UNDERGRADUATE

G000145690

THE OBJECTIVE of the Europ[...]
develop in young people the kno[...]
for international management.

Set in a beautiful campus in the heart of London, the
EUROPEAN BUSINESS SCHOOL offers the only degree-
level course in the UK which combines business studies,
management skills and two foreign languages. The four year
course leads to the Diploma in European Business
Administration (DEBA) and offers the opportunity to:

- *acquire a sound understanding of business disciplines*
- *learn management of innovation and entrepreneurialism*
- *become effective as a business communicator*
- *participate in a multinational student environment*
- *master three European languages*
- *study in two of: France, Germany, Italy, Spain*

On completion of the course, the EBS graduate will be
trilingual, possess an excellent grounding in business together
with an international outlook and have undertaken 48 weeks
of in-company work experience in a minimum of three
countries. Not surprisingly EBS graduates achieve excellent
positions in international companies.

Applicants should have A-levels or the equivalent and also
knowledge of one of the following languages: French, German,
Italian or Spanish.

For further details contact: The Registry
European Business School
Inner Circle, Regents Park, London NW1 4NS
Tel: 071-487 7400
Fax: 071-487 7465

THE STUDENT BOOK 1992 – EUROPEAN EDITION

DON'T LEAVE SCHOOL WITHOUT IT!

The essential guide to higher education – invaluable for parents and teachers as well as every sixth-former and would-be student – newly revised and updated for the European Community in 1992.

'Full of facts and helpful advice' *New Scientist*

- **Step-by-step guide to applying for and obtaining a place**, including how to get the money, survive your first year and equip yourself for Europe
- **Full details of over 280 universities, polytechnics and colleges:** who to apply to, main study areas, accommodation, amenities, what it's really like, what it costs and European Community links and languages
- **Extensive subject and places index**
- **What to study** – 75 teachers in Higher Education define their own study area and the approach to teaching them in UKCPUs from *Accountancy* to *Zoology*

'If there is only room for one guide for would-be students on the careers room bookshelf, this is it'
Times Educational Supplement

The Student Book 92

The applicant's guide to UK colleges, polytechnics and universities

Editors:

**KLAUS BOEHM
JENNY LEES-SPALDING**

With the compliments of NatWest Students Service

First published 1979 by
PAPERMAC
a division of Macmillan Publishers Limited
Cavaye Place London SW10 9PG
and Basingstoke
Associated companies in Auckland, Delhi,
Dublin, Gaborone, Hamburg, Harare, Hong
Kong, Johannesburg, Kuala Lumpur, Lagos,
Manzini, Melbourne, Mexico City, Nairobi,
New York, Singapore and Tokyo

Thirteenth edition 1991

British Library Cataloguing in Publication Data
The Student Book 1992: the applicant's guide
to UK colleges, polytechnics and universities.
—— 13th ed.
1. Universities and colleges —— Great Britain
—— Directories
I. Boehm, Klaus   II. Lees-Spalding, Jenny
378.41   L915

ISBN 0-333-56700-5

Computer typeset by Rowland Phototypesetting Ltd, Bury St Edmunds, Suffolk

Printed in Great Britain by Richard Clay Ltd, Bungay, Suffolk

WHAT YOU NEED TO KNOW IN SIX SECTIONS

HOW TO GO ABOUT IT   7

Before you apply   9

How to apply   19

How to get the money   31

How to survive your first year: A-Z   49

What's what in higher education   77

WHERE TO STUDY   101

MAPS   487

SUBJECT AND PLACES INDEX   499

WHAT TO STUDY   569

INDEX   737

About the Editors

Klaus Boehm specialises in reference books and publishing sponsorship. He works with a number of publishing houses, developing titles including the **Dictionary of the History of Science, British Archives, The Royal and Ancient Golfer's Handbook, Macmillan and Silk Cut Nautical Almanac** and **The European Community** ('the best single source on Europe').

Jenny Lees-Spalding was academic registrar at the City Poly, dealing with the students on first degree courses and the related academic administration. She left to develop reference books with Klaus Boehm. Their current titles are **The Student Book**; a companion volume, **The Careers Book**, published for much the same readership but offering a unique guide to becoming your own boss (not a bureaucrat); and **The Equitable Schools Books**, the discriminating parents' guide to over 580 independent secondary schools ('the Wisden of the fee paying circuit').

Books edited jointly by Klaus Boehm and Jenny Lees-Spalding share a common editorial philosophy: that information is best communicated directly to readers, rather than masked in the bureaucratese so often favoured by academic institutions, the professions, British corporate employers and (probably the best example of all) the European Commission. After that it is up to readers to get on with it – make their own shortlists, read prospectuses and institutional literature, consult, visit, interrogate and generally *find out for themselves*.

Foreword

BEFORE YOU APPLY – THINK EUROPE

If you are starting a degree course in 1992, the chances are you were born after 1 January 1973, the date Britain joined the European Community. So you have always been 'European' though many British schools have been so slow to adjust that you could be forgiven for not taking Europe seriously. But by the time you graduate it will be 1995 or 1996, the single European market will be up and running and you will probably have to work within it.

What does this mean to you? In a nutshell, it means you will be free to practise/work in continental Europe and their citizens in the UK; you will need to be equipped to work in the member states (currently Belgium, Denmark, Eire, France, Italy, Germany, Greece, Luxembourg, Netherlands, Portugal, Spain, UK). This will face British graduates with two linked challenges – to communicate effectively and fluently in the community (the fact that many other Europeans speak English is not enough) and to compete professionally at a local level which implies understanding the national environment, including the networks which provide jobs/contracts for the boys.

Will your British degree course help? Now is the time to find out, not when you've started and it's too late to change! This means working at it.

There are practical arrangements for *some* students in *some* faculties in *some* UKCPUs to develop their European languages and to study for part of their British degree course in a linked European institution. It's not enough, but it's a start, and you'll find that when you begin thinking Europe many British undergraduate prospectuses will tell you little or nothing – at least that was the position at the time of writing. The European Commission is aiming for 10% first degree students to spend part of their course elsewhere in the community so undergraduate prospectuses should become more informative.

There's lots of EC money to encourage student mobility – provided by the Erasmus programme. *BUT* beware! Europe is seen as big money by some UKCPUs and some impressive lists of European links may be a smokescreen; the UKCPU may just be a member of various Euro-groupings, with students coming *to* the UK to polish up their English (normally meaning cash for UKCPU) but few or no students going to Europe. Many UKCPUs can tell you down to the last fiver how much they have got in grants from the Erasmus scheme but have no idea how many of their own students go to other EC countries. These smokescreens are accompanied by a mass of indigestible prose and gnomic acronyms (even more gnomic than UKCPU that we use) – Erasmus, Comett, Text, Lingua, Science, Tempus.

But there *are* lots of exciting things going on so make sure you make the most of them. At some UKCPUs, language teaching is now available to all first degree students; there are opportunities for student exchanges (maybe through Erasmus) and work-placements in Europe (possibly through Comett). In **The Student Book 1992** we have for the first time given some European indicators for the UKCPUs eg what proportion of their students take an EC language and spend 6 months or more in another EC country as a part of their course; some information on the UKCPU's exchange links. There are other indicators but this should help you start your shortlist. After that it's up to you to find out. The UKCPU may have impressive Euro-credentials but no opportunities for *you* to go to another EC country; languages may be on offer to all courses but yours.

Apart from large grants to UKCPUs, Erasmus also offers top-up grants to students to go to another EC country (20,000 were planned across the community in the last three years). Erasmus is proud of the fact that it has a total budget of 85 million ecu (perhaps by the time you read this, people might know what an ecu is). There are two other interesting developments on exchanges. Firstly, there are moves to allow the work you do on an exchange to be accepted for credit towards your degree at your UKCPU – five subjects are involved in a three-year pilot scheme, masterminded by Erasmus. It is called ECTS (European Community Course Credit Transfer Scheme). The other, developed by individual UKCPUs with individual partners in Europe, allows you to get a diploma from the other EC university/college for your work there as well as your degree from your home UKCPU.

So – find out before you apply what's on offer. Start with **The Student Book 1992**; if you're lucky, the UKCPUs' 1992 prospectuses will be more revealing than the 1991. Some are doing a lot, many are not. Very few Students' Unions have Euro-contacts but, for example, there is a European Medical Students Association promoting exchanges. It's up to you to find out. But remember, there's no point in going to Europe if, once you get there, your life is dogged by loneliness, you are living in a British ghetto and never meet local students and you are locked out of overcrowded lectures – all of which happens. Some UKCPUs have been in this game for a long time and are canny at making sure you get a worthwhile educational experience and an adequate roof over your head; others have cashed in on the bandwagon and wouldn't know how to stitch together a good exchange agreement if they tried. Polish up some searching questions – have they *visited* the Euro-universities they send you to; what are the rooms like there; . . . ? NUS advice is to make absolutely sure of both money and accommodation before setting off.

So – use **The Student Book 1992**. Think Europe. Get a strategy. Best of luck.

ABOUT THE BOOK

The Student Book is a consumer book. To be precise, it is a book for potential consumers of first degree courses or equivalent in UK Colleges, Polytechnics and Universities. We call these institutions UKCPUs.

The book makes no pretence to cover higher national diplomas or any further education. Nor is it a catalogue of degree **courses**, which you can find elsewhere. It is intended to allow you to produce a strategy and shortlist of UKCPUs teaching the subject(s) you want to study. You can then get hold of the prospectuses.

We are grateful for the help we have received from the named contributors and from the student correspondents and the administrators of over 250 UKCPUs. In particular, we have been helped by Adam Gaines and Tim Walker of NUS; Mike Miller of Royal Holloway and Bedford; Maxine Penlington of Birmingham Poly; Brian High and Margaret Kilyon of City Poly and Tom Dodd of Manchester Poly. Our special thanks go to James Tomlinson and Pat Edwards for reading our handwriting and to Bryan Reading for the cartoons.

Klaus Boehm
Jenny Lees-Spalding

How to go about it

BEFORE YOU APPLY

HOW TO APPLY

HOW TO GET THE MONEY

HOW TO SURVIVE YOUR FIRST YEAR: A-Z

WHAT'S WHAT IN HIGHER EDUCATION

THE INSTITUTE OF CHARTERED ACCOUNTANTS IN ENGLAND AND WALES

Aims *To advance the theory and practice of accountancy and to train members.*
Membership *Over 93,000 members and 17,000 students.*
Qualifications *Associate (ACA)/Fellow (FCA)*

Entrance Requirements

5 GCE/GCSE passes, 2 of which must be at Advanced Level. Subjects must include English Language and Mathematics. Students must also have a degree (in any subject) or have passed the Accountancy Foundation Course, which is normally studied full time for one year at approved Polytechnics and Colleges. Some part-time courses are also available. These are the minimum requirements and it is likely that firms will be asking students to have obtained at least 'C' grades at Advanced Level together with a first or second class degree or a distinction or credit pass in the Foundation Course Examination. At present, over 90% of our students are graduates.

Training

All students are required to sign a training contract with an organisation which has been authorised by the Institute to train students. Until recently, the only way to qualify was via a training contract with a firm of chartered accountants. In future, training will be available in some industrial or commercial organisations as well. The contracts are of 3 years duration for graduates and 4 years duration for non-graduates and students are paid a salary during their training. Students undertake a programme of work experience and study for the Professional Examinations. Students receive paid study leave during their contract and employers pay for the course fees and examination fees at least for the first attempt at the Examinations. Students usually attend private tutors on a block release basis but much of the studying has to be carried out by the student in his or her free time in the evenings and at weekends. New syllabuses are being introduced and most students entering training in Autumn 1991 are likely to be affected. There will continue to be 3 main stages to the Examinations (Foundation, Intermediate and Final) which will cover a range of business subjects, such as Financial Reporting and Auditing and Financial Management.
The work experience gained will vary according to the training environment (size of firm is an important factor to consider if training in public practice). Students should think carefully about the type of experience they would enjoy most and which would give them most benefit for their future plans.

Opportunities on qualification

The Institute of Chartered Accountants in England and Wales is one of the world's leading accountancy bodies.
Around half the Institute's members work in public practice as sole practitioners, partners or employees in accountancy firms. These firms provide financial services to clients ranging in size and complexity from private individuals to the largest multinational corporations. The services provided include the preparation of accounts, auditing, tax, design of systems for financial and management control, advice on computer systems, special investigations and insolvency work. For many firms, particularly the larger ones, auditing represents the greatest part of the work as every company in the UK must have its annual accounts audited by an independent accountant to ensure that its financial statements present a "true and fair view" to shareholders and other interested parties.
Auditing provides an unparalleled opportunity to acquire detailed experience and a practical overview of a wide range of different companies and business activities.
Chartered accountants also play a major role in industry and commerce where their influence extends far beyond the preparation of accounts. They are found at every level of corporate activity from the boardroom to the computer department; they include managing directors, finance directors, financial controllers, management accountants, project analysts and internal auditors.
Training to be a chartered accountant has proved to be an excellent foundation for a career in general management.

To find out more

Further information may be obtained from the Student Recruitment Section at the address below.

The Institute of Chartered Accountants in England and Wales
PO Box 433
Chartered Accountants' Hall
Moorgate Place
London EC2P 2BJ. Tel: 071-628 7060

BEFORE YOU APPLY

IS A DEGREE WORTHWHILE?

SHOULD I DO A DEGREE NOW OR LATER?

IF I WANT TO DO A DEGREE NOW — WHAT NEXT?

The Student Book

Basic reference books worth getting

Library reference books worth consulting

Prospectuses

Alternative prospectuses

Open days

ENTRANCE REQUIREMENTS

MAKING A SHORTLIST — UKCPUS

MAKING A SHORTLIST — SUBJECT

GET A STRATEGY

Is a Degree Worthwhile?

You have to decide this for yourself. There are no useful general answers – the only worthwhile answer is one tailor-made for you.

If you are one of the very few who know what they want to do in life then you can work it out from the qualifications needed to get there. These can either be a legal requirement for entry into a profession such as medicine or a selection criterion used by employers for shortlisting job applicants: no degree, no interview.

If you do not know what you want to be doing in five years' time then it's all more complicated. There are lots of important factors to take into account including the opportunity to study in depth without the distraction of having to earn a living, the new range of talented people you will meet, the chance to develop your acting, musical, political or sporting prowess and of course the chance to keep your options open for another few years.

So how do you begin to work it out for yourself? You could of course write to John Major and ask him whether he thinks he would have got further if he had a degree. Alternatively you could try looking at it as a personal invest-ment decision – weighing the future benefits against the current sacrifices to decide whether your investment is likely to pay off. Admittedly this is a pretty dry approach but it might find some support in Downing Street.

If you want to look at the decision in purely financial terms you could use a framework commonly applied elsewhere. Try this:-

A   Costs
B   Benefits
C   Net Balance

A.   Costs

1. Earnings.
   You lose income by studying instead of working, even with a grant. However, assess your chances of getting a job. If the alternative is unemployment you've nothing to lose.
2. Expenses.
   If you don't get a grant you'll have to pay fees (and you *may* have to, even with a grant). Everyone has to buy books, equipment etc. You don't need a suit but accommodation and travel may be more expensive than if you were working or living at home. Overdrafts/loans have a finance cost or interest. Beware!
3. Length.
   The number of years your course lasts determines the total of these costs. Sandwich or language courses usually mean more years of cost (but maybe higher future income to offset them).

B.   Benefits

1. Better Chance of a Job.
   Graduates are less likely to be unemployed – in some areas they are screaming out for graduates and the shortages will get worse.

2. Higher Income.
   Graduates tend to earn more than non-graduates. For some professions a degree is a prerequisite; for others it means higher entry on the promotion scale; for most it's a sign of ability.

C. Net Balance

If these benefits outweigh the costs, then acquiring a degree is worth it as a financial investment. Even if it isn't, take account of the non-pecuniary benefits (and costs) which cannot be valued directly in financial terms. A new college lifestyle, greater independence, satisfaction from study, longer holidays and the prospect of more interesting and satisfying work when you leave are all significant benefits. Conversely prolonged financial dependence on parents may be a considerable cost not to mention paying back loans.

Allow for the benefits occurring later than the costs. Most of us would prefer to consume now rather than in the future. As a student you won't be able to maintain your desired level of consumption so the weight you give to present costs against future benefits depends on how much you value what you have to give up.

The cost benefit analysis framework is a valid economic approach for making your decision even if, for most, the motives are not solely financial. It should at least help you to identify the major reasons for and against studying further. If you don't know what you want to do now, you could do a lot worse than use the time at a university, poly or college to find out.

Should I Do a Degree Now or Later?

Taking time off between school and going to UKCPU can mean deferring your entry for just a year or some longer period. Many UKCPUs favour one year off and will accept applications in 1991 for entry in 1993; for some subjects eg agriculture they may require it. If you have a year or more between, a degree course ceases to be the only alternative; the decision is made more by you rather than parents or teachers. You're likely to be more independent and better able to cope with the rigours of student life. Returning to old study habits may be difficult, but at least you're sure it's what you want.

A year off may help when you start looking for a job too; many leading industrialists are in favour of a year off between A-levels (or equivalents) and going to a degree course. But of course any time off must be well planned. Loafing about in sun-spots abroad won't count for much in career terms, however enjoyable. You can contact GAP Activity Projects Ltd (44 Queen's Street, Reading, Berkshire RG1 4BB; 0734 594914). They can set you up with 6 months overseas voluntary work in schools, businesses, hospitals, farms . . .

Abigail Dawson, who took a year off, writes:-

'A whole year dossing. After the joys of A-levels that would probably sound a very enticing prospect, and it's quite feasible. There's nothing to stop you taking a year off and doing absolutely nothing with it. But what a waste. For the first and possibly last time in your life you have fifteen months at your disposal which, given money and parental support and sometimes without, you can spend exactly as you want.

There are endless good reasons for taking the year. In my case it enabled me to leave the hassles of UCCA until the relative calm of the post A-level period. It was a breather – I didn't feel I could go straight on from A-levels and start a degree course with much energy or enthusiasm. I'd heard how 'challenging and character-building' the year could be – at the time I took that with a deserved pinch of salt, but I have to report that it's probably true.

I'm no expert – I can't tell you the ins and outs of how to go about planning what you will do. That's up to you, your inclination to use your local library or careers centre and, to an extent, your school or college. I was lucky enough to find a place teaching in a school in Malaysia, before travelling round Singapore, Indonesia and Malaysia. There are also opportunities to participate in the GAP scheme, working abroad (with sheep in New Zealand, vines in France . . .) or with a mission in Africa, at home in industry with INDEX, or doing voluntary work of some kind – a friend spent an unforgettable few months with down and outs in East London.

Just about everything I encountered during the year was new: from a regular 9–5.30 job in a department store before Christmas (the definition of exhaustion, but good fun) and working behind a bar, to earn the cash to go away; to arriving in Malaysia expecting to give English conversation lessons and finding I was English teacher to 28 11-year-olds and general supply teacher to the rest of the school. travelling alone on decrepit buses full of livestock, accommodation at 30p per night, wonderful beaches, the odd volcano, religious ceremonies and festivals at which I was always made welcome, the humbling experience of fasting during the month of Ramadhan, beautiful temples, delicious (cheap!) food . . . and so on. I have met people who 'just' travelled during their years off. Looking back, most wish they'd taken some kind of job. But you can always play it by ear (two girls I met worked for bed and board for a week, teaching in a snow-bound Nepalese mountain village). I found the tourist trails of Malaysia and Indonesia so well-trodden by back-packers that travel was easy, cheap and quite well-organised (ignoring the odd break-down and ubiquitous con-artists, charging five times the standard rate. A sense of humour and a good guide-book helped).

So I started my degree course – refreshed and more self-confident and self-sufficient than a year before. There is an endless range of ways you can fill the year. If I have been preaching to the converted, I hope you have as good a time as I did. On the other hand you may be reading this in mid-October at 3pm, after your nth cup of coffee, sitting in your pyjamas and wondering what to do until it's time to go back to bed again. It's never too late. Get going and make the most of an invaluable opportunity.'

If I Want to do a Degree Now – What Next?

Find out as much as you can for yourself.

The Student Book

Once you've decided in general that you want to go on studying you need to be able to reduce the masses of information available to a shortlist of opportunities: where to study, what to study and how to go about it. *The Student Book* is the best place to start (obviously). It's divided into separate sections which give you this basic information:
- *How to go about it*
- *Where to Study (and maps)*
- *What to Study*

In the *Subject and Places Index*, it also shows you which UKCPU prospectuses are worth looking at if you want to study a particular subject. Use it intelligently (browse, then read, then shortlist); then write direct to the UKCPU for its prospectus.

Basic reference books worth getting

Not a lot. These ARE worth the effort of getting hold of for yourself if you are considering their subject matter.

ADAR Scheme Handbook (ADAR, Penn House, 9 Broad Street, Hereford HR4 9AP)

Directory of CNAA First Degree and Undergraduate Courses (Council for National Academic Awards, 344–354 Gray's Inn Road, London WC1X 8BP; free)

Grants to Students and *Loans to Students* (both from Department of Education and Science, Publications Despatch Centre, Honeypot Lane, Canons Park, Stanmore, Middlesex HA7 1AZ; also available from your local education authority or school; free leaflet)

PCAS Guide for Applicants (Fulton House, Jessop Avenue, Cheltenham, Gloucestershire GL50 3SH)

The Polytechnics (Committee of Directors of Polytechnics, 12–14 Whitfield Street, London W1P 6AX; also available from your school/college; free leaflet)

Scottish Universities Entrance Guide (Scottish Universities Council on Entrance, 12 The Links, St Andrews, Fife KY16 9JB)

UCCA Handbook (Universities Central Council on Admissions, PO Box 28, Cheltenham, Glos GL50 3SA; free booklet)

Library reference books worth consulting

These are books you might want to refer to in your school, careers or local library.

Commonwealth Universities Yearbook (London: Association of Commonwealth Universities)

University Entrance/The Official Guide (London: Association of Commonwealth Universities for the Committee of Vice-Chancellors and Principals)

Polytechnic Courses Handbook (Committee of Directors of Polytechnics, 12–14 Whitfield Street, London W1P 6AX)

Guide to the Colleges and Institutes of Higher Education (Standing Conference of Principals, Edge Hill College, Ormskirk, Lancs L39 4QP)

Degree Course Offers (Career Consultants Ltd)

Designated Courses (Department of Education and Science, Elizabeth House, York Road, London SE1 7HP; also available from your local education authority or school/college)

Guide to Courses and Careers in Art, Craft and Design (National Society for Education in Art and Design, 7a High Street, Corsham, Wiltshire SN13 0ES)

Design Courses in Britain (Design Council, 28 Haymarket, London SW1)

Prospectuses

Many prospectuses are glossy marketing documents, which are difficult to use for finding out real facts – an astonishing number lack even an index or list of subjects available. Some are works of art, especially for those of the more ambitious art schools. Remember, they are public relations documents designed to sell you the UKCPU. Beware glossy photographs: a beautiful sylvan scene might not be the whole view; a turn of 180° may reveal the abattoir. Many prospectuses oversimplify and, while usually accurate in detail, sin by omission. They may contain valuable information on courses, degrees, accommodation (or lack of it), fees, facilities, if you can find it among lists of staff and sales puff. Read any prospectus several times – to make comparisons between UKCPUs and for the detail (though they date quickly). Read between the lines. Try to identify the UKCPU's ethos. See what the prospectus says its strengths are (eg sport, religion): they may or may not match yours. Constituent colleges of universities (eg Cambridge, London, Oxford) have individual prospectuses, so get hold of these. Departments/faculties often produce their own guides which list staff and research interests. You might be able to gauge the nature, direction and tone of a department from this. Some prospectuses/department guides are now giving the average entry A-levels, although these will change rapidly.

Alternative prospectuses

Some students unions (SUs) produce Alternative Prospectuses to give a 'truer' picture for potential applicants of what the UKCPU is actually like – at least one SU also has an alternative prospectus video. They can be bitchy, selectively informative and moderately amusing. Well worth a look, particularly if you're applying for UKCPU accommodation, want to know the political leaning of the SU, or the idiosyncrasies of the more obvious student cliques.

Open days

Some UKCPUs hold open days for prospective students. These give you the opportunity to see the campus and town as well as any facilities that are particularly relevant to your choice of course (computer centres, labs etc). If your school or college doesn't have the details of these contact the UKCPU to find out if and when they take place. They may only be available to those who have been offered a place. If open days are offered – go. Don't even think of spending three years of your life in a place you haven't visited.

Entrance Requirements

You'll need to know about entrance requirements in general and the requirements of the UKCPU/courses that interest you in particular.

The present normal **minimum** for a first degree course (other than art & design) are: 5 subjects to a minimum of grade C GCSE, of which 2 are passed at A-level; or 4 subjects to a minimum of grade C GCSE with 3 passed at A-level. (For the oldies, O-level passes grade C or above and CSE grade 1 passes are accepted in place of GCSE). Most UKCPUs will accept (even enthuse over) AS-levels in addition to the basic 2 A-levels; but individual admissions tutors vary. BTEC Certificates or Diplomas at a good standard are also accepted. 4 Scottish Highers are the minimum for Scottish UKCPUs but may not be acceptable without further study in the rest of the UK. A recognised qualification in English Language, such as GCSE or JMB test, is normally required. If you have qualifications which do not appear in the prospectus (eg Scottish Highers outside Scotland; International Baccalaureat) check directly with the UKCPU. In addition there may be special **course** or **faculty** requirements.

Remember that in practice most UKCPUs have higher requirements than these and they change yearly. Offers are expressed either specifically in terms of A-level grades you must actually get or a number of points your AS or A-level results add up to on a scale when

for AS level	for A-level
A = 5	A = 10
B = 4	B = 8
C = 3	C = 6
D = 2	D = 4
E = 1	E = 2

You will find people at university with higher grades than average. Have a look at UCCA Press Releases (sent to your school/college from September on). Some polytechnics and colleges of higher education may accept the minimum requirements for some courses. The moral: badger and negotiate and remember A-level grades are not reliable pointers to future academic development. Don't waste applications; if in doubt consult the UKCPU. Have a look at *University Entrance* and Brian Heap, *Degree Course Offers* (Career Consultants Ltd) in your school/college library.

Many UKCPUs welcome applications from mature students and when you reach 21 (23 in some UKCPUs) you may no longer have to satisfy all the formal entry requirements for many degree courses. If (but only if) you can prove your willingness and ability to learn, you could be accepted for a course you would have been unable to get onto at 18. Polytechnics and colleges may be better bets than universities.

There are increasing numbers of Access Courses, which help you returning to study, or pick up eg science basics before starting a science degree. Some UKCPUs have their own so check – or consult *Access to Higher Education Courses Directory* (from ECCTIS, Fulton House, Jessop Avenue, Cheltenham, Gloucestershire GL50 3SH).

Making a Shortlist – UKCPUs

Apart from finding a place which is congenial to spend the next few years of your life (and don't just go by the name), there are other considerations in making your first UKCPU shortlist. Here are some thoughts:

Cuts

There are government pressures of two kinds on UKCPU staff:– (1) lack of money and (2) diminishing/diminished national status. The response of many UKCPUs is to cut staff, and close or merge departments and there are yet more mergers of UKCPUs in the offing. Make sure your subject and UKCPU will survive for the duration of your course and that it won't be turned into a minor liberal arts college when you are half-way through your course.

Popularity

If you're really good, you will get into the really popular places. If you're not, you are probably wasting a valuable choice if you apply. It's all part of the game of accurately assessing yourself and your chances.

Failure rates

There are rumours beginning of Paris-style failure rates: the UKCPU takes in its full quota to ensure its money and then fails large numbers of students at the end of the first year. Find out.

Research

If you want to use your degree as a stepping stone to a research post, you'll find it easier if you go to a UKCPU which has good research in your chosen area.

Employability

On the whole, employers are fairly conservative and still prefer graduates of Oxbridge or the universities well known in their field (eg Imperial for physics; LSE for economics). Having said that, graduates from poly-technics and colleges are more likely to find a permanent job within 6 months of graduation than their university counterparts. Ask about the employment record of the UKCPU when you go for an interview or open day.

Making a Shortlist – Subject

Getting in

Some subjects are highly competitive; in others they are crying out for students. Bear this in mind although don't, of course, apply for something you can't do. It's well known that medicine and law are two of the most difficult subjects to get into but do you know that over 100,000 people apply for business studies? If you have the minimum A-levels – or a science access course – you can walk into physical science degrees all over the country. There are all kinds of incentives around to attract people to engineering courses, particularly if you missed out on the right A-levels.

Employability

The demand for good graduates is now very strong. What it will be like in the mid-90s is another question but you should think Europe when you are shortlisting. At present, there are lots of vocational degrees, which is fine if you want to stay in that area after graduation. Otherwise the subject you take probably doesn't matter very much. What does matter is that you get a good degree. And getting a good degree is partly dependent on selecting a subject that will grab you for the full duration of the degree course. So, if you **want** to read Akkadian, go for it – and worry about the demands of industry later.

If you are going to be a mature student – beware. Employers (outside the civil service) don't treat you as equally recruitable after the age of 25. You'll need to talk to a careers adviser.

Get a Strategy

By now you'll be sick to death of UKCPU literature, teachers, careers services, relatives and 'friendly advice'. The golden rule is to listen to everything anybody can tell you and then ignore two-thirds of it. The choice of where to study and what to study is yours and yours alone. Find out about things like course structure and assessment (exams or in-course assessment) and choose what suits you best. Avoid tunnel vision and don't be frightened of trying something you haven't done before. Don't be indoctrinated – no-one knows your strengths and weaknesses better than you. Remember, you're choosing how to spend the next 3 years or more of your life. So get a strategy.

Make a shortlist

HOW TO APPLY

HOW TO APPLY IN GENERAL

Applicant's calendar for a 1992 start

Filling in forms

References

Interviews

How you are chosen

Offers (including POP)

Mature students

If you don't quite make it – action list

What if you come completely unstuck?

HOW TO APPLY IN PARTICULAR

Art and design applications

College and institute of higher education applications

Education college applications

Polytechnic applications

University applications

How to Apply in General

Applicant's calendar for a 1992 start

1991

June-September:
Absolute must: get a strategy. Prepare your own shortlist of UKCPUs.
Write for prospectuses and spend your summer having a good read.
Reduce your shortlist to five applications through UCCA (universities
and affiliated colleges), four through PCAS (polytechnics and most
colleges and institutes of HE). There is no limit for colleges not in
clearing systems. Find out more about UKCPUs as places. Comb
prospectuses.

From 1 September:
Application forms accepted by UCCA (university and affiliated college
applications) and PCAS (polytechnic and most college/institutes of HE
applications). They have a joint application form and you pay a £7 fee
to apply only through UCCA or PCAS, £14 to apply through both.
Find out where to apply for grants – normally your LEA (local
education authority). Write for forms and apply as soon as possible.

October:
Send applications in to colleges not in any clearing system.

15 October:
Last date for applications for Cambridge and Oxford to reach UCCA
from your educational referee.

15 December:
Last date for applications to reach UCCA and PCAS. Remember your
educational referee will need the form at least a week beforehand.

1992

February:
Application forms available for ADAR (for art and design courses in
polys and colleges in England and Wales and some in Scotland).

31 March:
Last date for ADAR applications to reach first choice colleges from
your educational referee (ADAR's schedule may change – check).

February/March/April:
Interviews with UKCPUs, if necessary, and offers of places.
For applications through ADAR, first choice interviews from 1 April
(decision by 9 May).

15 May:
Not more than one firm offer each through UCCA and PCAS may be
held after this date, with a further offer through each as an insurance.

May/June:
For ADAR applications, second choice interviews from 16 May (decision by 5 June).

Normally the final deadline for submitting grant applications. Each LEA has its own date. Late applications are accepted but the grant may be paid late. So get yours in as early as you can.

16 June:
ADAR clearing; interviews held from 23 June.

September:
Clearing for UCCA and PCAS: if you do not have a place, you will be sent information about clearing. But anyway ring round the UKCPUs – they now fill vacancies, sometimes accepting lower grades than before. You can also get help from your school or your LEA. Information on unfilled places is widely available, including the national press and various databases (Prestel, Campus 2000).

September/October:
Keep on ringing, there might still be places.

Allow for postal delays

Filling in forms

Going to UKCPU means filling in forms. Tough, but keep at it. If you think you need help, ask your teachers/tutors/careers officers. Going to UKCPU also means filling in forms **clearly**. PCAS and UCCA now have a joint form – you write and ask for the single form and the UCCA Handbook and/or PCAS Guide for Applicants. When you send your form back, it will be copied to all your choices *except* your PCAS choices are *not* sent to universities and your UCCA choices are *not* sent to polys. So you can still apply for courses in Chinese through PCAS without the (UCCA) medical schools ever knowing.

Just as the prospectus is the UKCPU's selling document, your own completed application form(s) is yours. Sell yourself. (But don't flannel – remember you may be interviewed by someone with this form in hand.) If you fail to do yourself justice, the chances are the selectors will reject you without giving you a second chance. Forget your reservations about the archaic school reward system (eg prefects) and write down any laurels you've earned. Remember selectors are looking for good grades; whether your reference indicates promise for the future; wide (but not necessarily 'straight') interests; and positions of responsibility. In short they want to know whether you look like benefiting from their degree course. But getting a place is a worse lottery than marriage – so keep at it.

Print boldly in **black** ink/biro/pentel. **Remember:** mess up an application form and you mess up your chances. Sign and date all application forms. Many applicants don't. This causes aggro and unsuccessful applications.

The information you are usually asked for is this:-

1. Personal details.
Fairly straightforward unless you are an overseas student.

2. Address.
Fairly straightforward unless your address for correspondence is different from your home address. If this is so, remember correspondence will continue until September next year. So make sure your correspondence address lasts this long or arrange for mail to be *efficiently* forwarded.

3. Choice of UKCPU and course (for UCCA & PCAS)
Browse through *The Student Book*. Then make a shortlist of about ten, consult prospectuses, reference books and **get it right for you**. Reduce to the relevant minimum (eg 5 for UCCA, 4 for PCAS) and fill in using the correct codes. Look in the handbook for how you can bracket choices. Practices at UKCPUs vary.

4. Education from age 11 in date order.
Straightforward – don't be too detailed.

5. Examinations for which results are known.
Put down everything even failures/low grades. It tells the UKCPU more about you, eg coming back from a failure/disappointing result indicates persistence, motivation and determination. Remember: one poor performance earlier in your school/college career won't count against you.

6. Examinations to be taken.
Again, put in everything even if not directly to do with your subjects.

7. Further information.
This is the most difficult section but use the space positively and draft it out in rough first. This is the only chance you've got to sell yourself, so give relevant and precise information. Include everything which gives you some 'depth' but don't put down (say) 'reading' as an interest; you're expected to read. Be specific. Then you can answer actual questions if you get an interview. Make yourself stand out from the

crowd. Say if you have a career in mind (shows motivation) but don't lose sleep if you don't know.

Remember to alter the form if you are applying for deferred entry.

References

All applications to UKCPUs must be supported by an educational reference. Increasing importance is being attached to it in selection procedures, so get the best you can. Your head teacher/tutor/lecturer will usually write the reference – and an academic reference carries more weight than one from a friendly clergyman. Don't go out of your way to flatter your teacher/tutor but show interest, motivation, persistence and that you're teachable. References are often held to be confidential, but some teachers/tutors show references to students and discuss them. Anyway badger whoever writes your reference to write a full and fair one. And make sure you give your referee enough time to write it, and that they send it in on time.

Interviews

If you are called for an interview, find out if it is part of the selection procedure rather than a visiting or open day. If it is part of the selection procedure then prepare for the interview by predicting questions like: why are you applying to this UKCPU, why have you particularly chosen this degree? Ask your teacher/tutor to give you a mock interview. When at the interview, show you have the personal qualities for a degree such as enjoying learning/reading/writing essays/lab work, wanting to argue and talk about new ideas, and being eager to find out new things for yourself. If you have more than one interviewer reply to the one who asks the questions and then bring the others in. Don't mumble, don't chew gum, don't pick your nose. Relax yourself as much as possible and wear what you feel most comfortable in. Wait to be told to sit down, and don't smoke. Try to repress all distracting mannerisms. Prepare questions for the interviewer at the end. Above all don't be cowed: you're interviewing them too.

How you are chosen

Being chosen implies some kind of rationality. Well, there isn't any. Each UKCPU sets itself a target number of new students and it will want to meet this target with the best applicants possible. UKCPUs also want teachable students so they adopt one (or both) of two ways of going about this:
1) A-level offers, made to a large number of candidates; so the A-level exams do the choosing
2) more reliance on interviews and reports from heads/course tutors; so lower offers can be made with more assurance on final student numbers.

Remember that the UKCPU's predicament is to get acceptable candidates onto its courses while leaving not a single place unfilled. Their predicament could be your opportunity.

After the A-level results are known, some UKCPUs top up their targets with people they would have rejected earlier in the year. Don't lose heart if you haven't got a place at this stage; keep badgering, even after the beginning of the autumn term. Selectors usually try very hard to be fair. But they might as well use a pin.

Offers

You may be offered a place at a UKCPU in one of two ways – **unconditionally** or **conditionally**. Unconditional offers are what they say! Conditional (or provisional) offers are dependent upon your getting, for example, specified A- or AS-level grades or points, and sometimes extra GCSEs.

What they **say** they are offering in a **particular year** is catalogued annually by Brian Heap in *Degree Course Offers* (Careers Consultants Ltd). Use it with discretion: as in any other marketplace (eg Stock Exchange) today's actual price is not necessarily the price quoted in this morning's *Financial Times*! The permutations involved in the offer/acceptance bargaining are mind-boggling. It's all supply and demand; if you get an offer based on 2 As and a B, it **may** be a better course than one offering 3 Ds – it's certainly more popular.

You may be expected by this system to balance your guess as to what you will achieve in A-level in the **future** with a **current** offer that involves you in weighing up the attractions of a variety of UKCPUs, subjects and courses. It is useful to have some sort of a multi-dimensional checklist in your head, or preferably on paper. If you are the sort of person who thinks better on paper than on your feet, why not try a DIY POP (Personal Offers Planner), using the proforma POP on p.25 and tailoring it to your own personal needs?

After 15 May you are allowed to hold only one offer, with another as insurance, through each of UCCA and PCAS. When the crunch comes, choose the UKCPU you want. The rejected UKCPUs won't approve, but it's your life.

POP

DIY – Personal Offers Planner

	What you think you'll get			Points
A-level grade	Subject (1)	Subject (2)	Subject (3)	
A	10	10	10	
B	8	8	8	
C	6	6	6	
D	4	4	4	
E	2	2	2	
AS-level grade	Subject (1)	Subject (2)	Subject (3)	
A	5	5	5	
B	4	4	4	
C	3	3	3	
D	2	2	2	
E	1	1	1	
				Total: _____

Your own shortlist/ offers	Grades needed						Points needed
	Subject (1)	Subject (2)	Subject (3)	Subject (4)	Subject (5)	Subject (6)	
UKCPU/COURSE (1)							
UKCPU/COURSE (2)							
UKCPU/COURSE (3)							
UKCPU/COURSE (4)							
UKCPU/COURSE (5)							
UKCPU/COURSE (6)							
UKCPU/COURSE (7)							
UKCPU/COURSE (8)							
UKCPU/COURSE (9)							

Instructions: Make up a POP when you are **beginning** to develop a strategy and keep it until August so that if you do not get the grades/points you need you can get cracking with clearing.

Mature students

Mature students are on the increase; some courses accept as many as 1 in 4; some are designed specially for them. If you are qualified for a degree course, you should have no problem. If you are not but you can persuade admissions tutors that you can benefit from the course and will be successful, you can still be accepted. For some you may have to take an exam; for others you will be interviewed. There is also an increasing number of access courses you can take to bring yourself up to the required standard. As a general rule, the polytechnics and colleges may be easier for what is called 'non-standard entry' but some universities (eg Salford) have imaginative schemes. For advice and further information, approach LEA careers advisers, or ECCTIS 2000 Ltd.

If you have taken a course before – even if you did not complete it – you may be exempted from part of a degree. This is called 'advanced standing'. If you think you may qualify, make sure you say so on your form and expect to be asked for syllabuses, transcripts etc. If you want advice, you can contact CATS (Credit Accumulation and Transfer Scheme, CNAA, 344–354 Gray's Inn Road, London WC1X 8BP). In some cases you can get credit for work experience and in-service training courses – CATS can tell you about that too.

If you don't quite make it – action list

If you don't get the grades you have been asked for first check that they won't take you on the course anyway. Speak to course tutors – don't just assume you're not wanted. UKCPUs have to fill their places with someone and lots of others may have missed the grades too. Then –
— Keep shopping around.
  UCCA and PCAS will automatically send you details of clearing in August/September if your conditional offer is not confirmed. This gives you another chance to get a place, even if it is not at one of the UKCPUs you originally chose.
— Keep up with last minute information available:
  – get in touch with your school/college
  – look in the national press – some list vacancies
  – look in local press for advertisements
  – listen to local radio services
  – use one of the electronic databases – Prestel and Campus 2000 – which are constantly updated
  – ring the *Observer*/Middlesex Poly telephone vacancy service, which is constantly updated but better at giving general advice than a screen
  – ring UKCPUs direct – the more enterprising have specially staffed units.
The intended order of clearing often breaks down (particularly in a postal strike). Many UKCPUs, desperate to meet targets precisely, take telephone applications (which are real) in preference to applications through

clearing (which might not materialize). Some UKCPUs even by-pass the system and actively recruit by phone for hard-to-fill courses.

This leaves you in an impossible situation: do you run up a huge phone bill and maybe strike lucky; or do you wait your turn through clearing and not make it. It's up to you. Good luck!

What if you come completely unstuck?

Tough but not the end of the world.
You can think about the following options –
— resit at school or a crammer or do something different at your local FE college.
— apply for a BTEC Higher Diploma if you have one A-level. If you choose a UKCPU with a diploma and a degree course in your subject you **might** be able to transfer later.
— forget all about it and do something else. There's always the chance you can come back to it later, when you're older and wiser. (Over 21 or, in some cases 23, the minimum entrance requirements can be waived on some courses, so long as you can persuade admissions tutors you will benefit.) Get a copy of *The Careers Book*, a companion book to *The Student Book* for all those who eventually want to become their own boss.

How to Apply in Particular

Art and design applications

The structure of art and design education is complicated and does not match tidily with most of higher education. Start by reading the article on *Art and Design* in the **What to Study** section; then return to the summary of application procedures below.

A few universities run practical art courses, for which you apply through UCCA. Most degree courses in art and design are run in art schools, colleges and polytechnics and you apply through ADAR (or direct to Scottish colleges outside ADAR). ADAR, the Art & Design Admissions Registry, is at Penn House, 9 Broad Street, Hereford HR4 9AP (0432 266653).

The minimum entrance requirements for art and design degree courses are not as inflexible as for other degree courses. After taking GCSEs, some students take A-levels, some BTEC diplomas, most a foundation course at an art college or polytechnic. Some are taken just on their portfolio. If you are one of the many who want to take a foundation course apply direct to the UKCPU – early.

The ADAR system may change in 1992 – but at the moment, you send for forms at the beginning of February with £8 (or £16 if you want to hedge your bets and apply for both BA and HND). Fill them in and ask your referee to ensure they reach your first choice college no later than 31 March. Your first choice interviews start after 1 April and you should be told of their decisions by 9 May. Second choice interviews start after 16 May and you should be told **that** decision by 5 June. If you are still not successful, you go into clearing. You will be told of the remaining vacancies on 16 June and clearing interviews start after 23 June.

Competition for art courses is stiff – make sure you know what you are going to do if you are turned down. You may find *Guide to Courses and Careers in Art, Craft and Design* (National Society for Education in Art & Design, 7a High Street, Corsham, Wiltshire SN13 0ES) and *Design Courses in Britain* (Design Council, 28 Haymarket, London SW1), useful.

College and institute of higher education applications

These are all different. For colleges affiliated to universities, you usually apply through UCCA. For the others, you apply through ADAR for art and design courses; direct or, more usually, PCAS for other courses. Check in **Where to Study** and the prospectuses.

Education college applications

Apply through UCCA or PCAS – check in *Where to Study* and the prospectus.

Polytechnic applications

Applications to degree courses at polytechnics and most colleges/institutes of HE in England and Wales are made through the **Polytechnics Central Admissions System (PCAS)**. This does not include art and design courses – apply through ADAR. You need the PCAS Guide for Applicants (it gives the codes you will need). Get this, together with the application form (and UCCA Handbook if you want it) from schools and colleges, or from PCAS, Fulton House, Jessop Avenue, Cheltenham, Gloucestershire GL50 3SH (0242 227788).

For autumn 1992 entry your application form should reach PCAS between 1 September and 15 December 1991. There is provision for late applications, but they will only be considered if suitable vacancies remain.

The form will be copied and reduced in size so write neatly and in black ink. (See *Filling in forms.*) To apply through PCAS, you should complete a single copy of the PCAS/UCCA application form, on which you may name up to four different polytechnics or colleges in alphabetical order (not order of preference). When you have completed your form, hand it to your referee with your fee (£7 for 1991 entry; £14 to apply to both UCCA and PCAS). Once your referee has completed a confidential report and sent the form and fee to PCAS, you will be sent an acknowledgement (normally same day) and a copy of your form is sent to each of the UKCPUs named.

Each of your choices will consider your application and make a decision, which is sent to you through PCAS; your reply to any offer made is also transmitted through PCAS. You may hold two offers through PCAS (in addition to any offers you hold from elsewhere).

If your first four choices don't come up, PCAS operates a clearing procedure in September, by which unplaced applicants are considered for admission to places unfilled earlier in the year. Details of clearing are sent to you automatically if you become eligible.

If you apply through PCAS and UCCA, your applications are considered separately in each scheme despite their common application form. Decisions are made independently in the two admissions systems and your polytechnic choices are not revealed to your chosen universities. You may hold offers through both UCCA and PCAS until after the exam results are published in the summer.

University applications

The Universities Central Council on Admissions (UCCA), PO Box 28, Cheltenham, Glos GL50 3SA (0242 222444), operates the central admissions scheme for full-time first degree courses at eighty-eight institutions (but apply direct to the Open University).

Applicants fill in a single application form (see *Filling in forms*) and name a maximum of five courses, usually at different universities. UCCA forwards copies of the applicant's form to the named universities which send their decisions to you through UCCA. Applications for entry in the autumn 1992 must be with UCCA by 15 December 1991 – or by 15 October 1991 if one of your choices is Oxford or Cambridge, when you must also apply direct to the university concerned (see Oxford and Cambridge prospectuses).

If you apply through UCCA and PCAS, your applications are treated quite separately despite their common application form; your university choices are not revealed to your chosen polys.

Normal application procedure is: obtain the application form and handbook – you must have this because you can't fill in the form without it, as it has the all-important institution and course codes. You can get copies of the *UCCA Handbook* for the year you want to start your course from your school/college, or from UCCA if you have left school. Consult prospectuses; choose five courses; fill in form (black ink only and be meticulous about UCCA's reference codes); make out a postal order for £7 (£14 if you are also applying through PCAS) for application fee; give form and fee to a referee (usually your headteacher); ask referee to forward form, fee and confidential statement to UCCA. UCCA will send an acknowledgement of your application up to a month after receipt of your form, but allow six weeks for acknowledgement of applications received around 15 December. The acknowledgement letter will contain an UCCA serial number and the universities to which the form has been forwarded. These details must be checked. You cannot change your mind or submit a second application until the following year. By 15 May, you may hold one firm offer and another for insurance.

If you are unsuccessful in all five choices, there is the summer scramble known as **clearing** when you might still find a place as the universities try to fill all remaining vacancies. You will be sent the information if you are eligible. Remember, UKCPUs know the number of places they have, but have no real idea of how many offers to make, so if you have no offer of a place do shop around during clearing. There is nothing to prevent you from getting in touch with any university and you might get a verbal offer which will later be confirmed through UCCA.

HOW TO GET THE MONEY

HOW MUCH DO I NEED?

Income and expenditure budget

Fees

Poll Tax (Community Charge)

WHERE DO I GET IT?

Grants of all sorts

LEA mandatory grants

LEA discretionary grants

LEA application procedure

How much?

Parental contribution

Loans – ten questions answered

Mature students

Access funds and other hardship funds

Part-time work when you're at UKCPU

Banks, charities, company educational trusts, sponsorship and scholarships

Social security benefits

OVERSEAS STUDENTS

How Much Do I Need?

Income and expenditure budget

This sounds really boring. It is an accountants' device for discovering whether you can afford to do what you want to do. Try one out **before** you commit yourself to going to UKCPU and make sure your income and expenditure are not too far out of balance. Don't assume you don't need to do this because you expect an LEA grant and a student loan. **Your** view of your minimum expenditure is almost certainly not the same as the **government's** view of your necessary income.

Income each academic year		Expenditure each academic year	
Cash in bank	£	Tuition fees★	£ ....
Grant	£	Exam fees★	£ ....
Loan	£	Accommodation (don't underestimate)	£ ....
Parental contribution (actual)	£	Food/drink	£ ....
Vacation earnings	£	Travel at UKCPU (incl any field courses)	£ ....
		Vacation expenses	£ ....
		Books	£ ....
		Stationery	£ ....
		Clothes	£ ....
		Leisure (fags, flicks, contraceptives, societies etc)	£ ....
		Interest on overdraft/credit cards	£ ....
		Poll tax (Community Charge)	£ ....

TOTAL £ ....   TOTAL £ ....

BALANCE £ ....

★at present, normally paid direct to UKCPU if you are on an LEA grant, but check.

Don't forget to mutiply the resulting balance by the number of years of your course to see whether you will be solvent at the end.

Fees

All UKCPUs charge fees but precisely what they are is often a mystery or trade secret ('Can I ask you why you want to know?') and their fee structure complex – one fees leaflet ran to 11 pages.

The UKCPU entries in **Where to Study** include the tuition fees for the academic year 1990/91. For most UKCPUs at the moment, the basic fee for home and EC students is set by the government – so most fees are about £1,675 in 1990/91. For 1991/2 the fee will depend on the course; so classroom-based courses may stay at £1,675, lab or studio courses rise to £2,500 and clinical courses to £4,500. Some UKCPUs add eg examination fees, registration fees. Hard-pressed UKCPUs are rumoured to be considering 'top-up' fees – ie charging a higher fee for courses they can fill even if it's pricey.

If you are on a grant, your fees should be paid direct to your UKCPU by your LEA. There are some exceptions – your grant may be discretionary and if so, so paltry that you/your parents are expected to pay them; there are some private colleges where the fees may not be covered in full (eg your grant will only cover £628 of the British School of Osteopathy fee for 1990/91); or top-up fees will not be covered.

Students from the European Community pay the same 'Home Fee' as UK students; and may not have to pay any fees at all if it appears they would have been eligible for a mandatory grant if they had been a UK student – now there's a bitter pill for UK students paying their own fees.

Students from outside the EC pay fees which are set by the UKCPU and are intended to cover the full cost of the course – 'Overseas Fees'. These range from £4,500 for classroom-based courses, through £6,000 or so for lab or studio courses to a staggering £10,500 or £11,500 for clinical courses – and that's only for one year.

Make sure you know what has to be paid, by whom, when and where.

Poll Tax (Community Charge)

Watch this space. Anything might happen to the poll tax between now and when you start your course.

At the moment the bad news is that students (full- and part-time) all have to pay it; the good news is that full-time students will 'only' have to pay 20% of it, while part-time students **may** get a rebate after paying 100%. The amount you pay varies from place to place. You can't (legally) get out of it, even if you are an overseas student. Tough. As a student you pay in the area where you will be living during **term-time**.

To get your reduction as a full-time student, you have to register with the Community Charge Registration Office in the area where you will live during term-time, and get your UKCPU to give you a certificate that you really are a full-time student (the Registration Officer may insist on seeing this). If you are part-time, you'll have to pay the 100% charge and try to claim a rebate from the Registration Office.

If you thirst for more information you can get a free leaflet *Students and the Community Charge* from: **Community Charge Leaflets**, PO Box 622, Bristol BS99 1TR.

Where Do I Get It?

Grants of all sorts

Do not assume that a grant is your automatic right. In particular, watch out that you do not lose your grant if you change course. Most UK first degree students have their tuition fees paid and are awarded maintenance grants by their LEA, topped up with loans. Overseas students have to depend on other sources such as the British Council (10 Spring Gardens, London SW1A 2BN) or World University Service (20 Compton Terrace, London N1). Some scholarships and loans are available from embassies and high commissions for their country's citizens; there are a few helpful charities, religious and others.

If your course is leading to a profession ancillary to medicine (eg physiotherapists, radiographers), grants are available from the DHSS, Room 109, North Fylde Central Office, Norcross, Blackpool, Lancashire FY5 3YA (0253 856123), and in Scotland from the Scottish Education Department, Awards Branch, 2 South Charlotte Street, Edinburgh EH2 4AP.

Useful books and booklets are:
NUS Information Service Sheets (on grants, welfare benefits etc for Students) and a parents' pack available from NUS, 461 Holloway Road, London N7 6LJ, with a large sae; *Guide to Students' Allowances* (Scottish Education Department, Awards Branch); 'Students' Grants', *Money Which?* (Consumers Association, 14 Buckingham Street, London WC2N 6BS).

LEA mandatory grants

Don't expect to survive on your grant alone. It won't go up however much the pound sterling goes down: grants are frozen at the 1990/91 level and student loans are intended to help you cope with the shortfall. A Labour government may change this in the future but for the time being you're stuck with this combination.

Regulations covering LEA awards are totally indigestible, as you'll see from the DES booklet *Grants to Students* sent to you by the LEA with your grant application form. Fundamentally you are eligible for a **mandatory** grant if you are ordinarily (but there are problems of definition) resident in the UK and have been so for at least three years; are doing a degree course or equivalent (DES decide the qualifying courses; the jargon is 'designated courses'); and have not done a course of this kind before. If you don't meet these conditions then the LEA can still make a

discretionary award but in the present financial climate you are lucky to get one. (The NUS has surveyed discretionary grant policies – see their LEA survey, from NUS, 461 Holloway Road, London N7 6LJ.) If you change courses or UKCPU with the approval of both course organisers and this is approved within 4 months of the end of your first year you should be able to transfer your grant too.

LEA discretionary grants

If you are not eligible for a 'mandatory' grant – either because you have held a grant before or because you are not on a 'designated course' (ie a degree course or similar, as judged by the DES), you are in the hands of your local authority – and the best of luck! Each local authority behaves differently, and they'll treat you differently if you're doing a 'non-designated' course such as a film course, foundation art or Law Society course than if you are an HND student transferring to the second year of a degree course or repeating a year. Some authorities will give no discretionary grants or payments at all and they may not give you as much if you had a mandatory grant. The policies of most LEAs are given in the NUS Local Education Awards Survey (from NUS, 461 Holloway Road, London N7 6LJ) and if they've changed, it'll be to give fewer.

The only general advice we can give to all students applying for a discretionary grant is:
* check direct with your LEA as soon as you think you may need a discretionary grant.
* expect to go through some arbitrary tests and assessment by the LEA before you can even hope for financial assistance and then you may hear very late.
* get the LEA answer *in writing*.
* finally, don't forget that if you are turned down, LEAs always have an appeal procedure – however longwinded – which usually involves elected councillors who can legitimately be lobbied. Appeal and lobby!

LEA application procedure

If you live in England and Wales you write for grant application forms to the LEA in whose area you normally reside. (In Scotland write to the Scottish Education Department, Gyleview House, 3 Redheughs Rigg, Southgyle, Edinburgh EH12 9HH; in Northern Ireland to your Education and Library Board.) You should do this very early. The completed forms often have to be returned to the LEA by the end of May or June (LEAs' closing dates vary) for a course starting in the autumn. Some authorities have a deadline irrespective of your having a place; others will not take your application unless you hold an offer. If you miss your LEA's deadline it can lead to delays, so find out their procedure and apply as **early** as you can. If yours is not a straightforward application, always confirm any conversations you have with your LEA in writing, or conduct dialogue by letters. LEAs do tend to say one thing and then several months later write something quite different. If your case is not straightforward, give *only* the information they ask for and get advice. LEAs have been known to turn down some applications on the basis of information which they needn't have been told in the first place.

If you have two possible LEAs, make enquiries and opt for the one which is the more reasonable. If you are moving, you should apply to the LEA where you will be resident on 30 June, prior to the autumn you start your course. LEAs often lose sight of their customers. Many have ansaphones to deter you from ringing from August to November and sometimes they don't reply to letters. So be persistent but without alienating the staff if you can help it.

Even if you get your forms in on time, you'll be lucky if your grant cheque is there at the start of term – so make sure you take some money to tide you over.

How much?

If you get an award your tuition fees will be paid (usually in full) and you will get a sum for maintenance based on a DES-fixed figure worked out on your/your spouse's/your parents' income. You may get more if: you study in certain places (eg London); you support dependants; you are over twenty-five and qualify for a mature student's grant; or you qualify for a disabled student's allowance.

Your grant, together with the stipulated parental contribution and loans, is supposed to keep you all year round – term-time and vacations (which is why you get less in your final year; no summer vacation). Most students have to work over summer vacations: for jobs get in touch with your students' union, or commercial agencies. Earned income does not affect your grant (although unearned income does).

To see how much you can expect to get, see our *Rough and Ready Reckoner*. If you think the figures at the top of each column are not enough, you have to go for a loan, find a friendly bank manager, win the pools – or all 3!

Parental contribution

Even if you are on an LEA grant, your parents (or a single parent) are expected to contribute to your maintenance if their joint (or single) income exceeds a certain amount (see *Rough and Ready Reckoner*). Certain deductions can be made which then leaves something called the 'residual income'; and the greater the residual income, the greater the parental contribution is expected to be. All you can be sure of, of course, is that as the residual income goes up, your grant goes down. Your LEA (local education authority) will tell your parents how much they are to contribute but it's not a legally binding requirement. The DES survey reveals that

GRANTS ROUGH AND READY RECKONER (1991–92)
Grants for 30 week academic year for one student

Residual income	Parental contribution	So your LEA will pay your fees and a grant of:-		
If your parents' residual income is:-	Your parents' contribution to you is supposed to be:-	For studying in London (£2,845 less parental contribution)	For studying outside London (£2,265 less parental contribution)	For studying while living at home (£1,795 less parental contribution)
up to £11,499	No contribution	£2,845	£2,265	£1,795
£11,500	£45	£2,800	£2,220	£1,750
£14,700	£388	£2,457	£1,877	£1,407
£18,000	£883	£1,962	£1,382	£912
£21,000	£1,333	£1,512	£932	£462
£24,000	£1,873	£972	£392	Nothing
£27,000	£2,435	£410	Nothing	Nothing
£30,000	£2,998	Nothing	Nothing	Nothing

If you need to spend time in the European Community as part of your course (and you're not getting paid) you should get a grant (less parental contribution) of:

£2,265 for Greece, Portugal and Spain
£2,670 for Italy and Luxembourg
£3,080 for Belgium, Eire, France, Germany and Netherlands
£3,425 for Denmark

Parental contributions

40% of students fail to receive their full parental contribution; for these students there may be advantages in the loan system. Some parents even refuse to fill out the forms, so the grant is tiny. If your parents are expected to make a sizeable contribution and then don't pay, you'll be hard pressed to survive on your grant, even with the loan, so work persuasively on your parents.

Your parents are not expected to contribute if you are over 25, you have been self supporting for three years or have been married for two years. Get in touch with your students' union (SU) if you are in difficulties. The NUS (National Union of Students) also provides helpful information.

Loans – ten questions answered

The Student Loans Company, based in Glasgow, was formed to administer student loans. You can telephone their Student Helpline (0345 300 900) for specific answers to questions which concern you.

Answers to ten common questions are:

1. A student loan is a top-up loan. It is available to help you meet your expenses during your time as a student, supplementing any grant or parental contribution you may receive. No regard will be paid to the amount of your grant, or any other income you may have.
2. You can apply for the loan any time during the academic year.
3. If you decide not to take a loan in your first year, you can still apply in subsequent years if you are still eligible.
4. Generally loans will be available to full-time home students on designated courses in the UK. Briefly, the course must last at least one academic year, and you must satisfy basic residence requirements.
5. You can borrow any amount up to the maximum. The money will be

paid into your bank or building society account. You can ask for the money in up to three instalments.

6. There is an interest charge. The amount you have outstanding will be indexed to inflation. This means the value of the sum you repay will be the same in real terms as the value of the sum borrowed.

7. You start repaying at the April after you finish the course. Most students will repay over five years. In some circumstances deferral may be possible.

8. To apply, go to your UKCPU administration department. Find out when you enrol which office deals with loans; it varies from UKCPU to UKCPU. Before you go to apply, check what to take with you: generally your birth certificate, your award letter and evidence of your bank/building society account details. Your UKCPU administrator will check your eligibility. You will then be given an application form which you complete and send to the Student Loans Company. You will then be sent a loan agreement to sign and return. The money follows shortly after that.

9. The maximum loan amounts for 1991/92 had not been fixed when we went to press, but will be announced in spring 1991. The maximum loan amounts for 1990/91 were as follows:

	Full year in 1990/91	Final year in 1990/91
Students who live away from home: in London	£460	£340
or elsewhere	£420	£310
Students who live at home	£330	£240

Remember you can borrow any amount up to the maximum.
The loans are lower for the final year, as they do not cover a summer vacation.

ANDREA ANDREWS BA (ON LOAN)

10. The present arrangements for grants will continue. However, the cash value of the basic grant rates, together with the proportion of grant to be contributed by parents, will be frozen at the 1990/91 rate.

The total level of grant and loan will be reviewed annually, and any increase will be provided as loan not grant. This process will continue until loan and grant are almost equal proportions of the total support.

If you want more information phone: Student Loans Company, Student Helpline 0345 300 900.

Mature students

If you are over 26, you are eligible for a higher rate of grant – so long as your grant is mandatory; if it is discretionary, so is the amount. This age allowance is dependent upon your having earned £2,000+ in the three years before your course starts. Even so, things will be tough particularly if you are supporting a family. (Mature students are more likely to end their course in debt than younger undergraduates.)

Access funds and other hardship funds

There's a sweetie to help you swallow student loans, the freezing of grants, and the abolition of housing benefit – it's called an Access Fund. The government hands out money (£14 million for first degree students in 1990/91) to help individual students who find the financial pressures too much. The money is being distributed by each UKCPU (for example, Lampeter has £14,400 to distribute, Cambridge £363,700). This is the first year; and you may qualify for some money in one UKCPU and be ineligible in another. The UKCPUs' criteria vary or, in some cases, appear to be non-existent. Some use criteria similar to those for housing benefit, others are using the money to reduce fees for self-financing students or help with childcare. Anything might have happened by 1992.

UKCPUs often have their own hardship funds for students with short-term problems or those who come unstuck financially part way through their course. But you'll find there is rarely any long-term help for students at the start of their course, so don't bank on it.

Part-time work when you're at UKCPU

Because you'll find yourself with too little money you'll probably have to look for ways to supplement your income. (Nearly 60% of students take holiday jobs to augment their income.) This will fall into two broad categories: during the summer vacation, and during the rest of the year. For summer vacation jobs, look at the guides produced by Vacation Work Publications (9 Park End Street, Oxford OX1 1HJ; 0865 241978) who produce a pretty impressive list (send sae). For opportunities during the rest of the year things are a little dicier. Your best bet is to try your UKCPU students' union office. Be a little enterprising and look out for opportunities for part-time businesses such as car washing/window

cleaning. But do be prepared to experiment a bit by going outside the usual bar jobs or acting as hacks for academics. Two *awful warnings*: don't let your part-time work get in the way of your academic studies, *and* don't accept drug firms' money to act as human guinea pigs without checking carefully or you may risk your life. It is also probably a good idea to let your tutor know what you're up to, *but* informally.

Banks, charities, company educational trusts, sponsorship and scholarships

Banks

You'll need one, and a sympathetic bank manager; most students need an overdraft to get through. Basic equipment: a cheque book and a bank card. Don't touch credit cards unless you're unusually organised about money and can pay them in full each month; handle cashpoint cards with extreme caution. **Shop around** – banks are wooing students with glossy brochures, filofax and membership of the Youth Hostelling Association – their student packages are unveiled each August. Although all banks now offer free banking as long as you're in credit, it's well worth comparing what overdraft conditions you can get (several give overdrafts up to £300 interest free), and whether you'll get interest on any credit in your current account. You could open an account at your parent(s)' bank; or find out which bank has a branch at your UKCPU and either open one there or at a branch of the same bank back home; it may help to have one with a specially appointed student adviser. Make sure you choose a bank with a branch on or near campus (the building societies are not seen on campus much yet which is why you'll probably need a bank). Open an account **before** you go to UKCPU or you may find yourself with a grant cheque in the bank but no cheque book to use the money. The table on pages 44 and 45 gives some idea of what banks offered to students in 1990. Check this year's glossies before taking action.

Charities
There are lots of impoverished students chasing the little money handed out by educational charities. So don't pin much hope on getting very much. Write to the Educational Grants Advisory Service, 501 Kingsland Road, London E8 4AU, which specialises in educational charities.

Company educational trusts
Many large companies have these. Find out if the company where your parent(s) works makes grants to sons and daughters of its employees/staff. Be careful: the Court of Appeal has decided these are taxable as fringe benefits.

Sponsorship
Sponsorships, and supplementary awards, are offered by employers (industry, government and professional organisations) – particularly for

SUMMARY OF STUDENT BANKING SERVICES
(as at end 1990 – new whacky packages come out each August, so check)

	Free Banking	Interest on Current Account	Cheap Overdraft	Student Advisers	Low Cost Graduate Loan	Cheque Card	Cashpoint Card	Low Cost Loan	Where to Write for Further Information
Bank of Scotland	Yes (if in credit or agreed overdraft)	Yes	Yes to £500	No	Yes to £1,500	Yes	Yes	No	Marketing Department Bank of Scotland Orchard Brae House 30 Queensferry Road Edinburgh EH4 2UH
Barclays	Yes	Yes	Interest free to £250	Yes	Yes	Yes (on application)	Yes	Yes	Student Account Service Personal Sector Marketing Department Barclays Bank PLC PO Box 120 Longwood Close Westwood Business Park Coventry CV4 8JN
Clydesdale	Yes (if in credit or within any agreed overdraft facility)	Yes	Yes	Yes	Yes	Yes (on receipt of grant)	Yes	No	Clydesdale Bank plc 30 St Vincent Place Glasgow G1 2HL
Co-operative (Nothing special for students)	Yes (if in credit)	Yes	No	No	No (but have 'career development loans')	Yes	Yes (at some branches. Cash cheques at Co-ops during shopping hours)	No	The Co-operative Bank Head Office PO Box 101 1 Balloon Street Manchester M60 4EP
Girobank (Nothing special for students)	Yes (if in credit)	Yes	No	No	No	Yes (normally after 6 months)	Yes	No	Personal Banking Marketing Girobank plc Bootle Merseyside G1R 0AA

	Free Banking	Interest on Current Account	Cheap Overdraft	Student Advisers	Low Cost Graduate Loan	Cheque Card	Cashpoint Card	Low Cost Loan	Where to Write for Further Information
Lloyds	Yes	Yes	Yes; free to £300	No	Yes	Yes (on receipt of grant)	Yes	Low rate higher education loan for parents	Lloyds Bank Plc 71 Lombard Street London EC3P 3BS
Midland	Yes	Yes	Yes; free to £300, preferential rate thereafter, if agreed in advance	Yes	Yes	Yes (on receipt of grant)	Yes	No	Midland Bank plc Marketing Department PO Box 2 Sheffield S1 3GG
National Westminster	Yes	Yes	Interest free to £300 for first year students	Yes	Yes	Yes (on receipt of grant)	Yes	No	National Westminster Bank PLC 41 Lothbury London EC2P 2BP
Royal Bank of Scotland	Yes (if in credit or if overdraft is prearranged)	Yes	£300 interest free if agreed in advance	No	Yes	Yes	Yes	No	The Royal Bank of Scotland plc FREEPOST Edinburgh EH2 0DG (no stamp required)
TSB England & Wales	Yes	Yes	£300 interest free	No	No	Yes	Yes	No	TSB Bank plc 60 Lombard Street London EC3V 9EA
TSB Scotland	Yes (if in credit or up to £300 overdrawn)	Yes	£300 free of interest or charges	No	No	Yes	Yes	No	TSB Bank Scotland plc Head Office PO Box 177 Henry Duncan House 120 George Street Edinburgh EH2 4TS

engineering students, where nearly 30% students are sponsored by large firms such as British Telecom. A common formula is a bursary (perhaps £1,000 pa) plus paid and structured vacation work. Beware – your grant will be reduced by the amount of the bursary – or even killed completely if it's too much. Candidates are normally responsible for gaining their own admission to UKCPU. *Sponsorships* is published by COIC and available from the Department of Employment, ISCO 5, The Paddock, Frizinghall, Bradford BD9 4HD; some schemes are also advertised in the press.

Scholarships

This is a complex area. Many UKCPUs offer scholarships of some sort. Check prospectuses. There are also specialist scholarships (eg in arts and sport). Look out for sports scholarships at Bath, Liverpool, Newcastle, and Stirling Universities. You can find out about art/music scholarships from the Arts Council of Great Britain, 14 Great Peter Street, London SW1P 3NQ (071-333 0100) which publishes *Guides to Awards and Schemes* (free). If you go for a scholarship remember, it can affect the amount of your grant.

Social security benefits

Don't rely on them. The government is committed to removing most students' entitlements. Disabled students are the only ones recently to have got any extra cash.

Overseas Students

If you are an overseas student, other than from the EC, legally you can be charged higher tuition fees (£4,500 pa for classroom-based courses up to £11,500 for clinical) and are not entitled to an LEA award. Some UKCPUs have special overseas advisers and many of the staff make a special effort to be sympathetic towards your problems, so talk to them.

Like all DES regulations, the rules defining overseas students are complicated. Those qualifying as **home** students (as opposed to specified) for fees purposes include:

a) those who have been ordinarily resident in the UK for three years but **excluding** any time spent here primarily for the purpose of education;

b) EC nationals resident in the EC for the three years preceding the course;

c) UK citizens who have been abroad temporarily during the previous three years for the purpose of employment (or spouse's or parents' employment);

d) refugees, new immigrants and EC migrant workers.

Being 'home' for fees purposes does not necessarily make you eligible for an LEA grant. If you are not sure of your status, check with your LEA and with **each** UKCPU which offers you a place.

EC citizens resident in the EC pay the same fees as home students. But they pay no fees at all if they would have qualified for a mandatory grant had they been British. Make sure your UKCPU knows in advance if you think you qualify – they will have to ask you lots of boring questions.

If you want help in becoming/being an overseas student try contacting: British Council, 10 Spring Gardens, London SW1A 2BN (071-389 4383), they have an educational enquiry service which you can phone or visit (though opening hours vary – so check); UKCOSA (United Kingdom Council for Overseas Student Affairs), 60 Westbourne Grove, London W2 5FG (071-229 9268/9); WUS (World University Service), 20/21 Compton Terrace, London N1 2UN (071-226 6747).

HOW TO SURVIVE YOUR FIRST YEAR: A–Z

ACCOMMODATION

AIDS

ARRIVAL

BOOKS

CHANGING COURSES AND CHANGING UKCPUs

DISABLED STUDENTS

DROPPING OUT

DRUGS

FINANCE

GAYS

HARDSHIP FUNDS

HOME-BASED STUDENTS

INDEPENDENCE

INSURANCE

LEARNING

LIBRARIES

LONDON

MATURE STUDENTS

NORTH v SOUTH

OVERSEAS STUDENTS' SURVIVAL

PARENTS

POVERTY: COPING WITH IT

PREGNANCY

RACISM

READING DIFFICULTIES

REGISTRATION

SAFETY

SELF CATERING CHECKLIST

SEX

SEXUAL HARASSMENT

SEXUALLY TRANSMITTED DISEASES

STAFF–STUDENT SEX

STUDENT CONCESSIONS

STUDENT HEALTH

STUDENTS' UNIONS

STUDYING

TRAVEL

TYPING

VACS

VICTIMISATION

WELFARE

WHAT IF YOU DON'T SURVIVE YOUR FIRST YEAR

WHAT YOU CALL THEM/ WHAT YOU DON'T

Accommodation

Face up to it. More students than ever before will probably be starting courses at UKCPUs (nearly a quarter of a million of you) in autumn 1992 and if you don't keep your eye on the ball there may be nowhere for you to sleep. If you don't believe this, look at the newspaper coverage of the student accommodation crisis in 1989 and 1990.

Two warnings. Check before you arrive whether your UKCPU considers that your accommodation is its problem: some do, some don't. Also don't assume that UKCPUs necessarily repeat their mistakes; if they are caught out making more offers than they know how to accommodate one year, they're usually a reasonable bet the next, when another will get it all wrong.

In general your first assumption as a fresher should be that the best accommodation has already been nabbed (moral – make sure you look early, before Easter, for your second year). Get along there and sort it all out before the start of term. As one accommodation officer said 'Once the course starts, it's difficult to find the time to sort it out'. Everyone usually finds something in the end but a month or two kipping on someone else's floor can seem a long time and doesn't help you settle into your course.

If you're *very* lucky, your university or poly will have a policy of accommodating all first years; most will just do their best to help you find somewhere outside. In 1989 and 1990 the system fell apart and first years were crashing out wherever there was space – holiday camps, library floors, warehouses etc; at least one college was dealing with a known shortfall of 600.

Accommodation varies hugely; but it all costs a lot and rising. If you're lucky enough to have a choice, it's best to live in; it's easier to make friends, more clout with the landlord and should be cheaper and closer to college. You may have more luck with the universities – they usually have more accommodation than the polys. In the richer Oxbridge colleges, you may get a bedroom and sitting room of your own but have to cross the quad for running water. In the cardboard halls of the sixties, your neighbour's bedsprings or the curtains downstairs may keep you awake; noisy plumbing can disturb your dreams there or in Victorian piles where plumbing was an afterthought.

If college accommodation is beyond the pale or non-existent, you look outside. This gets harder each year, particularly where there are other sources of tenants (such as holiday makers in seaside towns) and/or there is a shortage of private rented accommodation (leafy suburbs). The UKCPU accommodation officer should be able to provide you with telephone numbers of likely pads; *you* provide yourself with a map – and off you go. You may also be given a list of things to check; obviously find out about the rent (do you need to pay it all in advance, is there a retainer for keeping it free during vacations, how much is the deposit, who is responsible for the rent if one of the sharers leaves prematurely?). One student, who had all his kit nicked in his first year and is trying to get rid of cockroaches from his new flat, would recommend you check the lock on the front door and take a close look at the cupboards. Get advice on the contract *before* you sign; it's too late afterwards. Assuming you can't afford a solicitor, you should be able to get help from the accommodation office or the SU. (Many students ignore the no-party clause which many contracts include.)

If you are going to study near home, your LEA will assume that you will live at home. It's certainly cheaper. But you may miss out on some of the social facilities and there is always the chance you will turn your course into an extension of school, which is a mistake. If you want to move away from home, talk to the UKCPU office which deals with grants; you may be able to get their support for you to move away from home on 'educational grounds'. You should definitely do this if you don't have proper facilities to study at home (a room of your own, as a start).

If all else fails, you can join the increasing band of student squatters. Some councils regard students as a privileged class of squatters and make an effort for them. You can get the excellent **Squatters Handbook** from the **Advisory Service for Squatters** (2 St Paul's Road, London N1 2QN; 071-359 8814). The ASS will also help if you get in trouble in a squat, although act fast as you often only get 2 days before you are slung out.

Paying for a roof over your head will take the lion's share of your grant/ loan (housing benefit has all but vanished). You should assume you may have to pay up to around £45 a week, plus extras such as retainers for vacations, electricity etc. Savage increases are reported across the country – except, curiously, in London but that was pricey enough to start with. Living in is usually cheapest; self-catering cheaper than all-found. Do your sums for the whole year carefully to make sure you can afford what you find (with or without an overdraft). Landlords have a nasty habit of asking for whole term's rents in advance – whether or not your grant cheque has come in.

You will, with luck, end up with at least a bed of your own, light, heat and somewhere to work. Cooking, washing and laundry facilities will invariably be shared. Find out if you need to take sheets, towels, saucepans, plates, cutlery, glasses . . . Plus whatever *you* need – garlic press, lemon squeezer, cork-screw, water filter, favourite duvet. Don't take valuables unless you can't live without them, your digs are really secure and you are well insured.

The horror stories that emerge at the start of each year affect the minority – and with luck it won't affect you. So even if you need to give your room a lick of paint, wash the curtains, cover it with posters or fill it with potted plants, you should be able to create an atmosphere in which you, personally, can flourish.

AIDS – Acquired Immunity Deficiency Syndrome

AIDS has, in recent years, become the concern of everyone. The great majority of cases have occurred in the high risk groups, male homosexuals, intravenous drug abusers and haemophiliacs. However, AIDS is now beginning to spread among heterosexuals and none of us can afford to be complacent.

As well as the clinical cases of AIDS, there are many thousands of people who are carrying HIV-1 (Human Immunosuppressive Virus) who may not develop the disease for up to ten years. During all this time they may infect others. There is at present no effective cure for AIDS and a vaccine protecting against it may take many years to develop. To complicate matters there is a variant virus, HIV-2, which is found mainly in Africa or in people who have been there and this is thought to be more transmissible by heterosexual intercourse.

For all these reasons we need to think more carefully about our sexual behaviour. Sticking to one sexual partner obviously helps. When there is any element of risk, with gay or bisexual men or intravenous drug abusers, it is safer to use a condom or sheath which acts as a physical barrier to the transmission of the AIDS virus.

AIDS victims suffer from many disadvantages on top of their inevitably fatal disease. They cannot get life insurance or mortgages and may be ostracised or persecuted by prejudiced people. Much of this prejudice is based on fear and ignorance. AIDS cannot be transmitted by normal social contact nor by sharing food, swimming pools or lavatory seats.

If you suspect that you may have been in contact with AIDS you should discuss this with your student health service or seek counselling at a sexually-transmitted diseases (STD) clinic. Blood tests for HIV-1 antibodies can be arranged, anonymously if necessary. If you lose weight for no obvious reason, develop persistent swollen lymph glands or suffer from frequent unexplained infections, you will need to consult your student health service. Usually the cause will turn out not to be AIDS.

For advice ring AIDS Helpline at the Terence Higgins Trust Ltd, 071-833 2971 or send a large SAE for leaflets from AIDS Helpline, Terence Higgins Trust Ltd, London WC1M 3X. A student information pack on HIV and AIDS is issued by the Health Education Authority, Hamilton House, Mabledon Place, London WC1H 9TX (071-387 0550).

Dr Peter Andersen,
Medical Administrator, Health Centre, University College London

Arrival

Everyone experiences culture shock (especially overseas students) when they arrive at UKCPU. Whatever the environment – red brick or ivory tower – it's new and it's unnerving. Don't worry, you'll get used to it.

Make sure you register in the right place at the right time. At least then you should get your grant. Find out what you have to do and when and make yourself out a timetable. It's embarrassing to be late, or lost. Once that's over submerge yourself in the first week's entertainment – usually a 'freshers fair', endless discos, wine and cheese parties and bar promotion nights. Don't waste money by joining ludicrous societies. Induction meetings will bore you to death, but you'll see the faces in power and you might sit next to someone interesting.

Tom Dodd describes his experiences thus:

'On your first day at UKCPU you will more than likely be overawed and a little intimidated – don't worry, all the other students will feel the same. (After going through the amazingly tedious registration procedure, anyone would feel at least stressed.) Try and talk to some of them – if you make the first move, people will gladly talk to you. However, be prepared to meet some strange people! You're bound to meet some cheery soul, who cracks obscure jokes and talks about Socrates. (They will soon frown, however, when you tell them that you thought he played well in the last England vs Brazil game.)

On the second day, you will get so sick of pamphlets, leaflets, booklets etc, that you'll more than likely dump the lot. Unfortunately, this means you will have no idea where your first introductory lecture is and it's embarrassing walking into a large lecture room full of people only to be told by the lecturer you are in the wrong place – I know!'

Books

In the first week of term if not before, most UKCPUs will present you with an exhaustive reading list. Don't go to the bookshop and buy everything you're expected to – you'll never be able to afford it and they should all be in the library. Second-hand text books are up for sale on most student union and department notice boards for a fraction of the price. If these are beyond your means try borrowing or splitting the cost with others on your course, or being inventive in your use of the library. Some books will have to be bought sometime, but make sure they're essentials and not just your tutors' latest failed publication.

Changing Courses and Changing UKCPUs

Once at UKCPU, changing courses can be difficult, and practices vary between UKCPUs. The dodges are known – getting on an under-subscribed course and then switching. But most UKCPUs are sympathetic and the usual procedure is first to see tutors and then seek whatever permission is necessary. But watch out you do not lose your grant.

Transferring from one UKCPU to another can be more difficult and an agreed procedure doesn't exist. However, CATS' procedures are becoming more common – ask CATS (CNAA, 344–354 Gray's Inn Road, London WC1X 8BP). Different UKCPUs, and different courses within them, will take different approaches to giving credit for earlier study. Check first before doing anything.

If you are on a grant, you should be able to transfer it to a new course – but only if a) you get the timing right: the transfer must be approved by the UKCPUs before a notional date which is 4 months after the end of your first year or b) you would be due to complete your new course no later than you expected to complete your old course eg moving from the end of the first year of one course to the beginning of the second year of your new course, if they are the same length and you don't take a year off between. But in either case, you can only transfer your grant if your course transfer is with the approval of **both** course organisers (or both institutions). So make sure you talk to everyone concerned before taking the plunge.

Disabled Students

Despite the many barriers that still exist, hundreds of students with disabilities graduate from UKCPUs each year having had successful and rewarding years of study.

Among the many obstacles are physical barriers of difficult or impossible access, attitudinal barriers of ignorance and discrimination, and difficulties of finding the extra costs of disability. Even so, the student with a disability probably has a better chance of getting a place at UKCPU than ever before. Some of the barriers can be overcome by a very early informal application, and choosing a college which can provide extra help and support when this is necessary.

A key person in most UKCPUs is the adviser to disabled students. They can arrange informal visits for you, help you decide whether the course you hope to follow is a realistic possibility, advise on support services, and help you throughout your time at college.

Students with physical disabilities may require special accommodation. Most UKCPUs will have some rooms available for students with disabilities, though few have the specialist accommodation available at, for example, the universities of Essex, Southampton and Sussex, and in Oxford (Taylor House) for the Oxford colleges. A few UKCPUs have their own personal care helpers; most will help you arrange help, for example from Community Service Volunteers.

Some UKCPUs will arrange readers for blind and partially-sighted students. Other help, including financial assistance, is available from the Royal National Institute for the Blind.

Only Durham University and Bulmershe Campus at Reading have their own interpreters for the deaf, although many other UKCPUs make use of local services provided by the local education authority. The Royal

National Institute for the Deaf have a higher education adviser who can help with information and advice.

Extra counselling and tutorial help may be available in some UKCPUs for students with disabilities, including students with specific learning difficulties eg dyslexia, or with emotional or mental illness problems.

Students with disabilities on mandatory grants can claim an additional 'disabled students allowance', for extra costs incurred as a direct result of disability and attendance on the course. The Snowdon Award Scheme for Disabled Students has also proved an invaluable source of help for many.

More information on all these matters, and a selection of publications on eg applying to higher education, are available from *Skill: National Bureau for Students with Disabilities*, 336 Brixton Road, London SW9 7AA (Tel 071-274 0565). *Skill* operates an information and advice service, and is in contact with all UKCPUs.

Richard Stowell,
Director, Skill: National Bureau for Students with Disabilities

Dropping Out

There are hundreds of reasons why students drop out after a year at UKCPU – they may succumb to family pressure to do something else, fall ill or in love, or just not like the course or the subject or the UKCPU they've chosen. Maybe they decide they didn't want to do a degree course at all. Men are more likely to drop out of a first year course than women. If you want to see if your UKCPU/subject have a good record, you can consult a report of the Committee of Vice-Chancellors with the snappy title of *University Management Statistics and Performance Indicators*. If you're reading engineering don't bother – drop out rates are up to 20%. If you're thinking of dropping out, make sure you talk to tutors and student advisers before you take irrevocable steps – and watch out for grants/loans.

Drugs

Many students will be tempted to experiment with drugs which alter their state of mind. Those that are legal, such as alcohol, nicotine and caffeine, will be sold in most Student Unions. Tobacco, particularly in the forms of cigarettes, causes a great deal of long term illness and increases the risk of circulatory side effects in those taking the contraceptive pill. Abuse of alcohol causes ill health and leads to loss of social inhibitions, sometimes with disastrous results, such as violence and unwanted pregnancies. Long term alcohol abuse often leads to poor concentration and study difficulties. However, the temperate use of alcohol, particularly wine, can be the source of much civilized pleasure.

Experimenting with illegal drugs can be a very dangerous occupation – apart from the possibility of fines or imprisonment. Heroin, cocaine, amphetamines, barbiturates, LSD and marijuana are all illegal. New drugs of dependency keep cropping up, such as ecstasy which is an amphetamine derivative and crack which is a refined form of cocaine. Heroin is the most dangerous, particularly if it is taken intravenously. Dependency develops very rapidly and soon takes over the addict's life. Those who are hooked may have to find up to £80 a day to feed their habit. This can lead to dealing in heroin, prostitution and other crimes. The intravenous route also leads to the possibility of developing blood infections, Hepatitis B and AIDS.

One aspect of drug dependency is often forgotten. Addicts are at the mercy of their suppliers who may cut or contaminate what they sell. With LSD, for example, there is no way of knowing what dose is being taken. An overdose may cause very frightening 'bad trips' and lead to psychotic episodes.

Marijuana, although illegal, is in a rather different category. It is relatively harmless and does not often lead to antisocial behaviour. However, there is a risk of causing foetal abnormalities during pregnancy. In Holland it has been legalised without any great increase in its use.

If you feel under pressure to experiment with any illegal drug, the best advice is '*don't*'.

Students who get into trouble with the police for taking or supplying drugs can get advice from Release or Narcotics Anonymous.

Dr Peter Andersen,
Medical Administrator, Health Centre, University College London

Finance

Once you've got your money don't spend it all at once. It probably won't last all term anyway, but try to contain your extravagances. Work out what you have to spend each week on rent, food and entertainment, and stay roughly within your limit. When you need an overdraft or overdraft extension go and see your student adviser at your branch which, if you are well organised, should be pretty close to your UKCPU. Don't keep withdrawing money regardless – bank managers hate it. If you get into dire straits, go to the student union or UKCPU welfare office and cry convincingly.

Gays

If you are gay, and it's estimated 5–10% of the population are, then the campus provides a better-than-average environment to come to terms with your own sexuality. Student trendiness promotes the cultivation of gay acquaintances: 'Some of my best friends . . .'. Trendy tolerance is easy but public hostility is growing, especially in the light of AIDS statistics and it's worth remembering that landlords may not welcome overt gays. It is not necessarily easy for a gay to tell an uncomprehending Mum or Dad about it all, but you can get help from your college gay society: most of the big UKCPUs have one. There you can meet other gays and, if you like, get into gay politics. But make sure you have read everything the government has dished up on the subject of AIDS and only go in for safer sex.

The gay rights movement was triggered off by a riot in Stonewall's bar in New York about twenty-five years ago, but since then Oscar Wilde's 'love that dare not speak its name' has turned into the reactionary's 'love that does not shut up'. Although gays are sometimes overly paranoid, they are often victims of prejudice and fear. The 1967 Sexual Offences Act legalised sex between consenting males over the age of 21 in private. Lesbian sex has never been illegal, allegedly because of Queen Victoria's refusal to countenance that women would do such a thing when giving royal assent to the act outlawing homosexuality. Groups like the Campaign for Homosexual Equality want an end to legal harassment and the age of consent lowered. More generally, gay groups are campaigning for society's acceptance, not just toleration of homosexuals.

For gay students, London is reckoned to be the best bet for its variety of gay social life. Gritty macho areas like the North East and strong church-going areas like North Wales and Northern Ireland are not advised.

Hardship Funds

Many UKCPUs have funds (which are their own, in addition to government access funds) that allow small loans to tide you over if your grant is late (banks may also offer interest-free loans in these circumstances) or if your money from overseas is delayed by exchange control. Some UKCPUs have more substantial hardship funds which allow reductions in tuition fees if you are not getting a grant and can prove hardship. Ask your

UKCPU welfare staff if you're in difficulties; they may know of educational charities that can help.

Home-based Students

Living at home might have advantages but it doesn't help you to cut the apron strings and you might find that you are a second-class student at your UKCPU by not being able to take advantage of all the academic and social facilities offered. It's also much more likely that you will turn UKCPU into a **continuation** of school which is a great mistake.

It is cheaper for LEAs if you are based at home rather than living in UKCPU accommodation. If you want to live away from home and your LEA has assessed you on a 'living at home' basis, talk to the office at your UKCPU which deals with grants. You may be able to get the LEA's assessment changed if the UKCPU supports your moving away from home on 'educational grounds'. You should definitely do this if you don't have proper facilities to study at home (a room of your own, for a start).

If your grant is discretionary, you are more in the hands of your LEA. If the course you want to do is offered locally, they may refuse to pay for you to study elsewhere (eg art foundation course).

Independence

Higher education will mean, for most, living away from home for the first time. Self-sufficiency both financial and emotional has to be learnt. Teach yourself to cook if you haven't already; budget your spending. Homesickness may be inevitable (it's said to affect some 60% students, though only some 12% suffer to the point they can't cope). For most it should gradually pass as you adapt to your surroundings. Making friends is important as you won't have parents, siblings or friends back home to rely on. Remember everyone's in the same boat. Don't rush into ephemeral friendships but equally don't avoid human contact for fear of getting hurt. Lasting friendships will form but not in the first five minutes. 'You'll find you spend half your second year shaking off the undesirable friends you made in the first.' (Evelyn Waugh, *Brideshead Revisited*.) If you find it hard to cope don't be frightened to use welfare services, or Niteline run by the SU at most UKCPUs, for advice and support. They'll be more use (and cheaper) than a bottle of Scotch.

Insurance

Best advice is not to take very expensive personal items with you – they might get nicked. It's worth getting anything you do take insured, whether you live in UKCPU residences or not. Try 'Possessions Insurance for Students' from Endsleigh Insurance Services, 20 The Promenade, Cheltenham GL50 3NR (0242 582563). SU or welfare services should be able to advise you on policies for musical instruments, bicycles etc. The most important thing is to get your insurances sorted out immediately you get to UKCPU so you are covered as quickly as possible. It could be costly if you don't.

There are occasional tales of unauthorised life insurance salesmen visiting halls and student flats. You are strongly advised not to sign anything and to inform the appropriate authorities. You'll also be sent unsolicited mail – ignore it. As a student any personal insurance policy you're offered is likely to be a waste of time and money.

Learning

Forget school and the way schoolteachers treated you. UKCPU teachers treat you as an adult. Having taken the trouble to get into an UKCPU to study for a degree, it is assumed that you enjoy your subject, are committed to it and want to find out more about it. If so, all well and good. But watch out – the pattern of work may be very different from what you've been used to. No spoonfeeding; you do it yourself at UKCPU. Before you go, you will probably be sent a booklist. You may not be advised which books to read, use your own judgement. You'll be given a timetable for lectures and tutorials, seminars and practicals. Some lectures and seminars aren't compulsory, but most tutorials and practicals are. It's quite easy not to attend lectures, but it's your loss if you don't. You will be expected to do a lot of written work and use a wide range of sources. Try to plan your time well, rushed work isn't usually good work. You might have to read your essay, for example, to your tutor or other students. Don't be put off by this. Criticism, painful as it can be, sharpens understanding. Don't be put off by more sophisticated students, they are not necessarily brighter. Use your own sense and go your own way. See D Rowntree, *Learn How to Study* (London: Macdonald); R A Carman and W R Adams, *Study Skills* (New York: Wiley & Sons). Some UKCPUs put on courses for students who seem to lack study skills but if you need help get it while still at school or college. Have a look at Harry Maddox, *How to Study* (London: Pan). Remember, you will have to handle much more information than you did for A-level.

Libraries

From UKCPU to UKCPU libraries vary in quality, quantity and size; some have specialist collections. Bear this in mind when you apply (see

Where to Study). As libraries will loom large in your student life, suss out your UKCPU library very early on and make sure you know how to use it. Also check opening times and days. Some are closed completely at weekends. It will probably use a different classification system from the one you were used to at school or college. Most libraries have information services and are only too pleased to explain how the library works and if there's a guide, get hold of it. Also ask other users about it – a useful topic of conversation at ghastly induction meetings.

London

London has over 50 UKCPUs and upwards of 100,000 students – somewhere. It is clearly a magnet for students but there are difficulties. Unless you're in UKCPU accommodation being a student in London can be very isolated. London UKCPUs tend to be splintered over various sites, and it's up to you to be in the right place at the right time both socially and academically. If you don't know your way around London or have never been there before, then you'll have to learn fast. Nobody is going to lead you round by the hand. Accommodation will be hugely expensive and may be difficult to find. Expect to travel some distance for work and play and again, expect travel to be expensive. Opportunities for entertainment are great but so is the cost. SU facilities will be invaluable socially and financially, so use them. Guides and agencies for help do exist (through your SU), but your own resources will be your best asset.

Mature Students

Jeanette Dodd writes: 'It was with great surprise that I found myself embarking upon a BA Honours degree course. Having waded through what seemed like an eternity of forms, interviews and exams, I felt as though I deserved a degree just for surviving the mature matriculation process. Indeed, the passage of a mature student through the clearing system is both confusing and difficult, even with the aid of *The Student Book*.

'My friends had regarded me with suspicion when I had announced my intention of giving up my job and entering the realms of higher education. Undeterred, I fought my way through and, after a year, was still glad I had persevered.

'On my first day at college, I met up with several other mature students who, I was relieved to see, looked as nervous as I did. Then we knuckled down to lectures, acquiring text books, and all that "studying stuff" we had heard about.

'So how did we all get on? Well, it became apparent that college was not the holiday camp it seemed at first after years of earning a living. We were actually expected to produce assignments, sometimes the first essays we had written for years. Families moaned they hardly saw us, and non-college friends complained we fell asleep in the pub after an exhausting week at college. We were usually found buried under piles of books in the library, that is when we were not raiding the younger brother's pencil case, or cramming a month's household chores into a thirty minute blitz!

'Meanwhile, on the campus the young students were very kind, opened doors for us and smiled encouragingly. The only complaint I heard was that no hooks were provided for our Zimmer walking aids!

'Seriously, college life is the most rewarding and stimulating experience. I enjoyed being part of a group, and the variety of people I came into contact with only served to increase my enthusiasm for learning. I even enjoyed all the reading and hard work – even after three years!

They say "life begins at forty", forget it, life begins at maturity!'

North v South

The well publicised north/south divide does not necessarily have to affect student life. Nevertheless, stereotypical attitudes regarding 'northerners' and 'southerners' still remain to an extent. However, don't be put off going to a northern UKCPU coming from the south, and a southern UKCPU coming from the north. Just remember that different attitudes towards politics, religion, sex etc exist in different areas and that a little tact might come in handy. People from all over the country (even the world) may be at your UKCPU; some from your home area will be there too.

Overseas Students' Survival

The first few weeks at UKCPU can be disorientating for anybody, but students from overseas may have the additional problems of coping with a different language and culture (especially if they haven't already spent much time in the UK) not to mention the behaviour of the immigration officials when they enter and re-enter the UK. Advice must be above all to keep your visa up to date if you need one. Many UKCPUs have special orientation programmes and societies for overseas students which offer counselling, help and support (as well as social events). You may not necessarily want to surround yourself with compatriots while you have the opportunity to meet the locals but it can be helpful to know that others share your specific worries/problems. The NUS produces good literature on everything from fees to what to do if the immigration authorities refuse to let you into the country; it also has a list of useful addresses (National Union of Students, 461 Holloway Road, London N7 6LJ; 071-272 8900).

You can also get useful advice and information and a contact at most UKCPUs from UKCOSA (UK Council for Overseas Student Affairs, 60 Westbourne Grove, London W2 5FG; 071-229 9268-9). The British Council (10 Spring Gardens, London SW1A 2BN; 071-389 4383) runs an information service, which you can telephone or visit (though check their office opening hours). Two useful books – *Studying and Living in Britain* (published annually for the British Council, ISBN 0746306199) and *How To Study and Live in Britain* (ISBN 0746303777) are both published by Northcote House Publishers Ltd.

Parents

Establish the ground rules before you go – parental contribution (when and how it's to be paid), frequency of correspondence, phone calls, visits home etc. You are now an adult with a separate life to lead. Preserve your independence but don't distance yourself too much, or it will make contact difficult and Christmas impossible. Pride and/or concern will mean they'll want to come and see how you're getting on. Warn them what to expect. Don't let them just turn up – it will be at the most inconvenient moment. Fix an exact time and date. Sundays are a good idea – everybody's in bed and no-one will ever see them.

Poverty: Coping With It

The amount that students have to live on – whether it's from grants or loans – has failed to keep up with inflation over recent years so the romanticised image of student life on a shoe-string is now a harsh reality for many. Your allowance for the term (if you get it all at once) may seem like riches beyond measure; it isn't, so be careful you don't blow it all in one glorious fortnight only to spend the rest of term trying to avoid your bank manager.

One student writes:

'At the end of my first year, I had an overdraft of £500. This was rather in excess of what the banks generally like to allow. The reason my bank was not attempting to lynch me was that I had got to know my student adviser by visiting him and he had got to know me personally. The moral is – get to know your student adviser. It keeps the bank happy if you have taken the trouble to discuss your finances with them.'

Depending on where and what you are studying, it is sometimes possible to supplement your income by finding part time work, maybe at the SU or in local pubs and restaurants. Your SU or nearest job centre may be able to help you with this.

Wherever it comes from (grant, parent, loan, job) you will want your money to go as far as possible. The *Pauper Notes* for each UKCPU (*Where to Study* section) will help by listing some of the cheapest local amenities. In general, UKCPU accommodation seems to be the best value although it is sometimes possible to find very cheap flat shares if you have the time and energy to hunt (and if you are lucky). Food, drink and entertainment are usually cheapest at the SU but keep an eye open for local alternatives (Chinese and Indian restaurants, student discounts at theatres, cinemas etc.). Some supermarkets produce student survival kits, including money-off vouchers and budget recipes.

This may all sound grim; try not to be put off. Although you won't have a lot of spare cash for clothes etc neither will anybody else; try not to skimp on books or food. Most people enjoy themselves at UKCPU in spite of their lack of money. After all, the best things in life are free . . . they say.

Pregnancy

Don't. It may seem like a good idea at the time but don't. For all but the most mature students there is plenty of time after UKCPU. Take one thing at a time and find out about contraception early.

Racism

Racial discrimination is still a sad fact of UKCPU life. Recent reports from the Commission for Racial Equality have shown that black students are discriminated against in some UKCPU admissions procedures, that many colleges have no policies to deal with incidents of racism and that black graduates face discrimination in the labour market. That aside, black students are likely to find that they are confronted with less racial prejudice at a UKCPU than in many other walks of life.

Most UKCPUs now have well organised Black, Jewish and Irish student groups, as well as societies representing overseas students and different national and religious minorities. Many of these groups are extremely active in the social and political life of the UKCPU and are a very good place to meet other students of a similar background. The existence of these groups, and national organisations such as the National Black Students Alliance and the Union of Jewish Students, has ensured that there is a constant challenge to racism wherever it appears on campus.

The desire to oppose racism wherever it occurs sometimes expresses itself in debates about whether people who are members of declared racist or fascist organisations should have the right to organise or speak at a UKCPU. Since the Government introduced a law safeguarding free speech on campus, students have found a variety of other means of showing their opposition to speakers who represent racist or fascist groups. The discussions about the issue still continue and often represent one of the most fascinating and educative debates on campus.

The black civil rights leader, Martin Luther King, once said 'If you are not part of the solution you are part of the problem'. Student Unions go to great efforts to involve students in campaigns against racism, and anti-racism 'weeks of action' and international cultural evenings are now common features in a student union calendar. Indeed it is events like these which lead to an interaction of the experiences, histories and cultures of the different ethnic minority groups with those of the student body in general. This provides a dynamic and enriching aspect of student life and helps to ensure that UKCPUs remain relatively free from overt racism and a strong barrier against the spread of racial hatred and intolerance. Contact student union officers, or your tutor, if you have a problem on account of your race – on or off the campus.

Patrick Younge

Reading Difficulties

If you have difficulties with reading first have your eyes tested. Then get hold of M and E de Leeuw, *Read Better, Read Faster* (Penguin) or T Buzan, *Speed Reading* (David & Charles). And your local college of FE may run short helpful courses. If you are dyslexic there are special units at certain UKCPUs and in extreme cases you may be able to dictate essays and exam papers. If all else fails, try READING UNIVERSITY.

Registration

Put up with registration – it only happens once a year and the first year is worst. Expect queues (take books, crosswords or try busking). Make sure you take everything the UKCPU asks for or it will be even more boring. If the UKCPU asks for the original certificates they will mean it, so get duplicates in advance if you've lost them (most accept the slips you were sent by your exam board only for the most recent exams). Take your GCSE/O-level certificates along too, if they ask you to bring *all* your certificates. Take a pen and don't lose your papers. If you've got problems with eg your grant, tell registration staff. It's a hellish time for everyone – staff and students – so we advise patience and getting your act together *before* you reach the head of the queue. You'll find it useful to take four or five recent passport photographs for ID, membership cards etc.

Safety

This is becoming more of an issue, particularly (but not only) for women. Try and make sure you can get to and from your lectures/parties etc safely – ie that your lodgings are close to public transport and surrounding footpaths are well lit; if they aren't, harry the authorities to get things changed. Some SUs run late night buses for women students only; some provide first year women with rape alarms – a sign of the times.

Self Catering Checklist

If you are in self catering accommodation here are some points you may find useful:
*   Find out what cooking facilities are available (oven, rings, grill etc gas or electricity?)
    How many others share them?

Are there restrictions as to when they can be used?
Make sure you know how to operate them properly.

* What about cooking utensils, pots, pans, cutlery, crockery etc?
Make yourself a list of things you know you will need and check how
many of them are provided. A basic list could start with:
kettle
frying pan
sharp knife
bread knife
plates
bowls
jug
ovenproof dish or bowl
at least 1 saucepan
chopping board/surface
wooden spoon/spatula
cutlery
cups
glasses
dishtowels
tin opener
then add whatever else you expect to use: fish slice, lemon squeezer,
garlic press, potato peeler, cheese grater, sieve, bottle opener and cork-
screw.

* What food storage space is available? It can make a big difference if
there is somewhere for you to store supplies (without fear of having
them stolen) rather than having to dash to the shops every day. This is
particularly noticeable during the summer if you don't have access to a
fridge.

* Many students find it better to share cooking and food buying. This
usually works quite well until somebody gets waylaid in the pub when it
was their turn to cook. If you decide to take it in turns to cook (which
will reduce considerably the time you spend cooking and shopping) it
pays to be organised about it, especially where money is involved. Set
up a kitty or an accounts book where everyone writes down how much
they spend on communal food etc. It's also important to work out
exactly what is communal and what isn't; milk, coffee, cleaning stuff
etc. If possible keep some sort of emergency supplies so that you won't
starve if your cook gets any last minute invitations on the way home.

* If you haven't done much cooking before, or even if you have and want
some quick, inexpensive recipes then try some of these books:
The Students Cookbook by Jenny Baker (Faber)
Cooking for One by Catherine Kirkpatrick (Hamlyn)
Cooking in a Bedsitter by Katherine Whitehorn (Penguin)
Frugal Food by Delia Smith (Coronet)
Not Just a Load of Old Lentils by Rose Elliott (Fontana)
Many supermarkets have series of recipe books that cater for all sorts of
tastes and pockets.

Sex

Many students spend much of their time thinking about sex, but relatively little time actually doing it. Nevertheless, liberal attitudes towards sex still prevail on campus despite obvious concerns about AIDS. (The use of condoms is now much more widespread.) The glib idea put about by certain sections of the press, that students have come full circle and now hold attitudes resembling those of Queen Victoria or Mary Whitehouse is simply not true. For students living in close proximity to each other, often for the first time free from parental control, the opportunity to experiment with sex is considerable.

Sexual Harassment

It probably happens everywhere to a greater or lesser extent. But the stories are most consistent and extreme in the old male preserves (medical schools; some Oxbridge colleges which have accepted women undergraduates for a number of years but still have a predominantly male staff and, therefore, ethos). Check the place out before you apply. If you do have trouble – from staff or fellow students – make sure you tell someone. There's an officer responsible for women's issues in most SUs – that should be a good start.

Sexually Transmitted Diseases (STDs)

STDs have always been a risk associated with sexual relationships. In 1913 about 10% of the British population had syphilis. By 1985 there were fewer than 3,000 cases of syphilis treated in STD clinics but the annual incidence of gonorrhoea was still over 50,000. Between the end of the last war until some ten years ago, the spread of STDs was contained by early diagnosis, effective treatment and contact tracing achieved by the STD clinics. In the past few years the AIDS epidemic has overshadowed the other STDs but they are still a threat.

Syphilis was in several ways an earlier model of AIDS. It could be caught by sexual intercourse, it could lie dormant for years, it was often fatal and until the advent of antibiotics it was largely untreatable. There was a period in the 1960s and 70s when all STDs were thought to be treatable, which coincided with the introduction of the contraceptive pill and the breakdown of sexual taboos. However, the arrival of genital herpes on the scene changed all that.

The commonest STDs now are non-specific urethritis caused by chlamydial infection, gonorrhoea and monilial vulvo-vaginitis (thrush). The first two can unfortunately infect women without producing symptoms and are a risk to their future fertility. Human wart virus is also transmissible, from men to women and may be a causative factor in cervical cancer.

You can greatly reduce the chances of catching any STD including AIDS if you avoid promiscuity and use condoms or sheaths if your partner has been at risk of previous infection.

If you develop an unusual vaginal discharge, any genital sore or ulcer or unexplained lower abdominal pain, it is essential to consult your student health service or an STD clinic, also known as departments of genito-urinary medicine (GU Clinics). These departments offer free advice, investigations and treatment and you can refer yourself directly without going through your GP.

Dr Peter Andersen,
Medical Administrator, Health Centre, University College London

Staff–Student Sex

It happens. Both male and female students can be at risk, heterosexually or homosexually. It can be very ego-boosting (but not much more) to be 'courted' by an older, and apparently wiser, person. At its worst it is simply sexual harassment.

An affair with a tutor can lead to awkwardness, and more importantly from your point of view it can increase pressure on you. And it can be very tacky if your tutor is your examiner. Permanent relationships have, very occasionally, been known but tread warily. Some UKCPUs are actively considering/introducing a code of conduct to regulate staff/student sexual conduct. If it happens to you and you don't welcome it, talk to your student counsellor (unless he/she is the offending party) or student union.

Student Concessions

Many shopkeepers give students a discount on proof of student status, usually a NUS card. You can also get some newspapers and journals cheap. Lists of local retailers offering discounts are available from UKCPU SU office. So use these. To get discounts on some 18,000 shops, restaurants etc nationally, plus travel, accommodation, theatres, museums etc internationally, you need an International Student Identity Card (ISIC). This is an internationally accepted proof of student status and is available to full-time students of any age for the price of £5.40 and a photo. It is valid from September to December of the following year and you will get free copies of the international student discount scheme handbook and travel guide. Get details and an application card from your local SU or student travel office or NUS Services (Bleaklow House, Howard Town Mills, Mill Street, Glossop, Derbyshire SK13 8PT; 0457 868003).

Student Health

Most UKCPUs have their own student health services linked to the National Health Service. It is advisable for new students to register with them as NHS patients in the first week of term. Your medical records from your family doctor at home will then follow you in weeks or sometimes months. When you are at home during vacations you can still see your family doctor as a temporary resident.

All the information you give to doctors, nurses and counsellors remains confidential and will not be passed on to the college authorities without your specific consent. If you prefer to have your medical problems dealt with outside your place of study, you are free to register with any NHS general practitioner near where you are living.

The staff in student health services are experienced in dealing with your particular needs. They will be able to offer advice on contraception, unwanted pregnancies, study difficulties and eating problems such as anorexia nervosa. They will discuss with you how to avoid sexually transmitted diseases including AIDS and drug and alcohol problems. Information on healthy nutrition and keeping fit is available. Some centres also have attached dentists, opticians and physiotherapists.

Most health services will also have facilities for dealing with psychological problems. They employ counsellors, psychiatrists and psychotherapists who may normally be in short supply in the NHS as a whole. Again, it must be emphasised that these services are confidential.

Many colleges have special arrangements for the physically disabled or chronically ill students but it is important to inform them in advance of any difficulties you may have. Some groups of students, eg medics and dental students, need special immunisation cover for their clinical work.

Remember that the health centre staff are just as interested in preventing illness as in treating it, so feel free to consult them before health problems develop.

Dr Peter Andersen,
Medical Administrator, Health Centre, University College London

Students' Unions

Most UKCPUs have their own SU (sometimes called guild or association) normally affiliated to the NUS. Every student is automatically a member of the SU, and each SU receives a grant based on the number of students in it (though the Tories want to abolish this closed shop). Whatever the slant of the union (left, right or uncertain), it is run by students for students – more or less. It's usually responsible for entertainments (bands, discos, bars) and for funding clubs and societies. Check for a union shop, which may be the cheapest place to buy stationery etc, and for 'Niteline' for personal problems. Most SUs now offer some form of welfare service which can be useful for advice and information on accommodation, work and money matters. How much you get involved in union activities and politics is up to you, but life could be very dull without them. Don't necessarily be put off by a UKCPU's reputation for radical or conservative student politics but keep your eye on whether its SU engages in political censorship or racist or anti-middle class activity. Things can change and your involvement could help to change them.

Studying

Do it! If you do not know how or want to improve on it, try reading *Study for Survival and Success* by Sander Meredeen (Paul Chapman Publishing Ltd). Many UKCPUs run formal short courses at the beginning of the first term to help you develop study skills.

Travel

Local travel can be little or no problem at some UKCPUs but at others it can be horrendous. At some small, single campus UKCPUs there is no need to travel at all while at others you may find that you are spending nearly as much time, energy and money on travel as the average local commuter. Check what's required before applying – you can get some idea from *Where to Study* and the UKCPU prospectus.

When you move to college you'll be leaving behind the family car, along with the personalised laundry service, free heating and the nagging parents. Once you're living on your grant/loan/savings, you'll find you can walk much further than you ever thought possible; and, unless your nerve has completely failed you, a pushbike or pair of roller skates will be useful, if not essential. Hitching may be possible, depending on the area but it's not recommended for women alone after dark (some SUs run night-time minibuses for women). Try to plan your local travel so that it does not eat into your grant/loan. If you can still talk, walk.

Travel further afield needs researching. Look for 'ride boards' at college, advertising lifts to home/London or to sport/cultural occasions. You can get reductions on train and coach fares once you've invested in the appropriate card. The Young Person's Card from National Express Coaches costs £5 for a year and allows you 1/3 off standard fares without restrictions (including the Rapide services) as well as discounts on some international services. The Young Person's Railcard costs you £16 and entitles you to 1/3 off most standard second-class fares (including savers and day returns with some restrictions). And what's more, if you buy it before November, it'll last you 15 months, rather than just a year.

If you have a Student Travel Office nearby it will help with your travel plans for the holidays. They sell the products of the 10 or so main student travel operators and have heaps of good advice on student/youth travel. Or try the **Student Travel Centre, Tours and Travel** (STCTT, 18 Rupert Street, London W1; 071-434 1306) or **Campus Travel** (headquarters at London Student Travel, 52 Grosvenor Gardens, London SW1W 0AG; 071-730 3402; and on 26 student campuses).

No student pays the full scheduled air fare. There are all the usual methods of getting cheaper flights – bucket shops, ads, charter flights, standby fares, and advance booking (APEX and ABC). In addition, there are lots of student specials. The most obvious are youth fares and student charters. Youth fares allow a range of reductions (up to 25%) off the standard economy fare to European countries and some others. Some have to be bought from the Student Travel Office, so ask there first. They are good value on long-haul and European flights, giving you full-fare service at student price. Student charter flights operate in each vacation to Europe, Israel and the USA. You can get on them with a valid International Student Identity Card (ISIC) – check your Student Travel Office.

Or you can take the train with a BIJ or Interrail ticket. BIJ (Billets International Jeunesse) issues a 2-month ticket which gives you up to 40% reductions on second-class train tickets (including the channel crossing) to destinations in Europe and Morocco. You can stop-over and you don't need to come back the same way as you go; there's an Explorer's Ticket, linking 22 centres, for a round trip. If you're under 26, you can buy a ticket from any British Rail station or your Student Travel Office (or some other Eurotrain/British Rail/Sealink agents). New this year, you can have a week's unlimited travel in Hungary for £18.50 and in Poland for an astonishing £10. If you want to hit the fleshpots of a number of European cities, you may prefer an Interrail card. This will currently set you back £155 (less with a Student Rail Card), is valid for one calendar month and entitles you to unlimited travel on national rail networks in 22 countries on the continent, as well as reductions on some hovercraft and ferry services. An Interrail and Boat card costs £180 and adds free travel on some shipping routes; an Interrail Flexicard, at £145, buys you the same for 10 days in any month. Go to your Student Travel Office or to British Rail or its agents.

Typing

Make sure you can.

Get a wordprocessor if you can; you can probably use the ones in the UKCPU if you can't.

Vacs

You'll never have holidays this long again until you retire, so make the most of them. It's probably essential to use them to inject some life into your bank balance as well, so look at some of the excellent books obtainable from **Vacation Work Publications** (9 Park End Street, Oxford OX1 1HJ; 0865 241078). The most general are *Summer Jobs in Britain* and *Summer Jobs Abroad*, £6.95 each. *Vacation Traineeships for*

Students lists companies which will give you business experience to bolster your cv. Make sure you get the up-to-date editions, published in January.

There are three well trodden student paths to overseas travel in the long vacation:
- starting from work in a summer camp in America/Canada;
- starting from work on a Kibbutz in Israel;
- setting off to see the world with a back-pack.

1. *Working Holiday in American Summer Camp*

American school kids spend much of their summer holiday in Summer Camps and armies of British students act as camp staff – a good way of getting to the States.

Basic requirements: special working holiday visa; usually be aged between 18 and 35 and like working with children (experience of youth or community work useful; additional skills in drama, art and sport welcomed). The work is usually as general counsellor or drama/arts/sports specialist; for those not suited to working directly with kids there are posts in Kamp – a programme for camp kitchen and maintenance staff.

Basic costs: typically a deposit of £100, which covers insurance and a special visa. Your pay varies – $150 to $450 for the season – plus a free return air ticket and board and lodging at camp. At the end of the camp, most stay on as tourists with a Greyhound bus ticket – unlimited travel on North American buses for 7 days (£80), 15 days (£125), or 30 days (£180).

First moves: Specialist agencies recommended; they will interview you and arrange a suitable job, camp place, visa, flight and arrival. Try **Camp America** which places 8,500 British students in over 1,000 summer camps. It is at 37a Queen's Gate, London SW7 5HR; 071-589 3223; or **BUNAC** (The British Universities North America Club) 16 Bowling Green Lane, London EC1R 0BD; 071-251 3472; it is a non-profit student club open to all degree students which specialises in arranging working holidays for young people in the US and Canada (also Jamaica and Australia).

2. *Kibbutz Working Holiday*

Not recommended if you really want the Costa del Sol and definitely not for lager louts, this is a good way of sampling a unique way of life/culture. **Kibbutz Representatives** say the best recommendation is that, despite vociferous complaints of overwork, terrible food, rotten accommodation and under-pay, many students repeat the experience the following year and some stay on and on and on . . .

Basic requirements: special working holiday visa (minimum 5 weeks, maximum 6 months); be between 18 and 32 and in **robust** physical and mental health. Expect to work hard – in agriculture, horticulture or light industry – possibly at unsocial hours (eg daily six hour hatchery shift starting at 4.00am).

Basic costs: typically £30 registration fee gets you a visa and a Kibbutz place; return air fare £200. On the Kibbutz it's all found, including sport, and you'll be paid pocket money for toothpaste etc from the subsidised Kibbutz shop. Off the Kibbutz you're a tourist like any other and your costs are what you make them (Israeli buses are good). Most set off after they've finished, either from Haifa to Cyprus and Greece or down to Egypt.

First moves: Pukka agency with good Kibbutz contacts recommended. It will brief you and arrange your Kibbutz place, visa, flight and arrival. Try: **Kibbutz Representatives**, 1a Accommodation Road, London NW11 (081-458 9235) or **Project 67**, 10 Hatton Garden, London EC1 (071-831 7626).

3. *Seeing the World*

Once you've earned enough money to see you through the next term, you can put on your back-pack and set off to see the world. You need to be flexible, adaptable, resourceful and able to live without the usual creature comforts.

Basic requirements: Totally portable luggage, which won't destroy your back. Some ideas – where you're off to, how you're going to get there and where you're going to stay. Enough money to fund your ideas and any visas you need along the way. If you want to stay in youth hostels (there are some 5,300 across the world), join the **Youth Hostels Association** and take your International Accommodation Guide. Depending on the style of accommodation you're aiming at, you may want to take your sleeping bag.

Basic costs: Well what do you want to do? An Interrail Card will cost you £155 and you can assume about £2–£10 a night in a Youth Hostel in Europe (depending on location and whether there are showers/heating/shops etc or whether it is 'simple'). Or you can break the bank for a flight east and accommodation may be as low as 30p a night. Or get a cheapie flight to North America and sleep on Greyhound buses – so a month's ticket of £180 will cover travel and accommodation.

First moves: Visit your Student Travel Office. They can tell you about cheap flights, overlanding, package holidays, you name it . . . They can also provide you with an Interrail Card. To join the **Youth Hostel Association** – cost £2.00–£7.60 in 1990 – send for details to Trevelyan House, 8 St Stephen's Hill, St Albans, Hertfordshire, AL1 2DY (0272 40211); in Scotland to the **Scottish Youth Hostels Association**, 7 Glebe Crescent, Stirling SK8 2JA (0786 51181); in Northern Ireland, **YHANI (Youth Hostels Association of Northern Ireland)**, 56 Bradbury Place, Belfast BT7 1RU; (0232 324733).

Victimisation

If you think you are being victimised for reasons of politics, race, religion or sex you should contact your SU or try one of the following:

Campaign for Homosexual Equality (CHE)
PO Box 342, London WC1X 0DU (071-833 3912)

Catholic Students Council
186 St Paul's Road, Balsall Heath, Birmingham B12 8LZ (021-440 3273)

Commission for Racial Equality
Elliot House, Allington Street, London SW1 5EH (071-828 7022)

Communist Party Youth and Student Committee
6 Cynthia Street, London N1 9JF (071-278 4443)

Conservative Collegiate Forum
Westminster Palace Gardens, Artillery Row, London SW1P 1RR (071-799 1041)

Equal Opportunities Commission
Swan House, 52 Poland Street, London W1V 3DF (071-287 3953)

National Council for Civil Liberties
21 Tabard Street, London SE1 4LA (071-403 3888)

National Organisation of Labour Students
150 Walworth Road, London SE17 1JT (071-701 1234)

Student Democrats Youth Office
4 Cowley Street, London SW1P 3NB (071-222 7999)

Union of Jewish Students
Hillel House, 1/2 Endsleigh Street, London WC1H 0DS (071-380 0111)

Welfare

UKCPUs generally are supportive. They normally provide specialist help for a range of problems. The NUS publishes an excellent Welfare Manual – intended for student advisers but you may be able to consult a copy in your library or SU office or contact NUS (461 Holloway Road, London N7 6LJ).

The Government is stopping all social security benefits to students (with some exceptions eg disabled or single parents). More information from DSS leaflets from local DSS offices or Citizens Advice Bureaux.

DSS Information Service: Dial 100 and ask for freefone DSS. Dental and eye checks are means tested once you are 19 – get the appropriate forms from your dentist and optician to claim free checks.

What If You Don't Survive Your First Year

Work out what went wrong
If you're not up to higher education, look for a job. If you fancy eventually becoming your own boss, buy the *The Careers Book*.
If it was the wrong course, try changing course (fast, to keep your grant).

If it was the wrong UKCPU, or the wrong place, try changing UKCPU (fast, to keep your grant).

If the reasons are personal or financial, try giving it a break. You **may** be able to return later, transfer credit to another institution (though the systems are still sticky on this) or continue part time at some other UKCPU.

What You Call Them/What You Don't

(ie formal address for UKCPU academics). Below are the terms for **formal** address in speech and writing – what you call academics **informally** is up to you.

Status	Speech	Writing
Vice-Chancellor	Vice-Chancellor	Dear Vice-Chancellor
Principal	Principal	Dear Principal
Director	Director	Dear Director
Master (applies to some women's UKCPUs as well)	Master	Dear Master
Warden	Warden	Dear Warden
Professor (even if knighted)	Professor Bloggs	Dear Professor Bloggs
Readers		
Senior Lecturers	Dr/Mr/Ms/Mrs	Dear Dr/Mr/Ms/Mrs
Lecturers	Bloggs	Bloggs
Tutors		

Do not use Dear Sir, Dear Madam, or Dear Sir/Madam, when writing to tutors.

WHAT'S WHAT IN HIGHER EDUCATION

ABBREVIATIONS

ACCESS

ADAR

AGRICULTURE

A-LEVEL and AS-LEVEL GRADES

AMERICAN COLLEGES

ART COLLEGES

BOGUS DEGREES

CATS

CNAA

COLLEGE

COLLEGES/INSTITUTES OF HIGHER EDUCATION

COMMUNITY SERVICE VOLUNTEERS

CONTINUING EDUCATION

CORRESPONDENCE COURSES

CREDIT TRANSFER

DEGREE-EQUIVALENT COURSES

DEGREES

DES

DIPLOMA IN HIGHER EDUCATION (DipHE)

DRAMA

ECCTIS 2000

EUROPEAN COMMUNITY

EXTERNAL DEGREES

FILM EDUCATION

INFORMATION TECHNOLOGY (IT)

LEA

MATURE STUDENTS

MERGERS

MILITARY, NAVY AND AIR FORCE EDUCATION

NORTHERN IRELAND

NUS

OPEN UNIVERSITY

PCAS

PERFORMANCE ARTS

POLYS

PROFESSIONAL QUALIFICATIONS

SANDWICH COURSES

SCOTLAND

TEACHING

UCCA

UNIVERSITIES

WALES

Abbreviations

British and European higher education is jargon-laden with a welter of confusing and confused terms (eg semester strictly speaking means a half academic year but in some places means a term, ie third of a year) and abbreviations and acronyms. Regrettably, the list continues to grow: 800 plus at the last count. Here are a few useful ones:

A-levels – GCE passes at advanced level; ADAR – Art and Design Admissions Registry; AFEIS – Advanced Further Education Information Service; APL – Assessment of Prior Learning; AS-levels – Advanced Supplementary levels; BBA – Bachelor of Business Administration; BTEC – Business and Technician Education Council; CACC – Council for the Accreditation of Correspondence Colleges; CATS – Credit Accumulation and Transfer Scheme; CCE – Cambridge Colleges' Examinations; CNAA – Council for National Academic Awards; COMMET – Community Programme in Education and Training for Technology; CRCH – Central Register and Clearing House; CSE – Certificate of Secondary Education; DES – Department of Education and Science; EC – European Community; ECCTIS – The Educational Counselling and Credit Transfer Information Service; ECTS – European Community Course Credit Transfer Systems; EGA – Educational Guidance for Adults; ERASMUS – European Community Action Scheme for the Mobility of University Students; FE – Further Education; GCE – General Certificate of Education; GCSE – General Certificate of Secondary Education; GTTR – Graduate Teacher Training Register; HE – Higher Education; HEISU – Higher Education Information Service Unit; HNC – Higher National Certificate; HND – Higher National Diploma; IB – International Baccalaureate; ICP – Inter-University Co-operation Programme; JCR – Junior Common Room; LEA – Local Education Authority; LINGUA – Community Action Programmes to Promote Foreign Languages Competence in the European Community; NAB – National Advisory Body; NCDT – National Council for Drama Training; NGAA – National Grant-Awarding Authority; NUS – National Union of Students; O-levels – GCE passes at ordinary level; ONC – Ordinary National Certificate; OND – Ordinary National Diploma; PCAS – Polytechnic Central Admissions System; PCFC – Polytechnic and Colleges Funding Council; PICKUP – Professional Industrial and Communications Updating; Poly – Polytechnic; PSHE – Public Sector Higher Education; QTS – Qualified Teacher Status; SA – Students' Association; SCE – Scottish Certificate of Education; SCR – Senior Common Room; SED – Scottish Education Department; SRC – Students' Representative Council; STEP – Sixth Term Examination Papers (entrance exam for Cambridge University); SU – Students' Union; UCCA – University Central Council on Admissions; UFC – University Funding Council; UGC – University Grants Committee; UKCPU – a United Kingdom College, Polytechnic or University.

Access

This is a new buzz word. Widening access means opening up higher education, particularly to non-standard students. There are also access funds – government money distributed to students by UKCPUs, for those in financial hardship; and access courses which are designed to prepare you for a degree course if you were not previously qualified – particularly science and engineering. Some are excellent some are suspect. Check what extra qualifications you need for the UKCPU and degree course you want before you embark on an access course. A useful directory to access courses is available from ECCTIS (Access to Higher Education Courses Director).

In the *Where to Study* section, we use access to mean how you get there – bus, rail etc. How old fashioned.

ADAR

The Art and Design Admissions Registry, Penn House, 9 Broad Street, Hereford HR4 9AP (0432 266653). It processes all applications for art and design degree courses and higher national diploma courses in design and associated studies in polytechnics, colleges and schools of art and design in England and Wales.

Agriculture

Agriculture is taught at first degree level and higher national diploma. First degree courses are available at a number of UKCPU (for prospectuses worth getting hold of see **Subject and Places Index**). Several agricultural colleges teach for the higher national diploma only and in general tend to be concerned more with vocational training and lay less emphasis on the scientific aspects of the subject. You can take your choice.

Below we list some distinguished agricultural teaching institutions and how to get hold of them:

Cirencester ....See **Where to Study**
Harper Adams ....See **Where to Study**
Hertfordshire College of Agriculture & Horticulture, Oaklands
   Hatfield Road, St Albans, Herts AL4 03A (0727 50651)
Scottish Agricultural College, Aberdeen
   581 King Street, Aberdeen AB9 1UD (0224 480291)
Scottish Agricultural College, Auchincruive
   Ayr KA6 5HW (0292 520331)

Scottish Agricultural College, Edinburgh
  West Mains Road, Edinburgh EH9 3JG (031 667 1041)
Seale-Hayne................See **South West Poly** in **Where to Study**
Welsh Agricultural College, Llanbadarn Fawr, Aberystwyth, Dyfed
SY2 3AL (0970 624471)
Writtle – See **Where to Study**.

A-Level and AS-Level Grades

UKCPUs accept grades A–E as passes, these are often turned into points.
For AS level, A=5, B=4, C=3, D=2, E=1; for A-level, A=10, B=8,
C=6, D=4, E=2. If you have a conditional offer, you may well be asked to
gain specific grades or a cumulative minimum number of points. A-level
grades are not always regarded by UKCPUs as reliable pointers to future
academic development. But *your* job is to get your A-level grades. If you
have to play the grades game, invaluable advice and information is given in
Brian Heap, *Degree Course Offers*, Careers Consultants Ltd. UKCPUs
will normally accept two AS-levels in place of a third A-level but will often
require two A-levels. But there may be course requirements, so check.

American Colleges

Many American colleges have a UK campus which admits British
students. They are very variable and British students may find it difficult
to get employers and professional bodies to accept a degree from some of
them as equalling a British degree. Some of the American colleges
represented in the UK are of international standing.

Art Colleges

Some, but not all, colleges of art offer CNAA degrees. Where they do
you'll find them in the **Subject and Places Index** together with university

art courses. Some have become departments in polys or colleges of higher education (after much grumbling, some very justified). In London, a number have joined together in a loose federation called the London Institute, although there is some closer 'clustering' expected within the Institute. The individual colleges still maintain individual identities (at the moment) and you apply to them through ADAR. This trend has been followed in other parts of the country – Essex, Cornwall etc.

Work out what kind of institution you want to go to, but often grants for the foundation courses are not available for those outside your immediate area. Many offer foundation courses, which is one route to a degree. Our *Study Areas* distinguish between **fine arts**, which is art history, and **fine art** (which, together with graphic design, photography, textiles/fashion and three dimensional design, form the Art & Design *study area*).

Art at University

Some universities offer degree courses that combine fine arts (art history) with practical studio work. These university courses are often taught in conjunction with local art colleges.

Bogus Degrees

A number of bogus degrees are offered by post, mostly postgraduate degrees. Sometimes the degree is for sale, sometimes a thesis is required. There is seldom any course of instruction. No UKCPU offers or accepts them. Under the Education Reform Act 1988, it is a criminal offence to award or seek to offer to award a UK degree if you do not have express authority to award it, and the Secretary of State for Education provides lists of bodies authorised to award UK degrees. If in doubt contact the DES. There is no such constraint on offering certificates or diplomas, so beware!

CATS

A scheme operated by CNAA (344–354 Gray's Inn Road, London WC1X 8BP) to help students with unusual backgrounds or aspirations, throughout the UK and particularly in London.

CATS stands for Credit Accumulation and Transfer Scheme. It should be able to help you if you:
* want to carry credit to a degree course, perhaps on the grounds that you have already taken a course at a UKCPU or have work experience that duplicates part of the course.
* want to study for a CNAA degree at more than one UKCPU, perhaps because there is no UKCPU teaching the combination of studies you seek – eg Arabic and Hebrew.
* want to alternate periods of study with other activities – eg producing a family or earning your living.

You can make use of CATS in two different ways – either purely for obtaining advice before you apply to a UKCPU for a course leading to a CNAA degree *or* by registering directly with CATS so that you become a CATS student and can then study at a number of UKCPUs. A growing number of companies' in-house training schemes (eg IBM, W H Smith and even Wimpy) and professional bodies' qualifications (eg IPM, CIMA) can count for credit too.

CNAA

Colleges and polys, unlike universities, cannot award degrees in their own right. The Council for National Academic Awards awards degrees to students who have satisfactorily completed CNAA-approved courses. In each UKCPU profile you will see who awards the degree. Recently CNAA has delegated much of its authority to over 40 polys and colleges and so they will, in effect, be awarding their own degrees although you will still get a CNAA degree certificate. Make sure you know whose degree you are getting. CNAA's *Directory of first degree and Diploma of Higher Education courses* is available from CNAA, 344–354 Gray's Inn Road, London WC1X 8BP (071-278 4411).

College

This is a portmanteau word. Its usage can range from Garret Tutorial College, Hackney, to the Royal College of Surgeons. Some universities have a number of constituent colleges. No other word exists to describe this odd assortment. Some colleges teach first degrees. Most don't. Check a college's academic standing.

Colleges/Institutes of Higher Education

Colleges, in some cases institutes (and there's no real difference) of higher education, emerged in the 1970s as a third kind of higher education. They run a variety of advanced, ie post-A-level, and non-advanced courses. We include them as UKCPUs in *The Student Book* when they offer first degree courses from CNAA or 'parent' university. Not all of them do and degree students may be in the minority. Their history is various: some are stitched together from teacher training colleges and some are former colleges of technology. There appears to be a trend for colleges of HE to merge with their 'parent' university or associate formally with local polytechnics if they cannot themselves gain polytechnic status.

Most now use PCAS for degree applications unless they are affiliated to universities when they use UCCA. Most receive money from the same place as polys (PCFC – Polytechnics & Colleges Funding Council). Some have remained as LEA run colleges.

Community Service Volunteers

Are you uncertain about what to do when you leave school? – or have you decided, but would like to try something completely unconnected with work or college? Then community service volunteers could be the answer.

CSV is a national volunteer agency which involves young people in full-time community work in a wide range of projects throughout the UK, normally away from home. For example, volunteers are currently working with adults and children with learning difficulties or physical disabilities, with the homeless, the elderly, children whose families have broken up, young offenders, immigrants who want to learn English, battered wives and children on adventure playgrounds and play schemes. You don't need experience or qualifications to become a CSV – just the enthusiasm to commit yourself to the community and to improving the quality of other people's lives. No offer of service is refused: provided you can give between 4 and 12 months full-time and are over 16, CSV will find a project for you. As a volunteer, you'd receive full board and lodging plus £18.50 per week spending money and travelling expenses. If you think you might be interested in becoming a CSV, write for more information and an application form to CSV, 237 Pentonville Road, London N1 9NJ (071-278 6601).

Continuing Education

Another educational term which means what its users want it to mean!
Essentially it means that you can't expect your education to end when
you've got your first degree (we thought that'd cheer you up) but you can
expect periods of re-education and re-training during your working life. So
you could be going back to UKCPU for up-dating in your subject. This
contrasts with studying for a **higher** degree which is intended to take you
deeper into your subject.

Correspondence Courses

These are essentially part-time courses by postal tuition. There have been
abuses, and the responsible correspondence colleges have established the
Council for the Accreditation of Correspondence Colleges (CACC). But
accreditation is voluntary. CACC produces a list of colleges which it
accredits. It's obtainable from CACC, 27 Marylebone Road, London
NW1 5JS (071-935 5391). For advice on UK degrees available by correspondence, contact the DES (Department of Education and Science).

Credit Transfer

You may find that you want to change course or take a break from higher
education for a year. If you do change course or return to higher education
after a break you may be able to transfer the credit for the work you did in
your earlier course to your new one so maybe take less time to complete
your new course. This is called a credit transfer in UKCPU jargon. You
can carry a credit from one UKCPU to another, or from one course to
another within the same UKCPU. You will need the help (and maybe the
approval) of the course tutor from your first course so make sure you keep
him/her informed. Also, if you are on a grant, watch out you don't lose it
when you change course (see separate entries).

Some transfers are easier than others – from a DipHE to a linked degree
course in the same UKCPU will probably be automatic. But you wouldn't
expect to carry any credit to a physics degree on the basis of previous study
in the social sciences now would you? You can now get credit (through
CATS at CNAA) for an increasing number of companies' in-house
training courses though.

But the overlap in subject matter is not necessarily simple for admissions
tutors to assess and in many UKCPUs there is a noticeable reluctance even
to try. Indeed, within UKCPUs there can be a wide variation of approach
to credit transfer between the different courses. Some modular courses

can, and do, admit a large number of students with credit. So if you can't find (or don't want) a clone of your first course, they are a good point to start looking.

There are a number of developments aimed at breaking down some of the inflexibility of higher education. One is CATS (see separate entry) run by the CNAA, which aims to allow students the maximum credit, if necessary by registering them as students of CNAA rather than of a single UKCPU. The other is the establishment of a number of local higher education consortia (eg the Manchester Consortium consists of Manchester and Salford Universities, UMIST, Manchester Business School and Manchester Poly). These are in various stages of development and have differing aims but in general they aim to improve the possibility of transfer between the member UKCPUs and possibly lead to some common courses. Some consortia include local further education colleges, so it may be easier to move to local degree courses from these, possibly with some credit. It will be a chance in a million that you will benefit from them but they are a step in the right direction for higher education as a whole. If you want to find out whether your previous work will count for credit, ask when you apply to UKCPU. If that doesn't work, asks CATS.

If your UKCPU is part of the Erasmus Scheme, you can study somewhere else in the EC for credit – so long as you don't expect special treatment at the host institution because the assessment system and language are unfamiliar.

Degree-Equivalent Courses

To help you pick your way through the thickets of diplomas etc the DES (Dept of Education and Science) provides a free publication **Grants to Students: A brief guide**, available from your LEA (local education authority) or the DES (Publication Despatch Centre, Honeypot Lane, Canons Park, Stanmore, Middlesex HA7 1AZ). Generally speaking, mandatory grants are available for first degree courses, Diploma of Higher Education (DipHE) courses, Higher National Diploma courses, and courses of initial teacher training. Some other degree-equivalent courses are eligible for mandatory grants in the following subjects: accountancy, architecture, art and design, chemistry, drama, environmental health, landscape architecture/design, music, textiles and town/town and country planning. These are listed in a free leaflet, available from the DES, Designated Courses. Scotland is different: contact the Scottish Education Department, Awards Branch, Gyleview House, 3 Redheughs Rigg, Southgyle, Edinburgh EH12 9HH (031-556 8000).

The degree-equivalent courses covered in **The Student Book** are not necessarily the same as those attracting mandatory grants. They are degree courses and those that, in the opinion of the editors, are real alternatives to a degree. No less valid than the DES view!

Degrees

First degrees are the main concern of *The Student Book*, either honours or ordinary (sometimes called pass). Most degree courses are now honours, and ordinary degrees are awarded if a student fails to achieve honours standard. But, there are some courses leading only to an ordinary degree, eg Open University and some part-time courses.

Usually first degrees lead to the award of bachelor status (BA, BSc, BEd or LLB) but there are many variants eg many Scottish first degrees lead to an MA and not all bachelor degrees are first degrees (eg BPhil). Higher degrees are usually masters or doctorates (MA, MSc, PhD), again with many variants. When applying for first degrees, don't get worried by the letters – course content matters much more. Honours degrees are usually classified into first, upper second (2.1), lower second (2.2) or third. There are different types of degree depending on the course structure: **single** (where a single subject is studied for the length of the course, although a wide variety of topics may be covered and the first year may be broad); **joint** (where components of two single subject degrees are taken; you don't do twice as much work – but check the proportions); **combined** (where components from any number of single degrees can be put together; check how the degrees are combined – are they just stitched together to appear trendy or do they cohere as a real educational whole?); **multidisciplinary** or **interdisciplinary** (often terms for combined degrees so do check as for combined degrees); **modular** (where students structure their own degrees out of options, or modules).

There are also different kinds of approach: **theoretical** (a specialist study without immediate applications); **vocational** (the degree is directly linked to work applications); **sandwich** (part of the course is spent in a work placement). Think hard about what degree course structure and kind of approach will suit you best. Each UKCPU has its own language about its degrees so check thoroughly that it will provide what you expect. Check how the degree is assessed (eg examination, continuous assessment, project work). This can vary within a UKCPU depending on the course. Make sure you find out the assessment procedure and that it suits you.

Universities give their own degrees to their students, those in affiliated colleges and some colleges which do external degrees. Polys and most colleges/institutes of HE give CNAA degrees.

Degrees from foreign universities (eg American universities) are offered in the UK but *The Student Book* does not cover them. So long as the foreign university makes it clear that what is offered is not a UK degree but (say) a US degree, it is quite acceptable to the British authorities. But beware: the degree may not be acceptable to British employers or professional bodies. Check thoroughly before paying any fees.

DES

The Department of Education and Science, Elizabeth House, York Road, London SE1 7PH (071-934 9000) is the central government department responsible for education in England and Wales. For Northern Ireland the equivalent is the Northern Ireland Department of Education, Rathgael House, Balloo Road, Bangor, County Down BT19 2PR (0247 270077), and for Scotland the Scottish Education Department, New St Andrews House, Edinburgh EH1 3SY (031-556 8400). Most matters concerning grants are dealt with by your LEA.

Diploma in Higher Education (DipHE)

This is a two year diploma course which, in theory, is equivalent to the first two years of a degree course. They could be of interest to mature students not wishing to commit themselves to 3 years' study. Some UKCPUs allow you to transfer from DipHE to degree courses; others haven't heard of them. **Don't** embark on a DipHE without ensuring that transfer to a degree is possible.

Drama

Because grants for drama students are discretionary (ie your LEA will decide for itself whether it will give you a grant and, if so, how much) it is particularly important that you should get onto an approved course. The National Council for Drama Training (5 Tavistock Place, London WC1H 9SS, 071-387 3650) publishes a list of accredited courses. UKCPUs offering drama as a first degree subject are listed in **Where to Study**. The NCDT list of accredited courses is:

ALRA (Academy of Live and Recorded Arts); Arts Educational School; Birmingham School of Speech Training and Dramatic Art; Bristol Old Vic Theatre School; Central School of Speech and Drama; Drama Centre, London; Guildford School of Acting and Drama Dance Education; Guildhall School of Music and Drama; London Academy of Music and Dramatic Art; Manchester Polytechnic School of Theatre; Mountview Theatre School; Rose Bruford College of Speech and Drama (BA Theatre Arts); Royal Academy of Dramatic Art; Royal Scottish Academy of Music and Drama; Webber Douglas Academy of Dramatic Art; Welsh College of Music and Drama.

There are also lists of accredited courses in Community Theatre and stage management, and one year post-grad drama courses.

ECCTIS 2000

Educational Counselling and Credit Transfer Information Service, Fulton House, Jessop Avenue, Cheltenham, Gloucestershire GL50 3SH (0242 518724). Provides comprehensive information on all further and higher education courses and their entry requirements and handbooks on access courses and credit transfer. ECCTIS data (30,000 courses and due to increase) is stored on a computer which can be searched on-line to answer enquiries about courses. You can enquire direct through the Campus 2000 national viewdata system, or by letter (Freepost enquiry forms on request) or telephone.

European Community

The aim is for 10% undergraduates in the European Community to spend part of their degree course in a different EC country. British ministers fret about a one-way traffic to the UK. This could be your opportunity to break with insularity and become a European. For points to look out for, read **Foreword: Before You Apply – Think Europe** (page 3).

Erasmus, an EC action programme, helps organise student mobility between member countries. Students can spend a fully recognised period of study in another member country. For information on schemes and grants approach your UKCPU or UK Erasmus Students Grants Council (The University, Canterbury CT2 7PD; tel: 0227 762712) or the Erasmus Bureau in Brussels (Rue d'Arlon 15, B-1040 Bruxelles; tel: 0101.32.2.233.01.11).

Fritz Dalichow writes: 500 years ago, the Dutch humanist Desiderius Erasmus spent his school, university and working life as a university professor in different parts of Europe, moving freely both as a student and teacher. He learned and taught in places like Deventer/The Netherlands, Paris/France, Cambridge/England, Bologna, Turin and Venice/Italy, Leuven/Belgium and Basle/Switzerland. The Erasmus Programme (European Community Action Scheme for the Mobility of University Students), tries hard to bring back academic mobility in view of the Common Internal Market in 1993 and thereafter. This year there will be some 44,000 students spending a study period in an EC member state other than their own under Erasmus.

The Erasmus Programme was adopted on 15 June 1987 by the 12 member states of the European Community. As its name implies, the programme's main objective is to increase significantly the number of students who spend a period of study in one of the other European Community (EC) countries. However, the programme is broader than this in that it also provides funding for a wide range of other co-operative activities. Firstly, Erasmus provides grants to universities which, in this context, refers to all types of higher education institutions as defined nationally, for the purpose of designing, developing, operating, maintaining and evaluating programmes for the mobility of students and/or teaching staff. The totality of the programmes thus supported forms, what is known as, the European University Network. The emphasis is on programmes which enable students to spend a period of at least three months in another community country for which they receive full academic credit from their home university. Tuition fees are mutually waived. In the case of the staff mobility programmes, preference is given to arrangements whereby the visiting staff members provide integrated teaching input of significant duration, ideally at least a month, into the programmes of the host institutions.

In addition, universities may receive support for the joint development of new curricula and for carrying out intensive programmes of short duration, involving students and teaching staff from several Community countries. All four types of programme are collectively known as inter-university co-operation programmes (ICPs). Grants for these various activities vary considerably depending on the nature and complexity of the programmes concerned. For establishing student mobility programmes, they average $9,300 per university, per programme, per year.

Secondly – and this is the element of Erasmus which gives the programme both its title and its main focus – Erasmus provides mobility grants to students in the form of top-up grants to help cover the additional costs incurred by students wishing to study in another community country. These costs include such items as language preparation, cost-of-living differential and, of course, travel. The average grant, Community-wide, is around $2,000 for a full year's study, and students of all levels (up to doctorate) are eligible, though grants are not normally awarded to students in their first year of higher education. Priority is given to students moving to another EC country within the framework of ICPs supported under Erasmus.

Thirdly, the Erasmus Programme seeks to promote a number of measures designed to improve the possibilities for students to receive academic recognition or credit for study periods effected, and qualifications obtained, in other member states. In addition to the network of nationally based information centres on the assessment of foreign educational credentials which has been established for this purpose, a European Community course credit transfer system (ECTS) is now operational, launched in 1989/90, the pilot phase of this project will span a six-year period. Within ECTS, automatic credit transfer arrangements are being progressively introduced in five subject areas (mechanical engineering, medicine, chemistry, business studies and history), between the total of some 80 institutions, which will form the core of the pilot project.

Finally, the programme encompasses a number of complementary measures designed to assist in creating a favourable climate for the future development of Erasmus. These include in particular a 'visits' scheme to enable university teachers and administrators to visit other community countries for the purpose of preparing future exchange programmes, to carry out brief teaching assignments, or merely to familiarise themselves with aspects of the higher education systems in the countries visited. Support is also provided for specific projects of university associations and consortia operating at European level, for the preparation of publications related to university co-operation, and for various information activities.

The Commission of the European Communities is assisted in the operational implementation of the Erasmus programme by an agency called the Erasmus Bureau. The student grants' component of Erasmus is administered on a decentralised basis by nationally designated agencies, co-ordinated in Brussels and working according to jointly agreed guidelines.

Particularly important with regard to Erasmus is its comprehensive nature: it embraces 12 European countries and is open to all types of higher education institutions, all academic disciplines and levels of study, and provides support for a number of different types of co-operation activity.

Erasmus is by far the biggest programme for inter-university co-operation and exchange ever launched at European level, with a budget currently fixed at some 200 million ecu for the three year period 1990-92. Moreover, along with Comett, the EC programme for higher education-industry co-operation in the field of technology-related training, it has brought the higher education sector into the mainstream of policy-making for the EC as a whole. In helping to create a vastly increased pool of young people with first-hand experience of living and studying in another country, it has an important role to play in the run-up to 1993, the year in which internal barriers to trade and professional mobility within the Community should be dismantled, and takes its place alongside other measures designed to create what is becoming known as the 'People's Europe'.

(Fritz Dalichow is Assistant Director of the Erasmus Bureau in Brussels, responsible for academic recognition and credit transfer matters. This article is mainly based on an article written by Alan Smith (director of the Erasmus Bureau) for the review Higher Education Policy ('The Erasmus Programme of the European Community – Some Implications for International Exchange and Co-operation', *in:* Higher Education Policy, Vol 1 No.4 1988, pp 51-52). The views expressed in this article are those of the authors and do not necessarily represent those of the Commission of the European Communities or the European Cultural Foundation).

External Degrees

These are issued by a university, eg Kent University, which validates the teaching at another UKCPU. They are less common now that polys and colleges mostly offer CNAA degrees.

Film Education

Film education normally now includes TV film education. An invaluable list of film courses in higher education is available from the Educational Advisory Service, British Film Institute, 21 Stephen Street, London W1P 1PL (071-255 1444). See also Film Studies in **Subject & Places Index**.

Information Technology (IT)

IT is an umbrella term for a whole set of techniques, old and new, and definitions of IT can be cumbersome. But its central notions are simple – IT denotes the application of one central technology (eg cheap computer circuitry on silicon chips) and a small set of ancillary technologies to two basic activities: communication and calculation. Communication and calculation underpin our work and leisure and increasing these activities will restructure most people's lives. It is the combination of computing with new telecommunications (including fibre optic cables) which gives IT its present impact. To the electronic engineer, all forms of information – printed text, speech, music, pictures, numerical data or control signals – are stored in computer memories and transmitted, displayed or transformed in the same way. The wider spread of IT will be a part of higher education's involvement in innovation. There are an increasing number of first degree courses in IT and at some UKCPUs IT can be taken as a final year option or a component of electronics/computer science/technology courses.

LEA

This means your local education authority in England and Wales. It is to your LEA that you apply for a grant but also contact your LEA for advice (address in 'phone book). In Scotland apply for a grant to the Scottish Education Department, Awards Branch, Gyleview House, 3 Redheughs Rigg, Southgyle, Edinburgh EH12 9HH. In Northern Ireland apply to your area Education and Library Board.

Mature Students

For grants purposes, mature students are those over 26 on 1 September in the year they wish to start at UKCPU and then they should get more money. You can have your grant assessed independently of your parents before that if you have worked for three years.

Entrance requirements for mature students vary. Polys and colleges can be more flexible about entrance requirements for mature students though. But many universities are making encouraging noises and have positive policies, so don't give up.

There is a useful Mature Students' Union but the president, and so the union's address, changes each year. Write to the NUS (executive member responsible for mature students) and ask for the current president. See also: *Mature Students: university degree courses*.

Mergers

'Big is beautiful' is back. Under present financial arrangements, it's difficult for small institutions to survive and merger mania has struck. There are polys proposing merger with each other; colleges merging with universities, polys, each other or even FE colleges; colleges affiliated to universities are making more of their affiliation. UKCPUs can change dramatically, so make sure your UKCPU will survive your course in a recognisable form. The new generation of mergers will make split sites in a city look like a tight-knit campus. Many are spread over 50 miles.

Military, Navy and Air Force Education

Five UKCPUs offer this (see **Where to Study** – Cranwell; Dartmouth; Manadon; Sandhurst; Shrivenham). See also Strategic Studies in **Subject**

and Places Index. Military bursaries are paid to selected students while you are at UKCPU, if you promise to go into the service when you graduate. If your heart is set on this, then go ahead. But don't forget that after three or four years at UKCPU you mightn't want to return to service life. If you pull out you will probably have to pay the money back. Contact your local recruiting office for details of the various schemes.

Northern Ireland

Northern Ireland has two universities, Belfast and Ulster. Grants regulations are the same as for the rest of the UK although you apply to your Education and Library Board. Despite the political unrest student life is surprisingly normal. Students are affiliated to both the UK and the Eire NUS.

NUS

The National Union of Students, Nelson Mandela House, 461 Holloway Road, London N7 6LJ (01-272 8900) is the central organisation for UK students. You may or may not agree with its politics but student politics change rapidly – locally and nationally. NUS is a federation of students unions. You join your local SU automatically and, as a collective body, it decides whether to join NUS – 98% UKCPUs do. If you are at an UKCPU that is affiliated you will receive its benefits – its information services and student concessions are invaluable. Take grant and disciplinary problems to your UKCPU students' union.

Open University

Founded in 1969 to cater for part-time, mature students, the OU (Walton Hall, Milton Keynes MK7 6AA; tel: 0908 274066) now accepts applicants of 18 years and over onto degree courses.

Although OU degree courses usually take longer to complete than other full-time degree courses (4–6 years), the fact that they only require part-time study (10–15 hours a week) together with the flexibility of the inter-disciplinary course structures offered, makes the OU a good alternative for those who can't or don't want to commit themselves to a full-time degree course or who find it more satisfactory to study at home from the material provided by the OU.

(See Open University in **Where to Study**.)

PCAS

Polytechnics Central Admissions System, Fulton House, Jessop Avenue, Cheltenham, Gloucestershire GL50 3SH (0242 227788). PCAS operates the central admissions scheme to polytechnics and many colleges/institutes of higher education. This covers all full-time and sandwich degree courses (and DipHE & HND) except those in art and design. The PCAS Guide lists the PCAS courses. Get hold of it either direct or through your school/college.

Performance Arts

This term has been coined through the need to find a description for an area of study that includes experience in those arts which involve an element of performance. The word **performance** rather than **performing** is generally used to make clear that courses so designated are not vocational courses of training for would-be professional actors, singers and dancers, but rather intended to provide opportunity for a practical and theoretical study of these arts in a non-vocational context. This does not mean that students who follow such courses are debarred from a professional career, if they have the necessary talent (and a high standard of performance is usually required); but that they are degree courses offering an education in the understanding of the arts rather than a training in their practice.

Performance arts courses are usually CNAA degrees offered by polytechnics, rather than universities. This is a very complex area, study the various syllabuses with great care and write to the institutions to find out precisely the scope and objectives of the course and what options there may be.

John Allen

Polys

Polytechnics were first founded in the early seventies largely to teach vocationally oriented courses. But polys and universities now compete. Polys were often formed out of amalgamations of existing colleges, which has resulted in some split-site campuses. They are financed by the PCFC (Polytechnics and Colleges Funding Council). Scotland has its own Scottish Central Institutions which are increasingly calling themselves polys. Degrees at polys are normally awarded by the CNAA (Council for National Academic Awards). Two excellent guides are produced by the Committee of Directors of Polytechnics, Kirkman House, 12-14 Whitfield Street, London W1P 6AX (071-637 9939): *Polytechnic Courses*

Handbook and a leaflet *The Polytechnics: Full Time and Sandwich Courses* (free).

The thirty-three polys (look them up in **Where to Study**) are:

Birmingham, Bournemouth, Brighton, Bristol, City, Coventry, East London, Hatfield, Huddersfield, Humberside, Kingston, Lancashire, Leeds, Leicester, Liverpool, Manchester, Middlesex, Napier, Newcastle, North London, Nottingham, Oxford, PCL, Portsmouth, Sheffield, South Bank, South West, Staffs, Sunderland, Teesside, Thames, Wales, Wolverhampton.

Professional Qualifications

Degrees in themselves do not normally license you to practise a profession. A professional qualification is also necessary. The list below gives enquiry points from which details of the qualifications necessary for practice are available. You will also be told how long professional qualifications take and what exemptions your degree will give you.

Accountants

(Certified): Association of Certified Accountants, 29 Lincoln's Inn Fields, London WC2A 3EE (071-242 6855); *(Chartered):* Institute of Chartered Accountants, Chartered Accountants Hall, Moorgate Place, London EC2P 2BJ (071-628 7060); *(Scotland):* Institute of Chartered Accountants of Scotland, 27 Queen Street, Edinburgh EH2 1LA (031-225 56737); *(Cost and Management):* Chartered Institute of Management Accountants, 63 Portland Place, London W1N 4AB (071-637 2311); *(Public Finance):* Chartered Institute of Public Finance and Accountancy, 3 Robert Street, London WC2 (071-895 8823).

Acoustics

Institute of Acoustics, PO Box 320, St Albans, Herts AL1 1PZ (0727-48195)

Actuaries

Institute of Actuaries, Staple Inn Hall, High Holborn, London WC1V 7QJ (071-242 0106)

Advocates

(Scotland):
Faculty of Advocates, Advocates Library, Parliament House, 11 Parliament Square, Edinburgh EH1 1RF (031-226 5071)

Air Force

See Cranwell in **Where to Study**

Air Pilots, Engineers & Navigators

Guild of Air Pilots and Air Navigators, 291 Grays Inn Road, London WC1X 8QF (071-837 3323)

Architects

Royal Institute of British Architects, 66 Portland Place, London W1N 4AD (071-580 5533); Royal Incorporation of Architects in Scotland, 15 Rutland Square, Edinburgh EH1 2BE (031-229 7205)

Army

See Sandhurst and Shrivenham in **Where to Study**

Barristers

(England and Wales):
Council of Legal Education, 4 Grays Inn Place, London WC1R 5DX (071-404 5787);

(Northern Ireland):
Council of Legal Education (Northern Ireland), Institute of Professional Studies, Queen's University, Belfast BT7 1NN (0232 245133)

Dentists

General Dental Council, 37 Wimpole Street, London W1M 8DQ (071-486 2171)

Dietitians

Council for Professions Supplementary to Medicine, Park House, 184 Kennington Park Road, London SE11 4BU (071-582 0866)

Doctors

General Medical Council, 44 Hallam Street, London W1N 6AE (071-580 7642)

Engineers

Fellowship of Engineering, 2 Little Smith Street, London SW1P 3DL (071-222 2688)

Mathematics

Institute of Mathematics and its Applications, 16 Nelson Street, Southend-on-Sea, Essex SS1 1EF (0702 354020)

Navy, Royal

See Dartmouth and Manadon in **Where to Study**

Navy, Merchant

Department of Transport (Marine Division), Sunley House, 90–93 High Holborn, London WC1V 6LP (071-405 6911)

Nurses

(England and Wales):
UK Central Council for Nursing, Midwifery and Health Visiting for England and Wales, 23 Portland Place, London W1N 3AS (071-637 7181);

(Northern Ireland):
National Board for Nursing, Midwifery and Health Visiting for Northern Ireland, RAC House, 79 Chichester Street, Belfast BT1 4JE (0232 238152);

(Scotland):
National Board for Nursing, Midwifery and Health Visiting for Scotland, 22 Queen Street, Edinburgh EH2 1JX (031-226 7371)

Physiotherapists

Chartered Society of Physiotherapy, 14 Bedford Row, London WC1R 4ED (071-242 1941)

Radiographers

College of Radiographers, 14 Upper Wimpole Street, London W1M 8BN (071-935 5726)

Social Workers

Central Council for Education and Training in Social Work, Derbyshire House, St Chad's Street, London WC1H 8AD (071-278 2455).

Solicitors

(England and Wales):
Law Society, 113 Chancery Lane, London WC2A 1PL (071-242 1222);

(Northern Ireland):
Council of Legal Education (Northern Ireland), Institute of Professional Legal Studies, Queen's University, Belfast BT7 1NN (0232 245133).

(Scotland):
Law Society of Scotland, Law Society's Hall, 26 Drumsheugh Gardens, Edinburgh EH3 7YR (031-226 7411)

Speech Therapists

College of Speech Therapists, Harold Pastor House, 6 Lechmere Road, London NW2 5BU (081-459 8521)

Surveyors

(Chartered): Royal Institution of Chartered Surveyors, 12 Great George Street, Parliament Square, London SW1P 3AD (071-222 7000);

(Quantity): Royal Institution of Chartered Surveyors (address as above)

Teachers

Department of Education and Science, Elizabeth House, 39 York Road, London SE1 7PH (071-934 9000)

Town Planners

Royal Town Planning Institute, 26 Portland Place, London W1N 4BE (071-636 9107)

Transport

Chartered Institute of Transport, 80 Portland Place, London W1N 4DT (071-636 9952)

Veterinary Surgeons

Royal College of Veterinary Surgeons, 32 Belgrave Square, London SW1X 8QP (071-235 4971)

Sandwich Courses

These are ways of alternating courses of study at UKCPUs with periods of professional/industrial training out at work (50,000 students do). Periods vary in length (eg one pattern is six months 'in' and six months 'out') and there are 'thick' and 'thin' sandwiches. Find out the pattern from the UKCPU prospectus and ask for more details at the interview if you get one. Sandwich courses give good work experience and help your employability later; but some UKCPUs are finding it increasingly difficult to place their students. Watch out.

Scotland

Scotland has eight universities: Aberdeen, Dundee, Edinburgh, Glasgow, Heriot-Watt, St Andrews, Stirling, Strathclyde. Ordinary or pass degrees take three years, honours four. It also has one polytechnic, Napier; the Central Institutions, including art colleges; and the Royal Scottish Academy of Music and Drama. A full list is in the *Directory of Day Courses* (available from the Scottish Education Department, New St Andrew's House, Edinburgh EH1 3SY; 031-556 8400). *The Scottish University Entrance Guide* gives details of university courses and requirements (available from Scottish Universities Council, Kinnessburn, Kennedy Gardens, St Andrews, Fife KY16 9DR; 0334 72406).

There has been a tradition of Scottish students going straight on to a degree course after taking Scottish Highers in the fifth form (thus the four year honours courses). This does still survive but many UKCPUs now require you to take A-levels or Certificate of Sixth Year Studies.

Teaching

If you want to teach there are two routes involving a first degree course: Either get a degree in the subject you wish to teach, then take a Postgraduate Certificate of Education (PGCE). Or take a bachelor of education. Traditionally this has been a BEd but the trend now is towards a BA(Ed) or BSc(Ed); almost all the universities have made this change now because they believe the BA/BSc has higher standing.

Apply as stated in the UKCPU profile.

UCCA

The University Central Council of Admissions, PO Box 28, Cheltenham, Glos GL50 3SA operates the central admissions scheme for full-time first degree courses at all universities and affiliated colleges (but apply direct to the Open University).

Universities

Universities have charters to award their own degrees. They are funded by central government through the Universities Funding Council. There are 48 universities:

Aberdeen, Aston, Bath, Belfast, Birmingham, Bradford, Bristol, Brunel, Buckingham, Cambridge, City, Cranfield, Dundee, Durham, East Anglia, Edinburgh, Essex, Exeter, Glasgow, Heriot Watt, Hull, Keele, Kent, Lancaster, Leeds, Leicester, Liverpool, London, Loughborough, Manchester, Newcastle, Nottingham, Open University, Oxford, Reading, Royal College of Art, St Andrews, Salford, Sheffield, Southampton, Stirling, Strathclyde, Surrey, Sussex, Ulster, Wales, Warwick and York.

Wales

Wales University is a federation of six institutions: Aberystwyth, Bangor, Cardiff, Lampeter, Swansea, Wales College of Medicine. There is also Wales Poly (the only one still run by an LEA) and several institutes of higher education.

THE LONDON
● INTERNATIONAL ●
FILM SCHOOL

LOUGHBOROUGH COLLEGE of Art & Design

Principal: IEUAN PUGH

Foundation Course in Art & Design
A course of one year's duration prior to students entry
to advanced courses in Art & Design. (see also under BTEC below)

BA (Hons) Degree Courses in Art & Design
1. Textiles/Fashion with chief studies in Printed and
   Woven Textiles and Embroidery.
2. Three Dimensional Design with chief studies in
   Ceramics, Silversmithing and Jewellery, and
   Furniture.
3. Fine Art with major studies in Painting, Sculpture
   and Printmaking.

BTEC National Diploma Courses (2 years full-time)
1. Graphic Design
2. Fashion
3. General Art and Design

BTEC Higher National Diploma Course
   (2 years full-time)
Graphic Design.

Sandwich Course

A course of one year's duration (full-time sandwich
course) offering training for entry to professional
employment in Design,. Fashion or Textiles.

Further particulars on all courses are available from
**The Admissions Officer, Loughborough College of
Art and Design, Radmoor, Loughborough,
Leicestershire LE11 3BT.**

WE'RE A DEGREE OR TWO DIFFERENT FROM OTHER POLYTECHNICS

If we say we offer first-class education and excellent leisure facilities you'll probably think, "so does every other polytechnic" - but we'll say it anyway because it's true.

But it isn't every polytechnic that can offer such a breadth of choice, innovation and flexibility as Wolverhampton Polytechnic.

The town itself is at the very centre of Britain between the modern European city of Birmingham and the picturesque countryside of Shropshire with very reasonably priced accommodation and easy access to the country's major road, rail and air networks.

At the Polytechnic we fit our courses to the needs of business and the student, so you can either specialise in one area or choose a multi-subject programme of study. Whatever course you choose, you'll get a first-class education in an establishment that's nationally - and internationally - respected.

You'll find us accessible to both you and your ideas.

We offer courses in the following subject areas:

Applied Sciences; (0902) 321051.	Biology, Chemistry, Environmental Science
Art and Design; (0902) 321055.	Fine Art, Design for Communication (Graphic Design, Photography, Illustration and Electronic Media) Design for Manufacture (Ceramics, Glass, Wood, Metal and Plastics, Carpets and Floorcoverings).
Business; (0902) 321059	Accounting, Business Systems, Economics, Finance, Human Resource Management, Industrial Management, Marketing, Public Sector Finance and Management.
Computing and Information Technology; (0902) 321053.	Computing, Information Technology, Mathematics and Statistics, Business Information Systems.
Construction; Engineering and Technology; (0902) 321052.	Building, Civil Engineering, Quantity Surveying. Engineering Design CAD/CAM, Product Design , Electronics and Physics, Mechanical Engineering, Agricultural Engineering, Production Engineering, Manufacturing Systems, Materials Technology.
Education; (0902) 321050.	Initial Teacher Training for Primary and Secondary Schools, Teacher Training for Further Education, In-Service Training, Research, Higher Degrees and Specialist Centres.
Health Sciences; (0902) 321054.	Psychology, Biomedical Science, Nursing, Physiotherapy, Health Studies.
Humanities and Social Sciences; (0902) 321056.	American Studies, Drama/Theatre Studies, Economics, English, European Cultural Studies, Geography, History, History of Art and Design, Media and Communication Studies, Minority Cultures Philosophy, Politics, Racism and Ethnicity, Social Policy, Social Work, Sociology, War Studies, Women's Studies.
Legal Studies; (0902) 321058.	Law.
Languages and European Studies; (0902) 321057.	French, German, Spanish, Russian, English as a foreign language.
The Polytechnic in Shropshire; (0952) 292309.	Postgraduate Management, Business Enterprise, Business Studies, Personnel Management, Computer Studies, Business and Finance, Public Administration.

There are specialist degrees in most of these subjects, ie: BA (Hons) Business Studies; BSc (Hons) Computer Science; LLB ... There is also a menu of over 50 subjects which can be combined to make a programme for study leading to a multi-subject award ie: BA (Hons) English and History; BSc (Hons) Applied Sciences; BSc (Hons) Computing with German.

So you can select a course appropriate to your career needs and interests ...

WOLVERHAMPTON POLYTECHNIC

HOW TO FIND OUT MORE:

Call Central Switchboard (0902 321000) or ring the department direct on the numbers above

THE HIGHER EDUCATION SHOP (0902) 321032.

The shop is a unique facility, offering information and advice on the possibilities offered at Wolverhampton Polytechnic.

SCHOOL LIAISON

Careers officers/teachers should contact the Higher Education Shop, to arrange visits to the Polytechnic, talks by Polytechnic staff, or representation at careers events.

In the Heart of Britain

GLASGOW
EDINBURGH
LEEDS
MANCHESTER
WOLVERHAMPTON POLYTECHNIC
BIRMINGHAM
LONDON
BRISTOL

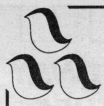

TRINITY COLLEGE
CARMARTHEN, DYFED SA31 3EP

Principal: D. CLIVE JONES-DAVIES, J.P., M.A., M.PHIL., F.R.S.A.

AN ASSOCIATED INSTITUTION OF THE UNIVERSITY OF WALES

* B.Ed (Honours)

* B.Ed Bilingual Education (Honours)
  Educational, Professional Studies and one of the following Major Fields:
  English, Welsh, Mathematics, Science, History, Geography, Religious Education,
  Music, Physical Education and Art, Design and Craft.

* B.A. Humanities (Honours)
  English/Welsh, History, Religious Studies, Theatre Studies and Welsh Studies

* B.A. Studies in the Rural Environment; Geography and Biology

* Post-graduate Certificate in Education
  (primary; secondary for Religious Education only)

**For further details and to arrange an interview telephone or write to the
Registrar, Trinity College, Carmarthen, Dyfed SA31 3EP (0267 237971)**

SOUTHERN ENGLAND
NURSERY TRAINING COLLEGE
(S E N T C)

PRIVATE RESIDENTIAL COLLEGE OFFERING
THE NATIONAL NURSERY EXAMINATION BOARD
NNEB PROFESSIONAL QUALIFICATION

STUDY IN THE BEAUTIFUL AREA OF BOURNEMOUTH
PROVIDING EXCELLENT STUDENT CARE,
ACCOMMODATION, EDUCATION & TRAINING

APPLY TO:
THE REGISTRAR
SENTC
ADMISSIONS OFFICE
81 LANSDOWNE ROAD
BOURNEMOUTH BH1 1RP
TEL: (0202) 780010

Where to Study

This section tells you about UK Colleges, Polytechnics and Universities (UKCPUs). Each UKCPU has a map reference, so you can find it on the *maps* (next section). Each UKCPU is profiled in two different ways: a Top and a Bottom.

TOP – from the UKCPU's administration and/or prospectus.

BOTTOM – *What It's Like* and *Pauper Notes* usually derive from the students.

You should not necessarily expect a complete match between the TOP and BOTTOM of each UKCPU profile.

CAN'T FIND WHAT YOU'RE LOOKING FOR? USE THE INDEX!

ABERDEEN UNIVERSITY

University of Aberdeen, Regent Walk, Aberdeen AB9 1FX (0224 272000) Map A, D2

Student enquiries: Schools liaison officer (0224 272090)

Main study areas – as in What to Study section: *(First degree):* Accountancy, agriculture horticulture and forestry, anatomy, biochemistry, biology, botany, chemistry, civil engineering, computing, economics, electrical and electronic engineering, English, environmental sciences, environmental studies, European studies, fine arts, geography, geology, history, Latin American studies, law, mathematical studies, mechanical and production engineering, medicine, microbiology, modern languages, music, Near East and Islamic studies, pharmacology, philosophy, physics, physiology, politics and government, psychology, religious studies and theology, sociology, women's studies, zoology. *Also:* Land economy, safety engineering.

European Community: 6% first degree students take EC language as part of course and 1% spend 6 months or more in another EC country. Formal exchange links (very few limited to language students) with 30+ EC universities/colleges: Belgium (3); Eire (3); France (5); Germany (6); Greece (4); Italy (3); Netherlands (3); Portugal (2); Spain (4). Approved Erasmus programme 1990/91 and links growing constantly.

Application: UCCA. **Founded:** King's College 1495, Marischal College 1593 merging to one university in 1860. **Main awards:** MA, BSc, BD, BTh, LTh, LLB, BLE, MB ChB, B Med Biol, BEng, BScEng. **Awarding body:** Aberdeen University. **Special features:** Summer school for Baltimore and Maryland Law Schools. Visiting professors in engineering and international relations. **Structural features:** New centres for the Study of Germans and Austrians in exile in Great Britain; remote sensing and mapping science; philosophy, technology and society. **Academic features:** New access courses and summer school; new combinations law and languages. New courses in tropical environmental science, Celtic civilisation, petroleum geology, Western Europe in the Renaissance, safety engineering, land use and marine resource management, countryside and environmental management. **Site:** 3 sites (King's College in Old Aberdeen, Marischal College in New Aberdeen, new medical buildings at Foresterhill). **Accommodation:** 2,400 places in halls, students houses and flats. **Library:** 5 library buildings, over a million and a quarter volumes, inter-library loan service, short loan collections for course books in heaviest demand; informal classes on use of library. **Specialist collections:** Jacobite material, transport and photographic collections, pre-1800 British and European works, first editions of early science and medical volumes. Almost 250,000 maps, many historical. **Other learning resources:** Interactive video; satellite TV for language teaching. **Welfare:** 3 doctors, dentist, health centre, university chaplaincy, academic and personal advisory systems at faculty and departmental levels; university counselling service. **Hardship funds:** Limited funds available. **Special category:** Every 3 years students elect Rector to represent them on University governing body. **Careers:** Information and advice service, regular vacancy bulletins. **Amenities:** Union building with snackbar, cafe, sewing room, launderette, 3 bars, music room with record library, supermarket; also large refectory with many facilities; SRC babysitting agency, vacation employment office, university symphony orchestra, choral society and chapel choir. **Sporting facilities:** Swimming pool, two extensive sports fields including running tracks, artificial ski slope, rowing on River Dee, Cairngorms and Grampians (mountain hut) within easy reach for climbing and walking.

Duration of first degree course(s) or equivalent: 3 years Ordinary/Designated, 4 years Honours; 5 years MB ChB; Divinity 4 years. **Total first degree students 1989/90:** 5,350; **Number of overseas students:** 420 (+ 100 nongrads). **Male/**

female ratio 1989/90: 5:4 **Teaching staff: full-time:** 571 **part-time:** 54 **Total full-time students 1989/90:** 6,814 **Postgraduate students:** 1,044. **Tuition fees, first degrees, 1990/91:** Home: £637; Overseas: £4,650-£11,470.

What it's like

Aberdeen, the Silver or Granite City, oil capital of Britain, is in NE Scotland with good access by rail and plane. Approaching its 500th anniversary. Based on medieval burgh with attractive landscaped campus. Main campus 10 minutes from halls and 5 minutes bus from city centre, where second site and union building are. About one-third housed in single study bedrooms and self-catering flats for 6 (same sex only). Hall place guaranteed for 1st year students. Private accommodation supply fluctuates; not too cheap. Student/admin relations good, SRC effective. Newly renovated SU building with 4 bars, function hall etc. 150 societies, sporting, political and many others. Some continuous assessment, more on the way. Failure and drop-out rate both below average. Changing courses is quite easy, as in Scotland you're admitted to a faculty, not a department. Most students are Scottish, but lots of English, Welsh, Irish and overseas. Less private school people than average. Some recognition given to Scottish Gaelic.

Pauper notes

Accommodation: Not much cheap accommodation but moderately priced is plenty enough. Lots of Hall places (squatting is illegal in Scotland). **Drink:** Real ale at various outlets and, of course, excellent range of whiskies almost everywhere. Regular cheap nights at the Union. **Eats:** Indian/Chinese/Italian very good, but not cheap. Radar's (pasta and American specialities) is always popular. Don't miss Jaws wholefood cafe. **Ents:** Several rock venues, including Union. Active folk scene, theatre, concert hall, arts centre, world cinema season (excellent value), alternative music festival. **Sports:** Facilities on campus (many free), for almost every sport imaginable. **Hardship funds:** Very little: university arranged. **Travel:** Scottish students can still claim travel awards, expensive to travel south by train. **Work:** A fair amount is available and the Students' Council runs a popular babysitting agency.

Alumni (Editors' pick)

Sandy Gall (ITV newscaster), Iain Cuthbertson (actor), Douglas Henderson, James Naughtie, Dr G Hadley (Convenor, Grampian Regional Council), David McLean MP, Alistair Darling, Denys Henderson (Chairman, ICI), Earl of Strathmore, Ian Crighton Smith, Catherine Gavin, Nikki Campbell (disc jockey), Kenneth McKeller, Gigi Callender, Glen O'Glaza, Dominic Addington.

ABERYSTWYTH

University College of Wales, PO Box 2, Aberystwyth, Dyfed SY23 2AX (0970 623111) Map A, C7

Student enquiries: Registrar

Main study areas – as in What to Study section: *(First degree):* Accountancy, agriculture & horticulture, American Studies, art & design, biochemistry, biology, botany, business studies, classics, computing, drama, economics, education, electrical and electronic engineering, English, environmental science, environmental studies, European studies, fine arts, geography, geology, history, information technology, law, library and information studies, mathematical studies, microbiology, modern languages, physics, politics and government, theology, zoology. *Also:* Celtic studies, space, Welsh studies.

CAN'T FIND WHAT YOU'RE LOOKING FOR? USE THE INDEX!

European Community: 6% first degree students take EC language as part of course; language and Erasmus exchange students spend 6 months or more in another EC country. Formal exchange links with 4 EC universities/colleges: Dublin (biochemistry and maths), Galway (Celtic studies), Limburg (economics and business), Wurzburg (law). Approved Erasmus programme 1990/91. European liaison office; growing emphasis on transnational co-operation in teaching and research.

Application: UCCA. **Structural features:** Part of Wales University. **Academic features:** Industrial year scheme. New courses: Computer science with European languages; rural resources management; agricultural and environmental biochemistry; accounting and finance; software engineering. Flexibility of degree schemes, students do not have to commit themselves until the end of their first or second year. Pickup programme. New Institute of Earth Studies. **Special features:** John Wain, Ralph Maud, Paul Ferris, Professor C Ricks are visiting lecturers. **Founded:** 1872, receiving charter in 1889, and joining with Bangor and Cardiff in 1893 to form University of Wales. Merged with College of Librarianship 1988. **Main awards:** BA, BSc, BScEcon, LLB. **Awarding body:** University of Wales. **Site:** Old College on sea front and Penglais campus of over 400 acres overlooking Cardigan Bay. Llanbadarn campus with accommodation within walking distance of Penglais. **Access:** Nearly all students live within walking distance of main teaching buildings. **Accommodation:** 1,900 places provided in halls and self-catering units, for 70% of student population. **Library:** 600,000 volumes, 3,000 periodicals; new library on Penglais site with over 500,000 volumes and 500 reader places; departmental collections. Access to National Library of Wales (copyright). **Specialist collections:** 600 books printed pre-1701; private press books; first editions collection (Matthew Arnold, Swinburne and Shelley), Catherine Lewis Gallery of prints and watercolours and 1747 edition of Shakespeare annotated by Samuel Johnson. **Other learning facilities:** Computer unit, microprocessor development laboratory, language laboratories with satellite receiving facilities. **Welfare:** College medical centre, college chapel (available for baptisms and marriages), Students' Union Welfare Service, Children's Centre. **Hardship funds:** Keasbey Awards, Gwilym & Dilys Edmunds Awards, and Thomas Charles Edwards scholarships. **Careers:** Information and advice (also available to those who do not complete their courses). **Amenities:** SU buildings on Penglais campus include lounge bar, bank, shop selling reduced records, 4 student bars; restaurant; over 50 societies; studio theatre and college theatre (part of Aberystwyth Arts Centre), 4 student newspapers. **Sporting facilities:** Over 50 acres of playing fields on town outskirts; Cader Range and Snowdonia within easy reach. Outstanding new sports hall with wide range of indoor sports and heated indoor swimming pool; highest proportion in UK of sports teams per student population.

Duration of first degree course(s) or equivalent: 3 years; 4 years (Modern Languages) **Total first degree students 1989/90:** 2,961 **Number of overseas students:** 238 **Number of mature students:** 14% **Male/female ratio 1989/90:** 1:1 **Teaching staff:** full-time: 298 part-time: 27 **Total full-time students 1989/90:** 3,635 **Postgraduate students:** 674 **Tuition fees, first degrees, 1990/91:** Home: £1,675 (£628 if self-financing); Overseas: £4,560 (eg politics), £6,050 (eg physics).

CEFNDIR

Sefydlywyd y Brifysgol yn 1872 mewn cyfnod o ymwybyddiaeth gynyddol o Gymreictod. Datblygodd o'r cychwyn cynnar yn yr adeilad ar lan y mor i fod yn Brifysgol brysur gyda 3000 o fyfyrwyr. Hyfforddir y mwyafrif ohonynt ar Gampws Penglais, a adeiladwyd yn y chwechdegau. Ceir golygfa wych o dref Aberystwyth a Bae Ceredigion o'r campws ac yn ychwanegol at hyn mae gennym gampws llai o faint ond mewn safle bendigedig yn Llanbadarn lle mae'r Coleg Amaethyddol a Choleg Llyfrgellwyr. Mae hawl gan holl fyfyrwyr Aberystwyth i ddefnyddio'r cyfleusterau ar y ddau gampws.

Daw mwyafrif y mwyafrif o du allan i Gymru, ond ymhlith y rhai o Gymru Cymraeg yw iaith gyntaf tua 400 ohonynt felly hefyd mae 50% o'r boblogaeth o

10,000 yn y dref ei hun. Mae digon o gyrsiau ar gael i'r sawl sy'n dymuno dysgu'r iaith. Lleolir Aberystwyth tua hanner ffordd i lawr arfordir Gorllewinol Ccymru, ac er mai araf deg yw'r daith, mae'r golygfeydd yn fendigedig. Oherwydd yr anhawster teithio, bydd llawer o fyfyrwyr yn aros yn Aberystwyth dros y penwythnos pryd y darperir gwledd o adloniant byw a disco.

Mae'r Coleg yn gofalu am letya holl fyfyrwyr y flwyddyn gyntaf – ar y campws ac ar lan y mor. Ar ol y flwyddyn gyntaf gall myfyrwyr ddewis rhwng neuaddau a lletu yn y dref.

Mae chwaraeon yn ffynu yn Aberystwyth – trefnir cynghreiriau yn y rhan fwyaf ohonynt a gall myfyrwyr gystadlu ar nifer o lefelau.

A rhaid nodi Rag Aber – un o Apeliadau Elusennol Myfyrwyr mwyaf yn Ewrob. Mae'n hwyl anhygoel i fynd ar daith Rag i gasglu arian ledled y DU.!

What it's like

Founded in 1872 at a time of growing Welsh national consciousness. Now a busy university of 3,000 students, most of whom are taught at the Penglais Campus, built in the 1960s with a superb view of Aberystwyth town and Cardigan Bay. Another smaller, beautifully sited campus at Llanbadarn which has the Welsh Agricultural College and College of Librarianship; facilities at both campuses can be used by all students at Aberystwyth.

Most students come from outside Wales. Those from Wales approximately 400 have Welsh as their first language. Plenty of courses available for those who want to learn Welsh. Town itself (population around 10,000) is about 50% Welsh speaking.

Aberystwyth is about halfway down the west coast of Wales. Travel by rail or road is slow, but the scenery for miles around is beautiful. Because of difficulty in travelling, many students stay in Aberystwyth over weekends, and there is plenty of weekend disco and live entertainment at the Union.

Student accommodation provided by the College for all first years, some on campus and some on the sea front, from then on people can choose halls or town digs. Sport is thriving with leagues in most sports. Students compete at local, Welsh and UK levels.

Last, but not least, is Aber Rag, one of Europe's biggest student Charity Appeals. It's great fun going on Rag trips collecting money anywhere in the UK!

Pauper notes

Accommodation: variety of halls with different catering systems. A few married quarters available. **Drink:** Two new, very 'plush' Union bars serving good, cheap beer; Ushers, Banks, etc. **Eats:** Good facilities, the 'Beacon' refectory and an excellent Pizzeria. **Sports:** Everything catered for at £8 pa. Large campus sports centre, track and pool. **Ents:** Large concert venue (1,000 seats). Regular live events and discos, variety of musical clubs and societies. Student discounts at Aberystwyth Arts Centre based on campus. **Hardship fund:** Interest free loans and donations for extreme cases. **Travel:** Travel shop on campus offering advice on student travel. **Work:** Part-time work mainly in hotels, pubs and restaurants.

Nodion Pauper

Llety (e.e. sgwatiau myfyrwyr, llety priod: Amrywiaeth o neuaddau gyda sistemau arlwyo gwahanol. Ychydig o lety priod ar gael. **Diod (e.e. mannau rhesymol/da, bragdai da lleol):** Dau far Undeb Newydd gyda chwrw am bris rhesymol – Ushers, Banks etc.). **Bwyd (e.e. rhesymol/da yn y campws/y dref):** Microbeiotig/ llysfwyd/ethnig. Cyfleusterau da i fyfyrwyr, yn Ffreutur y Beacon a Pizzeria arlderchog. **Adloniant (e.e. rhesymol, grwpiau newydd/ffilmiau/dramau ar/i ffwrdd o'r campws):** Neuadd gyngerdd fawr (1000 sedd) digwyddiadau byw rheolaidd, a discos, armywiaeth o glybiau a chlybiau cerddorol. **Chwaraeon (e.e. canolfannau chwaraeon rhesymol/da ar/i ffwrdd o'r campws, pyllau nofio, cyfleusterau trafnidiaeth):** Popeth ar gael am gost o £8 y flwyddyn. Canolfan Chwaraeon mawr ar y campws, trac a phwll. **Cronfeydd Caledi (i godi'r myfyrwyr tlawd ar eu traed):** Benthyciadau dilog a chyfraniadau i achosion eithafol o dlodi. **Teithio (e.e. ysgoloriaethau teithio, bodio, tocynnau myfyrwyr):** Swyddfa

CAN'T FIND WHAT YOU'RE LOOKING FOR? USE THE INDEX!

Deithio ar y campws, sy'n rhoddi cyngor ar deithio myfyrwyr. **Gwaith (i ych-wanegu at y grant yn ystod y tymor/gwyliau/ar/i ffwrdd o'r campws, agwedd i'r dol:** Gwaith rhan-amser yn bennaf mewn gwestair, tafarndai a thai bwyta.

Alumni (Editors' pick)

Lord Cledwyn, Arthur Emyr, Most Rev George Noakes (Archbishop of Wales), Berwin Price, Angela Tooby.

ALRA

Academy of Live and Recorded Arts, Royal Victoria Building, Trinity Road, London SW18 3SX (081-870 6475) Map D, B3

Student enquiries: The Administrator

Main study areas – as in What to Study section: *(First degree):* Dance, drama. Also: stage management, technical television.

European Community: No languages or exchanges.

Application: Direct. **Academic features:** Actor's course (3 years or 1 year postgraduate); stage management course (1 year); performing arts dance course (3 years). Teaching methods based on forward-looking approach to modern technology and performing arts media and on Sorrel Carson's unique philosophy of acting simply expressed as 'acting is reacting'. Modern and classical theatre, dance, voice, singing and recorded arts. **Special features:** Guest speakers and directors from professional theatre and related fields. Guest lecturers from Cambridge University. Professional TV studio. **Largest fields of study:** Acting, performing arts, stage management. **Founded:** 1979. **Site:** In listed (Grade I) Victorian building on Wandsworth Common. **Access:** Good road access; BR Clapham Junction, Wandsworth Common; bus to central London. **Accommodation:** Variety of private flats available for rent in locality; £40 exclusive of meals and public services. Rent: no student accommodation or rent controlled by academy. **Library and Learning Resources:** Two theatres, dance and rehearsal studios; stage management workshop; professional television studio; sound studio. **Careers:** Information and advice given; placement service when possible. **Welfare:** Active help with finding accommodation. Student welfare officers. Information pack given to new students regarding housing, public libraries, doctors and health centres, banks etc. Student Social Committee. **Hardship funds:** 3 scholarship places (up to value of £12,000 in fees) available each year. Bursaries for students encountering hardship awarded at Academy's discretion. **Amenities:** Active social life. Regular student/staff informal social gatherings. Student cabaret in theatre club bar. Several plays produced each term. Showings of film and television productions. Student common room and bar. **Sports:** Good local sports facilities.

Duration of first degree course(s) or equivalent: 3 years **Others:** 1 year **Total first degree students 1989/90:** 170 **Number of overseas students:** Less than 5% **Male/female ratio 1989/90:** 2:3 **Teaching staff: full-time:** 10 **part-time:** 30 **Total full-time students 1989/90:** 190 **Postgraduate students:** 15 **Tuition fees, first degrees 1990/91:** £5,070.

What it's like

Some drama schools take a selection of 'types', who are already 'good' young actors or good auditionees. ALRA looks at people as they are and finds the actor within them. It has no preconceptions of who will make an actor or who won't. The entry audition process does not use audition pieces but allows individuals to display their ability through improvisation, voice and movement workshops.

Royal Victoria Patriotic Building is beautiful, light and spacious. Good working environment. Comprehensive training has prepared me to enter the acting profession. Fully equipped TV studios give you the opportunity to realise yourself in the recorded medium and gives you the confidence to offer yourself and work in TV. Extensive movement and voice work – I enjoyed the special skills such as stage combat and mask work. Studying both classical and modern theatre very satisfying. Project work includes Greek theatre, Shakespeare and Restoration comedy as well as American, English and Irish drama. Working with guest directors and tutors who bring experience from their professional backgrounds means that students can make an immediate connection with what they learn in school and the reality of the profession.

ALRA is a young school – only 11 years old, constantly providing each new intake with a clear incentive and approach. It gives many students a chance where other schools have not. It's real. It's down to earth. It's genuine. And it wants to help.
Emily Murray

Alumni (Editors' pick)
ALRA is a new institution. Graduates commencing their careers, can be seen at the National Theatre, RSC, West End, BBC, ITV, American television and Hollywood.

ANGLIA

Anglia Higher Education College, (1) Victoria Road South, Chelmsford, Essex CM1 1LL (0245 493131)
(2) East Road, Cambridge CB1 1PT (0223 63271)
(3) Sawyers Hall Lane, Brentwood, Essex CM15 9BT (0277 216971)
(4) Danbury Park Management Centre, Danbury, Chelmsford, Essex CM3 4AT (0245 415511)
Map A, F7

Student enquiries: Admissions Unit

Main study areas – as in What to Study section: *(First degree):* Accountancy, agriculture, biology, business studies, chemistry, computing, economics, education, electrical & electronic engineering, English, European studies, geography, geology, history, law, modern languages, music, nursing studies, philosophy, sociology. *Also:* Building and construction, quantity surveying.

European Community: 10% first degree students take EC language as part of course and 10% spend 6 months or more in another EC country. Formal exchange links with college in Berlin. Approved Erasmus programme 1990/91.

Application: PCAS. **Academic features:** All courses available on modular, credit accumulation basis. New post-experience BEng in telecommunications systems. **Special features:** Professor Ivor Seeley, Emeritus Professor, Nottingham Polytechnic visiting professor. **Largest fields of study:** Law, education, English, history, built environment. **Founded:** 1989, merger of Essex Institute and Cambridgeshire College of Arts and Technology. **Main awards:** LLB, BEd, BSc, BA. **Awarding body:** CNAA. **Site:** Chelmsford town centre, Cambridge city centre, Brentwood and Danbury Park. **Access:** Good train connections with London from all sites. **Accommodation:** 100 hostel places, 350 places in college administered houses, 800 places in approved lodgings. **Library:** Library at all sites; 275,000 volumes, 650 periodicals, 700+ study places. **Other learning resources:** Computer centre, CAD/CAM centre. **Specialist collections:** Law, education and management, music, French Resistance Archive. **Welfare:** Counselling, medical and health education services. **Hardship funds:** None available but help given through student services and access funds. **Careers:** Information, advice and placement and Access funds. **Amenities:** Bookshop on all main sites, SU buildings with bars, sports centre, soccer, table tennis, volleyball, judo, golf, hockey, netball, keep-fit, rugby, squash, fencing, horse-riding, karate, canoeing, trampolining,

CAN'T FIND WHAT YOU'RE LOOKING FOR? USE THE INDEX!

weight-training, yoga, drama, music, pottery and lots more! Mumford Theatre (at Cambridge), creche.

Duration of first degree course(s) or equivalent: 3 and 4 years **Total first degree students 1989/90:** 2,600; **BEd students:** 400 **Number of overseas students:** 150; **Number of mature students:** 20% **Male/female ratio 1989/90:** 1:1 **Teaching staff: full-time:** 100 **part-time:** 100 **Total full-time students 1989/90:** 4,000 **Postgraduate students:** 500 **Tuition fees, first degrees, 1990/91:** Home: £1,675 (£651 if self-financing); Overseas: £4,600.

What it's like (Cambridge)

Enjoys a sometimes uneasy, sometimes mutually beneficial relationship with the prestigious university – many students use their rather more luxurious facilities, whilst many university students prefer Anglia's more relaxed and informal environment. Largely due to the efforts of the NUS area organisation a sense of homogeneity is gradually evolving amongst Cambridge students as a whole.

Excellent academic reputation, particularly for humanities/social studies; well developed and dynamic SU ensures that student services, entertainments and welfare issues are not neglected. The major problem is accommodation. SU has been campaigning on this issue for many years.

Wide variety of students from degree, through HND, A-level and day release. The opportunities are there for anyone with initiative to get on and pursue almost any field of endeavour they choose.

Pauper notes

Accommodation: Some cheap digs (£20–£25 pw) through housing associations. **Drink:** SU bar best value, local brews – Abbot Ale. **Eats:** The Tram Depot, SU Batman Cafe. **Ents:** Bands and gigs on campus, also at The Junction. **Sports:** Kelsey Kerridge sports hall and Parkside swimming pool open free to students at certain times. **Hardship funds:** SU will loan up to £700. **Travel:** STA Travel, Campus Travel, good hitching after long walk to starting points. **Work:** Pubs, SU bar, restaurants, factories.

Alumni (Editors' pick)

Sacha Count (own lingerie firm), John Swinfield (presenter of ITV programme, Enterprise), Pink Floyd, Adam Ant, Fluck and Law ('Spitting Image'), Tom Sharpe (lecturer).

What it's like (Essex)

Sites at Brentwood and Chelmsford; not very beautiful places. Teaching generally good. Small so atmosphere tends to be very friendly with everyone knowing each other.

Most entertainment is college-based; gigs, discos, cabaret. Accommodation a problem; town isn't, there aren't enough students to bother them! Students get involved in societies and college activities and most people enjoy their time here.

Pauper notes

Accommodation: Expensive private places, cheap council houses (very few). **Drink:** College bar (Placcy), local brew Adnams, Ridleys. **Eats:** Good bar food in Placcy: town, Indian (loads), Chinese. Bad provision for vegetarians. **Ents:** About the only regular local venue. Town has theatre plus 2 cinemas. **Sports:** New sports centre, cheap tickets available in college sports dept. **Hardship funds:** Student services fund. **Travel:** No student discounts, expensive bus fares. **Work:** Part-time work in town available also vacation work.

Alumni (Editors' pick)

Mike Smith.

CAN'T FIND WHAT YOU'RE LOOKING FOR? USE THE INDEX!

ARCHITECTURAL ASSOCIATION

Architectural Association School of Architecture, 34–36 Bedford Square, London WC1B 3ES (071-636 0974) Map E, C2

Student enquiries: Registrar's Office

Main study areas – as in What to Study section: *(First degree):* Architecture.

European Community: No students take languages or spend time in EC; no formal exchange links.

Application: Direct. **Special features:** International character of school reflected by teaching staff offering a wide range of design options and teaching styles. Students recognised as individuals and expected to demonstrate a high level of self motivation to benefit from rich and varied programme which includes seminars and tutorials with professional consultants and members of allied disciplines. **Academic features:** 1-year foundation course is offered to develop creative skills in intensive programme of studio work. **Founded:** 1901. **Main awards:** Exemption from RIBA Parts 1 and 2, AA diploma. **Awarding body:** RIBA, AA. **Site:** Central London. **Access:** Tottenham Court Road underground station. **Accommodation:** None provided but advisory service. **Library:** 24,000 books; 5,000 slides; 50 study places. **Specialist collections:** Yerbury slide collection (4,000 slides on buildings of 1920s and 1930s). **Welfare:** Pastoral care and individual counselling available. **Careers:** Information and advice from Practical Training Adviser. **Amenities:** International exhibition centre, specialist bookshop, restaurant, bar, darkroom, video studios, workshop, computer facilities. **Employment:** Architecture.

Duration of first degree course(s) or equivalent: 5 years **other:** 1 year **Total first degree students to AA Diploma 1989/90:** approx 260 **Overseas students:** 80% **Mature students:** 20% **Male/female ratio 1989/90:** 2:1 **Teaching staff: part-time:** 120 **Total full-time students 1989/90:** 311 **Tuition fees, 1990/91:** (home and overseas) £7,400.

What it's like

Features a 5-year programme (plus a one-year foundation) for RIBA Parts I and II and AA Diploma. Choice of units (like studios) ranging from conceptual to rigorously architectonic, all nevertheless experimental and none aim to advocate any house style. Pass from year to year based on quality of work presented in a final oral presentation of unit work as well as successful fulfilment of 3 other submissions: General Studies, Communications (life drawing, etching, video, photography, colour studio) and Technical Studies (including Computer Studio). Traditional university structure does not exist, as nothing is strictly compulsory during the year, but high standards are expected and students are given a great deal of independence which makes the system more difficult as it requires a great deal more resilience to maintain one's own standards without being spoonfed – sometimes a mild shock to those arriving from A-level. An intense and sometimes competitive atmosphere prevails, diluted in the evenings as students and tutors collect themselves at the treasured Rosebud's bar. School year consists of sustained periods of intense work interrupted by equally intense parties, an unofficial institution is the annual carnival which consumes all of the 3 Georgian Buildings as well as most of the AASU budget.

SU made up of a non-hierarchical committee of six students (3 elected each year for a 2-year term) and one paid student union secretary. Not associated with the NUS. Unlike any other school in the UK, students permitted to attend and occasionally vote at AA Council Meetings. No general student political affiliation or tendency. School attracts an international mix of students which at best brings a variety of influences and dialogues which creates a fragmented environment and indifferent student body.

In addition to the basic school environment the AA features a superb evening lecture series, with speakers from all over the world in many different disciplines.

CAN'T FIND WHAT YOU'RE LOOKING FOR? USE THE INDEX!

There is a good but expensive bookstore, featuring in-house publications. The slide library is extensive. Decent workshop for working with metal and wood, and an ever-growing CAD studio.

There are problems. Darkroom is completely inadequate for serious work, etching studio closed three days a week, and library quite limited. No sense of campus, no extra-curricular organisation and no sport. The working studio space near the school has been cut back and the shortage is now being dealt with by the AASU.

However, it's without doubt one of the best Architecture schools in the world, if not the best. So if you really love the cutting edge of architecture, and you can't wait to express your commitment and fascination without being stifled by the inane requirements of what passes for education these days, then you must apply.

Pauper notes

Accommodation: SU list of cheap accommodation weekly in hostel or digs. **Eats:** Cafe Monaco, Jimmy's Greek restaurant, Pollo Bar, all nearby in Bloomsbury and Soho. **Ents:** SU fortnightly films, students' standby at West End theatres and galleries (reduced rates). **Sports:** none at AA, ULU facilities nearby. **Hardship funds:** Loans from AA, very limited AASU aid. **Travel:** Travel scholarships from AA, other institutes (architectural). **Work:** AA offers employment to students and part-time in practices possible during term time.

Alumni (Editors' pick)

Richard Rogers (architect for Lloyds Building/Pompidour Centre), Mark Fisher (designer of Pink Floyd concerts), Ron Arad (furniture designer), Zaha Hadid (architect), Eileen Gray (architect, designer) Janet Street Porter (notorious).

ASTON UNIVERSITY

Aston University, Aston Triangle, Birmingham B4 7ET (021-359 3611) Map A, E7

Student enquiries: Admissions Officer

Main study areas – as in What to Study section: *(First degree):* Accountancy, administration, biology, business studies, chemical engineering, chemistry, civil engineering, computing, electrical & electronic engineering, mathematical studies, mechanical and production engineering, modern languages, pharmacy, physics, politics and government, psychology, town & country planning. *Also:* Ophthalmic optics.

European Community: 32% first degree students take EC language as part of course and 24% spend 6 months or more in another EC country. Formal exchange links with 28 EC universities/colleges: Belgium (1); France (17); Germany (9); Spain (1). Approved Erasmus programme 1990/91.

Application: UCCA. **Structural features:** Technological university. Many departments in new or very recently modernised facilities. Excellent and extensive computing facilities. Aston Science Park adjacent to campus. **Academic features:** Strong European focus, eg international business and modern languages, European business management, wide range of engineering disciplines with European studies, computer science with European studies, transport management and modern languages. Most degree programmes have foreign language option. **Special features:** 65% of students are on 'sandwich' courses. Close links with industry and business. **Largest fields of study:** Engineering, Management, Modern Languages and Science. **Founded:** 1895. Central Technical School 1927. College of Technology 1951. College of Advanced Technology 1956. University Charter 1966. **Main awards:** BSc, BEng, MEng. **Awarding body:** Aston University. **Site:** Modern, increasingly 'green' 40 acre campus. **Access:** Close to Birmingham city centre.

CAN'T FIND WHAT YOU'RE LOOKING FOR? USE THE INDEX!

Accommodation: Most live on campus; two-thirds of all students in university accommodation; all first years accommodated in university residence. **Library:** 215,000 monographs, 115,000 bound periodicals, 1,460 current periodicals; guides issued to students; computerised catalogues, circulation and information services, on-line access to databases throughout the world; audio-visual laboratory, 800 reader places. **Welfare:** Accommodation officer, doctor, dentist, FPA, psychiatrist, solicitor, chaplains, counsellor, careers & appointments officer. **Hardship funds:** A fund is available, and 3 annual travel scholarships. **Special category:** Married students' flats, nursery facilities. **Amenities:** Guild of Students bookshop, arts centre, chapel, banks, travel agent, language laboratories, CAD laboratory, tutored video instruction system (TVI). **Sporting facilities:** Most indoor sports, including swimming pool, squash courts and two sports halls on campus. 90 acre centre for outdoor sports twenty minutes from campus. **Employment:** High graduate employment record in industry, commerce, the professions.

Duration of first degree course(s) or equivalent: BSc: 3 years full-time, 4 year (sandwich), BEng/MEng: 3–5 years full-time and sandwich **Total first degree students 1989/90:** 3,325 **Male/female ratio 1989/90:** 3:2 **Number of overseas students:** 35 **Number of mature students:** 88 **Teaching staff: full-time:** 236; part-time: 18 **Total full-time students 1989/90:** 3,637 **Postgraduate students:** 1,176 (350 full-time) **Tuition fees, first degrees, 1990/91:** Home: £1,675; Overseas: £5,887 (eg politics); £6,706 (eg physics).

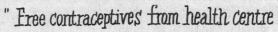

" Free contraceptives from health centre "

What it's like

Easily accessible by coach, car or train. Small, compact campus; very friendly. Accommodation on campus in single-sex, self-catering flats or 4 miles away in Handsworth Village (hall for first years and more self-catering flats). Both sites have launderettes. SU pioneered housing scheme for 200, 10 minutes walk from campus. Good city bus service, many all night routes.

Close to city centre facilities. SU active (about 70 societies, 35 sports clubs). Varied ents including one of the best student light shows in the country. Library open until 11 pm weekdays, 5 pm Saturday. Sunday opening in term 3. Campus health centre with full-time counsellor; understanding attitude towards contraception.

Courses increasingly modular usually with one year placements. Good graduate employment record. High entry grades but felt worth it by those that make it.

CAN'T FIND WHAT YOU'RE LOOKING FOR? USE THE INDEX!

Pauper notes

Accommodation: Non-university accommodation averages £19–£20 pw. **Drink:** SU the best prices in town, regular promotions. Campus pubs also very popular with students. **Eats:** SU offers good variety, reasonable prices. In town – wide choice from Austrian to Caribbean. Veggie food in SU; good curry houses nearby. **Ents:** SU provides films, discos, bands + cabaret. Campus Arts Centre caters for other tastes – good films (late night showings). **Sports:** 2 sports centres on campus plus swimming pool. University sports centre few miles out of town. Very active Athletic Union. **Hardship funds:** Only for the most deserving cases (mixture of grants and loans). **Travel:** New travel bureau in SU offers all advice, discounts etc. **Work:** Extremely hard to come by, SU, campus pubs offer bar jobs. Welfare now advertises jobs.

BANGOR

The University College of North Wales, Bangor, Gwynedd LL57 2DG (0248 351151) Map A, C6

Student enquiries: Academic Registrar
Main study areas – as in What to Study section: (*First degree*): Accountancy, agriculture, horticulture & forestry, biochemistry, biology, botany, chemistry, computing, economics, education, electrical & electronic engineering, English, history, linguistics, mathematical studies, modern languages, music, psychology, religious studies and theology, sociology, welfare studies, zoology. *Also:* Banking, finance, oceanography, Russian, Welsh studies.

European Community: 7% first degree students take EC language as part of course and 6% spend 6 months or more in another EC country. Formal exchange links with about 10 EC universities/colleges: Essen, Tubingen, Passau, Lena, Rennes (accounting, finance); Munster (accounting, banking); Mons, Siena (banking); Milan (banking); Namur (economics); Paris (banking, insurance, finance). EC initiatives: Staff/student exchanges (Tempus, Erasmus).

Application: UCCA. **Academic features:** Number of courses available through the medium of Welsh. **Structural features:** Part of Wales University. Centre for Social Policy Research and Development, National Coaching Centre established (one of only two in UK universities), Regional Centre for Language Awareness. Centres of excellence in telecommunications and in structural biocomposites. Menai Technology Enterprise Centre. School of Welsh Medium Studies. **Special features:** Sponsorship available with 4 major UK banks and a leading insurance company for degrees in banking, insurance and finance and with industrial companies for BEng/MEng. Honorary Professors: Dr W W M Brown, Dr W W McBride Brown, and Dr D S Wood (ocean sciences); Emyr Humphreys (English); Dr D Crystal and A R Thomas (linguistics); Dr I M James, Dr C E M Yates (mathematics); Dr C Milner, Dr S J Lockwood (biological sciences); The Most Hon The Marquess of Anglesey (history); Dr R C Roberts (agricultural and forest sciences). **Largest fields of study:** Biological sciences, electronic engineering science, ocean sciences, accounting, banking, economics, psychology, agriculture and forestry. **Founded:** 1884. **Main awards:** BA, BD, BMus, BSc, BEng. **Awarding body:** University of Wales. **Site:** Town centre. **Access:** 2 hrs travelling distance from M56, which links with M6. A55 is coastal road and A5 the trunk road through N Wales. Regular fast trains to and from London, Birmingham, Manchester. **Accommodation:** 7 halls (including 1 self-catering) offering approx 1,300 places, 1,200 places in lodgings/flats. All first years normally accommodated in hall, £668–£1,041 pa. Rent: 48% in accommodation where rent controlled by college. **Library:** 6 library buildings including ocean sciences library. 400,000 volumes in total, 2,200 periodicals, 800 study places, short loan scheme for texts in heavy demand. **Other learning facilities:** Ocean-going research boats, college farms, botanical garden, field station, zoology museum, computer building, language labs. **Welfare:** 4 part-time doctors, psychiatrist,

CAN'T FIND WHAT YOU'RE LOOKING FOR? USE THE INDEX!

nursing sister, college chaplains, college counsellors, Students' Union welfare office. **Hardship funds:** Some bursaries available to help students in financial difficulties complete course. Students' union interest free loan scheme for desperate cases. **Special categories:** Nursery run by Psychology Department, Playgroup, SU 'Niteline'. **Careers:** Information, advice and placement. **Amenities:** Professional theatre, concert halls, museum, art gallery. **Sporting facilities:** Sports centre, 56 acres of playing fields, unparalleled opportunities for outdoor activities in Snowdonia. **Employment:** Teaching, manufacturing industry, management and administration plus specialist openings for graduates in banking and insurance, accountancy, electronic engineering, agriculture, fisheries and forestry.

Duration of first degree course(s) or equivalent: 3 years; 4 years (languages), 4.5 years (BEng/MEng) **Total first degree students 1989/90:** 2,682 **Number of overseas students:** 452 **Number of mature students:** 616 **Male/female ratio 1989/90:** 4:3 **Teaching staff: full-time:** 271 **part-time:** 6 **Total full-time students 1989/90:** 3,328 **Postgraduate students:** 646 **Tuition fees, first degrees, 1990/91:** Home: £1,675 (£658 if self-financing); Overseas: £4,560–£6,050

What it's like

Small city, easily accessible by train, bus and car. University dominant; early 20th century building overlooking town centre, and main road lined with departments. SU central to campus; all halls and departments within 10 minutes walk (admittedly very hilly though!). Regular bus service/easy hitch or cycle journey to Menai Bridge (for Marine Sciences) 3 miles away.

College accommodation for 48% of students – mainly in Halls (mixed or single sex, self catered or catered) prioritized for first and third year. Private accommodation difficult to get, varies in quality. Laundries in all hall sites and in SU, cooking facilities passable in even catered halls! Wide variety of food shops/supermarkets etc, good prices.

Friendly atmosphere and good mix of students. Occasional trouble with locals, although active Community Action organisation in SU to socialise and work with/for the local community. Students represented well by SU on most College committees. Academic and personal advice available through colleges. Study facilities affected by government cuts, although arts, science and public libraries hold extensive (albeit sometimes dated) material and many periodicals.

Academically excellent in all areas – although cuts affect the number of courses offered, particularly in the Arts. Departments such as Electronic Engineering, Economics, Marine Studies and Agriculture/Forestry expanding; considered among the best in the UK.

Welfare Services in SU. Run by sabbatical officer and permanent staff member, confidential advice on academic, legal, financial, drugs, careers, housing, benefits, personal (including health education) etc. College health centre and part-time counsellor along with moral tutors. SU welfare handbook to all first year students at registration.

SU houses travel office, shop, restaurant, creche (all at discount rates), bank, insurance co. and Athletics Union. Two bars offer cheap drink, venues for many and varied entertainments (recent appearances by The Waterboys, The Bhundu Boys, The Fall, Bliss . . .). Clubs and societies active within SU – from Real Ale to War Games, Labour Club to Plaid Cymru, Agriculture to *Y Seren* (bi-weekly newspaper), as well as Community Action, Rag, and many more. Showers, laundry, snooker room, table tennis room, games room and meeting rooms also housed in SU building.

Not overtly political but facilities for students to become active in areas of interest or concern. Active bilingual policy enforced, and campaigns organised to counter racism, sexism, homophobia. Local and national campaigns also run for students to involve themselves in the running of the SU via general meetings and on committees as well as on campaigns. For information telephone (0248) 353709 or 362075.
Martin Purcell

CAN'T FIND WHAT YOU'RE LOOKING FOR? USE THE INDEX!

Pauper notes

Accommodation: Limited availability, esp at year start – mainly bedsits and shared houses, approx £25 pw. **Drink:** SU bars cheapest. Very extensive range of beers. **Eats:** SU Fat Freddies – omniverous, vegetarian and vegan specials and menu; college refec – set menu and salad bar (both outlets SU/college v cheap); 3 Crowns best/cheapest pub grub. Various English/Italian/Greek/Indian/Chinese eats; Herbs Restaurant – wide range of salads and healthy food. **Ents:** SU better reputation as venue for indi/up and coming bands. 2 main venues (refec × 800, main bar × 250). Discount for SU cardholders at cinema. **Sports:** College run centre; rates reduced for Athletic Union members (join in SU). College sports hall walking distance (squash, weights, multigym, large multiple sports area), swimming pool with diving facilities. **Hardship funds:** Loans Committee of SU can in exceptional circumstances (hardship) give temp loans to students. **Travel:** Student travel office, with many discount schemes, in Union building; many overseas scholarships – eg US and Canada. Hitching good with new coastal road Ireland link (but as always not recommended to individuals). Boats to and from Dublin v cheap. **Work:** Surprise, surprise SU biggest employer term-time (bars, bouncing, catering casuals). College bar staff also. Not very much casual work available.

Alumni (Editors' pick)

Dr Robert Edwards (pioneer of test-tube babies), Roger Whittaker (singer, songwriter), Dr David Rees (Director of National Inst for Medical Research), Ann Clwyd (MP), Robert Einion Holland (Chief General Manager, Pearl Assurance), Dr Dafydd Elis Thomas MP (President, Plaid Cymru), John Sessions (poet and impressionist).

BANGOR NORMAL COLLEGE

Bangor Normal College, Bangor, Gwynedd, N Wales LL57 2PX (0248 370171) Map A, C6

Student enquiries: Admissions Officer

Main study areas – as in What to Study section: *(First degree):* Main study areas: Communication studies, drama, education, English, environmental studies, history, humanities, mathematical studies, music, religious studies and theology, welfare studies. *Also* Welsh studies.

European Community: No students take EC language as part of course; no exchange links.

Application: PCAS. **Structural features:** Associate institution of Wales University. **Largest fields of study:** Education (primary). **Founded:** 1858. **Main award:** BA, BEd. **Awarding body:** Wales University. **Site:** Two sites, one mile apart: residential site in Upper Bangor; other site (residential, teaching, recreational) on outskirts of Bangor, overlooking the Menai Straits. **Access:** Coach and train (Bangor station on London-Holyhead line). **Accommodation:** 430 places on site, additional places in flats and houses as need arises. **Approx cost:** £25 without meals; all accommodation self-catering. **Library:** 60,000 volumes, 200 periodicals, 175 study places. **Specialist collections:** Children's books, Welsh history and literature. **Other learning facilities:** Language centre with learning lab, resources centre with printing facilities, child-study centre, 2 open-access computer networks based on Acorn/Apple computers. Part of European Pluto network for teacher education. **Careers:** Personal tutors offer advice. **Employment:** Teaching (BEd), environmental centres, public administration (BA). **Welfare:** Nurse on site daily; college doctor's surgery weekly. Each student allocated a personal tutor; help also available from deans. **Hardship funds:** Government access funds. **Amenities:** Variety of societies; SU bar; drama studies, hall. **Sports facilities:** Large sports hall,

CAN'T FIND WHAT YOU'RE LOOKING FOR? USE THE INDEX!

2 gymnasia, multi-gym, playing fields, tennis courts on campus. Bangor city swimming pool and Snowdonia National Park within easy reach for walking, climbing etc.

Duration of first degree course(s) or equivalent: 3 years (BA), 4 years (BEd). **Total first degree students 1989/90: 460 Number of BEd students:** 338; **Number of mature students:** 93 **Male/female ratio 1989/90:** 2:5 **Teaching staff: full-time:** 49; **part-time:** 2. **Total full-time students 1989/90:** 515 **Postgraduate students:** 55 **Tuition fees, first degrees, 1990/91:** Home: £1,675.

BATH COLLEGE

Bath College of Higher Education, (1) Newton Park, Bath BA2 9BN (0225 873701; FAX: 0225 874123) (2) Sion Hill Place, Lansdown, Bath BA1 5SJ (0225 425264; FAX 0225 445228)
Map A, D8

Student enquiries: Senior Registrar (Newton Park address)

Main study areas – as in What to Study section: *(First degree):* Art & design, education, music. *Also:* Home economics.

European Community: 6% first degree students take EC language as part of course but none spend 6 months or more in another EC country. Formal exchange links with 2 EC universities/colleges: Hildesheim (art/music, combined studies); Munchen (graphic design). Erasmus and Tempus exchanges. Faculty of Home Economics, Science and Humanities has contacts in France, Germany and Netherlands resulting in short study exchanges.

Application: PCAS except BA Art and Design (ADAR). **Founded:** 1983 Ex Bath College of Higher Education and Bath Academy of Art. **Main awards:** BA, BEd, BSc. **Awarding body:** CNAA. **Site:** Newton Park and Sion Hill, about 3 and 1.5 miles respectively from Bath city centre. **Access:** Rail, road (M4/A4), local buses. **Accommodation:** 595 places in college halls. Cost: £30.50 (single room); £26.50 (shared room). Rent: 40% in accommodation where rent controlled by college. **Library:** 1 library at each site; 154,000 volumes, 5,500 AV resources in total, 500 periodicals, 150 study places. **Other learning resources:** Computer systems; desk top publishing facilities, sound recording studio. **Welfare:** Doctor, student welfare officers, p-t counsellor. **Hardship funds:** Government access fund. **Careers:** Information and advice, no placement. **Employment:** Teaching, home economics, music, art and design.

Duration of first degree course(s) or equivalent: 3 years; BEd 4 years **Total first degree students 1989/90:** 1,303 **Total BEd students:** 620 **Number of overseas students:** 43 **Number of mature students:** 465 **Male/female ratio 1989/90:** 1:4 **Teaching staff: full-time:** 105 **Associate staff:** 17 **Total full-time students 1989/90:** 1,474 **Postgraduate students:** 73 **Tuition fees, first degrees, 1990/91:** Home: £1,675; Overseas: £4,550.

What it's like

It's divided between two sites: Sion Hill, 15 minutes walk from town; and Newton Park, four miles from Bath towards Bristol. There is a regular bus service from Bath to the college. Halls are for first years, all self catering. They are split into courts at Newton Park and houses at Sion Hill, where rooms are in a crescent, and each has its kitchen shared with other students. Each site has canteen open for lunch, coffee and snacks in the morning and afternoon. Bars on each site are subsidised – beer is £1 per pint whereas in local pubs it is £1.40. SU very active, holding events each week and liaising with university. At Newton Park there is a new sports hall and college teams hold matches, home or away, each week.

CAN'T FIND WHAT YOU'RE LOOKING FOR? USE THE INDEX!

There is a strong student presence in Bath with students from university and college of further education all trying to share same pubs and clubs. There are a lot of very individual pubs; most popular with the college are: Salamander, Hatchets, Cellar Bar, Boater and the House. In accordance with an old by-law in Bath, many of the clubs are underground such as Tiergarten, Players, the Island Club and Moles, where you have to be a member. BCHE students have concessions on Monday night. There are several markets throughout week eg Great Western antique market, indoor market, and on Saturdays a large flea market on Walcot Street. At the same time as living in Bath the college is on the bus route to Bristol, so you have the amenities of both a large town and city.
Rachel Hawkins

Pauper notes

Accommodation: Expensive and difficult to find. **Drink:** Good real ales, BX, Buttcombe, Eldridge Pope. Excellent pubs with atmosphere. The Bell, The Curfew, The Hat and Feathers, Hatchets. **Eats:** From veggie burgers to a-la-carte, eating places for all walks of life, eating habits and more importantly pockets. **Ents:** Venues for all tastes. Moles nightclub, gigs at the Uni and BCHE, much jazz, rock, pop and classics – Bristol 9 miles away. **Sports:** College teams play on a regular basis, also Bath leisure centre, with pool, squash and tennis. **Work:** Many bar and p-t jobs available throughout year.

Alumni (Editors' pick)

Anita Roddick (Body Shop), Mary Berry (cook), Sue Cuff (TV), Howard Hodgkin, Martin Potts (painters), Nicholas Pope, Veronica Ryan, Nigel Rolfe, Peter Randall-Page (sculptors).

BATH UNIVERSITY

The University of Bath, Claverton Down, Bath BA2 7AY (0225) 826826
Map A, D8

Student enquiries: Senior Assistant Registrar

Main study areas – as in What to Study section: *(First degree):* Aeronautical engineering, agriculture, architecture, biochemistry, biology, business studies, chemical engineering, chemistry, computing, economics, education, electrical & electronic engineering, environmental science, European studies, mathematical studies, mechanical and production engineering, metallurgy and materials science, modern languages, pharmacology, pharmacy, physics, politics and government, sociology. *Also:* Crop technology.

European Community: 9% first degree students take EC language as part of course and 9% spend 6 months or more in another EC country. Formal Erasmus links with large number of EC universities/colleges: education (France, Germany, Greece, Netherlands); mechanical engineering (France, Germany, Greece, Portugal); languages (France, Germany, Italy, Spain); management (France, Germany, Netherlands); physics (Netherlands); electrical engineering (Eire, France, Germany, Greece, Italy); maths (Italy, France); social sciences (Eire, Greece, Netherlands, Portugal, Spain); architecture (Denmark); chemical engineering (Italy).

Application: UCCA. **Largest fields of study:** Engineering, social sciences. **Founded:** 1894, as Merchant Venturers' Technical College, full university status 1966. **Main awards:** BA, BPharm, BSc, BEng, MEng. **Awarding body:** Bath University. **Site:** Campus 1 mile from Bath city centre. **Academic features:** Joint degree with Cirencester (Royal College of Agriculture), in crop technology and resource management. **Access:** Buses. **Accommodation:** 1,600 residences, 300 lodgings (mixed and segregated). Approx cost: Average £27 pw. Rent: 50% in accommodation where rent controlled by university. **Library:** 200,000 volumes,

3,000 periodicals, 500 study places, course books on short loan. **Welfare:** Counsellor, doctors, psychiatrist, chaplain, dentist. **Hardship funds:** Some funds available. **Special categories:** Some accommodation for married students, some facilities for disabled, nursery (15 places, £5 a day). **Amenities:** Bookshop, banks, general shop (SU), chapel, supermarket, travel agency, post office, newsagent and hairdresser. **Sporting facilities:** Include an excellent sports hall and swimming pool. All playing fields on campus. **Employment:** 76% of 1989 graduates employed. Strong tradition in engineering and pharmacy.

Duration of first degree course(s) or equivalent: 3 years f-t; 4 years (sandwich) **Total first degree students 1989/90:** 3,565 **Number of overseas students:** 233 **Number of mature students:** 320 **Male/female ratio 1989/90:** 2:1 approx **Teaching staff: full-time:** 379 **part-time:** 10 **Total students 1989/90** 4,109 **Postgraduate students:** 544 **Tuition fees, first degrees, 1990/91:** Home: £1,675; Overseas: £4,625 (eg arts), £6,115 (eg science).

What it's like

650 feet above city of Bath, exposed and windy. Modern buildings are concentrated round central pedestrian area – functional but not attractive. Some courses in biology based in separate building on campus. Expanding facilities include SU shop, travel bureau and coffee bar. Welfare provisions include sick-bay, dentist, nursery, twice weekly FPA and contraceptive supply. No chemist. 4 banks, all with cash points. Residences all self-catering, low rise blocks quietest. Refectories include wholefood counters and fast food.

Academic concentration on science/technology, especially sandwich courses; hence strong links with industry. Very good employment prospects. High proportion of continuous assessment. Training course for all new lecturers. Library not perfect but long opening hours, including Sundays. Links with town good, with plenty of opportunity for individuals to join in local life. Campus (but not town) quiet at weekends because much more going on in town. Small city but Bath has 7 cinemas, theatre, 6+ nightclubs, numerous fudge and book shops and pubs. Good cosy student town. Some alternative activity eg community bookshop, co-op printing press, active non-political SU with 70 clubs, 50 sporting clubs, high standard in teams and competitions – good national standing.

Pauper notes

Accommodation: A third of students live on campus, and this is increasing; there are now campus places for disabled students. City accommodation often expensive (about £35-£40 per week) and hard to find. Help given by University accommodation office. No campus places for married students. **Drink:** Plenty of pubs. Bath is real ale paradise (Wadworths, Mendip, Butcombe, Marstons, Ushers, Ruddles, etc); cheap but strong scrumpy often available. **Eats:** Range of food on campus inc good vegetarian. Wholefoods in town ('Harvest' and Huckleberrys). Kebabs, curries, fish and chips, pizzas and burgers. Wide range of restaurants. **Ents:** SU night at a club every Tuesday with live band; regular big gigs. Extensive freshers' week. Student's card gets some discounts at shops, cinemas, restaurants. 'Standby' cheapest way to get into theatre. Cheap local gigs advertised in papers. **Sports:** Swimming pool and excellent facilities (4 squash and 8 tennis courts) on campus free to students. Many teams and clubs (from snooker to hot-air ballooning). Sports centre in town more expensive. **Hardship funds:** University fund mainly for overseas students. Small loans from SU, plus welfare advice. **Travel:** Many hitch from town to campus as bus fares very expensive. Good rail and coach links (but check Sundays). London 75 minutes by train. SU travel bureau on campus for discount travel and holidays. **Work:** Some tourism-related work and summer work. Work on campus and pub jobs in town.

Alumni (Editors' pick)

John Kiddey (TV reporter), Martin Hedges (world champion canoeist), Chris Martin and David Trick (England Rugby Union internationals).

CAN'T FIND WHAT YOU'RE LOOKING FOR? USE THE INDEX!

BEDFORD COLLEGE

Bedford College of Higher Education, Lansdowne Rd, Bedford (0234 51966) Map A, F7

Student enquiries: Assistant Academic Registrar

Main study areas – as in What to Study section: *(First degree):* Computing, dance, drama, education, English, environmental studies, European studies, geography, history, modern languages, sociology. *Also:* Sports studies.

European Community: Very small number of first degree students take EC language and spend time in another EC country. No formal exchange links.

Application: CRCH for BEd, PCAS for BA. **Largest fields of study:** Education, human movement, English, geography, history. **Founded:** 1976 by merger of 3 colleges. **Main awards:** BA, BEd. **Awarding body:** CNAA. **Site:** Split on 3 sites. **Accommodation:** 400 places in halls of residence. **Library:** 1 library on each site: 110,000 volumes in total; 880 periodicals; 190 study places. **Specialist collections:** Hockliffe collection of children's literature. **Welfare:** Doctor, FPA, psychiatrist, chaplain, counsellor, accommodation officer. **Careers:** Information and advice service. **Amenities:** Students' Union; close to town centre; theatre; day nursery. **Sporting facilities:** Playing-fields; gymnasia; dance/drama areas; swimming pool; sports halls.

Duration of first degree course(s) or equivalent: 3 years; 4 years BEd. **Total first degree students 1989/90:** 973 **BEd students:** 720 **Number of mature students:** 390 **Male/female ratio 1989/90:** 2:3 **Teaching staff: full-time:** 95 **Total full-time students 1989/90:** 1,000 **Postgraduate students:** 71 **Tuition fees, first degree, 1990/91:** Home: £1,675; Overseas: £4,750.

What it's like

Spiralling towers and crumbling edifices of Bedford symbolise its history and tradition. Timeless reputation for producing first-rate teachers and questioning graduates. Sporting reputation. Excellent standing nationally in producing primary teachers of outstanding calibre. BA course with new modular programme incorporates new teaching innovations alongside time honoured lecturing standards upheld by dedicated teaching staff.

Facilities for such a small college are plentiful and well maintained. Student accommodation recently refurbished to highest standard. Main student block set in beautiful surroundings of Victorian terrace housing with picturesque gardens.

Social life well supported by two bars with their convivial atmosphere; hectic entertainment calendar. Balls usually sell out and are always massively enjoyed. Variety is our middle name and recent events have included hypnotism, comedy, karoake, pantomime and all manner of music. At Bedford College we don't mind working, but we do like to have a good time.

Pauper notes

Accommodation: Residence contract more expensive than many colleges. Accommodation register to assist students who wish to live out. **Drink:** 2 college bars recently refurbished. Bedford is the home of Red Strip brewed by Charles Wells so has many thriving pubs. Greene King. Many excellent country pubs. **Eats:** Multiracial town with varied eating establishments. **Sports:** Very good facilities (swimming pool needs upgrading). Local squash club at reduced rate. Sports clubs run by students with expert staff coaching if wanted. High standard in teams. **Ents:** Varied with both local bands and big bands eg Amazulu, Geno Washington, Ghoast Dance, Real Thing. Also 3 colleges within 12 miles radius offering more events. **Societies:** Christian Union, film, women's group, drama etc. Also mountaineering society which travels somewhere (Scotland, Wales, Devon) at least every second weekend.

CAN'T FIND WHAT YOU'RE LOOKING FOR? USE THE INDEX!

Hardship funds: College fund now in operation. **Shops:** Student discount available in some. **Work:** Pubs, swimming pools, sports centres, taxis (if over 24).

Alumni (Editors' pick)
Mandy Pickles (England U-21 hockey team), Lisa Black (Olympic rhythmic gymnastics team).

BELFAST UNIVERSITY

Queen's University of Belfast, University Road, Belfast BT7 1NN, Northern Ireland (0232 245133) Map A, B4

Student enquiries: Admissions Officer

Main study areas – as in What to Study section: *(First degree):* Accountancy, aeronautical engineering, agriculture, American studies, anatomy, archaeology, architecture, biochemistry, biology, botany, business studies, chemical engineering, chemistry, civil engineering, classics, computing, dentistry, economics, education, electrical & electronic engineering, English, environmental studies, food science & nutrition, geography, geology, history, information technology, law, library & information studies, mathematical studies, mechanical & production engineering, medicine, microbiology, modern languages, music, pharmacy, philosophy, physics, physiology, psychology, religious studies & theology, sociology, zoology. *Also:* Byzantine studies, Celtic studies, history of science.

European Community: 4% first degree students take EC language as part of course and 4% spend 6 months or more in another EC country. Formal exchange links with 35 EC universities/colleges: social anthropology (Belgium, Denmark, France, Germany, Greece, Netherlands, Spain, Portugal); law and computing (Netherlands); business studies and management science (Belgium, France, Spain); electrical engineering (Denmark, Eire, France, Germany, Italy, Netherlands); biochemistry (Belgium, Eire, France, Germany); mechanical engineering (Germany, Greece, Netherlands, Portugal). Approved Erasmus programme.

Application: UCCA. **Special features:** Writer in residence, J Simmons. **Founded:** 1850. **Main awards:** BA, BAgr, BD, BDS, BEd, BEng, BLS, BMus, BSc, BSSc, LLB, MB, BCh, BAO, MEng. **Awarding body:** Queen's University of Belfast. **Site:** Main site with various buildings about 1 mile from city centre; medical site about 2 miles from main site. **Access:** Most live within 1 mile of main site. Public transport available, if necessary, to those coming from home. **University accommodation:** 1,500 places in halls, university houses and apartments, 150 reserved places in Biggart House for medical and dental students; 92 flats for married students and over 170 places in associated halls and hostels. **Library:** Main library (central site), science library, medical library and agriculture and food science library. Over 900,000 books in main libraries, plus 80,000 in departmental libraries. **Other learning facilities:** Computer centre, marine biology station, astronomical observatory, audio resources centre, visual aids unit, conservation laboratory, phytotron, palaeoecology centre, Murlough Field Centre, electron microscope unit, microprocessor laboratory. Centre for Information Management, Information Technology Planning and Development Unit; N.I. Centre for Genetic Engineering (NICGENE), N.I. Technology Centre, Policy Research Institute; Queen's University Environmental Science and Technology Research Centre (QUESTOR). **Hardship funds:** Some funds for cases of financial hardship. **Amenities:** SU building with supermarket, record shop, bars, discos, etc; cinema on campus, bookshop, appointments and Careers Advisory Service, University Health Service, Student Counselling Service, Officers' Training Corps, Air Squadron. **Sporting facilities:** Excellent playing fields and physical education centre.

Duration of first degree course(s) or equivalent: 3 or 4 years; 5 years MB BCh BAO. **Total first degree students 1989/90:** 6,735 f-t; 631 p-t **Total BEd students:**

CAN'T FIND WHAT YOU'RE LOOKING FOR? USE THE INDEX!

1,279 **Number of overseas students:** 536 (f-t), 39 (p-t) **Number of mature students:** 287 **Male/female ratio 1989/90:** 6:5 **Teaching staff: full-time:** 941 **part-time:** 117 **Total full-time students 1989/90:** 7,868 **Postgraduate students:** 1,062 **Tuition fees, first degrees, 1990/91:** Home: £607; Overseas: £3,370 (eg politics), £4,495 (eg physics).

What it's like
Politically contentious city, student body holds itself apart from the troubles. 50% of students live at home. For many it's an extension of school and school friends. Most NI schools are single-sex and denominational although this is slowly changing. Academic standards high. Fair proportion of graduates go overseas for jobs, most remain at home. University area one of the most beautiful in Belfast, bordering posh Malone Road. Facilities good: 2 diners, coffee lounge, 2 bars recently renovated and a snack bar. One of the best creche facilities in UK. SU active especially over cuts etc. Some sectarianism. Accommodation facilities improving, though many students live in poor privately rented accommodation. University area centre of night life. Public transport until 11.00 pm. Renaissance of pubs and eating places recently – 158 in mile between City Hall and University. Three major cinema complexes showing national releases. Excellent alternative films in Queen's Film Theatre. Annual festival, second only to Edinburgh in site and diversity. Major pop acts play in Belfast. Also regular discos and gigs in the SU and around town.

Abortion still illegal. Student Health Service liberal in attitudes and Ulster Pregnancy Advisory Service sympathetic. Main drug is alcohol. Police over-stretched but active in student area.

Pauper notes
Drink: Lots of good bars in University area. SU still cheapest. **Eats:** Pizza, kebabs, Wimpy, Kentucky fried chicken and burger joints abound. Most pubs do lunches. **Ents:** SU main venue for bands and discos. Gigs also in Ulster Hall, Whitla Hall, King's Hall. New groups in Abercorn and Crescent bars. **Sports:** Excellent facilities on campus. Also wide range of leisure centres. New ice rink and ten pin bowling. Sports shop in SU building. **Hardship funds:** Bursar's loans easily available. **Travel:** Cheap travel on railways at certain times or if in possession of travel save stamp. Hitching not practical for obvious reasons. Excellent travel shop in SU. **Work:** Bar work, cloakrooms, bouncers.

CAN'T FIND WHAT YOU'RE LOOKING FOR? USE THE INDEX!

Alumni (Editors' pick)
Trevor Ringland, Nigel Carr and Philip Matthews (all rugby players), Brian Mawhinney (Minister of Education for N Ireland), Seamus Heaney (poet), Bernadette McAlliskey (nee Devlin), Kenneth Branagh (actor), Sir Francis Tombs (Chairman of Rolls Royce), Brian Moore (writer).

BIRKBECK COLLEGE

Birkbeck College, University of London, Malet Street, London WC1E 7HX (071-580 6622) Map E, C1

Student enquiries: Registrar

Main study areas – as in What to Study section: *(First degree):* Biology, botany, chemistry, classics, computing, economics, English, environmental science, fine arts, geography, geology, history, mathematical studies, modern languages, philosophy, physics, politics & government, psychology.

European Community: 13% first degree students take EC language as part of course but no exchanges or links. Approved Erasmus programme 1990/91.

Structural features: Part of London University. **Student publication:** SU diary/ handbook. **Special features:** Birkbeck College (which is outside the UCCA scheme) provides degree level teaching and research facilities for students 'engaged in earning their livelihood' – so is primarily part-time. There is provision to change from part-time to full-time study with the permission of the college. Applications from under-18 students not welcomed. Application is direct but you will need to get hold of prospectus as qualifications for, and schemes of, admissions are complex. **Main awards:** BA, BSc. **Awarding Body:** London University. **Access:** In London University's central precinct in Bloomsbury; easily reached by underground (near Russell Square, Goodge Street, Warren Street and Euston stations) and close to a number of bus routes. **Library:** 250,000 books; 1,000 periodicals. Late opening hours particularly designed to provide good study conditions for part-time students. Students also use main London University library next door in Senate House. **Other learning resources:** Language Centre: self-tuition courses available in a number of languages, with a four-booth language laboratory; language teaching lab with computer-assisted language learning packages; expanding collection of recordings in major European languages, sound-recording studio and tape facilities. **Computing facilities:** Access via terminals and micros to both college and university machines; advisory service; college Central Computing Service produces range of technical bulletins and regular newsletter.

Duration of first degree course(s) or equivalent: 4 years: 3 years for some advanced students **Total first degree students 1989/90:** 1,756 **Number of mature students:** 90% **Male/female ratio 1989/90:** 1:1 **Teaching staff: full-time:** 147 part-time: 15 approx **Total full-time students 1989/90:** 315 (mostly postgraduate) **Postgraduate students:** 1,556 **Tuition fees, first degrees, 1990/91:** Part-time: £498 (£408–£458 if self-financing); full-time Home: £1,675 (£628 if self-financing); Overseas: £5,400 (arts degrees), £6,600 (science degrees)

What it's like
Unique college catering primarily for mature, working people who choose to gain a London University degree through part-time study; classes are held between 6 and 9 pm and students range from early 20s to late 70s. Students without formal qualifications are often accepted. Degrees take 4 years instead of 3 and students may transfer to full-time after two years. (Postgraduate and research degrees can also be gained through part-time and/or full-time study.)

CAN'T FIND WHAT YOU'RE LOOKING FOR? USE THE INDEX!

Needs of both full-time and part-time students accommodated. Union shop and office, library and snack bar are open in the evenings as well as daytime, also new dining club, serving hot meals from 5 pm weekdays. Other facilities include a nursery, lively bar, SU magazine – *Spectrum* – encouraging student contribution, two annual careers fairs and a freshers fair, a careers officer, and over 30 other SU funded clubs and societies, which include own sports ground, an active drama group, and a Bat Society! Birkbeck students highly motivated, so they still manage to put time into Union activities, clubs, and societies on top of work and study; incredible, but true.

University of London Union (ULU) nearby, housing the major sports and social facilities; so are Senate House Library, the British Library (used by many research students), and Dillons bookshop. Located in the heart of academic London, Birkbeck is well served by public transport, and nearby shops, entertainments, and places of interest abound.

Pauper notes

Drink: SU bar. **Eats:** SU snack bars. ULU next door. **Ents:** Filmsoc – free film each week. Free live music/cabaret each week. **Sports:** Own sports association, own ground at Greenford, as used by QPR FC. **Hardship funds:** Some college assistance possible. **Travel:** ULU Travel is next door. **Work:** Ask SU for help – some casual work.

Alumni (Editors' pick)

Anthony Cornish, Baroness McFarlane of Llandaff (head of department of nursing, Manchester University), Elizabeth Esteve-Coll (Director of the V & A Museum), Frank Sidebottom (cabaret singer), Sidney Webb (founder of LSE and other things).

BIRMINGHAM CONSERVATOIRE

Birmingham Conservatoire, Paradise Place, Birmingham B3 3HG (021-331 5912) Map A, E7

Student enquiries: Director of Studies

Main study areas – as in What to Study section: *(First degree):* Music.

European Community: 40% first degree students take EC language as part of course; none spend 6 months or more in another EC country. No formal exchange links with EC universities/colleges but numerous informal exchanges.

Application: Direct (twice yearly, autumn and spring). **Academic developments:** Initial full-time courses lead to BA degree (CNAA) or to a graduate diploma (GBSM); new modular structure. Postgraduate diploma (part-time) in performance studies also available. GBSM students take either 3-year academic/teaching or a 4-year performing course. Only music college offering BA degree with band option. Other options in ethnic music, music administration, jazz and improvisation, music technology and recording techniques. Students come from all over UK, from schools with good music departments or with A-level music. Graduates of the teaching course especially well-placed for employment. **Structural features:** New concert hall complex recently completed. Distinguished teaching staff drawn from Midlands, also nationally and internationally. The City of Birmingham Symphony Orchestra has its administrative headquarters within the Conservatoire's Adrian Boult Complex and many of CBSO's principals teach at school. **Founded:** 1886 as part of Birmingham and Midland Institute; now a faculty of Birmingham Poly. **Main awards:** BA, GBSM. **Awarding body:** Birmingham Conservatoire and CNAA. **Access** 10 minutes walk from railway station. **Site:** City centre. **Accommodation:** Places at Cambrian Hall; and Halls of Residence, Faculty

CAN'T FIND WHAT YOU'RE LOOKING FOR? USE THE INDEX!

of Education, Westbourne Road. Apply to Birmingham Poly (Perry Barr, Birmingham 42) for both. Rent: 10% in accommodation where rent controlled by college. **Library:** 41,000 volumes, 30 periodicals, 32 carrels. **Specialist collections:** Dodd Bows. **Welfare:** Medical facilities of Aston University. **Hardship funds:** Harrod Fund; Centenary Appeal Fund. **Careers:** Information and advice, but no placement service.

Duration of first degree course(s) or equivalent: 3 years; **others (performing):** 4 years **Total first degree students 1989/90:** 93; **Number of overseas students:** 3 **Number of mature students:** 3 **Male/female ratio 1989/90:** 1:1; **Teaching staff: full-time:** 17 **part-time:** 92; **Total full-time students 1989/90:** 270; **Postgraduate students:** 30 **Tuition fees, first degrees, 1990/91:** Home: £1,675; Overseas: £4,295.

What it's like

It's ideally situated in modern purpose-built city centre development, with easy access to transport and main arts centres including town hall and repertory theatre. New concert hall and practice rooms should make it possibly best equipped UK music college. Most first years live in poly hostels (Cambrian Hall most accessible 4 mins walk). List of flats and digs available. Provides valuable opportunities for dedicated musicians with emphasis on professional discipline. Ample time for private practice. Staff/student relationships good. It combines a high practical and academic standard, with the centrality on the 1st study. Demand for places very high. Musical life centres around orchestras, choirs and bands, and growing chamber music dept. SU discos, barn dances and film shows. Birmingham night life ranges from cheap student bars to top international clubs. Very few students do not complete course.
Alison Knight

Pauper notes

Drink: The Shakespeare (M & B), Prince of Wales (Ansells), The Night and Day (if there isn't much time). The Grapevine. **Eats:** Lots of reasonable restaurants especially Nataraj on Broad Street. 'American Food Factory' on New Street. **Ents:** Rock and classical concerts with regular big names. **Hardship funds:** Official fund for students without a grant. **Shops:** Very interesting shops in suburbs of Harborne and Moseley. **Travel:** Midlands travelcards cost about £14 a month for unlimited travel on bus and trains in region. **Work:** Some Xmas shows offer work plus chance to gain experience; pub work always available in term-time.

Alumni (Editors' pick)

Ernest Elemont (violinist), Peter Aston, Paul Beard, Brian Ferneyhough, Jean Rigby, Nicholas Wood, orchestral musicians, singers in major opera companies, professors of music, music advisers, directors of music companies.

BIRMINGHAM POLY

Birmingham Polytechnic, Perry Barr, Birmingham B42 2SU (021-331 5000) Map A, E7

Student enquiries: Academic Registry

Main study areas – as in What to Study section: *(First degree):* Accountancy, architecture and landscape, art & design, building studies, business studies, communication studies, computing, economics, education, electrical & electronic engineering, English, fine arts, hotel & catering management, information technology, law, library & information studies, manufacturing & production engineering, modern languages, music, nursing studies, politics and government, sociology,

CAN'T FIND WHAT YOU'RE LOOKING FOR? USE THE INDEX!

speech sciences, town and country planning, welfare studies Also: chiropody & podiatry.

European Community: 5% first degree students take EC language as part of course and 5% spend 6 months or more in another EC country. Formal exchange links with EC universities/colleges not known.

Application: PCAS, except art and design (ADAR). **Academic features:** Current study on the needs of women engineers. New courses: building surveying; applied software engineering; export engineering; nursing. **Structural features:** Birmingham Business School recently established. **Largest fields of study:** Business studies, engineering, art and design, built environment. **Founded:** 1971, ex North and South Birmingham Technical Colleges, Colleges of Commerce and Art & Design, and Birmingham School of Music; later joined by City of Birmingham and Bordesley Colleges of Education and Anstey College of PE. Bourneville College of Art joined in 1987 and with Faculty of Art & Design constitutes the Birmingham Institute of Art and Design. **Main awards:** BA, BEd, BSc, BEng. **Awarding body:** CNAA. **Site:** Split on several sites. **Access:** Buses and railway from Birmingham city centre. **Accommodation:** approx 650 study/bedsits. Halls of residence reserved for first year students. Rent: approx 10% in accommodation where rent controlled by polytechnic. **Library:** Six specialist libraries containing 400,000 volumes, 2,000 periodicals, 140,000 non-book materials, 800 study places, course books on reference. **Specialist collections:** Rare books collection; collection of children's books; large collection of sheet music; Marion Richardson archive. **Other learning resources:** Computer Services Department (IBM 9370 system, 3 Prime 50 series mini computers plus workstations with access to institutional, national and international networks); Learning Methods Unit (research on improving teaching methods and offering study skills services). **Welfare:** SU welfare services. Student Services Centre at Perry Barr. **Hardship funds:** Limited fund at SU and Student Services. **Careers:** Information, advice and placement. **Amenities:** Bookshop, general shop, bank, travel shop, insurance broker, legal advice, medical services, creche.

Duration of first degree course(s) or equivalent: 3 years **Other:** 4 years **Total first degree students 1989/90:** 5,990; **BEd students:** 339 **Number of overseas students:** 232; **Number of mature students:** 1,466; **Male/female ratio 1989/90:** 7:6 **Teaching staff: full-time:** 630 **part-time:** 66 **Total full-time students 1989/90:** 7,006 **Postgraduate students:** 1,342; **Tuition fees, first degrees, 1990/91:** Home: £1,675; Overseas: £4,295.

What it's like

An amalgam of modern/old buildings split over seven sites, the largest being Perry Barr, then Gosta Green (arts), Westbourne Road (teacher training), Conservatoire (music school), Bourneville, Margaret Street (Arts), and the Jewellery School. Halls places limited, most students share houses. Communication helped by SU magazine – *Polygon.* SU provides social life – running bars/shops at Perry Bar and Westbourne Road. Sports and societies run by SU but limited by lack of facilities. Entertainments varied to cater for diversity of students. Large population – 14,500 students, many part-time/mature. Access to sites good, problems with car parking. Many good courses – business and music school especially. Birmingham is a student city – many cheap 'student nights' in clubs, also some discounts on theatres, cinemas, many cheap shops/markets.
Brigitte Marulli de Barletta

Pauper notes

Accommodation: Halls places extremely limited, poly housing scheme: fairly restrictive contracts; accommodation available around main site. **Drink:** SU bar comparatively cheap, many real ale pubs, Black Country Beers. **Eats:** Poly food not amazingly cheap, B'ham renowned for its curry houses. **Ents:** Many local events, bands, especially student stuff – B'ham and Aston Univs. Many discounts, nightclubs, theatres, cinemas. **Sports:** Poly facilities poor. SU hires good pitches/

CAN'T FIND WHAT YOU'RE LOOKING FOR? USE THE INDEX!

halls from city. **Hardship funds:** Poly provides emergency cover (minimum). **Travel:** Cheap, good buses and trains in city, B'ham is easy to get to and from! **Work:** Usual – pubs and clubs, and anywhere.

Alumni (Editors' pick)

Alfred Bestall (the creator of Rupert Bear); Judy Simpson, Kathy Cook (Olympic athletes), Betty Jackson (fashion designer); Larry (cartoonist).

BIRMINGHAM UNIVERSITY

The University of Birmingham, Edgbaston, Birmingham B15 2TT (021-414 3344) Map A, E7

Student enquiries: Academic Secretary (Prospectus)

Main study areas – as in What to Study section: *(First degree):* Accountancy, African studies, American studies, anatomy, archaeology, biochemistry, biology, biotechnology, botany, business studies, chemical engineering, chemistry, civil engineering, Classics, computing, dance, dentistry, drama, economics, education, electrical & electronic engineering, English, fine arts, geography, geology, history, law, mathematical studies, mechanical and production engineering, medicine, metallurgy and materials science, microbiology, modern languages, music, Near East and Islamic studies, nursing, philosophy, physics, physiology, politics and government, psychology, public administration, religious studies and theology, sociology, town and country planning, welfare studies. *Also:* Medieval studies, physical education, sport and recreation studies.

European Community: Number of first degree students who take EC language as part of course unknown; 1% spend 6 months or more in another EC country. Formal exchange links with 3 EC universities/colleges: Lyon, Karlsruhe and Bordeaux.

Application: UCCA. **Academic features:** New degrees in fine arts and art history; East Mediterranean history; Greek and Roman studies; mechanical engineering and business studies; commerce with languages; public and social policy management. **Founded:** 1828, as Birmingham School of Medicine and Surgery, and 1875 Mason College; granted charter in 1900. **Main awards:** BA, BCom, BDS, BEng, BEng and Man, BEng and BCom, MEng, BMus, BSc, BSocSc, LLB, MB, ChB. **Awarding body:** Birmingham University. **Site:** 2.5 miles from city centre (Edgbaston). **Access:** Just off A38; buses between university and city centre, trains between University Station (on campus) and New Street Station, in city centre. **Accommodation:** 2,000 places in halls, 1,950 in self-catering flats in three student villages; accommodation guaranteed for first year students. Independent hostels for Anglican and Jewish students; university accommodation officer helps with flats and lodgings. Rent: 40% in accommodation where rent controlled by university. **Library:** Main library with 1,300,000 volumes plus various subject libraries; guide issued to students. **Other learning facilities:** Computer centre, television and film unit, language laboratories, Barber Art Gallery. **Welfare:** Student welfare officer. University health centre with adviser, Guild of Students welfare service; medical and dental service both obtainable by telephone; all students asked to complete health questionnaire before coming up; sight testing by appointment at health centre. Day nursery for children of students and staff close to main campus. **Hardship funds:** A hardship fund, administered by the university, available for help in individual cases. **Careers:** Information and advice centre (including videotape presentations of various careers). **Amenities:** Union building controlled by Guild of Students with hall, bars, etc; bookshop, banks and barbers on site; Barber Institute of Fine Arts. **Sporting facilities:** Multi-activity centre with swimming pool, gymnasia, etc; seventy acres of playing fields; Raymond Priestley centre for

CAN'T FIND WHAT YOU'RE LOOKING FOR? USE THE INDEX!

rock climbing, sailing, and sub-aqua diving adjacent to Coniston Water in Lake District.

Duration of first degree course(s) or equivalent: 3 years; 4 years including language courses, MEng, BCom, and dentistry; 5 years medicine **Total first degree students 1989/90:** 8,641 **BEd students:** 681 **Number of overseas students:** 521 **Number of mature students:** 680 **Male/female ratio 1989/90:** 3:2 **Teaching staff: full-time:** 990 **part-time:** 53 **Total full-time students 1989/90:** 10,420 **Postgraduate students:** 1,624 f-t, 810 p-t **Tuition fees, first degrees, 1990/91:** Home: £1,675; Overseas: £4,690 (eg politics), £6,180 (eg physics) £11,280 (maximum).

What it's like

Centrally located in the Midlands, it is a campus university on outskirts of Birmingham. 10,000 full-time students, 1,700 part-time students', create a thriving atmosphere. The university is one of the top in the country; the students' union is amongst the top four. The Guild of Students (ie SU) not only has an impressive facility, housing the area's most popular bars, eating places and entertainments, but is also an active campaigning organisation for the rights and welfare of students and community. There are over 200 clubs and societies, as well as the Guild Athletic Union, which organises sport for all levels.

Campus facilities are outstanding, and nationally respected. The campus and halls of residences are all tree-lined and landscaped; once on campus it is easy to forget how conveniently close the city centre is. Birmingham is usually the first or second choice, so most students are happy here. There is good support network, and almost all can find some means of help, academically or personally. Excellent choice if you want to make the most of four years at university.
Jan Abramson

Pauper notes

Accommodation: 7 Halls; 5 self-catering sites; accommodation available for family units; most settings are extremely picturesque. New bus connects halls with the Guild. **Drink:** 5 Guild bars, the cheapest in the area; minibus takes you home. Favourite watering hole for miles around. **Eats:** Guild is excellent. 5 lunchtime catering outlets; meals in evening (fast food, sandwiches, pasta and salad bar; pizza; jacket potatoes). **Ents:** Thrice weekly nightclub until 2 am; cabaret, bands, Sunday night jazz, midweek trivia quizzes, videos (NEC also nearby). **Sports:** One of top five in country. Coaching for different levels. Large sports area and good sports centre. **Hardship funds:** Jointly run by University and Guild of Students for students who fall on hard times. **Travel:** Excellent travel in SU for student travel. **Work:** Available in and around campus but don't forget work and socialising. Guild has a large force of student employees.

Alumni (Editors' pick)

Sir Alex Jarratt (Jarratt Report), Victoria Wood (comedienne/writer), Sir Austin Pierce (Chairman, British Aerospace), Haslam, Desmond Morris (writer/ broadcaster), Sir Peter Walters (Chairman BP), Ross Whitley, The Hon J J Bossano (Chief Minister, Gibralter), Dr D M Mutasa (Speaker of Parliament, Zimbabwe). People who failed to get a degree – Simon Le Bon. People disciplined – Chris Tarrant.

BOLTON INSTITUTE

Bolton Institute of Higher Education, Deane Road, Bolton BL3 5AB (0204 28851); Fax 0204 399074; Freephone 0800 262117
Map A, D5

Student enquiries: The Marketing Officer

Main study areas – as in What to Study section: *(First degree):* Biology, business studies, engineering, computing, education, electrical & electronic engineering, English, history, mathematics, mechanical & production engineering, philosophy, psychology, strategic studies.

European Community: No first degree students take EC language as part of course; less than 1% spend 6 months or more in another EC country. Some links with France.

Application: PCAS. **Founded:** 1982, ex Bolton Institute of Technology and Bolton College of Education (Technical). **Main awards:** BA, BEd, BEng, BSc. **Awarding body:** CNAA; Manchester University (in-service teacher education degrees). **Site:** Bolton town centre. **Access:** Easily reached by road and rail. 10 miles north of Manchester. **Accommodation:** Halls, hostels and private lodgings; accommodation manager. **Library:** 145,000 books and related materials together with microfilms, microfiches, audiocassettes and tape slide presentations. **Other learning resources:** Access to PRESTEL. Provision made for on-line access to major bibliographic machine readable databases. **Welfare:** Student services unit specialist staff; chaplain. **Careers:** Information, advice and placement. **Amenities:** SU with numerous clubs and societies. Octagon Theatre, Bolton Little Theatre, Art Gallery and museum, Indoor and Outdoor Markets, Travel shop Water Place. **Sporting facilities:** Sports hall, playing fields, squash court.

Duration of first degree course(s) or equivalent: 3 years full time; 4 years sandwich **Total first degree students 1989/90:** 1,971; **Total BEd students:** 62 **Number of overseas students:** 79 **Number of mature students:** 758 **Male/female ratio 1989/90:** 3:2 **Teaching staff:** full-time: 37; part-time: 1. **Total full-time students 1989/90:** 2,275 **Postgraduate students:** 80 **Tuition fees, first degrees, 1990/91:** Home: £1,675; Overseas: £4,250.

What it's like

On 3 campuses. The buildings are a mixture of old Victorian schools (Gt Moor Street) and modern glass and concrete. Deane campus accommodates all technology based courses. Chadwick, the teaching department and humanities. Both are within cartwheeling distance of town, although at opposite ends of it. Chadwick has SU offices, bar, squash courts and library and tends to cater mainly for mature students, although its parochial image is gradually changing. Deane caters for 'younger' students. It also accommodates SU offices, SU bar, sports hall, Solomon Mahlangu common room, travel shop, photocopying service etc. Regular ents are provided at both sites by a rapidly expanding SU. Despite its 'in the sticks' image, Bolton is quickly becoming something of a commuter town for Manchester. Huge town centre developments are under way. SU has very close links with the bigger higher education institutions in Manchester twenty minutes train journey away. SU clubs and societies are very active. For the past 3 years, ethnic clubs have taken the lead in union activity. BISU is very firmly placed on the national map as a strong politically campaigning union.

Accommodation is difficult to find in Bolton; Institute accommodation is generally expensive and available only in first year. 3 hostels are more aesthetically pleasing than the halls, but still expensive.

SU has excellent relations with the Institute which has firm commitment to student representation and scarcely breathes without first consulting SU.

Most degrees are CNAA validated with sound standing. There is a reckonable

CAN'T FIND WHAT YOU'RE LOOKING FOR? USE THE INDEX!

student drop-out rate, mainly by yuppies and intellectual snobs at the end of their first year. However students from a multitude of backgrounds meet easily and naturally, often forming 'permanent relationships'. SU is committed to anti-racist, anti-sexist policies; working with the Institute to implement an equal opportunities policy and guidelines to protect overseas students from slipping through the holes in the British education system.
Nikki Francey

Pauper notes

Accommodation: Private sector accommodation very poor and difficult to obtain. No married quarters. Approx 150 places in college accommodation. **Drink:** Loads of pubs. Greenhall Whitley, Witches, Pendles. **Eats:** Good SU pizza franchise + pies & peas. Refectory food is usually good, averagely priced. Little veggy choice. **Ents:** Good on campus. Live Bands (middle market), regular film nights, alternative discos, heavy etc. Apart from pubs local ents are negligible. **Sports:** On campus sports hall, squash courts, bowling green, 1,000,001 local sports centres, gyms, swimming pools. **Hardship funds:** SU has welfare fund to help but this is limited. **Work:** Bar work for hard-up students.

BOURNEMOUTH POLY

Bournemouth Polytechnic, Talbot Campus, Fern Barrow, Dorset BH12 5BB (0202 524111) Fax: 0202 513293
Map A, E9

Student enquiries: Academic Secretary

Main study areas – as in What to Study section: *(First degree):* Accountancy, archaeology, business studies, communication studies, computing, electrical & electronic engineering, food science & nutrition; hotel & catering management, information technology, law, nursing studies. *Also:* Advertising, engineering business development, heritage conservation, public relations, tourism.

European Community: All students can study a language as an extra subject and work for certification of competence; none spend time in another EC country at present. Currently, links with 6 EC universities/colleges: France (2); Germany (2); Netherlands (1); Spain (1) but number increasing. Undergraduates will shortly be able to go on exchanges particularly in business management and tourism. Approved Erasmus programme 1990/91. New BA international marketing management, which includes 2 EC languages.

Application: PCAS. **Academic features:** Degrees in communication, retail management, health and community studies, public relations, nursing. Sandwich course in international marketing, engineering business development, product design, electronic systems design, information systems management. **Special features:** Visiting fellows: J Smith (nursing), J Foster (communication & media), A J C Solway (information systems), Albert Roux (catering), Sidney Silver (tourism), D Bebo, P Bird, D Hasted (business management). **Founded:** 1990; as Dorset Institute in 1976, ex Bournemouth College of Technology and Weymouth College of Education. **Main awards:** BA, BSc, BEng. **Awarding body:** CNAA. **Site:** 2 sites. **Access:** Buses. **Accommodation:** 250 places in student village, lodgings, self-catering flats and bedsits. **Library:** Libraries on each site; total of 130,000 volumes, 1,300 periodicals, 600 study places, restricted loan collection. **Welfare:** 2 full time counsellors, 2 accommodation officers, chaplain, full-time nurse, doctor, dentist, FPA, psychiatrist, solicitor, financial adviser. **Careers:** Information, advice and placement. **Amenities:** Good resort amenities, especially for sailing; arts centre at Poole plus Arndale Sports Club (squash, swimming, gymnastics); good sports halls, 2 squash courts and a weights room, together with cricket nets and wall-climbing facilities at Wallisdown. Large SU bar with refreshment and entertainment facilities.

CAN'T FIND WHAT YOU'RE LOOKING FOR? USE THE INDEX!

Duration of first degree course(s) or equivalent: 3 years (full time); **Other:** 4 years sandwich **Total first degree students 1989/90:** 2,400 **Male/female ratio 1989/90:** 1:1 **Teaching staff:** 250 **Part-time:** 30 fte **Total full-time students 1989/90:** 3,270 **Postgraduate students:** 280 **Tuition fees, first degrees, 1990/91:** Home: £1,675; Overseas: £4,630.

What it's like

Dorset Institute changed its name and status and is now Bournemouth Polytechnic. The college expanded in order to comply with qualifications required to become a poly, which has meant a huge increase in number of full and part-time students and the rapid introduction of new and innovative courses (eg BA in public relations) and also better library facilities. This has strained SU resources and left new poly in poor position to cope due to limited facilities. Growth rate will now stabilise as the goal has been reached. This year SU has been allocated a larger area and building has almost been completed for a new bar to accompany the old one. Houses of residence have been completed and have a capacity of 250 students, so majority of freshers would continue to live in hotels for the first term (£43 for dinner, bed & breakfast), before moving out into fully furnished rented accommodation.

College has 'hi-tech' 'hands-on' policy; lots of Macintosh personal computers on open access, though not enough to cope with peak times as most courses 'prefer' assignments done on the Mac word processors. (Learn to type before coming if poss.)

College is a large concrete rabbit hutch and a smaller sci-fi building. Nearly all courses are practical (biggest business studies and catering) which makes this the government's model college, and fact that most students are white, middle class and either conservative or unconcerned probably helps too. A high proportion of students own cars, making parking a serious problem.

SU active although not radical, maintains a good relationship with college administration and provides a number of good services. Both bars are under SU control as well as 'Herb Garden' which is excellent catering outlet providing both vegetarian and vegan meals as well as meat dishes. The Sugarmine (main bar) has a new PA system and lighting rig which provides an excellent venue for bands and discos.

The welfare and support services are good and extensive. SU provides a full-time sabbatical welfare officer, it is also a registered Citizens' Advice Bureau and so can give a high level of advice to students covering anything from housing to course work. The welfare service also produces its own student leaflets. There is a small hardship fund which is operated under strict rules and is generally used for rent. The loan agreement is quite flexible about the amount of time in paying it back. Some counselling services are provided by college and these are generally good with some excellent outside agencies in Bournemouth, ie Well Woman Clinic, Alcoholics Anon, etc.
Jessica Williams

Pauper notes

Accommodation: Capacity 250 in houses of residence, B&B hotels for 1st term at college, then majority of students go into fully furnished rented accom. **Drink:** College bar cheapest, although still not cheap. The Fiveways in Charminster good. Some good clubs. Old Thumper good strong local beer. **Eats:** Refectory not cheap. SU runs 'Herb Garden' which sells daily special vegan/vegetarian meals. Henry's, very good vegetarian in town. Fatty Arbuckles cheap burgers – big portions. **Ents:** Lots of clubs. Bands play on Friday nights in SU bar. Canon & UCI cinemas give student concessions on weekdays. **Sports:** Sports hall, multi-gym and squash courts on campus, off campus for playing fields and swimming pool (concessions). **Hardship funds:** Small fund operated under strict rules. Normally used for rent. Maximum payment £100. **Travel:** Poly is running a bus service for students from suburbs to college, experimental this year. **Work:** Part-time work in catering/bar establishments easy to get, pay average.

CAN'T FIND WHAT YOU'RE LOOKING FOR? USE THE INDEX!

BRADFORD & ILKLEY

Bradford & Ilkley Community College, Great Horton Road, Bradford BD7 1AY (0274 753026) Map A, E5

Student enquiries: Admissions Officer

Main study areas – as in What to Study section: *(First degree):* Art and design, education, welfare studies. *Also:* Community studies, home economics, organisation studies.

European Community: Number of first degree students taking EC languages or spending time in EC, not known; exchange links not known.

Application: PCAS; ADAR for art courses. **Founded:** 1982 ex Bradford College and Ilkley College. **Main awards:** BA, BEd. **Awarding body:** CNAA. **Sites:** Bradford and Ilkley. **Academic features:** Open and distance learning facilities available. **Accommodation:** 400 single rooms; lodgings officer supplies list of flats. **Library:** 220,000 volumes; 1,250 journals. **Specialist collections:** Slide collection of over 60,000 journal reprints. **Welfare:** Student service centre (including tutor to West Indian Youth, tutor for students with special needs, doctor and nursing staff). **Hardship funds:** Fully staffed student service gives advice and assistance. **Special categories:** Day nursery. **Careers:** Advisory service. **Amenities:** SU building with several bars; Bradford Alhambra Theatre, concerts, plays and recitals; library, theatre; National Photographic Museum. **Sporting facilities:** Shared with Bradford University; Richard Dunn Sports Centre in city of Bradford.

Duration of first degree course(s) or equivalent: 4 years; **others:** 3 years art and design, and organisation studies **Total first degree students 1989/90:** 702; **BEd students:** 270 **Number of overseas students:** 3 **Number of mature students:** 300 **Male/female ratio 1989/90:** 1:1 **Teaching staff: Full-time:** 485 **Part-time:** 1,000 **Total full-time students 1989/90:** 3,615 **Postgraduate students:** 110 **Tuition fees, first degrees, 1990/91:** Home: £1,675; Overseas: £4,500.

What it's like

Huge college (largest in UK? Europe?) – 33,000 students. Non-elitist community college. High proportion of overseas and mature students, with home students on minimum grant. SU active; on speaking terms with admin. Students represented on all college committees. Excellent counselling, careers accommodation services. Hall for 240, predominantly self-catering. Excellent social life.

Pauper notes

Accommodation: Housing lists from Student Services at the University. From £16-£35 per week. **Drinks:** SU building at Queens Hall and at Ilkley. Good local brews include Old Mill Bitter. Cellar Bar, Queene Hall: Old Mill, Ruddles, Courage, Theakstons, Batemans, Trough ales. **Eats:** Bradford home of foreign culinary delights at very cheap prices. 8 restaurants around Union campus – vegetarian meals inc. Curry restaurants, Italia cafe, Last Pizza Show, Oasis (Arabian), Mayflower (Chinese) and Lunch Box. **Ents:** One of the best and cheapest SU live music venues in England at Queens Hall – close to Alhambra Theatre and St George's Hall – discounts available. **Sports:** Excellent sports facilities. A lot shared with University. **Hardship funds:** Access funds and student services hardship grant – college administered. **Travel:** Hitching OK, esp from Leeds (M1), cheap student bus/train passes for West Yorkshire, Travel Trust for course related trips. **Work:** Part-time bar work, some portering etc, work in college, temping etc. Vacancy lists from SU.

Alumni (Editors' pick)

David Hockney – artist; New Model Army – group.

CAN'T FIND WHAT YOU'RE LOOKING FOR? USE THE INDEX!

BRADFORD UNIVERSITY

**University of Bradford, Bradford, West Yorkshire BD7 1DP
(0274 733466)** Map A, E5

Student enquiries: Schools Liaison Officer. Visitors welcome

Main study areas – as in What to Study section: *(First degree):* Archaeology, biochemistry, business studies, chemical engineering, chemistry, civil engineering, communication studies, computing, economics, electrical and electronic engineering, environmental science, European studies, food science and nutrition, geography, history, information technology, mathematical studies, mechanical and production engineering, microbiology, modern languages, nursing studies, pharmacology, pharmacy, philosophy, politics and government, psychology, sociology, strategic studies, welfare studies. *Also:* Medical sciences, ophthalmic optics.

European Community: 13% first degree students take EC language as part of course and 13% spend 6 months or more in another EC country. Formal exchange links with 7 EC universities/colleges: France (Montpellier, Nancy, Nice, Toulouse); Germany (Hamburg, Munich); Spain (Oviedo, Valladolid). Approved Erasmus programme 1990/91. BA management studies and German; BEng/MEng electronic engineering with European studies; modern languages facilities available to other students.

Application: UCCA. **Special features:** Opportunity to add range of practical skills (team work, presentation, report writing etc) and to become computer literate. Fellowships in music and theatre ensure a very active student arts scene. **Founded:** 1966. **Main awards:** BA, BEng, BPharm, BSc. **Awarding body:** Bradford University. **Site:** Close to city centre. **Academic features:** A positive and encouraging attitude towards non-standard and mature applicants; wide range of qualifications and/or experience accepted for entry. 70% of students are on sandwich degree courses. Engineering courses with foundation year for applicants with non-standard qualifications; BSc in electronic imaging and media communications, BSc in archaeology. **Structural features:** Part-time BA degree in social studies (evening classes). Continuing education extended. **Accommodation:** 900 places for men, 580 for women in halls; accommodation service for flats, bedsitters and furnished houses. Rent: 38% in accommodation where rent controlled by university. **Library:** 2 sites; 450,000 volumes; 2,000 current periodicals; 920 study places. **Other learning resources:** Personal computer connections for all staff and students to a large campus network giving access to electronic mail, university library, campus computer hosts, information bulletin boards and other services. Network access points being installed in offices, work areas and study bedrooms in student halls. Special prices and deferred payment terms available for personal computer purchases. **Welfare:** Student counselling service, overseas student advisers, student health service. 15 place day nursery. **Hardship funds:** Loans or small grants available from SU and from university in strictly defined circumstances. **Careers:** Information and advice service (with overseas section); annual recruitment fairs. **Amenities:** Communal building with 3 bar areas, dance floor, disco bar; SU travel office; bank and bookshop on campus; open air amphitheatre, studio theatre; campus radio; darkroom; SU shop and bar in Richmond Building. **Sporting facilities:** Indoor sports centre, plus solarium, sauna bath and 25 metre pool shared with Bradford College; sports grounds 3 miles away; additional squash courts and artificial turf areas at halls of residence.

Duration of first degree course(s) or equivalent: 4 years sandwich; **others:** 3, 4.5 and 5 years (sandwich) **Total first degree students 1989/90:** 3,898 **Number of overseas students:** 232 **Male/female ratio 1989/90:** 3:2 **Teaching staff: full-time:** 410 **part-time:** 160 **Total full-time students 1989/90:** 4,606 **Postgraduate students:** 708 **Tuition fees, first degrees, 1990/91:** Home: £1,675 (£665 if self-financing); Overseas: £4,500 (eg politics), £5,900 (eg physics).

CAN'T FIND WHAT YOU'RE LOOKING FOR? USE THE INDEX!

What it's like

Small, friendly campus university, five minutes walk from city centre. 4,800 students, 400 of whom based at Management Centre, 2 miles from main campus, on main bus routes. Technological university awarded Charter in 1966 (formerly Bradford College of Technology). Academic strengths – engineering, modern languages, business studies.

Accommodation: 1,700 places in university halls of residence, mostly self-catering. Private accommodation averages £15-20 pw, mostly in large, Victorian terraced houses within 2 miles of campus.

SU offers 4 bars on campus, shop, travel agency, print shop, welfare service, wide range of clubs and societies.

City – formerly Victorian textile capital, now extremely cosmopolitan and friendly. Cheap entertainment and food (cheapest and best curries in the country – try them or be forever socially inadequate!!) Products of 20 different real ale breweries can be sampled in the city.

Students – friendly and down-to-earth, no failed Oxbridge complex here. Despite being cheapest university city in the country, students rumoured to have largest per capita overdrafts (after London) – must be enjoying themselves.

Pauper notes

Accommodation: Most non-Hall accommodation is in 4/8 bedroom houses. Mainly close to campus and cheap £15–20 pw. But you can get what you pay for. **Drink:** SU bars cheaper than pubs. Watch for promos. Best beers are Tetleys, Websters, Theakstons and Youngers. **Eats:** Great value Indian, Pakistani, Chinese, Greek, Arabian, Italian all close to campus. All the burger and pizza places in town. **Ents:** Virtually all week on campus, gigs, cabaret, discos. Famous Alhambra Theatre and National Museum of Film Photography & Television nearby. 3 screen cinema near, ie it's brill. **Sports:** Cheap sports centre on campus ie swimming 20p. Playing fields 3 miles away on direct bus route. **Hardship funds:** Funds run by Union and University. **Travel:** Near to motorways therefore good for hitching. **Work:** Some local casual and bar work (some in SU) available.

Alumni (Editors' pick)

Dr Barry Seal MEP, Roland Boyes MP, Ian Bruce MP, David Hinchcliffe MP, Alice Mahon MP, Ann Taylor MP, Michael Meaowcroft (ex MP), Tony O'Riley (chairman of Heinz International).

BRETTON HALL

Bretton Hall, West Bretton, Wakefield, West Yorks WF4 4LG (0924 830261) Map A, E5

Student enquiries: Admissions Co-ordinator or Registrar

Main study areas – as in What to Study section: *(First degree):* Art and design, dance, drama, education, English, environmental studies, fine arts, music. **Also:** fashion and textiles.

European Community: No first degree students take EC language as part of course or spend time in another EC country.

Application: UCCA. **Academic features:** Integrated Arts course within BEd; BA Dance centred on community dance. New BAs: drama theatre crafts (technician), and fashion. New part-time MA in art & design education. New range of part-time BAs for mature students. **Special features:** Over 20 visiting artists and writers scheduled to be in residence, work and teach during the year. Lawrence Batley Centre for the National Arts Education Archive. **Founded:** 1949. **Main awards:**

CAN'T FIND WHAT YOU'RE LOOKING FOR? USE THE INDEX!

BA, BEd. **Awarding body:** Leeds University. **Site:** 18th century buildings in 260 acre rural setting. **Access:** 1 mile from M1 (Junction 38); public transport from Wakefield, Barnsley. **Accommodation:** 170 places on campus; excellent self-catering accommodation for 120 students nearby. College accommodation reserved for first-year students – 80% housed. 10% of students are home-based. **Library:** 50,000 volumes, 400 periodicals, 65 study places, reference or short term loan. Videos and microfiche reader facilities. **Other learning facilities:** Media resources centre. **Welfare:** Doctor, chaplain, counsellors, sick bay (staffed). **Hardship funds:** A general fund available for extreme hardship cases. **Amenities:** Bookshop on campus, boating, playing fields; Yorkshire Sculpture Park; Bretton Lakes Nature Reserve. National Art Education Archive.

Duration of first degree course(s) or equivalent: 3 years (BA); 4 years (BEd); **Total first degree students 1989/90:** 346; **BEd students:** 114 **Overall overseas students:** 10 **Overall mature students:** 317 **Male/female ratio 1989/90:** 1:3 **Teaching staff: full-time:** 88 **part-time:** 55 **Total full-time students 1989/90:** 1,097 **Postgraduate students:** 157 **Tuition fees, first degrees, 1990/91:** Home: £1,675 plus £321 university fee in first year; Overseas: £4,563 plus university fee of £321.

What it's like

Based around an 18th century mansion, set in 260 acres of beautiful landscaped parkland, which includes the Yorkshire Sculpture Park, Nature Reserve, Country Park and two lakes. Wakefield, Barnsley (7 miles) and Huddersfield (9 miles) within reach adequate public transport.

Around 170 students live on campus. College has bought a chunk of the Park Green housing estate, near Normanton. About 100 first years housed in self-catering accommodation.

Campus accommodation is catered, most say badly. Basically workers are not paid enough for the service to improve. SU supported campaigns wangled a snack bar, supposed to sell vegetarian food but now has salad, burger and chips!

Small college; not many societies despite the ease with which new ones can be established. Recently several have folded. SU making effort to get college involved with and recognised by other UKCPUs.

Lack of funding and space means no creche. Overworked counselling service unsupported by college management. Inadequate careers service. Regular bus service to and from Barnsley (twice daily) and Smirthwaite (3 times a day).

Pauper notes

Accommodation: Off-campus accommodation increasingly hard to find. SU Accommodation Officer compiles a Housing Advice Pack. Government destroying rent rebates. **Drink:** West Bretton one of only 3 dry villages in England! SU bar saves the world, with good selection of subsidised beers etc. John Smiths, Old Mill, Hoffmeister, Miller Lite, Taunton ciders, bar refurbished 1987. **Eats:** Vegetarian food usually best bet in canteen. SU bar sells hot snacks, SU shop sells fresh sandwiches and snacks. **Ents:** Regular events, plus outside trips; Ents Saver-card. **Sports:** All students entitled to free Passport to Leisure for Wakefield MDC's sport/leisure facilities. Sport at Bretton depends on involvement of students. **Hardship funds:** limited, through College Registrar, Vice-Principal. **Travel:** Student season tickets available for local buses and trains. **Work:** Possible to get bar/shop jobs part-time, transport permitting. BEd/PGCE employment over 90%; no figures for BA.

Alumni (Editors' pick)

Anne Collins (opera singer), Colin Welland (actor/playwright, author), David Rappaport (founder of Hull Truck), Nicholas Parsons (TV personality), John Godber (playwright), Ken Robinson (TIE/Arts in Education).

CAN'T FIND WHAT YOU'RE LOOKING FOR? USE THE INDEX!

"Lots of girl students go through initial heady Isadora Duncan-type period "

BRIGHTON POLY

Brighton Polytechnic, Lewes Road, Brighton, East Sussex BN2 4AT (0273 600900) Map A, F8

Student enquiries: The Registrar

Main study areas – as in What to Study section: *(First degree):* Accountancy, architecture, art & design, biology, business studies, chemistry, civil engineering, computing, dance, drama, economics, education, electrical & electronic engineering, English, fine arts, geography, history, hotel & catering management, information technology, library & information studies, linguistics, mathematical studies, mechanical and production engineering, music, pharmacy, physics, tourism, welfare studies. *Also:* Podiatry/chiropody, sports science.

European Community: 18% first degree students take EC language as part of course and 5% spend 6 months or more in another EC country. Formal exchange links with some 20 EC universities/colleges: France (11); Germany (7); Italy (2); most open to non-language specialists. Approved Erasmus programme 1990/91.

Application: PCAS; art and design, ADAR. **Academic features:** New courses: BA international tourism management; BSc Podiatry; BSc building surveying. **Structural features:** Centre for Business Research (Brighton Business School). **Largest fields of study:** Art, design and humanities; education (including physical education); engineering; business management; health; information technology. **Founded:** 1970, ex Brighton College of Technology and Brighton College of Art. Brighton College of Education and East Sussex College of HE incorporated later. **Main awards:** BA, BEd, BSc, BEng, MEng. **Awarding body:** CNAA. **Site:** 3 major sites at Brighton; Eastbourne site. **Access:** Bus and train services provide regular inter-site travel. **Accommodation:** At least 30% of first year students housed by poly, some catered, others self-catering. Accommodation officers assist with finding lodgings in private sector. Rent: 25% in accommodation where rent controlled by polytechnic. Approx cost: £34-£42 pw halls (with meals), £26-£30 pw (self-catering), £35-£50 pw (lodgings). **Library:** 7 libraries, over 500,000 volumes, 3,250 periodicals, 12,000 videotapes, 820 study places. **Other learning resources:** Media units for film and video, including darkroom and graphic design studio. 600 computer terminals/micros linked to each other and to VAX computers. Over 300 introductory documents to computing service. Advisory service also operates.

CAN'T FIND WHAT YOU'RE LOOKING FOR? USE THE INDEX!

Welfare: Welfare and accommodation officers, doctor, personal counsellor and chaplain on each site; recreation tutor. **Hardship funds:** Limited funds available for some final year students. **Careers:** Careers counsellor and careers information room for Brighton and Eastbourne campuses. **Amenities:** Bookshops at Moulsecoomb and Falmer sites; swimming pool (near Olympic standard) at Eastbourne campus; recreation facilities, including extensive playing fields in Brighton and Eastbourne, 6 gymnasia, dance studios, licensed bars.

Duration of first degree course(s) or equivalent: 3 years; **others:** 4 years (teacher training and sandwich) **Total first degree students 1989/90:** 5,639 **Total BEd students:** 847 **Number of overseas students:** 371 **Number of mature students:** 627 (in 1st year) **Male/female ratio 1989/90:** 1:1 **Teaching staff: full-time:** 540 **part:time** 550 **Total full-time students 1989/90:** 6,442 **Postgraduate students:** 698 **Tuition fees, first degrees, 1990/91:** Home: £1,675 (£651 if self-financing); Overseas: £4,500.

What it's like

2,500 part-time and over 6,000 full-time students spread over 4 sites. The main site is at Moulsecoomb which holds about 3,000 students studying sciences, business, architecture and interior design; near the town centre is the art college at Grand Parade. The Falmer site is 4 miles out of town, the home of library and information studies, humanities, social administration and teacher training. The Eastbourne site is 25 miles from Brighton, but has its own thriving social scene and will be your home if you decide to go there to study sports science, teaching, chiropody or hotel and catering.

Accommodation is pretty nightmarish. Poly can accommodate around 700 in halls; average rent for a student house in Brighton is £35+. Watch out for accommodation agencies, there are a few dodgy ones about. The accommodation people in student services are very helpful.

Doctors' surgeries on each site. The SU has 54 clubs, 49 societies and runs the Basement Bar where gigs are staged. Ongoing SU project is the Biko Scholarship scheme where the Union pays for a South African student to come and study at Brighton and the poly waives the fees.

Brighton is a great, if expensive, place to live and many students stay there after their courses have finished.
Cameron Paine, President.

Pauper notes

Accommodation: Limited – but not impossible; a lot of rubbish. Hardly any squats. **Drink:** SU club – The Basement for cheap drinks (next to the art college). **Eats:** Burger bars galore including the mighty Grubbs and Uncle Sams, a good range of vegetarian and vegan eating places, eg Food for Friends. Brighton has it all, whatever it is. **Ents:** SU gigs in Basement; films at the Duke of Yorks, Odeon and Cannon. Plays at the Gardener Arts Centre and the Theatre Royal. Bands play the Brighton Centre and at the Dome, loads of nightclubs, always something to do. **Sports:** Eastbourne campus has Olympic standard facilities, both the King Alfred and Prince Regent sports centres have swimming pools King Alfred (in Hove) also does snooker, ten pin bowling and water slides. **Hardship funds:** There are limited SU hardship loans. **Travel:** Excellent day train between Brighton–Falmer–Eastbourne; bus service varies, and night travel can be difficult. Hitching is not bad. **Work:** Summer jobs not too difficult to find, but beware the glut at the start of the summer holidays when 4,000 people try to go for 400 temping jobs. If you are planning to work in Brighton over the summer holidays, find your job early. Some part-time jobs for term times are available.

Alumni (Editors' pick)

Michael Hodson (art director), Gary Day Ellison (art director), Scott Crolla (of 'Crolla', wonderful menswear shop).

CAN'T FIND WHAT YOU'RE LOOKING FOR? USE THE INDEX!

BRISTOL OLD VIC

Bristol Old Vic Theatre School, 2 Downside Road, Clifton, Bristol BS8 2XF (0272 733535) Map A, D8

Student enquiries: The Principal

Main study areas: *(First degree):* Performance arts, movement studies, theatre design.

European Community: Number of students taking EC languages or spending time in another EC country, not known.

Application: Direct. **Academic features:** Strictly vocational training for theatre, and related media. **Structural features:** Close ties and working arrangements with the Bristol Old Vic Company, BBC Radio, HTV, university and polytechnic. **Special features:** Visiting specialists in all fields of the profession. All permanent staff have wide professional experience. **Largest fields of study:** Acting and stage management, design and wardrobe. **Founded:** 1946. **Site:** Main Clifton site with other venues around the city. **Access:** Adjacent 'Dart' bus stop. **Accommodation:** Private accommodation in nearby areas. Apply to Accommodation Officer to help find digs 3 weeks before commencement. Approx cost: Allow £1,000 per academic year. **Library:** No formal library, though the school stocks many play sets, individual texts and music. The Central and Reference libraries and the University theatre collection are open to certain student use. **Other specialist collections:** Sound and video editing, prop making etc. **Welfare:** The University student health service is available. **Hardship funds:** No special hardship funds. Advice about grant-making trusts is available. **Careers:** Information and advice given. No guarantee of placement. Main areas of employment: theatre and related media. **Sporting facilities:** The usual city facilities.

Duration of first degree course(s) or equivalent: 3 years; **others:** 2 and 1 years **Male/female ratio 1989/90:** 3:2 **Teaching staff: full-time:** 15; **part-time:** 21 **Total full-time students 1989/90:** 110 **Tuition fees, 1990/91:** £4,650.

What it's like

Training ground for all aspects of theatre/drama. Small institution with enormous amount of energy. One, two and three year acting courses, a two-year stage-management course, a theatre design course and a costume course.

Life can be emotionally and physically exhausting, yet rewarding and worthwhile. Claims to treat its students as professionals, allowing them a glimpse, we are told, of what it's like in the biz. This means rigorous discipline and, sometimes, not enough room for error and human fallibility.

Teaching is traditional with little radical input on the curriculum. Sometimes the rewards can be outweighed by the frustrations. Training is realistic and totally practical; most students are employed within six months of leaving.

The building is small and claustrophobic. If the atmosphere is family-like, then there is a lot of incest. Facilities vastly improved over last two years. No chance of late-night working as you have to be off the premises by 9 pm.

The commitment to a hard, penniless, unglamorous career in theatre has to be total, otherwise you will not endure the course and someone else could have had your place. Good luck!

Pauper notes

Drink: The Alma Tavern, Alma Vale Road; The Coronation Tap, University Union Bar. **Eats** University SU, York cafe, Cafe 59. **Ents:** Watershed, Arnolfini, Old Vic (half-price NUS). **Sports:** All Bristol SU facilities available. **Hardship funds:** The Madeleine Farrell Trust. **Work:** Front of house work at the Bristol Old Vic Theatre. Lots of bar/restaurant work.

Alumni (Editors' pick)

Daniel Day Lewis, Miranda Richardson, Jane Lapotaire, Christopher Cazenove, Jeremy Irons, Greta Scacchi, Gene Wilder, Simon Cadell.

CAN'T FIND WHAT YOU'RE LOOKING FOR? USE THE INDEX!

BRISTOL POLY

Bristol Polytechnic, Coldharbour Lane, Frenchay, Bristol BS16 1QY (0272 656261) Map A, D8

Student enquiries: Admissions Officer

Main study areas – as in What to Study section: *(First degree):* Accountancy, aeronautical engineering, art & design, biology, biotechnology, business studies, communication studies, computing, economics, education, electrical & electronic engineering, English, geography, history, information technology, law, mechanical & production engineering, modern languages, nursing studies, physics, politics and government, sociology, town and country planning. *Also:* Estate management, housing and construction, surveying.

European Community: 11% first degree students take EC language as part of course and 25% spend 6 months or more in another EC country. Formal exchange links with many EC universities/colleges, eg Bologna, Catania, Haarlem, Lyons, Nice (all business school links); Barcelona, Bordeaux, Mainz, Rennes (languages). Approved Erasmus programme 1990/91. Poly is moving towards a languages-for-all policy.

Application: PCAS except art and design (ADAR). **Academic features:** BEng manufacturing systems engineering; modern languages element in BSc systems design; diploma in broadcast journalism. **Structural features:** Bristol Business School. **Largest fields of study:** art & design, business studies, humanities, science, surveying. **Founded:** 1969, ex Bristol Technical College, College of Commerce and West of England College of Art; later joined by colleges of education. **Main awards:** BA, BEd, BSc, BEng, BTP. **Awarding body:** CNAA. **Site:** 6 main campuses. **Access:** Buses from Bristol city centre to all sites. **Accommodation:** 900 places in halls/hostels (65% reserved for first years). Approx cost: £20–£25 pw (single) (self-catering), £1,014 pa (poly residence). Rent: 20% in accommodation where rent controlled by polytechnic. **Library:** 6 libraries, total of 300,000 books, 2,000 periodicals, 930 study places, course books on loan. **Other learning resources:** Centre for Educational Services. **Welfare:** Student health service, welfare and counselling service, two nurserys (student discount). **Hardship funds:** Some funds available. **Careers:** Information, recruitment fairs, careers and 'milk round' programme. **Amenities:** Bookshops on 4 sites, chaplaincy centre, student union shops, bank, centre for performing arts. SU: supermarket, bars, TV and games room, advisory services. **Sporting facilities:** Excellent volleyball facilities (sponsored by Sports Council), gymnasium, playing fields (soccer, rugby, cricket, hockey), squash and tennis courts, provision by SU for large variety of minor sports e.g. canoeing, windsurfing, water-skiing.

Duration of first degree course(s) or equivalent: 3 years; 4 years (BEd & sandwich). **Total first degree students 1989/90:** 5,446 **Total BEd students:** 1,442 **Number of overseas students:** 77 **Male/female ratio 1989/90:** 1:1 **Teaching staff: full-time:** not known. **Total full-time students 1989/90:** 4,942; 2,121 (sandwich) **Postgraduate students:** 703 **Tuition fees, first degrees, 1990/91:** Home: £1,675 (£651 if self-financing); Overseas: £4,500.

What it's like

6 sites across the city. Main site, Coldharbour Lane, to the far north just off the M4 and M32. Typical early seventies architecture offers little sympathy to the surroundings. 6 miles from city centre, transport can be a problem; slowly being rectified by new half hourly bus service and a late night and lunchtime minibus service run by SU. 550 residences on campus. Outstanding academic reputation, especially in humanities, social sciences, law, many sciences and the arts.

Attractive and active student city. Wide range of pubs, nightclubs, theatres and

CAN'T FIND WHAT YOU'RE LOOKING FOR? USE THE INDEX!

cinemas. Rapidly becoming recognised as a centre for the arts, attracting international exhibitions and artistes throughout the year. Housing in the city is short, but not a major problem for poly students as there is an excellent accommodation office. SU is particularly active, politically and commercially. Bars, shops and services currently turn over nearly £1.5 million; major developments planned for the coming years. The education, welfare and information unit is rapidly expanding; new SU nursery. With over 70 different clubs and societies there is a fair deal of involvement in SU, which also means that campaigns are well supported.

Pauper notes
Accommodation: Gloucester Road and Bedminster areas cheaper housing. Montpelier and St Paul's licensed squats. Housing Association. Bristol rents high. **Drink:** SU does a lot of promotions on all drinks. Local pubs good; vary in price. Smiles – local bitter. Local cider, of course, commonly known as rough. Places depend on person – Sloane/Rugby Club; the Victoria in Clifton/hippy; Old England Montpelier/trendy. **Eats:** SU shop has a good range of food. Canteen food fairly priced (does vegetarian). Gloucester Road and Whiteladies have many good cheap restaurants. York Cafe, Special K's, Cafe de Daphne (not cheap). Refectory prices high (polytechnic run) – SU shop sells pasties etc. **Ents:** SU discos on 3 sites every week, gigs every week. Film club, films every weekday, local cinemas £1 on Wed. BPSU good reputation for promoting up and coming bands on Friday night at Coldharbour Lane – cheapest ents run by SU – £1 for most bands. **Sports:** Many different clubs play in BPSA and SWSSA. Transport provided. Good local clubs. SU subsidises many sports. Kingsdown Sports Centre in town is cheap. **Hardship funds:** Max £100 controlled by SU and Student Services. Must show severe conditions. Students with children £25 per dependant on top. Bank very good. **Travel:** Number of scholarships. Hitching from Coldharbour Lane OK. SU Travel Shop – only place in Bristol with genuine student discounts. **Work:** The usual bar work, temping, some in SU.

Alumni (Editors' pick)
Jack Russel (England wicket keeper),Wreckless Eric (Stiff Records artiste).

BRISTOL UNIVERSITY
University of Bristol, Senate House, Tyndall Avenue, Bristol BS8 1TH (0272 303030) Map A, D8

Student enquiries: The Registrar

Main study areas – as in What to Study section: *(First degree):* Accountancy, aeronautical engineering, anatomy, archaeology, biochemistry, biology, botany, chemistry, civil engineering, classics, computing, dentistry, drama, economics, electrical & electronic engineering, English, fine arts, geography, geology, history, Latin American studies, law, mathematical studies, mechanical and production engineering, medicine, microbiology, modern languages, music, pharmacology, philosophy, physics, physiology, politics and government, psychology, religious studies and theology, sociology, veterinary science, zoology. *Also:* Mediterranean studies.

European Community: 11% first degree students take EC language as part of course and 12% spend 6 months or more in another EC country. Arrangements under Erasmus to send undergraduates to 70¢ EC universities/colleges in 1990/91. Member of Santander Group (links 23 European universities) and Coimbra Group (links 22 universities) with aims of establishing special academic, cultural and socio-economic ties. Founder member of Medical Schools' European Credit Transfer Scheme, allowing medical students to spend 1 term to 1 year at another EC university, which contributes to final degree (currently unique in UK). Range of innovative courses eg European legal studies; history, with term at Giessen or year at Bordeaux; all branches of engineering offered with European studies.

Application: UCCA. **Academic features:** Degrees in music, biology, botany, zoology and computer science can be studied on a part-time basis by extended study and soon also in philosophy and social science. Research centre on Mediterranean studies; Reckitt & Colman psycho-pharmacology research unit. New company called Language Consultants for Industry Ltd (in conjunction with Bath University and Bristol Polytechnic) so university's European expertise available to industry, providing linguistic teaching and support, such as translation for business. **Largest fields of study:** Science. **Founded:** 1876, charter granted 1909. **Main awards:** BA, BDS, BEng, MEng, BSc, BVSc, LLB, ChB. **Awarding body:** Bristol University. **Site:** ¼ mile from Bristol city centre. **Access:** Walking, good bus services. **Accommodation:** 3,120 places in halls, flats and student houses. Rent: 38% in accommodation where rent controlled by university. **Special categories:** Residential facilities for overseas married students and disabled students. **Library:** Main Library (arts and social sciences and headquarters) and 12 branch libraries. 1,000,000 volumes, 6,300 periodicals, 2,250 study places. Late night opening in Main Library (term time). Short loan collections for heavily used course books. Library has own computer and an automated circulation system for issuing books in some libraries. On-line public access terminals in all libraries give access to information about books and periodicals. Strong emphasis on reader service and guided tours provided for new students. **Specialist collections:** Sir Allen Lane Penguin collection of autographed works, Wiglesworth ornithological collection, Exley mathematics library, medical library collections, manuscript and early printed rare books, original notebooks and sketch books of Isambard Kingdom Brunel, complete collection of election manifestos since 1892. **Other learning resources:** Computer centre; image analyser; Apollo Domain network for computer-aided design. **Welfare:** Health centre, chaplains, day nursery, counselling service, adviser to students with disabilities, adviser to overseas students. **Amenities:** Three theatres, Van Dyck Gallery, university bookshop. Active SU with bars, restaurants, recreational facilities. **Sporting facilities:** Indoor sports facilities include full sized swimming pool, excellent indoor fitness training facilities, squash courts, martial arts areas and a multi-use modern synthetic hockey/soccer pitch and excellent grass pitches for rugby, soccer and cricket.

Duration of first degree course(s) or equivalent: 3 years; 4 years (MEng and BA modern languages); 5 years (MB, ChB, BDS and BVSc) **Total first degree students 1989/90:** 6,796; **BEd students:** 40 **Number of overseas students:** 402 **Number of mature students:** 612 **Male/female ratio 1989/90:** 4:3 **Teaching staff:** full-time: 726 **Total full-time students 1989/90:** 7,744 **Postgraduate students:** 948 **Tuition fees, first degrees, 1990/91:** Home: £1,675; Overseas: £4,770 (eg politics), £6,360 (eg physics); £11,600 (maximum).

What it's like

Bristol University sprawls considerably, one of the first things to strike you. Departments embedded in the city – some in elegant Georgian squares, others in grey, square blocks called modern architecture. But never judge a book . . . most departments have excellent facilities and reputations, which keep student morale high and compensates those that are upset Oxbridge rejected them!

Student accommodation sprawls well away from the departments. Many of the first-years' halls are three miles away with a long walk or long bus-wait. Second and third-years face an accommodation crisis (bed-sits near the university are rapidly being converted into yuppie flats). It usually costs more than a grant to live in Bristol.

Much of the student-sprawl is brought together by the SU – the largest SU building in Britain, so 7,000-odd(!) students trek their way there to meet up. The SU is one of the wealthiest in NUS so lots of money is spent on hundreds of societies and entertainments. Good societies include ballooning, sky-diving, political (many MPs

CAN'T FIND WHAT YOU'RE LOOKING FOR? USE THE INDEX!

come to speak), dance and debating. The notorious Bad-Value drinking club might appeal, as might the Union swimming-pool, bars, restaurant and burger-bar.

Some big name bands play at the Union but many more play in the city. Like London, Bristol has developed a number of centres rather than just one. Clifton is Studentland, Broadmead is a shopping centre, St Pauls has a great annual festival. Look out for the Tropic-club and the Moonclub. West-country real-ale and scrumpy are pub specialities.

The general sprawl and vastness of Bristol mean that typical students are hard to define. There are a few stereotypes (Sloanes and southerners; conservative and bookish; preoccupied with sex and rock'n'roll) . . . Be wary of stereotypes . . . the university is ultimately cosmopolitan.

Pauper notes

Accommodation: Some squats in Montpelier/St Paul's. House/flat shares for £15/£16 in Hotwells/Redland if lucky. **Drink:** Epicurean (Union) Bar, Hall bars are cheapest. Kings Street/Clifton Village popular, but expensive. Cider in Coronation Tap. **Eats:** Restaurant in Union, University Refectory, York Cafe. Vegetarian: Wild Oats II, Ronam Cafe. **Ents:** SU bands, comedians etc. Lots of local/student bands in pubs (eg Bristol Bridge, Kings Arms). **Sports:** University Centre at Woodland House; pool attached to Union building. Sports fields 4 miles out. **Hardship funds:** £50 loan from the Union – once a year. May be raised to £75. **Travel:** University scholarship schemes. Easy access for hitching to London. **Work:** P-t work in bars, pubs, restaurants. Many students sign on in vacations.

Alumni (Editors' pick)

Sue Lawley (BBC newsreader), Susan Engels (actress, RSC), Frances Horovitz (poet), Hugh Cornwell (lead singer with The Stranglers), Paul Boateng MP, David Hunt MP (Secretary of State for Wales), Alistair Stewart (BBC newsreader).

BRITISH INSTITUTE IN PARIS

British Institute in Paris, University of London, 11 rue de Constantine, 75007 Paris (4555 71 99)

Student enquiries: In Paris: Secretary to French Department
In England: The London Secretary, British Institute in Paris, Senate House, Malet Street, London WC1E 7HU (071-636 8000)

Main study areas – as in What to Study section: *(First degree):* Fine arts, modern languages. *Also:* Aspects of French civilisation; literature, society and culture courses, translation studies.

European Community: 100% first degree students take EC language as part of course and 80% spend 6 months or more in another EC country. No formal exchange links.

Structural features: Part of London University. **Application:** Direct, to Paris or London office. **Academic features:** Courses leading to Certificate in French and English translation; Certificate of Proficiency in French; and Certificates in French for Business. 1 year course in French language and literature and in either political science or history for joint honours undergraduates taught partly at the Institute and partly at the Institut d'Etudes Politiques or the University of Paris. Distance education offered in translation and proficiency in contemporary French. The Certificate in French and English Translation and the Certificate of Proficiency in French can be prepared fully by correspondence. Short refresher courses organised for teachers of French at secondary level. **Special features:** Institute has dual purpose; its French department for English-speaking students (age 18+) can study

CAN'T FIND WHAT YOU'RE LOOKING FOR? USE THE INDEX!

French language, literature and history; its English department for French students to study English language and literature. Many British universities give financial support, though London University is responsible for Institute as a whole. French language courses are at 5 levels: Beginners, Elementary, Level 1 (UKCPU first year or third year remedial), Advanced Level 1 and 2 (UKCPU majoring in French at third year level). French is language of instruction; minimum period one term. Also correspondence courses and some vacation seminars. Institute is recognised centre for London and Cambridge examinations. Publishes an academic journal, Franco-British Studies. **Founded:** 1894, as private organisation, becoming Senate Institute of London University in 1969. **Access:** Situated in Central Paris. On bus routes 63, 83, 93, 69, 28, 49 and on metro routes 'B', Saint-Denis – Genevilliers – Montparnasse, and Balard-Créteil. **Accommodation:** Institute is non-residential, but accommodation secretary will assist. Some places for university students at Cites Universitaires in the Paris area; good rooms and paying-guest accommodation for early birds. **Library:** British Institute French Library, Cultural Centre English Library (lending and reference). **Other learning resources:** Tape and video-tape library, computer-assisted learning, film resources. **Welfare:** Best to take out insurance before you go. 'Mutuelle' (ie supplementary health scheme) available for full-time students. **Hardship funds:** Working scholarships available (full fees in exchange for light duties 2 hours a day). **Amenities:** Student club and cafeteria.

Duration of course(s): 1-2 years (Certificate/Diploma courses only) **Total first degree level students 1989/90:** 292 **Number of overseas students:** 49 **Number of mature students:** 22 **Male/female ratio 1989/90:** 1:3 **Teaching staff: full-time:** 6 **part-time:** 13 **Total full-time students 1989/90:** 78 (full year), 172 (part year) **Postgraduate students:** 2 **Tuition fees for full-time courses 1990/91:** Home: £900; Overseas: £1,150.

What it's like

Refreshingly different. The best of Britain squeezed into a magnificent building overlooking the Esplanade des Invalides. For the English student abroad it offers a friendly and homely environment. Vast range of courses provide a very interesting and thorough insight into French culture and life, from Stendhal to the latest in arts, to commercial and contemporary French. Very important for the English student is the asset that classes are always conducted in French. All teaching staff are warm, friendly and make you feel at home. One slight disappointment; the Institute houses an English department for French students but English tend to keep with English and French with French. Institute accommodates every student's need and taste. If you make the most of what it has to offer, your year will be rewarding, in terms of certificates and diplomas and also in terms of the many aspects of French life you are introduced to.
Katerina Moustacas

Pauper notes

Accommodation: Lots of garrets and rooms with French families available; only for very early birds. **Drink:** French wine so prevalent that the Institute's Club serves English beer as a nostalgia jerker. **Eats:** French university restaurants excellent dietetically, and fairly cheap (15 Francs a meal). **Ents:** Paris has 380 cinemas showing up to 450 films a week. The Institute's 'What's on this year' course provides intellectual support. **Sports:** Not good in Paris – however there are good walking areas within 15 minutes of centre, and swimming is plentiful. **Hardship funds:** Work available in the Institute bar, library etc, for deserving paupers.

Alumni (Editors' pick)

Poets: Carmela Moya, Adrian Mathews; Dramatist: Michael Sadler.

CAN'T FIND WHAT YOU'RE LOOKING FOR? USE THE INDEX!

BRITISH SCHOOL OF OSTEOPATHY

The British School of Osteopathy, 1-4 Suffolk Street, London SW1Y 4HG (071-930-9254) Map E, C3

Student enquiries: The Registrar

Main study area: *(First Degree):* Osteopathy.

European Community: No students take EC language as part of course or spend time in another EC country. No formal exchange links.

Application: Direct. **Academic features:** Course is student-centred with a focus on problem solving in a clinical context. **Structural features:** The School has links with eg medical schools and polytechnics for specialist areas of the teaching course and research activities. **Special features:** The undergraduate programme includes contribution by eminent osteopaths and medical practitioners (UK and abroad). Postgraduate programme includes a distance-learning advanced course in osteopathy and specialist courses in aspects of osteopathy. **Founded: 1917. Main award:** BSc. **Awarding body:** CNAA. **Site:** Single site in central London. **Access:** Underground and mainline stations within easy reach; also on various bus routes. **Accommodation:** Mainly private rented (especially shared) or hotel accommodation. Approx cost: £35.50; £55-£70 with meals. **Library:** 7,000 volumes, 110 periodicals, 70 study places. **Specialist collections:** Collections of rare books on osteopathy. **Other learning facilities:** Well-equipped human performance laboratory and anatomy resource room. **Careers:** Literature; promotional video and slides available; informal enquiries welcomed (any registered osteopath could provide information). **Employment:** Normally private practice as osteopaths. Some study for a higher degree and/or contribute to teaching. **Welfare:** Full-time counsellor. SU elects Welfare Officer each year and there is an active interest in student welfare through a committee of staff and students. **Special categories:** Facilities for students with families available in neighbourhood (list available from Counsellor) but none yet on site. **Hardship funds:** Students advised to apply to registered educational charities (lists from public reference libraries). On completion of first year, students may be eligible for support from the Osteopathic Educational Foundation (OEF). **Amenities:** Host of cultural facilities in central London. SU active in organising social functions with similar institutions. Squash court and weights room on-site. Student sports' clubs make arrangements externally for playing facilities with other institutions, eg local Medical Schools.

Duration of first degree course(s) or equivalent: 4 years **Total first degree students:** 370 **Number of mature students:** 39 **Overseas students:** 15 **Mature students:** 39 **Male/female ratio 1989-90:** 1:1 **Teaching staff: full-time:** 2 **Teaching staff: part-time:** 110 **Postgraduate students:** None **Tuition fees, 1990/91:** Home: £4,600.

What it's like

With its out-patient clinics, it's the largest alternative medicine training centre in Europe, based in a large corner building of traditional architecture just off Trafalgar Square, central London. Inside it's a maze of staircases and corridors leading to lecture theatres, treatment rooms, administrative offices and library containing largest collection of osteopathic medical literature. Access easy; close to Piccadilly Circus and Charing Cross tube stations; many buses stop in Trafalgar Square; Charing Cross BR station nearby; many other mainline London stations are short walk away. Strong railings around the building for locking bicycles to, but cycling in London has its special dangers. School and SU help find accommodation. BSO is a private college; it has now achieved mandatory grant status but grant still considerably less than fees! So get additional financial backing before starting (eg low interest rate loans, similar to those offered to medics and law students).

CAN'T FIND WHAT YOU'RE LOOKING FOR? USE THE INDEX!

SU is active in providing welfare advice, and is affiliated to NUS. Run by a non-sabbatical executive with no permanent employees, it concentrates on welfare, social activity, sport and maintaining relations with the BSO staff, with little time for political issues.

Loving: All lavatories in the building contain Mates condom machines; all forms of contraception are covered as part of the course, so no student can remain in ignorance for long. Course involves a great deal of physical contact between students while learning and practising osteopathic technique. Combined with the more formal lectures in anatomy, this means that all BSO students become remarkably relaxed about stripping off to their underwear in front of each other. But this does not mean that training at the BSO is akin to a four-year orgy. What it does mean is that sex, sexuality and intimacy become demystified and pointless social mores become recognised for what they are – an essential part of training for a lifetime of treating semi-naked patients and a valuable part of students' personal development.

Counselling: Full-time counsellor provides confidential support over any personal problems, not just on sexual relationships. Four years of a heavy course, often with financial problems too, can wear down even the most resilient of characters.

Central London's cheapest booze in BSO's bar, a club with membership restricted to staff and students (guests can be signed in). Events throughout the year, main ones Christmas and graduation balls. Central London's cheapest grub in basement canteen. Squash court and a weights room (and showers!) in building; any other sports or activities can be organised if enough people interested. Most popular sports are horse-riding and hang-gliding. Being based right in the middle of London, the BSO is in the centre of the country's largest entertainment complex! Everything is on offer somewhere. The National Gallery and St Martins in the Fields with its lunchtime concerts, are 30 seconds walk; the Coliseum about a minute away; Theatre Royal Haymarket just around the corner; countless cinemas nearby. Pubs, wine-bars, restaurants and nightclubs too numerous to be counted, but geared up for tourists/people with incomes, and pretty pricey.

Workload phenomenal. The course is much the same as at medical school except with one year less to do it in! However, there are some important differences: training takes an 'holistic' approach, ie health and illness are looked at in terms of the patient rather than the disease. Instead of treating the disease with drugs or surgery, the osteopath treats the patient in order to activate his/her own healing ability; there is slightly less emphasis on biochemistry and pharmacology than there is at medical school, since osteopathy is a drug-free system of medicine. Anatomy is of vital importance and students should know the entire body at a level of detail that doctors only approach when doing postgraduate surgical training. Large part of course is osteopathic technique; new techniques are always practised on fellow students before being used in school's clinic on actual patients. Clinical training takes place throughout course, including during so-called 'holidays'. It starts with observation in first year and gradually increases, under supervision, until fourth year students are taking patients all the way through from taking case history to providing the final treatment session. Most training in BSO premises but some physiology practicals at South Bank Poly and dissection classes at Guy's Hospital Medical School.

Most clinical staff part-time; as qualified osteopaths they have their own practices to run. Work assessed by combination of written exams, viva voces, essays and 'Objective Structured Practical Examinations' (or 'OSPEs'). Large-scale projects in second and third years; 'final' exams throughout fourth year. With such a heavy workload there is inevitably some attrition, mostly in the first year.

400 students from a very wide age range can be divided into three groups: about a third to a half are 18-22 year-olds who have come straight from sixth form or who have changed from another degree course elsewhere; another third to a half are between 25-35, for many of them this is their second degree, after a non-medical first degree/occupation; and the remainder are in their late 30s, even into their 40s, having decided to do what they have always wanted to do before it gets too late!

CAN'T FIND WHAT YOU'RE LOOKING FOR? USE THE INDEX!

Upon graduation, most start as an assistant in an existing practice, using any spare time for building up their own practice. Osteopathy still has no statutory legal status, so all practices are necessarily private. European standardisation in 1992 will before long probably enable osteopaths to offer their skills through NHS. All in all, BSO provides vocational training for a career of self-employment (ie freedom!) that provides a comfortable living from relieving suffering. What could be better! *Martin Preston*

Pauper notes

Accommodation: College doesn't provide accommodation but it offers help in finding it, as does SU. **Drink:** SU has cheapest drinks in central London. Fullers, from west London brewery, is the main beer but bar is fully-stocked with a wide range of drinks. **Eats:** Large canteen in basement. Very good value. **Ents:** Lots of SU social events, plus whole of London! **Sports:** Squash court, gym, weight-training room, all on campus. Off campus access to any sport you can think of if enough people interested. Good rugby team. **Hardship funds:** Two welfare officers in Union. Osteopathic Education Foundation can help some students from 2nd year. **Travel:** Close to Charing Cross & Piccadilly Circus tube stations. Lots of bus routes. Railings to lock cycles to (for suicidal!). **Work:** It's a heavyweight course and students do clinical work during the so-called 'holidays'. Good time-management and masses of energy should enable people to earn some money if needed.

BRUNEL UNIVERSITY

Brunel University, Uxbridge, Middlesex UB8 3PH (0895 74000)
Map A, F8

Student enquiries: Academic Secretary

Main study areas – as in What to Study section: *(First degree):* Anthropology, biochemistry, biology, botany, business studies, chemistry, communication studies, computing, economics, education, electrical and electronic engineering, environmental science, European studies, information technology, law, mathematical studies, mechanical and production engineering, metallurgy and materials science, microbiology, modern languages, physics, politics and government, psychology, public administration, sociology. *Also:* design & technology with education.

European Community: 9% first degree students take EC language as part of course and 5% spend 6 months or more in another EC country. Formal exchange links with Lille and Stuttgart. Approved Erasmus programme 1990/91; individual departmental links in Eindhoven, Hanover, Milan and Paris.

Application: UCCA. **Academic features 1991-92:** Most degree courses follow thin-sandwich pattern. Student exchanges with Plzen Univ (Czechoslovakia). New science park on campus. Engineering course with options in French or German; optional 1 year extensions to BEng courses for MEng or Diploma in engineering management. Special engineering programme, enhanced course for developing top industrial managers. New 3-year, broad-based course in 'Natural Sciences'. **Structural features:** Management input from Henley Management College and new Brunel Business Management Centre into some courses: New centres in research into innovation and the culture of technology. Wolfson Centre for Materials Processing. Institute of Bioengineering, directed by Prof Heinz Wolff (BBC's Great Egg Race). **Largest fields of study:** Engineering, mathematics, sciences. **Founded:** 1966. **Main awards:** BSc, BA, BEng, LLB. **Awarding body:** Brunel University. **Site:** Main campus near Uxbridge, West London; second campus near Egham, Surrey. **Access:** Uxbridge underground, West Drayton and Egham main line stations, M4, M25 and M40. **Accommodation:** 650 study bedrooms, 645 places in self-catering flats, 400 study bedrooms on Runnymede campus. First and fourth years offered accommodation. Approx cost: £28.00 pw. Rent: 55% in accommodation where rent controlled by university. **Library:** 280,000 volumes, 2,000 periodicals, 2,500 items of AV and microform material. **Other learning facilities:** Computer centre, audiovisual centre, EFL/Language Centre, experimental techniques centre, Metrology Centre. **Welfare:** Medical centre, chaplaincy, counsellors. **Hardship funds:** SU operate 'welfare loans' up to £100. **Careers:** Information and advice services (many Brunel graduates are offered posts by companies that provide their periods of industrial training). **Amenities:** Bookshop, supermarket, travel shop, newspapers, radio station, nursery, coffee and snack bars, university art gallery, art and music classes, student music bursaries. **Sporting facilities:** Sports centres, playing fields, all-weather playing surface. Programmes of coaching, classes, etc. Centre of excellence for weightlifting, basketball. Rowing, sailing, canoeing.

Duration of first degree course(s) or equivalent: 4 years **Others:** 3 years **Total first degree students 1989/90:** 2,650; **Number of overseas students:** 83 **Number of mature students:** 387 **Male/female ratio 1989/90:** 2:1 **Teaching staff: full-time:** 240 **part-time:** 20 **Total full-time students 1989/90:** 3,090 **Postgraduate students:** 1,442; 653 p-t **Tuition fees, first degrees, 1990/91:** Home: £1,675 (£665 if self-financing); Overseas: £4,560 (eg politics), £6,050 (eg physics).

What it's like

An engineering and science based university, but with important social science influence, ideally situated on the outskirts of London – ideal because direct tube-line but tourists never bother to come to Uxbridge.

The only university in the country which operates the thin sandwich system in large-size portions. Nearly every student spends 4 years at Brunel, 3 of which are spent divided into 6 months' study and six months' related work experience. The advantage is that Brunel students graduate very employable; the disadvantage is that you don't get 3 months' *normal* university vacation.

Two-campus university; Uxbridge, built in the 60's of concrete slabs, so hideous that a 'comic strip' episode was made there; and Runnymede, abundant with rabbits and trees, the St Trinian's films were made there.

Academia aside, Brunel is what you make of it. A relatively small university it has 4 bars, 2 disco/band venues and an active SU with over 90 clubs and societies (WRL to role playing) and a creche for younger members.

The male to female ratio isn't exactly even but then nothing's perfect.
Eileen O'Hara & Samm Smith

Pauper notes

Accommodation: Cheapest areas on campus. Other areas – Hayes, Southall. **Drink:** SU bar presently stocks Courage, S&N and Bass brews. Good selection. **Eats:** Fast food – Gallery; bar food – (both on campus). **Ents:** Nightclub venue – The Academy. On campus include regular bands, 'Now Dance!', 'New Variety'; alternative cabaret plus clubs and societies events. **Sports:** Sports centre on campus. Swimming pool – nearest Uxbridge. **Hardship funds:** Short term welfare loans from SU. **Travel:** Service on campus. **Work:** As all students are on sandwich courses, they are in full-time employment during summer term and holidays (dole offices can be 'difficult').

BUCKINGHAM UNIVERSITY

The University of Buckingham, Hunter Street, Buckingham MK18 1EG (0280 814080) Map A, E7

Student enquiries: Admissions Office

Main study areas – as in What to Study section: *(First degree):* Accountancy, biochemistry, biology, business studies, computing, dance, economics, English,

CAN'T FIND WHAT YOU'RE LOOKING FOR? USE THE INDEX!

European studies, history, hotel & catering management, law, mathematical studies, modern languages, politics and government, psychology.

European Community: 11% first degree students take EC language as main part of course, 50% as supporting course. 4% spend 6 months or more in another EC country. Formal exchange links with 5 EC universities/colleges in France (Lille and Strasbourg) and Germany (Augsburg, Holstein and Tubingen). Some students can transfer onto MBA programme at Strasbourg or Tubingen after graduating, completing within year.

Application: UCCA. **Academic features:** Degree courses in business economics, European business management with French or German, dance and related arts. **Special features:** Britain's only independent university receives no direct government financial support. 2-year degree courses, and a range of cross-disciplinary supporting courses. Academic year is 4 terms long and runs January–December. Law course entry also available in July. Applications welcomed from mature students. University has funds for scholarships and bursaries. **Structural features:** Validates degree course in dance at London College of Dance. **Largest fields of study:** Law, accounting and financial management, business studies. **Founded:** 1974. **Main awards:** BA, BSc, BSc(Econ), LLB. **Awarding body:** Buckingham University. **Site:** 2 sites near Buckingham town centre. **Access:** Buses from Aylesbury and Milton Keynes (both have main line railway stations). **Accommodation:** Accommodation guaranteed to all first year students, thereafter help given by accommodation officer. Approx cost: £50-60 pw (1992 estimates). Rent: 50% in accommodation where rent controlled by university. **Library:** 2 libraries; 60,000 volumes in total, 495 periodicals, computerised catalogue, 207 study places, short loan collection. **Other learning resources:** include audio-lingual language labs; satellite TV viewing room for live broadcasts in 6 European languages; video facilities; library of audio and video recorded materials in over 12 languages. Computer labs with IBM-compatible microcomputers, peripherals connected to Orion minicomputer. **Welfare:** University medical officer, student advisory system, student counsellor. **Hardship funds:** Student hardship fund in operation: scholarship, bursary system and loan system; bursaries adviser. **Careers:** Information and advice service, full-time careers adviser. **Amenities:** Student social centre; concert hall; on-campus accommodation; Oxford 23 miles away; Milton Keynes 12 miles away. **Sporting facilities:** Access to sports and recreational facilities.

Duration of first degree course(s) or equivalent: 2 years (8 terms) **Others:** 9 terms; 3 years **Total first degree students 1989/90:** 720 **Number of overseas students:** 465 **Number of mature students:** 356 **Male/female ratio 1989/90:** approx 3:2 **Teaching staff: full-time:** 70 **part-time:** 20 **Total full-time students 1989/90:** 762 **Postgraduate students:** 42 **Tuition fees, first degrees, 1990/91:** Home: £7,450; Overseas: £7,450.

What it's like

Between the stately city of Oxford and the butt-of-all-jokes Milton Keynes, lies the former market town of Buckingham, still getting used to being a university town. UB (as it is known) has much to offer – a small, compact campus, a dazzlingly cosmopolitan student body, and a succinct two-year degree course (Jan–Dec academic year) which dispenses with the lazy, hazy days of summer and delivers you into your chosen career in the time it takes you to say 'graduate' (almost). Not too many distractions from study but with ingenuity (and wheels) it doesn't take too long to reach Culture in Oxford or the Cinema in the great MK. Although predominantly lawyers, the student body abandons all labels (and many other things) during the yearly Rag Week – all in aid of charity and local breweries. Two balls – the mega-Graduation Ball in February and the Summer Ball, both provide an excellent outlet for the pent-up emotions of two years' hard labour.
Mark Silva

CAN'T FIND WHAT YOU'RE LOOKING FOR? USE THE INDEX!

Pauper notes

Accommodation: Accommodation for 1st years only. Private accommodation available but not easy to find. **Drink:** University bar; Courage Beer; Woolpack, Buckingham; New Inn, Buckingham; The Mitre, Buckingham; Verney Arms, Verney Junction; Old Thatched Inn, Adstock. **Eats:** Dipalee Tandori Restaurant, Buckingham, Verney Arms; Old Thatched Inn; Golden Chicken Take-away; Geordie Lass Take-away. **Sports:** On campus – 4 all weather tennis courts, multi-gym, snooker room, fencing, martial arts. Off campus – swimming pools, squash and badminton courts. **Shop:** SY shop; on campus 'The Buck Shop' sells UB souvenirs, confectionery, tobacco, 2nd hand books, stationery etc, groceries, frozen food, text books, clothing.

BUCKINGHAMSHIRE COLLEGE

Buckinghamshire College of Higher Education, (1) Queen Alexandra Road, High Wycombe, Bucks HP11 2JZ (0494 22141) (2) Newland Park, Chalfont St Giles, Bucks HP8 4AD (02407 4441) (3) Missenden Abbey Management Centre, Great Missenden, Bucks HP16 0BD Map A, E8

Student enquiries: Admissions Officer (address 2)

Main study areas – as in What to Study section: *(First degree):* Art & design, business studies, computing, environmental studies, nursing, sociology, welfare studies. *Also:* Furniture production, wood technology.

European Community: 60% first degree students take EC language as part of course and 50% spend 6 months or more in another EC country. Formal exchange links with some 12 EC universities/colleges: Denmark (2); France (3); Germany (2); Italy (1); Netherlands (1); Spain (3); many open to non-language specialists.

Application: PCAS. **Academic features:** Degree in European business studies includes a year in France/Germany/Italy/Spain; International business administration includes year in the USA; international office management; timber technology and 3-dimensional design, and furniture production industry. MA in European marketing management (part-time/distance learning). **Largest fields of study:** Art and design, business studies, furniture and timber. **Founded:** 1975, ex High Wycombe College of Technology and Art and Newland Park College of Education. **Main awards:** BA, BSc. **Awarding body:** CNAA. **Site:** 3 sites: near High Wycombe city centre; Newland Park, 12 miles from High Wycombe, near Chalfont St Giles; Missenden Abbey, near Great Missenden. **Access:** All sites served by excellent roads and railways; about 40 mins from London. **Accommodation:** 530 places in halls. Approx cost: £30 pw residence only, meals at cost. Rent: 50% in accommodation where rent controlled by college. **Library:** 3 libraries, over 100,000 volumes, multi-media services, 700 periodicals, 350 study places. **Welfare:** Doctor, dentist, FPA, psychiatrist, solicitor, chaplain. **Careers:** Information, workshops, vocational counselling and placement service. **Amenities:** SU bar, theatre. **Sporting facilities:** Sports centre, gymnasium, and playing fields at Newland Park.

Duration of first degree course(s) or equivalent: 3 years full-time, 4 year (sandwich) **Total first degree students 1989/90:** 846 **Number of overseas students:** 31 **Male/female ratio 1989/90:** 3:2 **Total full-time students 1989/90:** 2,798 **Postgraduate students:** 97 **Tuition fees, first degrees, 1990/91:** Home: £1,675; Overseas: £5,000.

What it's like

On 2 sites connected by union: Newland Park and High Wycombe. Former is fairly isolated college near Chalfont St Giles village. Life mostly campus-based in pleasant

CAN'T FIND WHAT YOU'RE LOOKING FOR? USE THE INDEX!

rural setting. Buildings mainly modern (1960's) grouped around Georgian mansion. 450 live on campus, some in comfortable modern accommodation but some in prefabs. Students mostly at degree/diploma level – courses include: business, management and social studies. Newland Park has SU bar, student centre, sports and drama: mostly attractive campus but far from any other major signs of life. High Wycombe site is mostly 1950's buildings with recent extensions in town centre. Fairly attractive town with some social life – pubs, sports centre, college bar, film club, and furniture industry providing jobs for students finishing art/design and furniture courses. Most students live at home, are aged 16–19 and on diversity of courses from YOP students to A-levels. Degree students aged 19–23 (plus mature students) come from further afield – rooms in halls for most 1st years. Halls of residence are comfortable and house 100; generally, not over-exciting but college and town fairly pleasant and bearable. Strong SU; growing and expanding clubs and societies; many student services eg help for overseas students, accommodation advice.

Pauper notes
Accommodation: Off-campus is expensive, some reasonable, others dire. College accommodation reasonable – no married quarters. **Drink:** SU bar cheap – main brewery names. Pubs are not cheap: £1.30+ per pint (lager). **Eats:** College refectory not particularly high standard and quite expensive. High Wycombe site greater choice, as in town. Newland Park more difficult to go off campus unless you have transport. Off campus food – good variety. **Ents:** Student Bar is where most ents go on – bands, quizzes, discos etc, Off campus not an exciting place – pubs have bands on. **Sports:** High Wycombe site – good sports centre (quite expensive) next to halls. Normal sports offered at college. Newland Park has reasonable facilities. **Hardship funds:** SU has emergency loan fund. **Travel:** Shuttle bus between sites but no discounts on local travel except trains (railcard) and coaches (coach card). **Work:** Temporary work available through agencies, reasonable amount of part-time work available during term-time eg Tescos, Sainsburys etc.

Alumni (Editors' pick)
Howard Jones, Martin Grierson.

BUCKLAND

Buckland University College, Ewert Place, Oxford OX2 7YT (0865 53570) Telex: 449793 TELSER G; Fax: 0793 617415 Map A, E7

Student enquiries: Academic Registrar

Main study areas – as in What to Study section: *(First degree):* Law.

European Community: No first degree students take EC language or spend time in another EC country.

Application: Direct. **Largest field of study:** Law. **Founded:** 1963. **Main awards:** LLB. **Awarding body:** London University. **Site:** Oxford, a mile north of city centre. **Access:** Fast London-Oxford coach and rail links; local buses. **Accommodation:** college assists with finding accommodation locally and has links with halls of residence in Oxford. **Rent:** no accommodation where rent is controlled by university. **Library:** 30 study places; open 9-6; special short-term loan scheme. **Welfare:** College welfare officer. **Careers:** Information, advice and placement service provided by London University. **Amenities:** Common room; leisure centres and sports facilities nearby; cultural and social amenities of Oxford. **Employment:** Law, commerce, teaching.

Duration of first degree course(s) or equivalent: 3 years **Total first degree students 1989/90:** 78 **Number of overseas students:** 36 **Number of mature**

students: 30 **Male/female ratio 1989/90:** 1:1 **Teaching staff: full-time:** 2 **part-time:** 16 **Total full-time students 1989/90:** 96 **Number of postgraduate students:** 5 **Tuition fees, first degrees, 1990/91:** £2,900 (Home students on LEA grant, fee reduced by £628); Overseas: £2,900.

What it's like

Small, independent specialist law school providing courses for London University degrees and the Bar Final examination. Classes are small: lectures of up to 30 students, seminars in groups of no more than 8 or 9. Most of teaching is done by visiting lecturers from other universities or colleges, but small scale means staff take a personal interest in students' progress. Lot of stress on full attendance and submission of written work. There is a reference and lending law library in college and access to other libraries in Oxford.

Since September 1990 the college has been in a pleasant, modern building round a small, quiet quadrangle in the Summertown district of Oxford. Facilities for socialising in college are modest, but there are pubs, restaurants and shops just a few yards away; programme of social events developing and a list of sports fixtures with other colleges in the area. BUC has a good mix of overseas students and mature students as well as 'home' students straight from school.

Pauper notes

Accommodation: College has links with inexpensive hostels, especially for overseas students. **Work:** Vacation work often available in Oxford.

CAMBERWELL COLLEGE OF ARTS

Camberwell College of Arts, Peckham Road, London SE5 8UF (071-703 0987) Map D, C2

Student enquiries: College Administrator

Main study areas – as in What to Study section: (*First degree*): Art & design, fine arts.

European Community: Number of students taking EC language and spending time in another EC country, not known.

Application: ADAR; PCAS for the History of Drawing & Printmaking. **Structural features:** Constituent college of the London Institute. **Largest fields of study:** Fine art painting/sculpture, graphic design, 3 dimensional design, history of drawing and printmaking, conservation. **Founded:** 1898. **Main awards:** BA. **Awarding body:** CNAA. **Site:** Main building and 2 annexes. **Access:** Waterloo, Peckham Rye, Elephant & Castle stations, then bus; bus from Oval, Vauxhall, or Victoria station. **Accommodation:** Limited places in the London Institute's halls of residence. Approx cost: £35–£50 pw. Rent: proportion of students housed in accommodation where rent is controlled by college: not known. **Library:** 40,000 volumes, 85 periodicals, 40 study places. **Other learning resources:** Word processing available, video viewing. **Welfare:** Easy access to all facilities, consult professional student counsellor. **Careers:** Information and advice service. **Amenities:** college shop. **Employment:** Graphics, ceramics, silversmithing, metalwork and paper conservation; students are successful in finding employment in craft or design studies related to their training.

Duration of first degree course(s) or equivalent: 3 years **Total first degree students 1989/90:** 423 **Number of overseas students:** 13 **Number of mature students:** 45 **Male/female ratio 1989/90:** 2:3 **Teaching staff: full-time:** 32 **part-time:** 120 **Total full-time students 1989/90:** 642 **Postgraduate students:** 30 **Tuition fees, first degrees, 1990/91:** Home: £1,675; Overseas: £5,750.

CAN'T FIND WHAT YOU'RE LOOKING FOR? USE THE INDEX!

What it's like

Built on 3 sites. The main one on Peckham Road is an ugly sixties monstrosity tacked on, rather uncomfortably, to a beautiful, Victorian purpose-built art school. The other two sites are a prefab sculpture annexe and an old grammar school. The diversity of the architecture is outdone only by the diversity of the students. Courses ranging from fine art to art history and paper conservation.

SU provides opportunities for meeting in a crowded, smoky atmosphere to exchange drunken conversations over loud music in friendly and inexpensive bar. Regular termly bashes with bands, cabarets etc. SU flourishing after a few bad years; the number of clubs is growing by the minute.

Accommodation in London is expensive and difficult to find but it is probably easier to find somewhere to live near Camberwell than other London art schools. Being in the capital means almost every type of entertainment is available (at a price).

All the courses require hard work, application and self-motivation. Support facilities, such as the library and media resources departments are excellent. Most of the staff are highly respected practitioners in their field.

" Main building looks like abandoned transistor radio "

BIG TURN OFF

Pauper notes

Accommodation: Some flats available through college; local council; squats in SE London: rented accommodation expensive but available. **Drink:** Popular SU bar cheap. Popular pubs: Grove, Phoenix and Firkin. **Eats:** College canteen. **Ents:** SU provides entertainment and Camberwell is very close to the centre of London. **Sports:** New sports centre 5 mins away in Peckham. 2 mins swimming pool. SU cricket and football teams. **Hardship funds:** See student Welfare Officer. **Travel:** Some college trips abroad: possibility of exchange trips to America. **Work:** Jobs in SU bar. Part-time work not difficult to find in London if you don't mind what you do.

CAN'T FIND WHAT YOU'RE LOOKING FOR? USE THE INDEX!

CAMBORNE SCHOOL OF MINES

Camborne School of Mines, Trevensen, Pool, Redruth, Cornwall TR15 3SE (0209 714866) Map A, B9

Student enquiries: The Academic Registry

Main study areas – as in What to Study section: *(First degree):* Geology, metallurgy and materials science. *Also:* Mining and mineral engineering.

European Community: No first degree students take EC language as part of course or spend time in another EC country. Formal exchange links with EC universities/colleges being developed; current feasibility study for mining engineering at school of mines in France.

Application: PCAS. **Special features:** Experimental mine. Occasional lectures from visiting industrial consultants. **Largest fields of study:** Mining engineering; mineral process engineering. **Founded:** 1859. **Main awards:** BEng. **Awarding body:** CNAA. **Site:** Outskirts of Camborne, Cornwall. **Accommodation:** 50 single study bedrooms (priority to 1st year students); wide variety of furnished accommodation including 4 flats for married students (unsuitable for children). Approx cost: £26–£42 pw. Rent: 24% in accommodation where rent controlled by college. **Library:** 8,000 volumes, 168 periodicals, 40 study places, course books kept in closed access. **Specialist collections:** Rare early mining publications. **Welfare:** Personal tutor system. **Hardship funds:** Student hardship fund. **Careers:** Use of Polytechnic South West Careers Service. **Amenities:** Carn Brea leisure centre and purpose built student club with squash court, bar, TV and billiards room. **Employment:** Mining and mineral, UK and abroad.

Duration of first degree course(s) or equivalent: 3 years **Total first degree students 1989/90:** 125 **Number of overseas students:** 15 **Number of mature students:** 33 **Male/female ratio 1989/90:** 14:1 **Teaching staff: full-time:** 26 parttime: 2 **Total full-time students 1989/90:** 245 **Postgraduate students:** 45 **Tuition fees, first degrees, 1990/91:** Home: £1,675; Overseas: £5,800.

What it's like

There cannot be too many places of higher education where the President of the SU is on first name terms with all students and academic staff. I, at the Camborne School of Mines, am. Briefly put, the CSM is more of a community of students than a gathering or crowd of students. Please do not misunderstand me. There are enough students at CSM to offer a wide range of activities and societies. Being mining, minerals, mineral surveying or geological engineers, most students are generally involved with outdoor activities. Therefore sports have a large influence with what CSM students do in their spare time. CSM provides teams for all major sports along with other minority sports such as surfing (CSM is only 4 miles from best surf beach in Europe), rock-climbing (the School has its own climbing wall), scuba-diving, gliding etc.

The School is situated in UK's main tourism area. It is thus able to offer students the chance to study in an area of outstanding natural beauty that also has a thriving night-life. The School is less than 3 miles away from both the grandeur of the Cornish coastline and entertainment at the best night-club in south-west.

Students run own social club which contains a bar, squash courts and other less physical pursuits, as well as acting as headquarters for many a night out.

Basically, the CSM has a wonderfully friendly environment both during studies and free time, and is probably able to offer the greatest number of pursuits per person than any other institution in the UK.
John Ross

CAN'T FIND WHAT YOU'RE LOOKING FOR? USE THE INDEX!

Pauper notes

Accommodation: Cheap modern hostel and married quarters provided by the college. Numerous low-priced holiday houses during autumn, winter and spring. **Drink:** Cheap comprehensive bar in students' club. Numerous friendly pubs within easy staggering distance. **Eats:** Cheap on-campus food at catering department of Cornwall Technical College, including vegetarian. **Ents:** Recently modernised, well equipped students social club. Regular very successful SU functions. Several good local discos. **Sports:** College rugby, soccer, hockey, squash, cricket, badminton. Large sports centre near campus – free use to students once weekly. **Hardship funds:** Co-operative local bank managers. College hardship fund for those in dire straits. **Travel:** Regular international exchange schemes. Nearby main-line station and direct intercity coach service. **Work:** Local mining operations. Frequent overseas summer job opportunities.

CAMBRIDGE UNIVERSITY

University of Cambridge, Cambridge, England CB2 1TN (Registry 0223 332200) Map A, F7

Student enquiries: The Tutor for Admissions, ... College, Cambridge

Main study areas – as in What to Study section: *(First degree):* Aeronautical engineering, anatomy, anthropology, archaeology, architecture, Asian studies, biochemistry, biology, botany, chemical engineering, chemistry, civil engineering, classics, computing, economics, education, electrical & electronic engineering, English, environmental science, European studies, fine arts, geography, geology, history, industrial relations, Latin American studies, law, linguistics, mathematical studies, mechanical and production engineering, medicine, metallurgy and materials science, microbiology, modern languages, music, Near East & Islamic studies, pharmacology, philosophy, physics, physiology, politics and government, psychology, religious studies and theology, sociology, veterinary studies, zoology. *Also:* Astrophysics, history of medicine, history and philosophy of science, land economy, pathology, Serbo-Croat, Slavonic studies, Turkish.

European Community: 7% first degree students take EC language as part of their course and spend 6 months or more in another EC country. No formal exchange links with EC universities/colleges at university level. Approved Erasmus programme 1990/91.

The University and Colleges: Each college is a self-governing community which elects its own fellows, admits its own first degree undergraduates and provides academic, sporting and social facilities. Colleges are not confined to particular subjects although some acquire a reputation in a particular subject. Most admit undergraduates to read all the subjects at Cambridge, although some smaller colleges discourage applications in minority subjects. For most undergraduates the college is the focal point of their life at Cambridge.

CAN'T FIND WHAT YOU'RE LOOKING FOR? USE THE INDEX!

THE COLLEGES

There are 28 undergraduate colleges:

Women only:
Lucy Cavendish (Mature only)
New Hall
Newnham
Men and Women:
Christ's
Churchill
Clare
Corpus Christi
Downing
Emmanuel
Fitzwilliam
Girton
Gonville & Caius
Homerton (separate profile; look up under H)

Jesus
King's
Magdalene
Pembroke
Peterhouse
Queens'
Robinson
St Catharine's
St Edmund's (Mature only)
St John's
Selwyn
Sidney Sussex
Trinity
Trinity Hall
Wolfson (Mature only)

HOW TO APPLY TO CAMBRIDGE UNIVERSITY

Entry is on the basis of results of A-level papers already taken or to be taken, sometimes in conjunction with the new Sixth Term Examination Papers (Step). It is possible to apply either to a college of first preference or by submitting an Open application not naming any colleges of preference. For details refer to the *Cambridge Admissions Prospectus* which you should consult as early as possible. In either case a preliminary application form should be submitted as early as possible, and by 15 October at the latest. The form may be obtained either from your school or from the Admissions Tutor of any Cambridge college, or from the Cambridge Intercollegiate Applications Office. You have also to submit a completed UCCA form in which you should name Cambridge as one of your university choices: **THIS MUST REACH UCCA BY 15 OCTOBER. You may not apply to Oxford as well as Cambridge in the same year unless you are a candidate for a choral/organ award.**

Cambridge Admissions Prospectus is distributed annually to all schools on the UCCA mailing list. If you miss yours, write to The Cambridge Intercollegiate Applications Office, Tennis Court Road, Cambridge CB2 1QJ (0223 333308). Students' Alternative Prospectus available from Cambridge University Students' Union, 11/12 Trumpington Street, Cambridge CB2 1QA price £2.50 (cheques made payable to Cambridge University Students' Union).
Duration of first degree course or equivalent: 3 or **4 years. Total first degree students: 10,190 Total number of BEd students: 271 Number of overseas students: 569 Number of mature students: 218 Male/female ratio: 3:2 Teaching staff: 2,500 Postgraduates: 3,533 Total full-time students: 13,723 Tuition fees 1990/91:** Home: £1,675; Overseas: £4,503 (eg politics), £5,907 (eg physics) plus college fee of £2,000-£3,000.

What it's like
It is its collegiate structure that makes Cambridge 'different'. Colleges largely self-contained (eg sports clubs and facilities and a larger amount of teaching). Don't spend too much time worrying about which college to apply to – it doesn't really

CAN'T FIND WHAT YOU'RE LOOKING FOR? USE THE INDEX!

matter. Don't believe the rumours about the 'character' of a particular college – they aren't true. The main points to consider are whether a college is mixed or single sex; its location; its wealth; whether it is old or new. Teaching in science subjects is mainly through lectures (6 mornings a week), supervisions and practicals. In arts, lectures are often ignored (very few are relevant or well integrated into the course) but students on average write 2 essays per week for supervisions. Seminars and other group teaching are virtually non-existent. Work-load is usually very heavy. Courses are assessed by exams. Changing courses is not too difficult. Drop-out and failure rates are low. Social life can often become too intense. There is a distinct pressure on students to cram a wide variety of activities into a very short space of time. University and college societies cater for every possible interest from drama to tiddlywinks. Cambridge suffers from a lack of a central focus for activities – there is no central SU building and no central venue for gigs, discos or for meeting.

Nicole Smith writes 'Some general points about Cambridge: Central town entirely geared towards students (and tourists) – allegedly more pubs per head of population than any other town in England. Also market town – good fruit 'n' veg plus second-hand clothes stalls. The Corn Exchange attacts motley variety of bands from New Model Army to the Inspiral Carpets – via Hawkwind! 'The Junction', a new venue, attracts more indie bands and 'alternative' theatre/dance groups.'

Pauper notes

Accommodation: Very expensive (average £36.00 per week). Most students live in college or in hostels. Students wanting to live out tend to congregate in the Chesterton Rd or 'trendy' Mill Road areas. **Drink:** Cambridge is reputed to have more pubs per square mile than other towns. Popular pubs include the Maypole (for hacks), the Eagle (just reopened), the Salisbury Arms (real ale and jazz on Sundays), King St pubs, Zebra (best food for miles), the Burleigh Arms (local bands almost every night), The Mill (local brews, with scrumpy that knocks you out). **Eats:** College food varies from OK to stodgy to good. Most do vegetarian. King's Pantry (veggie restaurant on King Street). 'Upstairs' on Castle Hill (Eastern food), Oasis (Green St) sells good late night kebabs and pizzas (ditto most shops in Mill Rd). Town is crammed full of Pizza Huts etc. For a more expensive treat try Footlights (Mexican), Shades (buffet) or Sweeny Todds (pizzas). **Ents:** College Bobs, occasional college ents (Emmanuel bar – Sundays, Clare Cellars). Local bands play the Burleigh Arms or the Alma. No venue for larger bands or nationally known big names within university, but Corn Exchange in town sees most tours. **Sports:** No University swimming pool (town one small and crowded). Most colleges have own sports facilities – eg there are 20 boathouses in Cambridge and as many rugby pitches. **Hardship funds:** Access funds are being used to help students in hardship. Colleges are able to give assistance in exceptional cases. **Travel:** Most colleges have funds – ask tutor. Zacharama, STA and Campus for cheap flights to Europe and USA. **Work:** Term-time work not permitted by university regulations apart from in college bars. Plenty of vacation work in and around Cambridge. Regulations (and usually no time) – except for college bars; for determined/resourceful plenty of vac work in Cambridge – fruit-packing, teaching in language schools and tutorial colleges, punting tourists in summer, college kitchens (boosts your street credibility to mingle with workers); Tory Reform Group personal assistant scheme can offer stimulation (at Westminster) rather than money.

Alumni (Editors' pick)

Milton, Darwin, Marlowe, Steve Coleridge, Brooke, Forster, Keynes, Pepys, Plath, Hughes, Erasmus, Wilberforce, Wordsworth, Palmerston, Cromwell, Bacon, Marvell, Dryden, Newton, Macaulay, Byron, Thackeray, Tennyson, Cleese, Frost, Burgess, McLean, Philby, Blunt, Drabble, Pitt the Younger, Trevelyan, Trollope, A A Milne, HM King Edward VII, Dr David Owen, Rajiv Gandhi, Lord Mountbatten of Burma, Bertrand Russell, E M Forster, Ian McKellan, Sir Arthur Bliss, Griff Rhys-Jones.

CAN'T FIND WHAT YOU'RE LOOKING FOR? USE THE INDEX!

CHRIST'S

Christ's College, Cambridge CB2 3BU (0223 334953)

Maintenance charge 1990/91: Fixed charge of £58 per term for meals. **Accommodation available:** All students can be accommodated in college or college-owned property. **Eating arrangements:** Choice of formal or informal meals. Fixed charge as above, plus breakfast (98p), lunch (£1.33), dinner (£1.84). **Gate/guest hours:** None. **Admission:** Pre A-level, by matriculation or conditional offers; some places offered on A-level results, school reports and interview. **Scholarships:** Unlimited number of scholarships (£100) mainly awarded on results of university examinations (approx 80 awarded for 1990/91). **Travel grants:** Approx 75 available each year (from £50 to £1,000). **Library:** Modern (1976) college working library; old library with antiquarian collection. **Other college facilities:** Theatre, concert hall, auditorium, playing fields, boathouse, squash courts, and modern public rooms. Medieval Dining Hall. Chapel.

European Community: Number of students learning an EC language or spending time in another EC country, not known.

Undergraduates: *Men:* 235 *Women:* 132
Postgraduates: *Men:* 68 *Women:* 27

What it's like

A medium-sized college, enjoying an excellent location in the centre of town, with shops, market, pubs and cinema all close at hand. The college combines old and new: the 16th-century First Court and the Fellows' garden are very picturesque, whilst Mandela Court, built in the 70's and known as 'The Typewriter', is less universal in its appeal.

There are 370 undergraduates with a broad mix of subjects and social backgrounds. About 35% are women – room for improvement but reflects the university average. Above all, Christ's is a friendly and tolerant student community.

Practically all first and third years live in college; most second years live in college-owned hostels and landlady/lord accommodation. Size and quality of rooms vary considerably; best facilities usually come with more modern rooms, although these often lack space and character. Cooking facilities are limited.

Food in college is subsidised by a fixed charge levied on all students. The Upper Hall (canteen) is cheap-ish and convenient but food tends to be stodgy and repetitive. Or you can dine in formal Hall which is enjoyable and filling. There are two bars: the Buttery has a good, cosy atmosphere but restricted hours, whilst the Wine Bar is lively if you can stand the appalling interior design.

Just about every sport or interest is catered for at university level, and Christ's has many of its own clubs and societies. Standards aren't always exceptional but the motivation is there; rowing and drama are particularly strong. Political interest is largely confined to university-based groups, but the college's SU is active. Christ's has its own squash courts, library and theatre.

Pauper notes

Accommodation: College provides accommodation for everyone at reasonable prices, far cheaper than can be found in the town. **Drink:** Many good pubs, especially off the breaten track; several good, cheap college bars. **Eats:** Variety of cafes and restaurants, with range of prices too! 'Nettles' and 'King's Pantry' for vegetarians. Pub lunches good. **Ents:** College film society costs about £1. Many pubs have live music evenings. ADC Theatre for student productions. **Sports:** Free squash courts in college. Best way to play cheaply is through college societies. **Hardship funds:** Hardship funds though small are readily available if you go and see your tutor. **Travel:** Travel grants, varying in amounts, are easy to obtain. **Work:** During the vacation it is relatively easy to get a job.

Alumni (Editors' pick)

General Smuts, John Milton, Charles Darwin, Mountbatten, C P Snow.

CAN'T FIND WHAT YOU'RE LOOKING FOR? USE THE INDEX!

CHURCHILL

Churchill College, Cambridge CB3 0DS (0223 336202)

Academic features: Word-processing and computing courses. Churchill Archives Centre: 20th-century British history. **Maintenance charge 1990/91:** £160-£260 per term, plus meals. **Accommodation available:** Modern bedsitting rooms or sets. Undergraduates in college all 3 years. **Eating arrangements:** Self-service breakfast, lunch and dinner; formal dinner. Vegetarian available. **Gate/guest hours:** None. **Admission:** Conditional offers: for sciences: usually AAA and a 1 in S-level or Step; for arts: usually AAB (no S papers). Virtually all candidates interviewed. Undergraduates not admitted for education, land economy, theology. **Travel grants:** Small long vacation travel fund. **Hardship funds:** Some available. **Library:** 2 undergraduate libraries open 24 hours a day. Books in greatest demand lent during limited period only. **Other college facilities:** Buttery, bar, theatre; extensive playing fields and tennis and squash courts within college grounds; multi-gym; 15 BBC computers, 5 PC workstations and 8 AppleMacs for student use, music recital and practice rooms.

European Community: Modern languages students spend 6 months or more in EC country. Formal exchange links for engineering students with Ecole Centrale, Paris.

Undergraduates: *Men:* 287 *Women:* 93
Postgraduates: *Men:* 170 *Women:* 37

What it's like

Founded in 1962 as the national memorial to Churchill, it quickly adopted a liberal approach; among the first to admit women. Very few restrictions, a relaxed friendly and unpretentious atmosphere. Strong science bias but arts still alive and kicking. High proportion of state school students; less cliquey than many other Cambridge colleges.

Resembles Stalag 17 from the outside; inside the rooms are light, airy, with all mod-cons; no visiting restrictions enforced. Dining hall serves a wide range of food, sometimes a little stodgy. Also a well equipped kitchen with phone(!) for every dozen students.

Large playing fields, tennis and squash courts and a multi-gym. Opportunities are numerous and include a thriving boat club, 3 or 4 football (1 women's), 2 hockey (one of each), 3 cricket (1 women's) and 2 rugby teams.

Large, well-equipped, air-conditioned lecture theatre-cum-cinema, home to 3 of the best film societies in Cambridge who each show weekly films. Also a frequently packed bar and weekly discos.

Library open 24 hours a day and caters well for most subjects; librarian very willing to fill any gaps.

Although almost a mile from the town centre, not as isolated as many would have you believe – almost everyone enjoys their 3 years here.

Pauper notes

Accommodation: Squats are few and far between and tend to meet with disgruntled reaction. Churchill can house all undergraduates. Cambridge is not an easy place to find housing and it's almost as expensive as London. There are the Wolfson Flats, as well as various college-owned houses, for married students. **Drink:** College bar big and popular. The Cow and Calf and Town and Gown college locals. **Eats:** College food much complained about but not that bad. Recent healthy eating drive resulted in near eradication of chips. 'Tatties' – basically jacket potatoes with toppings of numerous variations! **Ents:** Brilliant Pleasure Machine disco in college, 3 weekly film socs, annual, Spring Ball and Albert Scratchings night; JCR bar-b-q. Numerous cocktail parties. **Sports:** Good multigym in college, so you don't have to cycle to the other side of town to Kelsey Kerridge gym. Churchill quite 'sporty'.

CAN'T FIND WHAT YOU'RE LOOKING FOR? USE THE INDEX!

Good well kept pitches on college. Tennis, squash courts, strong boat club, rugby and football, good hockey. Chess, aerobics, canoeing, mountaineering – you name it! **Hardship funds:** Yes, but you need to be in dire straits. **Travel:** Generous – various travel grants, both for study and for recreation. Easy to hitch – close to M11. Rail station 4 miles, bus station 2 miles. **Work:** In college: bar-work (sometimes); helping porters with keys and car-parking; Vac work available in college particularly over summer. But work load too great to give you much time to earn vac money whatever your subject.

CLARE

Clare College, Cambridge CB2 1TL (0223 333246)

Maintenance charge 1990/91: Sample (for 2 room set and all meals in college) £1,160 pa. **Accommodation:** Mixture of sets, bedsitters and hostels available in all 3 years. **Eating arrangements:** Self-service buttery, formal dinner in hall Mondays–Thursdays. Ticket system. **Gate/guest hours:** Porter lets college members in all night; guests not booked in overnight expected to leave by 2 am. **Admission:** Most candidates apply during fourth term in sixth form. A levels plus Step is the most common method of entry but many offers are based on A or A plus S levels. **Scholarships:** Organ scholarship (£250 pa) every other year; an average of 7 choral and 2 instrumental exhibitions (£100 pa). **Travel grants:** Funds available at college's discretion; 3 major Parkin Grants and 8 Thirkill Grants for those who have played a prominent part in college life; Mellon Fellowship for third year undergraduates who spend 2 years at Yale. **Library:** Forbes Mellon Library New building. 20,000 volumes, collection of past examination papers, Law reading room. **Other college facilities:** Music and record libraries, music room, music practice rooms, computing and word-processing facilities and link to university mainframe, picture guild, pianos, harpsichord, meeting rooms, darkroom, studio and pottery room (with wheel and kiln); squash courts near college, outstanding playing fields (about 1.5 miles away), rowing, punts available in summertime. **Hardship funds:** Available in cases of unavoidable hardship.

European Community: 10% first degree students take EC language as part of course and 10% spend 6 months or more in another EC country. Formal exchange links with 2 EC universities/colleges (Heidelberg, Paris).

Undergraduates: *Men:* 242 *Women:* 167
Postgraduates: *Men:* 75 *Women:* 42

What it's like

Central, beautiful college on 'the Backs' – has an old bridge over the willow- and garden-bordered river Cam. Closeish to shops/lectures: foot or bike always adequate. 99% of students live in; all have the option. Accommodation varies from grotty bedsits (few) to spacious sets (also few) to houses for groups of c. six; most rooms are middling-good, generally good value. Minimal cooking facilities; coin-op washing and drying machines. No problems with mixed accommodation.

Keen on attracting overseas/exchange students. Very good relations between 'the college' and students.

Hours of libraries/labs/gyms/shops generally convenient. SU active in providing facilities, running social events, improving quality of life (eg low rents); politically reflects college's centre-left apathy. No visiting restrictions. Cambridge students not allowed cars. Counselling/advice services comprehensive, confidential, helpful. 'Little Blue Book' of info on contraception/sex/etc sent free to all first years. Active societies: rowing, mountaineering/hillwalking, music, rugby; plus inevitable drinking societies. Central Cambridge dominated by students, but relations not always good between town & gown: students seen as an 'overprivileged few'. Good cinema, market, major chain stores, many pubs.

CAN'T FIND WHAT YOU'RE LOOKING FOR? USE THE INDEX!

It's fairly easy to meet students from other colleges, but most people's time is largely spent within college: Clare offers a lot.

Courses mainly academic rather than practical, sometimes frustratingly so. Changing course easy. Work loads vary considerably, can (esp in sciences) be pretty heavy. No sandwich courses. Language courses have year abroad. Lecturers vary a lot: some very good, some useless. Cambridge degree has good reputation nationally and internationally. Work is assessed (in terms of degree results) only at the end of each year; but 'supervisors', one for each area of your course, see you fortnightly. Failure rate low, not fixed. Courses can seem dull at first, but by second/third year they're more interesting.

Most students from south; roughly half from public schools (Clare has a higher percentage from state schools than most Cambridge colleges). Almost no dropout. Incidents of sexist/racist discrimination relatively rare. Typical student has 3 A's at A-level, various non-academic interests, will work in City after graduating.

Pauper notes
Accommodation: Varies in quality, but relatively cheap, large choice of accommodation eg house, single room, shared. Enough accommodation owned by college for 3 yrs 'living in'. **Drink:** Greene King. **Eats:** College canteen keeps non-vegetarians alive; good pub lunches nearby. **Ents:** In Clare an excellent choice of Jazz, Folk & Blues Nights – all cheap, quality performances, in college JCR. Local Arts Cinema – excellent films. **Sports:** Also local sports centre with gym for training. **Hardship funds:** Only under exceptional circumstances. **Travel:** Don't need to use transport within Cambridge. **Work:** You won't have time during term-time anyway.

Alumni (Editors' pick)
David Attenborough (naturalist and broadcaster), Paul Mellon (philanthropist), Harvey & one of his Wallbangers, Richard Stilgoe (entertainer), James Watson (Nobel Laureate – DNA), Chris Kelly (broadcaster), Hugh Latimer (martyr), Cecil Sharp (folk songs), Siegfried Sassoon (poet), Peter Lilley MP, Matthew Paris (journalist), Norman Ramsey (Nobel Laureate).

CORPUS CHRISTI

Corpus Christi College, Cambridge CB2 1RH (0223 338056)

Maintenance charge 1990/91: College consolidated fee £4,159. Room, rent and meals approximately £1,875. **Accommodation available:** Sets and single rooms for all college members during Cambridge residence. **Eating arrangements:** All meals provided in hall. **Gate/guest hours:** Entry after 11.30pm by key; unless resident, guests leave by 12 midnight. **Admission:** Primarily based on A-level results, school report and interview. **Scholarships:** None. **Travel grants:** Considerable sums annually. **Library:** Butler Library (working undergraduate library); Parker Library (medieval manuscripts and early books). **Other college facilities:** Extensive sports grounds; 7-acre garden with open air swimming pool; river boathouse.

European Community: 25% first degree students take EC language as part of course and 5% spend 6 months or more in another EC country. Formal exchange links with various EC universities/colleges.

Undergraduates: *Men:* 172 *Women:* 67
Postgraduates: *Men:* 83 *Women:* 35

What it's like
Small and central, the main buildings comprise Old Court, Cambridge's oldest and arguably prettiest court, and gothic style New Court. 2nd years live in college hostels up to 1/3 mile away, including the new comfortable Bene't Street development. Old Court rooms range from pokey to palatial, but can involve long wintry

CAN'T FIND WHAT YOU'RE LOOKING FOR? USE THE INDEX!

walks to the bathroom. 13-amp electricity, sinks and basic kitchens have all been recently installed.

Simple self-catering facilities are gradually being fitted throughout college. Food in Hall is generally good, but pricey; hefty fixed charge whether you eat or not. Regular Guest Nights are lavish, reasonable, very popular, but not as good value as they once were. The Buttery and Bar (refurbished) are extensively used. Lunchtime snacks (baked potatoes, burgers, rolls etc) are further victims of recent price rises, but still provide a cheaper alternative to lunch in Hall. The Bar is open late and serves several beers, lagers and wines from the college's extensive cellars.

Excellent sports facilities are 15 minutes away – squash courts, tennis courts, and in summer an open-air swimming pool. Sporting standards vary but in general emphasis is on taking part rather than winning.

Strong college drama, history, literary and wine societies. Video always available in the TV room. Impressive computing facility has just been installed.

Academic standards are fairly high – Corpus is in the top of Cambridge academic league table. College can provide supervisors for most subjects, though some may be farmed off to surrounding colleges. Top for law. Undergraduate relations with fellows are good. Money, or your lack of it, will always be dealt with sympathetically. Guest restrictions are minimal – just sign in. The college library is small, but about to be drastically expanded. Most departmental libraries are close by. The JCR has shaken off its former apathy and is now active in student politics.

No undergraduate group is dominant – good mix from all backgrounds. Corpus was one of the last colleges to become mixed, and the proportion of female undergraduates is still below the university average, but college is aiming to rectify this position.

College is surrounded by a welter of good pubs, and the Corn Exchange (an emerging venue for national name bands) is less than 100 yards away. *Richard Stephens*

Pauper notes
Accommodation: New college hostel for 2nd year accommodation. Some rooms available 2nd/3rd years for c£15 per week. **Drink:** Several good 'student' pubs within 100 yards of college. Wide variety of brews can be found. 'The Bath' specialises in cider. **Eats:** College food relatively expensive for a Cambridge college. Vegetarians have a lot to moan about. Cambridge itself has a huge variety of eating places at all price ranges. **Ents:** College video club and college drama and music are both very active. **Sports:** Good college facilities, univ/town facilities limited. **Travel:** College awards two sets of travel scholarships (several awards each of anything from £100 to £900). **Work:** Some work usually available in college during long vac.

Alumni (Editors' pick)
Christopher Isherwood, Sir Frederick Lawton (Lord Justice of Appeal), Lord Sieff of Brimpton (Marks & Spencer), Sir Eric Faulkner (Lloyds Bank), Mark Elder, Joe Farman (discoverer of hole in ozone layer), Christopher Booker (journalist/writer), E P Thompson (historian/nuclear disarmer).

DOWNING

Downing College, Cambridge CB2 1DQ (0223 334800)

Maintenance charge 1990/91: Not available. **Accommodation available:** All first year undergraduates in college; at least one further year in college (or in adjacent college hostels). Rent: 75% in accommodation where rent controlled by college. **Eating arrangements:** Undergraduates may take all meals in hall; self-catering available. **Gate/guest hours:** Gates always open. Guests not booked in overnight must leave by 1.45 am. **Admission:** All offers based on school reports, interviews

CAN'T FIND WHAT YOU'RE LOOKING FOR? USE THE INDEX!

and A-levels or equivalent. **Structural features:** New undergraduate common room and theatre/concert hall. **Scholarships:** Scholarships and exhibitions on performance in university exams. Organ scholarship (£100 pa), choral and instrumental awards every year. **Travel grants:** Endowed trust funds. **Hardship funds:** Some funds available. **Library:** Well-stocked college library. **Other college facilities:** Bar; 2 tennis courts and 2 squash courts in college precincts; sports ground 5 min cycle ride away; boathouse. **Largest fields of study:** Natural sciences, law, engineering, medicine.

European Community: 7% first degree students take EC language as part of course and 7% spend 6 months or more in another EC country. No formal exchange links with EC universities/colleges.

Undergraduates: *Men:* 240 *Women:* 130
Postgraduates: *Men:* 75 *Women:* 16

What it's like

In the south centre of Cambridge, next door to science sites and only a short walk from all faculties. Academically particularly strong in law, medicine, natural sciences and geography; thrives in all areas.

Outstanding open spaces and austere classical design. Much recent building in keeping with style. Howard Building (opened 1987) provides a luxurious Junior Combination Room and a theatre/lecture hall; new JCR bar and party room (1989); computer room (1989) equipped with latest IBM PC network hardware. Two-thirds live in college accommodation; all in their first year.

Active JCR concerned primarily with student problems rather than wider political issues. Good relationship between JCR and college authorities, eg co-operation over improvements in security for women. JCR bar, wholly run and staffed by students, is second cheapest in university.

Sporting reputation is well-deserved – champion rugby and football college, winners of the tennis and skiing University Cup competitions, 2nd in May Bumps rowing competition, captain of the University cricket team, and of both University tennis teams, karate internationals . . . the list goes on. Emphasis on participation rather than success, with most students joining in for fun rather than serious competition.

Music Society has weekly concerts of an excellent standard; Drama Society puts on a number of excellent productions each year. Journalism thrives in the form of a termly college magazine and a fortnightly newsletter. A stimulating and active atmosphere for students.

Pauper notes

Accommodation: Many rooms recently refurbished; additional new rooms for 30 students provided this year. **Drink:** College bar cheap, Greene King IPA & Abbot, hand-pulled. The Alma Brewery nearby for scrumpy. **Eats:** (In college) good quality, excellent salads, generous portions, vegetarian every day; (outside) many jacket potato, pizza and other restaurants. **Ents:** Parties, sweaty bops; bands in corn exchange; plays in new theatre. Many productions and revues throughout Cambridge. **Sports:** Uni sports centre, gym & weights free; swimming pool nearby (£1.10). Tennis and squash courts on campus. Large grass area on campus. **Hardship funds:** Funds available; awarded in cases where such hardship is evident. **Travel:** Various scholarships for travel come up; some standard links with USA. **Work:** CUSU give good advice on claiming benefits; bar work in college available.

Alumni (Editors' pick)

Sir Graham Smith (Astronomer Royal), John Cleese, F R Leavis, Lord Goodman, Prof Lord John Butterfield, Trevor Nunn, Brian Redhead, Michael Winner, Mark Cox, Michael Atherton, Dr Alan Howard, Sir Peter Hall, Trevor Nunn.

CAN'T FIND WHAT YOU'RE LOOKING FOR? USE THE INDEX!

EMMANUEL
Emmanuel College, Cambridge CB2 3AP (0223 334200)

Maintenance charge 1990/91: For room and 3 meals daily, approx £2,064 pa. **Accommodation available:** All first and third year undergraduates accommodated in college (old or modern rooms); second year undergraduates in college or college hostels. Rent: all undergraduates housed in accommodation where rent is controlled by college. **Eating arrangements:** No compulsory eating arrangements. **Gate/guest hours:** No gate hours but guests must leave by 2 am (unless registered as overnight guests). **Admission:** Conditional and unconditional offers only. **Travel grants:** 30 awarded annually to resident undergraduates. **Library:** Large college library; Sancroft Library (old books) and Watson Collection (illustrated books). **Hardship funds:** Funds available to both undergraduate and graduate students. **Other college facilities:** Grand piano, harpsichord and organ; 2 squash courts, table tennis room, tennis courts and open air swimming pool in college precincts; nearby playing fields and boat house.

European Community: 12% first degree students take EC language as part of course and 3% spend 6 months or more in another EC country.

Undergraduates: *Men:* 262 *Women:* 144
Postgraduates: *Men:* 111 *Women:* 59

What it's like
Known principally for its ducks, but also for being friendly and unpretentious, Emma has a strong college identity – caused in part by the best student-run bar in Cambridge. Students here are drawn from a large range of backgrounds – 40% are women and applications from state schools are actively encouraged. Though one of the richer Cambridge colleges, this will not affect your rent bill. However, it is reflected in full undergraduate housing for three years, generous travel awards, a commitment to tutorial teaching and an increasing provision for hardship funds.

The college SU is politically and socially very active and there are a lot of well-financed clubs.

It is not hard to enjoy Emma – its grounds and students, that is once you get used to the food. At present self-catering is not encouraged.
Tim Dornan

Pauper notes
Accommodation: All 1st and 3rd and most 2nd years in college accommodation. £250–£300 per term inc: heating, elec. Living out very expensive and rare. **Drink:** Student run college bar cheapest in Cambridge (90–100p a pint). No local brew of note. **Eats:** Compulsory fixed termly charge (£70) a bone of contention. Lunch and dinner £1.50. Formal hall £2.50. Quality varies. Many places nearby in town. **Ents:** Free entertainments weekly in JCR. Drama Society. No good venue in town, but Emma JCR is good. **Sports:** Good free sportsground 15 min away by bike. Closest college to sports hall and swimming pool. **Hardship funds:** Extensive facilities available via tutorial system – useful to have a good tutor. **Travel:** Fairly generous travel grants. Travelling in Cambridge easy. No cars allowed. **Work:** Not encouraged during term. Some services/office vacancies in vacations.

Alumni (Editors' pick)
Michael Frayn, Eldon Griffiths MP, Professor Sir Fred Hoyle, Tom King MP, Cecil Parkinson MP, Sir George Porter, Griff Rhys Jones, Graham Garden.

CAN'T FIND WHAT YOU'RE LOOKING FOR? USE THE INDEX!

FITZWILLIAM

Fitzwilliam College, Cambridge CB3 0DG (0223 332000)

Maintenance charge 1990/91: £2,242 pa + 8%. **Accommodation available:** 275 rooms in college, college houses and hostel, some college-rented flats; all first and third year, and some second year undergraduates accommodated. 61% in accommodation where rent controlled by college. **Eating arrangements:** Continental breakfast and lunch in hall, choice of self-service and formal dinner. Small house charge but most meals paid for as required. **Gate/guest hours:** Normally guests must leave college by 2 am; some overnight accommodation if certain conditions satisfied. **Admission:** By A-level results: conditional and unconditional offers on basis of interview and school report only. **Scholarships:** Scholarships and exhibitions awarded on university examinations. **Travel grants:** Contributions to travel costs made from Sir John Stratton Travel Fund and other college sources. **Hardship funds:** Small amounts (£100–£200) through the Tutors Fund and University's Bell, Abbott, and Barnes Funds. **Library:** College library (open all evening and in Easter term until 2 am). **Other college facilities:** Bar, laundry, guest rooms, music room, squash courts, playing fields near college.

European Community: 15% first degree students take EC language as part of course and 8% spend 6 months or more in another EC country. No formal exchange links; modern linguists study at EC university of their choice. EC students welcomed at college.

Undergraduates: *Men:* 287 *Women:* 127
Postgraduates: *Men:* 100 *Women:* 22

What it's like

It's not only Fitzwilliam's red-brick exterior that distinguishes it from the 'traditional' Cambridge college – the student intake helps too, since students from state schools make up 70% of the undergraduate population. The atmosphere is down-to-earth and friendly and there is a strong sense of community, perhaps due to the college's location slightly out of town. It is, however, still only a five-minute cycle ride into the centre, and the rest of the colleges are close enough to be able to enjoy what the university as a whole has to offer.

Academically, Fitz is rising in the university ratings and has done particularly well recently in modern languages and law. The student population is diverse, although women are still outnumbered by a 3:1 ratio and there are few black students. This reflects no overt discriminatory policy but a sad fact that is true throughout the university.

Accommodation is guaranteed for first and third years, consisting of corridors with eight rooms, a kitchen (two ring burners but no oven) and adequate bathroom facilities. Third-year rooms in New Court are palatial and trendily done out in black pine, hence a higher rent. Most second years and graduates live in privately rented accommodation, and this can prove expensive.

On the social front, Fitz is fast acquiring a reputation for having the best Ents in town. These take place twice termly, and are only a small part of the social life on offer, should you wish it. Clubs and societies range from human rights to aerobics, with music and drama growing quickly. Sport is well catered for, with opportunities for all, three squash courts in college, and a college-owned ground nearby.

An active JMA (SU) involves itself with a wide range of issues, and an excellent welfare system provides each student with a tutor (there to help and listen in any situation, fully confidentially) as well as access to a women's tutor and a chaplain. Though fairly apathetic politically, attitudes in general are healthy and egalitarian.

Also worth noting: there are few restrictions on visitors or overnight guests. Contraceptive machines can be found in central block toilets and advice is also readily available. All students have access to computing facilities – Apple Macs and BBC model Bs. Bar has two full-time bar staff, one of the best in the university.
Rachel Pope

CAN'T FIND WHAT YOU'RE LOOKING FOR? USE THE INDEX!

Pauper notes

Accommodation: No married quarters, rooms with and without basins. Good new block rooms. **Drink:** Bar cheaper than pubs (not as cheap as student run bars in Cambridge). **Eats:** Cafeteria good value. Varying standard but always a salad bar. Veggie options. **Ents:** JMA organises 2 Ents per term. One play in Michaelmas term. **Sports:** All sports free. Sports ground very close to college. Basketball, badminton, athletics, tennis, squash (3 courts), rugby, football, hockey, netball, darts, softball. **Hardship funds:** Taxi service for injuries. **Travel:** Max £250 travel grant for educational trips. **Work:** No term-time employment (University regulations), some holiday jobs in kitchen and maintenance staff.

Alumni (Editors' pick)

Norman St John Stevas, Dr A Szent-Gyorgi (Nobel prizewinner), Derek Pringle, Phil Edmondes (cricketers), Christopher Martin Jenkins (cricket commentator).

GIRTON

Girton College, Cambridge CB3 0JG (0223 338999)

Maintenance charge 1990/91: £195.30 per term + c£60.00 heating and £54.16 kitchen overheads. **Accommodation available:** 419 rooms (mostly single bedsits but some sets) available for undergraduates in college. 40 rooms in college houses. Rent: 98% in accommodation where rent controlled by college. **Academic features 1990/91:** Mathematics Tripos course to take account of candidates with single subject mathematics. Engineering course now 4 years. **Structural features:** Besides the main college, Girton has Wolfson Court in Clarkson Road, in the centre of Cambridge for both graduates and undergraduates. **Eating arrangements:** Optional books of meal tickets valid for academic year. No compulsory meals. Lunch arrangements with Clare, Downing and Pembroke Colleges. Formal dinner in Hall once a week. **Guest/gate hours:** College members must be back in college by 6 am (if without overnight exeats); guests after 10.30 pm only if accompanied by college member. **Admission:** Conditional offers on A-level with some Matriculation offers. Post A-level and candidates for deferred entry welcomed. **Scholarships:** Scholarships and exhibitions awarded on results of Tripos examinations; organ scholarships, choral and instrumental awards. **Travel grants:** Some available. **Library:** College library (80,000 volumes). **Hardship funds:** The Buss Fund for undergraduates; The Pillman Fund for research and graduates, Overseas Bursaries for overseas students. **Other college facilities:** Playing fields, croquet lawns, swimming pool, cricket, soccer and rugger pitches, boathouse, tennis courts, squash court. **Largest fields of study:** Biological and physical sciences; engineering; also high intake in English, history, geography, economics, law, mathematics, medical sciences, modern languages and veterinary medicine.

European Community: 8% first degree students take EC language and spend a year in another EC country as part of their course (modern and medieval languages students). Formal exchange link with Utrecht University.

Undergraduates: *Men: 268 Women: 228*
Postgraduates: *Men: 80 Women: 50*

What it's like

Set in pleasant, extensive grounds about 2.5 miles from city centre; most find bikes essential. Vast majority of undergraduates live in; most second and third years have good accommodation. Wolfson Court houses 100, is more modern and nearer town. Several college houses available, all next to Girton College. Fixed rent for all rooms (inc college houses), regardless of size. 50:50 m/f. Strong overseas contingent. No breakfasts; no Saturday or Sunday evening meal. Food quite cheap and quite good.

CAN'T FIND WHAT YOU'RE LOOKING FOR? USE THE INDEX!

Several choices and salads available. Vegetarian meals provided; vegan on request. Self-catering facilities on each corridor; old twin-tubs on each corridor (ineffective). A few coin-operated machines provided. Extensive, good library, with convenient opening hours. Friendly relations between senior and junior college members. College societies range from subject-related to music, drama and film club. Sports available on site – most facilities good: hockey, lacrosse, tennis, netball, rugby, soccer, squash, cricket, croquet. Also heated indoor swimming pool, multigym and successful rowing club. Lively bar, soon to have pool table. Busy most times, cheap. Serves the excellent Greene King bitter. Party rooms available; TV room. JCR hires out discotheque and organises annual ball, garden party and band nights and discos.

Academic standards average. Fairly easy to change subjects. Workloads realistic and despite traditional atmosphere of degrees, interesting and unpressurised. Part One (first year) engineering and some sciences have a heavy workload (be prepared). Friendly and relaxed atmosphere. Very mixed intake – varied educational and home backgrounds; down-to-earth and unpretentious.

Several cheap college bars open to all students. A kitchen reject shop sells cheap and useful kitchen/living essentials and non-essentials. Pubs good but not cheap. No restrictions on entry into college but after 8 pm entrance is by front gate only. Gate locked at 2 am but porter always on duty to open it.

All rooms, facilities, library, bar etc contained within one building (which can be cold in winter as it's all brick and wood). Frequent buses but not always running to time-table: approx cost 70p. Taxi approx £3.50. JCR bikes available for students in need of one. Small JCR-run shop sells very cheap stationery and other essentials.

Pauper notes

Accommodation: Accommodation for most undergraduates – some 2nd years live out. No married quarters but houses available (rooms same rent as room in college) very near to college. **Drink:** Greene King is one of the best bitters! (and quite cheap). College bars (have to know people in other colleges to drink in their college bars). **Eats:** Best eating places in town, some on Castle Hill (none around Girton). College meals about £1.00 each. **Ents:** Local bands in college bars – some more famous play in Corn Exchange – fairly expensive – other disco or band each week in Girton. **Sports:** Very good facilities – however swimming pool on cool side. Univ sports advertised at societies fair realistic prices. **Hardship funds:** Interest free college loans are available to hard-up students. **Travel:** Bicycles essential. Bus frequent but not always regular. Taxi to town £3.00. Hitching easy. Travel grants available for summer vacation. **Work:** Some work in college kitchens – otherwise during term not officially allowed – temping possible in holidays.

Alumni (Editors' pick)

Arianna Stassinopoulos (writer and broadcaster), Angelia Tilby (writer and TV producer), HM Queen Margarethe of Denmark, Prof Rosalyn Higgins (professor of international law, University College, London), Mrs Doris Wheatley (chairman and managing director, Cambridge Communications Ltd), Prof Dorothy Wedderburn (Principal, Royal Holloway and Bedford College, London).

GONVILLE & CAIUS

Gonville & Caius College, Cambridge CB2 1TA (0223 312211)

Maintenance charge 1990/91: £370 pa. **Accommodation available:** All unmarried students allocated room in college in first and third year; second years housed in college lodgings. **Eating arrangements:** Self-service breakfast and lunch; undergraduates encouraged to dine in hall as often as possible and there is minimum dining requirement. **Gate/guest hours:** No restrictions. **Admission:** On basis of A-level results already obtained; increasingly high proportion of places also offered to pre A-level candidates conditional on certain grades in A-level examinations.

CAN'T FIND WHAT YOU'RE LOOKING FOR? USE THE INDEX!

Candidates are usually asked to offer 1 or 2 subjects at S-level or Step (Sixth Term Examination Papers) if they wish to study maths or medicine. **Scholarships:** Unlimited scholarships and exhibitions on university examinations. **Travel grants:** Numerous minor travel grants plus Paton-Taylor travelling scholarship for projects of an academic nature; awards from Leonard Gluckstein Memorial Fund for travel associated with historical or archaeological studies; grants from Handson Bequest for medical projects (eg recent expedition to South America). **Library:** College library contains collection of modern books; also largest surviving medieval collection in university and various collections bequeathed by Fellows. **Other college facilities:** College boathouse and boatman; cricket pitch; sports ground. **Academic features:** Caius has more medical students than other colleges, and a teaching Fellow in every pre-clinical medical subject. It is one of the very few colleges with a French and German Lector in addition to modern languages teaching Fellows.

European Community: Number of students learning an EC language or spending time in another EC country, not known.

Undergraduates: *Men:* 275 *Women:* 147
Postgraduates: *Men:* 107 *Women:* 64

What it's like

The main college buildings (the 'Old Courts') are in the centre of town – beautifully situated; next to the Squire Law Library. The buildings are attractive and ornate – pretty flower beds! Most first years live in Harvey Court (1960s halls – but admired by architects) – 10 minutes' walk away – on the Backs, and next to the arts faculties and university library. 2nd years 'live-out' in college houses, allocated by ballot; ballot order is reversed to choose 3rd year rooms in the Old Courts.

Washing machines/irons etc are readily available (if rather antiquated) and 3-5 people share a 'gyp-room' (kitchen) which contains a fridge and cooking rings. Officially only 'minor cooking' is allowed, as it is compulsory to eat in hall 45 times a term. All staircases are now mixed. Approx 5–10% students are from overseas, more in the MCR. Special efforts are made to ensure their integration into college life. Little ostentatious wealth among students – few leave without an overdraft! Relations between the administration and students are friendly (each student has a personal tutor). The college SU is active and well-regarded: affiliated to CUSU and NUS it concentrates more on welfare issues than party politics – although members of the college are involved in all political spheres – from CUCA through the Greens to Uni-left. Much like other Cambridge colleges, the character of the college changes with each new intake of students – but generally thought of as a tolerant and relaxed atmosphere. Courts tend to be very sociable – there are three bars – 2 student run. Everyone knows everyone else because of the compulsory dinner system which brings the college together once a day. Some find it insular – but many current Caians are involved on a university level in various activities from the President of the ADC Theatre to the CU 'Hands On' Massage Society.

Strong subjects are history and medicine; economics, engineering and law are also well-represented. It is very easy to change subject for Part II (eg law to English, economics to SPS). Workloads vary hugely from individual to individual and between courses: arts subjects require self-reliance (1–2 supervisions a week, few lectures); natural sciences and medicine are much more structured. The college library is open 24 hours a day, and there is a separate law library.

Rowing and hockey are sports at which Caius excels – but most other sports are played at a more laid-back level. If your interest is not represented among the 40¢ clubs and societies in college, it is easy to start up a new one (eg women's rugby and mixed netball last year). Debating, music and drama are all thriving! The majority of students are from London/Home Counties: college is keen to attract more state school entrants but currently large majority public/private and grammar schools. Drop-out rate approx 1 a year (from 150). Lively women's group – women prominent in college, although only 30% of student body.
Nicole Smith

CAN'T FIND WHAT YOU'RE LOOKING FOR? USE THE INDEX!

Pauper notes

Accommodation: Balloted accommodation, 95% excellent. £200–£290 per term. Married quarters. All students housed in college-owned property. Modern 1st year halls; 2nd year houses; 3rd year 'Old Courts'. **Drink:** 3 college bars – good, vary a lot in character – 95p pint lager. Student run 'Late Night Bar' has dance floor and seedy atmosphere. **Eats:** College caters for all diets; good vegetarian restaurants and health food shops in town. **Ents:** Frequent (cheap) college bops and other events. Thriving drama society; regular (classical) concerts, plays. Seven/eight films a term. 'Arts' cinema in town is excellent; also Cannon cinema for mainstream films. **Sports:** Excellent sports ground with clubhouse – contains signable drinks (ie not cash!) and a yard! – and squash/tennis courts. Good standard. Town sports centre has good indoor facilities (swimming, badminton etc). Also open-air pool in town. **Hardship funds:** College has several schemes and is understanding and generous in cases of financial hardship. **Travel:** A large budget for travel grants each year (average £100); approx £6 return to London (coach). **Work:** Possible to work in college bars (for a pittance) but otherwise work is officially prohibited during term.

Alumni (Editors' pick)

Titus Oates, David Frost, Captain Wilson, Venn (of Venn diagrams), Harold Abrahams, Sir Nevill Mott (Nobel Laureate, physics), Kenneth Clarke MP, Mark Bailey (England rugby player).

JESUS

Jesus College, Cambridge CB5 8BL (0223 357626)

Maintenance charge: No fixed inclusive charge – varies with rooms and meals taken. **Accommodation arrangements:** All first years and most third years accommodated in college. Second years in bedsitters and sets of rooms adjacent external staircases or lodging houses. Rent: 95% in accommodation where rent controlled by college. **Eating arrangements:** Self-service with alternative formal Hall dinner. Each undergraduate pays kitchen fixed charge plus cost of meals taken. **Gate/guest hours:** Free access until 2 am. Overnight guests have to be signed in. **Admission:** By conditional offer, using STEP or S level in certain cases. Post A-level candidates admitted on basis of A-levels, school reports and interview. **Hardship funds:** Named funds plus college loans. **Travel grants:** Usually available for applicant in Lent term. **Library:** College library. **Other college facilities:** Bar, junior common room, party room, TV room, stereo-reproduction room, billiards room, launderette, sports fields adjacent to the college.

European Community: Number of students learning an EC language or spending time in another EC country, not known.

Undergraduates: *Men:* 290 *Women:* 145
Postgraduates: *Men:* 139 *Women:* 40

What it's like

Medium sized college just off the tourist track (an advantage in summer). Only 3 minutes' walk to city centre with full range of shopping facilities. College is one of the few in Cambridge that has all its sports grounds and facilities on site giving an atmosphere of openness as well as producing a strong sporting tradition, particularly in rugby, hockey and rowing. (The boathouse and river is again about 3 minutes away.)

Students are well-integrated from all social backgrounds, fairly active in University activities. Flourishing college music society and drama has received a recent revival.

Accommodation good though not the cheapest around; very few students have a landlady in any of their 3 years here. 1st year spent in; 2nd year out – literally

CAN'T FIND WHAT YOU'RE LOOKING FOR? USE THE INDEX!

opposite the College; 3rd year either in or out, with a number of 3 room sets available for 3rd years. Rooms tend to be warm and well-furnished, about 75% have washbasins. Food is quite good with Formal Hall (3 course waitress served meal to which gowns must be worn) rated as one of the best in Cambridge and only £2.10. Student bar is both lively and popular, with many outside visitors frequenting it regularly. Current price for a pint of bitter 95p. Also a full-sized snooker table, reading room, TV room and computer room.

Jesus positively encourages applications from state sector and across the board in terms of subjects; no strict quotas in operation. English and history are particular strengths, but overall well-placed in the academic stakes with perhaps one of the more friendly Fellowships, always approachable and willing to listen to students and their problems.

Pauper notes
Drink: Old Peculier, good but not cheap. **Sports:** Sport free on college site. **Hardship funds:** Mostly loans from Fund of £50,000. **Travel:** Travel scholarships available.

Alumni (Editors' pick)
Alastair Cooke, W John Biffen MP, Bronowski, Raymond Williams, Sam Brittan, Sir Peter Gadsden, Sir David Trench, S T Coleridge, Archbishop Cranmer, Sterne, Malthus, Prince Edward.

KING'S

King's College, Cambridge CB2 1ST (0223 350411)

Maintenance charge 1990/91: Approx £189–£224 per term for college or hostel room (plus compulsory heating charge for some). **Accommodation available:** All undergraduates offered accommodation for 3 years – mostly study bedrooms, some sets of living room and bedroom. **Eating arrangements:** Self-service cafeteria. Standing charge covers kitchen overheads, individual meals are paid for. **Gate/guest hours:** None. **Admission:** Great majority by conditional pre A-level offers; some places offered to post A-level applicants with high exam grades. Undergraduates not admitted for law or veterinary science. **Scholarships:** Choral scholarships and organ studentships awarded at entrance; academic scholarships also awarded on university examinations. **Travel grants:** Many undergraduates awarded travel grants (about £120), usually for second year summer vacation. **Library:** College library (110,000 volumes); extensive music section. Record library. **Other college facilities:** 2 bars, launderette, darkroom, arts centre, computer room, film projection room, picture loan collection, croquet garden, punts, sports grounds. **NB:** King's encourages applicants from all backgrounds and all kinds of school, and, by interviewing every candidate, attempts to assess potential rather than examination performance. No compulsory gowns or formal meals.

European Community: 9% first degree students take EC language as part of course and 9% spend 6 months or more in another EC country. No formal exchange links with EC universities/colleges.

Undergraduates: *Men:* 219 *Women:* 144
Postgraduates: *Men:* 161 *Women:* 45

What it's like
King's effectively has the best of both worlds – while from the outside it presents the best known and most impressive exterior in Cambridge, within its walls exist the most informal and relaxed college in the university.

In every field: social, academic, artistic, sports, King's can hold its own (at least) with the rest of the university. It is King's breakdown of Cambridge cliché that makes it stand out – here students, staff and fellows do actually achieve some sense of community.

CAN'T FIND WHAT YOU'RE LOOKING FOR? USE THE INDEX!

King's offers some of the highest ratios in Cambridge for women, state school, mature and graduate intake, resulting in a mature and well-balanced student body. 'Minority' subjects (such as SPS, history of art, philosophy etc) are a King's speciality. Meanwhile college facilities (in accommodation, music, food and virtually everything else) are the equal of anywhere.

The student activism of the 60s and 70s that gained us the tag of 'Red King's' has left its legacy – the college offers a unique degree of student representation and involvement both within Cambridge and the UK as a whole. Although still the effective centre of the university's left-wing, the college is home to most shades of opinion and is best seen as a tolerant place to be.

King's actively welcomes and encourages applicants from all backgrounds, and from the disabled – King's offers a set of rooms specially converted for wheelchair access.

Of course no sketch can effectively portray life here, so come on over and see for yourself at our open days.

And hey – it's a nice place.
Matt Parton

Pauper notes
Accommodation: All undergraduates can live in. Graduates usually get 1 year. Town accommodation is available, though expensive. College accommodation ranges from not bad to exorbitant. **Drink:** Expensive Southern beer, both locally and in college, with a weird College cocktail bar providing the only financial relief for the real drinker. **Eats:** Good choice in canteen, vegetarians well catered for and not too expensive. Town tends to be either Wimpy or expensive, with one good kebab shop. **Ents:** Ents is good for films and student plays both on and off campus, with music generally agreed to be crap. New venue just opened, 'The Corn Exchange' but £7.00 to see Lindisfarne . . .? **Sports:** Loads of very cheap sports facilities because colleges are rich and like sporty people. **Hardship funds:** Lots and lots of lovely lolly. **Travel:** Town is compact so little need for transport. Travel abroad can be easily funded by colleges. **Work:** Lots of badly paid tourist industry work in summer, also colleges themselves are quite good.

Alumni (Editors' pick)
Sir Robert Walpole, Rupert Brooke, J M Keynes, E M Forster, The King's Singers, Michael Mates MP, Salman Rushdie, Alan Turing.

LUCY CAVENDISH

Lucy Cavendish College, Lady Margaret Road, Cambridge CB3 0BU (0223 332190)

Undergraduate college fees 1990/91: £2,478 ¢ maintenance. **Accommodation available:** Two-thirds offered accommodation. **Eating arrangements:** Lunches every day; evening meal twice a week. **Admission:** Evidence of recent academic achievement required (normally 2 A-levels or equivalent recognised qualifications) in addition to college test and interviews. College only admits mature (21 and over) and affiliated women students. **Scholarships:** Some scholarships and smaller awards (details available from college). **Hardship funds:** Very limited. **Travel grants:** Limited number of smaller grants. **Library:** College library (10,500 books, currently expanding). **Other facilities:** Computer facilities. Fine gardens. **Largest fields of study:** English, law.

European Community: 28% first degree students take EC language as part of course and 6% spend 6 months or more in another EC country. No formal exchange links with EC universities/colleges.

Undergraduates: *Women:* 57
Postgraduates: *Women:* 36

CAN'T FIND WHAT YOU'RE LOOKING FOR? USE THE INDEX!

What it's like

It is a unique college within Cambridge University in that it caters exclusively for mature female undergraduates and postgraduates. The age for entry is now 21 (down from 25) though in practice most students are 25-55. Undergraduate numbers expected to expand to 100 over the next few years. Staff are used to coping with the particular problems of mature students and are very supportive.

Lucy Cavendish has an excellent atmosphere, and being small it is possible to know everyone. The college consists of 3 old houses, one of which contains the library, one the dining hall, there is a purpose-built new building opened in 1989. The majority of students live in, accommodation being either study bedrooms in the older houses, or shared flats in new Oldham Hall. It is a short walk or bicycle ride to centre of Cambridge. Lectures and teaching take place around university, some at faculty buildings and within other colleges. In all respects Lucy Cavendish is a full Cambridge college and all the facilities of Cambridge are available for students. A degree at Cambridge carries a very intense workload but most mature students take their work seriously and despite family and other commitments, do well in their degrees.

Food is excellent – there is always a vegetarian option and plenty of salads. Lunch available every day, with one formal dinner a week. The Students' Association of the college is social, rather than political, and organises parties, links with other mature students in the university and weekly aerobic and yoga classes. As it is a small college there are few facilities for team sports but many students row, play hockey, lacrosse etc in other college teams.

For many students the second chance Lucy Cavendish offers revolutionises their lives and many go on to careers in law, teaching, medicine and management in industry.

Sara Maloney

Pauper notes

Accommodation: Very nice study bedrooms about £30/week including heating, but no married or family accommodation. **Eats:** College food some of best in the university; vegetarian option. **Ents:** Cambridge and other colleges full of entertainment. **Sports:** Lucy Cavendish joins other colleges for most sport. **Hardship funds:** College bursaries help.

MAGDALENE

Magdalene College, Cambridge CB3 0AG (0223 332100, switchboard; 332135, admissions; 63637, fax)

Maintenance charge 1990/91: Average room rent plus heat/light/kitchen fixed charge approx £1,095 pa estimate. **Accommodation available:** Approx 380 rooms; all first and third, and virtually all second years accommodated in college or college hostels nearby. Rent: 87% in accommodation where rent controlled by college. **Eating arrangements:** Meals at cost (dinner £1.90), both formal and self-service facilities. **Gate/guest hours:** Gates shut 2 till 6 am. **Admission:** Conditional offers of a fairly high standard involving one STEP or S paper grade in about 30% of cases. Rarely are two such grades required. All candidates interviewed. Further mathematics A-level not required for mathematics or engineering. **Hardship funds:** Various special funds of moderate value exist. **Scholarships:** Choral and music awards every year and an organ scholarship every second year. Generous scholarships and bursaries available in all subjects. Scholarships awarded to those gaining first in Tripos. At least one full-cost research scholarship each year, plus some bursaries for overseas students. **Structural features:** College has been mixed since 1988. The amount of accommodation provided has been increased. **Travel grants:** Available (including research) in all subjects. **Library:** Over 25,000 volumes; also

Wigglesworth Law Library, Pepys library (including the diaries) and Old Library.
Other college facilities: Bar, film society; 2 grand pianos, harpsichord and organs;
launderettes; photographic darkroom; boathouse; squash court, fives court, table
tennis room; 25 acres of playing fields nearby (shared), 3 computer terminals.
Largest fields of study: Law, natural sciences, history, engineering. **Hardship
funds:** Available; plus various dedicated trust funds. **Specialist subjects:** Architecture, land economy, law, natural sciences.

European Community: 4% first degree students take EC language as part of course
and 4% spend 6 months or more in another EC country. No formal exchange links
with EC universities/colleges.

Undergraduates: *Men:* 233 *Women:* 70
Postgraduates: *Men:* 81 *Women:* 17

What it's like

It's a mixed college with about 420 students. With the longest river frontage of any
college, it is an extremely attractive place to read for a degree.

Magdalene has successfully shaken off its image as a haven for public school
chauvinists. The majority of students come from the state sector.

Sporting provision continues to be of the highest order; rugby is the sport where
Magdalene truly excels with numerous Blues coming from the college. Rowing is
growing and recently the standard has increased dramatically. For the less active
drama, music and journalism are fully catered for.

Law and engineering are particularly strong – the dons being very interested in
their students. As the college does not have a don for all subjects, care must be taken
to ensure adequate teaching will be forthcoming.

The bar is popular – particularly as no money need change hands. Formal has a
deservedly good reputation, the only candlelit hall in Cambridge is cheap and on
every night.

By 1991 every student will be housed. This is due to large investment in property
and renovation work, not least the splendid Quayside. Magdalene's college bill is
high but the standard of rooms is above average.

The most memorable aspect of college is its friendly and relaxed atmosphere.
David C B Soanes

Pauper notes

Accommodation: Room quality varies greatly from the very plush to store-box, but
extensive redevelopment and all are comfortable. Because of its all male heritage,
there is a dearth of cooking facilities. Washing machine provision has improved and
there is a laundry service. Married quarters to those merely contemplating marriage. **Drink:** Excellent bar, Ind Coope. 'Town and Gown' serves fine ale. Pickerel is
the Magdalene pub. **Eats:** Hall: good value. £1.90 for a three-course meal with
waiter service. Beware however of the fixed kitchen charge – currently £74 and paid
on the bill by everyone however often, or not, they eat in college. Ramsay Hall: a
cafeteria service – food adequate. Cheap Gardenia/Omars/Tommy Tuckers. **Ents:**
Limited in college. Excellent student bands regularly round town. **Sports:** Facilities – excellent and free at college/university level for major field sports; free playing
fields, squash, swimming and most others. Summary facilities – limited in town.
Hardship funds: College is poor but helps out readily. **Travel:** Excellent scholarships – especially the Power Scholarship to Michigan. Funds for individual travel
are increasing with more endowment becoming available. **Work:** No term time
work allowed officially. During vac college employs staff to help.

Alumni (Editors' pick)

Lord Ezra, Lord Justice Cumming-Bruce, Professor J Boardman, Sir Michael
Redgrave, Lord Ramsay, Nick Estcourt, Gavin Hastings, Anthony Jay, Bamber
Gascoigne, Samuel Pepys, I A Richards, Charles Kingsley, Lord Pilkington,

CAN'T FIND WHAT YOU'RE LOOKING FOR? USE THE INDEX!

Jonathan Ridgeon, William Burt, Viscount Melia, Lord Derby, Prince Szudek (of Poland).

NEW HALL

New Hall, Huntingdon Road, Cambridge CB3 0DF (0223 351721)

Maintenance charge 1990/91: £240 per term (single room including background heating) plus £66 per term kitchen overheads charge. **Accommodation available:** All first years in college (some shared, split-level rooms). Rent: 86% in accommodation where rent controlled by college. **Eating arrangements:** Cafeteria system (pay as you eat), formal meals and self-catering. **Gate/guest hours:** None. **Admission:** Most candidates admitted on conditional offer largely based on A-level only, although maths candidates will be asked to take Sixth Term Examination Papers or S-level. Some candidates, post A-level, admitted on school record and interview. **Academic features:** Library, computer facilities with links to University computer. **Scholarships:** Given to students in residence. **Hardship funds:** Funds available for personal maintenance, travel, equipment etc, for home and overseas students, but not full funding. **Travel grants:** Awarded annually. **Other college facilities:** Lecture room with projector, party room, art studio, sewing room, video room, squash court, tennis courts and croquet lawn; sports ground shared with Fitzwilliam and Churchill. **Largest fields of study:** Archaeology & anthropology, English, modern & medieval languages, natural sciences. **NB:** New Hall is one of the newer colleges of the university (founded 1954) and intends to continue to admit only women.

European Community: 13% first degree students take EC language and spend 6 months or more in another EC country as part of course. No formal exchange links with EC universities/colleges. Participates in Erasmus scheme.

Undergraduates: 301 (Women only)
Postgraduates: 70

What it's like
New Hall is known for its Dome and the fact it is an all-women's college. The atmosphere is friendly and relaxed and student/Fellow relationships are better than average. The college has many thriving societies including a boat club, music society, photographic society and many sports teams. There is a chance to get involved with the running of college by joining one of the Liaison Committees or the college Union. As well as looking after the welfare of the students NH Union organises regular entertainment including the summer event in May Week. All college facilities, including the library, computer room and laundry are accessible 24 hours a day. The cafeteria food is fine but if you prefer to cook for yourself there is an electric ring in each room and kitchens throughout the college. As well as cheap drinks, the bar has a pool table and juke box but most students seem to socialise in other colleges. New Hall students are well represented in the University societies and sports team (1989/90 CUSU President was New Hall). The college offers all tripos subjects and will arrange supervisors from outside college who are specialists in particular subjects.

Pauper notes
Accommodation: College or college hostel accommodation for all 1st and 3rd years. **Drink:** New Hall bar cheap. **Eats:** Cafeteria system (meal costs just over £1). Good vegetarian selection. Famous hall with waitress service on a Tuesday evening. No breakfast provided. Large selection of restaurants in town. **Ents:** Bands/discos evening twice a term – cost £1–£1.50; easy to go to discos, films at other colleges. 2 cinemas in town. **Sports:** Squash court, table tennis table, large boat club. Most

sports represented by college teams. **Hardship funds:** Hardship fund. **Travel:** Travel grants and vacation study grants available. **Work:** Not allowed during term.

Alumni (Editors' pick)
Tilda Swinton (film star), Joanna MacGregor (concert pianist).

NEWNHAM
Newnham College, Cambridge CB3 9DF (0223 335700)
Special features: Large grounds with plenty of accommodation and sports facilities on site. Artist in residence. **Academic features:** Good balance of academic subjects. New mathematical course in 1991. **Accommodation available:** Most undergraduates are given their own study-bedroom in college for all three years (no shared rooms). Rent: 95% in accommodation where rent controlled by college. **Maintenance charge 1990/91:** £1,032 pa. **Eating arrangements:** Modern dining room for cafeteria service, and hall for formal dinners. All meals paid for in cash. Guests welcomed. Undergraduates may also cater for themselves. **Gate/guest hours:** Students and their guests are free to come and go at all times. **Admission:** Mainly on A-level grades and interviews, with some use of S-papers or Sixth Term examination papers. **Scholarships:** Scholarships and exhibitions awarded on results of University exams. **Travel and book grants:** Funds available. **Hardship funds:** Several College and University funds available. **Library:** One of best working libraries in Cambridge; 85,000 volumes, large antiquarian collection. **Other college facilities:** Bar, undergraduate kitchens; launderette; sewing machines; a music room with harpsichord; practice rooms with pianos; table tennis room, nearby squash court, playing fields in college grounds; punt hire scheme in summer. Microcomputer and word processor with link to university's main frame computer. Multi-gym.

European Community: 9% first degree students take EC language as part of course (but all students have the option) and 9% spend 6 months or more in another EC country. Formal exchange links with large number of EC universities/colleges including Rome (all students may go in the summer).

Undergraduates: 390 (Women only)
Postgraduates: 90

What it's like
By Cambridge standards, it's a newish college. Victorian red brick buildings covered in climbing ivy enclose large gardens which are used by undergraduates for sunbathing and garden parties in summer. However our long corridor makes it possible to avoid the cold in winter.

Newnham is not on the main Cambridge tourist trail and so is left relatively undisturbed, but it is close to the Sidgwick Site of the university and about five minutes by bike from town centre, and other faculties.

Most undergraduates choose to live in for all three years, and rooms are large, fully furnished and well heated. First-year rooms are allocated, in subsequent years they are chosen by a ballot system. One modern building has rooms with sinks. No rooms are shared. Cooking facilities are above average in Cambridge and the buttery is reasonably priced, with vegetarian options.

In sport, Newnham has an active boat club with one of the fastest ladies' crews on the river. College teams also do well in tennis, cricket, football, netball, hockey, cross-country running and netball. All standards are welcome and for the very keen there are university teams in most sports. The college has its own multigym, as well as sports fields within college grounds.

The Raleigh Music Society has a large membership and gives weekly recitals in college hall. Drama is catered for by the Anonymous Players, newly formed but very active.

CAN'T FIND WHAT YOU'RE LOOKING FOR? USE THE INDEX!

Newnham is well represented in university societies such as the Union Society, the Industrial Society, various faculty societies, the University Air Squadron and the Officer Training Corps. Many Newnhamites are involved in student journalism.

Newnham's student-run bar is very lively, with special events and promotions organised frequently. It is very popular for socialising after the weekly formal hall, to which undergraduates often bring guests. The regular bops are always well attended. The first two Newnham May Balls (in 1988 and 1990) were student organised and hugely successful. Others will definitely follow.

Academically, Newnham students have less pressure on them than in other colleges, but still managed sixth place in the Cambridge league table of colleges' results in 1990. Standards are high in both arts and sciences with one of the best equipped libraries in Cambridge.

The JCR encourages recycling schemes for paper and glass.
Mary Lamont/Antonia Banks

Pauper notes
Accommodation: Live in all 3 years, but possible to live out. 3 graduate houses. **Drink:** Cheap college bars. Many town pubs – The Bath, The Anchor (jazz live), Cambridge Arms, The Granta (on the River Cam). **Eats:** Veggie: King's Pantry; Clowns; Tatties; The Little Rose Restaurant; Eraina. **Ents:** Cheap college 'bops' and bands in most colleges each term – Christ's and Robinson College film societies. Night Clubs – Route 66, Cinderella Rockerfellas. **Sports:** At Newnham – free multigym; hockey pitch/football, tennis courts, shared squash courts, University badminton courts. Kelsey Kerridge sports hall and swimming pool. **Travel:** Travel grants available. Bike hire scheme, student rates with NUS card. **Work:** College bar, catering during term. Work (eg in pubs) available in town. Vacation: catering dept; housekeeping, library.

Alumni (Editors' pick)
Baroness Seear, Baroness David, Julia Neuberger, Frances Gumley, Sarah Rowland Jones, Dorothy Hodgkin, Margaret Drabble, Germaine Greer, Sylvia Plath, Joan Bakewell, Susie Menkes, Miriam Margolis, Katharine Whitehorn, Shirley Williams, Emma Thompson, Ann Mallalieu, Mary Archer.

PEMBROKE

Pembroke College, Cambridge CB2 1RF (0223 338100)

Charge 1990/91: Room rents £250–£300 per term. **Accommodation available:** Mainly single study bedrooms centrally heated with wash basins; some 2-roomed sets. All first years live in college; others in college or nearby college hostels. Some married accommodation in flats and houses. Rent: 95% in accommodation where rent controlled by college. **Eating arrangements:** Self-service breakfast, lunch and evening meal. Formal dinner. Fixed charge (1990/91) of £174 pa; in addition meals are paid for as taken (eg dinner £2.30). **Gate/guest hours:** Gates closed 2 till 6 am, but with access for keyholders. Overnight guests permitted by prior arrangement; other guests leave by 2 am. **Admission:** Write to Tutor for Admissions to apply or for advice. Applications for admission on A-level or equivalent results or by conditional offer. **Scholarships:** College and Foundation scholarships, exhibitions and prizes awarded for merit in university examinations. **Hardship funds:** Some assistance may be given from Trust Funds. **Travel grants:** Limited grants towards cost of vacation travel for suitable projects, and to graduate students for research visits. **Library:** Reading and borrowing facilities in all degree subjects. Word processing and computing rooms, linked to CU data network. **Other college facilities:** Sports (cricket, hockey, rowing, rugby, soccer, squash, netball, tennis, table tennis), music (rehearsal rooms, pianos, organ, Instrumental Awards scheme), drama room, photographic darkroom. **Social:** Junior parlour, bar, party cellar, extensive gardens.

CAN'T FIND WHAT YOU'RE LOOKING FOR? USE THE INDEX!

European Community: 15.5% first degree students take EC language as part of course and 6.5% spend 6 months or more in another EC country. No formal exchange links with EC universities/colleges.

Undergraduates: *Men:* 239 *Women:* 113
Postgraduates: *Men:* 101 *Women:* 34

What it's like

Founded 1347: medieval courtyard, architecture pleasant and homely, beautiful gardens. Very central and well located for most subjects. College accommodation for all 1st years; in total 45% live in, others live in nearby college owned hostels. Standard variable but on the whole good. No provision for married students. Food available on a cafeteria basis; breakfast good, lunch and supper dull though an alternative waitress-service dinner (Formal Hall) each night is good. Cooking facilities are limited. JP (Junior Parlour – College SU) active socially rather than politically and relations with the Fellows are good. Undergraduates are outgoing, friendly and going places. Bicycles necessary (car ownership is very limited for Cambridge undergrads). Fine college library, bar, soundproof music rooms, party rooms, college catered private functions and a large sports ground. Officially no overnight guests of opposite sex but very rarely enforced (condom machine provided). Sport is very strong, especially rowing, boxing, rugby. Opportunities are also plentiful in the arts, notably drama and music. Strong subjects: natural science, English, law, economics, oriental studies. Changing subject fairly easy. 10% overseas.

Pauper notes

Eats: Market is very good for fruit and especially cheap veg due to proximity of Britain's best farmland. Cheap student restaurants nearby. **Ents:** Arts Cinema – get a season ticket 6 months £16.00 for 10 films. Much cheap and often good student theatre. Number of cheap college films and plays. **Sports:** Facilities excellent – own boathouse, rugby/cricket grounds, squash and tennis courts. University gym free. **Hardship funds:** Go to King's College. **Travel:** Number of travel awards – easy to get one. **Work:** Pembroke library supervision 65p/hour to sit and study.

Alumni (Editors' pick)

R Porter, Peter May, Ted Hughes, Tom Sharpe, Christopher Hogwood, Clive James, Peter Cook, Eric Idle, Bill Oddie, Tim Brooke-Taylor, Ray Dolby, R A Butler, David Monroe, William Pitt, Thomas Gray, Edmund Spenser, Sir Robert Sainsbury, Lord Prior.

PETERHOUSE

Peterhouse, Cambridge CB2 1RD (0223 338200)
Admissions Tutor (0223) 338273
Admissions Secretary (0223) 338201

Maintenance charge 1990/91: £400 per term approx (wide choice of room rents). **Accommodation available:** All first and third years offered rooms in college. All second years live in college accommodation, most adjacent to Peterhouse. **Eating arrangements:** All meals provided in hall (breakfast 86p or £1.22p, lunch £1.22p, dinner £1.98p). **Gate/guest hours:** Gates close at 2 am, when guests, other than overnight guests, required to leave; gate keys issued for out-of-hours use. **Admission:** Flexible admissions policy. Realistic level of offers, with low ratio of offers to places. All candidates interviewed: mode of admission tailored to individual cases. No undergraduates admitted for geography, land economy or veterinary medicine. **Scholarships:** Examination, prizes, scholarships and exhibitions (£50 to £150) for performance in Tripos; annual organ scholarship (£250); music awards (£40 plus tuition); further named college examination prizes in history, law, mathematics, engineering, medicine and music. **Hardship funds:** Fund administered by Tutors. **Travel grants:** Approx 30 travel grants awarded pa (average value £200). **Library:** Approx 35,000 volumes. A large new building recently opened. **Other college facilities:** Bar, croquet lawns, squash court, multi-gym, computer room, punts, washing machines, playing fields, boathouse. New library, theatre and concert hall. **Largest fields of study:** Engineering, history, natural sciences.

European Community: 10% first degree students take EC language as part of course and 3% spend 6 months or more in another EC country. No formal exchange links with EC universities/colleges.

Undergraduates: *Men:* 155 *Women:* 58
Postgraduates: *Men:* 62 *Women:* 10

What it's like

It's almost the smallest and certainly the oldest Cambridge college. Over the years a strong academic reputation has been built up, especially in engineering, history, natural sciences, English and mathematics. All first and third years are accommodated in college, with half of second year having to live in nearby houses. College rooms, most of which are of a good standard, are atmospheric due to their age and many overlook the beautiful grounds that are the setting for what is probably the best white tie May Ball in Cambridge.

Over the last year the college has seen various improvements, one being that the standard of college food (served in a wonderfully antique hall) has been enhanced greatly. On the subject of food, electric/gas rings are available making 'survival cooking' easy enough.

The undergraduate intake is now at least half state school students, unlike previous years. There are some 220 undergraduates, leading to a friendly atmosphere with mixing across subjects and years the norm. Despite the college's small size, all sports are played competitively at inter-collegiate level.

The college authorities are traditional in the extreme (party permits required!!), but the JCR (called the Sexcentenary Club) is becoming a stronger force socially, politically and environmentally. Overall, a good place to live and work.
J R Jensen

Pauper notes

Accommodation: All either college run or 'university syndicate' organised; prices OK. **Drink:** Free Press, The Old Spring, The Cross Keys; Greene King and IPA. **Eats:** Tatties for baked potatoes. Clowns teas, for coffee and carrot cake, the Curry Centre for variations on a theme, Old Spring for pub food. Martin's for cafe meals. Free Press – excellent food. **Ents:** Arts Cinema, Arts Theatre, Churchill, Peterhouse, Trinity Hall College theatres. Corn Exchange, ADC Theatre, Burleigh Arms. **Sports:** Excellent grounds a short bike ride away; boathouse near pub; Kelsey Kerridge for all indoor sports – student rates. Plus weights room within college. **Hardship funds:** College organised funds, open to all. **Travel:** Numerous faculty scholarships and college awards. **Work:** Oversubscribed – eg kitchen staff in colleges.

Alumni (Editors' pick)

James Mason (actor), Richard Baker, Kelvin (of absolute zero fame), Thomas Gray (poet).

QUEENS'

Queens' College, Cambridge CB3 9ET (0223 335540)

Maintenance charge 1990/91: Varies according to room. **Accommodation available:** All undergraduates can live in college for all 3 years (sets and bedsits, medieval and modern, all with central heating and modern bathrooms). 80% in accommodation where rent controlled by college. **Eating arrangements:** Self-service for all meals; formal dinner also available. **Gate/guest hours:** Very relaxed. **Admission:** Entry in all subjects is via conditional offers based on A-levels; S-levels or STEP, according to candidate's choice, are used **only** for mathematics, medicine and natural sciences. All candidates interviewed. Several open days each year for prospective candidates. Undergraduates not admitted to study following in first year: chemical engineering, education, electrical & information sciences, history of art, manufacturing engineering, management studies. **Scholarships:** Not awarded on entrance but on subsequent university examinations. Bursaries available for eligible overseas students. **Travel grants:** Awards made from college expedition fund and other funds as well as grants to individuals. **Library:** Undergraduate library with copies of all course books; full borrowing facilities both in term and over vacation. Law library. Micro-computers and terminals with access to University main frame. **Hardship funds:** Several funds to help those who suffer financial difficulty. **Other college facilities:** Bar, new 220 seat theatre, squash courts, table tennis, croquet, punts, organ, piano, harpsichord, record library, dark room, launderette, rooms for TV; new boathouse and playing fields nearby.

European Community: Number of students learning an EC language or spending time in another EC country, not known.

Undergraduates: *Men:* 272 *Women:* 168
Postgraduates: *Men:* 153 *Women:* 70

What it's like

Queens' has a central location with added advantages of a site straddling the Cam, joined by the famous Mathematical Bridge. The buildings are beautiful or have good facilities (usually not both) although self-catering facilities are inadequate. A new development has a set of squash courts and theatre (doubles up as disco). Students are bright (but not self-consciously intellectual) and generally apathetic, and a wide variety of races, backgrounds, and interests, as well as a high (for Oxbridge) proportion of women helps keep a very sociable atmosphere, with most social events well attended.
Yaza Mohammed

Pauper notes

Accommodation: Accommodation for all students, recently acquired a disused nurses' home. **Drink:** Local brews: Greene King, Tolly Cobbold. Bar relatively cheap – pubs in town varied. **Eats:** Town: wide variety from Pizza Hut to high class dining clubs – College: standard high – increasingly varied options. **Ents:** College: Films every Thursday, disco every (almost) weekend. Town: 2 large clubs, Corn Exchange good for gigs. **Sports:** Cheap/good sports centre 10 min walk. On college site: squash, badminton, gym – sports ground 1.5 miles. All major sports (even Tiddlywinks! European championships held in old hall!); strengths – rugby, football and rowing. **Hardship funds:** College very accommodating – quiet word to tutor goes a long way. **Travel:** STA Travel in town very cheap; college gives limited grants. **Work:** Some bar work/guided punting in summer – work during May Balls.

Alumni (Editors' pick)

Archbishop of Sydney, Stephen Fry, Erasmus, Graham Swift.

ROBINSON

Robinson College, Cambridge CB3 9AN (0223 311431)

Maintenance charge: Varies according to accommodation. **Accommodation available:** Accommodation for approximately 330 undergraduates (study bedrooms, majority with own bathroom). Rent: 80% in accommodation where rent controlled by college. **Eating arrangements:** Both cafeteria and formal Hall; residents required to pay fixed kitchen charge. **Gate/guest hours:** Unaccompanied guests not allowed after midnight. **Admission:** Applicants considered by all available entry routes. **Scholarships:** Scholarships awarded on Tripos results. **Hardship funds:** A Hardship Fund is available. **Other college facilities:** Cafeteria, bar, music rooms, auditorium; joint sports ground with Queens'; boathouse shared.

European Community: 10% first degree students take EC language as part of course and 3% spend 6 months or more in another EC country. No formal exchange links with EC universities/colleges.

Undergraduates: *Men:* 256 *Women:* 136
Postgraduates: *Men:* 63 *Women:* 20

What it's like
Robinson has none of the imagined hallmarks of a Cambridge college – Chariots of Fire, picturesque courtyards, crusty porters, students in tweeds and cravats. Built 15 years ago, funded by a man who made his money in radio rentals and racehorses, it makes up in originality what it lacks in tradition and antiquity. Average student is not the eccentric, loaded Oxbridge undergraduate many imagine; admissions procedure discriminates positively towards applicants from state schools, which makes for a good mix and friendly atmosphere.

Predominantly red brick, very unusual architecture; also built to be a conference centre, so superb accommodation: all rooms are centrally heated (not the norm in Cambridge), comfortably furnished. About 50% first year have a private bathroom. Dual-purpose nature also provides excellent facilities: best auditorium in Cambridge, well-equipped party room, record library and hi-fi room and dark room plus the usual music rooms, games room, laundry, common rooms etc. Bar is run by paid staff rather than students; very much the focus of College life – people go there to be sociable, not just to drink! Food fairly expensive but good.

Very active students' association aims to represent and campaign for students; provides a forum for students' views, a variety of social events and funds college sports clubs and societies. Rowing, rugby and hockey teams recently hot competition in their fields; anyone with an interest, however humble, can enjoy the excellent facilities provided. Chapel choir and Music Society, which with the Dramatic Society produces a musical each year. Other societies, include debating, films, art, photographic; you are sure to find something to your taste. Above all, Robinson is a College where anyone can fit in and feel they belong.

Pauper notes
Accommodation: Expensive but most people live in. **Drink:** Bar good, but not cheap by other student bars standards. Regular cheaper drinks evenings. **Eats:** Very good, if pricey cafeteria. Exceptional Hall twice a week. Bar snacks. **Ents:** Regular on campus films, bands, discos and 'events'. **Sports:** Boathouse, playing fields, squash and tennis courts, volleyball, table tennis room all near by. **Hardship funds:** Many available. **Travel:** Grants for holiday activities available.

ST CATHARINE'S
St Catharine's College, Cambridge CB2 1RL (0223 338300)

College Consolidated fee – undergraduate £2,454. Accommodation available: Most undergraduates spend 3 years in college accommodation. **Eating arrangements:** All meals available in college dining hall. No compulsory meals. **Gate/guest hours:** Keys issued on payment of deposit; guest rooms for limited periods. **Admission:** College makes conditional offers on A-level results, and occasionally also on S-level or STEP examinations. **Travel grants:** Various grants available. **Hardship funds:** Various funds available. **Library:** 3 college libraries. New library

CAN'T FIND WHAT YOU'RE LOOKING FOR? USE THE INDEX!

and JCR completed October 1986. **Other college facilities:** Large new 3 manual organ, music practice room with grand piano; sports field with pavilion, squash, badminton, and tennis courts; boathouse; computer facilities; new graduate common room.

European Community: 8% first degree students take EC language as part of course and 8% spend 6 months or more in another EC country. Formal exchange links with Heidelberg (open to all undergraduates).

Undergraduates: *Men:* 234 *Women:* 167
Postgraduates: *Men:* 82 *Women:* 29

What it's like

Visually not one of the most impressive Cambridge colleges, its relatively small size makes St Catharine's one of the most friendly. Most students are able to live in college accommodation for all three years of their degree course, accommodation which ranges from decidedly pokey to well above average; for the unfortunate few who have to live out however accommodation can be difficult to find in Cambridge, and is often fairly pricey.

Students come from a very wide range of backgrounds and most tend to accept one another regardless of social background. Politically the college's reputation seems to be shifting from that of a notoriously apathetic college to one with a very strong and active left wing, many students being actively involved in the university Labour students group. As with any college, however, the students hold a very wide range of views and there is the inevitable handful of bigots.

The JCR committee, elected by and from the undergraduate body represents students in all aspects of college life, including organising a wide range of entertainments, financing the numerous college sports clubs and societies, and negotiating with the fellows of the college via the College Consultative Committee, a body comprising the JCR committee and several selected fellows.

Within the university itself it is possible to become involved in virtually any activity you could wish for, including a wide range of sports, drama, film-making, the list is almost endless. There is also a very strong network of support groups to make a student's life at Cambridge bearable in times of stress, including an eating-disorder group, several women's groups, gay and lesbian societies and an overseas students' society.

Students discover their own niches no matter what their background or beliefs; the intimate atmosphere of St Catharine's provides a valuable sense of security whilst incorporating the obvious benefits of a large university.
Ruth Entwistle

Pauper notes

Accommodation: Cheap Cambridge accommodation very hard to find but it can be done if you look early and hard enough. **Drink:** A number of good pubs in Cambridge (The Mill being the closest to Cats) but tend to be quite expensive – college bars cheaper. **Eats:** All colleges cater for vegetarians; very wide range of restaurants in town, varying price ranges and qualities. **Ents:** Very good for films and plays, not so good for nightclubs, although college ents committees arrange regular bops. New venue 'The Junction' very good. **Sports:** Very strong in university. Town facilities good but fairly expensive. **Hardship funds:** Students have to be very definitely in need. **Travel:** Travel scholarships easily available. **Work:** During term frowned upon, not available in college. Vacation jobs can be found both in town and college.

Alumni (Editors' pick)

Howard Brenton (controversial playwright), Emma Thompson and Ian McKellan (actors); current ambassador to Kuwait!

CAN'T FIND WHAT YOU'RE LOOKING FOR? USE THE INDEX!

ST EDMUND'S

St Edmund's College, Cambridge CB3 0BN (0223 350398)

Maintenance charge 1990/91: not known. **Admission:** Primarily a graduate college. Admits some mature undergraduates (21 and over) for any subject except medicine. **Accommodation available:** 61 single students in college housing plus 12 apartments for married students. **Other college facilities:** Micro-computing facilities (terminal to university mainframe); bar; football pitch, tennis courts, boat club.

ST JOHN'S

St John's College, Cambridge CB2 1TP (0223 338600)

Maintenance charge 1990/91: £965–£1,135 pa. **Accommodation available:** Normally accommodation in college is available to undergraduates in all three years. **Eating arrangements:** Self-service buttery dining room; formal dinner also available 6 evenings a week. **Gate/guest hours:** College members may come and go as they wish; certain regulations regarding overnight guests. **Admission:** Candidates are welcome to apply for conditional offers (which may include S or STEP grades) or on the basis of A-levels already taken. **Scholarships:** Scholarships awarded to members of the college on the basis of examinations. Scholars receive generous book grants and other privileges. **Travel grants:** Available. **Library:** College library (early 17th century) with over 100,000 volumes, ranging from medieval manuscripts to modern university textbooks; reading rooms; full set of Law Reports; skeletons for medical students. **Other college facilities:** Bar, college orchestra and musical society, theatre in School of Pythagoras; Fisher Building including music practice rooms, art studio, drawing office and large auditorium; 26-acre playing fields near college; modern squash courts, table tennis and billiards rooms, pool for college punts. Book grants available for textbooks; computer room with data links to University network.

European Community: Number of students learning an EC language or spending time in another EC country, not known.

Undergraduates: *Men:* 373 *Women:* 156
Postgraduates: *Men:* 159 *Women:* 73

What it's like

Architecturally beautiful and can accommodate undergraduates for all 3 years often in large, comfortable sets of rooms. Excellent on-site facilities: theatre/cinema, sportsfields and squash courts, fleet of punts, bar and music rooms. College academically strong, particularly in science and law. Generous book grants and travel scholarships (college is rich). Strong rowing tradition. Active JCR committee puts on events throughout year. Guest restrictions tacitly ignored by all. Being in town centre, access to everything in Cambridge easy: most get involved in activities outside college. Major acting, debating and political societies currently run by St John's. College choir world-famous. St John's is one of Cambridge's foremost colleges.

Pauper notes

Accommodation: Reasonably priced; provided by the college for all 3 years. **Drink:** Quite cheap in college bar. **Eats:** Cheap in college buttery; vegetarians catered for. **Ents:** Good cheap ents in college most weekends. **Hardship funds:** Available from the college in real case of hardship. **Work:** Not really available or encouraged during term-time.

CAN'T FIND WHAT YOU'RE LOOKING FOR? USE THE INDEX!

Alumni (Editors' pick)

Jonathan Miller (author, producer, broadcaster), Lord Coggan (former Archbishop of Canterbury), J Michael Brearley (former England cricket captain), Piers Paul Read (novelist), William Wordsworth, Trevor Bailey, Douglas Adams, Rob Andrew, Derek Jacobi.

SELWYN

Selwyn College, Cambridge CB3 9DQ (0223 335846)

Accommodation available: All unmarried undergraduates live in college rooms for all 3 years. **Eating arrangements:** Breakfast, lunch and dinner taken in hall; informal self-service and formal dinner. **Gate/guest hours:** College gates closed between 2 and 6 am; late keys obtainable. Undergraduates permitted to put up a guest in their own rooms. **Admission:** By conditional pre A-level offer after interview; some places offered on A-levels, school reports and interviews. **ALL** applicants are invited for interview. **Scholarships:** Organ scholarships awarded 2 years out of 3; annual choral exhibitions; annual instrumental exhibitions; book prizes, scholarships and exhibitions awarded to firsts and other outstanding performances in university examinations. **Hardship funds:** Chadwick Fund, Keasbey awards. **Travel grants:** Available. **Other college facilities:** Bar, undergraduate shop, 3 rooms for private functions, drama facilities; music practice rooms; photographic dark room; shared sports ground with King's College. Newly extended library with law reading room; computer room. Choral evensong 3 times weekly (newly installed organ). **Largest fields of study:** Engineering, history, modern languages, natural sciences.

European Community: Majority of those reading English study an EC language as part of their course, in addition to modern linguists; majority of linguists spend a period in another EC country.

Undergraduates: *Men:* 215 *Women:* 115
Postgraduates: *Men:* 50 *Women:* 30

What it's like

Bravery, brashness and broccoli is the stuff of which men and women of Selwyn are made.

Most introspective, and least overtly intellectual of Cambridge colleges; life lived at high speed. With term lasting a mere eight weeks, the lecturers' determination to cram as much information into students' skulls is only matched by the same students' desire to put such cerebral pursuits firmly in their place and spend their time on the more important things of life. Most reach a suitable balance, thus satisfying both the expectations of their tutors and the demands of, for example, the determined and successful Boat Club.

What else? Musical menageries, variously attended societies, pointless parties, pseudo-intellectuals, committed Christians, strange slang, friendly Fellows, the cheapest (and best) Ball in town, a magazine named after the national bird of New Zealand. All this, and a library with a goldfish bowl extension that is almost impossible to get into. Truly a place with plenty of character, and a lot of fun.

Pauper notes

Accommodation: Good quality but quite expensive rooms in college. Kitchen fixed charge. **Drink:** Selwyn bar – cheaper than pubs around 75p per pint. Good local breweries inc Greene King, Abbot, Tolly Cobbold. **Eats:** Selwyn – cafeteria cheap and basic – 3 course meal about £1.25. Vegetarian and Kosher meals available. **Ents:** College – cheap and regular eg 4 per term: discos, bands, cocktail parties etc. Univ – sparse but improving. Ents tend to be college based and run. **Sports:** College

CAN'T FIND WHAT YOU'RE LOOKING FOR? USE THE INDEX!

– lively, good participation. Excellent facilities – ¾ mile from college. Univ sports centre 1.5 miles. Town sports centre 1.5 miles. **Hardship funds:** Selwyn College has two hardship funds. Students apply via their tutor. **Travel:** Cambs – bad for hitching. College **very** generous with scholarships for vac travel. **Work:** Univ/college authorities don't object. Work in pubs/restaurants easy to find.

Alumni (Editors' pick)
Malcolm Muggeridge, E R Nixon, Lord Rayner, D Trelford, D Lumsden, Simon Hughes MP, Rt Hon John Selwyn Gummer, Huw Davies.

SIDNEY SUSSEX

Sidney Sussex College, Cambridge CB2 3HU (0223 338800)

Maintenance charge 1990/91: £485 per term. **Accommodation available:** All undergraduates may spend all three years in college accommodation without sharing rooms. **Eating arrangements:** All meals may be taken in hall; also self-catering facilities. **Gate/guest hours:** Until 2 am; keys available for late admission. **Admission:** Places are given on the basis of performance in public examinations. Detailed advice is available from the Admissions Tutors. **Scholarships:** Unlimited number of scholarships, exhibitions and prizes awarded on performance in university examinations; Evan Lewis-Thomas Law Studentships for law graduates to prepare for practice as barristers and solicitors. **Travel grants:** Available. **Hardship funds:** There are separate funds to assist undergraduate and graduate students. **Library:** Modern, open 24 hours. **Other college facilities:** Music practice room with piano, grand piano and harpsichord, new organ; sports field and pavilion shared with Christ's College; modern boathouse shared with Corpus Christi and Girton, and squash and tennis courts; two common rooms, two bars.

European Community: 10% study an EC language and spend a period in another EC country as part of their course. No formal exchange links.

Undergraduates: *Men:* 198 *Women:* 104
Postgraduates: *Men:* 54 *Women:* 28

What it's like
Small (300 undergraduates), co-residential college with pleasant architecture/gardens and central location. Accommodation is among the cheapest in the university but is good quality and guaranteed to all undergraduates, either in college or in nearby house/hostel. All staircases have washing and catering facilities, though these vary enormously from staircase to staircase. Hall serves three self-service meals a day (except Sundays) and optional formal supper; culinary standard is also variable, but receptive to student suggestions; reasonable choice provided (including vegetarian and choice of salads). Laundry room. Wide and popular range of extra-curricular activities in which anyone, no matter what standard, can participate. Student-run bar doubles as a venue for fortnightly bops; sports facilities include playing-fields and tennis courts (a mile away), a boathouse and squash court; a very successful drama society, plus chapel choir and orchestra. Academically, a gifted Fellowship, reasonable library (open 24 hours/day) and good Tripos results, especially in geography, engineering, classics and economics. Reasonable relations with Fellows – students enjoy full representation on Governing Body and other college committees. Socially, very easy-going with few of the cliques found in other colleges. Probably the friendliest college. A very fair admissions policy means no-one should be discouraged from applying. Open Days from Christmas for sixth-formers. Thriving SU promotes student welfare and provides some focus for limited political debate and activity. Less political apathy than at other colleges.

CAN'T FIND WHAT YOU'RE LOOKING FOR? USE THE INDEX!

Pauper notes

Accommodation: Guaranteed for all undergraduates, married accommodation available. Graduates: some rooms available. **Drink:** College bar very cheap. Lots of pubs nearby because college is centrally located. Greene King beers recommended. Good pub: Cambridge Arms. **Eats:** Not very good value – very touristy. Not many take-aways. **Ents:** University theatre (ADC) nearby, weekly productions. Arts Cinema across the road – excellent variety. Bops organised by different colleges and advertised throughout. No good nightclubs. **Sports:** No University sports centre. Cambridge town sports centre relatively expensive. No great skill required to play sport at college level. Wide variety of sports available – emphasis on fun. **Hardship funds:** Fund has been doubled to £4,000 a year. **Travel:** For vacation travel small amount (about £50) available quite easily for second years. **Work:** Against rules for Cambridge students to work during term. However, nights available in college bar.

Alumni (Editors' pick)

John Patten, David Thomson, C T R Wilson, C F Powell, David Owen, Oliver Cromwell.

TRINITY

Trinity College, Cambridge CB2 1TQ (0223 338400)

Maintenance charge 1990/91: Average charge £700 pa (room, heat and light). **Accommodation available:** All undergraduates are offered rooms in college or college hostels for 3 years. **Eating arrangements:** Breakfast, lunch and dinner available in hall on cafeteria system, plus formal dinner. Fixed annual price of £180+ cash payment for individual meals. Small kitchens on all staircases. **Gate/guest hours:** Great Gate locked at 2 am but college members may enter or leave at any time. **Admission:** Pre A-level candidates considered for Conditional Offers which may include S-level papers or Sixth Term Examination papers. Post A-level candidates considered on their record. Most candidates will be interviewed. **Scholarships:** Scholarships on university examinations; organ scholarship (£250 pa) offered in alternate years, 6 choral exhibitions (£100 pa) offered annually; numerous college prizes. **Travel grants:** Grants for projects and research; small grants for vacation travel. **Library:** Magnificent Wren Library with over 50,000 volumes plus a reading room; separate law reading room. **Other college facilities:** 3 large common rooms, bar, games and party rooms, buttery, 2 launderettes, record lending library, music room with pianos and harpsichord, small theatre; 3 sports grounds, squash, tennis and badminton courts; boathouse with excellent modern facilities. **Largest fields of study:** Natural sciences, medical sciences, mathematics, economics, English, engineering, law, modern languages, history.

European Community: 10% first degree students take EC language as part of course and 7% spend 6 months or more in another EC country. No formal exchange links with EC universities/colleges.

Undergraduates: *Men:* 525 *Women:* 166
Postgraduates: *Men:* 193 *Women:* 66

What it's like

Trinity is very big, the biggest of all Oxbridge colleges. Not only is it very big, it is also very rich. This is largely a product of its royal connections since its foundation by Henry VIII in the sixteenth century and consequent accumulated land grants. For students, this wealth makes a noticeable difference, allowing the college to give generous grants for books and travel and provide various facilities for students including a well-equipped computer room, and an excellent library. In addition, room rents are kept low, although not abolished altogether, owing to pressure from

CAN'T FIND WHAT YOU'RE LOOKING FOR? USE THE INDEX!

other colleges who are concerned not to annually lose all the best prospective applicants.

Academically, Trinity has a high reputation, and does particularly well in mathematics, English and natural sciences. Strong academic emphasis and most students work hard (although this is a common feature of Oxbridge). Usual student activities exist, with thriving sporting, music and drinking societies continuing age-old traditions.

A fair balance exists between public school and comprehensive school entrants, and by virtue of Trinity's size, most undergraduates are able to find like-minded friends. There is a small proportion of female undergraduates, and a very small proportion of black undergraduates, although this is largely a reflection of relative numbers of applicants, rather than bias in selection procedures.

Past members of the college include such notables as Lord Byron and the current Prince of Wales, as well as several less reputable students. Trinity is occasionally referred to as the college at which Sir Isaac Newton discovered the speed of sound in dry air, and most of the greatest spies since the Second World War discovered small boys.
Jolyon Welsh

Pauper notes
Accommodation: 1st and 3rd years live in; so do 2nd years with high ballot nos. Otherwise nearby (5–10 min walk) college houses and hostels. Rents c£125–210 per term. **Drink:** College bar crowded (closes 11.30 pm). Decor improving. Range of drink expanding. Many bottled beers. Cheapest pint – John Bull 78p. **Eats:** Hall food used to have worst reputation in Cambridge – but really has improved, viz excellent value. Guest Hall and Meals – c£1 each. Fixed termly kitchen charge – £50. Vegetarian available. **Ents:** Loads of societies, mostly free. TCU sweaty bops justifiably renowned attracting students from all Cambridge. **Sports:** Excellent overall, eg 3 sports fields, boathouse, badminton and squash courts. **Hardship funds:** College generally sympathetic for real hardship cases (though not for those who drink their grant). **Travel:** Many travel scholarships. **Work:** Vacation grants available.

Alumni (Editors' pick)
King Edward VII, HRH The Prince of Wales, A E Housman, Francis Bacon, Viscount Montgomery of Alamein, J H W Lloyd and C G S Hardie (producers of Not the 9 o'clock News), Sir Isaac Newton, Lord Butler, J Nehru, A A Milne, R Vaughan Williams, G M Trevelyan, Byron, Tennyson, Bertrand Russell, Lord Rutherford, Macaulay, Wittgenstein; The Spies.

TRINITY HALL
Trinity Hall, Cambridge CB2 1TJ (0223 332500; Fax: 0223 332537)

Maintenance charge 1990/91: Not available. **Accommodation available:** All undergraduates accommodated in college or college hostels. **Eating arrangements:** All meals available in hall; paid for by computer card. Super Hall (special dinner) on Thursdays. **Gate/guest hours:** Gate closed at 2 am; undergraduates intending to return later borrow a night key. Guests may not enter college after 1 am and must leave before 2 am. **Scholarships:** Scholarships and exhibitions awarded on the results of university examinations taken while in residence; numerous college prizes. **Hardship funds:** Funds are available. **Travel grants:** Elmore travel exhibition annually on result of modern and medieval languages Tripos; grants from Benn and Gregson funds for vacation travel of educational or adventurous nature. **Library:** Separate law reading room; also historic library (chained books). **Other college facilities:** Bar, music room with piano and harpsichord; washing machines and driers; boathouse; squash and tennis courts; playing fields; micro-computers

CAN'T FIND WHAT YOU'RE LOOKING FOR? USE THE INDEX!

and main-frame terminals. **Largest fields of study:** Natural sciences, law, engineering.

European Community: 10% students study an EC language and spend a period of time in another EC country as part of their course. No formal exchange links with EC universities/colleges.

Undergraduates: *Men:* 203 *Women:* 97
Postgraduates: *Men:* 87 *Women:* 43

What it's like

Small college in pleasant setting on the Backs. Very central, yet relatively quiet. Friendly atmosphere; relations between staff and students relaxed (notably helpful porters). Amenities include a modern JCR complex of common room, theatre, music room – all adjoin the popular bar. New computer room. Accommodation varies considerably, but rents are reasonable: 1st years and some 3rd years live in college, everyone else on two other sites. Limited self-catering and washing facilities are installed on each site. College food is tolerable: cafeteria every day, as well as the occasional formal and super halls (usually good value), vegetarian alternatives usually available but not vegan.

Most sports catered for; playing fields, tennis and squash courts 10 mins from college. Several active societies: outstanding in music and drama. Apolitical JCR coordinates many of the college activities, as well as representing students in the governing body.

Fair proportion of public school descent; college seeks a wider range of applicants. Male:female ratio 2:1, relaxed attitude to co-residence. Academically high, main subject, law, though most mainstream subjects catered for. Size and good internal facilities make the college rather insular, perhaps even a little claustrophobic.

Pauper notes

Accommodation: Can get cheap rooms, £200 a term. **Drink:** Bar is reasonable but goes for quality not cheapness, Bop's exceptional value. **Ents:** College ents very cheap, active discos, films and plays. **Sports:** Main sports (hockey, rugby etc) are free at college level. **Hardship funds:** Available but limited. **Travel:** No need for public transport during term – everywhere is walkable. Travel scholarships readily available.

Alumni (Editors' pick)

Robert Runcie, Sir Geoffrey Howe, Norman Fowler, Samuel Silkin, A Nunn May, Rev David Sheppard, Nicholas Hytner, A H Mars-Jones, Lord Simon of Glaisdale, J B Priestley.

WOLFSON

Wolfson College, Cambridge CB3 9BB (0223 335900)

Maintenance charge 1990/91: Not known. **Accommodation available:** 42% in accommodation where rent controlled by college. **Eating arrangements:** Meals in hall. Chocolate machine, cafeteria in club room. **Admission:** Primarily graduate college but mature undergraduates admitted. **Scholarships:** No scholarships. Some bursaries and awards. **Hardship funds:** College hardship fund. **Travel grants:** College travel fund. **Library:** 10,414 books, 44 periodicals, 20 study places. **Other college facilities:** Tennis court, multigym. **Largest fields of study:** Law.

European Community: No students study an EC language, but 1.6% spend time in another EC country as part of their course. No formal exchange links.

CAN'T FIND WHAT YOU'RE LOOKING FOR? USE THE INDEX!

Undergraduates: *Men:* 35 *Women:* 30
Postgraduates: *Men:* 174 *Women:* 138

What it's like

It's cosmopolitan, relaxed, unpretentious and friendly. Students are over 21, doing every imaginable degree (mostly postgraduate), from every corner of the world, lawyers and land economists, particularly strong. Food OK. Twice weekly formal halls popular. Limited college accommodation. Excellent May Ball (in April).

Pauper notes

Accommodation: Some flats and single accommodation for all first years and some others. **Drink:** College bar good, local pub 'Hat & Feathers' serves food also. **Ents:** Rest of Cambridge and internal college events. **Sports:** Best gym in Cambridge college. **Hardship funds:** Some; more available via university. **Travel:** Some assistance. **Work:** Work in college bar and kitchen available.

Alumni (Editors' pick)

C Bowman (singer/entertainer, well-known in Ireland).

CARDIFF

University of Wales College of Cardiff, PO Box 68, Cardiff CF1 3XA (0222 874000) Map A, D8

Student enquiries: Academic Registrar

Main study areas – as in What to Study section: *(First degree):* Accountancy, anatomy, archaeology, architecture, biochemistry, biology, biotechnology, botany, business studies, chemistry, civil engineering, communication studies, computing, economics, education, electrical & electronic engineering, English, environmental studies, European studies, food science & nutrition, geology, history, hotel & catering management, industrial relations, law, maritime studies, mathematical studies, mechanical and production engineering, microbiology, modern languages, music, Near East & Islamic studies, pharmacology, pharmacy, philosophy, physics, physiology, politics and government, psychology, religious studies and theology, sociology, town and country planning, welfare studies, zoology. *Also:* Astrophysics, banking, Catalan, conservation, Welsh studies.

European Community: Number of first degree students taking EC language or spending time in another EC country, not known. Formal exchange links with over 35 EC universities/colleges: Belgium (4); Eire (2); France (8); Germany (8); Greece (2); Italy (4); Netherlands (3); Portugal (1); Spain (5); many open to non-language specialists. Approved Erasmus programme 1990/91. European office actively promotes teaching and research programmes in Europe.

Application: UCCA. **Structural features:** Part of Wales University. **Academic features:** 4 year integrated sandwich courses, 5 year two-tier courses in architecture and town planning. **Largest fields of study:** Business studies, engineering, law. **Founded:** 1988 when University College, Cardiff (founded 1883) and UWIST (founded 1866) merged to form new college. **Main awards:** BA, BD, BEd, BMus, BSc, BEng, BScEcon, LLB, BPharm. **Awarding body:** University of Wales. **Site:** Close to Cardiff city centre. **Accommodation:** Over 1,200 places in halls of residence; approximately 1,800 places in self-catering flats; all accommodation mixed, except for one females-only hall of residence. Sufficient college accommodation to meet expected demand. Approx cost: £42.40 pw halls, from £15.40 to £22.70 pw self-catering flats, majority cost c£20.60. **Rent:** 40% in accommodation where rent controlled by university. **Library:** 9 libraries; over 650,000 volumes for loan, 4,500 periodicals, ample study places. **Specialist collections:** Salisbury Library of

CAN'T FIND WHAT YOU'RE LOOKING FOR? USE THE INDEX!

Celtic and Welsh material. Deposit library for UN and EC official publications. Technical Reference Bureau; Company Information Unit; Thomson Foundation Bureau (journalism); Robbins-Langdon Collection (music). **Welfare:** Students' advisory, counselling and health services; international section to assist overseas students. **Other learning resources:** Computing service on campus, used for teaching and research by staff and students of all disciplines. **Hardship funds:** Funds are available for interest-free loans, remission of fees and maintenance grants. **Special categories:** Residential facilities for married and disabled students; nursery and playgroup. **Careers:** Information, advice and placement. **Amenities:** Anglican, Catholic, Baptist, Methodist and United Reform chaplaincies; large SU with bars, nightclub, dining facilities, TV and reading rooms; snooker and pool room; university bookshop on campus, Wales University Air Squadron; Officer Training Corps. **Sporting facilities:** Gymnasium; new indoor and outdoor sports complex (about 1 mile away); extensive playing fields (about 4 miles away); boat houses on river Taff; 8 squash courts; very wide range of sport including rugby, hockey, sport-para, cricket; outdoor pursuits centre in Snowdonia National Park.

Duration of first degree course(s) or equivalent: 3 years; **others:** 4 years, 5 years **Total first degree students 1989/90:** 6,558; **total BEd students** 64 **Number of overseas students:** 430 **Number of mature students:** 977 **Male/female ratio 1989/90:** approx 5:4 **Teaching staff: full-time:** 686 **part-time:** 63 **Total full-time students 1989/90:** 8,165 **Postgraduate students:** 2,491 **Tuition fees, first degrees, 1990/91:** Home: £1,675 (£656 if self-financing); Overseas: £4,560 (arts-based courses), £6,050 (science-based).

What it's like

Main college looks pretty impressive, Union looks like a pile of shoe boxes. Easy to reach, at end of M4; M5 accesses north–south. Most of campus easy to get to and close (5 mins) to city centre. College accommodation available for most 1st years – 3 traditional (one women only), 2 self-catering, one Welsh speaking. Most students move out after 1st year. High proportion of overseas (approx 12%) and mature students.

Amicable relations with college, whose generosity with block grant have helped make Cardiff Union one of the country's best. Very active SU with over 200 social/ sporting societies, nightclub complex, new bars and shopping area. New Astroturf hockey pitch and indoor sports hall – all worth £1.25 million.

Aberdare Hall (women only), University Hall Tower Wing (women only) restrictive on male guests. FPA clinic 5 minutes from SU. Confidential union and college counselling available.

October 1990 saw a re-designed union welfare and advice centre and the addition of a third member of staff. Private interview room available in centre. Not much mixing with town. All the advantages of a capital city – multiscreen leisure complex, covered shopping areas, cinemas, theatres, museums, galleries, castles, docklands, arts centres and nightlife. Gay scene small (3 pubs/clubs exclusively gay) but well patronised.

3 subjects taken in 1st year, easy to swap if you pass exams and A-levels high enough. Language courses with 3rd year abroad. Lecturers slowly coming round to the idea of training. Degree assessment a mix of exams and continuous. Fail mark in first year about 40%, usually retakes allowed in September. Engineering building recently renovated and extended (excellent mobility disability access here: rest of college not very accessible). Home economics offered as a degree course. English department very innovative with some excellent (and famous!) lecturers (eg Chris Norris, Terence Hawkes, Catherine Belsey). European community studies a small close-knit degree course (3rd year away).

Students mostly from Wales and England, mixed backgrounds, approximately 10% Welsh speaking. Most famous student – Neil Kinnock (pass degree in economics). Sexual and racial harassment not overt, but engineering faculty an

MCP stronghold. Some scholarships (£100 usually) and prizes available. Good careers service.
Hermione Conna

Pauper notes

Accommodation: Accommodation crisis beginning of 1989 and 1990 session. All expensive (average £29 pw). Cheap, acceptable accommodation getting harder to find as student numbers increase. Halls contracts last whole year. **Drink:** Union cheapest in town. Ruddles, Holsten and regular promotions. Brains is local brewery and worth getting to know as they own most local pubs. **Eats:** 1 Welsh, 2 Greek restaurants (although Greek society doesn't rate them very highly), 1 Portuguese (great!) and several Italian restaurants. SU cheapest, but lots of cafes and veggie/wholefood places. Lots of chippies, Chinese and Indian takeaways. **Ents:** Union nightclub and bars; entry £1.50 Wed and Sats. Cheap films in town with NUS card (£2.00). Nightclub redecorated (1990), new pa system in concert venue. Usually discounts available for theatres, concerts etc for students. **Sports:** Squash courts in SU, gym and weights room – all well used. National swimming pool, ice rink; very active athletic union. **Hardship funds:** College can give interest free loans or grants of up to £500. **Travel:** Travel shop in syndicate with Warwick and Sheffield and offers very good deals; member of ABTA. Some scholarships available depending on course for overseas travel. **Work:** Plenty of bar and casual work, both in SU and in town. Other work hard to find.

Alumni (Editors' pick)

Rt Rev Derrick Childs (Bishop of Monmouth), Professor Alun Hoddinott (composer and professor of music at Cardiff), Neil Kinnock MP, Tim Sebastian, Ian Edwards, Sian Phillips, Philip Madoc, Bernice Rubens, Sir Graham Day, Sir Ronald Mason, Sir David Phillips, Vincent Kane.

CARDIFF INSTITUTE

Cardiff Institute of HE, Western Avenue, Llandaff, Cardiff CF5 2YB (0222 551111) Map A, D8

Student enquiries: Information Office

Main study areas – as in What to Study section: *(First degree):* Art & design, biology, business studies, dance, education, fine arts, food science & nutrition, nursing studies, psychology, speech sciences, welfare studies. *Also:* Chiropody, human movement studies, medical laboratory sciences, physical education, tourism.

European Community: Number of first degree students taking EC language as part of course and spending 6 months in another EC country, not known. Formal exchange links with a number of EC universities/colleges in France, Germany, Netherlands, Portugal and Spain – open to students in art and design, industry and hotel and catering management. Approved Erasmus programme 1990/91. New French and Spanish language options for BEd.

Application: PCAS, except art and design (ADAR). **Academic features:** BA European administration. **Main awards:** BA, BEd, BSc. **Awarding body:** University of Wales or CNAA. **Site:** 4 sites in or near Cardiff city centre. **Accommodation:** Segregated halls of residence. Approx cost: £60 pw. Rent: no students housed in accommodation where rent is controlled by the Institute. **Library:** 4 libraries, total of 210,000 volumes, 1,000 periodicals, 430 study places; reference and short term collections; access, through library computer, to British Library and Library of Congress (London). **Special collections:** Permanent collection of prints and books on the work of the designer Erte. Extensive collection of slides. **Welfare:** Doctors,

CAN'T FIND WHAT YOU'RE LOOKING FOR? USE THE INDEX!

nurses, chaplains, professional welfare and accommodation officer. **Hardship funds:** Student loan fund. **Careers:** Careers Advisory officer. **Sporting facilities:** Sports hall, gymnasia, swimming pool, athletic track (international standard), access to all sporting facilities of Cardiff University and to National Sports Centre. **Employment:** Art and design, education, paramedical sciences, hospitals, sports, environmental health, museums/galleries/arts administration, tourism.

Duration of first degree course(s) or equivalent: 3 years; **others:** 4 years (BEd, BSc nutrition and dietetics, speech therapy, environmental health, tourism). **Total first degree students 1989/90:** 1,425 **Total BEd students:** 381 **Number of overseas students, excluding EC:** 3 **Number of mature students:** 169 **Male/female ratio 1989/90:** 1:2 **Teaching staff:** 396 **Total full-time students 1989/90:** 2,571 **Postgraduate students:** 228 **Tuition fees, first degrees, 1990/91:** Home: £1,675; Overseas: £4,563.

What it's like

Formerly South Glamorgan Institute of Higher Education, it's still on 4 sites. Accommodation, generally very good, reasonable cost, reasonable quality. Good access to all 4 college centres. 2 halls of residence – warm, reasonably priced – good community atmosphere with lots of trust, team spirit and fun!

Travel – cheap and accessible (taxi and bus), regular use of SU minibuses but nowhere is too far on a bicycle.

Entertainment – very strong. Serious drinking and eating more than most student institutions. Great atmosphere; very friendly and easy going. Constant bombardment from SU with dances, games, shows, bands, discos. Students from all sites are given access to all 'gigs' due to use of SU minibuses. Lots of drinks promotions with prizes and freebies.

Local areas (pubs, clubs etc) – good pubs with very good beer (price and quality). Claude Hotel – best student pub – landlord loves us; constantly provides for bands, sponsorship for SU clubs, freebies, fancy dress and parties (all because of liaison with SU). Clubs – quite expensive but good to visit in groups. Student nights very good.

Places of interest – beaches, hills, nature paths, rugby, football, skating, swimming, all strong in Cardiff and within its vicinity. Castles, museums, cinemas – you name it we've got it! Very much a student orientated city, with citizens of all nationalities. Very good relationship between students and locals.

Facilities at SU – sports excellent: swimming pool, physiotherapy service, squash courts, gymnasiums, sports hall, multigym, hockey pitches, football, cricket and first class rugby pitches. Best college rugby side in Britain. Clubs and societies provide equal sporting opportunities for men and women and there are plenty.

Students come from all over Britain, from all backgrounds. There is a highly impressive pass rate – FE courses as well as HE which range right across the board from PE to fine art. Regular exchange programme all over the world.
D J Langford

Pauper notes

Accommodation: Good accommodation, but must be searched for. **Drink:** Claude Hotel, Poets' Corner, Philharmonic, Brains Beers good, and SA very strong. For mega blitz try Hurlimans Lager at Roath Park. 42nd Street, Brain's concession to yuppie market. **Eats:** Campus food varies – Colchester Avenue and tuck shop good. Eating out: Broadway Steak Bar, Patrice (cheap), Bently's (cheap and late). **Ents:** Cardiff offers all facilities of large city. Chapter and Sherman theatres good for students. Nightclubs etc. **Sports:** Plentiful and free on campus, also plentiful in city, eg National Sports Centre. Various leisure centres, swimming pools, golf club etc. **Travel:** Accessible and easy for hitching, trains and good bus service. **Work:** Pubs and restaurants, youth club coaching etc. Reasonably accessible during vacation time.

CAN'T FIND WHAT YOU'RE LOOKING FOR? USE THE INDEX!

Alumni (Editors' pick)
Dewi Bebb, Lynn Davies, Peter Radford, David Pittaway, Gareth Edwards, Rhodri Lewis, Stuart Baxter, Sian Williams, Kevin Hopkins, Hugh Morris, Mike Pereybrune, John Devereux, David James, Grey Thomas, Sally Hodge, Nigel Cousins, Martyn Geraint, Robert Norster, Richie Collins, John Bevan, Jamie Hughes, Anne Diamond, Jill Dando, Michael Buerk, David Bryant, Paul John, Colin Laity, Jason Charles, Maxine Lock.

CENTRAL ST MARTINS

Central St Martins School of Art and Design, (1) Southampton Row, London WC1B 4AP (071-753 9090) (2) 107 Charing Cross Road, London WC2H 0DU (071-437 0611) (3) 3/27 Long Acre, London WC2E 9LA
Map E, C2

Student enquiries: Registrar

Main study areas – as in What to Study section: (*First degree*): Art & design, fine arts.

European Community: Number of students learning an EC language or spending time in another EC country, not known.

Application: ADAR. **Founded:** 1989, from merger of Central School of Art & Design with St Martin's School of Art. **Structural features:** Part of the London Institute. Organised as three schools: fashion and textiles (Charing Cross Road); graphics (Longacre); art (Southampton Row). **Largest fields of study:** Design, fashion and textiles. **Main awards:** BA. **Awarding body:** CNAA. **Site:** Central London. **Accommodation:** 35 places in hostels, 50 in mixed halls. Rent: number of students in accommodation where rent is controlled by the school, not known. **Library:** Libraries on main sites; 80,000 volumes, 250 periodicals, 126 study places, slide libraries, 100,000 transparencies. **Welfare:** Doctor, FPA and psychiatrist. **Hardship funds:** Not known. **Careers:** Teachers are practising artists and designers so can help students. **Amenities:** Shop selling course materials; Common room, canteen and coffee bar; dances, films etc organised by SU; TV and cine equipment; reprographic centre.

Duration of first degree course(s) or equivalent: 3 years, 4 years sandwich, 5 years part time **Total first degree students 1989/90:** Not known **Male/female ratio 1989/90:** Not known **Teaching staff:** Not known **Total full-time students 1989/90:** Not known **Postgraduate students:** Not known.

What it's like
It's the result of the merger of Central School of Art & Design, and St Martins School of Art. Based on three main sites in the heart of London, producing an art and design college which is both ancient and modern, true of the buildings and the staff alike. There are over 2,000 students, with more than two-thirds on degree or higher level courses. Courses are positively forward looking (as far as the financial constraints will allow) maintaining close links with industry and the arts through visiting professionals and being in the centre of London! Students are a mix of ages, backgrounds and interests, reflected in a diversity of personal styles.

No bars at the college; the bar at PCL, Red Lion Square (alongside Southampton Row site) shared by CSM students and staff. It's a friendly bar with cheap and plentiful drinks. Good sounds, a party every Friday which is very popular with a regular crowd. SU holds parties approximately once a fortnight at one of the three main sites. There are also nights at the Wag, Wardour Street on a Wednesday with reduced admission for CSM students.

CAN'T FIND WHAT YOU'RE LOOKING FOR? USE THE INDEX!

Pauper notes

Accommodation: Limited access to halls of residence. London Institute SU full-time temporary accommodation service. **Drink:** PCL bar – shared with Central St Martins. **Eats:** Rosie's Restaurant, Southampton Row site. Surrounded by sandwich shops and greasy-spoons. **Ents:** Cheap and cheerful college ents. **Hardship funds:** Money available to cover loss of housing benefit but it's a case of working out how to get it out of the London Institute at the moment. **Travel:** Expensive London Transport. **Work:** Work available in bar and coffee bars and at college ents.

Alumni: (Editors' pick)

Zandra Rhodes, Ralph Koltai (set designer for National Theatre), John Napier (set designer for RSC), Rachel Wilson (printmaker), Adam Elliott (actor), Lionel Bart (composer/playwright), Robyn Denny (fashion designer), Linda Kitson (Falklands war artist), Bruce Oldfield (fashion designer).

" absinthe in glasses has been superseded by Nescafé in polystyrene cups"

CENTRAL SCHOOL OF SPEECH AND DRAMA

Central School of Speech and Drama, Embassy Theatre, Eton Avenue, London NW3 3HY (071-722 8183) Map D, B1

Student enquiries: Registrar

Main study areas – as in What to Study section: *(First degree):* Drama, education, English, speech sciences.

European Community: Number of students studying EC language and spending time in another EC country, not known.

Application: UCCA (BA); PCAS (BEd, BSc). **Academic features:** BEd revised to emphasise urban context; all degree courses expanding the level of student-centred learning. **Special features:** BEd in drama and spoken language taught in conjunction with Thames Poly; BA in drama and a language jointly with Queen Mary & Westfield; BSc in speech and language pathology, jointly with PCL. Many well-known guest directors and tutors from the theatre, teaching and speech therapy professions. **Founded:** 1906. **Main awards:** BA, BEd, BSc. **Awarding body:** London University (BA), CNAA (BEd, BSc). **Site:** Swiss Cottage. **Access:** Swiss

CAN'T FIND WHAT YOU'RE LOOKING FOR? USE THE INDEX!

Cottage station, buses. **Accommodation:** School is non-residential. Student Services Unit helps to find lodgings within half hour of School. Approx cost: £45 pw. **Library:** 29,000 volumes, 40 study places. **Other learning resources:** Well-stocked Audio Visual Unit. **Specialist collections:** Drama, speech pathology. **Welfare:** Student Services Unit, including counselling facility. **Hardship funds:** Limited loans from a special fund. **Amenities:** Specialist drama studios. **Employment:** BEd graduates – speech and drama teaching, theatre in education. BSc – speech therapists.

Duration of first degree course(s) or equivalent: BA 3 years; BEd and BSc 4 years **Total first degree students 1989/90:** 277; **BEd students:** 75 **Number of overseas students:** 1 **Number of mature students:** 14 **Male/female ratio 1989/90:** 1:3 **Teaching staff: full-time:** 17 **part-time:** 20 approx **Total full-time students 1989/90:** 434 **Postgraduate students:** 45 on post-experience courses **Tuition fees, first degrees, 1990/91:** Home: £1,675; Overseas: £4,820.

What it's like
Main site at Swiss Cottage is centred around the Embassy Theatre. Stage management workshops, two drama studios, large library, speech therapy and teacher training facilities all adjoin. Small and friendly college of some 300 students split into acting, stage management, teacher training (BEd), speech therapy, ACSD, ADUS courses. All makes for a better social life than most drama schools or colleges. New student common room and bar. No halls but SU helps in finding accommodation. SU runs discos, dances, cabarets, bands; also good football team. Easy access to other sports facilities and also to West End. Work-load heavy. Continual assessment. Failure/drop-out rate low. Changing courses virtually unknown.
Wolf Willey

Pauper notes
Drink: Washington Pub in Eton Avenue, Swiss Cottage Pub, North Star in Finchley Road, SU bar for cheap booze. **Eats:** Conrad's in Belsize Village, The Sky (Chinese), Cosmo's (Swiss/Austrian), New Delhi (Indian) all in Finchley Road. **Ents:** All performances in Embassy Theatre and studio are free to CSSD students. **Sports:** Swimming pool and sports centre opposite school. **Hardship funds:** School/SU help out in extreme circumstances. **Work:** Part-time jobs in shops and bars around school, also in SU bar and SU coffee bar in the school.

Alumni (Editors' pick)
Many leading actors, directors etc, eg Vanessa Redgrave, Deborah Warner, French and Saunders.

CHARING CROSS AND WESTMINSTER

Charing Cross and Westminster Medical School, University of London, The Reynolds Building, St Dunstan's Road, London W6 8RP (081-846 1234) Map D, A2

Student enquiries: Admissions Officer (081-846 7202)

Main study areas – as in What to Study section: *(First degree):* Medicine.

European Community: No students take EC language or spend time in another EC country.

Application: UCCA. **Structural features:** Part of London University. **Special features:** Recent introduction of a fibre optic remote teaching system which enables clinical students on 4 hospital sites to receive lectures by cable from one centre at one time and also to communicate between sites. **Founded:** 1818 and 1834. **Main**

CAN'T FIND WHAT YOU'RE LOOKING FOR? USE THE INDEX!

awards: MB; BS; BSc. **Awarding body:** London University. **Site:** Fulham and Westminster. **Access:** Hammersmith and Baron's Court underground stations; Westminster underground station. **Accommodation:** 259 places in halls (accommodation nearly always provided for first year students). **Library:** 42,000 volumes, 300 periodicals; 250 study places. **Specialist collections:** History of medicine. **Welfare:** Doctor, dentist, FPA, psychiatrist, chaplain. **Hardship fund:** The Dean's Discretionary Fund. **Careers:** Advice and limited placement service. **Amenities:** All resources of London University. **Sporting facilities:** International size swimming-pool on site, squash courts and extensive playing fields. **Employment:** Medical practitioners.

Duration of first degree course(s) or equivalent: 5 years (MB, BS); 1 year (Intercalated BSc) **Total first degree students 1989/90:** 834 **Number of overseas students:** 22 **Number of mature students:** approx 75 **Male/female ratio 1989/90:** 9:8 **Teaching staff: full-time:** c220-240 **part-time:** c200-230 **Total full-time students 1989/90:** 864 **Postgraduate students:** 30 f-t; 87 p-t **Tuition fees, first degrees, 1990/91:** Home: £1,675; Overseas: £6,350 (pre-clinical), £11,700 (clinical).

What it's like

A very active and friendly medical school situated at two contrasting sites: Charing Cross Hospital, in Hammersmith, is a 15 storey modern building in the shape of a cross; Westminster Hospital is a gothic brown brick building in the heart of Westminster. However, Westminster Hospital will eventually be replaced by the new Westminster and Chelsea Hospital to be built on the Fulham Road. Both Charing Cross and Westminster are linked with associated teaching hospitals via a unique fibre-optic TV network allowing one to be taught by a lecturer ten miles away using 2-way audiovisual communication.

Modern SU building at the Charing Cross site. SU runs bar and bookshop and is responsible for maintaining the usual packed social calendar as well as representing students on various Medical School committees. The Union is also active in initiating and co-ordinating campaigns on any issues affecting student welfare. Extremely good facilities including library, TV and snooker rooms, cafeteria, changing rooms. Sports complex situated on site with swimming pool, squash courts and concert hall. Active clubs and societies include drama (Edinburgh Fringe for last five years), light operatic, rugby, soccer, hockey, water polo, squash, tennis, basketball, rowing, mountaineering, film, Christian Union and Catholic Society. 'Camp Cando' is a residential summer camp for mentally handicapped people organised and run by students.

Halls of residence at Notting Hill Gate and Westminster. All students promised first year in Hall. Afterwards most find private rented accommodation around Hammersmith. Medical School is noted for its progressive selection policy. No offers are made without interview; year out is favoured; and a large number of graduates are considered (20 selected each year). Good opportunities for an intercalated BSc degree, which is encouraged (65 students this year).
Roby Rakhit

Pauper notes

Accommodation: Hard-to-let council accommodation. **Drink:** SU bar is easily cheapest (85p/pint) otherwise pubs are quite expensive. **Eats:** Veg! The Windmill (Fulham Broadway), Tea House (Ravenscourt Park), The Galleon (Notting Hill Gate), Hospital canteen and medical school refectory. **Ents:** Riverside Studios (Film and theatre) and The Lyric (Hammersmith) have student standby tickets, Brentford Waterman's Art Centre. **Sports:** On site swimming pool and sports club. **Travel:** Scholarships for electives; good hitching for M4/M3. **Work:** Good jobs in Hammersmith, temp jobs at the local Exhibition Centre.

CAN'T FIND WHAT YOU'RE LOOKING FOR? USE THE INDEX!

Alumni (Editors' pick)
Professor Harold Ellis (world famous general surgeon).

CHELSEA

Chelsea College of Art and Design, Manresa Road, London SW3 6LS (071-351 3844) Map E, B4

Student enquiries: Manresa Road

Main study areas – as in What to Study section: *(First degree):* Art & design.

European Community: No students take EC languages or spend time in another EC country.

Application: ADAR. **Largest fields of study:** Painting, sculpture, printmaking. **Founded:** 1962. **Structural features:** Part of the London Institute. **Main awards:** BA **Awarding body:** CNAA. **Site:** 4 sites in Chelsea/Fulham. **Access:** Tube (South Kensington/Sloane Square); buses along King's Road. **Accommodation:** Limited number of hostel places. Rent: 10% in accommodation where rent controlled by college. **Library:** 3 libraries at Manresa Road, South Park and Lime Grove Buildings; 40,000 volumes, 200 periodicals, 30 study places. **Specialist collections:** Fine art at Manresa Road. **Welfare:** Student services officer. **Careers:** Information and advice. **Amenities:** Shops for students' materials on 3 sites. **Employment:** Strong tradition of freelance work.

Duration of first degree course(s) or equivalent: 3 years **other:** part-time or mixed mode 4-5 years **Total first degree students 1989/90:** 256 **Number of overseas students:** 13 **Number of mature students:** 53 **Male/female ratio 1989/90:** 2:3 **Teaching staff: full-time:** 10.5 **part-time:** 78 **Total full-time students 1989/90:** 745 **Postgraduate students:** 39 **Tuition fees, first degrees, 1990/91:** Home: £1,675 (less for self-financing); Overseas: £5,750.

What it's like

Small college, spread over 4 sites: Manresa Road (behind Chelsea Fire Station), Hugon Road (just off the Wandsworth Bridge Road), Bagleys Lane (near Chelsea Harbour) and Lime Grove (shared with Hammersmith & West London College) behind the BBC in Shepherds Bush. This means it lacks strong single identity despite efforts of staff and SU. Make sure you look round the site you're actually applying to. Chelsea site, housing the fine art courses, has the best facilities (most 'events' take place here) and the academic reputation to match. Beware, students are expected to motivate themselves and tutors with famous names can prove elusive. If you do the Foundation Course at Bagleys Lane you'll probably have a great time, and get a place on a higher course but you may have to create your own social life. Look carefully at where the BA Graphic Design course is, before you sign up for three years in Hugon Road, SW6. It's a converted school, with the atmosphere to match; shared uneasily with over a hundred BTEC students and a long walk from the tube.

Chelsea has a problem, being in central London, with accommodation. The cheapest rents are £50 pw with no housing benefit. There are 400 places in 2 halls of residence; however competition is stiff for these places with the other 8,000 students of the London Institute. Important to start looking early, it may take a few months to find adequate accommodation, years to find sought after housing co-op or council housing. Typical student is middle class (though that seems to be changing), easy going, pretentious but friendly and clad in shabby chic.

Welfare and amenities are not priority of college. There is 1 student services officer for 750 full-time and 300 part-time students, a small careers unit and overcrowded canteens. Student shops are open from a couple of hours a week to

CAN'T FIND WHAT YOU'RE LOOKING FOR? USE THE INDEX!

half-day every day and along with every other service are run in order to make a profit. However, SU has concrete plans to make bars on 2 sites. Chelsea concentrates its meagre resources on the libraries, which have 40,000¢ volumes, 200 periodicals and 68 study places. B&W and colour photocopying facilities and AppleMac, Nimbus and IBM computers for students' use. There are financial difficulties in studying at Chelsea but millionaires are certainly encouraged to apply! Chelsea's results are excellent due to the few quality staff and the excellent quality of students Chelsea has been able to attract.

Pauper notes
Accommodation: Hall accommodation for first years only. **Drink:** Good, cheap SU canteen at Lime Grove, student bar at Chelsea. **Ents:** Active film society, some plays too. **Sports:** Very limited, possible to get a free leisure pass for council sports facilities. **Hardship funds:** Student welfare fund. **Work:** If you don't mind what you do jobs are still plentiful in London.

Alumni (Editors' pick)
Notorious: Alexei Sayle – Throbbing Gristle, Graham Gough. Famous students: Tom Dixon (bass with Funkapolitan), Simon Edmonson (painter), Sarah Jane Hoare (stylist with Harpers & Queen). Famous students (from the past): Henry Moore, Vincent Price, Patrick Caulfield, Howard Hodgkin, John Berger.

"Typical student : easy-going spoilt, arrogant London trendy"

♫ MYBEE ITS BECORSE EIMER LONDONER ♫

CHELTENHAM & GLOUCESTER COLLEGE

Cheltenham & Gloucester College of Higher Education PO Box 220, The Park, Cheltenham GL50 2QF (0242 532825) Map A, D7

Student enquiries: Registry

Main study areas – as in What to Study section: *(First degree):* Accountancy, art & design, business studies, computing, education, English, fine arts, geography, geology, history, hotel & catering management, information technology, mathematical studies, religious studies & theology, town & country planning. *Also:* Cultural studies, fashion, sports studies, women's studies.

European Community: 3% first degree students take EC language as part of course and 5% spend 6 months or more in another EC country. Formal exchange links with

CAN'T FIND WHAT YOU'RE LOOKING FOR? USE THE INDEX!

6 EC universities/colleges: 4 in France (including Lyons College of Art), 1 each in Germany and Spain. All open to non-language specialists. Approved Erasmus programme 1990/91. More Erasmus exchanges being developed.

Application: PCAS except art & design (ADAR). **Special features:** American professor plus exchange students each academic year. Voluntary CofE Foundation. **Academic features:** Modular structure for undergraduate courses. Links with industry and commerce. **Founded:** 1990, from merger of College of St Paul and St Mary with GlosCAT HE. **Main awards:** BA, BEd, BSc. **Awarding body:** CNAA, Bristol University. **Site:** Cheltenham and Gloucester. **Access:** Train, coach, M5 motorway, Staverton Airport (Channel Islands). **Accommodation:** Over 800 places in halls of residence (priority given to first year students). Cost: £40 pw (full board). 80% first year students, 10% others in accommodation where rent controlled by college. **Library:** 200,000 volumes, 950 journals. **Specialist collections:** Early children's books; College archives from 1847; history of sport collection, the Osborn Rock collection. **Other learning facilities:** Resource centres with film and TV, dance and drama studios; microcomputer facilities. **Welfare:** Director of Student Services and a college counsellor; medical officer and nursing staff, academic counsellors, chaplain, personal tutors. **Hardship funds:** Chapel Council, bursaries for projects/visits. **Careers:** College and county careers officers. **Sporting facilities:** 40 acres playing fields, swimming pool (near Olympic standard). **Employment:** Less than 4% of recent graduates failed to gain employment.

Duration of first degree course(s) or equivalent: 3 and 4 years (BEd) **Total first degree students 1989/90:** 1,645; **BEd students:** 690 **Number of overseas students:** 46 **Number of mature students:** 517 **Male/female ratio 1989/90:** 4:6 **Teaching staff: full-time:** 275 **part-time:** 50 **Total full-time students 1989/90:** 2,100 **Postgraduate students:** 191 **Tuition fees, first degrees, 1990/91:** Home: £1,675; Overseas: £4,555.

What it's like

Until recently predominantly teacher training, now offers range of degree courses. 3 residential sites not too far from each other, a bike is very helpful! Meals provided; only a small amount is self-catering. Contrast between modern and old buildings in 30 acres of parkland and garden. First years offered residence in halls thereafter students encouraged to live out.

Sport plays an active part in college life; a large variety of different ones available. SU very active; provides twice weekly discos/bands as well as shops, bars and offices for information, advice and help.

Centrally situated in Cheltenham, an excellent place for shopping and entertainment, and in Gloucester.

Pauper notes

Accommodation: Currently approx 600 places in college halls. Digs in Cheltenham expensive and very hard to come by. Borough Council very unhelpful and discriminating against students. **Drink:** Variety of pubs and wine bars – competitive prices – good choice. **Eats:** Restaurants, very many in a small area – both cheap and expensive. Indian, Greek, Chinese, French, English etc. **Ents:** SU provides a variety of entertainment such as discos, bands etc. Fringe theatre; Everyman Theatre; literature and music festival; Town Hall; night clubs etc. **Sports:** The college offers excellent sporting facilities. There are a number of very good leisure centres in Cheltenham both public and private. **Hardship funds:** SU interest-free loans up to £100. **Travel:** College offers many student awards for travel – Eleanor Greenwood – £500, Jack Voyce etc. **Work:** Numerous bar and restaurant jobs available.

Alumni (Editors' pick)

Omar Arteh, Samuel Baldeh, David Bryant, P H Newby, Sarah Potter, Graham Brookhouse, Don Hale, Chris Broad.

CAN'T FIND WHAT YOU'RE LOOKING FOR? USE THE INDEX!

CHESTER COLLEGE

Chester College, Cheyney Road, Chester CH1 4BJ (0244 375444)
Map A, D6

Student enquiries: The Registry

Main study areas – as in What to Study section: *(First degree):* Biology, computing, drama, education, English, fine arts, geography, history, mathematical studies, modern languages, psychology, religious studies and theology. *Also:* Health and community studies, physical education and sports science.

European Community: Number of students taking EC language not known (language courses new); 2% spend 6 months or more in another EC country. No formal exchange links but possibility of new European links for work experience.

Application: UCCA. **Academic features:** BA (Health and Community Studies). All BA/BSc students have work-experience placements; employment-related 'enterprise' modules in first-year course. **Special features:** Staff and BEd student exchange with State University of New York and Plattsburg. **Largest fields of study:** Education, English, PE, history. **Founded:** 1839 by Church of England. **Main awards:** BA, BSc, BEd. **Awarding body:** Liverpool University. **Site:** 30 acre campus within walking distance of Chester centre. **Access:** 15 mins from M56, 45 mins from M6, buses from town centre to site. **Accommodation:** 300 places in halls of residence on campus; 150 places in college houses on campus. Approx cost: £42 per week. **Rent:** 40% in accommodation where rent controlled by college. **Library:** 100,000 volumes, 400 periodicals, 145 study places. **Other learning resources:** Human performance laboratory; satellite remote-sensing suite; CCTV studio and media centre. **Welfare:** Chaplaincy; student services centre on campus; personal tutorial system. **Careers:** Full-time careers service; work experience for all undergraduates. **Amenities:** Full range of specialist teaching facilities, new auditorium and seminar complex, new conference centre. Leisure facilities include 25 metre pool, squash courts, sauna/solarium and all-weather pitches. **Employment:** Wide range in the professions, business, commerce, media, personnel etc.

Duration of first degree course(s) or equivalent: 3 years; BEd 4 years; 6 years part-time BA **Total first degree students 1989/90:** 1,650; **total BEd students:** 450 **Male/female ratio 1989/90:** 1:3 **Teaching staff: full-time:** 98 **part-time:** 10 **Total full-time students 1989/90:** 1,500 **Postgraduate students:** 32 (full-time); 158 (part-time) **Tuition fees, first degrees, 1990/91:** Home: £1,657; Overseas: £4,017.

What it's like

Founded in 1839, situated on a 30 acre site ten minutes' walk from the town centre. All facilities are on the one campus and include library and media centre, health centre (with confidential counselling, pregnancy and contraception advice), bookshop, Union shop, launderette and social club bar. Sports facilities include 2 squash courts, 2 gymnasia, swimming pool, sauna and solarium, 6 tennis courts, all weather pitch and various grass pitches. Also Northgate Arena, five minutes' walk away. Sports teams are all above average as PE is a major subject. 460 first years are accommodated in the seven halls of residence, many in single study bedrooms. Student village on campus accommodates 84 final year students in self-catering houses. The college owns several houses for self-catering students a few minutes walk away. Most 2nd and 3rd years live around the nearby Bouverie Street 'ghetto', which has varying standards and prices of accommodation. Because the majority of students live so close to college there is a great community atmosphere. Mix of students has a 'cosmopolitan' feel with regular intakes of Hong Kong students and a regular exchange programme with the State University of New York, Plattsburgh. All sections contribute to clubs and societies administered by a generally non-political SU, whose elected representatives sit on all major college committees. Entertainment-wise there are twice weekly bops and films on campus as well as

CAN'T FIND WHAT YOU'RE LOOKING FOR? USE THE INDEX!

visiting bands (Bay City Rollers 1989!), novelty acts and theme nights with quiz nights in the bar. English, PE and primary education are the most popular courses all leading to a combined studies degree from Liverpool.
Julia Gregory

Pauper notes
Accommodation: If it's cheap it usually looks it. **Drink:** College bar. 'Old Peculiar' at Telfords Warehuse, 'Moonraker' at Clavertons, otherwise loads of pubs, mainly Greenhalls, although better beer can easily be found. **Eats:** Bombay Palace, Sixties, Muswells. Wide variety of burgers, pizzas etc and lots of good restaurants. **Ents:** Nominal charge for college ents, discount at theatres, cinemas, etc. Twice weekly films on campus. **Sports:** Campus swimming pool, gyms and squash courts. Northgate Arena. **Travel:** National Express coach cards, ISIC and Railcards available from SU. **Hardship funds:** On merit in SU. **Work:** Bunacamp, Camp America, Camp Beaumont. Bar and restaurant work in city centre.

Alumni (Editors' pick)
John Carlton (rugby international), Carol Lewis (assistant governor, HM Borstal), Walter Winterbottom (director of Sports Council), Richard Palmer (Secretary British Olympic Committee), Eric Bolton (HMI, senior staff inspector), The Venerable Francis William Harvey (Archdeacon of London), Lynn Davies (British long jump record-holder), George Courtney (top British football referee), Jim Bowen.

CHRIST CHURCH COLLEGE

Canterbury Christ Church College, North Holmes Road, Canterbury, Kent CT1 1QU (0227 762444) Map A, G8

Student enquiries: Admissions Tutor

Main study areas – as in What to Study section: *(First degree):* Art & design, education, English, fine arts, geography, history, mathematical studies, music, religious studies and theology.

European Community: Number of students learning an EC language or spending time in another EC country, not known.

Application: PCAS. **Academic features:** New degree courses in occupational therapy; business studies; tourism, leisure and recreation; information technology. **Special features:** College's own radio station now broadcasting. Mature students with one A-level or from an Access course accepted in special cases. **Largest fields of study:** English, education. **Founded:** 1962; merged with Canterbury School of Radiography in 1988. **Main awards:** BA, BA(Ed), BSc. **Structural features:** Link now established with local hospitals to develop degree courses in nursing. **Awarding body:** Kent University. **Site:** 10 min gentle walk from Canterbury city centre. **Accommodation:** 210 places in mixed and segregated halls, accommodation officer will advise on lodgings. Special feature: head-leased houses – ie college rents houses from landlords and sub-lets to students. **Library:** 120,000 volumes, 300 periodicals, 120 study places, short term loan collection. New extension about to be built. **Welfare:** Doctor, nurse, sick bay, chaplain, nursery facilities nearby. **Careers:** Information and advice. **Amenities:** Spacious new Student Building. **Sporting facilities:** 16 acres playing fields, tennis courts and squash courts, gymnasium. **Employment:** Teaching, commerce, civil service, research, management, media, occupational therapy, radiography etc.

Duration of first degree course(s) or equivalent: 3 years (BA/BSc); 4 years (BA(Ed) and BSc (occupational therapy)) **Total first degree students 1989/90:** 1,050; **total BEd students:** 550 **Male/female ratio 1989/90:** 1:4 **Teaching staff:**

CAN'T FIND WHAT YOU'RE LOOKING FOR? USE THE INDEX!

full-time: 120 **part-time:** 20 **Total full-time students 1989/90:** 1,350 **Postgraduate students:** 200.

What it's like

Although expanding both its campus and student population, Christ Church still manages to maintain a friendly and personal atmosphere. Christ Church (C4) is located in centre of city, and many of the 200 rooms in halls overlook the cathedral. Accommodation on campus is predominantly first year; rest live in rented housing in Canterbury area. Due to large student population in Canterbury, accommodation is both expensive and difficult to find, but college and SU have accommodation officers to help students search for housing.

SU building is centre of most student activity and social life. Purpose built five years ago, it contains two bars, a disco/band/events area, games room and two TV lounges. SU has many flourishing groups, clubs and societies, all run for students by students, including our own campus radio station. Events at C4 are renowned as some of the best in Canterbury, attracting regular visits from students at both university and art college, with large-scale annual fixtures such as the Christmas Ball, The Carnival and Summer Ball.

Students come from all over the country to attend C4, and there seems to be no such thing as a 'typical' student, although many are following vocational degrees, leading to careers in areas such as teaching, nursing and paramedics. Other courses on offer at C4 facilitate entry into media, industry and tourism, with 'hands-on' experience gained through coursework.
Susan Haldenby

Pauper notes

Accommodation: No married quarters – high rents, very few (if any) squatting opportunities. **Drink:** Large and varied selection of pubs in city – one of most crowded square miles in England! **Eats:** College investing a lot of money in the refectory. Union bar provides good, cheap meals, many suitable for vegetarians. **Ents:** Union runs events four nights per week including bands, discos, films, 'alternative' entertainment plus annual Summer Ball. **Sports:** C4 has many thriving sports clubs and teams, 4 squash and tennis courts on site (free for students). **Travel:** Hitching opportunities good for both Continent and London. **Work:** Mainly found in pubs, restaurants & supermarkets. Much summer work created by tourist industry, especially English language schools.

CIRENCESTER

Royal Agricultural College, Cirencester GL7 6JS (0285 652531)
Map A, D7

Student enquiries: Admissions Secretary

Main study areas – as in What to Study section: *(First degree):* Agriculture, horticulture and forestry, biochemistry, biology, business studies, economics, environmental science, microbiology, town & country planning. *Also:* Animal nutrition, animal science, ecology, estate management.

European Community: 28% first degree students take EC language as part of course and 12% spend 6 months or more in another EC country. Formal exchange links with 7 EC universities/colleges in France, Germany and Spain (Institut Supérieur Agricole de Beauvais; Lycée Agricole de Libourne-Montagne; Ecole Supérieur d'Agriculture d'Angers; Fachhochschule Nurtingen; Universidad Politécnica de Valencia; Wagerungen University; Larenstein International Agricultural College).

CAN'T FIND WHAT YOU'RE LOOKING FOR? USE THE INDEX!

Academic features: New BSc course in International Agribusiness Management combining agricultural science, business management and languages. **Special features:** Combination of technical and business teaching. Some courses lead to membership of Royal Institution of Chartered Surveyors – Rural Practice Division. **Largest fields of study:** Rural economics and estate management, agriculture and business studies. **Founded:** 1845. **Main awards:** BSc, Diploma in rural estate management (DREM). **Awarding bodies:** Reading University, Bath University, Buckingham University (BSc) Royal Agricultural College (DREM). **Site:** 1 mile from Cirencester. **Accommodation:** 226 beds in halls. Approx cost: £1,848-£2,184 pa full board. **Rent:** 31% in accommodation where rent controlled by college. **Library:** 13,000 volumes, 500 periodicals, 160 study places. **Other learning resources:** Own farm, 770 hectares. **Welfare:** Doctor, chaplain, personal tutors. **Hardship funds:** Various bursaries available. Grants generally available. **Careers:** Information, advice and placement. **Amenities:** Common rooms, bar, student union. **Sporting facilities:** Sports pitches including floodlit all-weather hockey and tennis, facilities for squash, rowing, water sports and field sports, gym. **Employment:** Farm, plantation, nursery and estate management, private and government land agency, leisure management, conservation, rural investment, advisory and development agriculture.

Duration of first degree course(s) or equivalent: 3 years or 4 years (sandwich) **Total first degree students 1989/90:** 506 **Number of overseas students:** 15 **Number of mature students:** 40 **Male/female ratio 1989/90:** 4:1 **Teaching staff:** full-time: 48 part-time: 7 **Total full-time students 1989/90:** 723 **Postgraduate students:** 38 **Tuition fees, first degrees, 1990/91:** Home: £3,018–£3,786; Overseas: £3,018–£6,102.

What it's like

The Cotswolds provide a great atmosphere for the college which is set in private grounds, one mile outside Cirencester. Accommodation for approximately 200 students, mainly first years. Remaining students live in cottages within about a 10-mile radius of the college.

The library is computerised and there are computers available for student use.

Range of sporting clubs and other activities can be arranged; floodlit all-weather pitch and a multi-gym.

Pauper notes

Accommodation: College rooms single and shared. Cottages rents from £20–£40 pw. **Drink:** College bar not subsidised but provides a meeting place for students. Local pubs also provide a variety of entertainment. **Eats:** College provides meals for resident students and others may buy rolls at lunchtime. **Ents:** College provides a full and exciting social calendar. **Sports:** The sports facilities are excellent and matches are played against a number of other university and college teams. **Work:** Majority of students find jobs during the holidays.

CITY POLY

City of London Polytechnic, 117 Houndsditch, London EC3A 7BU (071-283 1030; fax: 071-623 2858) Map E, D2

Student enquiries: Admissions Officer, India House, 139 Minories, London EC3N 1NL

Main study areas – as in What to Study section: *(First degree):* Accountancy, art & design, business studies, communication studies, computing, economics, environmental science, geography, information technology, law, mathematical studies,

CAN'T FIND WHAT YOU'RE LOOKING FOR? USE THE INDEX!

modern languages, politics and government, psychology, sociology. *Also:* furniture design, interior design.

European Community: 7.5% first degree students take EC language as part of course and 0.5% spend 6 months or more in another EC country. Formal exchange links not known. Approved Erasmus programme 1990/91.

Application: PCAS, except art and design (ADAR). **Special features:** Positive attitude to mature and disabled students; modular scheme enables students to specialise in 1 subject, or combine 2 or more, to honours level. **Academic features:** New BA financial services and BSc computing with human factors. **Founded:** 1970 from City of London College and Sir John Cass College; merged with London College of Furniture, 1989. **Main awards:** BA, BSc. **Awarding body:** CNAA. **Site:** 8 teaching sites in City and Whitechapel. **Access:** British Rail, London Docklands Railway, underground and bus services. **Accommodation:** 380 self-contained flats; 99 in hall of residence. Approx cost 1990/91: £36-£39 pw (accommodation only), £60 pw (in hall). **Library:** 6 libraries; 260,000 volumes in total, 1,500 periodicals, 700 study places, slide collections (art), map collection. **Specialist collections:** Fawcett Library (women's studies). **Other learning facilities:** Computer centre, TV studio, language laboratories, electron microscope. **Welfare:** Student counsellors; chaplain; full-time nurse; AIDS adviser; access to solicitor and doctor. **Hardship funds:** In addition to the government Access funds, modest fund established annually to help students facing financial hardship during their course. **Careers:** Information, advice and placement. **Amenities:** Refectories or snack bars on all teaching sites; SU building with bars, TV and games rooms, discos etc. **Sporting facilities:** Gymnasium, activities room, 2 fitness rooms with multigym facilities, 2 outdoor sports grounds.

Duration of first degree course(s) or equivalent: 3 years; **others:** 4 years (sandwich and language) **Total first degree students 1989/90:** 3,055 **Number of overseas students:** 357 **Number of mature students:** 921 **Male/female ratio 1989/90:** 1:1 **Teaching staff: full-time:** 280 **part-time:** 81 **Total full-time students 1989/90:** 4,188 **Postgraduate students:** 378 **Tuition fees, first degrees, 1990/91:** Home: £1,695 (£655 if self-financing); Overseas: £4,950.

What it's like

Spread over 8 sites in the City and East End; facilities such as libraries split and shared. Sites quite cramped, many facilities inadequate. Accommodation a problem, as it is everywhere in London. No students live less than 2 miles away, most commute much further. Housing expensive, many live with their parents. Distances affect academic and social life.

Academically, standards are high; most staff are amenable and good teachers. Reasonable teaching and workload. Most subjects excellent. The modular degree scheme probably the most flexible in the country; proximity to the City ensures business and law related courses have the best teachers and are highly respected. SU executive turning away from political infighting towards student needs. Particular priorities are welfare, integration with local community, educational issues, student representation and active involvement in the academic affairs of the poly at all levels. Campaigns eg for Gay rights; against cuts in education, poll tax, racism in the East End, withdrawal of benefits and sexism. 3 Union bars, 4 shops, a bookshop and 2 (healthy!) fast food bars. SU funds a large number of active clubs – from Afro-Caribbean to Windsurfing. Finds it difficult to compete against London's many attractions, but a full programme of varied entertainments is provided.

Pauper notes

Accommodation: Poly can provide about 500 places. Otherwise accommodation can be difficult to find and expensive. Try areas like Leytonstone, Plaistow and the Isle of Dogs first; be prepared to have to live further afield. Start looking early. **Drinks:** 3 excellent SU bars (Fairholt House, Moorgate and Commercial Road); both the City and East End abound in pubs famous and infamous. Most, though,

CAN'T FIND WHAT YOU'RE LOOKING FOR? USE THE INDEX!

are expensive. SU bar in Fairholt House cheapest in city – happy hours galore. **Eats:** Most Poly sites have refectories providing cheap, canteen-type food. SU runs coffee bar (Moorgate) and Buttery/Snack Bar (Fairholt). Also plenty of snackbars in the City, and lots of good 'ethnic' food (try Bloom's kosher takeaways and curries at Dee Daas and Nazrul, both in Brick Lane). **Ents:** SU provides full programme of Ents – something most days. Not just bands, but film shows, cabaret and outings. Fairholt SU building – cabaret etc. Also a lot of cheap, varied and different cultural activities in the East End, and the West End is only half an hour away. **Sports:** Full time sports organiser and many clubs – but not great facilities. 2 Poly sports grounds – Chigwell, Essex, and Grove Park, Kent – a long way from poly itself. However, Wapping Sports Centre, and Sedgwick Centre are close by. **Hardship funds:** Poly has hardship and newly created access fund. Also small amounts available from other poly-linked sources. **Travel:** Central location makes travel quite easy. All sites close to tube and buses. Also near Liverpool St, Fenchurch St and Moorgate BR termini, Docklands light railway. **Work:** Plenty of work in 10 student trading shops and bars. Quite a lot of summer and weekend work in Central London. East End is unemployment blackspot.

CITY UNIVERSITY

City University, Northampton Square, London EC1V 0HB (071-253 4399) Map E, D1

Student enquiries: Academic Registrar

Main study areas – as in What to Study section: *(First degree):* Accountancy, aeronautical engineering, business studies, civil engineering, computing, economics, electrical & electronic engineering, law, mathematical studies, mechanical and production engineering, music, nursing studies, philosophy, psychology, sociology, speech sciences. *Also:* Actuarial science, media studies, ophthalmic optics.

European Community: Number of students taking EC languages or spending time in another EC country, not known. Approved Erasmus programme 1990/91.

Application: UCCA. **Largest fields of study:** Business studies, engineering, computing, IT, clinical and health-related subjects. **Founded:** 1894 as Northampton Institute, university status in 1966. **Main awards:** BSc, BEng, LLB, MEng. **Awarding body:** City University. **Academic features:** Courses available as full-time or on sandwich basis. All offer introduction to information technology, development of communication skills and opportunity to learn a foreign language. New degree courses in business law; journalism; sociology and media studies; physiotherapy with human sciences. **Site:** Islington, close to City of London. **Access:** Angel or Barbican underground stations. **Accommodation:** 810 places in hall (priority given to first and final year students). University accommodation service administers 200 places in self-catering flats and maintains register of private accommodation. Approx cost: around £45+ pw self-catering; £60–£100 pw B+B or B+B with evening meal. Hall fee £550 per 10-week term. Rent: 40% in accommodation where rent controlled by university. **Library:** 290,000 volumes, 1,800 periodicals currently taken. **Specialist collections:** Anderson Music Library, Erna Auerbach Collection, London Society Library, Walter Fincham Optics Collection. **Other learning resources:** Non-book media with listening and viewing facilities; Business School Library. **Welfare:** University health centre, counselling service and chaplaincy. **Careers:** Information, advice and placement service. **Amenities:** Bookshop on site, SU recreational facilities. **Sporting facilities:** Saddlers sports centre (good indoor sports and sauna); swimming pool; squash courts; major playing fields in South London.

CAN'T FIND WHAT YOU'RE LOOKING FOR? USE THE INDEX!

Duration of first degree course(s) or equivalent: 3/4 years; **others:** 4/5 years **Total first degree students 1989/90:** 2,279 **Number of overseas students:** 306 **Number of mature students:** 410 **Male/female ratio 1989/90:** 2:1 **Teaching staff:** 304 **Total full-time students 1989/90:** 3,276 **Postgraduate students:** 1,940 **Tuition fees, first degrees, 1990/91:** Home: £665; Overseas: £4,560 (eg politics), £6,050 (eg physics).

What it's like

In the triangle formed by Angel, Old St and Barbican tubes – each 5/10 minutes walk away. Not a campus, but most activity takes place in main building; halls and academic sites also within the triangle. Main building 1960s brick and concrete; accessible by numerous buses. First and final year students, who want to, live in halls; others rent flats/houses in N or E London. Overnight guests allowed in halls for two nights in any one week – but no one ever checks. Counselling and advice on mating/contraception available from SU or Barts Hospital clinic (very close and very busy). SU very active; tasteful left wing bias – no platform for racists at SU meetings. Runs a community action project and a creche for working/student mothers in the half term holidays. Discos/bands on Fridays, films on Thursdays and other ents during the week. Islington's pubs are a walk away and a taxi back from the West End is affordable. Top subjects are banking and finance, business, engineering, computing, optics and social sciences. Many students are sponsored; years out for training or experience is usually no problem. Most students are here because of a desire to see London Town or sponsorship, and City has low graduate unemployment rate.

Pauper notes

Accommodation: All 1st and 3rd years in hall. 1 bedroom flats for married students. Block of flats in Whitechapel plus others close to the University. **Drink:** 2 Union bars – approx 20% off a pint. Youngs Special. Bars in both halls of residence. **Eats:** Best to shop at the markets (Chapel & Whitecross Streets). Good veg curry house – lunch – as much as you can eat for c£3.00. Campus food missable. **Ents:** Ents card at least 1/3 off all City ents. Club atmosphere + appropriate music. **Sports:** University sports centre very nearby + cheap for students. Swimming pool in main building. Sports ground being re-negotiated currently. **Hardship funds:** Union will haggle with finance office/banks on students' behalf – good relationship with both. **Travel:** Travelling bursaries awarded by ex-student club (The N'ions). London fares high – get a bike or be prepared for the costs. **Work:** Work for Union in bars or ents, or for university in halls of residence kitchens usually available.

Alumni (Editors' pick)

Charles Farnecombe (conductor), John Alvey, Michael Fish (Good evening to you . . .).

COLCHESTER INSTITUTE

Colchester Institute, Sheepen Road, Colchester, Essex CO3 3LL (0206 761660) Map A, F7

Student enquiries: Enquiries Office

Main study areas – as in What to Study section: *(First degree):* Music.

European Community: 10% first degree students take EC language as part of course but none spend time in another EC country.

Application: PCAS for BA; direct for other courses. **Academic features:** Liturgical music, composition, performance, dissertation, 3yr Graduate Diploma Course in Music, recognised as degree equivalent for teacher qualification and designated comparable to first degree for grants. **Special features:** Ensemble in residence,

CAN'T FIND WHAT YOU'RE LOOKING FOR? USE THE INDEX!

master classes. **Structural features:** Links with Britten-Pears School at Snape and developing academic programmes with Essex University. **Founded:** 1976 ex North East Essex Technical College and School of Art, Colchester, and St Osyth's College, Clacton. **Main awards:** BA, Graduate Diploma in Music, Foundation Diploma in Music. **Awarding body:** CNAA. **Site:** Colchester and Clacton sites. **Access:** Both sites near town centres. **Accommodation:** 150 places in halls of residence at Clacton. Approx cost: £33.80pw including 5 evening meals. **Library:** Units on main site and at Clacton; 126,000 volumes in total, 500 periodicals, 352 study places. **Welfare:** Qualified nurses, medical room, student counsellor. **Hardship funds:** Local authority support for handicapped students. Local charities also available. **Special categories:** Residential facilities for disabled students. **Careers:** Information and advice. **Amenities:** SU shop and handbook. **Sporting facilities:** Gymnasia, judo, fencing, etc; tennis, playing fields, weight training room, dance studio. **Employment:** Music performance/teaching/music industry.

Duration of first degree course(s) or equivalent: 3 years **Total first degree students 1989/90:** 180 **Number of overseas students:** 6 **Number of mature students:** 30 **Male/female ratio 1989/90:** 2:3 **Teaching staff: full-time:** 17 **part-time:** 45 **Total full-time students 1989/90:** 2,350 (220 music students) **Tuition fees, first degrees, 1990/91:** Home: £1,675; Overseas: £4,563.

What it's like

On 3 sites: 2 in Colchester – Sheepen Road and Endsleigh Annexe; 1 in Clacton. Sheepen Road site (SR) built in late 50's, early 60's has only day students covering a wide range of courses in BA music, engineering, printing, catering, A levels etc. North East Essex Art School based here and at Braintree FE College. Clacton site (CS) on the sea front, smaller with residential facilities. Catering, sports and business courses, visitors allowed in rooms, has a good bar. Refurbished accom. Relaxed, informal atmosphere; understanding of student difficulties. Well developed SU with full representation, printing facilities and a cheap stationery shop. SU has one sabbatical and full representation on each site. Average student age 16–22. Mature and disabled students very welcome.

Pauper notes

Accommodation: Clacton residential accom. Refurbished, price includes one main meal. Vocational courses, accom provided at Clacton – non-voc (A-levels) none provided by college. Difficult to find, however Accom Officer has details. **Drink:** Smart bar at Clacton site plus good pub crawl rate. Oliver Twist, Hole in the Wall, The Cups, Fagin's Den – student pubs. **Eats:** Town food cheap and good: St Mary's Arts Centre, Tilly's, Traders, Shanty more expensive – Wings (Mercury Theatre rest). Don't miss Carol's at Clacton. **Ents:** (CS) Two discos per week and regular bands at Clacton. Video machine hire available. Film Society – films every 2 weeks. Discos every month. **Sports:** Sports centre and swimming pool 3 mins from Clacton site. Limited gym also. **Hardship funds:** SU has limited (very) funds for helping with playgroup costs. First come first served. Similar limited funds for bankrupt students. **Travel:** Inter-site transport. Exchange visit to Germany. 1 week field trip for some students. **Work:** Bar work – Clacton site bar.

Alumni (Editors' pick)

Farnaby Brass Quartet, Ebony Wind Quartet, Martin Litton (jazz pianist).

CAN'T FIND WHAT YOU'RE LOOKING FOR? USE THE INDEX!

COURTAULD INSTITUTE

Courtauld Institute of Art, University of London, Somerset House, Strand, London WC2R ORN (071-872 0220) Map E, B2

Student enquiries: Registrar and Secretary

Main study areas – as in What to Study section: *(First degree):* Fine arts.

European Community: 90% first degree students take EC language as part of course but none spend time in another EC country.

Application: UCCA. **Structural features:** Part of London University. **Largest fields of study:** History of European Art. **Founded:** 1931. **Main awards:** BA. **Awarding body:** London University. **Academic features:** Postgraduate diploma course in the history of art. **Site:** Central London. **Accommodation:** Apply to London University accommodation office, Malet Street, London WC1E 7HU. **Library:** Over 110,000 volumes, over 200 current periodicals, approx 112 study places; a slide library with over 250,000 b/w and coloured slides. **Specialist collections:** Witt Library (photographs and reproductions of paintings, drawings and graphics), Conway Library (photographs of sculpture and architecture). **Centres of excellence:** Courtauld Galleries (French impressionist and post impressionist paintings, Flemish and Italian Old Master paintings and drawings, Turner watercolours). **Welfare:** London University facilities. **Careers:** Information and advice service. **Amenities:** SU is affiliated to ULU and students can make use of their gymnasium, swimming pool, squash, etc. **Employment:** Museums and art galleries.

Duration of first degree course(s) or equivalent: 3 years **Total first degree students 1989/90:** 81 **Number of overseas students:** 5 **Number of mature students:** 15 **Male/female ratio 1989/90:** 1:2 **Teaching staff: full-time:** 21 **part-time:** 1 **Total full-time students 1989/90:** 201 **Postgraduate students:** 120 f-t; 101 p-t **Tuition fees, first degrees, 1990/91: Home:** £1,675; **Overseas:** £5,015.

What it's like

The Courtauld has moved into its grand new residence by the Thames with lots more space and better facilities; the gallery installed in the building incorporating the Courtauld's world famous art collection. Good teaching rooms and own fully modernised lecture theatre.

Students have large comfortable common room space, a smart refectory selling cheap food and a bar.

Larger cross-section of students coming to the college and the 'finishing school' reputation is long gone. Still a high standard academically and all tutors expect complete dedication.

The social life revolves around frequent parties and Xmas and Summer Balls. Added to this is the more informal quaffing club whereby, when the college closes at 7pm (excepting party nights) anyone left in the building is encouraged to go to the pub.

There are video clubs, theatre groups, camping clubs and women's societies, and any student with an idea for an activity is encouraged to follow it up.

The Courtauld has no accommodation facilities itself and refers its students to the Intercollegiate Halls. As a member of London University, students can make use of all sporting facilities of the University of London Union at Malet Street.

The Institute is in easy reach of London's galleries and libraries and, of course, the West End and all the entertainments London has to offer.
Neil Grindley

Pauper notes

Accommodation: Intercollegiate halls. **Drink:** Hopefully student bar in college, otherwise King's college bar next door. **Eats:** Cheap refectory. **Ents:** Parties in

CAN'T FIND WHAT YOU'RE LOOKING FOR? USE THE INDEX!

college, video clubs. **Sport:** ULU facilities. **Hardship funds:** Emergency hardship loans.

Alumni (Editors' pick)
Giles Waterfield, Neil McGregor, Alan Bowness, Anthony Blunt, Anita Brookner, Vincent Price, James Sainsbury.

COVENTRY POLY

Coventry Polytechnic, Priory Street, Coventry CV1 5FB (0203 631313)
Map A, E7

Student enquiries: Academic Registrar

Main study areas – as in What to Study section: *(First degree):* Accountancy, aeronautical engineering, art & design, biochemistry, biology, business studies, chemistry, civil engineering, communication studies, computing, economics, electrical & electronic engineering, environmental science, fine arts, geography, history, industrial relations, information technology, law, mathematical studies, mechanical and production engineering, modern languages, nursing studies, physics, politics and government, town and country planning, welfare studies. *Also:* Information systems, engineering, modern studies, equine studies.

European Community: 15% first degree students take EC language as part of course and 5% spend 6 months or more in another EC country. Formal exchange links with over 25 EC universities/colleges, including some open to non-language specialists: Belgium (Brussels); Denmark (Odense); France (Strasbourg); Germany (Aachen); Spain (Valencia). Approved Erasmus programme 1990/91.

Application: PCAS; ADAR for art and design. **Special features:** Admissions policy for mature and handicapped students. **Structural features:** Coventry School of Art & Design; Coventry Business School. **Academic features:** Increasing modular provision; credit transfer; links with European institutions. BA technical communication. **Founded:** 1970 ex Lanchester College of Technology, Coventry College of Art and Design, and Rugby College of Engineering Technology. **Main awards:** BA, BSc, BEng, MEng, LLB, BTP. **Awarding body:** CNAA. **Site:** Coventry city centre; large modern campus. **Access:** 5 miles M6/M1 intersection; 30 mins Birmingham by train, 75 mins London Euston; adjacent to National Express coach station. **Accommodation:** 737 places in halls of residence; 922 in bedsitters/houses; 300 places in lodgings. Approx cost: £27.50 pw room, £39.75 full board and lodgings. Rent: 20% in accommodation where rent controlled by polytechnic. **Library:** Main library and art and design library; 192,250 volumes in total; 3,020 periodicals, 1,100 study places; short loan collection of 8,000 course books and articles. **Welfare:** Doctor, FPA, psychiatrist, multi-faith chaplaincy; international students office; student counselling service; resident tutors in halls of residences. **Hardship fund:** South African student scholarship. **Special categories:** Residential facilities for disabled students. **Careers:** Information and advice service. **Amenities:** SU building with 3-bar complex, shopping area and travel bureau; nursery. **Sporting facilities:** 37 acre playing field, sports centre; Coventry swimming pool (Olympic standard) and city sports centre adjoin campus.

Duration of first degree course(s) or equivalent: 3 years; **others:** 4 years (sandwich) **Total first degree students 1989/90:** 5,000 **Number of overseas students:** 650 **Male/female ratio 1989/90:** 2:1 **Teaching staff: full-time:** 600 **part-time:** 50 **Total full-time students 1989/90:** 8,000 **Postgraduate students:** 550 **Tuition fees, first degrees, 1990/91:** Home: £1,675; Overseas: £4,600 (eg politics), £5,088 (eg physics).

CAN'T FIND WHAT YOU'RE LOOKING FOR? USE THE INDEX!

What it's like

Convenient for city centre, adjacent to cathedral. Easy to get to – M1, M6, very near to bus station and about 15 mins walk to train station. Poly accommodation – very expensive – 1st year students only – priority to overseas and particular courses, eg occupational therapy. Priory Hall – expensive, catered weekdays only – poor cooking facilities. Laundry facilities recently renewed – still inadequate. Catering – no vegan and little vegetarian. Most students live in private rented accommodation. Still fairly cheap on national scale.

Greater number of part-time students and also mature students. Inadequate nursery facilities although nursery is excellent. SU runs half-term play schemes. Library – opens longer near exam time – inadequate books due to increasing student numbers. SU – good socially and good ents. Over 110 societies. Good campaigning. Very good welfare bureau. Women's priority transport provided every night. Coventry City – not particularly safe at night. Not really a student town but plenty of pubs where students are welcome. Good transport links with Birmingham for concerts, theatre etc. Very close to Warwick University. Warwick Arts Centre good. Many courses have national representation. Several specialist courses, eg horse studies. Planning to go Modular by 1992. Reasonable teaching facilities. Lecturers have good relationships with students. Good relationship with administration. Generally, good standard of education and good social life.

Pauper notes

Accommodation: Introducing new head tenancy scheme for 1st year students. Priory Hall – fully catered and expensive; Caradoc Hall – 4 miles out but OK, dodgy neighbourhood; 50 poly houses in various states of repair, mostly good; River House – some like it, some don't, self-catered as is Caradoc and Poly houses. **Drinks:** SU sells cheapest beer. Warwick Uni only 3 miles away on No. 12 bus. Pubs mostly M&B, with some Courage and Ansells. **Eats:** Granny's Restaurant popular, Colin Campbell, Hope & Anchor, good, cheap for lunch. Little vegetarian or vegan catering in the city. **Ents:** Tic Toc – good venue; Browns – new disco popular with students. Main music scene centred on the poly and Warwick Uni. Excellent cinema at Warwick Uni Arts Centre. **Sports:** New deal with Coventry Sports Centre – reduced rates with SU card. **Hardship funds:** Increased due to access fund – SU recommendations to poly. **Travel:** Hitching is easy from Coventry but obviously not recommended, especially for women students. **Work:** Work in SU – stewards crew, glass collectors, local bars. Not good for vacation work.

Alumni (Editors' pick)

John Kettley (TV weatherman), Steve Ogrizovic (Coventry City FC goalkeeper), Alan Smith (Arsenal footballer), Peter Hadfield (founder of Two Tone), Jerry Dammers (The Specials).

CRANFIELD

Cranfield Institute of Technology, Cranfield, Bedford MK43 0AL (0234 750111) Map A, F7

This is largely a post-graduate UKCPU; undergraduate courses are offered in two faculties at *Silsoe* and *Shrivenham* – see separate entries.

CAN'T FIND WHAT YOU'RE LOOKING FOR? USE THE INDEX!

CRANWELL

The Royal Air Force College, Cranwell, Sleaford, Lincolnshire NG34 8HB (0400 61201) Map A, F6

Student enquiries: The Inspectorate of Recruiting RAF, Officers' Careers, Government Buildings, London Road, Stanmore, Middlesex HA7 4PZ; or to RAF School's Liaison Officer, or any RAF Careers Information Office.

Main study areas – as in What to Study section: *(First degree):* Aeronautical engineering.

European Community: Numbers of students taking EC language and spending time in another EC country, not known.

Site: Rural setting 7 miles from Sleaford and 15 miles from Grantham. **Access:** Situated on B1429, just off the A17. Nearest British Rail station is Sleaford with connecting bus service to college. **Accommodation:** Cadets live in single-room permanent accommodation throughout their period of training. Officers attending specialist and postgraduate courses will live in one of the 3 officers' messes. **Library:** 2 extensive libraries covering all aspects of military aviation and associated technical subjects, together with a wide collection of historic documents connected with the early days of the RAF. **Welfare:** Medical, dental and chaplaincy services. **Amenities:** Wide range of sports facilities include gymnasium and competition standard indoor swimming pool. Also riding, flying and gliding, and extensive range of hobbies.

What it's like

RAF officers have been trained at Cranwell since 1920. College is set in fine grounds of which central feature is imposing College Hall building. All officer cadets and student officers wear uniform. Initial officer training is both mentally and physically demanding, and course is designed to make cadets into leaders and fit them for role as junior RAF officers. Courses run by other departments at college or Flying Training School last from a few weeks to a year and are also challenging.

Alumni (Editors' pick)

Sir Frank Whittle, HRH The Prince of Wales.

CREWE & ALSAGER

Crewe & Alsager College of Higher Education, Crewe CW1 1DU (0270 500661 (College Office); 0270 589995 (Admissions)) Map A, D6

Student enquiries: Admissions Office

Main study areas – as in What to Study section: *(First degree):* American studies, art & design, biology, chemistry, dance, drama, education, English, environmental science, environmental studies, geography, history, mathematical studies, modern languages, music, nursing studies, philosophy, physics, physiology, psychology, religious studies and theology, sociology. *Also:* Crafts, physical education, sports science.

European Community: 5% first degree students take EC language as part of course and 5% spend 6 months or more in another EC country. No formal exchange links.

Application: PCAS; ADAR for BA Crafts. **Academic features:** Writing option offered as part of BA Creative Arts. Modular degree allows combination of subjects. BA Cert Ed for intending primary teachers. **Special features:** Nationally-known

CAN'T FIND WHAT YOU'RE LOOKING FOR? USE THE INDEX!

artists and craftsmen teach part-time on courses; usually an artist or craftsman in residence. Resident theatre company ('Theatre exchange') and dance company. **Founded:** 1974, ex Colleges of Education of Crewe and Alsager. **Main awards:** BA, BEd, BSc, BA with Cert Ed. **Awarding body:** CNAA. **Site:** 2 sites 6 miles apart. **Access:** M6 and railway stations near both campuses; regular inter-site transport. **Accommodation:** 700 places in both mixed and segregated halls of residence (all first year students who wish to can normally be accommodated). Rent: 40% in accommodation where rent controlled by college. **Library:** Library on each campus; 200,000 volumes, 1,000 current journal subscriptions, plus collection of microfilms and audio-visual materials, 260 study places. **Welfare:** Centre on each campus, visiting doctors and psychiatrist; professional welfare officers. **Hardship funds:** From LEA on recommendation from College. **Careers:** Information and advice service from professional careers officer. **Amenities:** Bookshops, shops and launderettes; SU with bars, TV rooms, etc; arts centre at Alsager site: studio theatre, dance and drama studios. **Sporting facilities:** Extensive playing fields, swimming pool, squash court and weight-lifting/training rooms, including a twelve station multi-gym, national coaching centre and sports injuries clinic.

Duration of first degree course(s) or equivalent: 3 years;others: 4 years (BEd; BA Cert Ed) **Total first degree students 1989/90:** 1,400 **Total BEd students:** 600 **Number of overseas students:** 30 **Number of mature students:** c200 **Male/female ratio 1989/90:** 1:1 **Teaching staff: full-time:** 150 **part-time:** c65 **Total full-time students 1989/90:** 1,850 **Postgraduate students:** c250 **Tuition fees, first degrees, 1990/91:** Home: £1,675; Overseas: £4,600.

What it's like

2 sites approx 6 miles apart. Crewe campus on outskirts of small, industrial town, pleasantly landscaped with good road and rail links. Alsager campus, in rural, rolling Staffordshire is less accessible but good services to Crewe and Hanley. Intersite bus service provided by college with limited night services.

Halls on both sites, 5 at Crewe and 9 at Alsager; majority are mixed. First and final years entitled to places; 2nd years live out. All halls are fully furnished with cooking facilities, No self-catering option. Large number of Irish students and mature students but no creche facilities. Indifferent management/student relations. SU becoming increasingly active on both sites.

Officially no overnight visitors allowed – unregistered cars are liable to be clamped. Good medical services in Crewe and Leighton hospital and student counsellor for confidential counselling.

Active and successful sports clubs, particularly football, rugby, hockey, netball, badminton, lacrosse etc. Also active SU clubs, eg Christian Union, Women's Group, Lesbian and Gay Group and Afro-Caribbean Group. Certain areas of the town, eg Walthall Street inhabited almost entirely by students. Other areas of Crewe not so friendly. Students living out generally meet up at college discos.

Crewe campus mainly HND business studies, environmental studies. Alsager mainly sports science, arts & humanity degrees (BEds on both). Work load depends on course. Assessments based on course work and examinations. The college has recently become a National Coaching Centre, run by the National Coaching Foundation.

The typical student either wears a tracksuit and is loud and drunk; or wears a more creative form of clothing, but is less loud while drunk.
Andrew Rock

Pauper notes

Accommodation: Plenty of accommodation in Crewe, if sometimes rather expensive (£25-40/week). **Drink:** The Vine, Earl of Crewe, Barrel, Brunswick, Belle Vue and the Victoria in Crewe (just a few of many). In Alsager: The Lodge, Grove and Plough. **Eats:** Plenty of chippies, Chinese takeaways and kebab houses. Lakeside Chippie in Alsager does particularly good pizzas. **Ents:** Local Oakley Centre for bands etc. Both sites have good social facilities for bands. Alsager also has drama facilities. **Sports:** Good facilities at Alsager for a wide range of sports, but little on Crewe campus. Alsager Leisure Centre and health gyms in Crewe also welcome students. **Hardship fund:** None. **Travel:** Exchanges with Kutztown. Excellent for rail travel and Sandbach service station is a useful hitching point. **Work:** Plenty of bar work around pubs in Crewe.

Alumni (Editors' pick)
Peter Purves, Mary Whitehouse, Steve Bainbridge, Dewi Morris, Matt Duncan, Phil Lewis, Sue Metcalf, Martin Grimley, Max Robertson, Tom Bailey (Thompson twins).

DARTINGTON

Dartington College of Arts, Totnes, Devon TQ9 6EJ (0803 862224) Map A, C9

Student enquiries: Admissions Officer

Main study areas – as in What to Study section: *(First degree):* Dance, drama, music, performance arts. *Also* community arts, performance arts.

European Community: Number of students learning an EC language or spending time in another EC country, not known. But various links eg with Eire, Denmark, Germany, Netherlands, Belgium, Luxembourg and France. Approved Erasmus programme 1990/91.

Application: PCAS. **Academic developments:** The college is now (1991) associated with South West Poly. **Special features:** College enjoys a close relationship with the Dartington Hall Trust; a unique establishment concerned with industry, education, arts and community development in rural area. Known for interest in Indian and other cultures. **Founded:** 1961. **Main awards:** BA. **Awarding body:** CNAA. **Site:** Modern and medieval buildings in beautiful grounds on River Dart. **Access:** Road and rail access to Plymouth and Exeter (within half hour), 10 mins from Totnes. **Accommodation:** 68 single study rooms on campus, accommodation officer helps with flats and lodgings in district. **Library:** 40,000 books and scores, 3,000 sound recordings, slides, films. Other learning resources: specialist studio and workshops, practice rooms. **Welfare:** Nurse/health centre. **Careers:** Some emphasis on preparing students for arts work in community. **Amenities:** Social centre with common room, bar, laundry, theatre, cinema; extensive grounds and garden.

Duration of first degree course(s) or equivalent: 3 years **Total first degree students 1989/90:** 340 **Number of overseas students:** 14 **Number of mature students:** 140 **Male/female ratio 1989/90:** 1:1 **Teaching staff: full-time:** 26 **part-time:** 5 **Total full-time students 1989/90:** 380 **Postgraduate students:** not known **Tuition fees, first degrees, 1990/91:** Home: £1,675; Overseas: £4,563.

What it's like
Beautiful, isolated campus, 20-minutes walk from Totnes. Picturesque gardens, old buildings and trees. Small campus, intimate and comforting but claustrophobic at times – 380 full-time students. Provision for disabled students improving on a difficult campus – on the side of a hill. Child-care provision not good, but is a priority campaign and improving. A small college, no money for SU but still provides a good variety of events. A part-time administrative assistant and an Executive of 13 look after SU affairs.

Easy reach of Torbay, Plymouth, Exeter and Dartmoor, but public transport is scarce/non-existent.

CAN'T FIND WHAT YOU'RE LOOKING FOR? USE THE INDEX!

Attracts European and Asian students; positively encourages applications from mature students. Excellent relations between SU and Admin. Library hours good; provision of texts/recorded material very good. No visiting restrictions. Health care excellent. Information readily available and comprehensive. Awareness sessions for first years on AIDS, contraception, alcohol and drug abuse. Confidential counselling available.

Accommodation scarce – some winter lets, mainly academic year lets. Own transport a definite advantage. Good college accommodation officer.

Courses revised and revalidated with much input from students. Work loads high. High-class visiting lecturers ensure that courses relate to current thinking in all subject areas. Few find the combination of work-load and campus conditions unbearable and leave. Failure rate low.

Students from a wide variety of social and educational backgrounds. 2 out of 3 department heads are women, plus female acting principal.

Pauper notes

Accommodation: 3 residential blocks for 68 students, all single rooms with wash basins; kitchen and 2 showers per 11 students. **Drink:** Good, cheap local beer (Blackawton), cider (Luscombes) on campus. College bar not subsidised but prices are comparable with local pubs. Totnes pubs good. Wine bars OK if you like posing! **Eats:** Cafeteria on campus providing vegetarian meals. Wide variety of vegan/vegetarian eating in Totnes, also Chinese, fish and chips. Good value in village pubs. **Ents:** Visiting theatre companies, concerts of all kinds, art exhibitions run by Dartington Arts Society – concessions available. SU organises bands, quiz nights, excursions, video. Lots of home-grown entertainment, classical and modern. **Sports:** Squash courts all year round – mixed football and cricket. Outdoor pool and tennis in Summer term. Swimming in Totnes indoor pool. **Hardship Funds:** Not a lot really. **Work:** Some work on campus – bar and library. Seasonal fruit-picking and farm work.

DARTMOUTH

Britannia Royal Naval College, Dartmouth, Devon Map A, C9

Student enquiries: Commander Graham Kemp RN, The Officer Enquiry Section, Old Admiralty Buildings, Spring Gardens, London SW1A 2BE.

Main study areas: Navy studies, strategic studies.

European Community: Number of students taking EC languages or spending time in another EC country, not known.

Entry conditions: Candidates must be at least 17 years old and under 22, 23 or 26 (dependent on the type of entry). Minimum entrance requirements: 5 GCSE or equivalent (grade C or better), including English language and maths; 2 A-levels required for full career commissions; A-level passes in physics and maths for engineering specialisation for both full and medium career commissions; many graduate entrants. Before entry candidates must pass Admiralty Interview Board and medical examination. **Entry dates:** Main entries in September, January and May. **Special features:** Almost all naval (and WRNS) officers start their careers at Dartmouth, as do many officers of foreign navies. The time spent at Dartmouth depends upon course taken. After period of general naval training, students go on to specialist training either at sea, at Dartmouth, at Royal Naval Engineering College, Manadon (see Manadon), or at universities. **Founded:** Training on River Dart since 1863. College buildings completed in 1905. **Site:** Beautiful hillside setting overlooking the Dart estuary. **Access:** Nearest British Rail stations at Paignton and Totnes. **Accommodation:** Single or shared cabins for all students. **Welfare:** Excellent, including full medical and dental facilities. **Amenities:** Full range of sporting and

CAN'T FIND WHAT YOU'RE LOOKING FOR? USE THE INDEX!

recreational facilities, including gymnasium, swimming pool, sports grounds with hard hockey pitch; over 100 boats and yachts and a beagle pack.

Duration of first degree course(s) or equivalent: up to 4 terms. **Male/female ratio 1989/90:** 10:1. **Total full-time students 1989/90:** 600+.

What it's like

Dartmouth is the Royal Naval Officers' new entry training establishment. As such day-to-day life at BRNC is very different from that of a normal university or polytechnic as the students are here to learn how to be leaders in a military service as well as to acquire the academic knowledge that will equip them for their future careers.

The student population is predominantly male and includes a number of international students. Daily routine is full, varied and demanding, geared to producing a healthy body and an agile mind. Teaching staff is comprised full-time civilian lecturers and serving naval personnel and the academic courses cover a wide range of subjects from international affairs to celestial navigation.

Most students are accommodated in either single or double rooms and full board is provided. Visitors are welcome at the College but no provision for their overnight accommodation (abundance of small hotels and guest houses in the holiday town of Dartmouth). College is poorly served by public transport and although the town is an easy walk away, those wishing to venture further afield will find their own transport a necessity.

Wide range of cultural, recreational and sporting activities which include music, drama, sailing, rugby, riding, cricket and squash to name but a few.

Alumni (Editors' pick)

HRH Duke of Edinburgh, HRH the Prince of Wales, HRH the Duke of York and Admiral Sir Julian Oswald (present First Sea Lord).

DERBYSHIRE COLLEGE

Derbyshire College of Higher Education, Kedleston Road, Derby DE3 1GB (0332 47181) Map A, E6

Student enquiries: The Registry

Main study areas – as in What to Study section: *(First degree):* Accountancy, American studies, art & design, biology, business studies, chemistry, computing, drama, education, electrical & electronic engineering, English, environmental studies, fine arts, geography, geology, history, information technology, mechanical & production engineering, modern languages, music, nursing studies, religious studies & theology, sociology. *Also:* Chiropody, photography, radiography.

European Community: 6% first degree students take EC language as part of course and 3% spend 6 months or more in another EC country. Formal exchange links with some 6 EC universities/colleges: Belgium (Nemours); France (Caen, Paris and Tours) and Netherlands (Breda). Planned expansion of modern languages learning and extension of range of languages available.

Application: PCAS, BA photographic studies and textile design (ADAR). **Largest fields of study:** Design (textiles, fashion, graphic), education, earth & life studies. **Academic features:** New modular degree with 40 options; new degrees in nursing, occupational therapy, accountancy and environmental monitoring. Biological imaging degree. **Structural features:** New Institute of Health and Community Studies, in collaboration with health authority. **Special features:** Artist-in-residence. **Founded:** 1983, ex Derby Lonsdale College of Higher Education and Matlock College of Higher Education. **Main awards:** BA, BEd, BSc. **Awarding body:** CNAA, Nottingham University. **Site:** Split on 3 sites. **Access:** Buses from

CAN'T FIND WHAT YOU'RE LOOKING FOR? USE THE INDEX!

Derby city centre. **Accommodation:** 500 places in halls, 100 places in registered lodgings (priority given to first year students). Approx cost: £28 self-catering halls, £45 pw lodgings. Rent: 30% in accommodation where rent controlled by college. **Library:** Main libraries at Kedleston Road and Mickleover sites; 295,000 volumes, 1,900 periodicals, 364 study places. **Other Learning Resources:** Computer centre and media services centre. **Welfare:** Dean of students, assistant deans, wardens and college nurse, chaplaincy, student counsellor. **Hardship funds:** Directors administer a hardship fund. **Careers:** Information and advisory service. **Amenities:** SU shop and bar, bookshops and stationery kiosks at main campuses. **Sporting facilities:** Gymnasia, heated indoor swimming pool at Mickleover site.

Duration of first degree course(s) or equivalent: 3 years; others: 4 years (sandwich) **Total first degree students 1989/90:** 1,100; **BEd students:** 400 **Number of overseas students:** 66 **Number of mature students:** 200 **Male/female ratio 1989/90:** 6:5 **Teaching staff: full-time:** 278 **part-time:** 150 **Total full-time students 1989/90:** 1,800 **Postgraduate students:** 200 **Tuition fees, first degrees, 1990/91:** Home: £1,675; Overseas: £4,400.

What it's like

It's 'a poly in everything but name', concentrated on 3 sites in Derby. Main site, Kedleston Road on a hill, with magnificent views of the countryside from upper floors. All sites on main bus routes from town centre, with one, Green Lane, actually in town centre.

College accommodation varies from purpose built blocks eg Fitzherbert Hall and Lonsdale Hall to converted Victorian residences along Uttoxeter New Road. For 1990 there were also caravans but even so most people live in private rented accommodation.

The student body is individual in its variety: a large proportion of women (balance has been addressed), many overseas students from countries as far apart as Ghana and Malaysia; also American and EC students.

Library on each site. Gymnasium and a multi-gym for weight training on the Kedleston Road site. SU has developed rapidly in recent years and continues to be very progressive. There is a recreation room at Kedleston Road with a bar in separate building, and an SU block at Mickleover (recent facelift) where many events held. SU particularly effective representing student point of view on college committees; co-ordinates effective campaigns on multitude of issues; also runs variety of clubs and societies – the most active being mountaineering and caving, students against bloodsports, football and rugby. SU discounts for students in the city include Derby Playhouse the Roos Sports complex, sports and record shops. Wide range of pubs to choose from in town centre and plenty of country pubs. Most are supplied by Bass, Ind Coope, Marstons and Wards. Cheapest drinks are in SU Social Club bars where real ales start at 90p per pint and Miller Lite £1.00.

Nationally renowned art and design faculty and photography courses; geography option in earth and life studies degrees offers a field trip to Morocco.

Students friendly, not that politically active; everyone seems to get on very well. Community spirit maintained during college expansion. People find it easy to settle in and have a very enjoyable time.

Pauper notes

Accommodation: Cheap terraced housing available in Normanton. **Drink:** SU bar cheapest drinks in town – Ansells and Scotch bitter. Other good places are Ye Olde Dolphin Inn (oldest pub in Derby), The Spa Inn in Abbey Street – serves Burton ale, and the students' favourite – the Great Northern on Junction Street. **Eats:** College restaurant now with edible food. Best takeaway Tuminose on St Peter's Street (pizzas and bolognese burgers a speciality), Ronos on Abbey Street. Many good Indian restaurants – many give student discount. Abbey Street kebab shops best. **Ents:** Theme discos. Annual favourites – Freshers Ball, Halloween Party and Bonfire Night. Bands recently already included Asia Fields, Lilac Time and Ska

CAN'T FIND WHAT YOU'RE LOOKING FOR? USE THE INDEX!

Boom. Also many bands at the assembly rooms; Dial & Lord Nelson. College radio.
Sports: On campus – 2 gyms and multigym. College swimming pool – free to
students. In town Rollerworld, Roos Sports Centre and Moorways Sports Stadium.
Hardship funds: SU offers loans – up to £30, also directors fund. **Travel:** Centre of
country, so easy for all transport networks. Can obtain railcards and coachcards
from SU Office. **Work:** Plenty of bar work available in town. Those who want jobs
don't find it a problem.

Alumni (Editors' pick)
Russell Harty.

DUNCAN OF JORDANSTONE

**Duncan of Jordanstone College of Art, Perth Road, Dundee DD1 4HT
(0382 23261) Map A, D2**

Student enquiries: Assistant Registrar

Main study areas – as in What to Study section: *(First degree):* Architecture, art &
design, communication studies, hotel & catering management, town and country
planning. *Also:* Home economics.

European Community: 8% first degree students take EC language as part of course
and 1% spend 6 months or more in another EC country. Formal exchange links with
1 EC institution at Nijmegen (Holland), open to non-language specialists. Approved Erasmus programme 1990/91.

Application: UCCA for architecture, town planning, hotel and catering management and home economics; direct other degrees. **Academic features:** Degree
courses in art and design from common foundation course. Professional video and
microcomputer centre available to students as a secondary study. Post grad courses
in electronic imaging, public art and design, computer-aided design and European
urban conservation. **Special features:** Writer in residence. Staff/student exchanges
with Nova Scotia College of Art & Design (Canada); School of the Art Institute of
Chicago (USA). **Largest fields of study:** Architecture, art and design. **Main
awards:** BArch, BDes, BA, BSc(Arch), BSc. **Awarding body:** Dundee University.

CAN'T FIND WHAT YOU'RE LOOKING FOR? USE THE INDEX!

Site: Dundee city centre. **Accommodation:** 156 hostel places (80% for first year students). Approx cost: £19.60 pw. **Rent:** 15% in accommodation where rent controlled by college. **Library:** 36,000 volumes, 180 periodicals, 130 study places. **Other learning resources:** Computer facilities. **Welfare:** No on-campus facilities. Assistant Registrar provides advice and assistance whenever possible. Access to Dundee University Student Welfare Service. **Hardship funds:** SU offers a loan scheme. **Careers:** Information service. **Amenities:** Shop, student common room, refectory and coffee bar. University SU and sports facilities.

Duration of first degree course(s) or equivalent: 4 years; **others:** 5+1 years for architecture **Total first degree students 1989/90:** 930 **Number of overseas students:** 32 **Male/female ratio 1989/90:** 1:1 **Teaching staff: full-time:** 70 **part-time:** 60 **Total full-time students 1989/90:** 1,191 **Postgraduate students:** 54 **Tuition fees, first degrees, 1990/91: Home:** £1,675 (£628 if self-financing); **Overseas:** £4,300.

What it's like

Surrounded by university buildings, 5 mins walk from the city centre, with access to major shopping precincts (three in all). The original building was erected in 1955 to house mainly art-orientated courses but as the college's reputation gradually grew it became necessary to expand the premises; new building opened in 1974 housing a further 400 students on eg architecture and home economics. Social life is as good as you make it. 2 college functions a week, Wednesday night fund raiser discos for students and Friday night disco, with live music when affordable. Accommodation difficult to find but college has blocks of flats shared with local technical college (200 places) mostly for first and second year students. Rent includes lighting, heating and hot water but an off-putting contract has to be signed. Welfare officer will discuss financial or personal problems as will Student President if preferred. Continual assessment on most courses with an end of term show of work. Changing courses or taking a year out is possible but not encouraged. Student Association representation on all major governing bodies including appeals.

Pauper notes

Accommodation: Fairly hard to find – increased college residential accommodation. **Drink:** College surrounded by student pubs, SA coffee bar, external bar – competitive prices. **Eats:** Variety of Indian, Chinese, vegetarian within immediate vicinity. **Ents:** College discos twice weekly, theatre, cinema. **Sports:** University sports complex, leisure centre. **Hardship funds:** Dependent on availability of funds. **Travel:** University housed campus travel. **Work:** Bar work.

Alumni (Editors' pick)

Albert Watson (royal photographer: wedding July 1986), David Leslie (rugby international).

DUNDEE INSTITUTE

Dundee Institute of Technology, Bell Street, Dundee DD1 1HG (0382 27225) Map A, D2

Student enquiries: Registry

Main study areas – as in What to Study section: *(First degree):* Accountancy, biology, biotechnology, business studies, chemistry, civil engineering, computing, economics, electrical & electronic engineering, mathematical studies, mechanical and production engineering, nursing studies, physics. *Also:* Quantity surveying.

European Community: 10% first degree students take EC language as part of course; none spend time in another EC country.

CAN'T FIND WHAT YOU'RE LOOKING FOR? USE THE INDEX!

Application: Direct. **Academic features:** BSc biotechnology, BSc chemistry with business studies. **Special features:** All courses have strong vocational bias; good staff links with commerce and industry. **Largest fields of study:** Engineering, science, business and other professional disciplines. **Main awards:** BA, BSc, BEng. **Awarding body:** CNAA. **Site:** Main college building plus 2 sites in Dundee city centre. **Accommodation:** 390 places in college flats; 170 places in hall of residence (particularly suitable for first year students); over 150 places in lodgings plus accommodation in private flats. Rent: 26% in accommodation where rent controlled by institute. **Library:** 100,000 volumes, 15,500 journals and periodicals, 400 study places, tied book system, audio-visual material. **Specialist collections:** Annual reports of 3,000/4,000 companies. **Other learning facilities:** Media centre; computer centre has powerful UA4, available for use by all students. **Welfare:** Counselling and advice, medical and health, accommodation, chaplaincy. **Hardship funds:** City of Dundee Educational Trust; Angus Educational Trust. **Careers:** Information, advice and placement service. **Amenities:** Bookshop; SU building with bars, games rooms, etc. **Sporting facilities:** Indoor facilities at SU.

Duration of first degree course(s) or equivalent: 4 years; **others:** 5 years (BEng/sandwich), 1 yr less for unclassified. **Total first degree students 1989/90:** 1,500 **Number of overseas students:** 50 **Number of mature students:** 150 **Male/female ratio 1989/90:** 7:3 **Teaching staff: full-time:** 170 **part-time:** 60 **Total full-time students 1989/90:** 2,100 **Postgraduate students:** 130 **Tuition fees, first degrees, 1990/91:** Home: £1,675; Overseas: £3,900.

What it's like

Situated in Dundee city centre; one of Scotland's Central Institutions offering degree and HND courses.

Accommodation is all around Dundee; college accommodation is in city centre, or 2-4 miles outside. Private accommodation is fairly easy to get but can be expensive.

All college accommodation has laundry facilities, mostly self catering but halls of residence places are available. Overnight guests not allowed in college accommodation without prior permission and no mixed accommodation available.

SU (recently refurbished) has variety of facilities including two bars, games room (snooker, multi-gym, table tennis) well-stocked shop and an excellent food service.

Variety of clubs and societies, all very active.

Student welfare excellent and all counselling confidential.

Students regarded by Dundonians passively. Relations between other Dundee colleges and university good.

Approximately 15% of students receive minimum grant and an overseas student population of about 6%. The student population is varied and comes from many different backgrounds and social groups.

Pauper notes

Accommodation: Private accommodation only for mixed couples. **Drink:** SU cheapest. Several good real ale pubs. Beer usually of high standard and a wide variety. **Eats:** SU cheap and varied. Many pubs do good meals; Tally Ho Scottish bar food champ. **Ents:** Steps Theatre, cinemas and rep all have discounts. Good live bands both major and minor. **Sports:** City council has good facilities and two Scottish Premier league teams. **Hardship funds:** SA operates loan fund. **Travel:** Student fare system in operation. On main routes for easy hitching. **Work:** Pubs, PO at Christmas, potato and fruit picking during summer.

CAN'T FIND WHAT YOU'RE LOOKING FOR? USE THE INDEX!

DUNDEE UNIVERSITY

University of Dundee, Dundee DD1 4HN (0382 23181) Map A, D2

Student enquiries: Secretary

Main study areas – as in What to Study section: *(First degree):* Accountancy, American studies, anatomy, architecture, art & design, biochemistry, biology, botany, chemistry, civil engineering, computing, dentistry, economics, electrical and electronic engineering, English, environmental science, European studies, fine arts, geography, history, hotel and catering management, law, mathematical studies, mechanical and production engineering, medicine, microbiology, pharmacology, philosophy, physics, physiology, politics and government, psychology, town and country planning, welfare studies, zoology.

European Community: 2% first degree students take EC language as part of course and 1% spend 6 months or more in another EC country. Formal exchange links with 2 EC universities/colleges in France (Grenoble) and Netherlands (Nijmegen - open to town and regional planning students). Approved Erasmus programme 1990/91. Possible exchange with Luxembourg University.

Application: UCCA. **Academic features:** BEng in Manufacturing Engineering making use of the most advanced CAD/CAM system in Scotland. Students able to switch between science and engineering subjects before entering the second year. New courses in medicinal chemistry, science of electronic materials, financial economics, hotel and catering management. **Founded:** 1881. **Main awards:** BA, BAcc, BArch, BDes, BDS, BEng, BMSc, BSc, LLB, MA, MB, ChB. **Awarding body:** Dundee University. **Site:** Near city centre. **Access:** By foot, rail and road. **Accommodation:** 860 places in mixed halls; over 850 places in university houses (over half student body is accommodated, and approximately 20% is home-based). 40% in accommodation where rent controlled by university. **Library:** Main library with approx 450,000 volumes; medical, law and departmental libraries; photographic department; inter-library loan scheme. **Other learning facilities:** Computing service; microcomputer centre, Tay estuary research centre; central media service unit; language unit. **Welfare:** Student counselling service. Health service offers routine medical examinations by local GP. **Hardship funds:** Loans may be available to students who encounter financial hardship. **Careers:** Information and advice service. **Amenities:** SU building with swimming pool, shop, bars, restaurant, bookshop, coin laundry; chaplaincy centre; civic repertory theatre adjoining campus. **Sporting facilities:** Indoor sports complex; university sports grounds and water sports centre; more than 20 golf courses including St Andrews and Carnoustie within half an hour's drive; skiing, climbing and hill walking in surrounding countryside.

Duration of first degree course(s) or equivalent: 4 years; **others:** 5 years (architecture, dentistry and medicine) **Total first degree students 1989/90:** 3,596 **Number of overseas students:** 8% **Number of mature students:** 17% **Male/female ratio 1989/90:** 3:2 **Teaching staff:** full-time: 359 **part-time:** 45 **honorary:** 387 (mainly in medicine and dentistry and courses taught at Duncan of Jordanstone College of Art) **Total full-time students 1989/90:** 4,069 **Postgraduate students:** 473 **Tuition fees, first degrees, 1990/91:** Home: £1,675; Overseas: £4,630 (eg politics), £6,120 (eg physics), £11,220 (maximum).

What it's like

Campus a mixture of modern and 18th-century buildings. City centre 2 mins away, but no through traffic allowed. All facilities on campus with the exception of medical faculty which is on a separate campus 3 miles away. Ninewells Hospital is the largest teaching hospital in Europe. Plentiful accommodation, but not always the best. 7% overseas students, 5% mature students. Excellent relationship between university and students – community atmosphere, close liaison with city. Large, new library and excellent sports centre on campus. SU is centre of students' social life, but politically fairly quiet.

Most courses are very flexible; transfers are easy at beginning of each year. Many field trips, several abroad. Work load really what you make it. Work assessment varies from course to course – all include exams but large move towards continual assessment.

Complete student support network. Full-time student counsellor, careers service, health service, plus SU run welfare team. Free dental treatment provided in campus dental hospital.

Over 100 active societies – many sports orientated. City geared towards students who form about 5% of population. Many pubs, two theatres, three cinemas (one devoted to showing 'alternative' films). Easy to meet other students (two unions on campus, one 2 mins away).

Dundee University has never been out of the top 5 in the employment stakes. Permanently top in Scotland. Salaries good, but lower for arts students.
Jessica Smith

Pauper notes
Accommodation: 55% students in univ accommodation. Cheapest private flats found by word of mouth. **Drink:** Tavern, Perth Rd, cheap. Union definitely cheapest – famous for 'Green Monsters'. Excellent Heavy throughout city. Most pubs do special promos from time to time – watch noticeboards. **Eats:** Union bar cheapest and caters for vegetarians, also 'Tower Cafe' on campus. On campus Association Supermarket. For veg and ethnics try Wholefoods, Perth Road. **Ents:** Airlie Place Ents (union) new venture in ethnic music; theatre on campus. Also Caird Hall (pricey) and Fat Sams. **Sports:** Sports centre on campus. Swimming pool in Association; new leisure centre 10 mins from campus. Ice rink in city. **Hardship funds:** Both university and Association run hardship funds. Access funds now available from university. **Travel:** No travel scholarships. Cheap fares available through Campus Travel in Association. **Work:** Available often in Association – bars, security, ents, DJs, painting, decorating, advertising etc. Other work difficult.

Alumni (Editors' pick)
David Leslie (Scottish rugby captain; member of 1984 'Grand Slam' team), George Robertson MP, Selina Scott.

DURHAM UNIVERSITY

University of Durham, Old Shire Hall, Durham DH1 3HP (091-374 2000) Map A, E4

Student enquiries: Academic Registrar

Main study areas – as in What to Study section: *(First degree):* Anthropology, archaeology, Asian studies, biochemistry, biology, botany, chemistry, civil engineering, classics, computing, economics, education, electrical and electronic engineering, English, geography, geology, history, law, linguistics, mathematical studies, mechanical and production engineering, microbiology, modern languages, music, Near East and Islamic studies, philosophy, physics, politics and government, psychology, religious studies and theology, sociology.

European Community: 10% first degree students take EC language as part of course and 4% spend 6 months or more in another EC country. Formal exchange links with increasing number of EC universities/colleges including: geography – 8 universities – main exchange with Tubingen (Germany), Barcelona (Spain); history – Roskilde (Denmark); theology – Aarhus and Tubingen (Germany); engineering –

CAN'T FIND WHAT YOU'RE LOOKING FOR? USE THE INDEX!

Nat Univ of Greece; education – Duisburg (Germany). Approved Erasmus programme 1990/91.

Application: UCCA. **Special features:** University consists of 12 colleges and 2 societies, largely self-governing, although teaching organised centrally. **Founded:** 1832. **Main awards:** BA, BSc. **Awarding body:** Durham University. **Site:** Durham city centre and south of river. **Accommodation:** Accommodation provided for 80% of undergraduate student body. **Library:** Main library has over 750,000 volumes, plus departmental and college libraries. **Welfare:** Student health centre; sick-bay facilities in each college, particular concern with deaf students with special adviser. **Careers:** Advisory service. **Amenities:** Wide range of facilities in both colleges and centrally (bar, bookshop, minibus) at Dunelm House, modern SU building; small theatre; museum of oriental art. **Sporting facilities:** Sports hall; 60 acres of playing fields.

Duration of first degree course(s) or equivalent: 3 years; **others:** 4 years **Total first degree students 1989/90:** 4,538; **BEd students:** 263 **Number of overseas students:** 180 **Number of mature students:** 305 **Male/female ratio 1989/90:** 7:6 **Teaching staff: full-time:** 432 **Total full-time students 1989/90:** 5,299 **Postgraduate students:** 761 **Tuition fees, first degrees, 1990/91:** Home: £1,675 (£665 if self-financing); Overseas: £4,560 (eg politics), £6,050 (eg physics).

What it's like

An attractive medieval city with cobbled streets, dominated by an impressive cathedral. Often referred to as the oasis of the north. University made up of 12 colleges. Vary from the Castle (almost as old as the cathedral), old houses along the North Bailey to attractive modern buildings designed in the '60s. All colleges but one now co-ed; St Mary's will remain all female. Academic departments housed in old buildings in town or on the modern purpose built science site.

Colleges are important aspect of Durham student life; majority of undergraduates live in for whole three years; social life tends to be centred in colleges with active theatre and arts groups, regular social events such as discos and bands. SU provides central ents in the form of bigger name bands. Rag Week organised centrally as are clubs and societies which range from the cultural (Arts groups) to the political (all major parties, Amnesty International, Greenpeace etc) and social. SU welfare department for personal, academic, financial, legal etc advice and professional counselling.

For those wishing to escape from Durham's peaceful atmosphere, Newcastle is only 20 minutes by train and has three excellent theatres, (RSC, National opera and ballet, visit regularly). Professional orchestras visit and big name pop bands. A range of cinemas (including alternative cinema) and many night clubs.

Sport a major part of Durham life. University teams very high standard but colleges provide for all standards. Sports range from hockey to hang-gliding and from rowing to rugby. Town has ice rink.

Students in Durham tend to be conventional with more Sloanes than usual. However, university widening the mix of students – hoping to take more overseas, mature and state school applicants.

Pauper notes

Drink: All colleges have bars; Castle (in the undercroft) best surroundings; van Mildert, best selection of real ales. Good pubs with real ale and student/town mix – Vic and Colpitts; other student pubs Dun Cow, New Inn, Swan + Three Sygnets. **Eats:** Riverside (SU), Old Post Office Restaurant (Indian), Hong Sing (Chinese inc take-away), Castle Tandoori (Indian take-away), plus six Italian restaurants. **Ents:** SU provides cheapest ents – mainly local bands, comedy etc; Film Society screens films(!). **Sports:** Graham Sports Centre (university); council swimming baths. **Travel:** SU travel bureau; some colleges give small travel scholarships. **Work:** Little opportunity of local employment to supplement grant.

CAN'T FIND WHAT YOU'RE LOOKING FOR? USE THE INDEX!

Alumni (Editors' pick)
Judith Hann (presenter, Tomorrow's World), Harold Evans (ex-editor of *The Times*), Will Carling (England rugby captain), Nasser Hussain (England test cricketer), Hunter Davies (writer, *Punch*).

EALING COLLEGE

Ealing College London, St Mary's Road, Ealing, London W5 5RF (081-579 5000) Map D, A2

Student enquiries: The Admissions Unit (Ref: B61)

Main study areas – as in What to Study section: *(First degree):* Accountancy, American studies, art & design, business studies, communication studies, computing, economics, English, European studies, fine arts, food science & nutrition, geography, history, hotel and catering management, information technology, Latin American studies, law, library & information studies, modern languages, music, politics & government, psychology, sociology. *Also:* Film studies, personnel administration, publishing.

European Community: Approx 55% first degree students take EC language as part of course and 30% spend 6 months or more in another EC country. Formal exchange links with some 25 EC universities/colleges: France (5); Germany (7); Italy (1); Netherlands (3); Portugal (2); Spain (6), many open to non-language specialists. BA applied languages Europe, in collaboration with University of Aix-en-Provence and Fachhochschule, Koln or Universidad Granada. Approved Erasmus programme 1990/91. Increasing number of courses allow 1 semester study abroad in EC.

Application: PCAS. **Academic features:** New degree courses in design and media management; English studies for language teaching; information management; law, French law/language or German law/language; leisure management. National Centre for Computer Assisted Language Learning. **Largest fields of study:** Business studies, humanities, law, languages. **Founded:** 1928, as a technical institute; designated a college of higher education in 1978. **Main awards:** BA. **Awarding body:** CNAA. **Site:** Ealing. **Access:** Buses, Ealing Broadway and South Ealing underground stations. **Accommodation:** Accommodation officer arranges flats and lodgings locally. Rent: 1% in accommodation where rent controlled by college. **Library:** 150,000 volumes, 1,000 periodical titles, 470 study places. **Welfare:** Student services unit provides medical, counselling and welfare services. **Careers:** Information and advice service. **Amenities:** Bookshop and bank on site; newly refurbished SU with 2 bars, entertainments hall, disco, restaurant, duplicating machines, binding service, own handbook, magazine 'Phase' and pamphlet 'What's On'.

Duration of first degree course(s) or equivalent: 3 or 4 years; **Total first degree students 1989/90:** 2,456 **Number of overseas students:** 1,187 **Number of mature students:** 40% **Male/female ratio 1989/90:** 2:3 **Teaching staff: full-time:** 260 **part-time:** 100 **Total full-time students 1989/90:** 3,740 **Postgraduate students:** 788 **Tuition fees, first degrees, 1990/91:** Home: £1,675 (£651 if self-financing); Overseas: £4,250.

What it's like

30 minutes out of central London by tube; within easy walking distance of Ealing Broadway and South Ealing tubes. Caters for courses, apart from degree courses. Small campus undergoing some expansion. Impersonality of larger institutions avoided. Campus has friendly atmosphere. Lively, effective SU is expanding rapidly with new offices and extra staff. SU runs a wide range of social events and activities and supports a large number of clubs: standard sporting (most activities

CAN'T FIND WHAT YOU'RE LOOKING FOR? USE THE INDEX!

catered for), cultural and political groups; also ethnic groups (Afro-Caribbean, Asian etc student association). SU deals with wide range of problems. No halls of residence. Rents are high locally but revamped accommodation offices will attempt to deal with problems (as well as SU). Low drop-out rate. Comprehensive student support services. Improving facilities for students with disabilities. Good relationship between SU and College.

Pauper notes

Drink: Excellent, friendly student bar; much cheaper than local pubs. **Eats:** Cheap food in student refectory, SU common room and bar. **Ents:** Wide range of SU-based events – discos, cabaret, live bands, cinema etc. Plenty of local cinemas; local arts centre (Watermans); easy access to central London for theatre, films etc. **Travel:** STA office on campus – cheap flights, trains etc to Europe and rest of the world. Good foreign placements on various courses, ie USA, Russia, Germany etc. **Sports:** Discount at local sport shop (with SU card). **Hardship fund:** Student Counsellor has hardship fund. **Work:** With Pizza Hut, Macdonalds, local pubs and student bar, SU functions by rota, Wembley Arena (via SU). **General:** Free handbooks to all students on enrolment; freshers pack available to all students; SU is much more able to deal with student problems this year due to increased funding. SU has non-sexist and non-racist policy. Confidential counselling service available.

EAST ANGLIA UNIVERSITY

University of East Anglia, Norwich, Norfolk NR4 7TJ (0603 56161) Map A, G6

Student enquiries: Registrar and Secretary

Main study areas – as in What to Study section: *(First degree):* Accountancy, American studies, anthropology, biochemistry, biology, botany, business studies, chemistry, computing, drama, economics, education, electrical and electronic engineering, English, environmental science, environmental studies, European studies, fine arts, geography, geology, history, law, linguistics, mathematical studies, microbiology, modern languages, music, philosophy, physics, physiology, politics and government, sociology, welfare studies, zoology. *Also:* Comparative literature, film studies, oceanography, physiology, Russian studies, Scandinavian studies.

European Community: 14% first degree students take EC language as part of course and 3% spend 6 months or more in another EC country. Approved Erasmus programme 1990/91. Also participates in many EC research projects, from information technology to greenhouse warming.

Application: UCCA. **Special features:** Excellent links with contemporary writers; past fellows in creative writing include Adam Mars-Jones, Maggie Gee, David Lodge, Anthony Thwaite, the poet Matthew Sweeney, Gore Vidal and Stuart Frost (ice sculptor). With associated institutes (John Innes and Food Research) forms largest concentration of biotechnology research scientists in W Europe. Also Climatic Research Unit. **Academic features:** Most degree courses combine study of several related disciplines, and include continuous assessment. **Founded:** 1963. **Main awards:** BA, LLB, BSc. **Awarding body:** East Anglia University. **Site:** 2 miles from centre of Norwich. **Access:** Frequent bus service. **Accommodation:** 1,400 study bedrooms on campus, 600+ on outskirts of Norwich, 89 in centre of Norwich, lodgings (addresses from accommodation centre). All first year students guaranteed accommodation. Approx cost: £837 per 30 week licence. Rent: 60% in accommodation where rent controlled by university. **Library:** Over 600,000 volumes, including books, volumes of periodicals, music scores and material in microform. 1,000 reading places, 100 study carrels; restricted loan collection of

CAN'T FIND WHAT YOU'RE LOOKING FOR? USE THE INDEX!

books in heavy demand, computerised catalogue system. **Other learning facilities:** Computing centre, language service unit. **Welfare:** Medical centre on campus with sick bay and dental service. **Hardship funds:** Small fund available. **Special categories:** Nursery and playgroup on campus, plus some accommodation for married students. **Careers:** Information and advice service. **Amenities:** University House with common rooms, printing rooms, television studios, student radio station; bookshop, newsagent, supermarket, post office, banks, launderette, pub, cafeterias on site, coffee shop, Sainsbury Centre restaurant, carvery and buffet; music centre; Sainsbury Centre for Visual Arts (19th and 20th century European paintings and sculpture plus outstanding ethnographic collection); university art collection (20th century). **Sporting facilities:** Indoor and outdoor sports facilities. **Duration of first degree course(s) or equivalent:** 3 years; **others:** 4 years (for courses involving study abroad) **Total first degree students 1989/90:** 4,018 **Total BEd students:** 105 **Number of overseas students:** 616 **Male/female ratio 1989/90:** 7:6 **Teaching staff:** full-time: 388 **Total full-time students 1989/90:** 4,680 **Postgraduate students:** 1,236 **Tuition fees, first degrees, 1990/91:** Home: £1,675 (£665 if self-financing); Overseas: £4,560 (eg politics), £6,050 (eg physics).

What it's like

Back in the mists of the early 60's, some bright spark thought it would be really neat to build a university on the wind-swept plains of East Anglia (aka a hill outside Norwich) – UEA is that university. Situated approximately 2 miles from the centre of historic Norwich, perhaps one of the most architecturally stimulating concrete complexes of the mid-60's, sited on the edge of parkland and enjoying panoramic views of the Norfolk countryside (and no it's not all flat!). Certainly a pleasant place to be.

SU provides an impressive group of services; from a pub to a TV station to an independent welfare service. UEASU is a dynamic force for quality services and student well-being. And with well over 100 sporting and non-sporting clubs and societies and the best ever ents programme, UEASU can easily fill all those hours you are supposed to spend working. Fine record of academic achievement, some of the best brains in the country, world leaders in subjects as diverse as landscape archaeology and development studies. By deliberate policy, UEA allows a high degree of inter-disciplinary study, often enabling students to tailor-make their degrees to suit their own interests. Also by accepting students who come from a wide variety of academic backgrounds and not just those who have the traditional 3 A levels, UEA is as socially stimulating as it is academically.

All in all UEA allows for personal as well as academic advancement. Come here – nowhere else will do!
Phil Scott

Pauper notes

Drink: Best brews Adnams, Greene King and Abbot. **Eats:** Cheap – Pizza One, Waffle House. Vegetarian – Eat Naturally. **Ents:** UEA is the centre of Norfolk for gigs. **Hardship funds:** SU will give small loan to students in need. **Work:** Some work in bars (factory work, once staple, becoming increasingly rare).

Alumni (Editors' pick)

Jonathan Powell (BBC), Selina Scott (TV presenter), Jenny Abramsky (Radio 4), Ian McEwan, Kazuo Ishiguro (authors), Noelle Walsh (Editor, *Good Housekeeping*), Vanessa Evans (Editor, *Country Homes & Interiors*), Tim Bentinck & David Vann (actors), Andy Ripley (rugby player), J Richard Sandbrook (International Institute for the Environment & Development), Dennis Callopy (MD, E6 Music Group), Martin Tyler, Peter Rose, Clive Sinclair.

CAN'T FIND WHAT YOU'RE LOOKING FOR? USE THE INDEX!

EAST LONDON POLY

Polytechnic of East London, (1) West Ham Precinct, Romford Road, London E15 4LZ (2) Barking Precinct, Polytechnic of East London, Longbridge Road, Dagenham, Essex RM8 2AS (081-590 7722)
Map D, D1

Student enquiries: Assistant Registrar (Barking Precinct).

Main study areas – as in What to Study section: *(First degree):* Accountancy, architecture and landscape, art & design, biochemistry, biology, biotechnology, business studies, civil engineering, computing, economics, education, electrical & electronic engineering, environmental science, law, mathematical studies, mechanical and production engineering, microbiology, modern languages, nursing studies, pharmacology, physiology, psychology, sociology, welfare studies. *Also:* Cultural studies, engineering and management, humanities, industrial design, manufacturing systems, physiotherapy, surveying – general practice.

European Community: 4% first degree students take EC language as part of course and less than 1% spend 6 months or more in another EC country. Formal exchange links with 4 EC universities/colleges: 1 in France (manufacturing systems); 3 in Germany (business studies and manufacturing systems). Approved Erasmus programme 1990/91. Degree programmes in European social studies and new technology with European studies.

Application: PCAS except art and design (ADAR). **Academic features:** BA/BSc by independent study (full-time or part-time); BSc manufacturing systems management (sandwich course with local industry); BSc biophysical science (sandwich course) New courses: biomarketing management; industrial design; geographical and land information management. **Founded:** 1970. **Main awards:** BA, BSc, BEng, LLB. **Awarding body:** CNAA. **Site:** Split on 7 sites; divided into 2 precincts (Barking and West Ham). **Access:** Close to BR station, underground and bus routes. **Accommodation:** 800 places in housing association student flats, 60 YMCA places. Approx cost: £30–£50 pw. Rent: 12% in accommodation where rent controlled by polytechnic. **Library:** Several libraries with subject bias; over 300,000 books in total, 1,000 study places. **Specialist collections:** Science Fiction Foundation Library; Charles Myers Library of industrial psychology. **Centres of excellence:** Chemotherapy research unit. **Welfare:** Professional welfare officers, doctor, FPA, chaplain. Welfare officers provide access to external agencies, eg charities and aid centres. **Hardship funds:** South Africa scholarship. **Special categories:** Playgroup at Barking precinct and at Holbrook Centre. **Careers:** Information, advice and placement service. **Amenities:** SU officers and premises on each precinct, choir of over 60, music centre at Barking precinct. **Sporting facilities:** Wide range of sporting activities, swimming pool, fitness centre.

Duration of first degree course(s) or equivalent: 3 years; **others:** 4 years (some ft and sw); 5 years part time **Total first degree students 1989/90:** 5,141 **BEd students:** 10 **Number of overseas students:** 590 **Number of mature students:** 3,850 (ft & sw) **Male/female ratio 1989/90:** 1:1 **Teaching staff: full-time:** 450 **part-time:** 8 (fte) **Total full-time students 1989/90:** 5,712 **Postgraduate students:** 1,103 **Tuition fees, first degrees, 1990/91:** Home: £1,675; Overseas: £4,530 (eg arts), £4,755 (eg science).

What it's like

PEL stretches across five sites in East London, with one other site just touching Essex in Barking. But before you get any cute ideas about East End Cockneys and Albert Square cliches, here's a closer look at life and study in this capital institution. From the tumbling down ex-school house of 'Holbrook' (architecture is based here!) to the plush conference halls of Duncan House (business), or the stern

CAN'T FIND WHAT YOU'RE LOOKING FOR? USE THE INDEX!

schoolness of Barking (law) PEL has courses and atmosphere to suit every student. Courses range from the conventional teaching and accountancy to the unconventional independent study and cultural studies. London students have the good fortune (or financial frustration) of living in a capital where entertainment can be pursued in any sphere. Ents at PEL are sound with the plus that a 'closed' building brings ie safer/less harassed, plus some of the cheapest beer prices around. PEL SU runs a huge range of clubs and societies from the Ravers to land surveying.
Lucy Bishop

Pauper notes
Accommodation: PEL is fortunate in having (approx) 1,300 plus places of accommodation, half of which is reserved for first years. By 1992 an additional 500 places should have been built at Barking. Although there is not a shortage of private housing in East London, prices are not always realistic. **Drinks:** Two SU run bars – Barking and Maryland, where the beer is cheap and the atmosphere unharassed. The 'Eddie' is a popular student pub in Stratford. **Eats:** Poly food varies from the scarcely edible of Holbrook to the amazing cuisine of Duncan House. Has to be tasted to be believed. **Ents:** Good for supporting new (and often local) bands. Cabaret excellent; good local theatres. **Sports:** Excellent range of facilities available at Barking. West Ham's sport is non-existent. **Hardship funds:** Ha ha ha ha ha! This has never been more relevant since the withdrawal of students from the benefit system. A hardship fund does exist for the desperate; you'll have plenty of company. **Travel:** Only railcards, Isic-cards and National Express. **Work:** Bar work and telephone research popular.

Alumni (Editors' pick)
Garry Bushell (TV editor of 'The Sun'), Mark Frith (freelance journalist with 'Smash Hits').

EDGE HILL

Edge Hill College of Higher Education, St Helen's Road, Ormskirk, Lancashire L39 4QP (0695 575171) Map A, D5

Student enquiries: Admissions Officer

Main study areas – as in What to Study section: *(First degree):* Education, English, European studies, geography, history, welfare studies. *Also:* Humanities, organisation and management, urban policy and race relations.

European Community: Number of students taking EC languages or spending time in another EC country, not known.

Application: UCCA. **Academic features:** Common first year for BA and BSc courses. **Special features:** Links with the open college scheme operated by colleges in Lancashire and the north west. **Founded:** 1885. **Main awards:** BA, BEd, BSc. **Awarding body:** Lancaster University. **Site:** Open rural site edge of Ormskirk. **Access:** Motorway, rail link with Liverpool. **Accommodation:** 450 places in halls, 750 flats/bedsitters/lodgings. All first year students offered accommodation. Approx cost: Halls £1,400 pa (B&B plus evening meal); lodgings £15–£25 pw (B&B). **Library:** 130,000 volumes, 650 periodicals, 166 study places, reference and short loan collections. **Other learning facilities:** Educational resources centre; closed circuit TV and studio, computer centre. College a national centre for UK Reading Association. **Welfare:** Full time counsellor, college health centre, creche facilities. **Careers:** Information, advice and placement. **Amenities:** SU building with bar, snack bar and games room; bookshop on campus; good sporting facilities including a double gym and heated swimming pool.

CAN'T FIND WHAT YOU'RE LOOKING FOR? USE THE INDEX!

Duration of first degree course(s) or equivalent: BA/BSc 3 years; **others:** BEd 4 years **Total first degree students 1989/90:** 1,513; **BEd students:** 715 **Number of overseas students:** 5 **Number of mature students:** 392 **Male/female ratio 1989/90:** 2:5 **Teaching staff: full-time:** 158 **part-time:** 60 **Total full-time students 1989/90:** 1,750 **Postgraduate students:** 120 **Tuition fees, first degrees, 1990/91:** Home: £607; Overseas £4,260.

What it's like

Campus with attractive buildings, ranging from 1930's to modern smoked glass and steel. 45 acres of playing fields and beautiful gardens. A very relaxing and attractive place to study, just outside Ormskirk (a small ancient market town). Within easy reach of Southport (7 miles) and Liverpool (15 miles). Both provide excellent nightlife; clubs, cinemas, theatres, restaurants, etc. Also good shopping facilities. Ormskirk has a cheap market on Thursdays and Saturdays and a small indoor market.

Campus life very easy-going. Students generally settle in very quickly. Low drop-out rate. College rooms comfortable, warm and nicely furnished. Meals provided in refectory and cooking facilities available in Halls.

Twice weekly entertainments organised. Films on Thursdays. SU societies are all quite active, especially in the Athletic Union. Folk, alternative music, anti-Apartheid, Arts, drama societies very active. SU finances societies and provides an excellent welfare service. Very active community work scheme and a child care facility on campus.

Students seem happy with courses. 33% on BEd course. English, geography, social sciences also have large intakes. Courses assessed on 40% coursework, 60% exam. Good staff/student relations – each student allocated a Studies Adviser. Degrees validated by Lancaster University.

Pauper notes

Accommodation: Most non-resident students live in Southport – £17–£25 pw. Approx 450 in 11 halls (7 mixed, 4 single sex). Cost includes room, breakfast and dinner. **Drink:** College Club on campus (Tetleys bitter, Skol and Castlemaine XXXX lager is main attraction). Ormskirk has 13 pubs ranging from wine bars to scruffy and cosy. **Eats:** Good value lunchtime snack – campus coffee bar, veggies catered for. Good variety of pub lunches in Ormskirk. Couple of good pizza/pasta places plus dial-a-pizza service in Ormskirk. **Ents:** Disco every Wednesday. Bands etc on Fridays – frequent off-campus trips to local nightclubs – films on campus every Thursday. **Sports:** Active Athletic Union. Very good facilities, gym, swimming pool, tennis courts, weights room, local swimming with squash and sauna. **Hardship funds:** Provided by SU. **Travel:** Quite good hitching between Ormskirk and Southport as bus fares expensive (service every half hour). Trains to Liverpool every 15 minutes – cost about £1 with railcard. **Work:** Some students manage to get work in Ormskirk or Southport. Limited term-time work. Some students stay to work in summer vac on local farms.

Alumni (Editors' pick)

Francis Harmer (LEA careers officer), Ann McCormack (commercial planner, Metal Box Co), Duncan Pybus (area manager, Hornsea Pottery), Jonathan Pryce (actor).

CAN'T FIND WHAT YOU'RE LOOKING FOR? USE THE INDEX!

EDINBURGH COLLEGE OF ART

Edinburgh College of Art, Lauriston Place, Edinburgh EH3 9DF
(031-229 9311) Map A, D3

Student enquiries: Registrar

Main study areas – as in What to Study section: *(First degree):* Architecture, art &
design, environmental studies, fine arts, town and country planning. *Also:* Housing
administration, landscape, urban studies.

European Community: No students learn an EC language or spend time in another
EC country as part of their course. Formal exchange links with 6 EC universities/
colleges: France (4); Greece (1); Spain (1) – all open to non-language specialists.
Approved Erasmus programme 1990/91.

Application: UCCA; direct for art and design. **Largest fields of study:** Art and
design, architecture, landscape architecture and town planning. **Founded:** 1909.
Main awards: BA, BArch, BSc, MA (Fine Arts). **Awarding body:** Heriot-Watt
University, Edinburgh University. **Site:** Edinburgh city centre. **Accommodation:**
64 places in self-catering flats. Further information on halls of residence and
lodgings available from Accommodation and Welfare Officer. Rent: 10% in accommodation where rent controlled by college. **Library:** 83,500 volumes, 110,000
slides; 483 periodicals, 140 study places. **Other learning resources:** Computer
facilities. **Welfare:** Counselling and welfare services available. **Amenities:** College
shop; student common room, student snack bar, music room and photographic
dark room. Clubs and societies provide a wide range of social activities. **Hardship
funds:** Some discretionary funds.

Duration of first degree course(s) or equivalent: 4 years; **Others:** 5 years **Total
first degree students 1989/90:** 651 **Number of overseas students:** 12 **Number of
mature students:** 32 **Male/female ratio 1989/90:** 2:5 **Teaching staff: full-time:** 54;
part-time: 44 **Total full-time students 1989/90:** 655 **Postgraduate students:** 39
Tuition fees, first degrees, 1990/91: Home: £1,675 (£637 if self-financing);
Overseas: £5,405.

NB: These figures are for schools of art & design. Figures for architecture and town
& country planning are included in Heriot-Watt University entry.

What it's like
Established in 1909. Very central location, right underneath the Castle. Very
classical interior – holds one of the finest collections of antique classical casts (until
the college authorities decided to whitewash them). Associated with Heriot-Watt
University, but retains its own governing body and is independently funded, or
underfunded rather.

Consists of very highly regarded and very traditional drawing and painting
school; other schools include sculpture, design, architecture, landscape, planning
and film and TV. Tutors still tend to be white, male and over 50; (but Union is
pushing for more women on staff).

SU always busy, always active, and has a high media profile. Active on most world
issues, particularly green and human rights. Internally has a women's group, gay
society, architecture group, darkroom, occasional bar, music room, Christian
union, Albertinas (Union cafe). Works closely with NUS, particularly on loans and
poll tax. Left wing. Still attempting to form a creche.
Scott Lawrie

Pauper notes
Accommodation: Student flats in rather dank Cowgate area. **Drink:** Tap Still
around; The Doric (should one wish to rub shoulders with Muriel 'Wacky' Grey);
Laughing Duck, oldest gay pub. **Eats:** Albertina's (excellent veggie burgers);
Seeds, West Nicolson St – very good value wholefood restaurant; Sebos cafe;

CAN'T FIND WHAT YOU'RE LOOKING FOR? USE THE INDEX!

Miah's, Forrest Road, all you can eat for £3.50 one night a week plus cheap vegetarian Indian. **Ents:** Wee Red puts on benefits/cabaret etc; Filmhouse/Cameo cheap student matinees; Bedlam Theatre. **Sports:** Use Heriot-Watt/Edin Uni facilities. Edinburgh has numerous Victorian swimming pools, Infirmary Street is best one. **Hardship funds:** Loans of £75 available immediately from college welfare. **Work:** Some work at exhibitions, openings.

Alumni (Editors' pick)

Some has-been pop stars; John Bellamy, John Houston, Gwen Hardie, Liz Blackadder (painters); Sean Connery; Susie Wighton (primary health care worker Palestinian camps); Ron Brown and Roy Williamson ('The Corries').

EDINBURGH UNIVERSITY

University of Edinburgh, Old College, South Bridge, Edinburgh EH8 9YL (031-667 1011) Map A, D3

Student enquiries: Secretary

Main study areas – as in What to Study section: *(First degree):* Accountancy, agriculture, horticulture and forestry, anthropology, archaeology, architecture, biochemistry, biology, biotechnology, botany, business studies, chemical engineering, chemistry, civil engineering, classics, computing, economics, electrical and electronic engineering, English, environmental science, European studies, fine arts, geography, geology, history, information technology, law, linguistics, mathematical studies, mechanical and production engineering, medicine, microbiology, modern languages, music, Near East and Islamic studies, nursing studies, pharmacology, philosophy, physics, physiology, politics and government, psychology, religious studies and theology, sociology, veterinary studies, zoology. *Also:* Celtic studies, wild life and fisheries management, Scandinavian studies, Scottish studies.

European Community: Number of students taking EC languages or spending time in another EC country, not known. Approved Erasmus programme 1990/91.

Application: UCCA. **Academic features:** New courses in housing studies; Japanese and linguistics; social policy with gender studies; sociology with South Asian studies; computational physics; immunology. **Founded:** ~1583. **Main awards:** BA, BCom, BD, BDS, BEng, BMus, BSc, BSc(Med Sci), BSc(Soc Sci), BSc(Vet Sci), BVMS, LLB, MA, MA (Religious Studies), MA(Soc Sci), MBChB. **Awarding body:** Edinburgh University. **Site:** Edinburgh city centre (arts, law, music, social sciences, veterinary medicine and medicine); science 2 miles south. **Access:** Waverley BR station and central bus station (St Andrew Square) nearby. **Accommodation 1989/90:** 4,680 students in university controlled accommodation – halls of residence, flats and lodgings; 4,250 in private sector accommodation. Remainder at home or in lodgings. **Rent:** 50% in accommodation where rent controlled by university. **Library:** Main library is largest university library building in UK, also various faculty libraries, nearly 2 million volumes and pamphlets, multiple loan service. **Specialist collections:** Major computer network & associated facilities; Reid music library, Erskine medical library, European Institute library, law library, New College (Divinity) library, veterinary library; Russell collection of early keyboard instruments; also historic collection of wind instruments; Talbot Rice Gallery with permanent Torrie Collection of painting and sculpture and visiting exhibitions. **Careers:** Advice and placement. **Amenities:** SA bars and shops, over 140 clubs, sports centre, playing fields and Firbush Point field centre on Loch Tayside for climbing and water sports. **Hardship funds:** Government access funds; limited assistance also available from university bequests.

Duration of first degree course(s) or equivalent: 4 years (hons), 3 years (general); **others:** 5 years (medicine and veterinary medicine) **Total first degree students 1989/90:** 9,154 **Number of overseas students:** 361 **Number of mature students:**

CAN'T FIND WHAT YOU'RE LOOKING FOR? USE THE INDEX!

925 **Male/female ratio 1989/90:** 10:9 **Teaching staff: full-time:** 1,242 **part-time:** 144 **Total full-time students 1989/90:** 11,094 **Postgraduate students:** 3,018 **Tuition fees, first degrees, 1990/91:** Home: £1,675 (£637 if self-financing); Overseas: £4,560 (eg politics), £6,050 (eg physics).

What it's like

Student life at Edinburgh is as varied and cosmopolitan as the city itself. The city is one of the best parts of being a student at Edinburgh. Not only is Edinburgh one of the most desirable places to live in Britain but the large student community means that there are a wide range of pubs, clubs, restaurants and shops which cater especially for student tastes.

The Students' Association provides countless services to its students – largest such organisation in Scotland. The three union houses offer cheap food and drink as well as many different kinds of entertainment. Six weekly discos ranging from indie-pop to heavy metal (and everything in between). Regular large scale events in the Unions with bands and cabaret acts – eg Aztec Camera and Gerry Sadowitz. Walk-in advice centre – the only one of its kind in Scotland.

Edinburgh has an international reputation for academic excellence, beautiful surroundings and many student-specific services provided both by the community and the Students' Association. What more could you ask for?
Martin Quinn

Pauper notes

Drink: Union bars – frequent promotions and a Happy Hour every night. Chambers Street Union House offers the cheapest drink in Edinburgh. **Eats:** Union food is cheapest, ranging from pie and beans to full meals, vegetarian, pizzas and new pasta bar. All union houses offer vegetarian food, Potterton makes it a speciality. **Ents:** 1 or 2 bands every week, also many discos, clubs, cabaret, jazz – free in all unions. Full range of city nightlife. Filmsoc the largest in Britain. **Sports:** Large sports union, also Commonwealth pool beside main Halls and other championship facilities. **Hardship funds:** Joint university and SA loans scheme (£60). **Counselling:** SA Education and Welfare Adviser, Uni counselling service, 'Nightline' phone-in. New walk-in advice centre. **Travel:** Limited company owned by SA runs four travel outlets offering discounts.

Alumni (Editors' pick)

Sir David Steel, Julius Nyerere, Sir Walter Scott, Sir James Barrie, John Buchan, Thomas Carlyle, R L Stevenson, David Hume, Sir Arthur Conan Doyle, George Foulkes, Charles Darwin, Malcolm Rifkind, Lord Palmerston, John Lloyd, Russell Johnston, Lord Mackay of Cashfern, David Livingstone, Mungo Park, Robert Louis Stevenson, Linsey MacDonald, Gordon Brown, Sheena McDonald.

CAN'T FIND WHAT YOU'RE LOOKING FOR? USE THE INDEX!

ESSEX UNIVERSITY

**University of Essex, Wivenhoe Park, Colchester CO4 3SQ
(0206 873333)** Map A, F7

Student enquiries: Admissions Officer

Main study areas – as in What to Study section: *(First degree):* Accountancy, American studies, biochemistry, biology, chemistry, computing, economics, electrical & electronic engineering, English, environmental science, European studies, fine arts, history, Latin American studies, law, linguistics, mathematical studies, modern languages, music, philosophy, physics, politics and government, public administration, sociology, welfare studies. *Also:* Operational research, telecommunication engineering.

European Community: 9% first degree students take EC language as part of course and 2% spend 6 months or more in another EC country. Formal exchange links with some 40 EC universities/colleges: Belgium (3, including for law and history); Denmark (3, including for law and government); France (7, including history, law, literature, physics); Germany (7, including history, law); Greece (4, including literature, law, physics); Italy (7, including law, history, literature, physics); Netherlands (2, including history, law); Portugal (2, including physics); Spain (4, including history, law). Approved Erasmus programme 1990/91.

Application: UCCA. **Academic features:** New degrees in European studies; art history and theory/history/literature/philosophy/sociology and music; chemistry (four-year sandwich degree); chemistry and European business studies; English and European laws. **Founded:** 1962, Royal Charter received 1965. **Main awards:** BA, BSc, LLB, BEng, MEng. **Awarding body:** Essex University. **Site:** 2 miles east of Colchester. **Access:** Bus service from Colchester station and from town centre. **Accommodation:** 1,876 places in university-owned accommodation, 450 places in houses and flats leased by university. Guarantee of accommodation for single first year students. Approx cost: £22.40 pw for 39 weeks (October–July). Rent: 62% in accommodation where rent controlled by university. **Library:** 437,000 volumes, 2,900 periodicals, 650 study places; 3-hour loan system for course books. **Specialist collections:** Latin American and Slavonic collections. **Welfare:** Doctor, FPA, psychotherapist, chaplain, student counsellor, welfare rights advice. **Special categories:** Some residential facilities for married and disabled students; 50 nursery/playgroup places. **Careers:** Information, advice and placement service. **Amenities:** Bookshop, general shop, banks and post office; 217 seat theatre, exhibitions gallery; SU building with shop, bar, travel centre, print room, newsletter etc; film society; University Radio Essex; art studio. **Sporting facilities:** Sports hall; floodlit, all-weather playing area; gymnasium; wide range of sports including water sports association with club house and dinghies.

Duration of first degree course(s) or equivalent: 3 years; **others:** 4 years (eg languages, environmental and industrial chemistry, information and business systems technology) **Total first degree students 1989/90:** 2,815 **Number of overseas students:** 433 **Number of mature students:** 1,230 **Male/female ratio 1989/90:** 1:1 **Teaching staff: full-time:** 264 **Total full-time students 1989/90:** 3,486 **Postgraduate students:** 671 **Tuition fees, first degrees, 1990/91:** Home: £1,675 (£636 if self-financing); Overseas: £4,560 (eg politics), £6,050 (eg physics).

What it's like

Campus university, about 2 miles from Colchester, built in large park. Compact, with friendly atmosphere. Main features of concrete skyline are 6 residential towers. Accommodation on campus insufficient – supplemented by 600 rooms in purpose built flats on estate down the road. Towers divided into 14/16 flats with 13/16 people sharing kitchen, some flats mixed. Double flats and married flats at top of some towers. 1st years guaranteed campus accommodation. Visiting restrictions officially

CAN'T FIND WHAT YOU'RE LOOKING FOR? USE THE INDEX!

in force but nobody takes any notice. Off-campus accommodation varied; university owns property in Colchester; also operates contract housing scheme; otherwise private market. Distances 1 to 9 miles from university. Bus sporadic, especially to main BR station (no service after 6 pm on Sundays).

Live groups and discos, own radio station, newspaper plus sporting, cultural, practical and political societies, as well as student help and advice. Colchester garrison town 55 miles from London; relations with town poor (too many squatting). Wivenhoe, couple miles away, trendy ex-fishing village, now thriving port. Some reasonable pubs if prepared to look for them. During winter it is cold and very windy with North Sea winds prevailing.

Relations between students and university administration fairly good. Result of degree depends on continuous assessment and more traditional sit-down closed-book exams. Easy to change course. Almost all first-year courses unspecialised leaving open as many options as possible for final degree. Students mixed; some yuppies; many yearning for old, radical days of Essex students.

Pauper notes
Accommodation: No student squats. Accommodation in crisis. More undergrads expected and as yet no increase in univ accommodation. **Drink:** SU bar biggest and cheapest in East Anglia; many good pubs in Wivenhoe ('Sociology on Sea') and surrounding area. Many good local real ales – Greene King, Adnams. **Eats:** SU food good and cheap. Veggie food catered for. **Shops:** Second hand bookshop and SU shop (alternative food) on campus. SU travel agent, proliferation of Oxfam, Help the Aged shops etc in area and many popular jumblies! **Ents:** Very good uni film soc. Good uni theatre. Fairly good ents, but not many student campus bands. **Sports:** No swimming pool. Astroturf and cheap facilities. **Hardship fund:** Both university and SU funds available. **Travel:** Most travel scholarships abolished. Good SU travel shop. **Work:** Summer work on campus. Jobs available off campus in term.

Alumni (Editors' pick)
Brian Hanrahan, Virginia Bottomley MP, President Oscar Arias of Costa Rica (Nobel Peace Prize 1987), Peter Joslin (Chief Constable of Warwickshire), Gwyn Jones (Welsh Development Agency), Rodolfo Neri Vela (Mexico's only astronaut).

EUROPEAN BUSINESS SCHOOL

The European Business School, Inner Circle, Regent's Park, London NW1 4NS (071-487 7400) Map E, B1

Student enquiries: The Registrar

Main study areas – as in What to Study section: *(First degree):* Accountancy, business studies, economics, information technology, modern languages, public administration.

European Community: All students take EC languages as part of course and spend 6 months or more in another EC country. Own network in Paris, France; Parma, Italy; Frankfurt, Germany; Madrid, Spain (link with ICADE).

Application: Direct. **Academic features:** Integrated languages and business programme; two foreign languages; courses in leadership, public speaking and management skills. **Structural features:** Part of international group with centres in Austria, Czechoslovakia, France, Germany, Italy and Spain. **Special features:** In-company training periods for 9 months as part of 4 year course. **Largest fields of study:** Business administration, finance and marketing. **Founded:** 1967. **Main awards:** Diploma in European Business Administration. **Awarding body:** Combined Examining Board of the European Business Schools. **Site:** Single campus in the heart of Regent's Park, London. **Access:** 5 minutes walk from Baker Street underground and buses. **Accommodation:** 30 students on site. Others in bed-sits,

CAN'T FIND WHAT YOU'RE LOOKING FOR? USE THE INDEX!

flats etc in central London. Approx cost: £102 with good meal plan. Rent: 20% in accommodation where rent controlled by school. **Library:** 65,000 volumes, 600 periodicals, 100 study places. **Specialist collections:** Royal Institute of Public Administration, Overseas Development Institute and Institute of Linguists libraries; other special collections on international relations, journalism and media and American law. **Other learning facilities:** New computer laboratory; access to libraries of British Theatre Association and Centre on Language Teaching and Research. **Careers:** Information, advice and placement service. **Main areas of employment:** Managerial positions throughout Europe. **Welfare:** Full facilities available on campus-wide basis through Regent's College; personal tutors for counselling. **Hardship funds:** Scholarships and bursaries on application. **Amenities:** Music, drama, art gallery and other activities on campus. **Sporting facilities:** Access to football and tennis in Regent's Park; indoor facilities in central London.

Duration of first degree course(s) or equivalent: 4 years **Total first degree students 1989/90:** 450 **Number of overseas students:** 70% **Male/female ratio 1989/90:** 5:3 **Teaching staff: full-time:** 30 **part-time:** 100 **Total full-time students 1989/90:** 450 **Tuition fees, first degrees, 1990/91:** (all first year students) £4,800.

What it's like

More a way of life than an undergraduate course. Situated in the centre of Regent's Park, one of the most beautiful parks in London. Excellent campus with first class facilities including a large common room, bar, tennis courts, refectory, library; acres of park in centre of London. Emphasis on international business and professionalism. Four-year course involves studying in three of the five EBS centres: London, Paris, Frankfurt, Madrid and Parma – and 48 weeks in-company training. All students develop fluency in two foreign languages, so even with mix of European nationalities at EBS communication is never a problem. Pace of work and life is demanding. Course very practical, not all theory, the main subjects are economics, law, finance, marketing, international business. Special attention paid to personal skills for management, managerial skills and two languages. Graduate employment depends on specialisation chosen for the fourth year. Some graduates continue businesses they have founded whilst at EBS, others go straight to management in international companies. To date some 3,000 EBS graduates managing and running companies all over world. Four years EBS experience enables graduates to command high starting salaries. If you would like to meet some students, see the college and get some advice on getting a place, write to the President of the Student Council.

Pauper notes

Accommodation: Very expensive, single and double rooms. **Drink:** College bar – nice cork-panelled – reasonable prices. Drummonds. **Eats:** Regent's College refectory – very good food – great variety – nice surroundings – reasonable prices. **Ents:** Lots of student activities sponsored by the student council both on and off the campus. **Sports:** On campus tennis courts (2 grass, 1 hard). Football pitches in Regent's Park. Off campus: Seymour Leisure Centre. **Work:** 48 weeks within 4 years – in-company training.
Student European (Links): SMILE (Student Marketing Initiative Linking Europe) is a student organisation that exists at EBS Frankfurt and London and is involved in arranging marketing and Europe-related activities. The long-term goal is to establish a European network in at least all the EBS centres. All outside EBS-students are welcome – co-operation with other universities etc is welcome in order to fulfil the European idea behind the organisation.

Alumni (Editors' pick)

Felix Meyer-Morn (DEBA 1986), John Jesser (DEBA 1986), Nicholas J Davies (DEBA 1985), Georgina Swift (DEBA 1988).

CAN'T FIND WHAT YOU'RE LOOKING FOR? USE THE INDEX!

EXETER UNIVERSITY

University of Exeter, Northcote House, The Queen's Drive, Exeter
EX4 4QJ (0392 263263) Map A, D9

Student enquiries: Academic Secretary

Main study areas – as in What to Study section: *(First degree):* Accountancy,
American studies, archaeology, biology, botany, business studies, chemical
engineering, chemistry, civil engineering, classics, computing, drama, economics,
education, electrical and electronic engineering, English, environmental science,
fine arts, geography, history, law, linguistics, mathematical studies, mechanical &
production engineering, modern languages, music, Near East and Islamic studies,
physics, politics and government, psychology, religious studies and theology,
sociology.

European Community: Number of students taking EC language or spending time
in another EC country, not known, but includes all students taking languages as
single honours or combined with eg fine arts, drama, history, music, Arabic, Greek
and Roman studies, computer science, maths. Some students studying engineering,
geography, law or psychology may also spend time in EC. Formal exchange links
with 5 EC universities/colleges: 4 in France (Marseille and Rennes, for law, science,
engineering, arts, social policy, science, health service) and Germany (Saarbrücken,
for law). Approved Erasmus programme 1990/91.

Application: UCCA. **Academic features:** BSc courses in: geoscience and cognitive
science; BA in managerial statistics. **Founded:** 1955. **Main awards:** BA, BEd, BSc,
BEng, LLB, BA(Ed), BSc(Ed). **Awarding body:** Exeter University. **Site:** Modern
campus. 1 mile from city centre. **Access:** Bus from city centre. **Accommodation:**
Around 50% of students accommodated. **Library:** Over 700,000 volumes and
journals, separate faculty libraries, especially law and education. **Specialist collections:** Rare editions, examples of early printing. University houses Cathedral
Library (distinguished collections of Anglo Saxon and medieval works); and the
Devon and Exeter Institution Library (West Country material). **Welfare:** Health
centre; counselling service and family centre for 28 children run by Guild of
Students; chaplaincy. **Amenities:** Shops, bank, etc on campus; Guild buildings
with licensed bars, launderettes, etc; Northcott Theatre which has its own professional company but also provides for amateur productions. **Sporting facilities:**
Sports hall on main site, offering wide range of facilities; indoor heated swimming
pool and gymnasia at the school of education; open air pool during summer.

Duration of first degree course(s) or equivalent: 3 years; **others:** 4 years **Total
first degree students 1989/90:** 4,963; **BA(Ed) BSc(Ed) students:** 759 **Number of
overseas students:** 67 **Number of mature students:** Approx 500 **Male/female
ratio 1989/90:** 1:1 **Teaching staff:** full-time: 552 part-time: 16 **Total full-time
students 1989/90:** 6,300 **Postgraduate students:** 1,947 **Tuition fees, first degrees,
1990/91:** Home: £1,675; Overseas: £4,560 (eg politics), £6,075 (eg physics).

What it's like

2 sites: lovely wooded main campus (modern buildings), 1 mile from city centre,
and St Luke's site (school of education, 19th century buildings) half mile in opposite
direction. Climate warm and wet; pace of life reflective rather than frenetic. Main
campus amenities good: 2 SU buildings with bars, coffee bars, refectories, shops,
outdoor swimming pool, sports complex and theatre. St Luke's has excellent PE
facilities (indoor heated pool, gymnasia, etc), lively bar, coffee bar and shop.
Accommodation: most first years in hall. Facilities good but food variable. Halls
date from 1960s but a few converted 19th-century houses. Most 2nd and 3rd years
live off campus. Self-catering flats on campus convenient though cramped. University keen to recruit from wide social and geographical base. Guild provides plenty of
opportunities for non-conformists; politically non-aligned and enjoys good relations

CAN'T FIND WHAT YOU'RE LOOKING FOR? USE THE INDEX!

with University and is quite well formally represented. Confidential pregnancy and contraception advice. Guild promotes big name concerts in large hall (2,000 capacity) and varied minority arts events of high quality; also excellent welfare services. Excellent sporting reputation and over 100 recreational, academic, social and political societies. University traditionally 'under funded' by UFC. Exams: mainly unseens, varying amount of dissertation work. Personal tutor system could be improved. Teaching services centre provides study methods counselling. Difficult to change course (strict quota imposed by UFC). High academic standard. Drop-out and academic failure rates relatively low. Exeter is a typically conservative county town with good but unexceptional amenities. Town wary of students. If ivory tower gets claustrophobic, escape to nearby seaside and beautiful countryside.

Pauper notes

Accommodation: 50% of students live on campus – Mount Pleasant/Pinhoe popular student areas off campus. Many live in the country. **Drink:** College bars (the Ram and Ewe). The Black Horse – notorious hangout for sporty people, The Red Cow (spit & sawdust). **Eats:** Guild coffee bar, The Ram for cheapest and tastiest pot meals – in town Pizza Piazza, Crockers and the Ganges are in. **Ents:** Last year – Transvision Vamp, The Wonderstuff, De La Soul, Jasper Carrot among the 40 live shows the Guild put on – the biggest ents programme in the south-west. Late night films at 2 Northcott theatres are very popular. Arts Centre in town well frequented. **Sports:** 2 pools on campus – open-air on the main site – indoor at St Luke's. 2 pools in town 1 of them being The Plaza. **Hardship funds:** £50 loans available from Guild – sympathetic bank manager on campus! **Travel:** Scholarships for overseas travel, quick hitching (M4/M5)/rail links. **Work:** Guild bars – restaurants/pubs in town – students fit in with summer and arrival of tourists.

Alumni (Editors' pick)

Rob Ackerman and Paul Downton (sporting internationals), Tony Speller and Bowen Wells (Tory MPs), Paul Jackson ('The Young Ones').

FALMOUTH SCHOOL OF ART

Falmouth School of Art & Design, Woodlane, Falmouth, Cornwall TR11 4RA (0326 211077) Map A, B9

Student enquiries: Academic Registrar

Main study areas – as in What to Study section: (*First degree*): Art & design.

European Community: 2% first degree students take EC language as part of course and 2% spend 6 months or more in another EC country. Formal exchange links with 4 EC universities/colleges in France (Ecole des Beaux Arts in Strasbourg, Caen, Poitiers and Tours). Industrial placement in Europe through Comett.

Application: ADAR. **Academic features:** Courses include information and graphic design, copywriting, illustration, fine art, radio journalism and ceramics. Trend towards student centred learning. **Special features:** Visitors include Michael Weaver (reader at Oxford), Michael Edwards (Jungian psychoanalyst). **Structural features:** New institution on the Falmouth School of Art site with £1.5 million new building. **Founded:** Began as private venture, taken over by local authority in 1938. Became Falmouth School of Art & Design in September 1987. **Main awards:** BA. **Awarding body:** CNAA. **Site:** Near Falmouth town centre. **Accommodation:** 1 student hostel; list of approved lodgings sent to students. Approx cost: £30–35 pw. **Library:** 20,000 volumes, 160 periodicals. **Careers:** Advice service. **Amenities:** SU arranges social and sports activities; excellent sailing.

Duration of first degree course(s) or equivalent: 3 years; **others:** 4 years (sandwich course in graphic information design) **Total first degree students 1989/90:** 254

CAN'T FIND WHAT YOU'RE LOOKING FOR? USE THE INDEX!

Number of overseas students: 10 **Number of mature students:** 63 **Male/female ratio 1989/90:** 1:1 **Teaching staff: full-time:** 50 **part-time:** 15.5 **Total full-time students 1989/90:** 880 **Postgraduate students:** 24 **Tuition fees, first degrees, 1990/91:** Home: £1,675; Overseas: £4,995.

What it's like

Fourth biggest art and design college in the UK. Set in picturesque grounds on the southern peninsula of Cornwall. First year accommodation in two college hostels. Warm, friendly atmosphere. Good all-round facilities, including well-equipped workshops and new audio-visual computer centre. Diversity of styles encouraged. Space available for students to work or exhibit in college gallery. Design courses have excellent industrial contacts, regular term-time placements and very good career prospects. Recently merged and expanding rapidly with construction of new buildings. SU very actively involved in the community, organising charity events and school and hospital placements. Also organises a hectic social life and activities as diverse as film clubs, ballet, football and weight-training. Local discount scheme; dance, theatre, sports, alternative cabaret, poetry festivals, rock concerts and trips to all local events.

Pauper notes

Accommodation: Hostel £18.50 shared, £22.50 single, town £26. **Drink:** Chain Locker, Jacobs Ladder, Seven Stars, King's Head, good local brews. **Eats:** Good on campus, catering for vegetarians. Local restaurants for diverse tastes, many offer discounts. **Ents:** SU Film Club, weekly – wide range of films; lively series of parties plus trips to concerts, theatre etc. **Sports:** Discount use of weights/sauna etc at Fit Pit. Free use of Cam Brea Centre, interdepartmental sports. **Hardship funds:** Being arranged. **Travel:** 2nd year (Fine Art) trips abroad subsidised. Healthy exchange scheme – French colleges. **Work:** Summer college work grants available, seasonal work – tourist industry bars, hotels etc.

Alumni (Editors' pick)

Fergus Walsh (BBC Radio 4 home affairs correspondent), Juliet Morris (BBC TV presenter).

GLASGOW COLLEGE

Glasgow College, Cowcaddens Road, Glasgow G4 0BA (041-331 3000) Map A, C3

Student enquiries: Academic Registrar/Schools Liaison Officer

Main study areas – as in What to Study section: *(First degree):* Accountancy, biochemistry, biology, business studies, chemistry, civil engineering, communications studies, computing, economics, electrical & electronic engineering, geography, information technology, mathematical studies, mechanical and production engineering, modern languages, nursing studies, politics and government, psychology, sociology. *Also:* Actuarial studies, ophthalmic optics, public administration, quantity surveying, risk management.

European Community: 27% first degree students take EC language as part of course and 10% spend 6 months or more in another EC country. No formal exchange links at present but sandwich placements planned in Denmark, Greece, France, Spain, Ireland.

Application: Direct. **Academic features:** BEng sandwich courses with electronic and manufacturing options. Degrees in chemistry with information technology and instrumentation; risk management; applied physics and instrumentation. Integrated management development programme leading to MBA. **Founded:** 1971.

CAN'T FIND WHAT YOU'RE LOOKING FOR? USE THE INDEX!

Designated a Scottish central institution 1985. **Main awards:** BA, BSc, BEng. **Awarding body:** CNAA. **Site:** City centre. **Access:** Bus, underground, rail. **Accommodation:** Accommodation officer will advise. **Library:** 150,000 volumes, 1,200 periodicals, 750 study places; study copies held. **Other learning resources:** Computer intensive environment, learning resources unit. **Welfare:** Doctor, chaplains, welfare advisers. **Hardship funds:** SA provides short term loans; college fund for direct emergencies. **Careers:** Information, advice and placement service (most courses are vocational). **Sporting facilities:** Sports hall, gym.

Duration of first degree course(s) or equivalent: 3 or 4 years **Total first degree students 1989/90:** 4,228 **Number of overseas students:** 155 **Number of mature students:** 1,491 **Male/female ratio 1989/90:** 1:1 **Teaching staff: full-time:** 329 **Total full-time students 1989/90:** 5,262 **Postgraduate students:** 934 **Tuition fees, first degrees, 1990/91:** Home: £1,675; Overseas: £4,270.

What it's like

Built in 1971 it borders on the city centre with easy access to buses, trains and underground. Close to shopping precinct with cinemas, theatres, pubs and discos. Association provides a lively Union with cheap entertainments, booze and food. Also produces a magazine, has a Welfare Office and two sabbaticals who represent students on college committees, etc. Runs many clubs, societies and sports clubs, from political to sub-aqua. However, there is a lack of sports facilities at the college (a sports hall with a games hall and a weights room). Union shop sells confectionery, cigarettes and stationery at reasonable prices.

No college accommodation but, being in the city, there are many good flats and bedsits within easy travelling distance. Library situated in a modern building provides study areas etc, on campus. College buildings are all situated on a compact campus and have just about everything a student needs within it.

Pauper notes

Accommodation: West end of city and south side popular. Red Road flats and Cobbington Place with Glasgow District Council, David Naismith Building with YMCA. **Drink:** Union for good cheap spirits and beers – Becks, Bellhaven, McEwans Export, Budweiser. **Eats:** Union snack bar for tasty cheap food. Always has at least 1 vegetarian dish. **Ents:** Discos every weekend, 4 'all-nighters' a year and bands at Union, Pavillion, Barrowland and SEC. Plays at Citizens' Theatre. **Sports:** Easy transport to sports facilities off campus. Sports Club go on day/weekend trips. Games hall and weights room on campus (free to students). **Hardship funds:** College provides short term loans and has fund for direct emergencies. **Travel:** Transcard system for buses, trains and underground – all stopping near College. **Work:** Difficult to get vacation work as Glasgow has high unemployment. No adverse attitudes to the dole.

Alumni (Editors' pick)

Alan Christie (ex-chairman NUS UK, general secretary of British Youth Council), James Doran (Nationwide journalist), Pat Nevin (Chelsea FC and Scotland), Colin Calder (Radio Producer with BBC), Denise Holt (AA Roadwatch), Claire English (TV presenter), Peter Lawwell (Celtic FC).

GLASGOW COLLEGE OF BUILDING

Glasgow College of Building & Printing, 60 North Hanover Street, Glasgow G1 2BP (041-332 9969) Map A, C3

Student enquiries: Academic Registrar

Main study areas – as in What to Study section: *(First degree):* Civil engineering. Also: Quantity surveying.

European Community: No students take EC languages or spend time in another EC country.

Application: Direct. **Largest fields of study:** Quantity surveying and building, (non-degree courses in printing, photography, interior design). **Main awards:** BSc. **Awarding body:** CNAA. **Accommodation:** Not known. Rent: no students housed in accommodation where the rent is controlled by the college. **Library:** 30,000 volumes, 200 periodicals, 70 study places. **Careers:** Information and advice service. **Amenities:** Design centre, Scottish Exhibition Centre, public libraries, museums, workshops. **Employment:** Quantity surveying, construction management, interior and graphic design, building, photography, printing, surveying.

Duration of first degree course(s) or equivalent: 4 years; **others:** 3 years **Total first degree students 1989/90:** 142 **Number of overseas students:** 34 **Number of mature students:** 26 **Male/female ratio 1989/90:** 6:1 **Teaching staff: full-time:** 186 **Total full-time students 1989/90:** 1,300 **Postgraduate students:** 20 **Tuition fees, first degrees, 1990/91:** Home: £628; Overseas: £4,475.

What it's like

13 storey glass-fronted tower block overlooking George Square. Well placed for transport and faculties. Close to Glasgow College and Strathclyde University: reciprocal agreements. Parking at college impossible. Accommodation register compiled by SRC at start of academic year; no halls of residence. 3% overseas students. Approx 1,200 full-time and 3,200 part-time students.

Active students' association with shop, photocopier, common room, pool tables, videos games. Wide range of students due to variety of courses. Employment rate is high. Most students straight from schools in West, North and Central Scotland, many stay at home with parents and aspire to job, family, car etc. Average drop out rate. Ratio of male to female in full-time courses is 2:1. On part-time courses it is 7:1. SRC is active but not overly political.
Alan M Benzie

Pauper notes

Accommodation: Shared in local authority flats or private sector. **Drink:** Cheapest at other SUs, plenty of trendy pubs nearby. **Eats:** Canteen average, some vegetarian. Fast food readily available nearby. **Ents:** Plenty live bands at college; good discos/clubs around city centre. Local theatre and cinema. **Sports:** Underused college PE dept, with good facilities; swimming pool within travelling distance. **Hardship funds:** Available where grants/bursaries are late. **Travel:** Travel services at Strathclyde Univ Union. **Work:** Very little part-time/vacation work available.

GLASGOW SCHOOL OF ART

Glasgow School of Art, 167 Renfrew Street, Glasgow G3 6RQ (041-332 9797) Map A, C3

Student enquiries: Academic Registrar

Main study areas – as in What to Study section: *(First degree):* Art & design.

European Community: No students take EC languages or spend time in another EC country. Approved Erasmus programme 1990/91.

Application: Direct. **Largest fields of study:** Art and design. **Founded:** 1840. **Main awards:** BA. **Awarding body:** CNAA. **Site:** Glasgow city centre. **Accommodation:** 80 hostel places. Approx cost: £18.50/£23.50 pw. Rent: no students housed in accommodation where rent controlled by college. **Library:** 50,000 volumes, 257 periodicals, 150 study places, 60,000 slides, 200 videocassettes. **Welfare:** Full-time welfare officer, health centre and dental hospital close to school. **Careers:** Information and advice service. **Amenities:** Activities committee organises a comprehensive programme of exhibitions, annual fashion show and social functions including dances, gigs and clubs. **Employment:** Freelance design; community arts, teaching.

Duration of first degree course(s) or equivalent: 4 years **Total first degree students 1989/90:** 650 **Male/female ratio 1989/90:** 1:2 **Number of overseas students:** not known **Number of mature students:** not known. **Teaching staff: full-time:** 85 **part-time:** 35 **Total full-time students:** 713 **Number of postgraduate students:** 49 **Tuition fees, first degrees, 1990/91:** Home: £628; Overseas: £5,500.

What it's like

Centrally located for major shops, cinemas, theatres and nightclubs, although the Art School itself has regular film shows, courtesy of the Mackintosh Film Society, twice weekly discos with regular club 'Divine' on Saturday nights; highly successful annual fashion show and activities week (plays, recitals, gigs, talent show). Clubs and societies, partly funded by the SU range from Karate club to the Anti-apartheid club.

Own student pub, where most of our activities take place, the 'Vic Cafe Bar' open 6 days a week and offers full range of food and drink.

As well as art and design, college includes the Mackintosh Architecture School, and industrial and interior design courses. All materials for all courses are paid for by students.

Welfare services and counselling are available and are, of course, confidential. Limited self-catering hostel accommodation.

Pauper notes

Accommodation: Expensive; cheap rented accommodation usually substandard and limited to bare essentials. Art School hostel. **Drink:** Vic Cafe Bar, Art School bar. Traditional bars eg Horseshoe Bar, Saracens Head. **Eats:** Sauchiehall (various Chinese, Indian, Turkish, Thai, trad cafe, most offer veg food). **Ents:** Art School Union, GFT (student rate) cinema – RSAMD (regular theatre). **Sports:** Kelvin Hall Sports Centre, swimming pool (Woodside Baths). **Hardship funds:** Available on first come, first served basis. **Travel:** Many student discount schemes. **Work:** Difficult to find.

Alumni (Editors' pick)

Steven Cambel, Peter Howson, Adrian Wyzsneski, Ken Curry (painters), Robbie Coltrane, John Byrne, Muriel Gray, Pam Hogg.

CAN'T FIND WHAT YOU'RE LOOKING FOR? USE THE INDEX!

GLASGOW UNIVERSITY

University of Glasgow, Glasgow G12 8QQ (041-339 8855)
Telex: 778421 GlasuL-G Map A, C3

Student enquiries: Registrar

Main study areas – as in What to Study section: *(First degree):* Accountancy, aeronautical engineering, agriculture, anatomy, archaeology, architecture, biochemistry, biology, botany, business studies, chemistry, civil engineering, classics, computing, dentistry, drama, economics, education, electrical & electronic engineering, English, fine arts, geography, geology, history, Latin American studies, law, marine technology, mathematical studies, mechanical and production engineering, medicine, microbiology, modern languages, music, Near East and Islamic studies, nursing studies, pharmacology, philosophy, physics, physiology, politics and government, psychology, religious studies and theology, sociology, speech sciences, veterinary studies, welfare studies, zoology. *Also:* Celtic studies, film and TV studies, Gaelic, Slavonic studies, sports studies, topographical science.

European Community: 20% first degree students take EC language as part of course and 2% spend 6 months or more in another EC country. A wide range of exchanges exist with EC universities/colleges including: Belgium (Liège, performing arts); Eire (Dublin, performing arts); France (Grenoble and Toulouse, engineering; Strasbourg, business and management); Germany (Mainz, law; Kassel, language); Italy (Florence, education; Modena, law; Milan, economics); Netherlands (Antwerp, maths; Amsterdam, dentistry; Rotterdam, sociology, Nijmegen, biology; Utrecht, performing arts and literature); Spain (Zaragoza, veterinary medicine; Barcelona, geography; Pamplona, philosophy). Approved Erasmus programme 1990/91.

Application: UCCA. **Founded:** 1451. **Main awards:** BA, BAcc, BArch, BD, BDS, BEd, BMus, BN, BSc, BEng, MEng, LLB, MA, MB, ChB, BVMS. **Awarding body:** Glasgow University. **Site:** Compact central campus. **Access:** Within easy reach of bus and rail stations. **Accommodation:** 2,500 places in halls and student houses. Approx cost: £36 pw (most meals), £20.00 (self-catering). Rent: 25% in accommodation where rent controlled by university. **Library:** Main and departmental libraries with around 1.5 million volumes; separate reading room with all first year texts. **Specialist collections:** Extensive and valuable collection of books and manuscripts. *Also:* Hunterian Museum (anatomical and surgical drawings, instruments etc); Hunterian Art Gallery (old masters, Whistlers, Chadins, Charles Rennie Mackintosh House), ethnographic and Roman collections. **Other learning facilities:** Computer centre, language laboratories. **Welfare:** Student health centre (works in co-operation with students' own local doctor). Student counselling service, academic advisers for all students. **Careers:** Advice (including summer vacation jobs) and placement service. **Amenities:** SRC shops, travel bureau, bank, insurance bureau, printing and photocopying facilities; 2 student unions with lounges, bars, TV rooms, etc. **Sporting facilities:** Stevenson Physical Education Building offering wide range of indoor sports, 25 m swimming pool and fitness training programmes. Athletic grounds with bar and pavilion about 2 miles from campus. Access to Kelvin Hall Sports Arena (most modern UK university sports facilities).

Duration of first degree course(s) or equivalent: 4 years (hons); **others:** 3 years and 5 years **Total first degree students (full-time) 1989/90:** 11,702 **Number of BEd students:** 483 (in Associated College of Education, Jordanhill) **Number of overseas students:** 625 **Number of mature students:** 14% **Male/female ratio 1989/90:** 5:4 **Teaching staff: full-time:** 1,060 fte **Total full-time students 1989/90:** 11,547 **Postgraduate students:** 2,510 **Tuition fees, first degrees, 1990/91: Home:** £1,675 (£637 if self-financing); **Overseas:** £4,560 (eg politics), £6,050 (eg physics).

CAN'T FIND WHAT YOU'RE LOOKING FOR? USE THE INDEX!

What it's like

It's a strongly traditional university. It lost its all-male union in 79/80 and repeatedly voted to stay out of NUS. 2 SUs supply wide variety of social and recreational facilities. The 'Union' stands in Scotch Baronial splendour at foot of university and houses bars, libraries, smoke-room, dining room, buffet, disco, TV rooms, bedrooms, 11-table snooker hall and biggest debating union in UK (university has won all biggest debating trophies eg Observer Mace for last 2 years). Queen Margaret Union ('Q.M.') stands on other side of hill in modern glass and concrete creation sheltering similar but smaller excitements. Athletic Club's excellent Stevenson Building contains Olympic swimming pool and many indoor sports, as well as assisting university's teams and sporting clubs. All students automatically join one of Unions and Athletic Club on matriculation. Glasgow makes no concessions to trendy innovations but gives security of ancient Scottish university education, with wide-ranging chances in corporate life. Cultural and educational opportunities set in Gothic grandeur of 'varsity buildings refute slum-bound image of Glasgow; city (especially West End) where university situated, very attractive.

Pauper notes

Accommodation: 15 bedrooms at cheap rates in Union for members 'too drunk to go home'. **Drink:** Union beer bar cheapest, extension disco suite in Union for 'nicer' surroundings. **Ents:** Theatre Royal, Glasgow Film Theatre and Citizens Theatre all offer students discounts. **Shops:** Union barber (John) for short back and sides. **Travel:** Scholarships on offer include McGill, Georgetown and Freiburg universities. **Work:** Large number of student bar-tenders needed in summer.

Alumni (Editors' pick)

Ian McGregor, Teddy Taylor (MP, Conservative), John Smith (MP, shadow cabinet), William Boyd (novelist and short story writer), Pat Kane ('Hue and Cry').

GOLDSMITHS' COLLEGE

Goldsmiths' College, University of London, Lewisham Way, London SE14 6NW (081-692 7171) Map D, C3

Student enquiries: Registry

Main study areas – as in What to Study section: *(First degree):* Art & design, anthropology, communication studies, computing, drama, economics, education, English, fine arts, history, mathematical studies, modern languages, music, politics & government, psychology, sociology. *Also:* Art, craft studies, studio practice, textiles.

European Community: 10% first degree students take EC language as part of course and 10% spend 6 months or more in another EC country. Formal exchange links with some 10 EC universities/colleges: France (Avignon, Paris, Toulouse); Germany (Berlin, Koumln, Marburg, Tubingen, Weingarten) and Luxembourg. Approved Erasmus programme 1990/91.

Application: UCCA; ADAR for craft studies and textiles. **Structural features:** Part of London University. **Academic features:** Access to extensive evening study programme for all students. Many degree courses available part-time; many in combined subjects. Increasing student choice in degree courses. **Largest fields of study:** Art, English, communication studies, drama, mathematics, psychology, social sciences, music, education and modern languages. **Founded:** 1891, incorporated in London University 1904. Royal Charter in 1990. **Main awards:** BA, BEd, BMus, BSc. **Awarding body:** London University. **Site:** South east London. **Access:** New Cross Gate or New Cross station (British Rail and underground) and

CAN'T FIND WHAT YOU'RE LOOKING FOR? USE THE INDEX!

buses. **Accommodation:** 1,000 places in halls (preference given to first years, 90% of whom are housed). Approx cost: £36 pw (self-catering), £50 (five day catering). **Library:** New purpose-built central library; 333,000 volumes, 1,500 periodicals, audio visual collections with facilities, Prestel, computer-based literature search, 400 study places. **Other learning resources:** Language Resource Centre with language laboratories, computer-enhanced learning facilities, studios, satellite reception, audio and video cassettes. **Welfare:** Doctors, counsellors, psychiatrist, physiotherapist, solicitor (via SU), chaplains. **Special categories:** Nursery (30 places). **Careers:** Careers adviser; London University appointments board. **Amenities:** College bookshop, refectory and bar; art gallery, audio visual facilities, theatre; SU building with launderette, coffee bar etc. **Sporting facilities:** Sports campus and playing fields near Sidcup (30 minutes) and on site, swimming pool nearby. **Employment:** Teaching, media, public service, administration, banking, commerce and industry.

Duration of first degree course(s) or equivalent: 3 years; **others:** 4 years (European languages, BEd, design studies) **Total first degree students 1989/90:** 2,184 **Total BEd students:** 303 **Number of overseas students:** 31 **Number of mature students:** approx 15% **Male/female ratio 1989/90:** 2:3 **Teaching staff: full-time:** 310 **Total full-time students 1989/90:** 2,713 **Postgraduate students:** 515 **Tuition fees, first degrees, 1990/91:** Home: £1,675; Overseas: £4,560 (eg politics) £6,050 (eg psychology).

What it's like

Very attractive Victorian red brick building, surrounded by very modern library, halls of residence and administration block etc in the heart of a gradually yuppifying, though shabby inner city area – enough to make Prince Charles wince! 3 faculties: arts, education and social and mathematical sciences. Good reputation for drama, music, visual art, communications and sociology – makes for a very diverse and interesting, though terminally trendy, student population. Hall places for 1,032 out of approx 3,000 full time students, first years guaranteed hall place, though there is an accommodation crisis. Halls range from very attractive, converted houses in rather desirable areas, to utilitarian monolithic concrete blocks overlooking main London-Deal road on one side and scrapmetal yard on other. Teaching is done on one site, at New Cross, though history students sometimes venture into other London colleges for lectures; on-campus teaching space is often cramped. Many overseas students further enrich cultural diversity within college.

SU has earned reputation as one of the most politically vocal in the university; also at great pains to provide 3 bars, coffee shop, launderette, welfare services, clubs and societies (most popular athletics union, drama, soul club, lesbian and gay), sports and entertainments. Time Out described it as 'the best student venue for bands in London'. 1990 saw The Shamen, Del Amitri, and The Blow Monkeys perform in the Union Hall.

Local points of interest: Greenwich, for its park, historic ships and buildings, pubs and market; Blackheath, for its wide open space, where Cornish rebels fought in 1493 with 'such valour and stoutness', and its striking architecture; Lewisham, for its shops; Brockley, for virtually nothing and New Cross for Goldsmiths' and economically feasible Chinese and Indian takeaways.

Conveniently situated close to central London, trains from New Cross to Waterloo/Charing Cross (journey time – 12 mins) are frequent and it is well served by buses even late at night. On the whole, a good place to study for those city lovers who hate isolated, tight campus universities.

A student view: 'Basically Goldsmiths' is a completely cool place if you fancy getting horribly inebriated a great deal, being patronised by 3rd years during Freshers' Week, getting flanned by people in rabbit suits and sleeping in a toll booth restroom on the jail break during Rag Week. It's a laugh, come and join us, it's better than every other college under the sun. And no, I'm not biased!!'

CAN'T FIND WHAT YOU'RE LOOKING FOR? USE THE INDEX!

Pauper notes
Accommodation: Hard to find; squats popular but poor conditions and few amenities – in SE London married quarters are rare. **Drink:** Pubs tend to serve community not students; virtually all Courage. Union bar the cheapest by far. **Eats:** Many restaurants in surrounding areas. Italian, Chinese, Indian, Caribbean, Thai – you name it, SE London has it. **Ents:** Time Out says: 'Goldsmiths' still pursuing its excellent policy of being the place where you see big bands first.' Cheap and excellent also for budding cabaret stars. Of course, the delights of the capital city are also just a train ride and an overdraft away. **Sports:** Active athletics union. 2 swimming pools, 1 very plush with saunas and weight training at Ladywell. **Hardship funds:** Limited access fund, at discretion of college, with guidelines agreed by SU for distribution to worthy students. **Travel:** Near A2 – lots of traffic, STA travel – cheap train and coaches. **Work:** Temping and part-time in local businesses can be hard to find.

Alumni (Editors' pick)
Vic Charles (world karate champion), Linton Kwesi Johnson (poet and musician), Mary Quant (fashion designer), Merlyn Rees MP, Colin Welland, Jack Brymer, Graham Sutherland, Malcolm McLaren (former Union VP), John Cale (Velvet Underground), Tom Keating (artist), Derek Hatton (politician), Julian Clary.

GUILDHALL SCHOOL

Guildhall School of Music & Drama, Silk Street, Barbican, London EC2Y 8DT (071-628 2571) Fax: 071-256 9438 Map E, D2

Student enquiries: Registrar

Main study areas – as in What to Study section: *(First degree):* Drama, music. Also: Technical theatre – stage management.

European Community: No students take EC language. No exchange links.

Application: Direct. **Special features:** All teachers active in their professions outside the School. The Takacs Quartet, quartet-in-residence. **Founded:** 1880, degree status granted 1945. **Main awards:** GGSM London and AGSM. **Awarding body:** Guildhall School of Music & Drama. **Site:** Barbican, central London. **Access:** Moorgate underground station. **Accommodation:** Welfare Officer helps with accommodation. Approx cost: £50 pw (room only), £50–£65 pw (all inclusive). Private lodgings, hostel and self-catering accommodation and flats. Rent: proportion of students housed in accommodation where rent is controlled by school, not known. **Library:** 60,000 volumes, 50 periodicals, 44 study places; listening facilities. **Specialist collections:** Alkan Society Collection, Appleby Collection (guitar music), Harris Collection (opera vocal scores), Merrett Collection (double bass), Rosencweig Jewish Collection, Worshipful Company of Musicians Westrup Collection. **Other learning resources:** Professional 16-track recording studio. **Welfare:** Welfare officer, doctor, counsellor, chaplain. **Hardship fund:** Limited funds available. **Careers:** Advice from Principal and senior members of staff. **Amenities:** Music hall, theatre (orchestra pit of 80), lecture recital room, John Hosier Practice Annexe (46 practice studios), theatre-training gymnasium, Barbican Centre. **Employment:** Music specialists in schools.

Duration of first degree course(s) or equivalent: 4 years (AGSM music) 3 years (GGSM music; AGSM acting) 2 years (CSM GSM stage management) **Total first degree students 1989/90:** 435 **Male/female ratio 1989/90:** 2:3 **Teaching staff: full-time:** 12 **part-time:** 275 **Total full-time students 1989/90:** 660 **Postgraduate students:** 200 **Tuition fees, first degrees, 1990/91:** Home: £2,700-£3,150; Overseas: £4,710.

CAN'T FIND WHAT YOU'RE LOOKING FOR? USE THE INDEX!

What it's like

Modern building of deep red brick and grey stone/concrete in the bowels of the Barbican Centre. (With the LSO and RSC so free/reduced tickets and rehearsal passes.) Practice bunker near Barbican tube station, with 46 rooms of varying shapes and sizes.

No halls of residence – some live at Barbican YMCA – around £48 per week for a double room, including all meals and no travelling expenses (eligible for single room after 6 months; visitors must be out by 10 pm). Other accommodation includes Henry Wood House in Camberwell (shared with other music colleges) – cheaper than the YMCA, but further out and self-catering; visitors may stay overnight for a small fee. Otherwise look through papers, agencies, adverts or word of mouth. School Welfare Officer has an accommodation list.

Relations between admin and students generally good. Teaching staff, on the whole, are excellent personally and professionally – most are working with top orchestras, opera and theatre companies, so know the problems which students face.

Courses cover all aspects of the performing arts – music, drama, stage management and scene painting. Not much collaboration between courses, except for timetabled musicials/operas etc. Relatively easy to change courses/teachers; motives, personality clashes and ability all play a part. Exams are mainly sit-down, but trend towards continuous assessment. Dropout rate is virtually nil; general attitude is happy, if somewhat apathetic socially. 12% of students come from outside the EC; 3–4% from Europe. School Library is open until 7.15pm Mon–Thurs. Access to University of London Library at Senate House and the magnificent Barbican Library.

No sports facilities but thriving football/netball teams, darts, pool etc. Access to nearby City University Sports Centre and swimming pool.

Being in the City, almost everything closes early – shops at 5 pm and most pubs at 9 pm(!!) but West End is (almost) within walking distance.

School snack bar open 8.30 am–4.30 pm. Lauderdale Tower (a 5 minutes' walk through the Barbican) houses refectory, open 12 noon–2.00 pm and SU Bar Club (excellent, with a full range of drinks including real ales). Atmosphere very good and good range of food served in the evenings. Discos, jazz nights and other events held there too. Bar open Mon–Fri lunchtimes and 5.00 pm–11.00 pm.

SU helpful and efficient, strictly non-political. Publishes a regular newsletter and information sheet for freshers. Societies include Student Theatre Society, Contemporary Music Society, Early Music Society, Christian Union, Overseas Students Association etc.

Anne Templer and Jaynne Stevens

Pauper notes

Accommodation: Barbican YMCA – no real halls of residence for Guildhall students. Henry Wood House takes a number of Guildhall students. **Drink:** Subsidised SU bar at Lauderdale Tower. **Eats:** Canteen at Lauderdale Tower 5 minutes' walk from school. Food in SU bar in evenings – adequate if uninspired. **Sports:** Use swimming pool and other sports facilities at nearby City University – very cheap with SU card. **Hardship funds:** Many scholarships available. **Work:** Some private teaching; busking; outside engagements (mostly City Livery Company dinners); depping in West End shows; gigs.

Alumni (Editors' pick)

Sir Geraint Evans, Fred Astaire, James Galway, Claire Bloom, Dudley Moore, Jacqueline du Pré, Peter Skellern, Max Jaffa, Mollie Sugden, Julia MacKenzie, Benjamin Luxon.

CAN'T FIND WHAT YOU'RE LOOKING FOR? USE THE INDEX!

HARPER ADAMS

Harper Adams Agricultural College, Newport, Shropshire TF10 8NB (0952 820280) Map A, D6

Student enquiries: Academic Registrar

Main study areas – as in What to Study section: *(First degree):* Agriculture. *Also:* Agri-food marketing, agricultural engineering, land management.

European Community: Number of students taking EC languages and spending time in another EC country, not known. Approved Erasmus programme 1990/91.

Application: PCAS (or direct if early). **Academic features:** A modular system for most courses, allowing a range of options. **Structural features:** All degree courses are sandwich courses; teaching links with appropriate polytechnics. **Founded:** 1901. **Main awards:** BSc. **Awarding body:** CNAA. **Site:** Single campus for all teaching, living accommodation and recreation. College farm surrounds the campus. **Access:** M54 from the south; M6 and A519 from North. **Accommodation:** On-site accommodation for most first years and 50% of all students; 50% in private accommodation nearby. *Approx cost:* £54.00 pw (meals included at weekends). **Library:** 20,000 volumes, 650 periodicals. **Specialist collections:** Links with polytechnic libraries on joint courses. **Other learning facilities:** Covered soil working area, specialised laboratories, glasshouse complex, mixed commercial farm. **Welfare:** Regular surgeries held at College. **Special facilities:** Some college houses available for mature students with families. **Careers:** Information, advice and placement service. **Amenities:** 2 common rooms, SU bar, stage and auditorium, hall for dances etc. **Sporting facilities:** Squash courts, swimming pool, sports hall, sports fields – all on campus. **Employment:** Careers in marketing, farming, engineering and land management.

Duration of first degree course(s) or equivalent: 4 years sandwich **other:** 3 years full-time **Total first degree students 1989/90:** 400 **Number of overseas students:** 12 **Number of mature students:** 15 **Male/female ratio 1989/90:** 2:1 **full-time students 1989/90:** 865 **Postgraduate students:** 15 **Tuition fees, first degrees, 1990/91:** Home: £1,675; Overseas: £4,563.

HATFIELD POLY

Hatfield Polytechnic, College Lane, Hatfield, Herts AL10 9AB (0707 279000) Map A, F7

Student enquiries: Secretary and Registrar or appropriate Admissions Office

Main study areas – as in What to Study section: *(First degree):* Accountancy, aeronautical engineering, agriculture and horticulture, biology, business studies, chemistry, civil engineering, computing, economics, education, electrical & electronic engineering, English, environmental studies, geology, history, law, linguistics, mathematical studies, mechanical and production engineering, philosophy, physics, psychology, sociology, welfare studies. *Also:* Contemporary studies, medical electronics, printing and packaging, travel and tourism.

European Community: 30% first degree students take EC language as part of course; very few spend time in another EC country. Formal exchange links with 5 EC universities/colleges in Berlin, Esslingen, Tours, Offenburg, Poitiers. Approved Erasmus programme 1990/91. Member of ECTS for mechanical engineering. Polytechnic policy that all students should have possibility of a European dimension to their studies. This ranges from language study to study/work placement abroad.

CAN'T FIND WHAT YOU'RE LOOKING FOR? USE THE INDEX!

Application: PCAS. **Academic features:** High proportion of sandwich courses; most courses based on a common modular structure. Students over 25 make up about 30% of all students. **Founded:** 1952; designated polytechnic 1969. **Main awards:** BA, BEd, BEng, MEng, BSc. **Awarding body:** CNAA. **Site:** Three campuses in Hertfordshire, some 20 miles north of London. **Access:** Hatfield campus next to A1(M); Wall Hall campus near M1; Hertford campus near A10. All three campuses fairly near railway stations with regular fast services to London. Local buses between campuses and nearby towns like St Albans, Watford and Welwyn Garden City. **Accommodation:** 1,250 places in halls of residence (1,000 reserved for first-year students). Approx cost: £23.40 pw (self-catering). Rent: proportion of students in accommodation where rent is controlled by the poly, not known. **Library:** 250,000 volumes – on all three campuses. **Other learning facilities:** Observatory, computer centre, audio/visual aids service. **Welfare:** Personal Services Unit providing specialist help, in addition to personal tutorial system. General medical and nursing facilities, professional counsellors, chaplaincy and day nursery, financial and legal advisory services. **Hardship funds:** Reduction or deferment of fees in cases of unforeseen hardship (after first year). Poly and SU have small loan funds to help students overcome temporary hardship. **Special categories:** Residential facilities for disabled and families. **Careers:** Advisory and placement service. **Amenities:** Modern purpose built sports hall and SU building; music and drama centres; wide range of sports.

Duration of first degree course(s) or equivalent: 3 years; **others:** 4 years **Total first degree students 1989/90:** 4,360 **Total BEd students:** 140 **Number of overseas students:** 220 **Number of mature students:** 2,581 **Male/female ratio 1989/90:** 3:2 **Teaching staff: full-time:** c410 **part-time:** c170 **Total full-time students 1989/90:** 4,870 **Postgraduate students:** c750 **Tuition fees, first degrees, 1990/91:** Home: £607; Overseas: £4,380.

What it's like

It's accessible to London, Hatfield town and St Albans. Good Personal Services Unit. SU provides four bars; over 80 clubs and societies which range from archery to Zeu Wei (you can always set up a new club/society providing there is demand); a shop which sells general goods, eg clothing, stationery etc; snack bar; finance office and travel office. The PSU gives welfare advice to all students.

Polytechnic campuses are in surroundings both attractive and conducive to studying. Both Hertford and Wall Hall campuses have ornate and decorative buildings; Hatfield campus (near Hatfield House) has modern spacious buildings containing a library, computer centre and administration centre. There is also a sports hall, small gym and swimming facilities in Hatfield and Hertford.

Pauper notes

Drinks: SU bars: The Font (Hatfield), The Boathouse (Hertford) and Wall Hall (Aldenham). Others: The Goat, The Blacksmith, Two Feathers in St Albans; Wrestlers, Hatfield Arms, Hilltop in Hatfield; Lord Haig, White Horse, The Blackbirds in Hertford. **Eats:** Snack bar on Hatfield campus, lunches at Boathouse. **Ents:** Excellent discos and good bands at all sites, plus Campus Radio. **Shops:** Very good access to both Brent Cross & London. Huge superstores within 5 minutes of all sites. SU shop on Hatfield campus offering wide variety of goods at cheap prices. **Travel:** Railcard absolute necessity when travelling to London. 4 journeys will put you into profit! **Work:** SU bars, local pubs and supermarkets.

Alumni (Editors' pick)

Martin Dew (badminton), Delroy Alexander (student DJ of the year).

HERIOT-WATT UNIVERSITY

Heriot-Watt University, Riccarton, Edinburgh EH14 4AS (031-449 5111) Map A, D3

Student enquiries: Admissions Officer/Schools Liaison Officer

Main study areas – as in What to Study section: *(First degree):* Accountancy, architecture, art and design, biochemistry, biology, business studies, chemical engineering, chemistry, civil engineering, computing, economics, electrical & electronic engineering, information technology, mathematical studies, mechanical and production engineering, microbiology, modern languages, physics, town and country planning. *Also:* Actuarial studies, brewing, building, energy studies, estate management, interpretation & translation, furniture production, offshore engineering, quantity surveying, textile technology.

European Community: 5% first degree students (plus language specialists), take EC language as part of course and 2-3% (plus language specialists), spend 6 months or more in another EC country. Large number of formal exchange links in France, Spain and Germany. Some double degrees, where students can gain degree from Heriot Watt and equivalent qualification from partner institution in EC. Some industrial placements abroad with study at partner institutions, eg degree in chemistry with European language. Approved Erasmus programme 1990/91.

Application: UCCA. **Founded:** 1821, granted charter in 1966. **Main awards:** BA, BArch, BEng, BSc, MEng. **Awarding body:** Heriot-Watt University. **Academic features:** New degrees in brewing & distilling (Heriot-Watt is base of industry-backed International Centre for Brewing and Distilling), energy resources engineering, housing studies; new degrees in chemistry/mathematics/accountancy/economics with a European language, international business and languages. **Structural features:** Faculties of environmental studies (architecture and planning) and art and design are joint with Edinburgh College of Art; faculty of textiles (industrial design – textiles, colour science and technology, textiles & clothing studies) joint with Scottish College of Textiles. **Site:** Modern campus at Riccarton, 8 miles from central Edinburgh; Edinburgh College of Art (environmental studies, art and design) in central Edinburgh, Scottish College of Textiles at Galashiels in Scottish borders. **Access:** Bus from central Edinburgh. **Accommodation:** 750 places at Riccarton, in single and double study bedrooms, with full board or in self-catering student flats. Accommodation and welfare officer assists with lodgings. Rent: proportion of students in accommodation where rent is controlled by university, not known. **Library:** 140,000 volumes, 2,500 periodicals; on-line information system. **Other learning facilities:** Television centre, computer centre, computer-assisted learning. **Welfare:** GP and dental services. Personal counselling by accommodation and welfare officer, tutor/mentor, university chaplains. **Careers:** Information and advice service. University has an excellent record of graduate placement in employment. **Amenities:** New purpose-built SU at Riccarton; numerous clubs and societies. **Sporting facilities:** Excellent sports centre on Riccarton campus.

Duration of first degree course(s) or equivalent: 4 years; 3 years for some ordinary degrees; 5 years for some MEng **Total first degree students 1989/90:** 3,977 **Number of overseas students:** 595 **Number of mature students:** 550 **Male/female ratio 1989/90:** 2:1 **Teaching staff: full-time:** c400 **part-time:** c50 **Total full-time students 1989/90:** 4,898 (full & part-time) **Postgraduate students:** 921 (full & part-time) **Tuition fees, first degrees, 1990/91:** Home: £1,675; Overseas: £4,660-£6,150

What it's like

Split-site campus, building programme due for completion in 1992. Travel between sites by bus; train service to campus.

   Campus probably one of the most striking but not well designed. Accommodation reasonable: full board, self-catering flats and self-catering single rooms. Central laundry facilities and spin driers in each hall. All blocks mixed (corridors single-sex); no visiting restrictions. All the problems of campus universities; student ghetto etc, but advantage of being close to one of the most exciting cities in Europe. Limited residences, mainly for College of Art students. University leases flats from private landlords, most of which are very reasonable. Approximately 20% overseas students, predominantly from Malaysia and Norway, also from South (similar proportion). Many overseas students mature, fewer home students are. Main sports facilities on campus open 9-9 seven days a week; well used by students, staff and local community. Other facilities on campus; shop (open 7 days a week); library (7 days) are well used. In most matters relations with university administration are reasonably good.

Courses predominantly science and engineering; highly thought of business courses, economics, accountancy and finance and business organisation; highly respected interpreting course (one of very few in UK). Campus is science dominated and town, social sciences. Many unusual/unique courses including actuarial mathematics, marine biology and interpreting. All have high international standing, renowned as a technological institution. Heavy workload and specialised vocational courses. Scope for transfer (easiest in first or second year) to General degree provides a good safety net for those who have made the wrong choice or wish to keep their horizons broad. Main assessment by exam, some continuous. Much teaching goes alongside research so quite a few progress to further study.

New union building on campus. Free buses provided on major function nights. Entertainments range from bands, folk singers, drinks promotions to regular discos. Many active societies hold events such as speakers (debates), cheese and wine, pub crawls; cover wide range of interests. Edinburgh is a student city with two universities and several colleges. Excellent opportunity to meet and mix with other institutions. Many pubs, cinemas and theatres and reciprocal agreements allow students to use other unions.

Heriot-Watt University provides the pleasant combination of city night life and a peaceful campus environment.

Pauper notes

Accommodation: Careful reading of adverts in papers may yield bargains. No knowledge of squats. **Drink:** Union provides cheapest pint in town, other reasonable places selling local brews, for example The Athletic Arms. **Eats:** Food in residences is fair. Union provides wide range of cheap meals and snacks. **Ents:** Many local pubs offer free bands midweek and weekends. Several 'alternative' theatres and cinemas. **Sports:** Several good sports centres in city including ice rinks, swimming pools and all-round complexes. **Hardship funds:** Students' Association can loan £75. **Work:** Vacation jobs harder to come by but many departments help with course-related jobs.

HEYTHROP COLLEGE

Heythrop College, University of London, 11–13 Cavendish Square, London W1M 0AN (071-580 6941) Map E, B2

Student enquiries: Secretary and Registrar

Main study areas – as in What to Study section: *(First degree):* Philosophy, religious studies and theology. *Also:* Philosophy of religion.

European Community: No students take EC language or spend time in another EC country.

Application: UCCA. **Structural features:** Part of London University. **Special features:** Epstein Madonna and Child on south front. **Founded:** In 17th century Liège as a Jesuit college. Later providing a residential seminary for Jesuits and other students in Oxfordshire until transfer to London premises in 1970. Became college of London University in 1970. **Main awards:** BA, BD. **Awarding body:** London University. **Site:** Central London site. Collegiate non-residential scheduled building in Cavendish Square. **Access:** Oxford Circus underground station. **Accommodation:** Non-residential students are advised to apply to a London University hall of residence or to the University Catholic Chaplaincy (111 Gower Street, London WC1E 6AR). Students belonging to religious Orders usually have accommodation provided for them by that Order. Rent: no students housed in accommodation where rent controlled by college. **Library:** 250,000 items (many 17th century), 150 study places. **Welfare:** Students use the facility of the University Health Service. **Amenities:** College choir; proximity to theatres, cinemas, museums, galleries; coffee bar (run by Heythrop SU) and staff–student lunch facilities. **Sporting facilities:** Gymnasium (badminton etc); football and cricket teams. **Employment:** Christian ministry, teaching, social work, media, police force etc.

Duration of first degree course(s) or equivalent: 3 years **Total first degree students 1989/90:** 111 **Number of overseas students:** 5 **Number of mature students:** 50 **Male/female ratio 1989/90:** 3:2 **Teaching staff: full-time:** 19 **part-time:** 7 **Total full-time students 1989/90:** 180 **Postgraduate students:** 69 **Tuition fees for first degrees 1990/91:** Home & Overseas: £1,345.

What it's like

Around 180 students; in the last few years has taken on more younger students and a more vibrant atmosphere. Many students are members of, or studying to be a part of, religious orders. This, together with the close-knit atmosphere means it's not the average arty-student type place. Very friendly; most social life revolves around SU. Very active SU and football team.

Library probably the best in the country for theology; stocked well for philosophy. 3 JCR's incorporating chocolate and drinks machines, microwave, TV and stereo but no bar and no refectory. Eating facilities available in the poly around the corner!

Work is made up of an average 5 essays a term, 2 seminars and 1:1 tutorials. Lectures are compulsory and expert; obvious advantages to 1:1 tutorials.

On the whole, students must put a lot into the college, for which they'll gain a lot, in the form of close friends, a fairly active social life, and a good, well-recognised degree.

Pauper notes

Accommodation: Catholic chaplaincy in Gower Street, otherwise halls of residence. ULU accommodation office very helpful. **Drink:** ULU, Catholic Chaplaincy. No good local brews in London. **Eats:** ULU, Pie and Mash shops – lists of cheap places etc in free copy of Time Out given to all London students. **Ents:** Cinemas cheaper on Monday nights. Bloomsbury Theatre very cheap for students. ULU gig night. **Sports:** ULU. Sports centres out of Central London. **Hardship funds:** Discretionary college fund. **Travel:** Excellent travel cards save a good amount of money. **Work:** Security, cleaning, waiting, catering, stewarding – loadsawork!!

HOLBORN COLLEGE

Holborn College, 200 Greyhound Road, London W14 9RY (071-385 3377) Map D, B2

Student enquiries: Registrar

Main study areas – as in What to Study section: *(First degree):* Accountancy, business studies, economics, law. *Also:* Courses for professional law exams.

CAN'T FIND WHAT YOU'RE LOOKING FOR? USE THE INDEX!

European Community: No students take EC language or spend time in another EC country.

Application: Direct. **Academic features:** Full-time, part-time, distance learning and intensive revision courses available for most study programmes. **Founded:** 1970, as an independent college to provide courses for London University LLB external degree and for English Bar examinations. **Main awards:** LLB, BSc (Econ). **Awarding body:** London University. **Sites:** West Kensington, adjacent to Queens Club. **Access:** Baron's Court, West Kensington, West Brompton underground; buses. **Accommodation:** Student Information and Welfare Officer gives advice. Rent: no students in accommodation where rent is controlled by college. **Library:** Own reference library and reading room. **Other learning resources:** Group publishes own textbooks and course materials, Lawtel. **Careers:** Information and advice on legal, accountancy, economics and business careers. **Amenities:** Bookshop (textbooks, stationery), dining room, library, sports facilities, students' common rooms. Extra-curricular academic and social activities.

Duration of first degree course(s) or equivalent: 3 years **Total first degree students 1989/90:** 950 **Number of overseas students:** 750 **Number of mature students:** 50 **Male/female ratio 1989/90:** 1:1 **Teaching staff: full-time:** c43 **part-time:** c50 **Total full-time students 1989/90:** 1,200 **Postgraduate students:** 200 **Tuition fees, first degrees, 1990/91:** Home and Overseas: £3,100 (standard), £3,500 (eg economics).

What it's like

It's not in Holborn or 'tutorial' in academic approach. Syllabus covered by mix of lectures, seminars, written assignments and mock examinations. Lecturers and tutors from all branches of legal profession and academic fraternity; healthy mix of practitioners and academics. Staff very friendly; welfare and information officer and academic staff always someone available to discuss problems. College produces unique textbooks, casebooks, revision workbooks and suggested solutions to previous examination papers; results phenomenal (prizes from London University for past 10 years). Housed in former Chelsea School of Art converted with excellent facilities; main block houses 20 lecture rooms, dining room, student common rooms bookshop and academic offices. Outside blocks house library, reading rooms and administrative offices. Multi-purpose recreation area, use of local sports facilities and Fulham pools five minutes away. Extra-curricular activities strongly supported including moots, mock trials, guest lectures, including day-trips, concerts, theatre, discos etc. First academic institution to receive the Queen's Award for Export (1982).

Pauper notes

Accommodation: Several nearby student hostels, shared flats relatively easy to find in area. Assistance from student information and welfare officer. **Drink:** Good local pubs. **Eats:** College restaurant provides excellent food from around the world at reasonable prices. Bargains in North End Road market. **Ents:** Trips to theatre, concerts, weekends away, discos etc, students' society organises special events and annual glitter ball. Hammersmith Odeon, The Greyhound, and Riverside Studios. Also many amenities in local area. **Sports:** Use of all ULU facilities and of Int Students House, Fulham swimming pools nearby. **Hardship funds:** Genuine cases – always some help available. **Travel:** ULU card gives discount with student ID. You can get NUS discount card and ISIC card for cheap travel. **Work:** Assistance and advice given.

CAN'T FIND WHAT YOU'RE LOOKING FOR? USE THE INDEX!

"Canteen serves both English and Oriental food"

TANDOORI CHICKEN

THE TRADE DESCRIPTIONS ACT

HOMERTON

Homerton College, Hills Road, Cambridge CB2 2PH (0223 411141)
Map A, F7

Student enquiries: Admissions Secretary

Main study areas – as in What to Study section: *(First degree):* Education.

European Community: No students take EC language or spend time in another EC country.

Application: UCCA. **Structural features:** Part of Cambridge University. **Academic features:** BEd degree of Cambridge which incorporates 'qualified teacher status' including lower primary (4-8) or upper primary (7-12) age ranges. The BEd degree of the University is an internal degree with students studying tripos courses of the University in years 3 and 4. **Special features:** Links with Kokebe College (Ethiopia), Vanderbilt Univ (USA) and the Faculty of Education of the University of Guyana. **Founded:** Origins go back to 1695; in Cambridge since 1894. **Main awards:** BEd. **Awarding body:** Cambridge University. **Site:** A single site of 30 acres, with garden, playing fields and orchards, about one mile south of the city centre, and within easy reach of the railway station. **Access:** By rail, on the Liverpool Street – King's Lynn or Kings Cross – Cambridge line. By road, via the M11 or A604/A1. **Accommodation:** 182 single study bedrooms; 71 single and double study bedrooms in College-owned houses nearby. Approx cost: £1,510 pa including 1 meal per day. Rent: 35% in accommodation where rent controlled by college. **Library:** 100,000 volumes, 300 current periodicals. About 100 study places. **Specialist collections:** Education and Teaching Practice. **Other learning facilities:** Computing/Resources Centre. Physics, chemistry and biology laboratories. Drama studio. 3 art studios. 3 primary bases. Specialist room for geography, English, maths and history. **Welfare:** College sick bay on site, with nursing sister. Own doctor holds regular surgeries. Full range of University medical and counselling services. **Careers:** Information, advice and placement service. **Amenities:** All the societies of the University of Cambridge. **Sporting facilities:** Squash courts, playing fields for soccer and hockey, indoor facilities for badminton and gym. **Employment:** Mainly teaching in the maintained sector.

CAN'T FIND WHAT YOU'RE LOOKING FOR? USE THE INDEX!

Duration of first degree course(s) or equivalent: 4 years; **Total first degree students 1989/90:** 600 BEd students: 600 **Number of overseas students:** 20 **Number of mature students:** 30 **Male/female ratio 1989/90:** 1:10 **Teaching staff: Full-time (or unspecified):** 51 **Teaching staff: Part-time:** 29 **Total full-time students 1989/90:** 770 **Postgraduate students:** 170 **Tuition fees, first degrees, 1990/91:** Home: £1,996; Overseas: £4,871.

What it's like

Homerton is an independent voluntary college which is also an approved society of the University of Cambridge.

It's situated in spacious and attractive grounds one and a half miles from city centre, within easy reach of other university buildings. Facilities include science labs, art studios, drama and music workshops, language laboratory, new technical resources centre and dance studio which blend in well with lovely old red-brick buildings. Good library with well-stocked teaching practice section; very lively college bar and union room complete with new stationery shop. Residential accommodation in college or nearby college houses, guaranteed for all first year BEd students; rooms cosy, with brand new furniture, fitted carpets and new decor. Other students live in – 4th years priority – about 250 rooms. Finding somewhere to live in Cambridge a problem and expensive. Food generally good. Buttery open daily, serving snacks, filled rolls, sticky buns; cafeteria lunchtime. In good old Cambridge tradition 'Formal Hall' takes place about once a week and the Principal invites every 1st year to sit at 'High Table' for one evening – together with their supervisor and other guests. It's popular to invite friends from other colleges or for eg rugby club to reserve a block booking for a meal.

Mixed residency: Homerton is actually very relaxed about this – probably due to the very small number of male students on BEd course. No-one seems to think twice about having mixed washing facilities on all corridors!

Unusually high intake of mature students; PGCE students greater number of mature students. Very few overseas students apart from annual intake of about 15-20 JYA's (Junior Year Abroad Students) – spending year doing some main subject work, generally living it up in Cambridge – mainly from America – certainly add atmosphere to college life. Students from all parts of Britain, majority from 'south', background 50% private/50% state comprehensive; mostly affluent. Less than 10% males on BEd course means atmosphere can be a bit like girls' boarding school in the first year. Homertonians are unfortunately renowned for their apolitical natures – don't let this put you off applying and changing things. Relations between admin and students are good.

Libraries open 9.00am - 8.00pm Mon-Fri, Sat am and Sun pm. SU high profile, affiliated to CUSU. All main college entertainment provided by SU – freshers' bop, wine tasting, Christmas events, jazz and cocktail evenings, local bands and a summer May ball (this year hoping to go right through the night, culminating in a champagne breakfast!).

Resident students must sign out to be out later than midnight (or 2am Fri/Sat) – for fire regulations. College never shut at night, students free to come and go. Guests are supposed to be 'registered' simply by writing the number of extra persons in a student's room on a slip and leaving at porter's lodge.

Contraception and pregnancy advice – either through SU welfare team, resident sister, CUFU or advice centres in town. Counselling entirely confidential – Cambridge services include 'Linkline' and University Counselling Service.

Sport: right through from college teams and practises to representation on university teams where many Homerton students gain 'blues' eg rugby, cricket, netball. Sports range from water polo to highly popular women's football and rowing teams, to mountain club (where are the hills in Cambridge . . .?!). Great variety of activities including music, religious organisations, social groups, political parties at college/university level, not forgetting 'wacky' clubs such as Cupboard Society to serious philosophical groups. Wealth of opportunities is overwhelming.

Homerton has long-established reputation for education and training of teachers

CAN'T FIND WHAT YOU'RE LOOKING FOR? USE THE INDEX!

of highest calibre; it attracts well-motivated students who become full members of the university.

Students have tutor to look after their welfare and eventually write job references/reports; quality of lectures very good; work loads about right. Student representation on college committees excellent. Work continually assessed with a number of assignments counting towards grades of 2nd year intermediate examination. Main subject lectures in university departments. Students would welcome a more practical approach with lots of ideas for classroom activities – though things are improving eg with new computer/word processing/display course in 1st year. 75-80% of 4th years go on to teach immediately. Very very low failure rate – students tend to leave if they are dissatisfied. Teaching practice soons sorts out weeds!

HUDDERSFIELD POLY

Huddersfield Polytechnic, Queensgate, Huddersfield HD1 3DH (0484 422288) Map A, E5

Student enquiries: Assistant Registrar (Admissions)

Main study areas – as in What to Study section: *(First degree):* Accountancy, architecture, biochemistry, business studies, chemical engineering, chemistry, communications studies, computing, drama, education, electrical & electronic engineering, English, food science & nutrition, geography, history, hotel & catering management, information technology, law, mechanical & production engineering, modern languages, music, politics & government, psychology, sociology. *Also:* Chiropody.

European Community: 8% first degree students take EC language as part of course and 2% spend 6 months or more in another EC country. Formal exchange links with 3 EC universities/colleges in Denmark (South Danish Business School for business studies students); and France (Besançon and Rennes). Plans to make an EC language available in a wider range of courses. Approved Erasmus programme 1990/91.

Application: PCAS; ADAR for product design and textile design. **Academic features:** New courses: BSc in podiatry, BSc in product design. **Special features:** Hosts annual Huddersfield Festival of Contemporary Music. **Largest fields of study:** Engineering, business studies, catering studies, music. **Founded:** 1841, became a polytechnic in 1970. **Main awards:** BA, BSc, BEng, LLB, BEd. **Awarding body:** CNAA. **Site:** Huddersfield town centre. **Acess:** Within walking distance of main bus and railway stations. **Accommodation:** 1,000 places in halls of residence; first year students given priority. Rent: 18% in accommodation where rent controlled by polytechnic. **Library:** 250,000 volumes, 2,200 periodicals, 750 study places; multiple copies of recommended books, including copies for reference use only; separate music library. **Other learning resources:** Wide range of computing facilities **Welfare:** Counsellors, chaplain, overseas students' adviser, health centre. **Special categories:** Residential facilities for disabled students. **Careers:** Information, advice and placement service. **Amenities:** SU with bar, films, disco, etc. **Sporting facilities:** Polytechnic sports hall and playing fields. Municipal sports centre with Olympic standard facilities.

Duration of first degree course(s) or equivalent: 3 years; **others:** 4 years (sandwich); 2 years BEd **Total first degree students 1989/90:** 3,575 (full-time), 490 (part-time); **Total BEd students:** 90 (full-time), 160 (part-time) **Number of overseas students:** 140 **Male/female ratio 1989/90:** 3:2 **Teaching staff: full-time:** 370 **part-time:** 80 **Total full-time students 1989/90:** 5,420 **Postgraduate students:** 340 **Tuition fees for first degree students 1989/90:** Home: £1,675; Overseas: £4,400 (eg politics), £5,100 (eg physics).

CAN'T FIND WHAT YOU'RE LOOKING FOR? USE THE INDEX!

What it's like

Town centre location so no problem with communications. Three major supermarkets close to town, so shopping is easy and cheap. Many shops in town provide discounts to students on a range of goods.

Bus and train routes to the polytechnic and halls of residence are very good. As an added bonus, travel fares are subsidised in West Yorkshire with a maximum off-peak fare of 60p, so Bradford, Leeds and other areas of Yorkshire are accessible with no financial strain.

The standard of halls of residence generally good, with only one site relying partially on portacabins. Overall, the halls are close to campus, no more than a mile away and all accessible by bus. Polytechnic has not been able to house expanding number of first years but does provide a vetting service should private landlords wish to let to students.

Sports facilities are limited – a small sports hall and playing pitches two miles from campus. SU has many successful sporting clubs, too numerous to mention. Overall, SU has 80+ clubs and societies. It also provides regular bands, discos and cabaret.

SU building itself is small (probably the most delapidated building on campus) and with a fire limit of 650 – not much use with a full-time student population of over 4,500. The Union also has a travel unit, shop and coffee bar – prices in all are cheap. Polytechnic provides a refectory but quality is limited.

Pauper notes

Accommodation: Too variable to mention. **Drink:** Growing number of pubs do student nights. **Eats:** Union Coffee Bar, College Arms – wide selection of snacks offered. Union Poly refectory, Blue Rooms – superb vegetarian food. **Ents:** Cannon cinema; varied SU events; clubs and pubs; arts centre; sports centre. **Sports:** Not much. **Hardship funds:** 2 – 1 run by SU; 1 by Poly. **Travel:** Easy access to major cities and towns by bus or train. Hitching OK off M62. **Work:** Very little about. **Shops:** 'Magpies Nest' in town centre for good second hand clothes.

HULL UNIVERSITY

University of Hull, Hull HU6 7RX (0482 46311) Map A, F5

Student enquiries: Academic Registrar

Main study areas – as in What to Study section: *(First degree):* Accountancy, American studies, anthropology, Asian studies, biology, business studies, chemistry, computing, drama, economics, education, electrical and electronic engineering, English, environmental science, European studies, fine arts, geography, history, law, mathematical studies, mechanical & production engineering, modern languages, music, nursing studies, philosophy, physics, politics and government, psychology, public administration, religious studies and theology, sociology, welfare studies Also: Operational research, Scandinavian and Slavonic studies.

European Community: 12% first degree students take EC language as part of course and 11% spend 6 months or more in another EC country. Formal exchange links with 10 EC universities/colleges: Belgium (Brussels, Ghent); France (Angers, Bordeaux); Germany (Osnabrück); Italy (Bologna, Urbino); Netherlands (Rotterdam, Utrecht); Spain (Murcia). Approved Erasmus programme 1990/91.

Application: UCCA. **Academic features:** BSc engineering sciences for students without science A-levels. Many part-time degrees, some taught at Doughty Centre, Grimsby. **Special features:** Distinguished art collection, specialising in British art 1890–1940; and Thompson collection of 17th-century Chinese ceramics. **Largest fields of study:** Engineering, English, law, modern languages. **Founded:** 1927,

CAN'T FIND WHAT YOU'RE LOOKING FOR? USE THE INDEX!

charter granted 1954. **Main awards:** BA, BEng, BMus, BSc, LLB. **Awarding body:** Hull University. **Site:** North of Hull. **Access:** Easy access from Hull town centre. **Accommodation:** 1,583 places in halls, 1,193 places in student houses. All first years accommodated. Rent: 65% in accommodation where rent controlled by university. **Library:** 750,000 volumes, 5,800 periodicals, 1,750 study places, reserve collection of course books. **Other learning resources:** Audio-visual centre, language teaching centre, computer centre. **Specialist collections:** Philip Larkin collection, history of Labour and left-wing movements, 20th century social and political archives, 20th century poetry, emigration to North America, South-East Asian studies, fine printing 1890–1940, German expressionism, medieval France. **Welfare:** Doctor, FPA (referral system), psychiatrist, solicitor, chaplain. Nursery with 42 places (cost according to income), facilities for disabled students. **Careers:** Information, advice and placement service. **Amenities:** Bookshop on campus; SU bar, launderette, television rooms: Middleton Hall (auditorium of over 500). **Sporting facilities:** Indoor purpose-built sports centre and all playing fields on campus. **Employment:** Law, chartered accountancy, computing, electronic engineering, education.

Duration of first degree course(s) or equivalent: 3 years; **others:** 4 years **Total first degree students 1989/90:** 5,083 **Number of overseas students:** 10% **Number of mature students:** 9% **Male/female ratio 1989/90:** 1:1 **Teaching staff: full-time:** 352 **part-time:** 104 **Total full-time students 1989/90:** 5,815 **Postgraduate students:** 732 **Tuition fees, first degrees, 1990/91:** Home: £1,675; Overseas: £4,300–£5,700.

What it's like

Hull University has always had a reputation for being a friendly place, something you can only experience for yourself, so take up any opportunities you may get to visit on an Open Day and have a look for yourself.

All academic departments are on one campus about two miles out of the city centre. University accommodation is situated around this, and student houses (around £14.50 a week) back onto the central site. 3 miles away, the halls of residence stand in a local village (the biggest village in the country, more like a small town). University accommodation is about £29, that includes meals. The modern Lawns Halls are particularly popular, boasting their own balconies with each room. Being so flat, Hull is 'cycling city' and therefore you don't tend to notice the distance.

Most 2nd and 3rd years leave university-owned accommodation and move into private accommodation. Places in shared houses are cheap (around £18 a week). Such private accommodation can best be described as cheap and cheerful, certainly not luxurious.

Most social events centre around the halls in Cottingham, or more particularly, the SU. The SU is one of the best equipped in the country, the vast majority of students use it as their evening meeting place. The Union ents committee put on many bands throughout the term, some pop/chart material, and run lots of films. SU also acts as a centre for some 150 societies, and also 51 sporting clubs as part of an active athletic union. (Hull's big claim to fame at the moment is having the best university American football team!). SU manages the sports centre; new health and fitness centre.

Unemployment has hit Hull hard, and so the city can't be said to be thriving. However, many local clubs and pubs do seem to be doing well. Local venues provide a stream of lesser known acts which lead to a cheap, good night out. Theatre is extremely good in Hull, particularly Spring Street Theatre, home to Hull Truck Company (of Bouncers and Up and Under fame) which puts on late night cabarets, comedy, music and drama. The Film Theatre at the City Library shows films not on general release, which is always a good night out.

Pauper notes

Accommodation: Still quite cheap, but not always the best quality. **Drink:** SU bar. **Eats:** SU (2 different eating areas including vegetarian food) and cheap Italian restaurants in town. **Ents:** SU films, discos and concerts. Drama dept productions. Occasional concerts and theatre in town. **Sports:** Good sports facilities; and large Sports Centre actually on campus. **Hardship funds:** Are dwindling, but one can usually get help in cases of emergency. **Travel:** Travel Centre in SU. **Work:** Limited. Unemployment in Hull high. Pubs, parks and maybe packing fish.

Alumni (Editors' pick)

Sir Ron Dearing, Tony Galvin, Sarah Greene, Roy Hattersley MP, Chris Mullin, Roger McGough, Philip Larkin (was librarian), Ben Walton/Tracy Thorne (Everything but the Girl).

HUMBERSIDE POLY

Humberside Polytechnic, Cottingham Road, Hull HU6 7RT (0482 440550) Map A, F5

Student enquiries: Admissions Officer

Main study areas – as in What to Study section: *(First degree):* Accountancy, architecture, art & design, biology, business studies, chemical engineering, chemistry, communication studies, education, electrical & electronic engineering, English, environmental studies, fine arts, food science & nutrition, geography, history, information technology, mechanical & production engineering, modern languages, welfare studies. *Also:* Fishery science.

European Community: 19% first degree students take EC language as part of course and 19% spend 6 months or more in another EC country. Formal exchange links with 7 EC universities/colleges: business studies exchanges in Denmark (South Denmark Business School); France (Bordeaux, León); Germany (Münster); Netherlands (Rotterdam); Spain (Madrid); chemical technology link with Netherlands (Amsterdam). Students on BA European business studies spend half time in Germany/France/Spain. Approved Erasmus programme 1990/91.

Application: PCAS; ADAR for art and design courses. **Academic features** Summer School available in various subjects also Jazz Summer School. Students on BA contemporary studies and applied social science can spend a year in America, on BA European business studies spend half time in Germany/France/Spain. Encourages applications from those without formal entrance requirements; guarantees place on degree course to those passing Humberside-validated access course. **Largest fields of study:** Business, food science/technology, arts. **Founded:** 1976. **Main awards:** BA, BSc, BEng. **Awarding body:** CNAA. **Site:** In and around Hull city centre and Grimsby. **Accommodation:** 636 places in halls of residence. Approx cost: £38.85 pw. Rent: 16% in accommodation where rent controlled by polytechnic. **Library:** 200,000 volumes, 1,560 periodicals, 750 study places and Learning Resource Centres. **Other learning facilities:** Computer centre, sound and TV studios. **Welfare:** Medical, chaplain, independent financial adviser, student counselling service. **Careers:** Information, advice and placement service. **Amenities:** Sound and TV studios, training ketch and dinghies, marine simulator, wide range of sporting facilities, computer centre.

Duration of first degree course(s) or equivalent: 3 years; others: 4 years (sandwich) **Total first degree students 1989/90:** 2,761 **Number of overseas students:** 176 **Number of mature students** 1,042 **Male/female ratio 1989/90:** 5:4 **Teaching staff: full-time:** 278 **part-time:** 245 **Total full-time students 1989/90:** 4,025

CAN'T FIND WHAT YOU'RE LOOKING FOR? USE THE INDEX!

Postgraduate students: 302 **Tuition fees, first degrees, 1990/91:** Home: £1,675; Overseas: £4,260 (classroom based courses), £4,620 (studio or lab based courses).

What it's like

Four main sites – three in Hull, one Grimsby, ranging from picturesque to practical. Boasts an impressive range of highly respected courses from fine art to business studies and engineering. Emphasis on quality of learning environment, rather than extra-curricular activity. Sport and leisure facilities, and welfare services consistently eroded. Access for non-traditional students has been poor. Halls good, catering recently much improved. Atmosphere in Halls is lively and liberal. Increasing number of overseas students, particularly European. SU has a full-time welfare employee who works with and refers to local bodies BPAS, FPCs etc. Also has active societies including hockey, rugby, football, drama, Asian, ski club, mountaineering, Zambian, Labour and windsurfing. Hull, while having a large student body (also has a university) has less of a student culture but several student venues. Grimsby is less well catered for; no SU bar or shops which, along with distance, makes for an occasionally strained relationship. Accommodation in Hull is cheap and cheerful. Grimsby housing is expensive and hard to come by. SU politically left of centre, affiliated to NUS and the Area organisation, has 5 sabbatical officers, bars, shops etc. It continues to strive for equal provision on all sites, provides cheap Ents, beer etc and involves itself in campaigning work from welfare and sports facilities to grants and sexual politics.

Pauper notes

Accommodation: From £11 pw in Hull, expensive and limited in Grimsby. **Drink:** Cheap at SU, Hull Old Town and Cleethorpes pubs best. Minerva's Pilots Pride best real ale. Mostly Mansfield Brewery. **Eats:** Italians predominate, but also chippies, Indian, Chinese, Middle Eastern, Kebabs all good and cheap. **Ents:** Grimsby Grinders nightclub is a favourite, so is Exchange pub. In Hull Spring Street and Hull New Theatres, 2 OK cinemas, Central Library has unusual film programmes. Wellington Club is a favourite. Also boasts Adelphi Club – home of The Housemartins and best live independent venue in North East. **Sports:** Minimal at college, shared facilities with Grimsby FE, University Sports Centre available, good in Hull for most sport, particularly Rugby League. **Hardship funds:** SU resources very limited but can help occasionally, college has no provision. **Travel:** Easy access by road, Humber Bridge plus cheap ferries to Europe.

Alumni (Editors' pick)

Ann Brown and Christine Ford (England Women's Basketball team), Mary Parkinson (TV presenter/interviewer), Eliot Morley MP, Death by Milkfloat (independent pop band).

IMPERIAL COLLEGE

Imperial College of Science, Technology and Medicine, University of London, London SW7 2AZ (071-589 5111; Telex: 929484 IMPCOL G; Fax: 071-584 7596) Map E, A3
The Medical School, Norfolk Place, Paddington, London W2 1PG (071-723 1252; Fax: 071-724 7349)
(You can look up St Mary's Hospital Medical School separately)

Student enquiries: Senior Assistant Registrar (Admissions)

Main study areas – as in What to Study section: (*First degree*): Aeronautical engineering, biochemistry, biology, biotechnology, botany, chemical engineering, chemistry, civil engineering, computing, electrical & electronic engineering, geology, information technology, mathematical studies, mechanical and production

CAN'T FIND WHAT YOU'RE LOOKING FOR? USE THE INDEX!

engineering, medicine, metallurgy and materials science, microbiology, physics, zoology. *Also:* Energy engineering, mineral processing technology, mining, petroleum engineering.

European Community: Under 2% first degree students take EC language as a formal part of course or spend 6 months or more in another EC country (but increasing). Wide range of exchange schemes for undergraduates with prestigious technological institutions in Belgium, France, Germany, Italy, Netherlands, Denmark and Spain. Approved Erasmus programme 1990/91. Strong commitment to 'Year in Europe' courses (available with biochemistry, biology, chemistry, physics, materials, chemical engineering and civil engineering). Newly formed 'European office for student recruitment mobility.'

Application: UCCA. **Structural features:** Part of London University. **Academic features:** All 4 year engineering now MEng; most 3 year courses, BEng. New courses in: biology with management, information systems engineeering, mathematics with management. Humanities programme offering weekly lectures in associated studies and foreign language courses. **Special features:** Imperial College established by Royal Charter 'to give the highest specialised instruction, and to provide the fullest equipment for the most advanced training and research in various branches of science, especially in its application to industry'. Applications from women are strongly encouraged. Visiting lecturer and musician-in-residence, Richard Dickins, leads a variety of musical activities. Some 50 visiting professors. **Founded:** 1907, from Royal College of Science, Royal School of Mines, City and Guilds College. Amalgamated with St Mary's Hospital Medical School, 1988. **Main awards:** MEng, BEng, BSc, BSc(Eng), MB BS. **Awarding body:** University of London. **Site:** 25 acre site in South Kensington. Medical School in Paddington. **Access:** South Kensington underground station; Paddington or Edgware Road underground stations for medical school; buses. **Accommodation:** Almost 1,000 places on campus; others in student houses nearby; more in head tenancy scheme. All first year students except those living in the Greater London area guaranteed accommodation in college or university residences. Rent: 30% in accommodation where rent controlled by university. **Libraries;** Lyon Playfair Library for all course books: 300,000 volumes, 500 places; individual department libraries. For older material, college relies on Science Museum Library which adjoins college library: 500,000 volumes, 20,000 periodicals. Haldane Library (humanities and general reading) 35,000 volumes; music library, containing lending collection of records, tapes, CDs and scores. Medical School Library: 30,000 volumes and bound journals. **Other learning facilities:** College mine in Cornwall; computer centre on South Kensington campus; 240 acre college field station at Silwood Park (near Ascot). **Welfare:** Advisory committee; vacation training scheme; careers advisory service; student accommodation office; health centre, student counsellor, welfare adviser, 'Nightline', nursery. **Hardship funds:** A number of funds available to MB BS course students. **Amenities:** SU building with refectory, bar, bookshop, etc; wide range of societies. **Sporting facilities:** Sports centre on campus with indoor swimming pool; boathouse at Putney; 60-acre sports ground near Heathrow Airport. **Employment:** Traditionally industry; but increasing number of graduates enter banking, insurance, etc as well as general commercial areas. Medicine.

Duration of first degree course(s) or equivalent: 3 or 4 years (science and engineering); 5 years (medicine) **Total first degree students 1989/90:** 4,217 **Number of overseas students:** 583 **Number of mature students:** 94 approx **Male/female ratio 1989/90:** 7:2 **Teaching staff: total:** 650+ **Total full-time students 1989/90:** 6,077 **Postgraduate students:** 1,860 **Tuition fees, first degrees, 1990/91:** Home: £1,675 (£650 if self-financing); Overseas: £4,900-£6,500.

What it's like

It's in South Kensington near Hyde Park and the museums. All the benefits of central London and usual drawbacks of expense and accommodation. Halls off Exhibition Road; houses 20 mins walk away – most self-catering. Places also available at London University halls, a tube trip away. All first years offered places in IC residences, all undergraduates can spend at least one year in college accommodation. International reputation and very high academic standards. Course fairly intensive, 7% fail and 7% drop out. Men still outnumber women by 4:1, despite efforts to redress balance. 40% of students are postgraduates. SU not affiliated to NUS, tends to concentrate on college matters: supports a wide range of clubs from sporting motorcycle to Amnesty International, as well as social clubs for most cultural and ethnic groups (20% of students from overseas). Excellent student media led by weekly newspaper, *Felix*, radio station and television network. ULU facilities and events at Malet Street are open to IC students. 3 constituent colleges (City & Guilds College, Royal College of Science, Royal School of Mines) organise rag stunts, such as tiddly-winking down Oxford Street, and other social events. The Medical School (St Mary's, Paddington), is the most popular medical school on UCCA applications with friendly atmosphere and strong traditions for revues and rugby. IC adage: 'Work hard, play hard' – balance often difficult but student life very much what you make of it.

"Preponderance of 'grey' scientists...."

Pauper notes

Accommodation: Never cheap, single room in college halls typically £40 pw. **Drink:** SU bar for full range, including real ales; drinks up to 30p/pint cheaper than local pubs. All the Firkin pubs and Union bar supply real ale. **Eats:** Union runs cheap wholefood snackbar; college pizza bar OK. Local area expensive except Indian and pasta bar in South Kensington. Best: veggie S. Indians in Euston/ Notting Hill etc. **Ents:** Regular cheap events on campus. 'London Social Secretaries' card (available to all) gives discounts at all colleges. Still many free gigs/ exhibitions in London. Pub gigs good value. **Sports:** Campus sports centre very cheap for swimming, squash, weights. Group transport to excellent college grounds at Heathrow. **Hardship funds:** Limited availability. **Travel:** Bicycle + A–Z essential! For longer distances hitch, get coach card, rail savers. STA branch on

CAN'T FIND WHAT YOU'RE LOOKING FOR? USE THE INDEX!

campus. **Work:** Casual work available from college and union – if you have time. Always casual, part time work available (including tutoring) in London.

Alumni (Editors' pick)
H G Wells, Sir Lewis Casson, Sir Granville Bantock, Joan Ruddock MP, Sir John Egan, Trevor Phillips, Francis Wilson, Brian May.

INSTITUTE OF ARCHAEOLOGY

Institute of Archaeology, University College London, 31–34 Gordon Square, London WC1H 0PY (071-387 7050) Map E, C1

Student enquiries: Registrar, University College London, Gower Street, London WC1E 6BT

Main study areas – as in What to Study section: *(First degree):* Archaeology. *Also:* Archaeological conservation, environmental archaeology.

European Community: No students take an EC language as part of their degree course. Variable number of students spend time in another EC country (no formal links).

Application: UCCA. **Structural features:** Part of University College, London University. **Founded:** 1937. Joined University College London in 1986. **Main awards:** BA, BSc. **Awarding body:** London University. **Site:** Central London. **Access:** Warren Street and Euston Square underground stations. **Academic features:** 60+ optional course units available. 3-year courses in W. Asia archaeology include language options and some ancient history. 3 year specialist BSc in archaeological conservation; environmental archaeology options available to BSc and BA students; computer facilities open to all undergraduates. All staff are practising archaeologists or archaeological scientists. **Accommodation:** Students can apply to University intercollegiate halls of residence, University College London Student Residence Office and University accommodation officer. **Library:** Specialist archaeology library. 27,000 volumes (6,000 in store), 21,000 pamphlets, 800 periodicals, 60 study places; recommended books temporarily restricted for use of students. **Welfare:** College Health Centre, health service nearby. **Careers:** Advice on careers in archaeology. **Amenities:** The Institute's Society of Archaeology Students affiliated to University College London union and to ULU, so students can make use of their facilities and the sports ground at Motspur Park.

Duration of first degree course(s) or equivalent: 3 years **Total first degree students 1989/90:** 166 **Number of overseas students:** 24 **Number of mature students:** 55 **Male/female ratio 1989/90:** 1:1 **Teaching staff: full-time:** 27 **part-time:** 50 **Total full-time students 1989/90:** 229 **Postgraduate students:** 130 **Tuition fees, first degrees, 1990/91:** Home: £1,675; Overseas: £5,365 (standard); £6,995 (archaeological conservation).

What it's like
Rectangular and functional; not an inspired piece of architecture. Its redeeming feature is that it faces Gordon Square allowing an escape from city life (almost). Almost equidistant from UCLU and ULU and very handy for alcoholic post lecture refreshment. Vi provides drinks and snacks in our own common room throughout the day. Smokers confined to one Sin Bin which arouses mixed feelings.

Lots of approachable, friendly and enthusiastic staff – many let their hair down at the regular Institute shin-digs organised at intervals (free beer and food) by the SAS (Society of Archaeology Students – the remains of the Student Union).

CAN'T FIND WHAT YOU'RE LOOKING FOR? USE THE INDEX!

Library can become a battleground (especially in the 1st year) over set books; can be overcome by using one of the other libraries in the area.

Large range of courses – from European ethnoarchaeology and archaeology of disease to South American archaeology and computing – the only compulsory courses are in 1st year. Possible to take related courses in other departments and build up a degree to your own interest.

Environmental courses include lots of very cold field trips (Norfolk popular) on top of the general fieldwork requirement of 70 days. 10 of these days are spent getting your hands dirty learning basic excavation techniques whilst another 4 are taken up getting even dirtier battling with the elements in the English autumn on the primitive technology course, designed to test skill and ingenuity whilst attempting to live in the open using a pre-industrial lifestyle.

Cosmopolitan atmosphere with students from many different backgrounds, countries and of a wide age range.

Societies include: Underwater ArchSoc, VikingSoc (banquets and general skullduggery). Annual Trowel Trophy cricket match (staff vs students) and expeditions galore to far flung places (and a few nearer to home). *Jenni Heathcote*

Pauper notes

Accommodation: UCL and intercollegiate halls of residence. Cheapest accom in SE London (bring a bike and don't rely on London Transport). **Drink:** Cheapest ULU/UCLU. Best atmosphere: The Sun – wide variety of real ale etc, and Firkin brewery pubs. **Eats:** Union bars for cheap(ish) food, Institute canteen for limited hot food and sandwiches/snacks. The Greenhouse – good veggie food SOAS. Drummond St: veggie, Indian. **Ents:** 70p films at Bloomsbury Theatre. UCLU and ULU provide a wide range of ents. Institute parties eclipse all other entertainments though. **Sports:** UCL Waves Centre Swimming Pool, squash. **Travel:** Fieldwork grants for those in receipt of LEA grants. Various grants for travel/fieldwork.

Alumni (Editors' pick)

James Coppice Norman, Nick Branch, Andrew Hobley.

INSTITUTE OF EDUCATION

Institute of Education, University of London, 20 Bedford Way, London WC1H 0AL (071-636 1500) Map E, C1

This is a postgraduate UKCPU.

Student enquiries: Deputy Academic Registrar

Main study area: *(Not at first degree):* Education.

European Community: No students take EC language or spend time in another EC country.

Application: Direct; except PGCE to GTTR (3 Crawford Place, London W1H 2BN). **Structural features:** Part of London University. **Academic features:** Postgraduate teacher training course involving close partnership with schools. Modular masters and diploma courses in most educational specialisms, enabling students to accumulate credits over a period of time. Special short courses (3 months) in: management development for schools and services; special educational needs in ordinary schools; mathematics for secondary schools; a computer-based programme for mathematics teachers; teaching numeracy and vocationally related mathematics; economic awareness in the pre-vocational curriculum; retraining in

CAN'T FIND WHAT YOU'RE LOOKING FOR? USE THE INDEX!

mathematics; science coordination in primary schools. **Special features:** Postgraduate education and research. **Founded:** 1902, became Institute of Education in 1932. **Main awards:** PGCE, MA, MSc, MPhil, PhD, specialist diploma courses. **Site:** Bedford Way. **Access:** Russell Square underground. **Accommodation:** Students use London University accommodation office. 231 places in halls; a number of self-contained flats available for senior postgraduates on 1 year courses. Approx cost: £48.65 per person pw. **Rent:** 20% in accommodation where rent controlled by university. **Library:** 220,000 volumes, 1,900 periodicals, 240 study places. **Specialist collections:** ILEA Resources Collection. **Welfare:** London University health service, university chaplain, student adviser, nursery facilities (£49.50 pw for Institute students). **Hardship funds:** Loans available for students in temporary financial difficulties. **Special categories:** Facilities for married students. **Careers:** Information and advice. 90% of those on initial training course employed within 6 months. **Amenities:** Central London and London University. Dillon's 5 mins walk. **Employment:** Education.

Male/female ratio 1989/90: slightly more female students **Teaching staff: full-time:** 127 **part-time:** 33 **Total full-time students 1989/90 (all postgraduate):** 1,302 (1,409 part-time) **Tuition fees, 1990/91:** Home: £1,675 (diploma & PGCE); £1,985 (higher degree); Overseas: £4,650.

What it's like

Unlike most London University colleges, it's purely postgraduate. A world centre for study of education. It has a student body of over 2,500. Work falls into three broad categories: initial professional training; advanced courses for experienced qualified teachers; and research degrees – MPhil, PhD. For the first category the Institute offers 500 PGCE places. The Institute has a high reputation for research and, occasionally, this filters down to practical training. It is a fairly strange place to spend a year.

The SU Society is a fairly liberated Union, offering wide variety of services in the minute space allowed – a bar, snack bar, lunch counter and shop. Good relationship with the Institute, and many joint ventures are undertaken, such as the South African Scholarship Scheme. A lot of activity centres around educational issues, such as anti-racist and anti-sexist education. SU has cheap bar, free discos on a Friday, and general non-threatening environment.

Situated just off Russell Square, in a huge concrete and tinted glass monstrosity, it's near Euston & King's Cross BR stations. Nearby is Dillon's, also seriously trendy Lumiere Cinema, and the seriously untrendy ULU. The SU Society is popular with students from other colleges.

Pauper notes

Accommodation: Flats, self-catering accommodation and single/double rooms with food and heating included. **Drink:** Varies, but usually at least 2 real ales and 3 lagers. **Eats:** Cheapish meals in snack bar/lunch counter. A good variety of vegetarian and salads. **Ents:** Regular discos and sometimes bands are invited – cheap or free entrances. **Sports:** Join ULU facilities. **Hardship funds:** Hardship fund administered by college. Nursery subsidy. **Travel:** Cheap fares available from STA (round corner). **Work:** Bar work, stewardings, kitchen work for special events.

CAN'T FIND WHAT YOU'RE LOOKING FOR? USE THE INDEX!

JEWS' COLLEGE

Jews' College, Albert Road, Hendon, London NW4 (081-203 6427)
Map A, F8

Student enquiries: Academic Registrar

Main study areas – as in What to Study section: *(First degree):* Education, philosophy, religious studies and theology. *Also:* Jewish studies.

European Community: No students take EC language or spend time in another EC country.

Application: Direct. **Academic features:** Students not committed to any profession when they arrive. College linked to London University for all degrees. **Special features:** Lecturers regularly visit from Bar-Ian University, Israel. **Founded:** 1855, to train rabbis, leaders and teachers for the Anglo-Jewish community and overseas. **Main awards:** BA. **Awarding body:** London University. **Access:** Buses from central London. **Accommodation:** Students accommodated with local families or flats in area. Rent: no students in accommodation where rent controlled by college. **Library:** Outstanding reference and information centre for all things Jewish; 75,000 volumes, 142 periodicals; priceless 15th and 16th century manuscripts. **Welfare:** Student counsellor; honorary medical officer available for consultation. **Security:** Entrance door locked at all times. **Special categories:** Special arrangements for mature students. **Hardship funds:** Grants and scholarships available in appropriate cases. **Careers:** Direct links to United Synagogue for those wishing to pursue the ministry. **Amenities:** SU provides range of services.

Duration of first degree course(s) or equivalent: 3 years **Total first degree students 1989/90:** 28 **Number of mature students:** 3 **Number of overseas students:** 4 **Male/female ratio 1989/90:** 3:2 **Teaching staff: full-time:** 4 **part-time:** 10 **Total full-time students 1989/90:** 50 **Postgraduate students:** 80 **Tuition fees, first degrees, 1990/91:** Home: £607; Overseas: £1,100.

What it's like

Small, cosy college, with warm, friendly atmosphere. Good student/staff relationships. Modern purpose-built campus boasts the most extensive Judaica library in Europe, numerous conference rooms and the London based Institute of Jewish Education. Host to various Jewish Youth organisations, making available our services and facilities for week-end and evening seminars. SU offers programme of social and cultural events in conjunction with the Union of Jewish Students. College has enjoyed close contact with NUS and is represented at its Annual Conference. Degrees can lead to teaching, administrative, or ministerial posts within the community. Some graduates use their degree as a basis for entrance into the professions.

Location means most forms of entertainment are nearby. Prospective students are in for a busy and enjoyable time.

Pauper notes

Accommodation: College helps find kosher accommodation locally. **Eats:** Discounts at some kosher restaurants. **Work:** Bursaries available for needy students. Some vacation work etc available.

Alumni (Editors' pick)

Lord Jakobovits (Chief Rabbi), Rabbi Dr Jonathan Sacks (Chief Rabbi Elect) Prof S Greenbaum (London University), Dr Stefan Reif (Director, Taylor Schechter Geniza Research Unit, Cambridge), Prof Alan Corre, Dov Zackheim.

CAN'T FIND WHAT YOU'RE LOOKING FOR? USE THE INDEX!

KEELE UNIVERSITY

Keele University, Keele, Staffs ST5 5BG (0782 621111) Map A, D6

Student enquiries: Director of Academic Affairs

Main study areas – as in What to Study section: *(First degree):* American studies, anthropology, biochemistry, biology, chemistry, computing, economics, education, English, environmental science, European studies, geography, geology, history, law, mathematical studies, modern languages, music, philosophy, physics, politics and government, psychology, sociology. *Also:* electronics.

European Community: 16% first degree students take EC language as part of course and 12% spend 6 months or more in another EC country. Formal exchange links with 11 EC universities/colleges: France (4); Germany (4); Spain (3). Approved Erasmus programme 1990/91.

Application: UCCA. **Special academic features:** 4 year course (foundation year + 3 years) with few course requirements. 330+ dual honours combinations available and concurrent Cert Ed possible; over 300 3-year dual honours courses. New courses: human resource management, biomedical sciences, criminology, international politics, international history, environmental science, environmental management. **Special features:** Visiting Professors: J Bordas (physics from SERC Daresbury); K A Chittenden (electronics); G N Greaves (chemistry from SERC Daresbury); J F Hallstrom (music from Colby College, Maine); P E Secker (electronics from Royal Doulton); A M Stoneham (chemistry from AEA, Harwell). **Largest fields of study:** Computer science, English, law, management science, psychology. **Founded:** 1962, ex University College of North Staffordshire. **Main awards:** BA, BSc. **Awarding body:** Keele University. **Site:** Campus 2 miles from Newcastle-under-Lyme. **Access:** M6, buses to campus from Stoke station. **Accommodation:** 2,580 rooms. Approx cost: £23 pw. All first years and most others accommodated. Rent: 83% in accommodation where rent controlled by university. **Library:** 500,000 volumes, 1,500 periodicals, 685 study places, separate foundation year library. **Specialist collections:** Turner mathematics collection, Wedgwood archives. **Welfare:** Doctor, dentist, FPA, psychiatrist, solicitor (SU), chaplains, financial adviser, counselling service. **Special categories:** Nursery (50 places); playgroup (25 places). **Careers:** Information and appointments service. **Amenities:** Bookshop on campus, SU premises with bookshop, launderettes, supermarket, newsagent and banks. Italian pizzeria with bar, unisex hairdressing salon, sunbeds. **Sporting facilities:** Multi-purpose sports centre with adjoining playing fields, tennis courts and athletics track; 7 squash courts, climbing wall and fitness centre gymnasium; sports shop.

Duration of first degree course(s) or equivalent: 4 years (with foundation year); 3 years (without foundation year) **Total first degree students 1989/90:** 2,649 **Number of overseas students:** 390 **Number of mature students:** 310 **Male/female ratio 1989/90:** 1:1 **Teaching staff:** full-time: 280 part-time: 20 **Total full-time students 1989/90:** 3,119 **Postgraduate students:** 1,038 **Tuition fees, first degrees, 1990/91:** Home: £1,675; Overseas: £4,560 (eg humanities and social sciences), £5,300 (eg one principal science), £5,950 (eg two principal sciences).

What it's like

'Keele? Oh, the one stuck on the top of the hill in the middle of nowhere!!', a narrow-minded view held by a lot of the ill-informed. Keele is, admittedly, on top of a hill so a large supply of woolly jumpers is essential; but it's also the largest campus in England and by far the most picturesque.

2,900 of the full-time students at Keele are resident on campus so there's a good community atmosphere. The University hopes to increase its intake to 6,000 students by the year 2000. Keele courses are all joint honours so should fit in well with changes in schools, particularly the National Curriculum.

CAN'T FIND WHAT YOU'RE LOOKING FOR? USE THE INDEX!

Accommodation both on and off campus is some of the cheapest in the country. As a first year student you will be guaranteed a study bedroom in one of the four Halls of residence (spacious with washbasin and access to a kitchen; electricity and heating included in residence fees).

Your social life should be your main concern. There is a variety of entertainments, from gigs and Balls through comedy, plays and jazz nights to discos. Also over 100 societies covering a broad spectrum of interests and activities.

All in all, Keele is a brilliant university, and all who leave miss the lifestyle and the friends they make here.

Pauper notes

Accommodation: Limited off campus. With only two bus routes onto campus, own transport useful, or wellies in winter. **Drink:** 3 union bars, 4 hall bars and 2 pubs nearby. **Eats:** Refectories try but SU snack bar and 'Oysters' deliver. Veggie available at SU. Evening snack bar. New pizza place in sports centre – well worth a visit. Off campus – trendy cafes such as Stones and Gios in Newcastle. **Ents:** Discos, bands, cabaret, promotions nights all at SU. Localwise – new Vic Theatre, gigs at Victoria Hall, Hanley; Stoke Beer Festival – first week. 24 track recording studio. Several nightclubs – Ritzy, Maxims and Hudsons (Newcastle) and Excalibur (gay) in Hanley. **Sports:** Everything but the swimming pool – that's in Newcastle-under-Lyme. **Hardship funds:** Hall fund, SU and Vice-Chancellor's discretionary fund. **Travel:** SU travel bureau. Travel scholarships, PMT/Crossville buses and excellent access to M6. Cheap runabout passes from campus travel office. **Work:** Behind SU bar, local pubs, typing and delivering publicity circulars and Julie's Pantry at Keele Services (M6). Security/stewarding for gigs and discos.

Alumni (Editors' pick)

John Golding MP, David Pownall, Bamber Gascoigne, Jack Straw, Gerry Northam and Sue Robbie, Alun Michael, Ian Taylor, Bernard Lloyd.

KENT INSTITUTE

Kent Institute of Art and Design, Oakwood Park, Oakwood Road, Maidstone, Kent ME16 8AG (0622 757286) Map A, F8

Student enquiries: Marketing Officer

Main study areas – as in What to Study section: *(First degree):* Architecture, art & design, communication studies, fine arts. Also: Community arts and film

European Community: No students take EC language or spend time in another EC country as part of degree course. Exchanges with Düsseldorf (architecture) and fine arts links with colleges in France, Germany, Netherlands and Spain. Approved Erasmus programme 1990/91.

Application: ADAR; direct for architecture. **Academic features:** New degree in communication media; study in Public Art; all degrees being converted to modular structure to allow greater student choice of study. **Founded:** 1987 by merger of Canterbury College of Art, Maidstone College of Art and Medway College of Design. **Main awards:** BA. **Awarding body:** CNAA. **Site:** Three separate campuses, each shared with other educational establishments, each close to a town or city centre (Canterbury, Maidstone, Rochester-upon-Medway). **Accommodation:** Full-time officers arrange student accommodation. Rent: 9% in accommodation where rent controlled by institute. **Library:** Three separate libraries, each approximately 15,000–20,000 volumes.

Duration of first degree course(s) or equivalent: 3 years **Other:** 5 years (part-time BA) **Total first degree students 1989/90:** 508 **Number of overseas students:** 37 **Number of mature students:** approx 30 **Male/female ratio 1989/90:** 1:1 **Teaching**

CAN'T FIND WHAT YOU'RE LOOKING FOR? USE THE INDEX!

staff: full-time: 27 part-time: 132 **Total full-time students 1989/90:** 1,585
Postgraduate students: 76 **Tuition fees, first degrees, 1990/91:** Home: £1,675;
Overseas: £5,850.

What it's like – Maidstone

On the edge of town. Looks terrible; don't be put off, there are very good courses in
illustration, graphics, film, video and foundation. Externally threatened with
closure by the government but atmosphere is good. SU active. Own canteen/
common room and run own gigs and parties. Quite near London but there's lots
going on in college. Proportion of overseas students increasing.

Pauper notes

Accommodation: Varies – cheapest is college owned Terrace Road. Small squatting movement beginning. **Drink:** 'Druid Arms' in town is popular. 'The Pilot' has
wicked real ale especially 'Old Devil'. **Eats:** Refectory good value. Eating out in
town usually expensive. **Ents:** SU organises parties, gigs, films, trips to nearby gigs
etc. A few nightclubs in town. 'Albion' in town has live music on Thursdays.
Cheques cashed at 'Admiral Gordon', 'Walnut Tree' and 'Minstrel' small wicked
real cider (local), also good wines. **Sports:** Westborough sports centre on campus.
Mote Park swimming pool on other side of town. **Work:** Usually available in pubs
and fast food places. Hop picking in summer.

What it's like – Canterbury

1960 type building just outside the city walls with view of the cathedral. Nice town
with good traditional feel and large student population. College shares campus with
the Tech. Virtually no accommodation in Canterbury itself and what there is is
expensive. Students move to Herne Bay or Whitstable which are cheaper. Foundation students mostly home-based. Other courses recruit nationally or internationally – many from the north. Art and design courses taught by practising
artists. Good studio space and all courses have good facilities especially fashion and
design. College has own accommodation and welfare officers though no careers
officers but the staff are helpful and you can use the university.

Pauper notes

Accommodation: Available through accommodation officer and local press. **Drink:**
College bar cheapest, best local brew is Shepherd Neames (give Canterbury bitter a
miss). Also, 'City Arms', 'Millers Arms', 'Bell and Crown', 'The Dolphin' and
'Simple Simons'. **Eats:** College canteen plus whole food and vegetarian canteens
part of SU, refectory at Tech. 'Sarnies' and 'Alberrys' (St Margaret's St) – both
vegetarian. Most restaurants and night clubs offer student discounts. **Ents:** SU has
good local bands, something on twice a week; also at University and Tech. **Sports:**
Tech sports centre; swimming pool/sports centre in town. **Travel:** Some fine arts
scholarships for travel. **Work:** Some part time work in SU, or MacDonalds if you
like work but not money.

KENT UNIVERSITY

**University of Kent at Canterbury, Canterbury, Kent CT2 7NZ
(0227 764000)** Map A, G8

Student enquiries: Office for Undergraduate Recruitment Services, University Registry

Main study areas – as in What to Study section: *(First degree):* Accountancy,
African studies, American studies, anthropology, Asian studies, biochemistry,
biology, biotechnology, business studies, chemistry, classics, communication studies, computing, drama, economics, electrical and electronic engineering, English,

CAN'T FIND WHAT YOU'RE LOOKING FOR? USE THE INDEX!

environmental science, European studies, fine arts, geography, history, industrial relations, law, linguistics, mathematical studies, materials science, microbiology, modern languages, philosophy, physics, politics and government, psychology, public administration, religious studies and theology, sociology, town and country planning, welfare studies. *Also:* Actuarial studies, Caribbean studies, film, microbial technology, operational research, Renaissance studies, visual and performed arts.

European Community: Number of students learning EC language or spending time in another EC country, not known. Formal exchange links with 18 EC universities/colleges: France (9); Germany (5); Italy (1); Netherlands (1); Spain (2). Approved Erasmus programme. 1990/91: 4-year courses in English and French/German/Spanish law; 4-year BA course in French with 2 years at the University Stendhal (Grenoble III) to include award of Maîtrise de Lettres Modernes.

Application: UCCA. **Academic features:** 4-year course, with 1 year abroad, offered for BA European management science, BSc in biochemistry, chemistry, electronics, microbiology and physics, as an alternative to normal 3-year courses. Unique African and Caribbean studies BA; electronic engineering with medical electronics BSc. New degrees in communication and image studies and physics with space science and systems. **Special features:** Number of distinguished scholars from various parts of world in residence for all or part of the year as Visiting Professors/Scholars. Edward K Brathwaite (eminent writer) gave T S Eliot Memorial Lectures, 1990. **Structural features:** Institute of Social and Applied Psychology; Canterbury Business School; Space Sciences Research Unit; Channel Tunnel Research Unit. **Largest fields of study:** English and American literature, biochemistry, computer science, law, electronic engineering. **Founded:** 1965. **Main awards:** BA, BSc, LLB. **Awarding body:** Kent University. **Site:** 300 acre campus, on outskirts of Canterbury. **Access:** Good road and rail links with London and Europe. **Accommodation:** All first-years guaranteed accommodation in 1 of 4 colleges, or self-catering accommodation. Approx cost: £360 per term (single room in college), £30 pw (self-catering). **Library:** 565,000 volumes, 110,000 pamphlets and official publications, 135,000 microforms and related materials, 117,000 slides, 4,000 periodical titles. **Specialist collections:** Links with the Library of Canterbury Cathedral; university library houses Lloyd George Collection (signed copies), Pettingell Collection (19th century plays), Maddison Collection (history of science), John Crow Collection (English literature); and Centre for Cartoons and Caricature (70,000 originals). **Welfare:** Personal tutorial system; medical service; SU provides legal and financial advice; student counselling service, travel bureau. **Careers:** Information and advisory service. **Amenities:** Dillon's bookshop on site; Gulbenkian Theatre; Cinema 3 (The Regional Film Theatre). **Sporting facilities:** Sports centre provides facilities for over 30 different activities (including coaching to international standard).

Duration of first degree course(s) or equivalent: 3 years; **others:** 4 years **Total first degree students 1989/90:** 3,711 **Number of overseas students:** 576 **Male/female ratio 1989/90:** 5:4 **Teaching staff: full-time:** 370 **part-time:** 14 **Total full-time students 1989/90:** 4,621 **Postgraduate students:** 543 **Tuition fees, first degrees, 1990/91:** Home: £1,675 (£665 if self-financing) plus £133 college fee; Overseas: £4,620 plus £133 College fee (eg politics), £6,120 plus £133 College fee (eg physics).

What it's like

It overlooks Canterbury, which is about half-an-hour's walk away. Campus life tends to be based around the four colleges – Darwin, Rutherford, Eliot and Keynes. College rooms small and expensive (£36 per week, including compulsory catering subscription scheme) but reasonably comfortable – if you can get one! Cooking in college accomodation is hopeless – a small stove/no fridge. Parkwood kitchens have had most cutlery and pans etc withdrawn for a reason only known to the university.

CAN'T FIND WHAT YOU'RE LOOKING FOR? USE THE INDEX!

Double rooms – Rutherford College; bunk-bedded rooms very small. Eliot – small rooms, no bunk beds. Darwin – fairly large. Keynes – no double rooms. Accommodation a major problem – most people get into college or Parkwood (Brookside style self-catering houses, £30 pw) in the first year, but if you manage this in the second and third year you're one of the lucky ones. New accommodation of 'higher quality' – therefore higher price – Becket Court £45 pw, with en suite shower etc. Overseas students (quarter of all students) tend to get better deal on campus accommodation. The university is taking on more students each year but providing a token amount of new accommodation – be prepared to hunt for a house, many end up in Herne Bay (10 miles away).

Some courses, like geography, taught at campus and at Christ Church College – about one and a half miles away.

University-owned bars in each college on pricey side (lager £1.10 pint) for students, unfortunately open until 10.30 pm (11 pm Friday and Saturday) but this may improve. Food in colleges is nothing to write home about – by the end of the year you'll be glad of your mum's cooking! Fast food service in Keynes most nights.

Safety: after an incident, followed by an occupation, university installed extra night porters, 7 security guards, extra lighting, better locks, spyholes, late night minibus.

SU excellent, politically and socially active. No SU building means social life can be a bit fragmented and provides some problems for ents; but across the 4 colleges there are 9 venues, with regular bands, discos etc in each one. Minor bands cost £1.50-2.50. Major ents have recently included 'The Darling Buds' and 'The Real Sounds of Africa' – £4.50-5. Campus societies also stage ents often. Films shown 3 nights a week (film card costs £4 for 3 films), plus another showing from the Film Society. The Gulbenkian Theatre and Cinema 3, both on campus, are used by public and students alike – attracting major productions. Little entertainment in town, only one nightclub – but loads of pubs, some good, some bad – most expensive! Shops are tourist-orientated – lots of gift shops! Restaurants excellent.

Cuts are being felt – long queues in library, dining halls, classes increasing in size; facilities not improved very often.
Sarah Brown

Pauper notes
Accommodation: Few married quarters on campus, a lot of b&b, student houses are scarce! **Drink:** Rose & Crown (promotions), Simple Simons/New Inn (good beers). Falstaff Tap (good cider/atmosphere). **Eats:** Vegetarian alternatives most restaurants/all dining halls. Cheap pub food in Thomas A'Becket and City Arms in Canterbury. Restaurants – Chinese, Thai, Mexican, American, Italian, pizze and pasta – vary in price! Cafe specialising in Mexican food offers different and cheap breakfasts/lunches etc. Very trendy. **Ents:** On campus films and ents (90 films approx 60 ents) with a £20 a year ents card (65p a week). Good ents at art college and Christ Church College; Kent is good campus for drama and film. **Sports:** Excellent sports facilities on campus but there is a charge. Swimming pool in Canterbury is good but expensive and crowded. **Hardship Funds:** Access funds (government scheme). **Travel:** No problem hitching into the city centre – hitching to London also easy. Coach under 2 hours to London, train 90 mins – Capital card, tube and train good value. **Work:** Summer in Canterbury means tourists and all the jobs associated with them (language schools/bars/shops etc); Also farm work in season. Bar work, dining halls – on campus. Fierce competition for vac jobs.

Alumni (Editors' pick)
Kazuo Ishiguro, Ted Harrison, Colin Lazzerini (founder of Loose Tubes).

CAN'T FIND WHAT YOU'RE LOOKING FOR? USE THE INDEX!

KING ALFRED'S COLLEGE

King Alfred's College, Sparkford Road, Winchester SO22 4NR (0962 841515) Map A, E8

Student enquiries: Admissions Officer

Main study areas – as in What to Study section: *(First degree):* American studies, archaeology, drama, education, English, history. **Also:** Design and technology.

European Community: No students learn an EC language or spend time in another EC country.

Application: PCAS. **Academic features:** Computer studies built into BEd for all students. BA design and technology. **Founded:** 1840, as diocesan training college for teachers. **Main awards:** BA, BEd. **Awarding body:** CNAA. **Site:** Overlooking city of Winchester. **Accommodation:** 560 places in halls of residence; (accommodation provided for first year students). Approx cost: £47 board and lodging. Rent: 41% in accommodation where rent controlled by college. **Library:** 100,000 volumes, 565 periodicals, 300 study places. **Welfare:** Health and counselling committee. **Special categories:** Some residential facilities for married students. **Careers:** Information, advice and placement service. **Amenities:** Theatre; television centre, learning resources centre, computer studies centre, library, art/design workshop, arts centre, human movement studio, sports hall, SU building with bar, laundry, bank, etc. **Sporting facilities:** Gymnasium, sports hall, squash courts, small open air pool, playing fields. **Employment:** Teaching, industry, commerce, civil service, media etc.

Duration of first degree course(s) or equivalent: 4 years; **others:** 3 years some BA courses; 2 years BEd design and technology. **Total first degree students 1989/90:** 1,117 **Total BEd students:** 733 **Number of overseas students:** 2 **Number of mature students:** 286 **Male/female ratio 1989/90:** 1:3 **Teaching staff: full-time:** 102 **part-time:** 16 **Total full-time students 1989/90:** 1,324 **Postgraduate students:** 42 **Tuition fees, first degrees, 1990/91:** Home: £1,675; Overseas: £3,300-£5,400.

What it's like

Attractively situated on hillside 10 mins' walk from Winchester city centre. Modern blocks contrast with traditional stone buildings. Accommodation varies. Most students live in: 1st years in converted houses within half mile of college; 2nd years mainly in college and approved digs; 3rd and 4th years in single study bedrooms on campus. Laundry and shop in SU building.

Well developed and confidential counselling service. Social life centres around SU; discos, dances, bands, parties, cocktail evenings, film and video shows and regular excursions. Winchester has a fine selection of pubs, a theatre, a disco, good shops and two markets. Southampton is twelve miles away, 20 minutes by train.

Excellent new sports complex on site, playing fields a mile from campus. Strong reputation for drama – regular student productions and visiting companies.

40 students a year study in America for a term. Most interesting developments: Shoei College for Japanese students and possibility of a Polish exchange. Relatively easy to change course during 1st year. Quality of staff varies. Workload reasonable to heavy, emphasised by use of continuous assessment as well as exams. Good academic reputation. SU active both socially and politically. Anti-Racism Group, Gay Society. Provides welfare and marketing services, social and sporting amenities, a newspaper, weekly TV programme, magazine and an annual handbook. Majority of students from south of England with a wide variety of backgrounds. College has a very close knit atmosphere. Dropout rate low.

Pauper notes

Accommodation: College married quarters available but limited. Creche available for 3–5 year olds. **Eats:** Cheap food in campus dining hall. A great quantity

CAN'T FIND WHAT YOU'RE LOOKING FOR? USE THE INDEX!

including vegetarian, but quality leaves a lot to be desired. Good selection available in college and town. **Drink:** Winchester pub prices average to high. **Ents:** Active Ents committee at college. 2 film socs. Multitude of good theatre on and off campus. Good range of active clubs and societies. **Sports:** Swimming pool and new sports complex on campus. Also recreation centre and swimming pool in town. **Hardship funds:** College give loans as do the SU. **Travel:** SU sells Rail cards, ISIC hitching relatively easy. **Work:** Plenty and varied. Winchester has country's lowest unemployment rate.

KING'S COLLEGE LONDON

King's College London, Strand, London WC2R 2LS (071-836 5454) Map E, C2

Student enquiries: Central Registry
You can look up King's College School of Medicine and Dentistry separately.

Main study areas – as in What to Study section: *(First degree):* Anatomy, archaeology, biochemistry, biology, biotechnology, botany, business studies, chemistry, civil engineering, classics, computing, dentistry, education, electrical and electronic engineering, English, environmental science, European studies, food science and nutrition, geography, history, humanities, Latin American studies, law, mathematical studies, mechanical and production engineering, medicine, microbiology, modern languages, music, nursing studies, pharmacology, pharmacy, philosophy, physics, physiology, religious studies and theology, strategic studies, zoology. *Also:* Physiotherapy.

European Community: 15% first degree students take EC language as part of course and 11% spend 6 months or more in another EC country. Formal exchange links with a large number of EC universities/colleges; most open to all undergraduates. New BA European studies (1992). Approved Erasmus programme 1990/91.

Application: UCCA. **Structural features:** Part of London University. **Founded:** 1829. **Main awards:** BA, BMus, BSc, BEng, MEng, BSc(Eng), LLB, MBBS, BDS, BPharm, BSc with RGN, BSc with Physiotherapy, BSc with PGCE. **Awarding body:** London University. **Special features:** Number of visiting professors contribute to the life of the college by giving lectures, participating in seminars, symposia etc. **Site:** in Strand, Kensington and Chelsea. Development of new buildings will allow operation from a single site based around the Strand. **Access:** Good underground and bus services to all campuses. **Accommodation:** Approx 1,440 places in college halls and some places in intercollegiate halls; high proportion of first years offered a hall place. Approx cost: £1,100 (1990/91) self-catering, £1,865 (fully catered) for a 30 week session (reduction for shared rooms). **Rent:** proportion of students in accommodation where rent is controlled by college, not known. **Library:** Book stock of over 800,000, periodicals, microfilms, tapes, videos, computer tapes, slides and filmstrips; reserved collections in most popular subjects. **Specialist collections:** Eng (classics); Burrows (modern Greek and Byzantine studies); Box (Old Testament); Liddell Hart (military studies); Ford (science); Adam Archive (Portuguese). **Welfare:** Doctors, psychotherapists, chaplains, student advisers. **Hardship funds:** Every effort made to help students who encounter financial hardship; government access fund. **Careers:** Information, advice and placement service. **Amenities and sporting facilities:** All facilities of ULU (including swimming pool); King's College union of students buildings; sports ground, boat club and sailing club; a particularly central position for London's cultural amenities.

Duration of first degree course(s) or equivalent: 3 years; **others:** 4 years **Total first degree students 1989/90:** 4,572 **Number of BEd students:** 20 **Number of**

CAN'T FIND WHAT YOU'RE LOOKING FOR? USE THE INDEX!

overseas students: 495 **Number of mature students:** 30 **Male/female ratio 1989/90:** 7:4 **Total teaching staff: full-time:** 513 **part-time:** 50 **Total full-time students 1989/90:** 5,790 **Postgraduate students:** 2,106 **Tuition fees, first degrees, 1990/91:** Home: £1,675; Overseas: £5,200 (eg politics), £6,600 (eg physics), £11,750 (eg medicine).

What it's like

One of the largest colleges in London, formed in 1985 by King's, Queen Elizabeth and Chelsea colleges merging. Increasingly, departments and faculties are focusing on the Strand which has created space difficulties but makes for a lively and busy atmosphere. Students work hard; impressive academic results. Large range of courses available; diverse course structure/teaching techniques. Large range of sports clubs and societies.

Strand campus next to Somerset House (which houses the Courtauld galleries), and is within walking distance of all the tourist sites of London and many theatres. Chelsea campus is on the Kings Road – it's all here – from alcohol to aspirins, text books to trainers. Pubs tend to be trendy or Sloaney; campus SU bar very popular. Kensington campus is between Notting Hill Gate and High Street Kensington, so students can enjoy the hustle and bustle of busy shopping areas and escape to Holland Park for peace and quiet. Each site has a different flavour and atmosphere so, if you're looking for a relaxed, friendly college and a busy vibrant, and stimulating three years, KCL is the place to be!

Pauper Notes

Accommodation: King's owned; also London University Intercollegiate Halls of residence. Excellent short life and head-leasing schemes run by college accommodation office. **Drink:** SU run the Strand ('Waterfront', completely refurbished summer 1990) and Kensington bars; college runs Chelsea one. All much cheaper than London pubs. **Eats:** SU catering outlets at Strand and Kensington serve pizzas, rolls etc. College offers self- and waitress-service refectories. **Ents:** Excellent varied SU ents programme – weekly discos on all campuses, cabaret, balls, Karaoke, quizzes, gigs etc – one of the best reputations in London University. ULU has trendy bands. **Sports:** Excellent indoor facilities at ULU. Developing college outdoor sports facilities; sports ground at Mitcham. **Hardship funds:** As well as Access funds, there are educational trusts/loans available – see college registry for details. **Travel:** Exchange programmes, scholarships. ULU travel shop at Strand. **Work:** SU offers casual work in bars, catering, shop and at ents. Plenty of work available in London.

Alumni (Editors' pick):

Archbishop Desmond Tutu, Sir Shridath Ramphal, Chapman Pincher, Sir Hugh Rossi MP, Lord Edmund-Davies, Susan Hill, Angela Rumbold, Arthur C Clarke, Pat Reid, Jonathan Kohn.

KING'S COLLEGE SCHOOL OF MEDICINE

King's College School of Medicine & Dentistry, University of London, Bessemer Road, London SE5 9PJ (071-274 6222) Map D, C3

Student enquiries: Medical School Office (ext 4017) or Dental School Office (ext 2541)

Main study areas – as in What to Study section: *(First degree):* Dentistry, medicine.

European Community: No students learn an EC language or spend time in another EC country.

CAN'T FIND WHAT YOU'RE LOOKING FOR? USE THE INDEX!

Application: UCCA. **Structural features:** Part of King's College, London University. **Special features:** Densely populated urban area with some 1,000 beds, and over 100,000 dental patient attendances, so both medical and dental students have clinical contact with many patients. **Founded:** 1831. **Main awards:** BDS, MBBS. **Awarding body:** London University. **Site:** College in the Strand and in Camberwell Green/Denmark Hill area. **Access:** British Rail from Victoria, Holborn or London Bridge stations to Denmark Hill station; underground to Brixton, Elephant & Castle, or Oval, and then bus; various buses from central London. **Academic features:** Basic medical and dental sciences taught in multi-faculty environment of King's College London. Medical students also admitted from Oxford and Cambridge Universities for clinical studies only. **Accommodation:** Halls of residence of King's College London and the University of London. **Library:** 27,000 books and bound journals, 65 study places at Denmark Hill. **Other learning resources:** Use made of videos and computer-assisted learning packages. **Welfare:** Doctor, dentist, FPA, psychiatrist, chaplain, independent financial adviser, hospital chapel. **Careers:** Information, advice and placement service. **Amenities:** All facilities of London University. **Employment:** Medicine and Dentistry.

Duration of first degree course(s) or equivalent: 5 years **Total first degree students 1989/90:** 532 (clinical students only) **Number of overseas students:** 31 **Male/female ratio 1989/90:** 3:2 **Teaching staff: full-time:** 111 **part-time:** 30 (clinical only) **Total full-time students 1989/90:** 568 **Postgraduate students:** 145 **Tuition fees, first degrees, 1990/91:** Home: £1,675; Overseas: £6,600 (pre-clinical), £11,750 (clinical).

What it's like

Spending two (or three) years in King's College on the Strand before coming down to the Hospital in Camberwell does make life rather interesting, since King's College London is one of the largest multi-faculty colleges of London University. Two or three years spent with non medics or dentists tends to broaden one's outlook and gives an experience of 'student life'. As well as being just down the road from Covent Garden, National Theatre and the whole West End, it means that while one still has some overdraft facilities, London life is there to be enjoyed.

Once finished in the Strand, students come down to Camberwell, to meet patients and be assimilated into hospital life. Rather than lectures, as at the Strand, learning is emphasised at the bedside, with importance being attached to speaking to and examining patients, so that a 'whole' view of the patient is obtained. A lot of learning is absorbed by a sort of osmosis as students are expected to spend some time following House Officers. This is exciting as patients are seen first-hand as they appear in Casualty with anything from haemorrhages or heart attacks to knife wounds. Not all the course is in King's – two months are spent in outside district hospitals which is popular as teaching is generally enthusiastic and atmosphere more relaxed.

Once at the hospital students are also members of SU, called the Guild. Apart from one of the most pleasant bars in London, also boasts one of the best mobile discos in south London, and provides cheap entertainment every week plus many bands during year. Also provided in 'The Penthouse' are TV/games rooms. The Guild has many clubs and societies, as well as brand new sports ground in Dulwich Village, which makes us rather unique in that students walk to 'the Griffin' rather than overcoming an obstacle course provided by London Transport and BR!

Outside the hospital, Camberwell and Brixton, while not being the West End, do provide many alternative night spots which are fairly cheap such as 'the Fridge' in Brixton and the Ritzy – an independent cinema. It's obviously an up and coming area judging by the wine bars springing up everywhere. Student reductions available at sports centres locally.

A few general points. Once outside King's the label 'student' is not automatically applied which provides independence with the friendly back-up of large student body. Accommodation provided in first year at least, free advice and information

CAN'T FIND WHAT YOU'RE LOOKING FOR? USE THE INDEX!

provided thereafter. Life is more expensive than outside London but Camberwell is cheaper than many other areas; there is a 'community' feeling in Camberwell not the 'lost in London' effect which is found in other areas. And because the hospital is in a varied community, medical teaching is varied, interesting and of a high standard.

Pauper notes

Accommodation: Squats through King's College London – £15-20/week. Short life because houses are condemned and to be demolished but this rarely occurs. **Drink:** Penthouse and Strand bars – £1/pint Kronenburg/Courage best. **Eats:** Cheap refectory at hospital, local kebab houses. Cheap pasta locally and excellent Thai food. Wine bars. **Ents:** Penthouse on campus plus Brixton Ritzy – alternative and box-office hit films cheap and interesting. Student reductions in London for plays. **Sports:** Brixton Sports Club – all sports. Cheap membership gives reductions. Griffen Sports Club – tennis, netball, hockey, rugby, multigym, bowls and squash courts. **Hardship Funds:** Some for poverty-stricken students. Apart from KCL Hardship Fund, there are some companies providing help. **Travel:** 15 seater minibus. Few travel scholarships for elective students; many local secondhand bike dealers. **Work:** Working on the bar, waitering/waitressing – very easy to find work, fairly well paid.

Alumni (Editors' pick)

Dr Reita Faria (ex-Miss World, now practising doctor), J L Dawson (Surgeon to Royal Household), Sir R M Feroze (President, Royal College of Obstetricians and Gynaecologists), Graeme Garden ('The Goodies').

KINGSTON POLY

Kingston Polytechnic, Penrhyn Road, Kingston upon Thames KT1 2EE (081-549 1366) Map D, A4

Student enquiries: Admissions Officer

Main study areas – as in What to Study section: *(First degree):* Accountancy, aeronautical engineering, architecture, art & design, business studies, chemistry, civil engineering, computing, economics, education, electrical and electronic engineering, English, environmental science, fine arts, geography, geology, history, information technology, law, mathematical studies, mechanical and production engineering, microbiology, modern languages, music, politics and government, sociology, welfare studies. *Also:* Estate management, quantity surveying.

European Community: 25% first degree students take EC language (open to all as a non-examined subject) and 25% spend 6 months or more in another EC country. Formal Erasmus links with a number of EC universities/colleges: in economics (Spain); politics (France, Germany, Spain); business (France, Germany, Netherlands, Spain); information systems (Eire, France, Greece, Spain); design (France, Netherlands); public administration (Belgium, Denmark, Eire, France, Germany, Greece, Italy, Netherlands, Spain); chemistry (Germany). Approved Erasmus programme 1990/91.

Application: PCAS except for art and design (ADAR). **Academic features:** Courses in information systems design, business information technology, aerospace engineering, geographic information systems, manufacturing engineering, cell and molecular biology, biomedical science, business studies (European programme), music technology. **Special features:** Medici string quartet. Links with Gateway School of Music/modern music rehearsal centre and recording studio. Two Picker Fellows in art and sculpture. Three visiting professors in physical science, aerospace engineering and business. **Largest fields of study:** Applied science, business studies, engineering and modern arts. **Founded:** 1970, ex Kingston Colleges of

CAN'T FIND WHAT YOU'RE LOOKING FOR? USE THE INDEX!

Technology and Art, joined in 1975 by Gipsy Hill College of Education. **Main awards:** BA, BEd, BSc, BEng, MEng. **Awarding body:** CNAA. **Site:** Kingston area. **Access:** British Rail (Kingston or Surbiton stations), buses. **Accommodation:** 1,250 hostel places cost c£30 pw, 500 bedsitters cost £30–35. Accommodation usually found for first years, who have priority for hostel places. Rent: proportion of students in accommodation where rent controlled by poly not known. **Library:** On 4 sites, total of 350,000 items consisting of books, periodicals, tapes, records; 930 study places; short loan service for course books; slide library at Knights Park Centre, music library at Gipsy Hill Centre. **Other learning resources:** One of largest academic computing facilities in Europe. **Welfare:** Full-time welfare unit, part-time doctors; Counselling service, student services department. **Hardship funds:** Dealt with by student services department. **Careers:** Information, advice and placement service. **Amenities:** SU building with bar, common room, etc. SU bars on all four sites. **Sporting facilities:** Gymnasiums, playing fields, wide range of sporting activities. Poly teams have excellent records at national college/polytechnic level.

Duration of first degree course(s) or equivalent: 3 years; **others:** 4 years (sandwich) **Total first degree students 1989/90:** 6,535; **total BEd students:** 120 **Number of overseas students (including EC):** 290 **Number of mature students:** approx 650 **Teaching staff: full-time:** 483 **part-time:** 200 **Total full-time students 1989/90:** 7,383 **Postgraduate students:** approx 850 **Tuition fees, first degrees, 1990/91:** Home: £1,740 (£903 if self-financing); Overseas: £5,050.

What it's like

Contrary to the appearance of the official prospectus, Kingston is not all romantic sunsets over the Thames and peaceful strolls down tree-lined boulevards. Want to know the truth? Well, here it is in all its naked glory.

Kingston town centre is a road planner's disaster area with traffic wardens to match. Too many cars, too many buses, and far too many students but shopping facilities excellent and so is public transport into central London (Waterloo 20 mins – no tube). Many good restaurants to suit all tastes and budgets; several popular student pubs although London prices make SU bars the usual alternative; two very average night clubs with occasional student nights and 'Options' has three cinemas with a half-price twilight saving at 6pm.

The polytechnic is most renowned for its fashion and engineering depts. Many sandwich and modular courses, work experience opportunities and field trips. The Erasmus scheme means good relations with European academic institutions and strong language dept. Also linked to some American colleges. Changing course obviously depends on requirements and subscriptions but generally poly is very helpful. Highest drop-out rate is on HND courses because of extremely high workload. Overall academic standard is very good but food is dreadful (go to SU snack bars instead: much nicer and much cheaper).

Kingston Poly SU (KPSU) is very active, although not very radical. Provides major Kingston venues and ents: weekly bands, discos, comedians, cabarets and films. There are 5 bars, 3 shops, over 70 social, cultural, sporting and political clubs; a confidential welfare service; campus banking and insurance; travel agency and many part-time jobs. Most active societies are rugby, law, drama, surfing (trips to S of F), canoeing, mountaineering. Students contribute to town life; considerable opposition from residents; most ents are SU run.

Housing – the main drawback for Kingston Poly is accommodation. A very lucky few may manage to get into halls of residence for their first year, but most students live out. Although rented accommodation is usually of quite good standard, it is scarce and very expensive (approx £45 pw) and since the abolition of housing benefit and introduction of poll tax, things are getting harder. It's not all bad though; bus services are good and many students live in slightly cheaper surrounding areas of New Malden, Surbiton, Tolworth and Norbiton.

There is no such thing as a 'typical' student at Kingston other than the fact that

CAN'T FIND WHAT YOU'RE LOOKING FOR? USE THE INDEX!

most are from south and south-east and private or grammar schools. There is every type here ranging from the hyper trendy art students at Knights Park to conscientious engineers at Canbury Park and finally to the Golf GTI brigade in the law dept at Kingston Hill. Anything goes here.

Money is the bane of every student's life and Kingston is not a cheap place to live, however if you do find somewhere to sleep and don't own a car, it's a great place to spend your degree years. Most students who come here end up staying in the area, so it can't be all bad!
Kerstin Shields

Pauper notes

Accommodation: Expensive. **Drink:** SU bars average 30-35p per pint cheaper. Popular student pubs include The Kingston Mill, The Ram and The Railway. **Eats:** Bad poly service. Good SU snacks available (pizzas, rolls, samosas etc). Good restaurants, Indian/Italian/Chinese everywhere. **Ents:** Options cinema do half price twilight shows around 6.00 pm (3 films). SU provides major Kingston venues – weekly bands, discos, films. **Sports:** Many squash, tennis, golf clubs – cheaper if used through SU. Poly fitness rooms, squash courts, gyms, playing fields, tennis courts. **Hardship funds:** Small SU loans. **Travel:** SU travel office (STA). Hitching bad. **Work:** Many p-t jobs in SU plus many others in pubs, shops, restaurants in Kingston.

Alumni (Editors' pick)

Penny Jones (VP).

LA SAINTE UNION

La Sainte Union College of Higher Education, The Avenue, Southampton SO9 5HB (0703 228761) Map A, E8

Student enquiries: Mrs Pauline Wilson

Main study areas – as in What to Study section: *(First degree):* Biology, education, English, European studies, geography, history, mathematical studies, modern languages, religious studies and theology.

European Community: 15% first degree students take EC language as part of course and 15% spend 6 months or more in another EC country. Formal exchange links with 5 EC universities/colleges in France and Germany.

Application: UCCA. **Academic features:** Chiropody (Society of Chiropodists) course, 3 years full-time. Computer courses for students. **Special features:** Visiting literary figures and lecturers. **Founded:** 1904, by LSU sisters. **Main awards:** BA, BEd, BTh. **Awarding body:** Southampton University. **Site:** Southampton town centre. **Access:** 5 minutes from centre of Southampton. **Accommodation:** 360 places in college houses and hostels. (One third of students home based.) **Library:** 90,000 volumes, 366 periodicals, 142 study places, temporary reference collection. **Welfare:** Doctor, chaplain, nursery school. **Special categories:** RC and ecumenical services. **Careers:** Full advisory service. **Amenities:** SU coffee bar and bar, bookshop on campus, SU, CCTV. **Sporting facilities;** Heated indoor swimming pool, 2 gyms, tennis. **Employment:** Teaching; graduate careers in usual range for BA, BTh students.

Duration of first degree course(s) or equivalent: 3 (4 years languages) **Total first degree students 1989/90: 934 Total BEd students:** 352 **Number of mature students:** 167 **Male/female ratio 1989/90:** 3:7 **Teaching staff: full-time:** 67 **part-time:** 2 **Total full-time students 1989/90:** 934 **Postgraduate students:** 120 **Tuition fees, first degrees, 1990/91:** Home: £1,675 (plus £321 for first year only).

CAN'T FIND WHAT YOU'RE LOOKING FOR? USE THE INDEX!

What it's like

Small campus in pleasant grounds, close to city centre. Station 10 mins walk away; plenty of local buses; good taxi facilities. National coaches close. Small airport with many flights from Channel Islands and good hydrofoil and boat services to the Isle of Wight. Few students have cars; parking difficult.

All hostels on campus or within 100 yards. Small, mainly single study bedrooms, comfortable, usually carpeted, own sink. 1st years and some final years live in. Washing facilities available; all meals taken in college refectory. Some mixed hostels, others single sex; no real problems. Guests can stay in spare rooms. Relationship between administration and students good.

SU close to true unionism active in whatever students want to do – political, social, sporting or anything else. Small tuck shop and TV and video in board room. Plenty of info.

No college counsellors but chaplain and good personal tutor system. Union has part-time welfare and women's officer; access to university psychologists. Medical centre with trained nurse. Contraception advice careful due to Catholic nature of college.

Small, thus clubs and socs have limited resources but great deal of freedom to set up new ones and get involved in established ones. Good relationship with town. Plenty of pubs, increasing theatre provision and new cinema. Good student discounts.

Two-thirds doing initial teacher training; changing course is becoming increasingly difficult. Few overseas students (though 8-10 French/German exchange). Lots of students from Midlands, South Wales and London as well as many local. A lot from church schools.
Anne Patrick

Pauper notes

Accommodation: College: single room. Town: quite good on single rooms; little married accommodation. **Drinks:** Nasty Southern beers but some good Free Houses. Frog & Frigate brews its own, Gales pubs good and Huntsmans etc. **Eats:** More ethnic food becoming available inc Caribbean, Italian good. Good veggie restaurant close. **Ents:** Many clubs, theatre increasing. **Sports:** New Centre 2000 with flues, bowling, ice rink no more. Div 1 football and county cricket. **Travel:** Citybus do student card. **Work:** Local part-time work but Soton flooded with students during vacation.

LABAN CENTRE

Laban Centre for Movement and Dance Laurie Grove, New Cross, London SE14 6NH (081-692 4070) Map D, C3

Student enquiries: The Registrar

Main study areas – as in What to Study section: *(First degree):* Dance. *Also:* Dance theatre.

European Community: No students learn an EC language or spend time in another EC country.

Application: Direct. **Academic features:** MA in dance studies, dance movement therapy. **Special features:** Visiting artists as teachers and performers. Annual international summer school, special 1-year courses, junior year abroad scheme for US students. Access to buildings for the disabled. **Main awards:** BA. **Awarding body:** CNAA. **Site:** South East London. **Access:** New Cross or New Cross Gate stations (British Rail from Charing Cross); various buses. **Accommodation:** Private locally; no college (or college rent controlled) accommodation. **Library:** Dance

CAN'T FIND WHAT YOU'RE LOOKING FOR? USE THE INDEX!

collection, related subjects, notation scores, periodicals, record collection, Peter Williams dance archive, 40–45 study places, access to Goldsmiths' College libraries. **Welfare:** Doctor, psychiatrist, chaplain, solicitor through SU. **Hardship funds:** Small interest-free loans available for short term. **Careers:** Information and advice. **Amenities:** Purpose-built studios, sound studio, music rooms, well-equipped modern studio theatre and wardrobe department. Fully-equipped pilates studio for body training. In-house publications: Dance Theatre Journal and international working papers. **Employment:** Performing arts and teaching. Community art. Dance animateurs. Choreography. Notation. Research.

Duration of first degree course(s) or equivalent: 3 years **Total first degree students 1989/90:** 140 **Number of overseas students:** 15 **Number of mature students:** 0 **Male/female ratio 1989/90:** 1:10 **Teaching staff: full-time:** 16 **part-time:** 25 **Total full-time students 1989/90:** 215 **Postgraduate students:** 27 **Tuition fees, first degrees, 1990/91:** £5,775.

What it's like

Housed in a converted church with purpose built dance studios and pilates studio, attached to the Goldsmiths' College campus. British Rail and tube available for easy access to Central London. SU has no Sabbatical Officer, but is run by a committee of present students who are determined to make the Union active and effective. Laban students have the chance to use many of the Goldsmiths' facilities. Timetable heavy – 9 am until 6 pm Monday–Friday and weekends when necessary, plus written work especially for BA students. Drop out rate high. Many overseas students. Wide range of courses available and overall teaching standard is high, but relations between students and administration staff can be distant.

Pauper notes

Accommodation: College provides details of local accommodation. SU can provide details of squats, co-ops etc. **Drink:** Goldsmiths' SU bar next door, many local pubs. **Eats:** Goldsmiths' provide vegetarian food and many Indian/Chinese/Italian restaurants (reasonably priced) nearby. **Ents:** Goldsmiths' SU discos, gigs etc regularly. Laban students, staff and outside company performances. **Sports:** Local pool (New X baths) free for residents of Lewisham. Sports centre (Lewisham) with discounts for residents. **Hardship funds:** College provides loan fund, although amounts not very large and payback time quite short. **Travel:** Lisa Ullman fund provides opportunity for dance students to travel abroad. Goldsmiths' SU provide safe women's transport after social events. **Work:** Local work in pubs, restaurants. Plenty of temp jobs in summer holiday.

Alumni (Editors' pick)

The Cholmondeleys, David Massingham, Matthew Bourne, Geographical Duvet, Adventures in Motion Pictures, Action Syndicate (all ex-Laban BA students), Lea Anderson, Jacob Marley (choreographers).

LAMPETER

St David's University College, Lampeter University of Wales, Dyfed, Wales SA48 7ED (0570 422351) Map A, C7

Student enquiries: Admissions Officer

Main study areas – as in What to Study section: *(First degree):* Archaeology, classics, English, geography, history, library and information studies, modern languages, Near East and Islamic studies, philosophy, religious studies and theology. *Also:* Environmental archaeology, Swedish, Victorian studies, Welsh studies.

CAN'T FIND WHAT YOU'RE LOOKING FOR? USE THE INDEX!

European Community: 7% first degree students take EC language as part of course and 3% spend 6 months or more in another EC country. Formal exchange links with The Netherlands (Nijmegen). Approved Erasmus programme 1990/91.

Application: UCCA. **Structural features:** Part of Wales University. **Academic features:** Joint honours courses in archaeology, church history, Victorian studies, Swedish and Islamic Studies; first year has 3 subjects of equal weight including main degree subject(s). Information studies available to all first year students and as part of joint degree in informatics. **Largest fields of study:** English, history, geography, theology and religious studies. **Founded:** 1822, becoming part of Wales University in 1971. **Main awards:** BA, BD. **Awarding body:** Wales University. **Site:** Lampeter town centre. **Accommodation:** 392 places in halls of residence; 110 places in self-catering hostels; rooms in halls of residence automatically allocated to all first year students. Approx cost: £630. Meals paid for as taken in the refectory. Rent: 80% in accommodation where rent controlled by university. **Library:** Main library and old library; 200,000 volumes in total, 950 periodicals, 190 study places. **Specialist collections:** Tracts collection; early Welsh periodicals; Bibles, prayer-books, hymnals, catechisms and ballads; MSS collection including 15th century Books of Hours. **Welfare:** All facilities available in Lampeter; chaplain. **Hardship funds:** Principal's Hardship Fund – limited funds available. **Special categories:** Residential facilities for disabled students; children's playgroup. **Careers:** Information, advice and placement service. **Amenities:** Bookshop on campus; purpose-built SU. **Sporting facilities:** Sports hall; playing fields less than 5 mins from campus; use of town swimming pool; college sailing club at Aberaeron.

Duration of first degree course(s) or equivalent: 3 years; **others:** 4 years (philosophy, Welsh, modern languages) **Total first degree students 1989/90:** 832 **Male/female ratio 1989/90:** 1:1 **Teaching staff:** full-time: 70 part-time: 18 **Total full-time students 1989/90:** 864 **Postgraduate students:** 71 **Tuition fees, first degrees, 1990/91:** Home: £1,675; Overseas: £3,950.

What it's like

Smallest university college in Britain with c900 students. Numbers rising and should reach 1,000 by 1992. Very pretty single campus dominated by the Old Building (built 1822). Accommodation good, but on the small side; competition growing for on-campus accommodation as numbers grow. Rents relatively cheap on and off campus but some off-campus housing pretty grim.

Student population mixed. High percentage of mature students (not that you'd notice most of the time). About 10-15% are Welsh with half of them being Welsh speaking. There is an exchange scheme with Canadian and Swedish universities. About another 50% of students are from the Home Counties.

There are no visiting restrictions and few other restrictions although there are quiet halls for those who enjoy tranquility.

Due to isolated position of Lampeter many students have cars. The remoteness of the place means that much of the entertainment is home-grown although some surprisingly large name bands have played here. Entertainment is centred on the Union building and arts hall. The Union itself is quite active but not at all party-political.

There are many shops and societies from rugby club to shopping society. On campus squash and tennis courts, gym and hockey pitch.

Pauper notes

Accommodation: Generally good, majority of students (500 out of 800) live on campus. Facilities not so good for married students and those with children (but good creche). Cheap but rising; as little as £18 pw in very poor accommodation. **Drink:** Bar is cheapest hostelry around and has good atmosphere; there are many pubs in town. **Eats:** College refectory cheap but nasty; SU Pooh's Corner more upmarket and caters for vegetarians. Again wide variety of cafes and restaurants in

CAN'T FIND WHAT YOU'RE LOOKING FOR? USE THE INDEX!

town including Chinese take-away and Indian restaurant. **Ents:** Groups about three or four times a term in arts hall – from £3 to £5, regular discos and twice weekly films. Regular plays by Elinfach Theatre (6 miles off campus) often in Welsh. **Sports:** Use of town pool and sports hall on campus also tennis and squash courts, all free. **Hardship funds:** Available from SU but only in cases of dire emergency. **Travel:** Isolated so difficult. No BR station in Lampeter though there are rumours that rail-link is to be re-opened by late 1990s. There are buses. It is a good area to hitch to and from. **Work:** Hard to find. Students work behind bar and in Pooh's Corner, also sometimes available at the Co-op and at a vegetable packing factory.

Alumni (Editors' pick)

T E Lawrence (of Arabian fame), Sulak Sivaraska (Thai human rights campaigner), Sue Slipman (former NUS chief now involved in SDP/Democrats), George Gordon (arrested for impersonating a priest in a hospital(!)).

LANCASHIRE POLY

Lancashire Polytechnic, Preston PR1 2TQ (0772 201201) Map A, D5

Student enquiries: Access and Student Recruitment

Main study areas – as in What to Study section: *(First degree):* Accountancy, agriculture and horticulture, American studies, art and design, biochemistry, biology, biotechnology, business studies, chemistry, computing, economics, education, electrical and electronic engineering, English, environmental science, European studies, fine arts, geography, history, hotel and catering management, information technology, law, linguistics, mathematical studies, mechanical and production engineering, microbiology, modern languages, nursing studies, pharmacology, physics, physiology, politics and government, psychology, sociology, welfare studies. *Also:* Astrophysics, building technology, European business studies.

European Community: 10% first degree students take EC language as part of course (language training is available for all students) and 5% spend 6 months or more in another EC country. Formal exchange links with some 30 EC universities/colleges (more in pipeline): Eire (1); France (10); Germany (7); Netherlands (3); Portugal (2); Spain (6). Approved Erasmus programme 1990/91. Opportunity to work abroad on Commett grant.

Application: PCAS; ADAR for art and design. **Academic features:** New courses include fashion promotion, product design, employee relations, financial services, community studies, horticultural technology and management, applied physics for Europe with business skills, electronic design, medical electronics, design and manufacture; combined honours programme of 60¢ subjects. Work studio approach to teaching of BEng (mechanical engineering), CATS (Credit Accumulation and Transfer Scheme) being introduced. ACOL (Analytical Chemistry by Open Learning). Languages for all initiative. **Special features:** John Thompson (IBA), first visiting professor in journalism and broadcasting; Ian McDiarmid (British Aerospace), visiting research fellow. Links with universities in China, USA and Europe where students may take part of their course. **Founded:** 1973 as Preston Polytechnic, name changed 1984. **Main awards:** BA, BSc, BEng. **Awarding body:** CNAA. **Site:** Central site of c. 38 acres. **Access:** Road and rail. **Accommodation:** 250 places in halls, 700 (approx) in Poly residences and Poly-controlled hostels/houses. Approx cost: Halls/hostels c£27.50 pw, poly houses c£19pw (both self-catering). Rent: 20% in accommodation where rent controlled by polytechnic. **Library:** 260,000 volumes in total, 1,700 periodicals, 700 study places; restricted loan collection; slide library, video & audio cassettes. **Specialist collections:** Preston Incorporated Law Society Library; collections of illustrated books and local history. **Welfare:** 2 counsellors and 3 accommodation officers, health centre, FPA,

CAN'T FIND WHAT YOU'RE LOOKING FOR? USE THE INDEX!

legal advice centre, multi-faith centre, creche, adviser for overseas students and adviser for students with special needs, racial equality unit. **Hardship funds:** Individual cases of financial hardship considered for assistance. **Careers:** Information Officer; advice and placement service; 2 careers advisers. **Amenities:** Arts centre, sailing centre, sports centre with human performance laboratory, good outdoor sports facilities, observatories, bookshop, pre-school centre, health centre, students' union with shops and travel agency, banking facilities, conference facilities, catering service.

Duration of first degree course(s) or equivalent: 3 years; **others:** 4 years (sandwich) **Total first degree students 1989/90:** 3,410 (full-time), 1,028 (part-time) **Number of overseas students:** 94 **Number of mature students:** 1,500 (full-time), 2,600 (p-t) **Male/female ratio 1989/90:** 5:4 **Teaching staff: full-time:** 500 part-time: 175 **Total full-time students 1989/90:** 5,500 **Postgraduate students:** 300 (f-t); 325 (p-t) **Tuition fees, first degrees, 1990/91:** Home: £1,675; Overseas: £4,563.

What it's like

Preston is undergoing large re-development that makes it quite a busy town. Still maintains its friendly atmosphere without letting its abundance of rain dampen the spirit. Poly also expanding, taking on new students and new courses each year (though not increasing accommodation and library resources) to go hand in hand with that!

Purpose built Union building houses 2 bars, food outlets, admin offices, plus 750 capacity 'Venue'. (This is proving inadequate for the increasing number of students.)

Pauper notes

Accommodation: New 400-bed halls (1991). Poly is expensive – private sector not much better; squats impossible. **Drink:** SU bars reasonable, good selection. Local pubs offer Robinsons, Theakstons, Thwaites and Matty Brown. **Eats:** SU offers a good range of burgers – few vegetarian restaurants, many Indian, few Chinese. Roobarb for vegetarian near Poly library. **Ents:** Local Odeon offers cheap student entry. New 10-screen cinema offering student discounts. **Sports:** Poly has no playing fields of its own. **Hardship funds:** None from SU. Poly has some funds. **Travel:** Good for hitching (on M6/M61). **Work:** Good bar work – term time on and off campus.

Alumni (Editors' pick)

Joe Lydon (rugby league international).

LANCASTER UNIVERSITY

Lancaster University, University House, Lancaster LA1 4YW (0524 65201) Map A, D5

Student enquiries: Undergraduate Admissions Office

Main study areas – as in What to Study section: (*First degree*): Accountancy, American studies, art & design, biochemistry, biology, business studies, chemistry, classics, communication studies, computing, drama, economics, education, electrical & electronic engineering, English, environmental science, geography, history, industrial relations, information technology, law, linguistics, mathematical studies, mechanical and production engineering, modern languages, music, philosophy, physics, politics and government, psychology, religious studies and theology, sociology, welfare studies. *Also:* Medieval studies, operational research, women's studies.

CAN'T FIND WHAT YOU'RE LOOKING FOR? USE THE INDEX!

European Community: 15% first degree students take EC language as part of course and 8% spend 6 months or more in another EC country. A wide range of opportunities; particularly strong links with Copenhagen University and Copenhagen Business School. There are programmes in (among others) management, medieval studies, geography, linguistics and law. Approved Erasmus programme 1990/91. Member of the European Credit Tranfer System in business administration.

Application: UCCA. **Academic features:** Course structure flexible (easy to change course) and allows specialisation. Flexible BSc combined science; new BA in culture and communication. Admission policy welcomes mature students (details from Director of Admissions). **Special features:** Medici String Quartet (artists-in-residence); John Clegg (pianist-in-residence). Exchange programme in many subjects with US universities, as well as Erasmus and Comett programmes in Europe. **Largest fields of study:** English, history, management, biological and environmental sciences. **Founded:** 1964. **Main awards:** BA, BBA, BMus, BSc, LLB, BEng, MEng. **Awarding body:** Lancaster University. **Site:** Bailrigg, south of Lancaster. **Access:** On main London–Glasgow line; A6 and M6 main roads. **Accommodation:** 2,800 rooms on campus (accommodation available for all first years). Rent: 57% in accommodation where rent controlled by university. **Library:** About 800,000 items, over 3,000 periodicals, 800 reader places; short loan system for course books. **Specialist collections:** Redlich collection (music); Quaker collection; library of Burnley Grammar School. **Other learning resources:** Language resource centre, TV studio. **Welfare:** Collegiate advisers, doctors, psychiatrist, chaplains, professional student counsellors. **Hardship funds:** Student Aid Fund assists students with unforeseen financial difficulties. **Special categories:** Residential facilities for disabled and some married students; nursery (40 places, free or subsidised for students). **Careers:** Information, placement and advice service. **Amenities:** Bookshop; second-hand bookshop run by students; various shops and banks on campus; Peter Scott art gallery; Jack Hylton music rooms; Nuffield theatre studio. **Sporting facilities:** Wide range of sporting and recreational facilities (including swimming pool, sauna, solarium, and rock-climbing wall); outdoor centre in the Yorkshire Dales.

Duration of first degree course(s) or equivalent: 3 years; others: 4 years (MEng, languages and sandwich courses); 5 years (sandwich MEng) **Total first degree students 1989/90:** 4,161 **Number of overseas students:** 850 **Number of mature students:** 749 **Male/female ratio 1989/90:** 7:6 **Teaching staff: full-time:** 421 **part-time:** 16 **Total full-time students 1989/90:** 5,202 **Postgraduate students:** 1,722 (inc part-time) **Tuition fees, first degrees, 1990/91:** Home: £1,792 (£782 if self-financing); Overseas: £4,560 (eg politics), £6,050 (eg physics).

What it's like

Attractive modern on-campus university in pleasant grounds 2 miles south of Lancaster. Very accessible – M6 and maritime London-Scotland rail link. Excellent location for outdoor activity – sea, Lake District and good access to other major cities.

Reasonable accommodation for 1st and some 3rd year students, on campus in colleges. Each of the 8 colleges has own bar, student run JCR and tradition. Keen rivalry between colleges producing a very good atmosphere. Active and powerful SU campaigning and providing information including: education and welfare department, Athletic Union (over 30 clubs), non sporting and cultural societies. Social events (Sugar House nightclub, on campus, concerts, balls etc). No visiting restrictions.

Courses extremely flexible – three subjects in first year. Staff generally very helpful and friendly. Almost all courses have some continued assessment (alternative prospectuses available from SU). Chance to study abroad in 2nd year.

Friendly university; excellent atmosphere, international flavour.

CAN'T FIND WHAT YOU'RE LOOKING FOR? USE THE INDEX!

Pauper notes

Accommodation: University headlease scheme, holidaymakers, flats on campus. **Drink:** 9 bars on campus and lots of local pubs provide good choice at reasonable prices. **Eats:** Usual fast food, takeaways etc plus good international selection of restaurants in town. **Ents:** Excellent on-campus Recreation Centre. **Sports:** Very good on-campus facilities. **Hardship funds:** Limited; varies from college to college. **Travel:** Good hitching. Bus system expensive but in turmoil. Some travel scholarships in colleges. **Work:** Some in Sugar House in term and in bars. Much tourist and conference trade in vacation.

Alumni (Editors' pick)

Eric Bolton (Senior Chief Inspector of Schools); Robert Fisk (award winning Middle East correspondent of *The Times*); Simon Smith (RU England International); Linda Lewis (reporter, BBC Television News); Gary Waller, MP.

LEEDS POLY

Leeds Polytechnic, Calverley Street, Leeds LS1 3HE (0532 832600)
Map A, E5

Student enquiries: Course Enquiries

Main study areas – as in What to Study section: *(First degree):* Accountancy, architecture, art & design, business studies, chemistry, computing, economics, education, electrical and electronic engineering, fine arts, food science & nutrition, history, hotel and catering management, law, library & information studies, modern languages, nursing studies, politics and governments, psychology, sociology, speech sciences, welfare studies. *Also:* Building and construction, physiotherapy, sports studies.

European Community: 15% first degree students take EC language as part of course and 12% spend 6 months or more in another EC country. Formal exchange links with over 40 EC universities/colleges: Belgium (4); Eire (3); France (13); Germany (6); Greece (6); Italy (1); Netherlands (3); Portugal (1) and Spain (6). Subject areas include: nursing, education, leisure studies, environmental health, European languages and institutions, European finance, information technology, graphic design, social work. Approved Erasmus programme 1990/91.

Application: PCAS except for art and design (ADAR). **Academic features:** BA consumer services, management and public relations; BSc courses in health sciences, physiotherapy, information systems for business; DipHe playwork. Several 4 year sandwich degrees. **Largest fields of study:** Education, European languages and business, business studies, hospitality management, informatics, law. **Founded:** 1970, from 4 existing colleges; joined by 2 further colleges of education in 1976. **Main awards:** BA, BEd, BSc, BEng, LLB. **Awarding body:** CNAA. **Site:** 2 campuses, in or near Leeds town centre. **Access:** Good road, rail and air links. **Accommodation:** 800 places in halls (priority given to first years); 200 places in hostels; 400 approved lodgings; 3,000 places supplied by Unipol (first year students apply to accommodation officer). Rent: 11% in accommodation where rent controlled by polytechnic. **Library:** Central library, plus smaller campus and subject libraries; 360,000 volumes in total, 3,000 periodicals, 1,000 study places. **Welfare:** 2 student health centres staffed by nurses; FPA; counsellors; students union welfare officer. **Hardship funds:** Student financial support scheme for existing students. **Special categories:** Nursery facilities available; 'night line' service; overseas students advisory group; Chaplaincy. **Careers:** Information, advice and placement service. **Amenities:** Bank and shop on central campus; SU building with bars and other recreational facilities; health and fitness suite.

CAN'T FIND WHAT YOU'RE LOOKING FOR? USE THE INDEX!

Sporting facilities: Specialist PE facilities, including swimming pool, dance studio, 'all weather' athletics track, regional gymnastics centre. **Employment:** Most courses vocationally slanted.

Duration of first degree course(s) or equivalent: 3 years full-time; 4 years (sandwich and others) **Total first degree students 1989/90:** 4,650 (full-time and sandwich); **BEd students:** 650 **Number of overseas students:** 220; **Number of mature students:** 340; **Male/female ratio 1989/90:** 1:1 **Teaching staff: full-time:** 645 **part-time:** 250 **Total full time and sandwich students 1989/90:** 7,000 **Postgraduate students:** 850 **Tuition fees, first degrees, 1990/91:** Home: £1,675 (£651 if self-financing); Overseas: £4,650 (eg arts courses), £5,400 (eg science courses).

What it's like

Leeds is not only the gateway to the north, but a greatly expanding city. The city centre consists of many shopping precincts, Victorian and Edwardian arcades, and a popular market. Virtually every well-known retail organisation has a branch within Leeds. Many cinemas with student discount, theatres, museums etc.

Leeds Poly is relatively large, with three main sites, and two smaller ones. These include main city site in Leeds and Beckett Park Site, Headingley (home of Carnegie Sports College and most poly halls of residence). Many students are accommodated in Headingley/Hyde Park area (Leeds 6). Plenty to do with many facilities geared towards students. Poly main site, 200 metres from university.

SU provides bars, cafes, shops, sports and cultural clubs, discos, concerts, alternative cabaret, information point, bank, discounts, welfare services and almost everything you need to survive your student life. No, not money!

If you want to make a success of your student life, Leeds Poly is a good start.

Pauper notes

Accommodation: Headingley most popular student area. Other places are cheaper. **Drink:** New SU bar. Pubs – Original Oak, Woodies, Hyde Park. **Eats:** SU bar, Coburg pub, all restaurants reviewed in SU handbook (good range). **Ents:** Poly discos, national bands, student nights at clubs, many cinemas with discounts. **Sports:** Excellent facilities, many sports/cultural clubs on campus. **Hardship funds:** Be nice to your bank manager! **Travel:** Usual student travel discounts. Next to M1/M62 for hitching. Excellent bus service from Headingley. **Work:** Plenty of casual work. SU bar/security, pubs, shops, cafes etc.

Alumni (Editors' pick)

Marc Almond (Soft Cell), Sir Henry Moore, Ron Pickering, Mick Hill, Bill Slater, Les Bettinson.

LEEDS UNIVERSITY

University of Leeds, Leeds LS2 9JT (0532 431751) Map A, E5

Student enquiries: Undergraduate Office (Admissions)

Main study areas – as in What to Study section: *(First degree):* Accountancy, American studies, anatomy, architecture, art and design, Asian studies, biochemistry, biology, biotechnology, botany, business studies, chemical engineering, chemistry, civil engineering, classics, computing, dentistry, drama, economics, electrical & electronic engineering, English, fine arts, food science & nutrition, geography, geology, history, industrial relations, Latin American studies, law, linguistics, mathematical studies, mechanical & production engineering, medicine, metallurgy and materials science, microbiology, modern languages, music, Near East and Islamic studies, pharmacology, philosophy, physics, physiology, politics and government, psychology, public administration, religious studies and theology, soci-

CAN'T FIND WHAT YOU'RE LOOKING FOR? USE THE INDEX!

ology, welfare studies, zoology. *Also:* Ceramics, colour chemistry, energy studies, minerals processing technology, mining, operational research, textile technology.

European Community: 10% first degree students take EC language as part of course and 9% spend 6 months or more in another EC country. Formal exchange links with over 35 EC universities/colleges, both Erasmus and other: Belgium (2); Denmark (1); Eire (1); France (14); Germany (2); Greece (2); Italy (4); Netherlands (2); Spain (7). Subjects include business studies, law, engineering, chemistry, food science, classics, maths, geography. Approved Erasmus programme 1990/91.

Application: UCCA. **Academic features:** New part-time degrees. New degree courses in Japanese. **Founded:** 1904. **Main awards:** BA, BChD, BEng, MEng, BSc, MBChB, LLB. **Awarding body:** University of Leeds. **Site:** Main central site close to city centre. **Access:** Nearby bus and railway stations; bus, or within walking distance of halls of residence. **Accommodation:** 1,800 places in halls, 3,000 places in university flats; almost all first year students accommodated. Approx cost: £1,500 for 30.5 weeks (full board). Rent: 48% in accommodation where rent controlled by university. **Library:** Over 2,000,000 volumes including microfilm, 2,500 study places. **Other learning facilities:** Audio-visual centre; central language laboratory (taped courses in over 30 languages available to all); computing service. **Welfare:** Health centre, advisers for handicapped and overseas students, day nursery, chaplaincies. **Hardship funds:** Students in financial hardship may make use of the Union's grant enquiry service or apply for a student loan or to Geoffrey Spink Hardship Fund. **Careers:** Advice and placement service. **Amenities:** Union with bars, coffee lounges, discos, newspaper; 600-seat theatre. **Sporting facilities:** Two sport halls on campus; sports ground within 3 miles; outdoor huts in Lake District and Pennines; Olympic standard swimming pool and golf in Leeds.

Duration of first degree course(s) or equivalent: 3/4 years; **others:** 5 years **Total first degree students 1989/90:** 9,622 **Number of overseas students:** 429 **Number of mature students:** 677 **Male/female ratio 1989/90:** 5:4 **Teaching staff: full-time:** 1,080 **part-time:** 50 **Total full-time students 1989/90:** 11,460 **Postgraduate students:** 1,600 (full-time) **Tuition fees, first degrees, 1990/91:** Home: £1,675 (£665 if self-financing); Overseas: £4,560 (eg politics), £6,050 (eg physics).

What it's like

It's one of Britain's largest universities with over 12,000 attending courses. Vast range of courses cater for most tastes. Campus is about 10 minutes' walk from city centre, avoiding isolation of some campus universities, yet retaining a separate identity. University accommodation is in halls and flats which stretch from the campus to the north of the city, about 4 miles away. Most first years live in and then move out into private accommodation which is plentiful and still reasonably cheap, compared at least to London and the South.

SU is one of the country's biggest. Supports 180 societies and 52 sports clubs including sub aqua, hunt saboteurs, ballroom dancing and lacrosse. SU boasts 3 bars (and is Britain's biggest bitter retail outlet!), its own stationery shop, ABTA registered travel shop, print room and exam paper sales, bookshop, card and ticket shop, fully equipped games room and a concert venue which has put on acts such as T'pau, The Pogues, Level 42 and Madness. Range of welfare services impressive; 4 full-time permanent members of staff advise on all aspects. Range of facilities is probably unmatched by any other SU.

Leeds is a large city of 3/4 million people, with a well-equipped city centre. For those of sporting bent there's football at Elland Road, rugby league and cricket at Headingley and an international swimming pool. Reasonable choice of theatres and cinemas, both large and small, with a new complex, the West Yorkshire Playhouse, recently built. Leeds is a lively and diverse city which can be recommended to anyone.
Andrew Berman

CAN'T FIND WHAT YOU'RE LOOKING FOR? USE THE INDEX!

Pauper notes

Accommodation: University accommodation expensive, plenty of private accommodation although rents beginning to rise. All first years offered place in university accommodation. **Drink:** 3 SU bars with very cheap beer, most local pubs are Tetleys. **Eats:** Cheap food in SU – chips, pies, pizzas, etc. Wide range of foreign cuisine particularly Indian and Italian. **Ents:** Good selection of entertainment on campus including large gigs. City good with new cinema/theatre complex. Leeds famous for being a Goth city. **Sport:** Local international swimming pool (home of Adrian Moorhouse!), excellent playing fields but 4 miles from campus. **Hardship funds:** Loans available from SU. **Travel:** Occasional travel scholarships available. M1 starts at Leeds; excellent rail links. SU has own ABTA travel shop. **Work:** Some work in SU bars and town.

Alumni (Editors' pick)

Sir Geoffrey Allen FRS, Sir George Porter, Mark Knopfler (Dire Straits), Nicholas Witchel (BBC newsreader), Jack Straw MP, Andy Kershaw, Andrew Eldritch (of Sisters of Mercy), Marc Almond.

LEICESTER POLY

Leicester Polytechnic, PO Box 143, Leicester LE1 9BH (0533 551551)
Map A, E6

Student enquiries: Academic Registrar

Main study areas – as in What to Study section: *(First degree):* Accountancy, architecture, art & design, Asian studies, biology, biotechnology, business studies, chemistry, computing, dance, drama, economics, electrical & electronic engineering, English, environmental studies, fine arts, history, information technology, law, mathematical studies, mechanical and production engineering, music, pharmacy, politics and government, public administration, speech sciences, welfare studies. *Also:* Building, estate management, footwear, furniture design, performance arts, surveying, textiles.

European Community: Number of students learning an EC language or spending time in another EC country, not known; includes some students in law, business studies and combined studies (possibly 14%). 1 formal exchange link with Germany. Approved Erasmus programme 1990/91.

Application: PCAS; ADAR for art and design. **Special features:** Policy of encouraging mature students and disabled students where feasible. **Largest fields of study:** Business, technology, construction. **Founded:** 1969; merged with City of Leicester College of Education in 1976. **Main awards:** BA, BSc, BEng. **Awarding body:** CNAA. **Site:** Split on 2 sites; at or within easy reach of Leicester city centre; plus site in Milton Keynes. **Academic features:** Semester structure operates for combined studies and engineering technology. New course in business information systems. Year 1 of combined studies available at franchise centres around the country (check with poly for nearest). **Access:** Central position, easy access by rail and road. **Accommodation:** 1,265 places in halls of residence (priority to first year students); 500+ lodgings; poly housing 400 places; monthly private housing list published; flats available through the Student Housing Association. **Library:** 2, at City campus and Scraptoft site; 270,000 volumes in total, 2,076 periodicals, 995 study places; collection of audio-visual material; micro-lab with 24 IBM-Compatible micro-computers. **Other learning resources:** Excellent computing facilities. **Careers:** Information, advice and placement service. **Welfare:** Counselling; student health service; chaplaincy; legal information service. **Amenities:** Bookshop; exhibition hall; SU; expanding computer facilities. **Sporting facilities:** Good sporting facilities. **Employment:** Strong links with textile and fashion, and

CAN'T FIND WHAT YOU'RE LOOKING FOR? USE THE INDEX!

engineering industries (employment record well above national average).

Duration of first degree course(s) or equivalent: 3 years; **others:** 4 years sandwich, 5 years extended **Total first degree students 1989/90:** 5,600 **Number of overseas students:** 159 **Number of mature students:** 757 **Male/female ratio 1989/90:** 5:4 **Teaching staff: full-time:** 650 **part-time:** 500 **Total full-time students 1989/90:** 7,472 **Postgraduate students:** 285 **Tuition fees, first degrees, 1990/91:** Home: £1,675 (£651 if self-financing); Overseas: £4,563 (eg politics), £5,029 (eg physics).

What it's like

Inner-city poly spread over half square mile, second 'country' campus at Scraptoft 7 miles away. Now has 7,000+ full-time and 2,500 part-time students. Buildings are a mix, mainly unattractive. Housing is a problem for first 3 weeks, but gets sorted after that. Most students live in private housing, you have to know where to look. Housing stock is diminishing with property boom. Scraptoft is a small campus; very tranquil, large field sports area, few students (300ish).

Leicester City is easily accessed by road and rail; only 75 mins by train to London. It's a reasonably cheap city, very cosmopolitan, good cultural mix, interesting and useful shops open all hours and days. Loads of varied local events.

Biggest art and design faculty in Europe; wide variety of courses, fine art to footwear design. Well recognised academically with excellent student services, counselling and medical. SU is well developed commercially and enjoys good relationships with poly.

Very difficult for cars; no parking, **millions** of traffic wardens. OK for bikes (motor/push), but lots of thefts. Lots of students in town and well catered for. Some hostility to students but generally good relationships. Good male/female ratio and lots of opportunities to make friends. Most students get jobs during course.

Pauper notes

Accommodation: Wide range of halls of residence. Some reasonable private lodgings with some excellent houses if you look in the right places. For bargains use information centre, union noticeboards, Accommodation Officer and ask current students before arrival. **Drink:** SU is cheapest (real ale bar) in Leicester for beers, and offers chilled 'tinnie bar' on function nights. Good beers, IPA, Becks, Scotch Bitter, Fosters and Castlemaine. **Eats:** SU catering includes pizza and salad bars at reasonable prices. Princess Charlotte 30p hot meals Saturday lunchtime. Fine selection of Tandoori restaurants and several excellent Chinese. **Ents:** LPSU Arena caters for 1,100, sell-out disco every Saturday. Phoenix Arts good local theatre and cinema managed by poly and City Council, Haymarket Theatre and Studio excellent. Very lively SU Ents programme. Good discos on Wednesdays and Fridays. **Sports:** Cheapest sport through SU clubs. City has very good sports facilities and Polysport centre provides excellent badminton, basketball, weights facilities as well as sauna, sunbeds and squash court. Very good facilities at Saffron House, Granby halls and St Margaret's baths. **Hardship funds:** Available through SU if hardship is not through one's own fault. **Travel:** Excellent Polytech travel bureaux with Prestel and telex services. Also Leicester well-placed for hitching – M1 (north, London), M69 – M6 (Midlands and north west), A47 – A46 (east and East Anglia). Trains each half hour to London. **Work:** SU employs many students (150) in security, catering and bars.

Alumni (Editors' pick)

Charles Dance (actor).

CAN'T FIND WHAT YOU'RE LOOKING FOR? USE THE INDEX!

LEICESTER UNIVERSITY

University of Leicester, University Road, Leicester LE1 7RH
(0533 522522) Map A, E6

Student enquiries: Admissions Officer

Main study areas – as in What to Study section: *(First degree):* American studies, archaeology, biochemistry, biology, biotechnology, botany, chemistry, computing, economics, electrical & electronic engineering, English, European studies, fine arts, geography, geology, history, law, mathematical studies, mechanical and production engineering, medicine, microbiology, modern languages, physics, physiology, politics and government, psychology, sociology, zoology. *Also:* Astronomy, mining, space and technology.

European Community: 14% first degree students take EC language as part of course and 7.5% spend 6 months or more in another EC country. Formal exchange links with over 35 EC universities/colleges: Belgium (sociology, biology history); Denmark (genetics, maths); Eire (geography, genetics); France (genetics, biology, law, English, arts, history, geography, French); Germany (medicine, English, arts, history, German); Greece (sociology); Italy (law, English, Italian, politics, genetics, arts); Netherlands (biology, history, genetics); Portugal (genetics); Spain (history, geography). Approved Erasmus programme 1990/91.

Application: UCCA. **Largest fields of study:** Law, medicine, engineering, biological sciences. **Founded:** 1918, receiving charter in 1957. **Main awards:** BA, BSc, BEng, LLB, MBChB. **Awarding body:** Leicester University. **Site:** 1 mile from Leicester city centre. **Access:** Railway station (15 mins walk); M1 and M69 motorways 5 miles from campus. **Academic features:** 3 types of first degree; single, joint and combined honours. Combined honours provides flexible choice of 3 subjects (arts) or 2 to 5 subjects (science). **Special features:** Research centres focusing on football hooliganism, youth employment, public order, federalism. Genetic fingerprinting discovered here by Prof Alec Jeffreys. **Accommodation:** 1,590 places in hall; 1,280 flats/bedsits (accommodation provided for 60%). Cost: £1,470 approx pa halls, £808 approx pa self-catering. **Library:** Main library has 923,000 volumes, 1,085 study places, multiple copies of prescribed textbooks on short loan. Also 3 subsidiary libraries. **Specialist collections:** Robjohn's Collection of Bibles; Works of Bunyan; English local history. **Other learning resources:** Audio-visual services, computer centre, language laboratory, university bookshop, Leicester University Press. **Centres of excellence:** Biochemistry, space physics, mass communication research, economic and social history/urban history, geology, sociology. **Welfare:** Doctors, welfare officers, personal tutors, FPA, psychiatrist, counsellors, chaplains, student legal advice centre, 'night line' telephone contact service. **Hardship funds:** Vice-Chancellor and SU both have modest funds for loans/grants for students in financial difficulties. **Special categories:** Nursery (independent) with favourable terms for student parents. **Careers:** Information and advice service. **Amenities:** Bookshop, general shops and banks on site; Leicester University Theatre (strong links with Haymarket and Phoenix professional theatres in Leicester); Archduke Trio (resident chamber music group). **Sporting facilities:** Excellent sports facilities including one of the finest athletics tracks in Midlands and two sports halls. **Employment:** 31% further study and training; 16% public sector; 24% industry and commerce.

Duration of first degree course(s) or equivalent: 3 years; others: 4 years (engineering, European studies, modern languages, mathematics (European Community), mathematics + astronomy (EC), mathematics + computing (EC)); 5 years (medicine) **Total first degree students 1989/90:** 5,461 **Number of overseas students:** 455 **Number of mature students:** 676 **Male/female ratio 1989/90:** 1:1 **Teaching staff: full-time:** 497 **part-time:** 43 **Total full-time students 1989/90:** 6,269 **Postgraduate students:** 1,175 **Tuition fees, first degrees, 1990/91: Home:** £1,675

CAN'T FIND WHAT YOU'RE LOOKING FOR? USE THE INDEX!

(£666 if self-financing); Overseas: £4,500 (eg politics), £6,000 (eg physics), £11,150 (maximum).

What it's like

The university is close to the city centre. Self-catering houses closest to campus and halls of residence about 3 miles away in pleasant foliage-adorned residential area. Most first years stay in university accommodation, second and third years have choice to move out into private accommodation, helped by SU's private accommodation service. All halls/self-catering are mixed, some single sex houses, students can indicate preference on admission.

Large proportion of overseas students; SU sabbatical overseas officer to look after their interests. Growing number of mature students; half-term play schemes offered as well as nursery subsidy provision.

The campus is busy most of the time – library and SU open at weekends; restaurants for evening meals open during weekdays. SU has over 60 clubs and societies and runs a very active sports association. Students have many opportunities to become 'politically' involved; fortnightly general meetings, union council, various committees. Political orientation tends to be of mixed outlook, with considerable attention to 'liberation' campaigns. SU has extremely successful and progressive entertainments programme including weekly discos, rock discos, pub quizzes, comedians, films and top name bands, ie New Model Army, Sam Brown. Runs very good 'Intro Week' for first years.

Plenty of opportunity to meet 'other halves' – no restrictions in halls and houses for visiting them once you've met them. Students with cars are few and far between because of parking restrictions on campus and halls of residence. Advice on contraception and pregnancy is offered both by Student Health Centre and SU, all advice free and confidential.

Leicester is definitely a student town, loads of pubs and restaurants on the cheaper side! Number of shops, cinemas, theatres in a student discount scheme – need NUS card (available at registration). Can also use this card to get into other universities and polys. SU on NME/MM circuit.

Biggest departments are medicine and law and there tends to be a concentration on scientific subjects, despite thriving arts and humanities courses. Trendy subjects include astronomy, astrophysics and mass communications; university building a much publicised 'Space Centre'. All courses have opportunities for field trips etc and university has many guest lecturers. Good choice of subsidary subject in first year. Subject changes are fairly easy depending a lot however on A-level grades. Work assessed by combination of examination and course work. Opportunities to resit exams are good. Very low degree failure rate. Workload can be heavy in first year for combined subjects, but varied coursework complements this.

Students come from all over the country and world! Mixture of state/private school; few public school. Drop-out rate is low. Discrimination by staff/students whether sexual, racial or religious can be dealt with by formal procedures. Help and confidential counselling always available at SU. Typical student takes work fairly seriously – aims for a 2:2 degree. Spends free time playing sport or drinking in the bar, and organising round-the-world back packing trip for summer vacation.

Graduates can look forward to salaries starting around £7,000-£8,000 pa with good prospects. Many go on to teacher training in the School of Education or other postgraduate work. Popular course with students who 'don't know what to do' when they've graduated is information technology.

Pauper notes

Accommodation: Catering hall accommodation for c1500 students. Self-catering flats for approx 1200. Others live in private accommodation. SU runs flat-finding service. **Drink:** SU bars cheapest in city (85p–95p per pint). Local breweries Hoskins, HOB (notable real ales), Everards (large Midlands brewery). **Eats:** SU refectory seats over 1,000 diners. University catering service provides a large central restaurant plus numerous coffee bars around campus. Leicester notable for Indian

CAN'T FIND WHAT YOU'RE LOOKING FOR? USE THE INDEX!

food. Rise of Mexican, Cajun food restaurants in town – good atmosphere. **Ents:** SU runs popular discos on Fridays and Saturdays and films on Mondays. Leicester University Theatre is funded by SU and provides regular performances, as does the Revue and Theatre Society. Haymarket Theatre in Leicester nationally famous for touring productions. Halls and sc houses organise their own entertainments frequently. **Sports:** University has 2 large sports grounds about 3 miles from campus, 1 adjacent to halls of residence. SU runs over 40 sports clubs. **Hardship funds:** SU hardship fund and Vice-Chancellor's fund. Grants above £200 are rare. **Travel:** Regular bus service from halls to campus (3 miles). Leicester being central is well connected for trains. London St Pancras is 1¼ hrs. **Work:** Union employs evening bar staff. Part-time work plentiful in Leicester. Union has a private job-shop. Plenty of agencies in town centre which are 'student friendly'.

Alumni (Editors' pick)

Professor John Ashworth, Professor Laurie Taylor, Professor Alan Walters (Economist), Professor Malcolm Bradbury, Heather Cowper, David Puttnam, J H Plumb, C P Snow, Ron Pickering, Mike Nicholson, Sue Cook, John McVicker.

LIVERPOOL INSTITUTE

Liverpool Institute of Higher Education, (1) St Katharine's College, Stand Park Road, Liverpool 16 (051-722 2361)
(2) Christ's & Notre Dame College, Woolton Road, Liverpool 16 (051-722 7331) Map A, D6

Student enquiries: Admissions Office, PO Box 6, (Address 1)

Main study areas – as in What to Study section: *(First degree):* American studies, art and design, biology, computing, drama, education, English, environmental studies, geography, history, mathematical studies, modern languages, music, psychology, religious studies and theology, sociology. *Also:* Occupational therapy, physical education.

European Community: 3% first degree students take EC language as part of course and 3% spend 6 months or more in another EC country. No formal exchange links in EC at present.

Application: UCCA. **Academic features:** Degree courses in combined subjects, American studies, theology and religious studies. **Special features:** First ecumenical institute of HE. **Largest fields of study:** English, history, education. **Founded:** Institute formed in 1980. **Main awards:** BA, BEd, BSc, BDesign. **Awarding body:** Liverpool University. **Site:** Rural outskirts of Liverpool. **Access:** Bus to Liverpool city centre; M62 within one mile. **Accommodation:** Over 900 places in hall on both campuses (all first year students can be accommodated). Rent: Approx 40% in accommodation where rent controlled by institute. **Library:** 2 libraries; 210,000 volumes, separate reference/reading room for first degree students; resource centre. **Other learning facilities:** Computer laboratory for interactive learning. Primary Resource Centre and Religious Education Centre. **Welfare:** Doctor, 2 chaplains, counsellor, two chapels (C of E and RC). **Careers:** Information, advice, work experience and placements. **Amenities:** SU common rooms, bookshop on campus, banking, playgroup. **Sporting facilities:** Gymnasia, squash and tennis courts, outdoor pursuits centre. **Employment:** Teaching (BEd). Wide range of employment (BA, BSc, BDes).

Duration of first degree course(s) or equivalent: 3 years; **others:** 4 years (BEd; BA American studies) **Total first degree students 1989/90:** 2,050; **BEd students:** 728 **Number of overseas students:** 10 **Number of mature students:** 400 **Male/female ratio 1989/90:** 1:3 **Teaching staff: full-time:** 160 **part-time:** 5 **Total full-time**

students 1989/90: 2,200 **Postgraduate students:** 150 **Tuition fees, first degrees, 1990/91:** Home: £1,675; Overseas: £3,950.

What it's like

Situated in Childwall, a pleasant suburb about 5 miles from Liverpool city centre; good communications via M62, British Rail, Speke Airport and Liverpool Docks. College field centre in Caerdeon (near Barmouth, Wales). Approximately 40% of students live on 3 sites in single bedsits (12 meals a week provided). Extensive building programme to cope with the increase in student numbers (which has affected the academic work of a number of arts based subjects). There is also a large percentage of mature students, for whom there are not adequate facilities eg creche, car parking. In general the Institute space and facilities find it difficult to cope with the number of students. On the plus side, those studying French have a chance to study in France; there are also exchanges with Potsdam and Wittenburg Universities (USA).

Pauper notes

Accommodation: Approximately 800 places in halls of residence. **Drink:** Derwent House and CND social club provide cheap drink; promotions nights. **Eats:** Refurbished call order bars on 2 sites; bar snacks available in 2 social clubs. **Ents:** Institute Social Club provides the campus based social activities. Live bands most weekends. Also a varied night life available in Liverpool city centre. **Sports;** Sports hall, gym, 2 squash courts, tennis courts, all-weather pitch as well as sports field. Numerous athletic clubs and non-sporting societies through SU.

Alumni (Editors' pick)

David Alton MP, Willy Russell (playwright).

LIVERPOOL POLY

The Liverpool Polytechnic, Rodney House, 70 Mount Pleasant, Liverpool L3 5UX (051-207 3581) Map A, D6

Student enquiries: Access Services – Admissions Section

Main study areas – as in What to Study section: *(First degree):* Accountancy, architecture, art & design, biochemistry, biology, business studies, chemistry, civil engineering, computing, drama, economics, education, electrical & electronic engineering, English, environmental science, fine arts, geography, geology, history, law, library & information studies, marine technology, maritime studies, mathematical studies, mechanical and production engineering, modern languages, nursing studies, pharmacy, physics, politics and government, psychology, sociology, welfare studies. *Also:* Building, estate management, sports science, surveying.

European Community: Number of students learning an EC language or spending time in another EC country, not known. Approved Erasmus programme 1990/91. International business studies degree courses with French, German and Spanish.

Application: PCAS except art and design (ADAR). **Special features:** Has links to 20+ access courses in the Merseyside region (through the Merseyside Open College Federation); positively welcomes mature students with non-standard qualifications or on access courses, and has long experience of supporting them. Provision for HND and accountancy, engineering, art and design, science foundation students to transfer to degree courses. **Academic features:** Integrated Credit Scheme offers range of subjects, single hons, joint hons, major/minor degree choice. **Largest fields of study:** Pharmacy, business studies. **Founded:** 1970. **Main awards:** BA, BEd, BSc, BEng, MEng. **Awarding body:** CNAA. **Site:** Various sites in Liverpool

CAN'T FIND WHAT YOU'RE LOOKING FOR? USE THE INDEX!

city centre and southern suburbs. **Accommodation:** 970 places in halls, 370 flats/
bedsitters. Approx cost: £38 pw halls, £20-£35 pw flats/bedsits. **Library:** On all
sites; 550,000 volumes in total, 3,000 periodicals, 1,209 study places. **Other
learning resources:** Audio-visual centres. **Welfare:** Doctor, chaplain, counsellor,
accommodation officer. **Special categories:** Nursery. **Careers:** Information, advice and placement service. **Amenities:** SU wine bar, book and stationery shop,
bank, bars on 3 other sites, 70 clubs and societies.

Duration of first degree course(s) or equivalent: 3 years (full-time); 4 years
(sandwich) **other:** extended degree courses 4 years (full-time), 5 years (sandwich)
Total first degree students 1989/90: 7,700 **BEd students:** 620 **Number of overseas
students:** 500 **Male/female ratio 1989/90:** 3:2 **Teaching staff:** approx 620 **Total
full-time students 1989/90:** 8,500 **Postgraduate students:** 311 **Tuition fees, first
degrees, 1990/91:** Home: £1,675 (£651 if self-financing, after first year); Overseas
£4,563.

What it's like

Spread over 11 sites, 9 in city centre, 1 in Aigburth and 1 in Calderstones.
Accommodation varies from poor to excellent – self-catered flats and traditional
halls. Most first years live in; over 1,000 places provided. Active SU with social/
political balance. Moderate left executive. More than 60 sporting, social and
political clubs and societies, magazine, regular, quality entertainments, 8 shops and
6 bars (cheap and plush), including the infamous Commerce and the recently
renovated Haigh.

Wide range of subjects. Good staff/student relations. Course manoeuvres arranged. Work load depends on course. Industry years and field trips on some
courses. Excellent staff. Continual assessment plus exams. Facilities average –
libraries, recreation, student services and careers service. No visiting restrictions.
Comprehensive welfare advice from Poly and SU – strictly confidential. SU
Handbook. Good relationship with community, but not a student town. Wide range
of theatres – from enormous Empire to tiny Unity. Art galleries and museums and a
good shopping centre from the Albert Dock to the St John's Centre and Church
Street. 2 large cinemas and SU film nights. SU bars and good pubs in abundance –
The Grapes, Ye Cracke, The Pilgrim, Casa Blanca. Excellent clubs – MacMillans
and the Mardi Gras.

40% students from Liverpool, high North West intake. 70% from comprehensive
schools. Ugly racism minimal. Sexism more blatant but still minimal. Typical
student – science/beer/rugby or humanities/trendy/politics – wide range!

Easy to get attached to Liverpool which is a vibrant and exciting city despite what
the media says. The best city and the best Poly in the land.
Sean O'Muirt

Pauper notes

Accommodation: Poly accommodation in city centre called 'Cathedral Parks',
excellent standard only five minutes from SU building. **Drink:** Places: Casablanca,
Haigh Building. Brews: Higsons, Stones, Whitbread. **Eats:** Off campus: Quiggins,
Trading Places, Munchies, Acorn Gallery. On campus: Haigh Building, various
site canteens. **Ents:** Off campus: Bluecoat Gallery, Liverpool Everyman, Playhouse. On campus: Haigh Building, wine bar. **Sports:** Everton Sports Centre,
Kirkby Sports Centre, Toxteth Sports Centre (all SU reductions). **Travel:** Campus
travel shop. **Work:** Various part-time employment available in city – bars to clothes
shops!

Alumni (Editors' pick)
Debbie Greenwood, Martin Offiah, Julian Cope, Con McConville.

LIVERPOOL UNIVERSITY

University of Liverpool, PO Box 147, Liverpool L69 3BX
(051-794 2000) Map A, D6

Student enquiries: Schools Relations Office

Main study areas – as in What to Study section: *(First degree):* Accounting, African studies, American studies, archaeology, architecture, Asian studies, biochemistry, biology, biotechnology, botany, business studies, chemistry, civil engineering, classics, communication studies, computing, dentistry, economics, education, electrical & electronic engineering, English, environmental science, geography, geology, history, Latin American studies, law, marine technology, mathematical studies, mechanical and production engineering, medicine, metallurgy and materials science, microbiology, modern languages, music, Near East and Islamic studies, nursing studies, pharmacology, philosophy, physics, physiology, politics and government, psychology, public administration, religious studies & theology, sociology, veterinary studies, welfare studies, zoology.

European Community: Number of students learning an EC language or spending time in another EC country, not known. Approved Erasmus programme 1990/91.

Application: UCCA. **Founded:** 1881. **Main awards:** BA, BArch, BCom, BDS, BEd, BEng, BMus, BSc, BVSc, LLB, MBChB. **Awarding body:** Liverpool University. **Site:** 85 acres in city centre. **Accommodation:** Halls of residence (2,300 places) near campus; all first years normally live in (except home students); self-catering accommodation. Approx cost: £1,185 pa. **Library:** 2 main libraries; 1,100,000 books; 1,100 study places. **Other learning resources:** Computing service. **Welfare:** Student counsellors, student health service, chaplains.

Duration of first degree course(s) or equivalent: 3 years and 4 years; **others:** 5 years (medicine), 5+ years (dentistry) **Total first degree students 1989/90:** 6,430 **Male/female ratio:** 5:3 **Total full-time students 1989/90:** 7,370 **Tuition fees, first degrees, 1990/91:** Not known.

What it's like

With the main campus half a mile from the city centre, student life in Liverpool is amongst the best you'll find anywhere. City has an extremely varied culture and people are warm and friendly – if you stay on the right side of them!

The Guild of Students (a Guild is same as a Union, name is different for historical reasons) has second largest building in Europe. It houses a television bar, disco bar, 1,000 capacity hall for major acts (like Squeeze or the Wedding Present), snooker rooms, table tennis and cafe bars. Guild has welfare department which is run partly by students, partly by staff.

Nearly all first years get place in halls of residence, which offer quite good accommodation – but food isn't haute cuisine! Living out is option for most second years onwards and there is still adequate housing to choose from. Be careful though, leaky roofs and damp are rife in Liverpool's private sector housing.

Socially, there is so much to do. At least six night clubs which are tuned to student tastes (honestly!), two theatres – the Everyman and Playhouse, an opera house and the Royal court – a 2,200 capacity live music venue. Add to that the Philharmonic Orchestra and you've got a city that offers plenty for everyone.
Martin Connor

Pauper notes

Accommodation: University accommodation for married students limited. Much less accommodation than before – harder to find places. **Drink:** Guild's good for cheap drink, many Yorkshire beers. **Eats:** Vegetarian restaurants and food shops in town. Good food on campus – but rarely open at awkward hours. **Ents:** Many new and 'up and coming' groups play, two films in Guild every week. **Sports:** Excellent

CAN'T FIND WHAT YOU'RE LOOKING FOR? USE THE INDEX!

university sports centre and swimming pool – free to students. **Hardship funds:** Access funds; unfortunately cannot offer hardship funds. **Travel:** Lime St Station can get you anywhere, most places direct. Student travel shop in Guild offers many reductions. **Work:** Average opportunities for restaurant/bar work term-time off campus. Little full-time holiday work.

Alumni (Editors' pick)

Hugh Jones (marathon runner), Judge O'Donoghue, Dr N Cossons (Director of Science Museum), Mike Thomas (SDP MP), Jon Snow (ITN reporter), Robert Kilroy-Silk (Labour MP), Steve Coppell (footballer), Dame Rose Heilbron (Lady High Court Judge), Phil Redmond (TV writer – Brookside), Lord Evans of Claughton, Graham Leach (BBC reporter), Hugh Jones (athlete, marathons), Ann Leuchars (TV newscaster), Maeve Sherlock (NUS President).

LONDON BIBLE COLLEGE

London Bible College, Green Lane, Northwood, Middlesex HA6 2UW (09274 26061) Map A, F8

Student enquiries: Academic Registrar

Main study areas – as in What to Study section: *(First degree):* Philosophy, religious studies and theology.

European Community: No students learn an EC language or spend time in another EC country.

Application: Direct. **Academic features:** MA in aspects of biblical interpretation. Part-time MA. **Special features:** Number of subjects available unusual in theology degrees, eg sociology of religion, missiology, linguistics and pastoral theology. **Largest fields of study:** Theology. **Founded:** 1943. **Main awards:** BA. **Awarding body:** CNAA. **Site:** 9 acres. **Access:** Metropolitan line to Northwood; by road off A404 Rickmansworth Road. **Accommodation:** Places in halls of residence (priority to first year, overseas and mature students). Rent: 50% in accommodation where rent controlled by college. **Library:** 23,000 volumes, 100 periodicals, 100 study places. **Welfare:** Doctor, chaplain. **Hardship funds:** Some bursary funds available. **Careers:** Information, advice and informal placement service. **Amenities:** Bookshop on college premises; games room, tennis courts. **Employment:** Christian ministry, overseas missionary work, and RE teaching.

Duration of first degree course(s) or equivalent: 3 years **Total first degree students 1989/90:** 133 **Number of overseas students:** 33 **Number of mature students:** 115 **Male/female ratio 1989/90:** 3:2 **Teaching staff: full-time:** 16 **part-time:** 4 **Total full-time students 1989/90:** 201 **Postgraduate students:** 20 **Tuition fees, first degrees, 1990/91:** £1,980.

What it's like

An international, interdenominational college community of 210 students from all 5 continents and 30 countries (including Eastern European) from all over the world. 25% students from overseas. The residential suburb of Northwood, 30 mins from Central London on the Metropolitan Line, and conveniently close to the M25.

Half the students live on campus in pleasant, spacious grounds; on-site facilities include a launderette, football pitch, tennis courts, a well-stocked bookshop (some publishers' discounts), a student-run stationery shop, and a modern student centre with TV lounges, kitchen, music rooms, table-tennis room, weightlifting equipment, a pool table and changing rooms. (No accommodation for married students on campus.) Average age of students is 28.9, almost all have some work-experience before coming here. Good academic standard, excellent library facilities.

CAN'T FIND WHAT YOU'RE LOOKING FOR? USE THE INDEX!

High motivation and commitment characteristic of students, who in addition to academic work perform some practical Christian activity each week, either in a local church or in a college team – drama, open-air evangelism, schools work, producing videos, preaching, children's work etc. Some practical assignments – sometimes overseas eg Southern Africa, South America, Europe (E & W), Middle East in 1990 – during the vacations, especially in summer.

Student–faculty relations are excellent; student reps sit on faculty and Governors' Board meetings.

Practical training department gives guidance for future work; students enter a wide range of full-time Christian (or secular) employment, several each year go on to post-graduate studies.

Overall the college has a very warm and friendly atmosphere, mutual respect and encouragement, groups of approx 15 act as support groups and provide forum for social events. Confidential counselling available.

Pauper notes

Accommodation: Not cheap in the area. Often local church members will rent rooms to LBC students at below the market rate. (College has a list of digs.) **Eats:** College meals very good; offers vegetarian food. Few cheap eating places in the area; non-resident students can sometimes get an evening meal in college free if a resident student is absent. **Ents:** Recently-released videos shown most weeks in college; also evening concerts by students several times a term. **Sports:** Soccer, rugger, cricket, volleyball teams; local squash courts and swimming pools have cheap afternoon slots which students can use. **Hardship funds:** College provides bursary funds to help with tuition fees (mostly for overseas students); students run a gift-fund to help day-to-day expenses if needed. **Travel:** Normal student discount schemes apply.

Alumni (Editors' pick)
Os Guinness, Derek Tidball, Clive Calver, Terry Virgo.

LONDON BUSINESS SCHOOL

London Business School, Sussex Place, Regent's Park, London NW1 4SA (071-262 5050) Map E B1

This is a postgraduate UKCPU.

Student enquiries: Information Officer, MBA Programme

Main study area: *(Not at first degree):* Business studies.

European Community: Number of students learning an EC language or spending time in another EC country, not known. Approved Erasmus programme 1990/91.

Application: Direct. **Academic features:** Case teaching a la Harvard, group assignments, visiting speakers, student consultancy projects, assessed class participation, videos. Formal exams at the end of every term. 25% of MBA programme go on exchange for a term with eg Amos Tuck, Berkeley, NYU, Chicago, Wharton, Cornell, North Western, MIT, British Columbia, Sao Paulo, Barcelona, Cologne, HES (Paris), ISA (Paris), Milan and Japan. Significant number of visiting professors from abroad as teaching exchange – lots of guest speakers. **Special features:** Research centres include economic forecasting, small business, finance and business strategy. **Founded:** 1965. **Main awards:** MBA, PhD. **Awarding body:** University of London. **Site:** Located at Regent's Park in an elegant Nash terrace overlooking the lake. 1 site. **Access:** Tube: Baker Street; road via Regent's Park. **Accommodation:** 75 rooms on site. Many students have their own homes – which they often share with other MBAs. Approx cost not known. **Library:** Corporate library includes comprehensive stock of annual reports and extel cards – online data

CAN'T FIND WHAT YOU'RE LOOKING FOR? USE THE INDEX!

base facilities available. **Other facilities:** Computer room; close-circuit TV centre. **Careers:** Information, advice and placement service. **Employment:** Merchant banking, finance, strategy consulting. **Welfare:** None on site – Lisson Grove Health Centre available to residents. Students have personal faculty advisers if needed. **Hardship funds:** Some scholarships and prizes are awarded by the school but no hardship fund. **Amenities:** Close to West End. **Sports:** On campus – gym and aerobics room; off campus – squash at Lord's cricket ground, soccer in the park.

Duration of degree course(s) or equivalent: 2 years full-time; 3 years part-time; **others:** PhD 3 years plus **Male/female ratio 1989/90:** not known **Teaching staff: full-time:** not known **research:** 50 **Total full-time students 1989/90:** 300 MBA (postgraduate) **Tuition fees, 1990/91:** Home: £6,500; Overseas: £7,500.

What it's like

A Nash terrace overlooking Regent's Park lake. An elegant facade hiding very well-equipped lecture theatres and computer rooms. Supposedly the best business library in Europe. On campus bedrooms small but functional. A well catered, subsidised restaurant and cafeteria, two bars and wine bar.

Fun but incredibly demanding. Not for the faint hearted. Students typically put in 80–90 hour weeks during the first year; weekends and evenings off are rare! A top business school; both students and faculty totally motivated and committed, with a strong career ethos among students, although not as deadly competitive as their Harvard counterparts. (These ones put high emphasis on team-work and group experience.)

A very international school; 60% students come from 35 different countries; international focus in curriculum as well as in various international projects and overseas field visits. An international exchange programme with students spending a term in other top business schools in continental Europe, Asia, North and South America: and probably highest percentage of women (30%) among world's best business schools.

Average graduating salary – £35,000 plus, although they will swear that is **not** why they are here! An exclusive, multi-layer admissions procedure with tough entry requirements, including minimum of two years' professional experience. Early application is essential as places on the programme are quickly filled. Low drop-out rate and few overall failures. Part-timers on MBA programme are usually sponsored and take three years to complete course.

A great emphasis is put on high quality of teaching and research. Most have had experience in business schools abroad and close links with industry/commerce through their consulting activities. Students are very vocal if they are not getting value for time or money and formal assessments by students of lecturers each term.

Football, aerobics and squash are popular and there's a lot of swimming, jogging and boating around Regent's Park. LBS has own gymnasium.

Careers clubs (such as finance and consultancy) are well attended and enable students to mix freely with guest speakers. Students' association non-political, purely administrative and social. 3 or 4 large events per term, well attended, especially the summer ball!

Pauper notes

Clearing banks offer low interest loans to UK students which most take up. All students earn money for their project works and in summer vacations.

Alumni (Editors' pick)

John Egan (Chairman, Jaguar Cars), Iain Vallance (BT Chairman), Matthew Carrington MP, Sir Ronald Deering (Post Office Chairman), Brian Taylor (CEO Glaxo), Richard Greenbury (MD Marks & Spencer).

CAN'T FIND WHAT YOU'RE LOOKING FOR? USE THE INDEX!

LONDON COLLEGE OF DANCE

London College of Dance, 10 Linden Road, Bedford MK40 2DA (0234 213331) Map A F7

Student enquiries: The Principal

European Community: No students learn an EC language or spend time in another EC country. No EC links.

Application: Direct. **Academic features:** New BA Dance, with classical ballet as core discipline. 3 year diploma course focuses on dance as a performing art, open to talented male and female students seeking an intensive training in a variety of dance styles. Strong emphasis is placed on developing the individual dance potential of each student. In-depth preparation in the theory and practice of teaching is integrated with the practical dance studies. **Special features:** Most members of the vocational staff have had careers in ballet, contemporary companies and the musical theatre. **Largest fields of study:** Dance studies and teacher training. **Founded:** 1944 as London College of Dance and Drama; became London College of Dance in 1986. **Main awards:** Diploma of London College of Dance; BA. **Awarding body:** CDET; University of Buckingham. **Site:** College situated in a pleasant part of Bedford close to the Lansdowne site of Bedford College of Higher Education so students benefit from atmosphere of a small community, combined with resources of a larger institution. **Access:** British Rail (direct Bedford/St Pancras line); easy access to M1 and A1. **Accommodation:** Private accommodation in town. **Specialist collections:** London College dance collection held at Bedford College of Higher Education. BCHE library facilities available to London College students. **Careers:** Prospective employers apply direct to the college. Students are placed in these posts. **Employment:** Teachers of dancing; theatrical performers. **Welfare:** Welfare and counselling facilities are available to college students in conjunction with BCHE. **Amenities:** All SU facilities plus private college events. **Sports:** Sports facilities available via BCHE.

Duration of first degree course(s) or equivalent: 3 years **Total number of Diploma students 1989/90:** 90 **Number of overseas students:** 10 **Number of mature students:** 5 **Male/female ratio 1989/90:** 1:8 **Teaching staff: full-time:** 9 **part-time:** 12 **Total full-time students 1989/90:** 79 **Postgraduate students:** 3 **Tuition fees, first degrees, 1990/91:** £4,600.

What it's like

Offers the dancer an ideal environment in which to develop dance and teaching skills; self-discipline and responsibility.

Spacious mirrored studios with sprung floors, air-conditioning, piano and music systems. 2 student common rooms, adequate changing and shower facilities. The Bowen-West Community Theatre, a stone's throw away, for student performances and many other shows.

3 year course allows exploration of many styles of dance and develops creative expression and performance skills. Practical lessons: music, anatomy, education and dance history studies to give a broader knowledge of the world of dance. Also now offers BA course providing a practical study of dance in its cultural context with emphasis on ballet.

Practical work is continually assessed; external exams are also taken. Written work assessed on 3 essays a year during the first 2 years; a long study in year 3 on any dance-related topic of special interest.

Second years teach in local primary schools and in the Dance Club (talented local children) to develop teaching skills and choreography for young children. In third year studio teaching practice gives a chance to teach both set and free work. Guest lecturers involved in many subjects, bringing varied styles, technique and expertise.

CAN'T FIND WHAT YOU'RE LOOKING FOR? USE THE INDEX!

Most students live in digs and cycle to college; good bus service. Access to library, medical, physiotherapy and sports facilities of Bedford College.

Organised visits to London theatres. Speakers and choreographers invited throughout the year.

College staff offer invaluable expertise and advice to all students in pursuit of their careers either as performers, teachers or dance-related arts.
Lynne Shapcott

Pauper notes

Accommodation: No halls of residence; plenty of outside accommodation (inspect it personally). **Drink:** Use of Bedford College bar facilities (reduced prices), good local pubs (including country ones if you have a car), one popular nightclub and one popular but expensive disco pub. **Eats:** Plenty of choice especially pizzas and Indian. Pubs also (close to college) have good, cheap meals. **Ents:** Many theatre trips locally and in the city (some subsidised); good cinemas (2 screens locally; 10 in Milton Keynes); and college's own theatre. **Sports:** Use of Bedford College sports facilities, public swimming pool, squash courts, leisure complex. **Hardship funds:** SU helps to best of their ability. **Travel:** Usually by bike – but good bus services. SU cards for reduced coach travel. **Work:** Many students find evening/weekend work: bars, restaurants, teaching dance.

LONDON COLLEGE OF MUSIC

London College of Music, 47 Great Marlborough Street, London W1V 2AS (071-437 6120) Map E, B2

Student enquiries: Registrar

Main study areas – as in What to Study section: *(First degree):* Music.

European Community: 20% students learn an EC language. No students spend time in another EC country.

Application: Direct. **Academic features:** 3-year undergraduate academic/ performing course; post-graduate course for singers, accompanists and in writing music for films & TV; Music-in-Schools Programme. Music theatre class. **Special features:** Emphasis on wide range of relationships within whole music industry, and with community needs. Audio Visual Unit. **Largest fields of study:** Music. **Founded:** 1887. **Main awards:** GLCM; FLCM; Diploma of Advanced Study. **Awarding body:** London College of Music. **Site:** Central London. **Access:** Oxford Circus underground station. **Accommodation:** Hostels etc, apply to registrar; no college accommodation. **Library:** c30,000 volumes, 20 study places. **Welfare:** Doctor. **Careers:** Information and advice service. **Employment:** Teaching music, and all areas of music industry.

Duration of first degree course(s) or equivalent: 3 years **Others:** 1 year **Total first degree students 1989/90:** 173 **Number of overseas students:** 20 **Male/female ratio 1989/90:** 3:4 **Teaching staff: part-time:** 89 **Total full-time students 1989/90:** 225 **Postgraduate students:** 49 **Tuition fees, first degrees, 1990/91: Home:** £2,463; **Overseas:** £4,250.

What it's like

Small and friendly college situated in the heart of London's West End; close to Oxford Circus tube. Many overseas students including Mexico, Italy and South East Asia, and quite a few mature students.

LCM runs a postgraduate course in composing music for films, a music theatre class for singers, as well as the two undergraduate courses. It has a thriving composition department and an innovatory 'Music in Schools' programme which

CAN'T FIND WHAT YOU'RE LOOKING FOR? USE THE INDEX!

gives a grounding in teaching principals. Some excellent staff help promote a good relationship with students and admin. SU aims to help in student welfare, education and enhance social lives.

College orchestra works under some of the best conductors in the country and covers much valuable repertoire. Twice weekly lunchtime recitals given by visiting artists or students.

Work load is as easy/hard as you make it. Those who put the most in gain the most from their course (and in the job market). Termly/annual exams. Teaching is 1 to 1, or 1 to 6. Most students are happy with their course/professors but changes are possible. The graduate course has a low failure rate and few drop out. Many students go on to do a one year PGCE teaching course or do a postgraduate year at LCM, Royal College of Music, Guildhall etc.

Obviously there are limitless options for leisure activities in London. LCM has a thriving Christian Union run by students. The SU organises many events including boat discos, free drinks night etc. Rag week not to be missed!

All parts of the UK are represented at LCM as well as those from abroad. Most previously attended comprehensive schools or junior music schools. Many students come to LCM with aspirations of a playing career but soon discover that there are many other varied and interesting jobs in the music world. Even those who are fortunate enough to find playing work supplement this by teaching. Don't even think of a career in music if you're fond of money!
Andrea Martin/Wendy Robson

Pauper notes
Accommodation: No college halls. Students live in hostels in Central London (cutting out travel time and costs), or paying substantially less to live in digs/shared houses in the suburbs (paying exorbitant tube fares and wasting time imitating sardines!). You can't win! **Drink:** SU has links with 2 local pubs – full introduction given to all 1st years! Best local beers are in the 13 or so Firkin pubs, and Youngs/Fullers houses. Ultra cheap (northern prices) drinks at ULU and PCL bars. **Eats:** SU provides details of local good grubberies – also a cheap snack machine. Plenty of Indian/Chinese/Veggie/Health food places in the area, plus the usual chains. **Ents:** Every conceivable variety available in London can be extra cheap with an NUS card on the standby scheme. About one SU bash per month for students and friends. **Sports:** Most of the facilities at ULU are available (swimming, weight lifting, sauna and more). **Hardship funds:** SU advises as far as possible, and offers assistance and official backing to those in difficulties. Financial assistance can only be given in small doses to the very needy – (we're skint!) **Travel:** Very expensive – likely to become worse. At present, the best buy is a monthly/termly Travelcard which allows unlimited travel on buses and tubes, within the zones paid for. Those in hostels in Central London have no such problems. **Work:** Of all varieties available in the West End, and throughout London. Casual playing work can be found – but finding it is generally a matter of luck!

Alumni (Editors' pick)
David Caddick (musical director, Royal Shakespeare Co), Martin Ellerby (composer), Raphael Terroni (pianist), Edward Blakeman (flautist, Head of Woodwind, LCM, Radio 3 presenter), John Treleaven (international tenor).

LONDON COLLEGE OF PRINTING

London College of Printing, Elephant & Castle, London SE1 6SB (071-735 9100) Map E, D4

Student enquiries: College Administrator

Main study areas – as in What to Study section: *(First degree):* Art and design, business studies. *Also:* Film and video, printing, publishing, radio journalism.

European Community: Number of students learning an EC language or spending time in another EC country, not known.

Application: PCAS and ADAR. **Structural Feature:** Part of the London Institute. **Founded:** 1894, ex St Brides School and School of Photo-engraving and Lithography. **Main awards:** BA. **Awarding body:** CNAA. **Site:** Elephant & Castle; annexes at Clerkenwell and Leicester Square. **Access:** Elephant & Castle underground station (Bakerloo and Northern lines). **Academic features:** BA media production and design is 4 year sandwich course with periods of 3 months spent in industry. Part-time BA in book production. Degrees in film and video, and photography. Postgraduate diplomas in radio journalism and scriptwriting. **Accommodation:** 115 places in hall (reserved for students residing outside Greater London). **Library:** Main library at Elephant & Castle, 100,000 volumes in total, 580 periodicals, 70 study places; textbook reference collection. **Specialist collections:** History of the book. **Welfare:** Literature concerning welfare and accommodation is available; majority of advice facilities. **Careers:** Information and advice service. **Amenities:** Resident bookseller; students through membership of college library have access to all major art centres in London. **Employment:** Design and printing; photography, film and television industries; teaching; journalism; publishing.

Duration of first degree course(s) or equivalent: 3 years **Total first degree students 1989/90:** 420 **Male/female ratio 1989/90:** 3:2 **Teaching staff: full-time:** 197; **part-time:** 250 **Total full-time students 1989/90:** 1,559 **Postgraduate students:** 102 **Tuition fees, first degrees, 1990/91:** Home: £607; Overseas: £4,800.

What it's like

Towering above traffic and subways of Elephant and Castle it's difficult to miss. One of the leading colleges in the communications industry; widely recognised courses in printing, journalism (radio and periodical), publicity, promotion, photography, film, TV, media production design and graphic design. Library quite strong in all these areas. Accessible by bus, British Rail and Northern and Bakerloo line tubes. Many students from the Home Counties commute; accommodation is difficult to find. Places available at three halls of residence; very limited so apply early. Most students part-time or block release; tends towards apathetic response to college events. SU is trying to change this with wild parties and bands. Groups for CND campaigners, Christians and women meet regularly, others spasmodically. With the West End nearby there is a wide variety of entertainment – the problem being money. The biggest of the 7 colleges in the London Institute. Now promoted as arts and print centre of excellence for Europe – looking towards 1992!

Pauper notes

Accommodation: Halls of residence. **Drink:** Social club bar, Oswin St, Watneys (20p cheaper than local pubs), and Goose and Firkin. **Eats:** Refectory, social club.

Alumni (Editors' pick)

Trevor McDonald (newsreader), Neville Brody (designer 'City Limits', 'The Face'), Dave King (Arts Council Designer).

CAN'T FIND WHAT YOU'RE LOOKING FOR? USE THE INDEX!

LONDON CONTEMPORARY DANCE SCHOOL

London Contemporary Dance School, 16 Flaxman Terrace, London WC1H 9AT (071-387 0152) Map E, C1

Student enquiries: School Office

Main study areas – as in What to Study section: *(First degree):* Dance.

European Community: No students learn an EC language or spend time in another EC country.

Application: Direct, followed by two-stage practical auditions (some first-stage auditions held regionally and overseas). Candidates for degree course must pass the certificate audition, although academic qualifications are not necessarily required. **Academic features:** Parts of the degree course are taught in liaison with other institutions including Central School of Art and Design. **Special features:** Part of Contemporary Dance Trust which also embraces a performing company, London Contemporary Dance Theatre. Leading centre for training professional dancers in contemporary dance and choreography in Europe. **Founded:** 1966. **Main awards:** BA. **Awarding body:** Kent University. **Site:** Off Euston Road. **Access:** King's Cross and Euston tube and BR stations, buses. **Accommodation:** Student services officer gives advice on accommodation. **Library:** Extensive collection of dance, arts, psychology and related studies in addition to a general collection. **Welfare:** School osteopath visits twice a week, school doctor in NW1. Resident full-time student services officer. **Hardship funds:** For 2nd and 3rd year students only – competitive scholarship/endowment fund. **Careers:** Personal contact service for jobs. **Amenities:** 9 dance studios, music studio, The Place Theatre for student workshop performances; restaurant, student common rooms. **Employment:** Combination of performance and teaching, further studies.

Duration of first degree course(s) or equivalent: 3 years; others: 1 year **Total first degree students 1989/90:** 38 **Number of overseas students:** 52 **Number of mature students:** 28 **Male/female ratio 1989/90:** 1:7 **Teaching staff: full-time:** 15 **part-time:** 6 **Total full-time students 1989/90:** 150 **Postgraduate students:** 8 **Tuition fees, first degrees, 1990/91:** £5,940.

What it's like

Large building in central London known as The Place. Home of The Place theatre and London Contemporary Dance Theatre, a professional dance company. Euston and King's Cross stations only a few minutes walk away. Some squats across road, hostels very close. Helpful student adviser/counsellor. 25% recruitment from overseas. School library open throughout college hours. SU very active, particularly in providing link between students and admin. Each year given different tutor and every group covers different topics throughout year. Degree course consists of practical work with theoretical contexts of dance; and is for professional dance students only. Generally, employment for successful candidates good, but training very rigorous and suited to dedicated dancers wishing for professional careers, prepared to work extremely hard. Drop-out rate 30%–40%.

Pauper notes

Eats: Restaurant, cafeteria for school and theatre on premises (caters for vegetarians) – cheap, healthy food. Also many local cafes. **Drink:** Local pub Mabels just across road. **Work:** Some available in theatre, theatre bar and in admin for students. Occasional teaching and demonstrating work.

Alumni (Editors' pick)

Richard Alston, Siobhain Davies, Robert North, Anthony Van Laast, Linda Gibbs, Ian Spink; entire performing members of London Contemporary Dance Theatre.

CAN'T FIND WHAT YOU'RE LOOKING FOR? USE THE INDEX!

LONDON HOSPITAL

London Hospital Medical College, Turner Street, London E1 2AD
(071-377 7000) Map D, C2

Student enquiries: Sub-dean for Admissions

Main study areas – as in What to Study section: *(First degree):* Dentistry, medicine.

European Community: Number of students learning an EC language or spending time in another EC country, not known. Exchanges with Denmark (Copenhagen Dental School), Eire, (Cork), France (Rennes). Approved Erasmus programme 1990/91; expanding involvement in Erasmus and becoming involved in Tempus scheme.

Application: UCCA. **Structural features:** Part of London University. **Academic features:** Full medical course for MBBS degree; 23 pa students join clinical course after pre-clinical studies at eg Oxbridge. **Special features:** Pre-clinical teaching centred on Queen Mary and Westfield College. **Largest fields of study:** Medicine, dentistry. **Founded:** 1785; joined London University in 1900. **Main awards:** MBBS, BDS, BSc. **Awarding body:** London University. **Site:** Off Whitechapel Road. **Access:** Whitechapel underground station. **Accommodation:** 182 places in halls, 75 flat/bedsitter places (preference given to those living outside London and with domestic or personal difficulties). Approx cost: £210–£245 pm halls, £100–£125 pm flats. Rent: 26% in accommodation where rent controlled by university. **Library:** Main library + several departmental libraries; 32,000 volumes, 350 periodicals, 100 study places. **Welfare:** Doctor, dentist, FPA, psychiatrist, chaplain. **Hardship funds:** Funds available in cases of special financial hardship. **Amenities:** SU building providing common rooms, shop with supply of textbooks. **Sporting facilities:** Athletics ground at Hale End; rowing club with boats at Chiswick, own cottage and boats at Burnham-on-Crouch. **Employment:** College provides approx 120 pre-registration house appointments.

Duration of first degree course(s) or equivalent: 5 years (MBBS); **others:** Intercalated BSc 1 year **Total first degree students 1989/90:** 866 **Number of overseas students:** 39 **Number of mature students:** 33 **Male/female ratio 1989/90:** 3:2 **Teaching staff: full-time:** 226 **part-time:** 137 **Total full-time students 1989/90:** 980 plus 216 part-time **Postgraduate students:** 329 **Tuition fees, first degrees, 1990/91:** Home: £1,760; Overseas: £6,552–£11,300.

What it's like

Noted for its friendly, informal atmosphere. London Hospital serves the East End community (including Dockland Yuppies) which provides an enormous variety of patients and disease for the clinical student. The oldest English medical school. Clubs Union, a union of 39 vibrant clubs, from bridge to drama (6–7 productions per year); sailing (own cottage at Burnham); various sporting clubs based at beautiful grounds at Hale End. Student life centres around SU building and lively bar in the hospital and college campus. Medical, dental and paramedical students and staff mix at discos, live concerts, balls and cabaret.

Famous Rag Week raises more than £50,000 in one week by entertaining and shocking the London public. Whitechapel tube (across the road) allows rapid access to the West End. East also has much to offer, street markets eg Brick Lane, cheap Indian restaurants, Half Moon Theatre and docklands. As far as pubs are concerned the East End 'lock-in' is not a thing of the past.

New and imaginative curriculum; preclinical students taught with Barts students at Queen Mary & Westfield, Mile End. About 1/3 of students are offered an intercollegiate BSc in their 3rd or 4th year.

A number of overseas and mature students. Selection Committee looks for students with interests and achievements outside medicine.

Come and join us!!

CAN'T FIND WHAT YOU'RE LOOKING FOR? USE THE INDEX!

Pauper notes
Accommodation: 1st year accommodated in college hostel, Pooley Hall (QMW + LHMC) or intercollegiate halls. Clinical students eligible for cheap college housing. Many students in cheap council housing or college. Rent approx £15.00 pw. **Drink:** Club Union cheap and friendly. Traditional East End pubs with friendly atmosphere, eg The Lord Rodneys Head, Prospect of Whitby, Falcon & Firkin, Blind Beggar (of Kray Brothers fame). **Eats:** Good canteen food for around £1, Carlo's Cafe opposite the hospital for the true fry up. Many cheap Indian and Chinese restaurants as well as Pizza One, Pancake Two in Bethnal Green. **Ents:** Union events, usually once a week, bands, cabaret, discos etc plus 4 balls per year. Cheap high quality off campus theatre, cinema. **Sports:** Hospital swimming pool, excellent sports clubs and grounds. City squash club and tennis courts. **Hardship funds:** College helps. **Travel:** Some elective scholarships. STA Travel down the road. **Work:** Bar work, portering/agency nursing, drug and research trials, library attendants.

Alumni (Editors' pick)
Frederick Treaves (physician to John Merrick 'The Elephant Man'), Dr Barnardo.

LONDON INTERNATIONAL FILM SCHOOL

London International Film School, 24 Shelton Street, London WC2H 9HP (071-836 0826) Map E, C2

Student enquiries: The Administrator

Main study areas – as in What to Study section: *(First degree):* Film studies.

European Community: No students learn an EC language or spend time in another EC country.

Application: Direct. (Courses begin each term). **Academic features:** Writing drama for film scripts. Directing workshops. Practical sessions with actors. Extramural course in music for films, with Trinity College of Music. Half time is practical film-making; half formal tuition. **Special features:** Acceptance depends upon educational achievement and examples of relevant work, eg photography, previous films, video, film scripts, story boards; experience in film, TV or related areas taken into account. **Main fields:** include script writing, direction, camera work, art direction, sound recording and editing. **Founded:** 1956 as London School of Film Technique. **Main awards:** Diploma, Certificate. **Awarding body:** LIFS. **Site:** Covent Garden area. **Access:** Covent Garden tube station. **Accommodation:** None. **Library:** Technical books, periodicals, 17 study places. **Welfare:** National health services nearby. **Careers:** Graduates are automatically acceptable as members of ACTT, with access to vacancy registers covering film and TV. **Amenities:** Two viewing theatres, two fully equipped studios, video rehearsal studio, comprehensively equipped camera, sound and editing departments. Equipment includes 35 mm Panavision, 35 mm Mitchell, 16 mm and 35 mm Arriflex cameras, Nagra sound recorders, Steenbeck and Magnasync editing tables, video camera and editing equipment. LIFS Film Society run by students. SU plays large part in school. **Employment:** Film industry.

Duration of first degree course(s) or equivalent: 2 years **Total first degree students 1989/90:** 120 **Number of overseas students:** 102 **Number of mature students:** 6 **Male/female ratio 1989/90:** 4:1 **Teaching staff: full-time:** 27 **part-time:** 24 **Total full-time students 1989/90:** 120 **Tuition fees, first degrees, 1990/91:** £9,696.

CAN'T FIND WHAT YOU'RE LOOKING FOR? USE THE INDEX!

What it's like

Housed in a former banana warehouse on the corner of Shelton and Langley Streets, Covent Garden, right in the heart of the theatrical and film world. Easily accessible by tube (Covent Garden, Leicester Square, Tottenham Court Road) and various bus routes into West End. No students live in. Some are on grants, mainly from governments of their countries of origin. Many UK students on LEA grants. School run as co-op charity by students, their union, administration and board of governors. One governor is student. SU lately gaining more influence. Film society very active. Main student meeting place school coffee shop. Covent Garden area abounds in pubs, cafes, coffee shops. LIFS has high reputation for technical expertise and primarily technical course in how to make film, use cameras, sound equipment, edit, dub sound, build sets, lighting, directing etc. Quality of lectures variable. LIFS diploma has high local and international standing; diploma recognised by ACTT and membership automatically available to graduates who find work. About 140 students including 40 different nationalities. Students passionate about film: some want glittering prizes, others want monk-like quiet. LIFS graduate should be able to handle any aspect of film-making, in 16 mm or 35 mm, as well as the principles of video. Most work in film/TV industry. Many students would like to see more money put into equipment and facilities. Recent student work appearing in numerous festivals.

Pauper notes

This is an expensive school in an expensive area.
Drink: The Two Brewers, Seven Dials; various places around Covent Garden. **Eats:** Cheapest but not worst: LIFS coffee shop; various places around Covent Garden and Soho. **Ents:** Film society evening screenings; numerous cinemas and theatres around London.

Alumni (Editors' pick)

Arnold Wesker, Mark Forstater, John Irvin, Franc Roddam, Les Blair, Mike Leigh, Michael Mann, Mark Kasdan, Don Boyd, Bill Douglas, Horace Ove.

LONDON UNIVERSITY

University of London, Senate House, Malet Street, London WC1E 7HU (071-636 8000)

Main study areas – as in What to Study section: *(First degree):* All Study Areas are taught in London University – see the entries for the constituent colleges.

Academic features: Colleges, Schools, Institutes and London's unique External System offer over 900 undergraduate and 400 Master's degree courses, and many Diploma and Certificate courses via the Birkbeck College/Centre for Extra-Mural Studies. London offers the biggest choice of courses in the UK. **Special features:** London is a federal university of Byzantine complexity. Don't bother about its bureaucratic structure but concentrate on its separate teaching institutions, all of which select their first degree students themselves. We have designated each of these institutions as UKCPUs – you can look up their profiles in *Where to study*.

London University UKCPUs are:
Birkbeck College
British Institute in Paris
Charing Cross and Westminster (Medical School)
Courtauld Institute
Goldsmiths' College
Heythrop College
Imperial College

CAN'T FIND WHAT YOU'RE LOOKING FOR? USE THE INDEX!

Institute of Archaeology (part of University College)
Institute of Education
Jews' College
King's College London
King's College School of Medicine (part of King's College)
London Hospital (Medical College)
LSE (London School of Economics)
Queen Mary & Westfield (College)
Royal Free (Hospital School of Medicine)
Royal Holloway and Bedford (New College)
Royal Veterinary College
St Bartholomew's Hospital Medical School
St George's (Hospital Medical School)
St Mary's Hospital Medical School (part of Imperial College)
School of Pharmacy
Slade (School of Fine Art; part of University College)
SOAS (School of Oriental and African Studies)
SSEES (School of Slavonic & East European Studies)
United Medical and Dental Schools (of Guy's and St Thomas's Hospitals)
University College London
Wye College

For applications: Mostly through UCCA; see UKCPU profiles. **London University UKCPUs** teach for London University degrees – science degrees on modular degree system. **External students:** The University will register and examine eligible students world-wide who are not registered at London University UKCPUs. First degrees in divinity, arts subjects, laws, music (examinations in UK only), economics. Diplomas include education, public administration. Higher degrees restricted to London graduates. Enquiries to Secretary for External Students, University of London, Senate House, Malet Street, London WC1E 7HU (071-636 8000). **Site:** Bloomsbury, including 35 acres between British Museum and Euston Road, on which University College, Birkbeck, SOAS and Institute of Education are located. Almost all London University UKCPUs are within a radius of 3 miles of this site except for Royal Holloway and Bedford New College in Surrey and Wye College in Kent. **Central Library:** Library has 1,300,000 books and 5,500 current periodicals; particularly strong in the humanities. Many distinguished specialist collections. UKCPUs have own libraries. **Students' union:** University union (ULU) is in Malet Street. Most London University UKCPUs have their own unions. The athletic ground is in Motspur Park, Surrey; University boathouse is at Hartington Road, Chiswick; sailing clubhouse is at Welsh Harp Reservoir, Brent. **Welfare:** See individual UKCPUs. There is a Central Institutions Health Service for the Institute of Education, Birkbeck College, SSEES, the School of Pharmacy and SOAS. **Hardship funds:** Vice-Chancellor's Discretionary Fund: unforeseen hardship **after** commencing a course of study. **Accommodation:** Enquiries to Accommodation Officer, Room 5, Senate House, Malet Street, London WC1E 7HU (071-636 8000). 37% in accommodation where rent controlled by university (varies from college to college). **Other learning resources:** The University has an excellent computer centre, one of two national facilities providing resources to university users all over the UK. It also has its own specialist collections and galleries as well being within easy reach of all London's museums and galleries.

Duration of first degree course(s) or equivalent: 3 years; **others:** medicine/dentistry 5 years **Total first degree students 1989/90:** 34,875 (full-time); 2,324 (part-time); **total BEd students:** 190 **Number of overseas students:** 4,016 **Number of mature students:** 3,425 (full-time), 1,812 (part-time) **Male/female ratio 1989/90:** 54% male (full-time), 46% male (part-time); 46% female (full-time), 54% female (part-time); **Teaching staff: full-time:** approx 4,900 **part-time:** 490 **Total full-time students 1989/90:** 46,042 **Postgraduate students:** 11,167 full-time; 8,169 part-time **Tuition fees, first degrees, 1990/91:** each college sets own fee.

CAN'T FIND WHAT YOU'RE LOOKING FOR? USE THE INDEX!

Alumni (Editors' pick)
Rt Rev George Carey, Archibishop of Canterbury (King's), Edwina Curry (LSE), Bob Geldof (honorary graduate), Robert Mugabe, President of Zimbabwe (external system), David Owen (UMDS), Jonathon Ross (UCL).

LOUGHBOROUGH COLLEGE OF ART

Loughborough College of Art & Design, Radmoor, Loughborough, Leics LE11 3BT (0509 261515) Map A, E6

Student enquiries: Admissions Officer

Main study areas – as in What to Study section: *(First degree):* Art & design.

European Community: No students learn an EC language or spend time in another EC country. Exchange links with Spain (University of Granada; fine art undergraduate numbers increasing); informal exchanges of art and design undergraduates with various schools of fine and applied arts. Approved Erasmus programme 1990/91. Credit rating of courses underway to facilitate exchanges.

Application: ADAR. **Academic developments:** Flexible course arrangements. **Largest fields of study:** Textiles. **Founded:** 1958. **Main awards:** BA. **Awarding body:** CNAA. **Accommodation:** 175 places in halls. Rent: 50% in accommodation where rent controlled by college. **Library:** 50,000 volumes, 400 periodicals, 124 study places; extensive slide collection and video library. **Other learning resources:** Artists' books collection, IT facilities. **Welfare:** Doctor, chaplain, counselling service. **Careers:** Information and advice service. **Amenities:** Bookshop in SU building. **Sporting facilities:** Swimming pool, running track, sports hall, sports pitches, squash courts, etc available to all students as members of the Loughborough SU.

Duration of first degree course(s) or equivalent: 3 years **Total first degree students 1989/90:** 379 **Number of overseas students:** 3 **Number of mature students:** 40 **Male/female ratio 1989/90:** 2:3 **Teaching staff: full-time:** 42 **part-time:** 39 **Total full-time students 1989/90:** 657 **Tuition fees, first degrees, 1990/91:** Home: £1,675; Overseas: £6,000.

What it's like

Shares campus with technical college, across the road from university. 10 minutes' walk from town centre. Usual facilities of a medium sized market town. Markets every Thursday and Saturday. Small shopping precinct off the market place. Equidistant from Nottingham, Derby and Leicester. SU one of the largest, over 12,500 student members from university, technical college and college of art and design. Building three minutes' walk from college with bars, travel bureau, fast food outlet, 7 shops and a nursery.

Many students are local. Courses are strongly vocational for practising artists, industrial designers and teachers.

12 halls of residence for approximately 200 students. Large houses on main roads into town. None are mixed though that might change. All are catered for. Most have kitchens for supplementary cooking. Refectory is adjacent to the main site, less than a minute's walk from all the buildings. Students not in hall either live in registered lodgings or at home.

Library is being extended but still inadequate for most courses. Visiting restrictions; visitors out by midnight. Own student-run internal affairs committee to promote and represent the general interests of the students of the college and to keep them informed on academic matters.

CAN'T FIND WHAT YOU'RE LOOKING FOR? USE THE INDEX!

Pauper notes

Accommodation: No married quarters in residential accommodation but available for tenants in town houses. Certain student streets in area – small ghettos, good atmosphere – always near a pub!! **Drink:** 5 bars in SU building – drinks up to 20p cheaper. Marstons Pedigree (real ale) still most popular. Regular drinks promotions, guest beers and a wide selection of soft drinks. A number of student pubs in town. **Eats:** College refectory. SU fast food outlet, baked potatoes, burgers, pizzas. Wine/bottle lounge bar in SU provides traditional and continental cuisine. A number of curry houses, Chinese and fish and chip shops in town. One vegetarian restaurant and a number of whole-food shops. Town has a profusion of supermarkets. **Ents:** Excellent – lot of top groups tour here; regular films, SU discos, a jazz band every week. Drama on University campus as well as in town and adjacent cities. Three nightclubs within area which offer student rates, also a five screen cinema. **Sports:** Best College/University facilities in country. Need look no further. University facilities open to SU Club members. **Hardship funds:** £75 interest free loans from SU and fund to help hardship cases in payment of nursery fees and childminding costs. **Travel:** New travel bureau recently opened in SU – provides cheap holidays for all students – can buy rail, coach and air tickets over the counter the same as at a High Street travel centre. Close to M1 for hitching. **Work:** Some part-time work available in the bars and shops plus occasional casual work and some work in the town's bars.

LOUGHBOROUGH UNIVERSITY

Loughborough University of Technology, Loughborough, Leics LE11 3TU (0509 263171) Map A, E6

Student enquiries: Senior Assistant Registrar (Admissions)

Main study areas – as in What to Study section: (*First degree*): Accountancy, aeronautical engineering, business studies, chemical engineering, chemistry, civil engineering, computing, dance, drama, economics, education, electrical & electronic engineering, English, environmental science, European studies, geography, information technology, library & information studies, mathematical studies, mechanical and production engineering, metallurgy and materials science, modern languages, pharmacology, physics, physiology, politics and government, psychology, sociology, welfare studies. *Also:* Building technology, design, operational research, physical education, sports studies, surveying, transport studies, urban studies.

European Community: 5% first degree students take EC language as part of course and 1% spend 6 months or more in another EC country. Formal exchange links with 16 EC universities/colleges (number increasing): Belgium (2; chemistry, human sciences); Denmark (2; civil and mechanical engineering); France (3; European studies); Germany (4; economics, European studies, mechanical engineering); Italy (4; chemical and mechanical engineering, polymer technology and materials engineering); Netherlands (1; human sciences). Approved Erasmus programme 1990/91. Increased language teaching planned and more opportunities to combine languages with other subjects.

Application: UCCA. **Academic features:** New courses in English and history of art and design; chemical engineering with environmental protection; chemistry and physical education and sports science; commercial management and quantity surveying; construction engineering management. 3-year undergraduate courses in aeronautical engineering, automotive engineering and mechanical engineering. BEng in mechanical and manufacturing, design and manufacturing, civil, electro-mechanical power, electronics and manufacturing, chemical and mathematical engineering, and engineering science and technology. **Special features:** Industrial

CAN'T FIND WHAT YOU'RE LOOKING FOR? USE THE INDEX!

professors (3-year appointments, several hours' teaching per week): chemical engineering – H A Duxbury; economics – J H B Tew; geography – J Sheail; library studies – M B Line; management studies – D Allen; physics – J M Walls; transport technology – G L Wilde. **Largest fields of study:** Electrical engineering, management studies, civil engineering. **Main awards:** BA, BSc, BEng, MEng. **Awarding body:** Loughborough University. **Site:** 216 acres about a mile from town centre. **Access:** 1 mile from M1, 1½ miles from railway station; 8 miles from East Midlands airport; bus service between town and campus. **Accommodation:** 3,670 places. Rent: 80% in accommodation where rent controlled by university. **Library:** Pilkington Library has 600,000 volumes, 700 study places. **Other learning facilities:** Computer Centre, Institute of Polymer Technology and Materials Engineering; Engineering Design Institute; Centre for Extension Studies. **Welfare:** Medical services, counsellors, chaplains, wardens. **Careers:** Active careers service. **Amenities:** Purpose-built SU building with 4 bars, wine/cocktail lounge bar, shop, travel office, banks, bookshop, performance area; day nursery/playgroup; student arts centre with darkroom, studio equipment, record and cassette library; associated music centre; drama studio with workshop; campus radio station. **Sporting facilities:** Excellent sports facilities including 3 sports halls, 2 gymnasia, 2 swimming pools, 7 squash courts, 2 floodlit all-weather areas, all-weather athletics stadium, dance studio, numerous major games-playing pitches and all-weather tennis courts.

Duration of first degree course(s) or equivalent: 3 or 4 years **others:** 4 or 5 years **Total first degree students 1989/90:** 4,851 **Number of overseas students:** 388 **Number of mature students:** 9% **Male/female ratio 1989/90:** 2:1 **Teaching staff: full-time:** 498 **part-time:** 28 **Total full-time students 1989/90:** 5,637 **Postgraduate students:** 786 **Tuition fees, first degrees, 1990/91:** Home: £1,675 (£643 if self-financing); Overseas: £4,520 (eg politics), £5,930 (eg physics).

What it's like

Tripartite SU derives membership from 4 constituent student bodies (including university, colleges of art and technology); 12,000 members in all, 15% overseas, 10% mature, mixture of private, state and comprehensive schools. Many part-time students. 30% own cars. Good SU facilities for students with disabilities: 200 about to start at new Blind College. Accommodation good, mixed; washing facilities poor; bike or local bus company's campus service.

SU politically and socially active. Confidential advice and welfare unit: financial assistance for pregnant women. Union on NME/MM circuits. Students meet easily, SU is centre of activity. Good town/student relations; student community action group. Lots of pubs, theatres, markets. Most active societies are the athletics union (50+ clubs) and Rag (largest in the country – raised £100,000 last year).

Engineering, technology and PE most popular subject areas, still plenty of arts students. Changing course in first year possible; workloads vary, science courses require a lot of time in practicals. Many courses have years abroad or in industry. Assessment through course work, exams and practical. No fixed failure rate. Students are hardworking; employment varies but many go into management.

Pauper notes

Accommodation: 80% of students in halls. Many 2nd/3rd year students choose to 'live-out'. Large number of student 'ghettos' – streets that primarily house students. Very few student squats. Little or no accommodation for married students in hall – housing open but sometimes difficult. **Drink:** SU is cheapest – 5 bars in SU building, drinks up to 20p cheaper. Regular promotions and wide selection of wine and soft drinks. Numerous pubs in town. **Eats:** Hall food OK– good vegetarian options. SU food outlets including fastfood restaurant type and pizza, baked potatoes etc, cafe. A number of curry houses, Chinese and fish & chip shops in town. One vegetarian restaurant and a number of whole-food shops. Town has a profusion of supermarkets. **Ents:** Excellent – a lot of top groups tour here; regular films in SU, discos, a jazz band every week. Also Rag and Hall events. Drama on university campus as well as in town and adjacent cities. 3 night clubs in area which offer student rates, also a 5 screen cinema. **Sports:** Best university sporting facilities in country – open to Loughborough Students Athletics Club members. University Athletic Union Champions 8 years for men, 9 years for women. **Hardship funds:** £50 interest free loans available on delivery of post-dated cheque. Nursery funding assistance available based on parental income with a sliding scale of charges. **Travel:** New ABTA Travel Bureau recently opened in SU – provides cheap holidays for students – can buy coach, rail, air tickets over the counter. **Work:** Casual work available at SU, also variety of part-time jobs in shops in town.

Alumni (Editors' pick)
Alastair Biggart (Channel Tunnel), Peter Bonfield (ICL), Rob Dickens (British Phonographic Industry), Sebastian Coe, David Moorcroft, Christina Boxer, Danny Nightingale and Steve Scutt, Sue Shoblon, Forbes Robinson, Jack Buckner, Tim Hutchings, Ernie Obeng, Bob Wilson, Tania Rodrigues.

LSE

London School of Economics & Political Science, University of London, Houghton Street, London WC2A 1AE (071-405 7686) Map E, C2

Student enquiries: Assistant Registrar (Admissions)

Main study areas – as in What to Study section: *(First degree):* Accountancy, anthropology, computing, economics, geography, history, industrial relations, law, mathematical studies, philosophy, politics and government, psychology, public administration, sociology, welfare studies. *Also:* Actuarial studies, management.

European Community: 3% first degree students take EC language as part of course and 1% spend 6 months or more in another EC country. Formal exchange links with 15 EC universities/colleges under Erasmus scheme; all open to non-language specialists (some for postgraduates only).

Application: UCCA. **Structural features:** Part of London University. **Academic features:** Unique concentration on economic and social sciences, taught in 15 departments. **Special features:** Numerous visitors attend every academic year. One year courses for overseas students. **Founded:** 1895, joined London University in 1900. **Main awards:** BA, BSc, BSc(Econ), LLB. **Awarding body:** London University. **Site:** Central London (just off Aldwych). **Access:** Aldwych, Holborn and Temple underground stations; buses. **Accommodation:** Halls and flats to accommodate approx 25% of student body (apply to Assistant Registrar, Admissions). Rent: approximately 25% students housed in accommodation where rent is under school's control. London University will advise on lodgings. **Library:** British Library of Political and Economic Science is a national collection in field of social science as well as School's working library; 881,000 volumes, 4,600 current periodicals. Teaching library: 31,500 volumes, with additional copies of more important course books; short loan collections of periodicals. Shaw Library: collection of general literature. **Centre of excellence:** Internationally renowned in social sciences. **Welfare:** Doctor, dentist, FPA, psychiatrist, nursing sister, chaplains, women's adviser, disabled students' adviser. **Hardship funds:** LSE 1980's Fund and other funds to help students facing hardship. **Special categories:** Nursery with 24 places. **Careers:** Information and advice service. **Amenities:** SU with restaurant, bar, shop, legal advice centre, newspaper and magazine; facilities of London University union in Malet Street. **Sporting facilities:** Sports grounds at New Malden; circuit-room, squash court and gymnasium on site.

CAN'T FIND WHAT YOU'RE LOOKING FOR? USE THE INDEX!

Duration of first degree course(s) or equivalent: 3 years; others: 4 years Total first degree students 1989/90: 2,557 Number of overseas students: 761 Number of mature students: Large number Male/female ratio 1989/90: 4:3 Teaching staff: full-time: 310 part-time: c200 Total full-time students 1989/90: 4,020 Postgraduate students: 2,064 (incl c600 part-time) Tuition fees, first degrees, 1990/91: Home: £1,675; Overseas: £5,425.

What it's like

Truly unique and cosmopolitan institution. High percentage of overseas and postgraduate students. Buildings lack the grandeur of Oxbridge; academic tradition strong. It's an 'international centre of excellence'. Most departments very strong: economics in top three in world, law department one of most radical in UK, social policy, accounting, government and social admin all strong. Virtually all assessment is exam based, no opportunity for September re-sits (apart from law). Easy to change courses; difficult to fail first year. SU: bar, cafe and shop and excellent welfare service with specialist advice on money problems and cheap/available housing in London. Politically as stimulating as ever. SU policy decided at weekly UGMs, often of 400 students. Wide range of political opinions and ferocious debates. School authorities tend to rely on reputation; relationship with students good. The library is the largest collection of social, economic and political material in Europe: tremendous asset. Sporting facilities relatively poor. Social life based on wide variety of societies.

Pauper notes

Accommodation: Poor but trying. SU offers excellent private accommodation service for students unable to get into halls. Only 20% in halls. Drink: Three Tuns Club newly refurbished. Eats: The Cafe – vegetarian restaurant – excellent food, excellent value, pies and pizza in The Three Tuns. Ents: Regular bands (eg Housemartins, Curiosity Killed the Cat, Blow Monkeys), Hall discos, film soc etc. Sports: Squash court and gym on campus, playing fields at New Malden, Surrey. Hardship funds: Gifts (up to £100) given to about 100 needy students each term; also Right-to-Choose fund to help pregnant women re access to abortions or help with childcare. Interest-free loans for some students. Shops: SU shop for very cheap stationery and other essentials. Travel: Rail cards, ISIC cards available – STA branch on campus. Work: Some casual work in Union – whole of London casual market.

Alumni (Editors' pick)

Frank Dobson, Clare Francis, Bernard Levin, Robert Kilroy-Silk, John F Kennedy, Mick Jagger, Pierre Trudeau, Edwina Currie, Maurice Saatchi, Michael Meacher.

LUTON COLLEGE

Luton College of Higher Education, Park Square, Luton LU1 3JU and Putteridge Bury, Hitchin Road, Luton, Beds (0582 34111) Map A, F7

Student enquiries: The Registrar (Park Square address)

Main study areas – as in What to Study section: (First degree): Accountancy, biochemistry, biology, business studies, computing, electrical and electronic engineering, environmental science, geography, geology, history, information technology, law, mechanical and production engineering, modern languages, nursing studies, psychology, sociology, welfare studies. Also: Building studies, instrumentation, mapping, Urdu.

European Community: 70% first degree students take EC language as part of course (including building and engineering students) and 40% spend 6 months or

CAN'T FIND WHAT YOU'RE LOOKING FOR? USE THE INDEX!

more in another EC country. Formal exchange links with 4 EC universities/colleges in Belgium, France and Spain. Approved Erasmus programme 1990/91. Development of language and exchanges in every faculty.

Application: PCAS. **Main awards:** BSc, BA, LLB. **Awarding body:** CNAA and University of London (LLB). **Site:** Town centre. Putteridge Bury site 3 miles from main campus. **Access:** 5 mins from M1, bus and railway stations and international airport. **Accommodation:** 100 places in self-catering halls; college managed houses also available via Accommodation Office. Rent: 20% in accommodation where rent controlled by college. **Library:** 69,000 volumes, 400 periodicals, 250 study places; microfilm and video facilities. **Other learning resources:** Computer Services: approximately 400 pc's for student use; Communication Services: TV, video and radio stations. **Welfare:** Senior tutor, personal tutor for each student, doctor, FPA, independent adviser. **Careers:** Information and advice service. **Amenities:** College bookshop, closed circuit TV, regional sports centre; Olympic standard swimming pool, library, theatre in Luton, first division soccer. **Employment:** Wide range of careers in science, business and public services.

Duration of first degree course(s) or equivalent: 3 years **Others:** 4 years (sandwich) **Total first degree students 1989/90:** 327 **Number of overseas students:** 120 **Number of mature students:** 350 **Male/female ratio 1989/90:** 2:1 **Teaching staff: full-time:** 200 **part-time:** 15 **Total full-time students 1989/90:** 1,401 **Postgraduate students:** 27 **Tuition fees, first degrees, 1990/91:** Home: £1,675; Overseas: £4,563.

What it's like

The college has three campuses. Main campus situated at Park Square, right in centre of Luton, next to parish church and Arndale Shopping Centre, which boasts all usual shops and good indoor market. Putteridge Bury campus, four miles away, a magnificent neo-Elizabethan mansion set in very attractive grounds, serves as a management centre. Third campus, next to Dunstable town centre, caters for vocational courses. Since entering Polytechnics and Colleges Funding Council (PCFC) last year, student population has increased by 53% and is forecasted to increase further over next couple of years.

Main campus is about two minutes (by taxi) from coach and railway stations and about 10 minutes (by taxi) from Luton International Airport. For those wanting excitement and who have money to spend, London is only half an hour away by train.

One hall of residence opposite main campus provides ninety single study bedrooms with shared kitchens. Downs Road provides further sixteen self-catering places. A head tenancy scheme run by college accommodation office provides shared housing for majority of student population, plus large percentage in private sector. Average rent works out between £30 and £35 pw with bills on top usually. Most accommodation within walking distance of college.

Socially, SU centre of all activities; being cheapest place to drink in town it is always packed out. Union building just revamped, resulting in two bars which sell all usual plus a number of real ales. Within the bar you can play pool, bar billiards, darts, watch television and videos on a large screen and deafen yourself listening to the CD jukebox. Regular discos weekly and a number of live bands every term plus all the usual things that happen within a thriving SU!

In town, Cannon cinema receives all latest releases very quickly; an arts cinema in town library shows unusual but usually brilliant films. Also arts centre near town centre has regular programme of live music, comics, exhibitions etc. A number of nightclubs in town; more popular have student night every week.

All usual fast food joints and pizza places scattered through town; excellent Chinese and Indian restaurants; odd Italian and French restaurants, usually hidden up some obscure little side street.

Contrary to popular belief, Luton is a fun place to go to college. The typical Luton student can be described as conscientious and hard-working but when

CAN'T FIND WHAT YOU'RE LOOKING FOR? USE THE INDEX!

necessary can go through a metamorphic change and become the ultimate party animal.

Pauper notes

Accommodation: Mostly average – same price, varying standard. Private accommodation generally poor and over priced; new head tenancy scheme helps but still needs a lot of work. **Drink:** SU bar cheap, good atmosphere and friendly. Pubs generally don't cater for students but the Cock good local. **Eats:** Two refectories on campus: Church Street fast food; Vicarage Street, good food but vegetarian provision not good. Plenty of chip shops, kebab, Chinese and Indian. Good veggie curry houses Leagrave Road. **Ents:** 1 cinema and town library has good cheap plays and films. SU is main source of ents but more student support needed. **Sports:** Good local sports facilities backed by college contacts. Within radius of 3 miles: 3 sports centres and baths and college playing fields. **Hardship funds:** Access fund (government); college welfare section and SU-run hardship fund (re-payable). **Travel:** Mostly walking; poor college transport; local transport good but expensive. Get a coach and rail card. Hitching fairly easy on M1. **Work:** Mostly pub/bar work, stewarding in SU etc.

Alumni (Editors' pick)

Paul Young (pop singer), Chairman of Rolls Royce.

MANADON

The Royal Naval Engineering College, Manadon, Plymouth PL5 3AQ (0752 553740 Ext 81213) Map A, C9

Student enquiries: Academic Registrar

Main study areas – as in What to Study section: *(First degree):* Naval engineering including aeronautical engineering, electrical and electronic engineering, marine technology, mechanical engineering, strategic studies.

European Community: No students learn an EC language or spend time in another EC country.

Special features: 3 year full-time residential engineering degree course (covering mechanical, electrical and control engineering), followed by up to a year's post-degree application training. New 2-year BA in maritime defence, management and technology. **Entry conditions:** Mainly RN engineering officers; also open to officers of the other armed services, and members of their associated civilian organisations; civilian students, sponsored by Ministry of Defence engineering contractors or by LEAs. **Founded:** 1880. **Main awards:** BEng, BA. **Awarding body:** CNAA. **Site:** Campus at Manadon, Plymouth. **Access:** Via Crownhill, 2 miles north of Plymouth city centre (regular bus services). **Accommodation:** 400 places in single and double rooms. Rent: 40% in accommodation where rent controlled by college. **Library:** 70,000 volumes, 500 periodicals, 90 study places. Micro-film and microfiche reader/printers, video cassette players for publications in non-book format. **Welfare:** Medical and dental facilities on site. Strong tradition of pastoral care. **Amenities:** Bank; sundries shop; theatre/cinema. **Sporting facilities:** Open air swimming pool; squash courts; full range of sporting facilities with gymnasium, excellent grounds and hard hockey pitch; recreational facilities covering a wide range of subsidised activities, including off-shore sailing.

Duration of first degree course(s) or equivalent: 3 years **other:** 2 years (BA) **Total first degree students 1989/90:** 240 **Number of overseas students:** 20 **Male/female ratio 1989/90:** 50:1 **Teaching staff: full-time:** 70 **Total full-time students 1989/90:** 420 **Postgraduate students:** 30 **Tuition fees, first degrees, 1990/91** £1,675.

CAN'T FIND WHAT YOU'RE LOOKING FOR? USE THE INDEX!

What it's like

Set in 100 acres of wooded grounds between the Dartmoor National Park and the City of Plymouth. It has a high academic standard and low drop-out rate as a result of a well structured course, regular assessment and excellent student/tutor ratio. The BEng course has recently been updated to allow earlier specialisation. The first and second years are lecture/tutorial intensive with the third year based around individual projects, undertaken in the college's modern, well-equipped labs. There are also powerful mainframe computer and computer-aided engineering facilities. An 11-week workshops course runs in conjunction with the degree to provide engineering application training as required by the Engineering Council for registration. A new BA degree has been designed and the first students arrived in September 1990.

All first year students live in the officers' mess, with the equivalent facilities of a good students' union, where accommodation, food and facilities are provided well within the students' means. A hectic social scene is the norm at Manadon; sporting, political, musical and theatrical activities run hand in hand with more traditional naval occasions, which include formal mess dinners.

Staff and students mix socially both in the mess and in the many sports the college caters for. Tennis/squash, playing fields, an astroturf pitch, a 9-hole golf course, swimming pool and multigym are all in the grounds, whilst sailing, rowing, climbing, flying and riding are available locally at little or no cost.

Plymouth has cinemas, excellent theatre, busy night life, a dry ski slope and Dartmoor National Park close by. The Barbican is especially popular with its character pubs and restaurants set in the historic port of Plymouth.

Many students have their own cars but Plymouth bus services are good as are road and rail links into the city. The majority of students are Royal Navy officers with varied social and academic backgrounds, but civilian students are welcomed and enjoy all the facilities on an equal basis. This contributes to a well-balanced, friendly professional atmosphere.
S/Lt Mark Malley, RN

Pauper notes

Accommodation: There is ample rented accommodation on campus and in Plymouth at reasonable rates. **Drink:** Manadon bars are busy and inexpensive. Plymouth and Dartmoor also have a wide range of historic ale houses and pubs. **Eats:** All meals are catered for on campus at good rates and there is a large selection of restaurants/pubs in Plymouth to suit all tastes. **Ents:** There are frequent social gatherings on campus. Plymouth Theatre Royal and Drum Theatre are easily accessible. **Sports:** All sports and outdoor activities are catered for at any level and all at minimal cost.

MANCHESTER BUSINESS SCHOOL

Manchester Business School, Booth Street West, Manchester M15 6PB (061-275 6311) Map A, D6

This is a postgraduate UKCPU.

Student enquiries: Admissions Secretary, Postgraduate Centre

Main study areas: *(Not at first degree):* Business studies.

European Community: 90% degree students take EC language as part of course and 15% spend 6 months or more in another EC country. Formal exchange links with 5 EC universities/colleges in France, Italy, Netherlands and Spain. Approved Erasmus programme 1990/91.

CAN'T FIND WHAT YOU'RE LOOKING FOR? USE THE INDEX!

Application: Direct. **Special features:** Manchester Business School is Faculty of Business Administration of Manchester University. MBA course combines management theory and practice leading in the second year to consultancy-type projects within organisations; Language teaching included. Doctoral programme involves one year of taught courses followed by a research project leading to the thesis. **Founded:** 1965. **Academic features:** 2 year MBA (Master's degree in Business Administration); 1 year Diploma in Business Administration and 3 year PhD (Doctoral Programme in business administration). All postgraduate and all available on part-time basis. Part-time Master in Business Management post-experience course. **Main awards:** MBA, PhD, Diploma in Business Administration, Master in Business Management. **Awarding body:** Manchester University. **Site:** University area of Manchester Education Precinct, 1 mile from city centre. **Access:** Regular bus service from most parts of the city. **Accommodation:** No accommodation within the school for graduates; advice from the University Accommodation Office. **Library:** 30,000 volumes, 800 journals, newsclippings and annual report files. **Other learning facilities:** Advanced computing facilities; commercial information services. **Welfare:** Emergency doctor, psychiatrist, chaplain, solicitor. **Careers:** Advisory and placement service. **Amenities:** University sports centre nearby (swimming pool, sauna, squash, etc). **Employment:** International commerce, finance, consultancy, marketing, line management (for case histories of graduates see prospectus).

Male/female ratio 1989/90: 6:1**Teaching staff: full-time:** 55 **Total full-time students 1989/90:** 235 **Total part-time students 1989/90:** 100 **Doctoral students:** 27 (including 2 part-time) **Tuition fees, first degrees, 1990/91:** Home: £4,550; Overseas: £6,400.

What it's like

Emphasis on putting theory into practice; use of projects as a major teaching tool, with less emphasis on more traditional exam and case study approach. Formal training in all the basic aspects of management, but the 'MBS project' dominates course. Subject matter varies but working with groups of fellow students is always required. This can be rewarding or frustrating – sometimes both, and teaches you how to rely on other people in pressurised situations. Strong individualists who find it difficult to work in teams have a tough time. Students are **all** postgraduate; from a

CAN'T FIND WHAT YOU'RE LOOKING FOR? USE THE INDEX!

wide range of backgrounds with degrees ranging from medieval English literature to banking. Most have had significant work experience varying from being a diplomat in Peking to being a small businessman. Two years with this body of students is a great source of learning. Courses require mental stamina and considerable personal commitment; the rewards in terms of personal achievement and learning within a group environment cannot be denied. Good chance of getting on the international exchange programme, to spend one term at a prestigious business school in the USA, Europe or Japan. MBS international club is affiliated to a network of European business school student clubs.

Notes
Drink: MBS club non-profitmaking (Newcastle Bitter). **Eats:** Cooked lunch £1.50. On the Eighth Day for vegetarian. **Ents:** University Theatre, postgrad film society, Royal Exchange Theatre and Space Capsule in Old Cotton Exchange, Halle Orchestra, Palace Theatre (Grand Opera and Ballet), Royal Northern College of Music, just across the road. Peak District close at hand, and sailing at nearby Tatton Mere. **Sports:** MacDougall Centre (plus swimming pool) within walking distance. **Work:** Almost all take on summer jobs with UK and overseas companies, as a basis for a dissertation.

Alumni (Editors' pick)
Joe Matthews (managing director, Adamson-Butterley), Terence Riorden (managing director, Benrose Ltd), Andrew Slinn (general manager for Europe – Readicut International), Chris Kirkland (business development executive, Burmah Oil), Tim O'Brian (project manager, Norcros), James Ross (Chief Executive, BP America), John Ward (President of Midland Montagu, America), David Varney (managing director of Shell, Sweden).

MANCHESTER POLY

Manchester Polytechnic, All Saints, Manchester M15 6BH (061-247 2000) Map A, D6

Student enquiries: Academic Registrar

Main study areas – as in What to Study section: *(First degree):* Accountancy, architecture, art & design, biochemistry, biology, business studies, chemistry, computing, drama, economics, education, electrical & electronic engineering, English, environmental studies, European studies, fine arts, geography, history, hotel & catering management, information technology, law, library & information studies, mathematical studies, mechanical & production engineering, metallurgy and materials science, microbiology, modern languages, nursing studies, philosophy, physics, physiology, politics and government, psychology, public administration, sociology, speech sciences, welfare studies. *Also:* Film studies.

European Community: 18% first degree students take EC language as part of course and 11% spend 6 months or more in another EC country. Formal exchange links with 4 EC universities/colleges: France (3); Germany (1) plus Erasmus links in Belgium (1); France (2); Netherlands (4). Approved Erasmus programme 1990/91. Courses with EC links include international hotel management; business in Europe; international economic studies (with university of Caen).

Application: PCAS except for art and design (ADAR). **Special features:** Some transfers possible between HND/HD and parallel degree courses for good students. **Founded:** 1970, ex Manchester College of Art & Design and College of Commerce and John Dalton College of Technology; joined 1977 by Didsbury College of Education and Hollings College and 1983 by City of Manchester College of Higher Education. **Main awards:** BA, BEd, BSc, BEng. **Awarding body:** CNAA. **Site:** In or near city centre, except for Didsbury site (6 miles away), Hollings (3 miles) and Elizabeth Gaskell (2 miles). **Access:** Regular bus service to Didsbury, Hollings and Elizabeth Gaskell sites. **Accommodation:** 1,400 places in halls (80% for first year students). Accommodation office helps with flats, bedsits, lodgings and council flats. Approx cost: catered hall £48.00 pw, self-catered hall £30.00 pw, full board/lodging £42.00 pw, private self-contained flat £30.00 pw (excl heating/lighting). Rent: 11.5% in accommodation where rent controlled by polytechnic. **Library:** 6 libraries, total of 750,000 volumes, 3,500 periodicals, 1,600 study places. **Specialist collections:** Book design, children's literature 1870–1930, local collections. **Other learning facilities:** Supermini computer system. **Welfare:** Counsellors, chaplains, educational adviser, learning skills adviser, nurse. Doctors (day emergencies only), FPA and nursery shared with university. All students required to register with local GP. Legal advice available from solicitors via SU. **Special categories:** 5 council flats for families, some accommodation for physically handicapped students in halls. **Careers:** Information and advice. **Amenities:** Horniman Theatre, art galleries and studios. SU building including bar, restaurant, shop, launderette and games room. **Sporting facilities:** Excellent sports facilities, including gymnasia, sports halls, tennis and squash courts, weight training and swimming pool. **Employment:** Public service, industry, commerce and professions.

Duration of first degree course(s) or equivalent: 3 years; **others:** 4 years (sandwich); up to 7 years (part-time) **Total first degree students 1989/90:** 10,292; **BEd students:** 849 **Number of overseas students:** 167 **Number of mature students:** 1,719 **Male/female ratio 1989/90:** 5:6 **Teaching staff: full-time:** 950 **part-time:** 350 **Total full-time students 1989/90:** 12,250 **Postgraduate students:** 1,704 **Tuition fees, first degrees, 1990/91:** Home: £1,675; Overseas: £4,495.

What it's like

Split site, spread over 6 miles. Main site in middle of Manchester, 200 yards from the university, UMIST and the Royal Northern College of Music. The poly (largest in Europe) has approximately 18,000 students: mixed backgrounds, races, religions, nearly 51% mature students. SU facilities on 5 sites, main purpose built building on main site. SU runs 6 bars, 3 catering outlets, 6 shops, 2 launderettes, 1 bank and travel service, many machine services and socials and events of all sorts. Manchester is an active and popular city with highest student population anywhere in Europe, so caters for most tastes. City has lot to offer but is ideally situated for trips to countryside. Poly offers many specialised and interesting courses. Union is active.

Pauper notes

Accommodation: Even more difficult this year – rents higher, no longer eligible for housing benefit – students are beginning to move into accommodation they may have rejected previously because of their lack of funds. **Drink:** Trendy: Dry 201, Archies, Flea & Firkin, Red Lion – Withington, Queen of Hearts – Fallowfield, the Didsbury Dozen (well known pub crawl), The Barleycorn – West Didsbury, The Beech and Dog and Trumpet – Chorlton. **Eats:** Rusholme for Asian food – vegetarian: Pie in the Sky (Withington), Greens, 8th Day, Billies (Chorlton). Good and cheap: Howling Smith Cafe, Basta Pasta, Corner House and Lime Tree Cafe. **Ents:** Weekly films, disco, gigs, bands, fashion show, comedy nights – all in main poly SU building. **Sports:** Moss Side Centre, Chorlton – swimming/badminon; Withington – karate, sauna, weightlifting, turkish bath, swimming and Victoria Baths; the poly's own All Saints Centre. **Hardship Funds:** Some available; contact welfare office or Student Services. **Travel:** Buses expensive – buy 'Clipper cards' or use a bike whenever possible. **Work:** Bar work, fast food chains, supermarkets, waiting, waitressing, washing-up, security (in poly).

CAN'T FIND WHAT YOU'RE LOOKING FOR? USE THE INDEX!

Alumni (Editors' pick)
L S Lowry (painter), Ossie Clark (fashion designer), Julie Walters (actress), Bryan Robson (footballer) Mick Hucknall (lead singer of 'Simply Red').

MANCHESTER UNIVERSITY

University of Manchester, Manchester M13 9PL (061-275 2000) Map A, D6

Student enquiries: The Registrar

Main study areas – as in What to Study section: *(First degree):* Accountancy, aeronautical engineering, American studies, anatomy, anthropology, archaeology, architecture, Asian studies, biochemistry, biology, business studies, chemistry, civil engineering, classics, computing, dentistry, drama, economics, education, electrical & electronic engineering, English, environmental studies, fine arts, geography, geology, history, information technology, Latin American studies, law, linguistics, mathematical studies, mechanical and production engineering, medicine, metallurgy and materials science, microbiology, modern languages, music, Near East and Islamic studies, nursing studies, pharmacology, pharmacy, philosophy, physics, physiology, politics and government, psychology, public administration, religious studies and theology, sociology, speech sciences, strategic studies, town and country planning, welfare studies, zoology. *Also:* Iberian studies, Irish and Welsh studies, medieval studies, Russian studies, Semitic languages, Slavonic studies, soil science, urban studies.

European Community: Number of students learning an EC language or spending time in another EC country, not known. Approved Erasmus programme 1990/91.

Application: UCCA. **Special features:** Whitworth Art Gallery. Lindsay String Quartet in residence. International Development Centre; Joint Centre for European Studies. **Academic features:** New degrees in Soviet studies, chemistry with industrial experience, chemistry with polymer science. **Largest fields of study:** Science and technology (latter at UMIST). **Founded:** 1851, charter granted in 1903. **Main awards:** BA, BA(Accg & Law), BA(Econ), BSc, BScBEng, BScMEng, BSocSci, BDS, BEd, BNurs, LLB, MBChB, MusB. **Awarding body:** Manchester University. **Site:** Centre of Manchester Education Precinct, 1 mile from city centre. **Access:** Bus. **Accommodation:** 6,788 places in halls and flats (all single first year students accommodated). Approx cost: £700-£1,278. **Library:** John Rylands University Library, over 3 million volumes, 8,000 periodicals, 650 study places, course books on reference. Also over 1 million mss and 800,000 microform titles. **Specialist collections:** Charters, early printed and rare books, manuscripts, military documents, archives (eg of Manchester Guardian). **Centres of excellence:** University Library (designed library of legal deposit), Nuffield radio astronomy laboratories at Jodrell Bank, department of computer science, nuclear reactor (shared with Liverpool University), department of audiology and education of the deaf, European Institute for the Media. **Welfare:** Central academic advisory service, doctor, dentist, FPA, psychiatrist, solicitor, SU welfare secretary, interdenominational chapel, SU creche. **Careers:** Information, advice and placement service. **Amenities:** SU bars, second-hand bookshop etc, McDougall Centre and Armitage Centre (indoor sports), wide range of outdoor sport, all cultural and recreational facilities of Manchester.

Duration of first degree course(s) or equivalent: 3 years; **others:** 4 years (some arts and science courses and nursing); 4/5 years (dentistry); 5/6 years (medicine) **Total first degree students 1989/90:** 9,977 **Number of overseas students:** 502 **Male/female ratio 1989/90:** 4:3 **Number of mature students:** 840 (f/t), 359 (p/t) **Total**

CAN'T FIND WHAT YOU'RE LOOKING FOR? USE THE INDEX!

full-time students 1989/90: 11,747 **Postgraduate students:** 1,770 (full-time) 1,288 (part-time) **Tuition fees, first degrees, 1990/91:** Home: £1,675; Overseas: £4,560 (eg politics), £6,200 (eg physics), £11,150 (clinical).

What it's like

Screw up your eyes and Manchester in May could look like Venice in January – university's central square shows more than passing resemblance to St Mark's Square for romantically inclined (difference being that one is surrounded by water, the other suffused in drizzle). OWENS (as university is, for some impenetrable reason, called) takes many of its characteristics from its mother city; it's gruff, grandly built, hard-working and friendly. 11,000-strong student body allows for huge range of tastes; somewhere in mass of Manch. Univ. there is someone who shares your interests and desires, whatever they may be. Halls of residence, especially Whitworth Park, known as The Toblerones, good bet for first years trying to establish social niche, but not cheap. Don't be fooled by southern jessy agitprop: students here are as sophisticated, polished and clever as any in home counties. Manchester University kicked off social science revolution in 60's – Anna Ford is one of its most agreeable alumnae. Before that, OWENS had established firm reputation in classics, arts and sciences. Course-switching easy, though lectures often remote, and being increasingly pressed by cuts.

Pauper notes

Accommodation: City council provides cheap flats in run-down areas eg Hulme.

Alumni (Editors' pick)

Mark Carlisle MP, Sir Rhodes Boyson MP, Sir Maurice Oldfield (MI6), Robert Bolt (playwright), Anthony Burgess (novelist), Christabel Pankhurst (suffragette), Peter Maxwell Davies (composer), Sir Frank Worrall (sport), Lord Lever (politician), Lord Winstanley (politician), Alan Gowling (sport), John Tomlinson (music), Anna Ford (broadcaster), C A Lejeune (film critic), Rik Mayall (actor), Francis Thompson (poet), Ian McNaught Davis.

MIDDLESEX POLY

Middlesex Polytechnic, Bounds Green Road, London N11 2NQ (081-368 1299) Map A, F8

Student enquiries: Central Admissions Enquiries

Main study areas – as in What to Study section: *(First degree):* Accountancy, American studies, art & design, business studies, civil engineering, communication studies, computing, dance, drama, economics, education, electrical & electronic engineering, English, environmental science, fine arts, geography, geology, history, hotel & catering management, information technology, law, mathematical studies, mechanical and production engineering, modern languages, music, nursing, philosophy, politics & government, psychology, religious studies and theology, sociology, welfare studies. *Also:* Cultural studies, European business administration, film studies, movement studies, performance studies.

European Community: 10¢% first degree students take EC language as part of course and 10¢% spend 6 months or more in another EC country. Formal exchange links with large number of EC universities/colleges including: Denmark (1); France (13); Germany (7); Greece (1); Netherlands (3); Spain (3). Approved Erasmus programme 1990/91. Language skills available on every course. No discipline which cannot be partly studied at an institution outside UK. Many work placements can be in EC. On some courses, students can graduate with both UK degree and qualification elsewhere simultaneously.

CAN'T FIND WHAT YOU'RE LOOKING FOR? USE THE INDEX!

Application: PCAS except art and design (ADAR). **Academic features:** New courses in production, construction, electronic engineering and management; environmental technology; Modular degree scheme offers wide range of joint honours degrees, including pathways in English literary studies, society and technology, studies in contemporary writing and historical studies. **Special features:** Special entry procedures for mature students including those without formal qualifications. **Largest fields of study:** Art and design, business studies and management, education, performing arts, engineering, humanities, social science. **Founded:** 1973, ex Enfield and Hendon colleges of technology and Hornsey College of Art; later also joined by Trent Park College of Education, New College of Speech & Drama, and College of All Saints, Tottenham. **Main awards:** BA, BEd, BSc, BEng. **Awarding body:** CNAA. **Site:** 7 sites in North London/Middlesex area. **Access:** All sites served by tube, bus or British Rail. Inter-site transport. **Accommodation:** 600 mixed places in halls; site accommodation officers help with private rented accommodation. Approx cost: From £37 pw (hall); from £40 pw plus bills (private/self catering); from £56 pw (private full board). Rent: 6% in accommodation where rent controlled by polytechnic. **Library:** 5 main libraries, total of 400,000 volumes, 2,200 periodicals, 1,150 study places, 6,000 video tapes, course books for reference. Audio-visual library at Trent Park with 7,000 records and tapes, 6,000 books on music. Art and design library at Cat Hill has 240,000 slides and illustrations. **Specialist collections:** Silver Studio Collection – complete archive of a London design studio 1880–1960. **Centres of excellence:** Microelectronics centre at Bounds Green, high level tennis, design, computer graphics, flood hazard research, criminology research, language centre at Enfield. **Welfare:** 3 student counsellors, 1 student advisory assistant, 5 health centres, co-ordinator for handicapped students, nursery (15 places), playgroup (18 places). Ecumenical chaplaincy. **Careers:** 3 careers advisers and 2 careers information officers, based at Enfield and Hendon sites, provide information, guidance and counselling including computer-based systems. **Amenities:** Bookshops at all main sites. **Sporting facilities:** Indoor and outdoor tennis courts, squash courts, saunas, indoor and outdoor swimming pools, playing fields, gymnasia including multigym.

Duration of first degree course(s) or equivalent: 3 years, 4 years (sandwich, BEd, MEng and part-time courses), modular course part-time 5–8 years **Total first degree students 1989/90:** 7,486; **BEd students:** 431 **Number of overseas students:** 491 **Number of mature students:** Over 50% intake **Male/female ratio 1989/90:** 1:1 **Teaching staff: full-time:** 434 **part-time:** 123 **Total full-time students 1989/90:** 8,145 **Postgraduate students:** 1,389 **Tuition fees, first degrees, 1990/91:** Home: £1,740; Overseas: £4,965 max.

What it's like

The 7 sites, up to ten miles apart, range from the most beautiful campus in London (Trent Park) to converted grammar schools and the prototype for the Pompidou Centre in Paris (Bounds Green). Communication and travel between sites are erratic: societies and student social life suffer as a result although the SU (its politics swinging annually between moderate and revolutionary) does its best to provide decent entertainments on its meagre budget. There are a total of 600 halls rooms spread around the sites, supposedly reserved for first years although many others get places; otherwise accommodation is at prohibitive London prices. Sports facilities are good; tennis team is nationally renowned. Art and design faculty (Cat Hill), said to be one of the best in the country.
James Wallis

Pauper notes

Accommodation: Halls of residence far cheaper than rented accommodation but limited places. **Drink:** Cheap bars on each site, SU bar at Trent Park. **Eats:** SU shops sell food at reasonable prices including veggie/vegan products. **Ents:** Two SU discos per week at Trent Park. Entry under £1. College ents usually much cheaper

CAN'T FIND WHAT YOU'RE LOOKING FOR? USE THE INDEX!

than London prices. **Sports:** Wide range of poly sports facilities available to all students. **Hardship funds:** SU can give loans of up to £50 and can give general financial advice. **Travel:** Limited minibus service between sites. Bicycle (and strong padlock) recommended. **Work:** Some temporary work with SU or in poly facilities during term.

Alumni (Editors' pick)

Adam Ant (pop star), Ally Capellino (Alison Lloyd and Jonathan Platt), Wendy Dagworthy (fashion); Ray Davies (pop star – Kinks), Lynsey de Paul (pop star), Richard Torry; Gerald Hoffnung, Anish Kapoor (international artist), Richard Wilson (sculptor).

NAPIER POLY

Napier Polytechnic of Edinburgh, Craiglockhart Campus, 219 Colinton Road, Edinburgh EH14 1DJ (031-444 2266) Map A, D3

Student enquiries: Information Office, Napier Polytechnic, Freepost, Edinburgh EH14 0PA (031-444 2266 ext 4330).

Main study areas – as in What to Study section: *(First degree):* Accountancy, biology, business studies, chemistry, civil engineering, communication studies, computing, electrical and electronic engineering, hotel & catering management, information technology, law, mathematical studies, physics. *Also:* Building, film studies, industrial design (technology), photography, publishing, quantity surveying, transport studies.

European Community: Number of students learning an EC language or spending time in another EC country, not known. Approved Erasmus programme 1990/91.

Application: Direct. **Largest fields of study:** Accounting, business studies, science, engineering, commerce. **Founded:** 1964. **Main awards:** BA, BEng, BSc. **Awarding body:** CNAA. **Site:** 3 major sites with four annexes. **Academic features:** Degree courses include interior design; applied physics with microelectronics; quantity surveying (multi-mode attendance); publishing; hospitality management; engineering systems; BEng electronic and communication engineering; BEd technology (with Moray House College of Education). Most courses are sandwich, all are vocationally oriented. **Special features:** Access courses in engineering, electronics, sciences, physics for those without formal entry qualifications. **Accommodation:** All students are helped to find accommodation if they wish. Full time accommodation officer. **Library:** 3 libraries; 2,130,000 volumes in total, 1,600 periodicals, 800 study places. **Welfare:** Medical officers, nurse, student advisers, chaplains. **Hardship funds:** Limited assistance can be given. **Careers:** Information, advice and placement service. Two full-time careers advisers on campus plus careers information assistant. **Amenities:** SU facilities at all main sites, sports dome, swimming pool; cultural facilities at Edinburgh.

Duration of first degree course(s) or equivalent: 3 or 4 years; **Others:** 4 or 5 years **Total first degree students 1989/90:** 2,450 **Male/female ratio 1989/90:** 2:1 **Teaching staff:** 460 **Total full-time students 1989/90:** 4,449 **Postgraduate students:** 334 **Tuition fees, first degrees, 1990/91:** Home: £628; Overseas: £4,300, plus exam fees.

What it's like

Napier Polytechnic of Edinburgh is only poly in Scotland and as such likes to think of itself as extremely forward thinking. This attitude has in the past not always been reflected in SA services and facilities.

Napier has around 8,000 students spread over 6 sites dotted around different

CAN'T FIND WHAT YOU'RE LOOKING FOR? USE THE INDEX!

areas of Edinburgh; a fact that, in itself, creates obvious problems of communications etc.

SA has bars and shops at 3 major sites but has no facility that is really suitable as a band or disco venue. Student accommodation: halls of residence based at one of main sites but provides places for only 173 students, and state of repair is pretty poor. There is an SA campaign for central site union, better halls facilities and an expansion of student services, both welfare and entertainment.

Academically emphasis placed on science, technology and commercial disciplines. Energy engineering and science with management studies especially strong. As with most other institutions, poly is expanding student intake although funding from the Education Department is not necessarily increasing proportionately. Most significant increase is in the number of short, high turnover, money spinning post-paid courses being offered mainly by the faculty of professional studies.

The poly at the moment appears to be filled to capacity and a large question mark hangs over its ability to maintain, far less improve, the teaching standards and resources on offer – although all credit to the poly, they have prioritised development in this area.

Pauper notes

Accommodation: Edinburgh generally very expensive; most advisable to view potential flats. Poly has very limited number of flats and halls of residences, fairly high quality and very reasonably priced. **Drink:** NPSA runs 3 bars at each of 3 major poly sites, each with its own unique atmosphere. Prices are some of cheapest in Edinburgh. McEwans 80 shilling is excellent and Scrumpy Jack Cider is not to be missed (in Snakebite form). Each bar has its own range of weird and wonderful cocktails both alcoholic and non-alcoholic. Other places to try: The Grassmarket, Rose Street, The Black Bull and The Oasis Rock Cafe. One thing Edinburgh is not short of is pubs. **Eats:** College and NPSA provide cheap wholesome meals. Edinburgh is very good for eating out whether your taste be sirloin steak, vegetarian, curry or traditional chippy. NPSA Malt Shop at Craiglockhart not to be missed. **Ents:** Edinburgh well served with theatres, cinemas, entertainments associated with the Festival. Nightclubs very poor but expensive: Edinburgh more a pub city. NPSA ents high quality, quantity and variety. **Sports:** Poly sporting facilities extremely limited. District council runs free or low cost sports centres. Students Association Sports Confederation runs clubs for every sport. **Hardship funds:** NPSA runs a limited hardship loan fund. **Travel:** Many student reductions on travel, most of which obtained from NPSA. **Work:** Very difficult to find in Edinburgh – conditions are poor and pay even worse – it's not worth the hassle.

Alumni (Editors' pick)

Ian Buchanan (ex student, Edinburgh councillor), Steve Jacks (ex student, Radio Forth DJ).

NATIONAL EXTENSION COLLEGE

National Extension College, 18 Brooklands Avenue, Cambridge CB2 2HN (0223 316644) Map A, F7

Student enquiries: Head of Degree & Professional Services

Main study areas – as in What to Study section: (*First degree – correspondence*): English, geography, law, modern languages, philosophy, religious studies and theology. *Also:* Building studies.

European Community: 33% first degree students take EC language; none spend time in another EC country.

CAN'T FIND WHAT YOU'RE LOOKING FOR? USE THE INDEX!

Application: First – Secretary for External Studies, London University, Senate House, Malet Street, London WC1 7HU (071-636 8000). Then – NEC. **Special features:** Home-based teaching by correspondence. Most NEC students are mature and teaching is by NEC tutors; work schedules are individually worked out. Assignments are sent regularly to tutors. Some courses designed to prepare students for degree work. **Largest fields of study:** English, divinity, law, languages. **Founded:** 1963, ex University Correspondence College. **Main awards:** BA, BD, LLB. **Awarding body:** London University (external). **Welfare:** Subject tutors are also personal tutors.

Duration of first degree course(s) or equivalent: 5 years **Total first degree students 1989/90:** 600 **Number of overseas students:** 150 **Number of mature students:** Most **Male/female ratio 1989/90:** 1:1 **Teaching staff: Part-time:** c75 **Total full-time students 1989/90:** 600 **Tuition fees, first degrees, 1990/91:** £120 plus approx £260 pa for assignments (£22 per assignment, home students; £24 per assignment, overseas students).

NATIONAL FILM SCHOOL

National Film and Television School, Beaconsfield Film Studios, Station Road, Beaconsfield, Bucks (04946 71234) Map A, E8

This is a postgraduate UKCPU.

Student enquiries: Admissions Secretary.

Main study area: *(Not at first degree):* Film studies.

European Community: School has strong links with other film-schools worldwide (Director, Colin Young, President of Centre International des Ecoles de Cinema et Television since 1980). Frequent exchanges of students and staff from other European Schools; School is a founding member of (recently formed) European Association of Film and Television Schools. Other links include Council of Europe; MEDIA '92.

Application: Direct (on basis of previous experience and/or supporting material). **Academic features:** 3 year course which has postgraduate status leading to an Associateship (ANFTS) with specialisation in training of producers, directors, directors of photography, editors, animators, art directors, sound recordists, documentary and film composers. 1-year course in script writing is also available. Students encouraged to interchange roles in any practical activity at same time as developing their specialisation. **Entrance:** Approx 35 students admitted annually (6-7 places reserved for overseas students). Average age, 27 years; previous experience in film or a related field expected. **Special features:** Resident tutors include: Rob Buckler, Roger Crittenden, Herb DiGioia, Chuck Despins, Jan Fleischer, Alma Godfrey, Tony Gurrin, Richard Jenkins, Walter Lassally, Simon Mallin, Jim O'Brien, Moia Tait, Barrie Vince, Colin Young. Visiting tutors include: Gaby Prekop, Ernest Walter, Maureen Thomas, Mark Le Fanu, Stephen Frears, Andre Mellin. **Founded:** 1970. **Main awards:** Associate of NFTS. **Awarding body:** National Film and Television School. **Site:** Beaconsfield. **Access:** British Rail. **Accommodation:** Not provided. **Library:** 2,500+ volumes, 35 periodicals. (Entire collection film-oriented.) **Careers:** Advice service. **Amenities:** Corporate member of British Film Institute, British Academy of Film and Television Arts, the Producers Association and CILECT (Centre International des Ecoles de Cinema et Television). **Hardship funds:** Own scholarship fund. **Employment:** Film-making for cinema and television (usually on a freelance basis).

Duration of post-graduate course(s) or equivalent: 3 years **Male/female ratio 1989/90:** 1:1 **Teaching staff: full-time:** 18 **part-time:** as required **Postgraduate students:** 100 **Tuition fees:** Home: £1,985; Overseas: £4,560.

CAN'T FIND WHAT YOU'RE LOOKING FOR? USE THE INDEX!

What it's like

Fully equipped school, having taken over the British Lion studio in Beaconsfield. Provides practical hands-on film training for a small number of students in all the major disciplines of film making: producing, writing, directing, camera, animation, editing, design, music, sound and documentary. Allows students to gain a considerable amount of useful experience, and to build up a showreel of work to promote oneself in the professional industry.

Being relatively young, the school has yet to sort out a structure which properly supports all students. It is left largely to the individual to structure his or her course, with little in the way of an organised curriculum. Although this provides great freedom, it also leads to considerable problems, and many students find it hard to work effectively in this environment. The first year is becoming increasingly structured as efforts are made each year to improve the curriculum. Definitely not a 9–5 place; most students come in a few days a week to make use of it as a facilities centre.

Beaconsfield is isolated. Most students live in London and commute out. There's little social life there – bar Christmas and summer parties. Reviving contacts with ULU. There is the possibility (long term) of the school moving into London.

A film course is only as good as the people who run it, whatever the structure. The NFTS has a certain amount of complacency in its staffing, and the few excellent tutors need their numbers boosting. Some are full time; some part time because they are working, which is good for contacts in the industry. At the end of the day, whatever the problems of the school, the level of practical film making experience is not matched anywhere else in the UK, and the benefits of that are enormous.
Toby Macdonald

Alumni (Editors' pick)

Directors: Mike Radford, Malcolm Mowbray, Brian Gilbert, Ben Bolt, Conny Templeman; Documentary: Nick Broomfield, Jeff Perks, Jana Bokova; Camera: Roger Deakins, Dianne Tammes, Oliver Stapleton; Animators: Phil Austin, Derek Hayes, David Anderson; Music: Trevor Jones; Writers: Shawn Slovo; Also Michael Caton Jones, Harry Hook, Terence Davies, Molly Dineen, Beeban Kidron, Jennifer Howarth, Nick Park, Mark Baker, John Keane, Steve Morrison.

NATIONAL HOSPITALS COLLEGE

National Hospitals College of Speech Sciences, 2 Wakefield Street, London WC1N 1PG (071-837 0113) Map E, C1

Student enquiries: BSc Administration

Main study areas – as in What to Study section: *(First degree):* Speech sciences.

European Community: 10% first degree students take EC language as part of course; none spend time in another EC country.

Application: UCCA. **Special features:** Students are undergraduates at University College London and simultaneously at the National Hospitals College of Speech Sciences. Students whose clinical profile is appropriately high are recommended to College of Speech Therapists for licence to practice. **Founded:** 1974, ex West End Hospital Speech Therapy Training School and Oldrey-Fleming School of Speech Therapy. **Main awards:** BSc. **Awarding body:** London University. **Site:** Bloomsbury (near St Pancras) – located at the former Royal Free Hospital School of Medicine building. **Access:** King's Cross, Euston, Russell Square underground stations; buses 18, 30, 73, 172. **Library:** Specialised library. **Specialist facilities:** Collection of language and speech assessments in test library; voice laboratory; adjacent clinic (with local DHA). **Amenities:** Students' common room and refectory on site; University College London with students' union facilities

CAN'T FIND WHAT YOU'RE LOOKING FOR? USE THE INDEX!

(swimming pool etc) within walking distance. **Hardship funds:** Limited charitable funds to assist students in their final year. **Employment:** Students wishing to practise as speech therapists must register with the College of Speech Therapists, in order to find openings both at home and abroad in an expanding profession; some 10% take up other employment in eg teaching, audiology, management consultancy.

Duration of first degree course(s) or equivalent: 4 years **Other:** 3 years **Total first degree students 1989/90:** 172 **Number of overseas students:** 12 **Number of mature students:** 25 **Male/female ratio 1989/90:** 1:40 **Teaching staff: full-time:** 22 **Total full-time students 1989/90:** 180 **Postgraduate students:** 19 **Tuition fees, first degrees, 1990/91:** Home: £1,675; Overseas: £6,995.

What it's like

At Wakefield Street WC1, near King's Cross, in a fully renovated medical school building. Speech pathology part of course taught here and building has common room, refectory and library with computer facilities. Students also have use of all facilities of University College in Gower Street, where many departments participate in teaching other aspects of course. Within easy reach of interesting spots, good for tube/bus. Range of people on course, some previously worked and/or took year out, have spent time in a clinic with speech therapist, others straight from school with three good A levels (C or above, usually).

Pauper notes

Accommodation: University College helpful in first and final years, in between you're on your own, although the accommodation office will help. Likely you'll need to contact other agencies which may prove expensive and time-consuming. **Drinks and eats:** London is saturated with places to eat and drink – including vegetarian, Greek, Chinese and Indian restaurants – you name it, London has it. Food on campus tends to be expensive; SU offers cheap food and drink including vegetarian. **Ents:** Wide range of societies for all needs/likes. Bloomsbury Theatre on site for films and theatre. **Sport:** Both UCL and ULU facilities and clubs for beginners to experts. **Hardship funds:** Limited trust fund to assist genuine cases of hardship. **Travel:** Expensive though once travel card purchased, free to explore London and use good network of trains, tubes and buses (including good night bus provision). **Work:** Usual opportunities for part-time and vacation work – secret is to apply well in advance.

NENE COLLEGE

Nene College, Moulton Park, Boughton Green Road, Northampton NN2 7AL (0604 715000) Map A, E7

Student enquiries: Academic Registrar.

Main study areas – as in What to Study section: *(First degree):* Accountancy, American studies, biology, business studies, drama, economics, education, English, environmental science, geography, history, law, mathematical studies, modern languages, psychology, sociology. *Also:* Building and construction, European business, leather technology, occupational therapy, podiatry.

European Community: 1% first degree students take EC language as part of course and 0.5% spend 6 months or more in another EC country. Formal exchange links with 3 EC universities/colleges in France (Poitiers); Germany (Trier) and Spain (Salamanca) – all for European business students; link with University of Florence (Italy) being developed in European business. French/German/Spanish diplomas awarded as well as degree. Approved Erasmus programme 1990/91.

Application: PCAS. **Academic features:** BSc/BA combined studies, including European business (business administration and German/French/Spanish). Degree in podiatry. **Special features:** International centre for leather technology in English-speaking world. **Founded:** 1975, ex Colleges of Education, Art and Technology. **Main awards:** BA, BEd, BSc. **Awarding body:** Leicester University. **Site:** Outskirts of Northampton. **Access:** Public transport; M1 5 miles away. **Accommodation:** 470 places in halls, 50 places in college houses. Approx cost: £38 pw (self-catering). Rent: 18% in accommodation where rent controlled by college. **Library:** 2 libraries; 200,000 volumes, 800 periodicals, 280 study places. **Other learning resources:** Resource centres at both campuses; computer centre; AVA; language labs. **Welfare:** Doctor, dentist, FPA, solicitor, chaplains, dean of students. **Hardship funds:** Extreme Hardship Fund (loans on limited basis). **Careers:** Full-time careers officer. **Amenities:** SU building and rooms, also bookshop on both sites, banking facilities. VAX 11/780 computer with extensive terminal network. Additional laboratories and teaching block completed 1985. **Sporting facilities:** 2 sports halls, all-weather pitch, playing fields, tennis courts. **Employment:** Teaching or related personal services; social and health services, chiropody, leather technology, industry and commerce.

Duration of first degree course(s) or equivalent: 3 and 4 years **Total first degree students 1989/90:** 2,050 **Total BEd students:** 500 **Number of overseas students:** 35 **Number of mature students:** 450 **Male/female ratio 1989/90:** 1:1 **Teaching staff: full-time:** 150 **part-time:** 18 **Total full-time students 1989/90:** 2,500 **Postgraduate students:** 49 **Tuition fees, first degrees, 1990/91:** Home: £1,675 (£651 if self-financing); Overseas: £4,563 (plus £321 registration fee for all students in their first year only).

What it's like

Two campuses with a student population of 8,000+ including a large mature student intake. Creche facilities available. New halls will be ready for 1991 intake. Planning stage for new SU building. Extended library services, including disabled computer link on campus. Adequate sporting facilities; watersports centre. SU runs two bars, one on each campus, both with late entertainments licences ensuring social events go with a bang. Local bands, top names, comedians and impressionists on a weekly basis.

SU encouraging increased involvement in NUS campaigns after some successful loans/poll tax demonstrations over the country last year.

Nene is rapidly increasing in size and ambition, but still retains its friendly and supportive atmosphere . . . it's fun.
David Arthern

Pauper notes

Accommodation: Halls on campus £29.00 pw. **Drink:** Favourite student pubs – Kingsley Park Tavern, the Racehorse, King Billy, Shipmans. Many Manns houses. Abington Hotel amazing home brew. SU Biko's bar. **Eats:** On campus OK but SU offers better value. Town has good vegetarian, burger/pizza places, with discounts. Cagney's Diner, La Cafe, Buddies. **Ents:** Events and late bar, Thurs/Fri/Sat. SU Film Society has weekly showings. Social committee puts on discos, bands and very successful Balls (4 per year). Societies run promos and contact with local theatre and major transport link to London + Birmingham for concerts, plays etc. **Sports:** SU parachutes, sailing, canoeing, fencing etc. **Hardship fund:** SU hardship fund, financial adviser, Midland Bank. **Travel:** Northampton accessible via M1 and A45. Hitching easy. Good bus service/easy rail links with London and Birmingham. No student travel service. **Work:** Fairly easy (low local unemployment).

Alumni (Editors' pick)

David Jay (Bahouse), Daniel Ash (Love & Rockets), Derek Redmond.

CAN'T FIND WHAT YOU'RE LOOKING FOR? USE THE INDEX!

NEWCASTLE POLY

Newcastle upon Tyne Polytechnic, Ellison Building, Ellison Place, Newcastle upon Tyne NE1 8ST (091-232 6002) Map A, E4

Student enquiries: Assistant Registrar (Registry)

Main study areas – as in What to Study section: *(First degree):* Accountancy, art & design, business studies, chemistry, computing, drama, economics, education, electrical & electronic engineering, English, environmental studies, fine arts, geography, history, information technology, law, library & information studies, mathematical studies, mechanical and production engineering, modern languages, music, nursing studies, physics, politics and government, psychology, sociology. *Also:* Building studies, estate management, media studies, physiotherapy, quantity surveying, secretarial studies, sports studies.

European Community: 6.5% first degree students take EC language as part of course (is increasing) and 4% spend 6 months or more in another EC country. Formal exchange links with a number of EC universities/colleges in Belgium, Denmark, France, Germany, Italy, Netherlands, Portugal, Spain. Approved Erasmus programme 1990/91.

Application: PCAS except art and design (ADAR). **Academic features:** Degree courses in media production, computing for industry, travel & tourism, criminal justice studies, history of modern art, design and film; business information technology, fashion promotion, communication engineering. **Special features:** National coaching centre. **Founded:** 1969. **Main awards:** BA, BEd, BSc, BEng and MEng. **Site:** 2 sites (Newcastle city centre, Coach Lane campus 3 miles away). **Accommodation:** 1,900 places available (1,100 places in hall; others in lodgings and tenancies). Priority given to first years. Halls mixed or female only. Approx cost: £40.95 pw (full board), £24.25 pw (self-catering). **Library:** Library at each site; total of 500,000 volumes, 3,750 periodicals, 1,100 study places, short loan only for recommended volumes. **Specialist collections:** EEC Documentation Centre. **Centres of excellence:** Microelectronics education centre, small business unit, handicapped persons research unit, European law centre, optoelectronics research group, North East centre for community studies. **Welfare:** Health services, welfare officer, student counsellor, accommodation service, chaplains. **Special categories:** Some places in hall for disabled students, 24 places in local authority flats for married students, playgroup. **Careers:** Information, advice and placement service. **Amenities:** One of the largest SU buildings in UK (300-seat theatre, ballroom, second-hand book shop). **Sporting facilities:** Indoor sports on city campus, outdoor sports 2 miles away, Newcastle swimming baths.

Duration of first degree course(s) or equivalent: 3 years (full-time); 4 years (sandwich), 3–6 years (part-time), **Total first degree students 1989/90:** 6,679; **BEd students:** 506 **Number of overseas students:** 363 **Number of mature students:** approx 25% **Male/female ratio 1989/90:** 1:1 **Teaching staff:** full- and part-time approx 650 **Total full-time students 1989/90:** 8,376 **Postgraduate students:** 587 **Tuition fees, first degrees, 1990/91:** Home: £1,675; Overseas: £4,325 (eg politics), £4,765 (eg physics).

What it's like

Nestles between A1 fly-over and civic centre: main site conglomerate of burnt brick and paving slabs. Campus handy for town centre, metro, buses. Also several suburban sites. Halls split between sites and 'residential' area: some self-catering places, personalisation possible with ingenuity.

Social life good with one of the biggest SU's in UK providing bands and discos every week, and facilities for many clubs and societies. SU a good mixture of political/social.

Many students are not straight from school, gives a more mature attitude. Many

CAN'T FIND WHAT YOU'RE LOOKING FOR? USE THE INDEX!

students from local community and region, and large population of part-time students; makes for less 'ivory-tower' atmosphere. SU has fully equipped theatre, bars, dark room, sports centre, playgroup (run by SU) and Gazette newspaper. Town has plenty of cinemas, nightclubs, pubs, community groups and special-interest activities. Metro has put campus within 20 mins of Whitley Bay and coast.

Useful welfare services include SU welfare officer, personal tutors, counsellor, accommodation officer and chaplains. SU has women's officer, and contact persons available for sexual and racial harassment procedures.

Term varies from 10–13 weeks and exams are mixture of continuous assessment and sit-down depending on course. New courses being set up include varied teaching modes. Authorities sympathetic to requests to change course if students genuinely unhappy. Appeals procedure for failure exists but is inadequate.

Several courses considered 'centres of excellence'. Library good – is best in region. SU tries to build and develop strong links with local community, to widen access to building and resources to groups in the city. Strong commitment to taking students 'out' into the community.

Pauper notes

Accommodation: Keelmen's flats. Local authority flats let to students. **Drink:** 3 bars on main site, 1 at Coach Lane, halls, all serve cheap beer. Happy hours in town bars. Newcastle Brown. **Eats:** A variety of excellent food available in SU refectory, ie veggie, vegan, brilliant stotties (sandwiches). **Ents:** On campus – cheap ents, discos, big name bands and local talent, films most weeks off campus. Try the Riverside, mecca of the alternative music freaks. **Sports:** Good sports centres all over region including Gateshead Stadium. **Hardship funds:** available to all students. **Travel:** Cheap travelcard for metro and bus. **Work:** Some chance of local work during term time.

Alumni (Editors' pick)

Steve Cram, Paul Shriek (fashion designer), Rodney Bickerstaff.

NEWCASTLE UNIVERSITY

University of Newcastle upon Tyne, 6 Kensington Terrace, Newcastle upon Tyne NE1 7RU (091-222 6000) Map A, E4

Student enquiries: Admissions Officer

Main study areas – as in What to Study section: *(First degree):* Accountancy, agriculture, anatomy, archaeology, architecture, art & design, Asian studies, biochemistry, biology, botany, chemical engineering, chemistry, civil engineering, classics, computing, dentistry, economics, electrical & electronic engineering, English, environmental science, fine arts, food science & nutrition, geography, history, Latin American studies, law, linguistics, marine technology, mathematical studies, mechanical & production engineering, medicine, metallurgy and materials science, microbiology, modern languages, music, Near East & Islamic studies, physics, physiology, politics and government, psychology, religious studies and theology, sociology, speech sciences, town & country planning, welfare studies, zoology. *Also:* Agricultural engineering, astronomy, film studies, management, marine biology.

European Community: 8% first degree students take EC language as part of course and 5% spend 6 months or more in another EC country. Formal Erasmus links with a large number of EC universities/colleges including languages, computer science, politics, chemistry, urban planning, neurolinguistics, theology, soil sciences, literature, civil engineering, medicine, chemical engineering, microbiology, chemistry, public administration, marine technology, geography, biology, architecture,

CAN'T FIND WHAT YOU'RE LOOKING FOR? USE THE INDEX!

education, mechanical engineering, business studies, materials science. Approved Erasmus programme 1990/91.

Application: UCCA. **Academic features:** New courses in: accounting and law; agricultural and environmental science; natural resources; molecular biology; 4-year engineering degrees for those without maths/science A-levels. **Largest fields of study:** Science, engineering, arts, medicine and dentistry, agriculture, economics and social sciences. **Founded:** Early 19th century, present title 1963 (formerly the Newcastle Division of Durham University). **Main awards:** BA, BSc, BEng, MEng, LLB, MBBS, BDS. **Awarding body:** University of Newcastle upon Tyne. **Site:** City centre. **Accommodation:** Approx 1,800 places in halls, about 1,350 in self-catering flats and 300 in student houses. Approx cost: £546–£1,197 pa. Rent: 44% in accommodation where rent controlled by university. **Library:** 800,000 volumes, 5,000 periodicals, 700 study places. **Specialist collections:** Archaeology (Gertrude Bell); History of Medicine (Pybus); English Literature (Robert White); Japanese Science and Technology (Robert Phillifent). **Other learning facilities:** Espin Observatory (largest telescope in north of England), Computing Laboratory, Museum of Antiquities, Greek Museum, Hatton Gallery, 2 farms, marine biological station, Moorbank Gardens. **Welfare:** Health Service (incl sick bay), counselling service, Union Society welfare adviser, chaplaincy. **Careers:** Careers advisory service, wide range of facilities including personal interviews, careers education programmes, talks, seminars, library and information service and employer contact. **Employment:** 1989 graduates – 60% direct into employment, 20% into professional training or further academic study, 4% unemployed. **Amenities:** Newcastle is regional capital of NE (excellent theatres, cinemas, bars, concert halls). SU one of largest in UK with wide range of facilities including 13 food and drink outlets, tennis courts, shops, sporting and cultural facilities, an 18 hole golf course, extensive outside sporting facilities and new sports hall.

Duration of first degree course(s) or equivalent: 3 & 4 years; **others:** 5 years town & country planning **Total first degree students 1990/91:** 7,195 **Number of overseas students:** 413 **Male/female ratio 1990/91:** 3:2 **Teaching staff: full-time:** 820 **part-time:** 67 **Total full-time students 1990/91:** 9,011 **Postgraduate students:** 1,295 **Tuition fees, first degrees, 1990/91:** Home: £1,675; Overseas: £4,560 (eg politics and physics).

What it's like

Fairly central location, good public transport and within walking distance of much student accommodation. Good social life – many good pubs but also many that students should avoid. Especially good for live music, several theatres, the Tyneside Cinema shows a wide selection of foreign and artistic films. Good nightclubs, eg Rockshots, Magic Roundabout, The Drop.

SU – six bars, provides a wide range of reasonably priced food, wide variety of ents – live bands, Friday night disco, quizzes and bingo. Runs a huge range of social, political and sporting clubs and societies. Students conservative (with a small c) but union still runs campaigns on most issues affecting students. Excellent welfare service. Good mix of students, just under 10% are from overseas.

Accommodation, private sector has been cheap and plentiful, however rents are starting to go up and there is more pressure on places. University accommodation – too little in the past but more being built.

Courses – many excellent ones but style and quality of teaching varies from dept to dept, eg economics has a high failure rate but is recognised as an excellent department nationally. Big for medicine, agriculture, engineering.
Mike Shallcross

Pauper notes

Accommodation: Private sector: very cheap and plentiful. Halls of Residence: as everywhere else. **Drink:** 6 SU bars: wide range of atmospheres with frequent

CAN'T FIND WHAT YOU'RE LOOKING FOR? USE THE INDEX!

promotions. **Eats:** SU main provider of campus; cheap and wide range; pizzas, salads, hot food, stotties, vegetarian and whole-food. **Ents:** Friday night discos, live bands in SU. Studio Theatre on campus. Tyneside cinema: cheap off circuit. **Sports:** No swimming pool, on site playing fields or rugby club. **Hardship funds:** Very difficult to obtain. **Work:** No work, this is Newcastle.

Alumni (Editors' pick)
Rowan Atkinson (comedian), Bryan Ferry (musician), Miriam Stoppard (TV doctor), Richard Hamilton (painter), Kate Adie.

NORFOLK INSTITUTE
Norfolk Institute of Art and Design
(1) Great Yarmouth Campus, Trafalgar Road, Great Yarmouth NR30 2LB (0493 843557); (2) Norwich Campus, St George Street, Norwich NR3 1BB (0603 610561) Map A, G6

Student enquiries: Chief Administrative Officer

Main study areas – as in What to Study section: *(First degree):* Art & design.

European Community: No students learn an EC language or spend time in another EC country. Formal exchange links with 5 EC universities/colleges: Germany (Aachen, Karlsruhe, Kiel); Netherlands (The Hague); Portugal. All open to non-language specialists and language tuition provided. Approved Erasmus programme 1990/91. Further links proposed with France and Italy.

Application: ADAR. **Founded:** 1989 ex Norwich School of Art and Great Yarmouth College of Art and Design. **Main awards:** BA. **Awarding body:** CNAA. **Site:** Norwich city centre and Great Yarmouth. **Accommodation:** Very limited hostel accommodation; a register of landladies is maintained by the college. **Rent:** 2% in accommodation where rent controlled by institute. **Library:** 24,000 volumes, 120 periodicals, 25 study places; slide library: 135,000 slides. **Welfare:** Student counselling service available. **Amenities:** Norfolk Museums Services; East Anglia University (UEA) library; Sainsbury Art Centre at UEA; Norwich School of Art Gallery.

Duration of first degree course(s) or equivalent: 3 years **Total first degree students 1989/90:** 327 **Number of overseas students:** 2 **Male/female ratio 1989/90:** 43% **Teaching staff: full-time:** 19 **part-time:** 100 **Total full-time students 1989/90:** 327 **Tuition fees, first degrees, 1990/91:** Home: £1,675; Overseas £4,563.

What it's like
A friendly place. Norwich Art School in town centre overlooking River Wensum. Several students live in boats on the river but most opt for private rented housing – limited college accommodation. Good staff/student relationships unique to smaller colleges. Merged with Great Yarmouth College of Art and Design 1989 to form Norfolk Institute.

Gigs and alternative music Jaquard Club, big name bands at nearby UEA. Various other venues throughout city. Theatre and cinemas offer student discounts. First Division football club. Art school football team is in the local league. Real ale at The Reindeer Bills Bery and Red Nose served. Also the White Lion – too many good pubs to mention. Several nightclubs.

Erasmus European exchange scheme offers the opportunity to learn a European language and study abroad for a term. Easy access to London (2 hrs train). Majority of students come from Home Counties.

CAN'T FIND WHAT YOU'RE LOOKING FOR? USE THE INDEX!

Pauper notes (Norwich)

Drink: Real ale: White Lion, Ten Bells, Golden Star, Ferryboat. Trendy – Murderers, La Rouen, Central Park, Ritzy Nightclub, Jolly Butcher Nightclub. The Red Lion unofficial SU bar, actively supports students with cheap nights, promo's, cheap nosh. **Eats:** Many places offering all types of food. Too many to list. Also ethnic, Mexican, Lebanese, Greek, Italian, veggie, Chinese, Indian, fish (through the price range). **Ents:** Film society provides constant pulp viewing, fringe cinema over the road, plus Cannons, Odeons etc. **Sports:** Loads of community centres plus UEA facility. **Hardship funds:** Hardship loans suspended, but SU arrangements with the big 4 banks. **Work:** Part-time bar work readily available.

NORTH CHESHIRE COLLEGE

North Cheshire College, Padgate Campus, Fearnhead, Warrington WA2 0DB (0925 814343) Map A, D6

Student enquiries: Admissions Officer

Main study areas – as in What to Study section: *(First degree):* Business studies, communication studies, information technology. *Also:* recreation studies, sports studies and tourism.

European Community: 5% first degree students take EC language as part of course and 5% spend 6 months or more in another EC country on work-based assignments. No formal exchange links with EC universities/colleges.

Academic features: Two modular joint honours degrees with wide range of modules and work-based assignment in year 2. Courses in media with business management; recreation with business management. **Largest fields of study:** Media studies, leisure & recreation, business management, information technology. **Main awards:** BA. **Awarding body:** Manchester University. **Site:** Extensive landscaped site, close to new shopping and leisure facilities. **Access:** Within easy reach of M6, M56 and M62 motorways. **Accommodation:** All years can be accommodated in single study bedrooms. **Library:** Number of libraries; over 95,000 books, range of periodicals, reading rights at Manchester Univ library. **Other learning resources:** Computer facilities; TV and sound studios, darkroom etc. **Welfare:** Student Services Centre offers careers guidance, counselling and welfare services. **Amenities:** Good sporting facilities; own SU complex; within easy reach of Manchester and Liverpool; town a short bus ride away.

Duration of first degree course(s) or equivalent: 3 years **Total first degree students 1989/90:** 350 **Number of mature students:** 110 **Male/female ratio 1989/90:** 1:1 **Teaching staff: full-time:** 50 **part-time:** 5 **Total full-time students 1989/90:** 350 **Tuition fees, first degrees, 1990/91:** Home: £1,675; Overseas: £4,563.

What it's like

A smallish college on the edge of Warrington. Higher education currently focuses on business management with variety of associated courses, all of which are becoming bigger and better, and facilities are (we're told) catching up. On-site students have gone up in number recently to about 360 (a vast amount for us with which to infiltrate the locals).

Warrington's best entertainment generally takes place on campus, so most students stick around; everybody knows everybody, and we have a great sense of community (alongside a notorious grapevine). Main gathering point on campus is new SU bar: probably the best of recent brilliant initiatives thought up by hardworking, forever active, always caring SU executive committee. Athletics

CAN'T FIND WHAT YOU'RE LOOKING FOR? USE THE INDEX!

union is equally active and well organised but possibly has a more questionable success rate!

Friends and visitors are always welcome and can be entertained in town centre (20 minutes bus ride) or in Manchester (15 mins by train), which is probably as good as London for pubs, clubs, eats and other cultural activities.

NCC graduates have been known to go into all walks of life from working in burger bars to executive stress. A few have even come back as lecturers most of whom are 'okay' but the Old Boys are naturally the most understanding. Even our director is 'quite a nice bloke!'

The drop-out rate is considerably low, and if you can cope with your lectures, your finances and your neighbours, your three years here will be an experience you will carry with you fondly for the rest of your life.
Pip Hunt

Pauper notes
Accommodation: Halls of residence quite cheap – often shared, very little accommodation in Warrington. **Drinks:** Tetly Walker, Scottish & Newcastle and special beers in (very cheap) SU bar. **Eats:** Nice Greek/Indian and veggi. **Ents:** Close to Manchester. Cinema reductions with SU card. Local theatre. **Sports:** Sports hall and multigym on campus – free. **Hardship Funds:** Limited but available from college. **Travel:** Close to M6, convenient for hitching. **Work:** Bar work in SU and locally; cinema likes students in evenings – work always available.

Alumni (Editors' pick)
Alan Bleasdale.

NORTH EAST WALES INSTITUTE

North East Wales Institute of HE
(1) Cartrefle, Cefn Road, Wrexham, Clwyd LL13 9NL (BA, BEd, BNursing) (0978 290390); (2) Deeside, Kelsterton Road, Connah's Quay, Deeside, Clwyd CH5 4BR (BSc, BEng) (0244 831531) Map A, D6

Student enquiries: Marketing Officer (address 2)

Main study areas – as in What to Study section: *(First degree):* Aeronautical engineering, business studies, chemistry, computing, education, electrical & electronic engineering, English, environmental studies, history, nursing studies.

European Community: No students learn an EC language or spend time in another EC country.

Application: PCAS; UCCA for nursing. **Academic features:** New courses in electronic and electrical engineering and manufacturing systems engineering (with new aerospace option). **Special features:** Mature students may be exempted from normal entry requirements. Specialist BEd business studies; possibility of some study in the United States. 1 A-level entry for BSc/BEng courses – these include study time also at Salford University. **Founded:** 1975; formed from two technical colleges and a teacher training college. **Main awards:** BA, BEd, BEng, BNursing, BSc. **Awarding body:** Wales University/University of Salford. **Site:** 4 sites – 3 in Wrexham on fringe of town, 1 at Deeside. **Access:** Public transport to each site; train service nearby Deeside site and Wrexham sites. Good rail and bus links to Chester. **Accommodation:** 245 places in halls, 135 hostel places (20% of students home-based). **Library:** Library on each site with subject bias – approx 10,000 volumes, 500 periodicals, 350 study places. **Other learning facilities:** Resources laboratories, computer links, TV studios. **Welfare:** Welfare officer, qualified nurses, doctor on call, chaplain, counsellors, on-campus nurseries. **Careers:** Information and advice service. **Amenities:** SU common rooms, bar and shops.

CAN'T FIND WHAT YOU'RE LOOKING FOR? USE THE INDEX!

Theatre Clwyd at Mold. Leisure centres: Plas Madoc (8 miles), Deeside. Deeside Ice Rink. **Sporting facilities:** Excellent boating and mountaineering. Good sporting facilities on campus, including weight training, gym and dry ski slope at Deeside. **Employment:** Good employment prospects due to high proportion of vocational courses.

Duration of first degree course(s) or equivalent: 4 years; **others:** 3 years (BSc computing, BA combined studies) **Total first degree students 1989/90:** 692; **Total BEd students:** 469 **Number of overseas students:** 47 **Number of mature students:** 499 **Male/female ratio 1989/90:** 1:2 **Total students 1989/90:** 559 **Postgraduate students:** 104 **Tuition fees, first degrees, 1990/91:** Home: £1,675; Overseas: £4,563.

What it's like
Standards of accommodation range from large well kept rooms to very small inadequate ones. Canteen facilities on campus but of poor quality so most students cook for themselves. Good cooking facilities, microwaves in many kitchens. Large proportion of mature students on some courses and many overseas students. Very small creche on site, much in demand. Relationship between admin and students generally good, but unnecessarily strict rules and regulations in hostels cause much resentment. Very strict visiting restrictions and tendency of admin to treat students as immature. Very active SU, emphasis on sport and social activities rather than politics. Contraceptives available in all toilets both male and female. Lots of contraception advice available, all counselling is strictly confidential.

Popular clubs and societies – canoeing, rugby, football, women's football, netball, mountaineering etc. SU bar very popular especially on the weekly Wednesday night disco. Wrexham contains a number of very good pubs, excellent beers, but the night clubs are a bit of a disappointment. Not a student town but has a lot of cheap eat-outs and many excellent food markets. Very friendly, everybody quickly gets to know everybody else.

Academic courses vary from laid back English/history to the more formal environmental studies. Lectures generally good but, lasting in many cases for 3 hours means much information not taken in by students. Lecturing time is heavy and there is often little time left for reading course books. Easy to change between BEd and BA if after a year you decide not to take up teaching. Assessment usually 60% exams 40% continual assessment. CQSW, nursing degree and youth and community work courses balance other purely academic courses.

Pauper notes
Drinks: SU bar. Plenty of pubs in town. **Eats:** Kentucky Fried Chicken, McDonald's, Wimpy, Pizza Chef, Pizzaland and hundreds of fish and chip shops. **Ents:** Good ents on campus, disco every Wednesday and often bands and discos on other days. Good local bands often play in town.

NORTH LONDON POLY

Polytechnic of North London, Holloway Road, London N7 8DB (071-607 2789) Map D, B1

Student enquiries: Communications Office (courses), extension 2030/1 (24 hour answering service 071-607 5755) 071-753 5066/7.

Main study areas – as in What to Study section: *(First degree):* Accountancy, architecture, art & design, Asian studies, biochemistry, biology, business studies, chemistry, classics, communication studies, computing, economics, education, electrical and electronic engineering, English, environmental science, European studies, food science & nutrition, geography, history, hotel & catering management, information technology, Latin American studies, law, library & information studies, mathematical studies, microbiology, modern languages, philosophy, physics, sociology, welfare studies. *Also:* Film studies, Irish studies, tourism.

European Community: 16% first degree students take EC language as part of course and 16% spend 6 months or more in another EC country. Formal exchange links with 9 EC universities/colleges: Belgium (3); France (1); Germany (1); Italy (4). Approved Erasmus programme 1990/91. Increasing opportunities for language study.

Application: PCAS. **Academic developments:** Newly structured modular courses in business; new subject combinations within the BSc science modular scheme. **Special features:** Development of flexible entry criteria and of foundation year programmes; commitment to mature students; strong local community involvement. **Largest fields of study:** Science and technology. **Founded:** 1971, ex Northern Polytechnic and North Western Polytechnic. **Main awards:** BA, BEd, BSc. **Awarding body:** CNAA. **Site:** Split on 3 sites. **Access:** Good rail, underground and bus connections. **Accommodation:** Over 400 places in halls plus a range of PNL managed council flats. Rent: 10% in accommodation where rent controlled by polytechnic. **Library:** 4 libraries; 300,000 volumes in total, 2,100 periodicals. **Specialist collections:** Librarianship, polymers, H G Wells. **Welfare:** Chaplain, student services office including advisers, counsellors and accommodation officer. **Hardship fund:** Fund for Hong Kong students. **Special categories:** Residential facilities for students with disabilities; limited nursery facilities. **Careers:** Information, advice and placement service. **Amenities:** Polytechnic theatre, The Rocket, a multi-purpose venue with an emphasis on Black Arts, music and dance; SU with own paper, offices and shops on all sites; bookshop and British Rail agency at Holloway Road. **Sporting facilities:** Sobell Sports Centre nearby; dance studio and gymnasium at Kentish Town; gymnasium at Holloway Road, poly playing fields.

Duration of first degree course(s) or equivalent: 3 years; **others:** 4 years (sandwich) **Total first degree students 1989/90:** 4,000 **Total BEd students:** 380 approx **Male/female ratio 1989/90:** 1:1 **Teaching staff: full-time:** 400; **part-time:** Over 200 **Total full-time students 1989/90:** 5,000 **Postgraduate students:** 640 **Tuition fees, first degrees, 1990/91:** Home: £1,675 (£657 if self-financing); Overseas: £4,865 (£4,625 if full fee paid by 1 November).

What it's like

Located on 6 sites in Camden and Islington mainly in converted factory space; you won't get facilities even second-rate universities enjoy. PNL is no ivory tower (because it can't afford to be), but has few mind-bending restrictions/traditions; its atmosphere is practical and relevant. Student body has consistent record of taking up issues forcefully and successfully. Student support services have welcome absence of condescension. No conventional student 'social' life but good mix between courses and faculties, with many opportunities for students to meet each other and have good time. You'll get the most out of it if you're prepared to travel (sites aren't more than 30 minutes apart). Your time at PNL can be interesting, enjoyable and educational.

Pauper notes

Accommodation: Use all contacts you have before main flat-hunting season (Sept–Oct) opens; poly accommodation reserved for 1st and 3rd years but can't take them all so apply early. **Drink:** Larger sites have own bars. **Eats:** Local cafes and family restaurants better price and quality than canteen food. **Hardship funds:** Poly has fund for fee-paying students and very limited loan fund – but don't rely on it. **Travel:** Buy a bike. **Work:** Wide choice of (usually poorly paid) jobs during term time and vacation.

CAN'T FIND WHAT YOU'RE LOOKING FOR? USE THE INDEX!

Alumni (Editors' pick)
Jeremy Corbyn MP, Garth Crooks (Tottenham Hotspur), Malcolm Fraser (CNAA Chairman), Claire Rayner, Neil Tennant (Pet Shop Boys).

NORTHERN SCHOOL OF CONTEMPORARY DANCE

Northern School of Contemporary Dance, 98 Chapeltown Road, Leeds LS7 4BH (0532 625359) Map A, E5

Student enquiries: The Administrator

Main study areas – as in What to Study section: *(First degree):* Dance.

European Community: No students learn an EC language or spend time in another EC country.

Application: Direct. **Academic features:** Classical and contemporary dance; choreography and allied arts; performance and related studies; theory and practice of dance in education design. **Structural features:** Collaboration on music/choreography with Leeds College of Music, on costume design with Leeds Poly. **Special features:** Artist in residence; strong links with local artists and musicians. **Largest fields of study:** Contemporary dance. **Founded:** 1985. **Site:** Leeds city centre, close to city library/art gallery, university and polytechnic. **Access:** Very accessible. **Accommodation:** Private accommodation available. Approx cost: £20.00 pw (excluding meals). **Welfare:** Own physiotherapist in attendance; counselling on tutorial system. **Careers:** Information, advice and placement service available. **Hardship funds:** Small student assistance fund. **Amenities:** Cultural and social facilities of Leeds. **Sporting facilities:** City facilities. **Employment:** Professional dance companies in UK and abroad.

Duration of first degree course(s) or equivalent: 3 years (full-time); **Total full-time students 1989/90:** 75 **Male/female ratio:** 2:3 **Teaching staff: full time:** 10 **part-time:** 1 **Total full-time students 1989/90:** 75 **Tuition fees, first degrees, 1990/91:** Home: £489; Overseas: £2,700.

NOTTINGHAM POLY

Nottingham Polytechnic (1) City Centre Site, Burton Street, Nottingham NG1 4BU
(2) Clifton Campus, Clifton Lane, Nottingham NG11 8NS
(3) Clifton Hall, Clifton Village, Nottingham (0602 418418)
Map A, E6

Student enquiries: Academic Registrar

Main study areas – as in What to Study section: *(First degree):* Accountancy, art & design, biology, business studies, chemistry, civil engineering, communication studies, computing, drama, economics, education, electrical & electronic engineering, European studies, fine arts, hotel & catering management, information technology, law, mathematical studies, mechanical and production engineering, modern languages, music, physics, politics and government, public administration, welfare studies. *Also:* estate management, operational research, performance arts, sports studies, surveying, textiles, theatre design.

CAN'T FIND WHAT YOU'RE LOOKING FOR? USE THE INDEX!

European Community: Number of students learning an EC language or spending time in another EC country, not known. Approved Erasmus programme 1990/91.

Application: PCAS except art and design (ADAR). **Academic features:** MEng in computer aided engineering and manufacturing systems engineering with management. Part-time MBA. **Special features:** Implementing the enterprise initiative. Credit accumulation. Negotiated study programmes. **Main awards:** BEd, BA, BSc, BEng, LLB, MEng. **Awarding body:** CNAA. **Site:** Nottingham city centre and Clifton. **Access:** City centre site near rail and coach stations; bus services from Clifton sites. Near M1 and East Midlands Airport. **Accommodation:** 1,000 places in halls and self-catering accommodation. **Library:** Main library on each site plus number of small reference libraries; 400,000 volumes in total, 2,500 periodicals, 1,250 study places. **Other learning resources:** Extensive computing facilities for all students; modern, open-access language laboratories. **Welfare:** Doctor, counsellors, chaplains, welfare officer. **Hardship funds:** Director's fund available to alleviate cases of temporary financial hardship. **Careers:** Information, advice and placement. **Amenities:** Students' union with films, concerts, subsidised social evenings, shop bar, hairdresser, bookshop and bank on each site; travel bureau, sports facilities, playgroup at all sites; closed circuit television studio, playing fields and athletic track at Clifton; cultural resources of Nottingham (museums, theatres, cinemas).

Duration of first degree course(s) or equivalent: 3 or 4 years **Total first degree students 1989/90:** 8,700 **BEd students:** 570 **Number of overseas students:** 250 **Number of mature students:** 6,700 (21¢) **Male/female ratio 1989/90:** 3:2 **Teaching staff: full-time:** 692 **part-time:** not known **Total full-time students 1989/90:** 8,167 **Postgraduate students:** 850 **Tuition fees, first degrees, 1990/91:** Home: £607; Overseas: £4,260.

What it's like

Nottingham Polytechnic (formerly Trent) is at present suffering from a rather severe case of confusion. Are we Trent or are we Nottingham? Are we a polytechnic or are we a higher education corporation? Nobody really seems too sure. Nevertheless, it's quite an enjoyable place to be.

It's split into two sites (City and Clifton) with a wide range of courses and activities at both. SU has offices at both sites. It's always ready to help out. The SU is the centre for all student activities. Facilities and services include a wide spectrum of clubs and societies (from the Communist students to the hang gliding club), a welfare department, community work agency, bars, shops, films etc. Indeed, serving the needs of its students is one of the things the SU has had to learn to do.

Even the entertainments department has improved, which considering its already high standard of excellence was something of an achievement. The Monday night free showcases are still as popular as ever, while bands such as the Stone Roses, the Real Sounds of Africa and Edwyn Collins grace the main refectory stage to rapturous applause (well OK, a bit over the top I admit, but the punters seem happy!).

As a city, Nottingham is large, busy yet surprisingly intimate and friendly. With every type of entertainment available for the taking, including more good pubs than I care to mention (see Naples and die, but see Nottingham and have a hell of a headache), there is never any need to have nothing to do! Prices of course are often geared to the student pocket, so don't let lack of cash be a problem.

So whether you're a budding Milton Friedman, Yves St Laurent or Herbert Marcuse perhaps you could do a lot worse than Trent, whoops! Nottingham Poly . . . honest!
Philip Hancock

Pauper notes

Accommodation: At present plentiful supply of decent privately rented accommodation at lower than average prices. **Drink:** A wide range of local and national

CAN'T FIND WHAT YOU'RE LOOKING FOR? USE THE INDEX!

beers, with more good pubs than even the rugby club can manage! **Eats:** Loads of good cheap cafes and bistros in Nottingham. **Ents:** The night life in Nottingham is extensive with most clubs and discos running a (cheap) student night. NPSU Gigs 'n' things now regarded as one of the major live venues in the area. **Sports:** Nottinghamshire is one of the best parts of the country for leisure and recreation. **Hardship funds:** Polytechnic Director. **Travel:** NPSU has an expanding travel shop with all the best deals. **Work:** Mainly in bars, leisure centres.

Alumni (Editors' pick)

Nicholas Hall (1987 Young Designer of the Year, Furniture Section).

NOTTINGHAM UNIVERSITY

University of Nottingham, Nottingham NG7 2RD (0602 484848) Map A, E6

Student enquiries: Registrar

Main study areas – as in What to Study section: *(First degree):* Accountancy, agriculture, horticulture & forestry, American studies, archaeology, architecture, biochemistry, biology, botany, business studies, chemical engineering, chemistry, civil engineering, classics, computing, economics, electrical & electronic engineering, English, environmental science, fine arts, food science & nutrition, geography, history, law, linguistics, mathematical studies, mechanical and production engineering, medicine, metallurgy and materials science, microbiology, modern languages, music, nursing studies, pharmacy, philosophy, physics, politics and government, psychology, religious studies and theology, sociology, welfare studies, zoology. *Also:* Agricultural economics, horticulture, mining, Slavonic studies.

European Community: Number of students learning an EC language or spending time in another EC country, not known. Approved Erasmus programme 1990/91.

Application: UCCA. **Academic features:** New courses in: electrical and electronic engineering with French/German; nursing; BSc with European studies in agricultural and food sciences; linguistics and beginners' Russian; history and Russian; part-time first degrees available in American studies, archaeology, economics, philosophy, politics, sociology, social policy and administration and joint honours American and English studies or philosophy. **Founded:** 1881. **Site:** 330 acre campus to west of city centre. **Access:** Buses from city centre and railway station; M1 4 miles from campus. **Accommodation:** 12 halls of residence on campus; all first year students can be accommodated. **Library:** Over 900,000 volumes and pamphlets, 5,000 periodicals; short loan collection for books most in demand. **Other learning facilities:** Cripps computing centre; university museum and art gallery. **Welfare:** Health service and chaplaincy, counselling service. **Careers:** Advisory service. **Amenities:** SU with shop, minibuses, travel agency, hairdressers, etc; 190 clubs and societies; campus bookshop; performing arts studio, theatre. **Sporting facilities:** Indoor sports centre, excellent playing fields, 2,000 metre international rowing course nearby.

Duration of first degree course(s) or equivalent: 3 years; **others:** 4 years; 5 years (medicine); 6 years (architecture) **Total first degree students 1989/90:** not known **Number of overseas students:** not known **Number of mature students:** not known **Male/female ratio 1989/90:** not known **Teaching staff: full-time:** not known **Total full-time students 1989/90:** not known **Postgraduate students:** not known **Tuition fees, first degrees, 1990/91:** Home: £607; Overseas: £4,300–£10,500.

CAN'T FIND WHAT YOU'RE LOOKING FOR? USE THE INDEX!

What it's like

Nottingham University is one of the most pleasant working environments. Being campus based it's very much self contained, with most amenities available within easy walking distance. The attractive campus and excellence of many academic departments can lead to a feeling of encroaching suburbia!

Campus social life is improving. The twelve halls of residence have a long established events programme, culminating in summer hall party extravaganzas. Almost all first years are placed in halls, but shortages of accommodation do occur. The SU have recently acquired and refurbished a large union bar and this, added to their other amenities of travel bureau, shop, printing unit, welfare centre, make the Union an integral part of university life. Participation in activities is high, especially in sport, Union clubs and societies, hall life, community work and charity fund raising.

The city centre is a ten minute bus journey away and has a wide range of pubs, clubs, cinemas, theatres, art galleries and shopping centres. Student discounts are available at many restaurants, theatres etc. Student housing is relatively plentiful and reasonably priced – student areas are buzzing with atmosphere.

The university has a strong community atmosphere and three years here are well spent.

Pauper notes

Accommodation: Generally good but always a rush to find houses in January/February. Landlord problems always exist but major problems are rare. **Drink:** Cheap hall bars and University bar. Local pubs popular with students: Happy Return, Three Wheatsheaves (Lenton), Greyhound (Beeston), Yates's Wine Lodge, Trip to Jerusalem. Local brew: Shipstones, Home Ales. **Eats:** Good Indian at Hyson Green, Beehive – vegetarian, Blue Lagoon (Hyson Green) – West Indian, Charlie Parker, Pizza Hut – Italian. **Ents:** Midland is 'trendy arts' theatre. Cheap student nights at Rock City, Zhivago's, Irish Social Centre. Reduced cinema prices at the Odeon, Savoy, also Unifilms – run by Students Union. **Sports:** Local swimming pools; on-campus well-equipped sports centre, University sports fields adjacent to campus and inter-Hall sports grounds about 1 mile away. **Hardship funds:** A Union-employed welfare assistant, possible Union assistant. **Travel:** Cheap bus travel offered for regular users – buses being privatised. **Work:** Temping available but low-paid. Bar jobs, local pork pie companies. Some theatre and sports concessions for UB40's.

Alumni (Editors' pick)

D H Lawrence, Brian Moore (England Rugby international), John Gunn (1988 Guardian Young Businessman of the Year).

OAK HILL COLLEGE

Oak Hill College, Chase Side, Southgate, London N14 4PS (081-449 0467) Map A, E8

Student enquiries: Admissions Officer

Main study areas – as in What to Study section: *(First degree):* Religious studies & theology.

European Community: No students learn an EC language or spend time in another EC country.

Application: Direct. **Founded:** 1932. **Main awards:** BA. **Awarding body:** CNAA. **Site:** Cockfosters/Southgate area. **Access:** Underground to Southgate (Piccadilly line); then walk or bus (about 1 hr from Westminster). **Academic features:** New module in homiletics. Successful DipHE candidates can transfer to degree course. Number of mature students admitted without the formal qualifications. **Special features:** Some modules may be taken at the Middlesex Polytechnic. **Accommodation:** 40 places in hall; 35 houses for married students; 8 flats/bedsitters; accommodation provided for all first year students. Approx cost: Maintenance fee £1,533 pa, £45 pw for married accommodation. **Library:** 15,000 volumes, 80 periodicals, 30 study places; course books placed on temporary reference; tape library, video library. Access to major London libraries. **Welfare:** Doctor, chaplain. **Special categories:** Houses for married couples. **Careers:** Advice service. Vocational placement scheme. **Sporting facilities:** Tennis courts; football field on site; municipal squash courts and swimming pool nearby; also cricket and rugby football. **Employment:** Christian ministry and various community services.

Duration of first degree course(s) or equivalent: 3 years **Total first degree students 1989/90:** 65 **Number of overseas students:** 10% **Number of mature students:** 100% **Male/female ratio 1989/90:** 4:1 **Teaching staff: full-time:** 11 **part-time:** 2 **Total full-time students 1989/90:** 104 **Postgraduate students:** 2 **Tuition fees, first degrees, 1990/91:** Home and Overseas: £3,162.

What it's like

A compact, much extended former stately house in 60 acres of parkland and woods. All singles and many marrieds in college-owned houses and flats on site and nearby. Individual studies for most students. Good food. Good washing and cooking facilities.

Most students training for Church of England ministry, some from other denominations, some not in ministerial training; all studying DipHE/BA in theological and pastoral studies; 30% part time.

Expanding library; good bookshop. Good relations with staff; student representation on all college committees. Prayer and worship an integral part of college day. Courses semester based; continuous assessment and/or examinations; varied teaching styles – seminars, lectures, workshops, role play, videos, tutorials; courses can be taken at Middlesex Poly. Modules on Biblical studies, counselling, sociology, world religions, communication, Greek, church history, doctrine, liturgy, preaching, philosophy.

Good placement system with London churches. College missions, block placements, and courses in hospital chaplaincy and urban studies in vacations. Social life mainly college based. Spouses welcome at all lectures, meals and services. Special programme in evening for wives. Tutorial groups for pastoral care.

Pauper notes

Accommodation: Study bedrooms for singles. Some year-round accommodation for singles available in certain circumstances. Houses for marrieds on and off campus. **Drink:** Various local pubs. **Eats:** College dining room (includes vegetarian). Range of restaurants locally. **Ents:** TV and video room. Social events arranged throughout year. Tube link to central London. **Sports:** On site: football, rugby, cricket, snooker, croquet; nearby: squash, swimming, tennis. **Hardship funds:** College bursary fund. **Travel:** Travel expenses for Sunday and block placements. **Work:** Paid manual work for college in vacation available.

Alumni (Editors' pick)

Michael Baughen (Bishop of Chester), Roy Williamson (Bishop of Bradford), David Gillett (Principal, Trinity College, Bristol), Cliff Richard, Tony Thisetton (Principal, St John's College, Durham).

OPEN UNIVERSITY

Open University, Walton Hall, Milton Keynes MK7 6AA (0908 274066)

Student enquiries: Central Enquiry Service (0908 653231 – answering service out of office hours)

Main study areas – as in What to Study section: *(First degree):* Biochemistry, biology, chemistry, communication studies, computing, economics, education, electrical & electronic engineering, English, environmental science, environmental studies, European studies, fine arts, geography, geology, history, humanities, information technology, mathematical studies, mechanical engineering, metallurgy and materials science, music, philosophy, physics, politics and government, psychology, public administration, religious studies & theology, sociology, strategic studies, welfare studies. *Also:* Very many specialised subjects in course unit system.

European Community: No students learn an EC language or spend time in another EC country.

Application: Direct. No educational qualifications required but students should be 18 or over and resident in UK at end of first teaching week. Early applications take precedence over later ones, so apply early. **Academic features:** Approx 140 courses, many multi- or inter-disciplinary, in arts, social sciences, mathematics, science, educational studies and technology. Degrees built up on course credits (6 for degree, 8 for honours) or individual courses may be taken on one-off basis for vocational, updating or as refreshers. Community education courses available in eg parent education, energy saving, consumer decisions. Postgraduate study also possible (taught and research based). **Special features:** Students study at home from specially written course texts, set books, radio and television broadcasts, other audio-visual materials and home experiment kits. Also face-to-face tuition at local study centres and, for some courses, annual residential summer schools. **Founded:** 1969. **Main awards:** BA. **Awarding body:** Open University. **Centres of excellence:** Centre for advice to others wishing to set up similar institutions. **Library:** For staff and full-time students only. **Careers:** Information booklet 'Career choices and degree planning'. **Hardship funds:** Funds for students experiencing hardship, including some specially earmarked for the unemployed. Some LEAs may help also and give funds for summer school. **Amenities:** Set book stockists from whom students can obtain course-related texts; network of more than 250 study centres. The Open University Students' Association, whose membership includes all currently registered students, provides support services in both education and welfare.

Duration of first degree course(s) or equivalent: 4–5 years average, 5–6 years average for honours **Total first degree students 1989/90:** 72,715 **Number of mature students:** Almost all **Male/female ratio 1989/90:** 1:1 **Teaching staff: full-time:** approx 670 **part-time:** approx 5,500 **Total full-time students 1989/90:** approx 200 **Postgraduate students:** approx 4,600 **Tuition fees, first degrees, 1990/91:** £202 for each full credit; £101 for each half credit (plus £137 if a summer school is involved).

What it's like

A large-scale distance teaching organisation; studying with it is a unique experience. The student is recommended to spend 10–15 hours a week studying, but this varies greatly. The well-organised and self-disciplined do just that, others cram everything into a frantic weekend of study closetted away from family and friends. The OU provide students with units of written information plus details of set books; these are supported with radio and television broadcasts. Unfortunately, the broadcasts are becoming increasingly inaccessible due to very unsocial transmission times. They are, however, available on video. All courses have tutorials; these vary greatly, the foundation course has considerably more than third and fourth level courses.

CAN'T FIND WHAT YOU'RE LOOKING FOR? USE THE INDEX!

Some also have summer schools (all the foundation courses do) held at universities throughout the country. The prospect of spending a week away from home with hundreds of strangers can be daunting, but everyone's in the same situation and most enjoy the intensive study and social life. Many OU students have problems with isolation. It's very easy to feel that you are the only OU student in your area (this is very unlikely to be true). One way out is through the Students' Association (OUSA) which exists to serve the needs of OU students via its welfare and services function; to promote the student voice via its representation and education function on OU boards and committees; and to fight for lower fees and mandatory grants for part-time students via its campaigning. Most study centres have an OUSA branch where students can not only meet like-minded people but derive inspiration and stimulation for further study. Studying with the OU is not cheap. Fees continue to rise; help with fees for registered unemployed or low waged. Applications should be made to the appropriate regional office (addresses from the OU). There is also a fund administered by the Students' Association to help with the other study related costs: details from OUSA, c/o The Open University, Walton Hall, Milton Keynes MK7 6AA. Being an OU student means being in charge of your own learning experiences. You can study what you want when you want; cross discipline areas and even take a year off. Study can be fitted into odd moments through the day or in the evening, weekend or holiday periods. The OU is no easy option. It's difficult to cope with all the demands on your time and keep up with the deadlines. However, its very popularity (by 1986 there were over 76,000 graduates) indicates how worthwhile its students feel it to be – not only in the acquisition of a qualification, but in proving to yourself that you can do it.

OXFORD POLY

Oxford Polytechnic, Headington, Oxford OX3 0BP (0865 741111)
Map A, E7

Student enquiries: Registry

Main study areas – as in What to Study section: *(First degree):* Accountancy, anthropology, architecture, biology, business studies, chemistry, civil engineering, computing, economics, education, electrical & electronic engineering, English, environmental science, environmental studies, fine arts, food science & nutrition, geography, geology, history, hotel & catering management, law, mathematical studies, mechanical & production engineering, modern languages, music, nursing studies, physics, politics and government, psychology, sociology, town and country planning, welfare studies. *Also:* Many other subjects within modular system; estate management, publishing, tourism.

European Community: 11% first degree students take EC language as part of course and 7% spend 6 months or more in another EC country. Formal exchange links with 3 EC universities/colleges: France and Germany (European business students); Italy (planning students). Approved Erasmus programme 1990/91.

Application: PCAS. **Academic features:** Modular course allows study on a full-time, part-time or mixed-mode basis including nursing and midwifery, visual studies or cartography. New courses in applied statistics, European business, nutrition and food science. Access courses at seven local centres give entry to Oxford Poly courses. **Founded:** 1865, as school of art, becoming polytechnic in 1970; in 1976 amalgamated with Lady Spencer-Churchill College of Education. **Main awards:** BA, BEd, BSc, BEng, LLB. **Awarding body:** CNAA. **Site:** Headington (1 mile from city centre) and Wheatley (6 miles from city centre). **Access:** Transport between sites. **Accommodation:** 1,284 hall places; 350 places in poly housing association; other students in lodgings or shared houses. Average rent for private accommodation in Oxford £35 self catering, £50 full board. Rent: 27% in

CAN'T FIND WHAT YOU'RE LOOKING FOR? USE THE INDEX!

accommodation where rent controlled by polytechnic. **Library:** 2 libraries, 270,000 volumes, 1,900 periodicals, 756 study places. **Other learning resources:** Computer Centre: 7 Prime 50 series with over 500 terminals, 6,000 registered users. Prime Nimbus and Appollo networks available 24 hours a day, 7 days a week. Educational Methods Unit: TV, graphics and photography. Consultancy and training in teaching methods, course design and evaluation. **Welfare:** Student services centre with 30 professional staff (counsellors, careers, accommodation, housing and chaplaincy staff, overseas student adviser, nurses, FPA and visiting GPs). **Amenities:** SU with bars and shop, banks, outdoor sports, fitness training room and multi-gym, choirs and orchestra, nursery. **Hardship funds:** A fund is available.

Duration of first degree course(s) or equivalent: 3 years; **others:** 4 years **Total first degree students 1989/90:** 4,792 **BEd students:** 210 (£bq 70 Inservice BEd) **Number of overseas students:** 263 **Number of mature students:** Approx 2,000 **Male/female ratio 1989/90:** 1:1 **Teaching staff: full-time:** 390 **part-time:** 70 **Total full-time students 1989/90:** 5,900 **Postgraduate students:** 730 **Tuition fees, first degrees, 1990/91:** Home: £1,675; Overseas: £4,550.

What it's like

2 sites, Headington and Wheatley; buildings on both sites functional. Access to Headington site average from city centre, excellent from London (190 bus stops outside). Intersite transport free and frequent: half-hourly, and hourly after 6pm. Halls of residence (full board and self-catering) and shared houses fiercely competed for and prices high (around £40+ pw, excluding bills). Halls accommodate only 20% of all students, ie 25% first years. Many students start off in lodgings.

Based on modular course system – most advanced in the country. Successful and popular. Non-modular courses available. Library and labs well-equipped and stay open late. Sports facilities average but dwindling – no central sports hall. Student services and SU both have good counselling service. SU organises good quality ents; bars on both sites. Top subjects: architecture, education, estate management, town planning, catering, business studies. Oxford is student city and geared to students' needs but expensive! Drop-out rate is low and most enjoy life. Social mix – mostly middle class – 70% students from public school background.

Pauper notes

Accommodation: Expensive, limited campus accommodation. **Drink:** SU has cheapest – £1.15; in local 'student pubs' £1.60!! **Eats:** Poor campus food – expensive and low quality. Good choice in town. **Ents:** Good ents. Recent bands: Carter, Ruff Ruff & Ready, Blur, Bass-o-Matic, David Grant. Recent run of 'Best of Alternative Comedy' eg Sean Hughes etc. **Sports:** Considering poor facilities, great range and quite cheap. Good teams. **Hardship funds:** Available in a long term, no interest loan fund. **Travel:** Easy hitch to London, regular buses, trains. **Work:** Poly takes part-time and full-time staff during vacations, locally jobs available but not mind-bending, usually barperson, salesperson, waiting etc.

Alumni (Editors' pick)

Adrian Reynard (Reynard Racing).

OXFORD UNIVERSITY

University of Oxford, Oxford, England OX1 2JD (Registry 0865 270000) Map A, E7

Student enquiries: (1) (University) Oxford Colleges Admissions Office, University Offices, Wellington Square, Oxford OX1 2JD (2) (Colleges) The Tutor for Admissions, ... College, Oxford.

CAN'T FIND WHAT YOU'RE LOOKING FOR? USE THE INDEX!

Main study areas – as in What to Study section: *(First degree):* Asian studies, biochemistry, biology, botany, chemistry, civil engineering, classics, computing, economics, electrical & electronic engineering, English, fine arts, geography, geology, history, law, mathematical studies, mechanical & production engineering, medicine, metallurgy & materials science, modern languages, music, Near East and Islamic studies, philosophy, politics and government, physics, physiology, psychology, religious studies and theology, zoology. *Also:* Human sciences, management.

European Community: 9% first degree students take EC language as part of course and spend 6 months or more in another EC country. University has links with large number of EC universities. Most exchanges at undergraduate level are for language specialists although number of opportunities in other subjects is increasing.

The University and the Colleges

Oxford is not a campus university – university and college buildings are scattered throughout the town centre. It is a federation of 35 colleges, 28 of which admit first degree undergraduates, together with 6 private halls. Each college selects its own students, houses them (for at least 2 out of 3 years), provides meals, common rooms, libraries, sports and social facilities and is responsible, through the tutorial system, for academic work. You apply to colleges for a BA degree. Your college will be the hub of your life.

THE COLLEGES

You can look up these colleges and private halls:

Women only:
St Hilda's
Somerville

Men and women:
Balliol
Brasenose
Christ Church
Corpus Christi
Exeter
Hertford
Jesus
Keble
Lady Margaret Hall
Lincoln
Magdalen
Manchester (permanent private hall for mature students)
Mansfield (permanent private hall)
Merton
New College
Oriel
Pembroke
Queen's
Regent's Park (permanent private hall)
St Anne's
St Catherine's
St Edmund Hall
St Hugh's
St John's

CAN'T FIND WHAT YOU'RE LOOKING FOR? USE THE INDEX!

St Peter's
Trinity
University College
Wadham
Worcester
There are three other permanent private halls – Campion Hall (men only, principally members of the Society of Jesus); Greyfriars (men only, principally members of the Franciscan Order); St Benet's Hall (men only, principally for Benedictines).

How to apply to Oxford University

Critical dates: Oxford Colleges Admissions Office must receive your completed application card and UCCA must receive your application form, both by *15th October*.

You may choose up to three colleges if you wish, or put in an open application to the university. (The Admissions Office will advise you or see the *Undergraduate Prospectus*.) All candidates will be considered by the colleges named in order of preference. Candidates not accepted by any of the colleges so named will then be available to all other colleges for consideration. You must complete your application in the calendar year before the year in which you wish to enter the University. The regulations are quite complicated and you should study the *Undergraduate Prospectus* carefully, but basically there are two methods of selection – Mode N (conditional offers) and Mode E (involving a written examination). There are 2 forms to be submitted:

Form 1: *The Oxford Application Card* – You must return this to the Oxford Colleges Admissions Office (University Offices, Wellington Square, Oxford OX1 2JD) by 15th October. There is an application fee of £10.00. Instructions for completing the cards are given in the *Undergraduate Prospectus* which is distributed, with the card, by the Admissions Office to schools or by application to the Secretary (Oxford Colleges Admissions Office, University Offices, Wellington Square, Oxford OX1 2JD).
Form 2: *The UCCA Form* – You must return this to UCCA before 15th October.

Applications to both Oxford and Cambridge:
It is no longer possible to apply to both Oxford and Cambridge in the same admissions year, unless you are a candidate for a choral/organ award.

Duration of first degree course(s) or equivalent: 3 and 4 years **Total first degree students 1989/90:** 9,924 **Number of overseas students:** 652 **Male/female ratio 1989/90:** 3:2 **Teaching staff: full-time:** 1,500 **part-time:** 200 **Total full-time students 1989/90:** 13,948 **Postgraduate students:** 3,773 **Tuition fees, first degrees, 1990/91:** Home: £635–£1,675; Overseas: £4,560 (arts), £6,050 (science), £11,150 (clinical); plus college fees of £2,000–£3000.

What it's like

Consists of over 30 semi-autonomous colleges scattered around the centre of city; many beautiful old buildings, some modern. Easily accessible by rail from London, the south-west and anywhere via Birmingham. There's also a cheap and frequent bus link to London. In Oxford cars are impractical and most students cycle, though there is a reasonable bus service. Accommodation (quality and quantity) varies from college to college; but everyone gets at least their first year in, some all three. Private rented sector is expensive. Two all-female colleges; the rest are mixed. A high percentage of overseas students, particularly graduates, but few mature students. Library opening hours vary from college to college; some 24 hour. Excellent university libraries too.
  Without a large central site the student union tends to be a campaigning and

representative force rather than a social one; though it has a cheap stationery shop and is the largest student union publisher in the country. Currently labour-led. Visiting restrictions vary from college to college but most fairly lenient. Contraception and pregnancy advice available in city; many colleges have condom machines; university has own confidential counselling service and there are numerous telephone help lines too. Enormous range of societies; ranging from things you've always wanted to be involved in to those you've never heard of. Relationship with the town is fairly good. Lots of pubs, student plays, excellent cinemas showing new releases, stuff that you missed first time around and trendy, arty films.

All subjects highly rated though courses generally traditional. You can change subject reasonably easily if it's because you want to rather than because you're terrible at your present one. Work load . . . some people claim they don't have one, others spend all their time in the library. In the end most people get seconds. Degrees awarded solely on performance in exams at the end of your final year (a stressful time!). Lecturers vary from interesting to abysmal but few people attend anyway (especially arts subjects). It's your tutorials that matter and you can change tutor if you really don't get on.

The south and private schools are over-represented but this is changing (at present 45% state schools). Sexism, racism and homophobia exist but don't let them put you off. There's far too much on offer here.

There's no such thing as a typical Oxford student; everyone finds their niche be it in the library, the bar, the theatre etc, and whether they become a high-earning merchant banker, an unpaid voluntary worker or something in between.

Alternative Students' Prospectus available from OUSU, New Barnett House, 28 Little Clarendon Street, Oxford OX1 2HU (0865 270777/6).
Mary Wimbury

Pauper notes

Accommodation: Houses outside city centre cheaper; area called Jericho (western edge of city) traditionally popular; Cowley Road is student-inhabited. **Drink:** College bars (especially St Catz & Somerville) cheapest – Morrells best beer; many pubs but surprisingly few outstanding ones: though all visit central Turf and King's Arms. **Eats:** Pak Fook (Chinese, on Cowley Road), number of good Indian restaurants on Cowley Road. Burger vans in High Street. Best college food in Merton and Lincoln. Vegetarian served almost everywhere. **Ents:** College discos cheapest, Oxford discos towny (as opposed to gowny) but can be fun, eg Downtown Manhattan (are you kidding) near Worcester Coll. Playhouse, good cinema (Phoenix in Walton Street carries an independent tradition of old Scala, which formed British Cinema – John Schlesinger, Lindsay Anderson). Also Penultimate Picture Palace (PPP) and Not the Moulin Rouge. Oxford Poly often has good bands to which all NUS members can go; also Jericho Tavern. **Sport:** Most colleges have good sports facilities – but no swimming pool in university as yet. **Hardship funds:** All colleges have them; some admins stony faced, some dons have been known to loan from own pockets. **Shops:** Covered market (fruit and veg, Camembert and well-hung game), Gloucester Green market (Weds), 3 Oxfam shops, contraceptive vending machines now in many colleges. **Travel:** All colleges have some funds (however piddling), most students too languid to claim them. Cheap coach travel to Lond (£3) by Citylink. **Work:** Quite a lot of part time shop and pub work, some teaching in summer and 'Undergraduate tours' (London-based) if you have car.

Alumni (Editors' pick)

Margaret Thatcher, Roy Jenkins, Harold Wilson, Michael Heseltine, Denis Healey, Benazir Bhutto, Roger Bannister, Rowan Atkinson, Dudley Moore, Willy Rushton, Melvyn Bragg, Sir Robin Day, Tony Benn, Kris Kristofferson.

CAN'T FIND WHAT YOU'RE LOOKING FOR? USE THE INDEX!

BALLIOL

Balliol College, Oxford OX1 3BJ (0865 277777)

Maintenance charge 1990/91: £720 pa (terms only, no meals). **Accommodation available:** All undergraduates offered rooms in college (usually bedsits) for their 1st year and either their 2nd or 3rd year and possibly both. Rent: 75% in accommodation where rent controlled by college. **Eating arrangements:** All meals taken in hall on cafeteria basis, JCR pantry for snacks and breakfast. **Gate/guest hours:** Gate locked at midnight. All students have keys. 2 guest rooms. **Admission:** Mainly by Mode N or Mode E except pre-A level candidates in medicine or modern languages who must apply by Mode E. No undergraduates admitted for botany, earth sciences, zoology. **Scholarships:** None at entrance. **Travel grants:** Some grants towards travel for academic purposes awarded annually on tutors' recommendations. Coolidge awards to enable undergraduates to spend summer vacation in USA, after finals. **Library:** Library aims to provide at least basic coverage in all main subjects. **Hardship funds:** Hardship Fund available. **Other college facilities:** Nearby sports field and pavilion (with 2 squash courts).

European Community: 5% students study an EC language and spend a period in another EC country. Formal exchange links in Paris and Munich.

Undergraduates: *Men:* 262 *Women:* 121
Postgraduates: *Men:* 95 *Women:* 47

What it's like

Good academically (especially in social sciences and classics) and active and energetic in other aspects. Co-residential, guaranteed 2-years-living in, some for 3 years. Separate graduate centre and middle common room. Lots of overseas students. Hall dining facilities and JCR pantry service (best and latest breakfast in town). Lively JCR both socially and politically. Excellent drama, sport and music facilities. Central sports field. Sunday night concerts free and famous in Oxford. Music room and Lindsay drama room are very actively used. Good library facilities (all-night law library). Active women's group – regular speakers and meetings. Progressive college with high academic standards and friendly and active atmosphere to suit all needs and interests. Most people love their 3 years at Balliol.

Pauper notes

Accommodation: In college quite cheap, most live out one year. More building planned. **Drink:** Cheap bar, good atmosphere, new bar in preparation. **Eats:** Hall provides cheap food, JCR alternative – cheap and good; some vegetarian choices. **Ents:** Big summer event, discos, famous cocktail parties, plays, Christmas panto. **Sports:** Close sports field with football, squash, tennis, rugby. Also darts, pool and video games. Nearest pool about 2m away. **Hardship funds:** College loans/grants help those living out. Book and travel grants. **Travel:** Grants, travel scholarships, 8 yearly awards to USA for summer. **Work:** Not many work during term, lots of holiday jobs. Some vacation grants.

Alumni (Editors' pick)

Harold Macmillan, Ted Heath, Bryan Gould, Graham Greene, H H Asquith, the Huxleys, Gerald Manley Hopkins, Peter Snow, Anthony Powell, Chris Patten, John Schlesinger, Denis Healey.

BRASENOSE

Brasenose College, Oxford OX1 4AJ (0865 277823)

Maintenance charge: Approx £1,300 pa. **Accommodation available:** All undergraduates can live in for two years, and some (if they wish) for a third year. Rent: 75% in accommodation where rent controlled by college. **Eating arrangements:** Breakfast, lunch and dinner in hall; tea available in New Buttery. **Gate/guest hours:** Unrestricted. **Admission:** Standard Oxford arrangements. No undergraduates admitted to earth sciences, human sciences. **Scholarships:** Awards no longer made on entry to any Oxford College, but will be made at the end of the first year. **Hardship funds:** The college has discretionary funds for assistance in case of hardship. **Library:** About 30,000 volumes, 90 periodical subscriptions; separate history and law reading rooms. **Other college facilities:** Shop, bar, sports ground, pavilion, squash and tennis courts about 10 mins walk from college; boathouse. **Largest fields of study:** Law, PPE.

European Community: 10% students take EC language as part of course and spend 6 months or more in another EC country. Formal exchange links in Strasbourg.

Undergraduates: *Men:* 230 *Women:* 115
Postgraduates: *Men:* 79 *Women:* 35

What it's like

Positioned along one side of Radcliffe Square, in the wake of the towering dome of the Camera, Brasenose is very central. All main libraries, the Bodleian, the Cordington and the Radcliffe Camera are extremely convenient; very close to shops, pubs and nightclubs. Though not one of the most imposing or palatial of the Oxford colleges, the 16th-century Old Quad and adjoining, ironically named, miniature Deer Park are very picturesque. Small enough for a sense of community; large enough not to be claustrophobic. Rooms tend to be cold and quaint, or warm and ugly – a 1960s/70s concrete box with glaring orange curtains. Undergraduates guaranteed accommodation for two out of three years. This may include a year in Frewin, the college annexe, which in terms of facilities, is far superior to the single JCR kitchen, sparse number of showers and inadequate college laundry.

Academically variable, lodged in the middle of the Norrington Table, after a brief spate of success. Widely known as the place for law and PPE. Tutors and library facilities are excellent in these areas. College library is less comprehensive in most other subjects, although historians do have their own modestly-sized library.

JCR generally moderate, incorporates students from a variety of backgrounds, schools and regions. In the past, however, the 2:1 male/female ratio has created a rather 'hearty', male atmosphere which still prevails. Situation has improved with the advent of a JCR Women's Officer, an SCR Women's Advisor and an active Target Schools Scheme, which is intent upon encouraging more women, state school, and disabled students to apply.

Reputation as a strong rowing college. Many other sports to a high standard; namely, rugby, netball, football and cross-country. Facilities are close-by and very comprehensive, including two football pitches, a rugby and a hockey pitch, squash, tennis and netball courts, and an excellent boathouse. College facilities feature a student-run bar, which bears a striking resemblance to an underground tube station with bare-brick walls and abstract murals. JCR possesses a mere two computers, the customary TV and video, a pool table, Coke machine and a tortoise called Addington. Runs societies as diverse as The Brasenose Players, Christian Union, Women's Group, Wine Society, as well as its own wittily malicious student Noserag.

Generally liked by its members, Brasenose is a good place to while away your three years at Oxford.

CAN'T FIND WHAT YOU'RE LOOKING FOR? USE THE INDEX!

Pauper notes
Accommodation: Live in college (usually) 1st and 2nd years. Accommodation in college character rooms, cold but attractive. Frewin Annexe good facilities, modern and warm. **Drink:** Student Sloanes go to The Turf, expensive but very quaint. Nearest pub to Brasenose is Kings Arms, very popular, crowded, difficult to get served. **Eats:** Hi-Low Jamaican Restaurant – good food (eg funky chicken) and interesting atmosphere – deafening reggae, dancing waiters. Price average. **Ents:** Caribbean Club – only really studentish club. Variety of music. Earthy Church Hall building £2 entrance. Jericho Tavern – very popular and good for bands. **Sports:** Every college has its own sports ground and facilities – they vary in their facilities. **Hardship funds:** Strictly means tested. Have to be absolutely broke and preferably injured to get one. **Travel:** A few available – not advertised very well so few actually apply. **Work:** Vacation residence for £14.50 per day given to those who need to be in Oxford for exams or holiday work (limited time for latter – 28 days in the academic year).

Alumni (Editors' pick)
Colin Cowdrey (cricketer), Michael Palin (Monty Python), William Golding (novelist), Robert Runcie (ex-Archbishop of Canterbury), Walter Pater, Sir Arthur Evans, John Buchan, Lord Scarman, Jeffrey Archer.

CHRIST CHURCH
Christ Church, Oxford OX1 1DP (0865 276151)

Maintenance charge 1990/91: The daily accommodation with dinner is £5.85p. Breakfast and lunch available on cash payment. Heat, light and laundry charges according to use. **Accommodation available:** All undergraduates offered accommodation in college (sets or bedsits) for first 2 years; nearly all will be able to stay in for whole course. **Eating arrangements:** All meals in hall. **Gate/guest hours:** Undergraduates have own keys. Guests not admitted before 9 am, and must have left by 2 am. **Admission:** By entrance examination or interviews (see University undergraduate prospectus). Undergraduates not admitted to botany, classics, English, electronic and structural materials engineering, geology/earth sciences, human sciences, metallurgy and science of materials, metallurgy, economics and management, modern history and English. **Scholarships:** The College will award scholarships and other prizes for meritorious work during residence. **Travel grants:** Limited assistance provided to encourage travel by undergraduates, irrespective of subject of study. **Library:** Over 100,000 volumes; collections of early printed books and manuscripts; large law library. **Other college facilities:** Picture gallery (Christ Church has a famous collection of Old Masters), music room, computer room, playing fields nearby, new sports pavilion, squash courts, boat house. Because Christ Church is both a college and cathedral it has a strong musical tradition. **Largest fields of study:** Law, modern history, PPE, English, modern languages, classics, geography, physics, mathematics, chemistry, engineering.

European Community: 9% first degree students take EC language as part of course and 9% spend 6 months or more in another EC country. No formal exchange links.

Undergraduates: *Men:* 282 *Women:* 129
Postgraduates: *Men:* 87 *Women:* 35

What it's like
One of the most architecturally outstanding and famous colleges in this university, which leads to much tourism and also a great deal of college pride. Easy access being in town-centre, although maintains relative peace and quiet. Large main college site means all college accommodation close together, rather than scattered around the

town. Accommodation excellent – mostly large and beautiful rooms in good state of repair. Almost no cooking facilities for undergraduates but food served in hall is adequate. Mixed college residency but no mixed room sets. Large majority white, British students but some racial cross-section and a few overseas students, particularly graduates. Good relationship between college administrators and students – students have certain amount of say in college policies.

No overnight guests allowed officially but this rule seldom enforced. Probably less than 10% students have cars, mainly because of very restricted parking facilities. Active JCR – mainly socially rather than politically orientated; involved in charity work.

No counselling service within college, but college nurse offers a certain amount. University-wide counselling service good and confidential. Hardship grants available to those with financial difficulties.

Active drama society in college, but focus particularly on music and sport – music particularly including the cathedral choir; sport active in many areas, particularly rowing and rugby. Good sports facilities all within walking distance of college.

Large student population means good social cross-section and therefore a tendency to be quite insular but nevertheless easy to meet students from other colleges through societies etc.

College especially good for history and law – good law library open all night and excellent college library. Expected to cope with heavy workload but not enormous academic pressure. Most students go on to jobs, many well-paid in the city etc. Prestigious college – high graduate employment rate. Relatively low drop-out rate – a few students per year, perhaps 2 or 3 out of 130. Students from public schools predominate but much less so now than in the past. Male/female ratio 2:1 but evening out.

Pauper notes
Accommodation: Rooms in college excellent almost without exception. Single rooms to suite of 4 rooms per person and double rooms available in college. Married flats available; more graduate and undergraduate accommodation being built. **Drink:** JCR prices 2/3 of town pubs. Half price cocktails at discos and other social events. New bar opening 1991. Many popular pubs near, off licence outside college. **Eats:** Food cheap and of reasonable quality. As well as dining hall food, breakfast, lunch and tea are served daily in JCR. Good health-food shop directly by college. Many reasonable restaurants in town. **Ents:** Discos and other entertainments regularly held. Amusement machines, pool table and dart board in JCR. Also table football. Thriving drama group within college. 3 good independent cinemas in town. **Sports:** Excellent sports facilities 15 minutes by foot from college. Strong traditions of success in most sports, particularly rowing and rugby. Health centre/ swimming pool at Temple Cowley does very cheap student package. College has own weights room, squash court and other free facilities. **Hardship funds:** Grants available from college and university by negotiation, if suitably broke. Also residence grant money for study abroad. **Travel:** Generous travel grants liberally distributed. Good student fares eg coach Oxford–London c£3 day return. **Work:** Officially permission needed for paid work 12 months of year, but never heard it enforced in vac!

Alumni (Editors' pick)
Lord Hailsham, Sir William Walton, OM, Sir Adrian Boult, CH, Rt Hon N St J Stevas, Sir Antony Acland, Sir Robert Armstrong, Judge James Pickles, Peter J F Green, Peter Jay, Mark Girouard, Lewis Carroll, Gladstone, Sir Alec Douglas Home, Antony Eden, Leon Brittan, Nigel Lawson, Hugh Cluarshie, Howard Goodall, Sir Robert Peel, W H Auden, ex-president Bhutto, Auberon Waugh, Anthony Howard.

CORPUS CHRISTI

Corpus Christi College, Oxford OX1 4JF (0865 276700)

Maintenance charge 1990/91: Likely average £1,182 pa. **Accommodation available:** All undergraduates offered rooms in college or annexes (in college for first and final year). All graduate students offered rooms in annexes for up to three years. Rent: 77% in accommodation where rent controlled by college. **Eating arrangements:** All meals available in college. **Gate/guest hours:** Keys available to all members. Some restrictions on frequency and duration of entertainment of guests in college. **Admission:** No special provisions or requirements differing from those applying to Oxford colleges generally (see Oxford University Undergraduate Prospectus). Undergraduates not admitted to botany, geography, geology (earth sciences, human sciences), music (except for organ scholars), oriental studies, zoology. Modern language students must offer Italian. **Travel grants:** Some available. **Library:** Old Library with unrestricted access but restricted borrowing hours. **Other college facilities:** Squash courts and playing fields; boathouse; music room, computer suite. **Largest fields of study:** Classics, history and PPE.

European Community: 5% first degree students take EC language as part of course and 1.5% (all modern linguists) spend 6 months or more in another EC country. No formal exchange links.

Undergraduates: *Men:* 143 *Women:* 72
Postgraduates: *Men:* 67 *Women:* 17

What it's like

Its strength lies in its size: this is Oxford's smallest college. Atmosphere intimate and friendly and peculiar interests may be followed. Large beer cellar provides meeting place for all. JCR increasingly active and well supported. Fundamentally an academic college with propensity towards classics, but strong in PPE, English and medicine and gaining strength in sciences and history. (No tutors in zoological sciences.) Work load high in all subjects; library amongst best (open 24 hrs a day). Corpus average sporting college and facilities good – squash court, boathouse, tennis courts, playing fields and pavilion. All years now fully mixed and female proportion increasing. Accommodation amongst Oxford's best, large percentage of undergraduates (and many graduates) live in. Food compares favourably with other colleges. Discipline tactful; poor work not tolerated. No aristocratic pretensions. Public/state school ratio roughly equal. Tolerant college, if gossipy – slightly left wing bias.

Pauper notes

Accommodation: Very good and expanding – in 2 years' time every undergrad will be able to live in college accommod. Married quarters – college houses. **Drink:** The Wheatsheaf, Chequers, The Bear (Halls, Morrells). **Eats:** Kebab vans, chippy, Kentucky, Wimpy – some healthy places too – college food nutritional and cheap. Sweeny Todds, Browns, The Moonlight (Indian) Restaurant, Pak Fook (Chinese). **Ents:** Phoenix, PPP, Moulin Rouge, Cannon cinemas, Oxford Playhouse; lots of college and university events, balls. **Sports:** Rowing good, other sports average. Watch 1st Division Oxford United, Univ teams from croquet to ice hockey. **Hardship funds:** Special fund; book grants and vacation residence grants. **Travel:** Scholarships from college and JCR, university awards, good student travel centres. **Work:** Can work on college maintenance staff; other temp work avail in Oxford.

Alumni (Editors' pick)

Sir Isaiah Berlin, Lord Beloff, William Waldegrave MP, J L Austin, Sir Robert Ensor, R Brinkley, G W Most (classics), Baron Hailey, Lord Clyde, E C Robertson-Glasgow, K H Bailey, Lord Cameron of Lochbroom, Brian Sedgemore MP, Michael Brock, Brough Scott, Sheba (the college tortoise).

CAN'T FIND WHAT YOU'RE LOOKING FOR? USE THE INDEX!

EXETER

Exeter College, Oxford OX1 3DP (0865 279600)

Maintenance charge 1990/91: Lodging charge (including standard catering charge) up to £945 pa. Cost of food is approx £3 per day if all meals are taken. **Accommodation available:** All students accommodated in College for first year, and many offered a second year (usually for finals). College also has hostels, flats and houses available; generally able to house all who do not want privately rented accommodation. **Eating arrangements:** Self-service breakfast and lunch and served dinner available in early 17th-century hall daily throughout term. Some self-catering facilities. **Gate/guest hours:** All members have late keys. No guests allowed between 2 and 8 am unless they have been booked in overnight. **Admission:** Undergraduates not admitted for biology, botany, zoology, human sciences, geography, oriental studies. **Scholarships:** and exhibitions awarded for meritorious work during undergraduate courses. **Travel grants:** Generous provision made from endowed funds for both academic and general purposes. **Library:** Well-stocked. **Hardship fund:** Well-endowed fund administered by the Rector and Tutors' Committee. **Other college facilities:** Bar, sports clubs, playing field, boathouse and multi-gym. College chapel has fine choir made up of students and boys from Cathedral school.

European Community: 12% first degree students take EC language as part of course and spend 6 months or more in another EC country. No formal exchange links. Many visiting EC students in residence.

Undergraduates: *Men:* 234 *Women:* 78
Postgraduates: *Men:* 47 *Women:* 21

What it's like

Small and cosy; everyone knows everyone else. Central position gives good access to shops and facilities. Friendly, with thriving JCR and entertainments committee. Facilities are being slowly improved – a new staircase and lecture room being built at the moment. Food is fairly good – dinner in 2 sittings; gowns worn for formal hall. Everyone has a late key. Cheap bar. Impressive Fellows garden. Exeter has settled at around the top of the Norrington Table, but non-academic pursuits are encouraged. JCR provides a wide range of facilities – newspapers, magazines, a drinks machine, table tennis table, pool table, televisions and video. Traditional links with West Country, but recently more people from Merseyside than from Devon. Healthy public/state school ratio.

Pauper notes

Accommodation: University married quarters. College building new accommodation. College owns flats, houses and hostels for students. **Drinks:** Cheap college bar at Exeter. **Eats:** Town has many good places. College food has improved recently, and is fairly cheap. (Chefs have been on vegetarian courses to give meals a little imagination.) **Ents:** Good local cinemas eg Phoenix. Excellent college entertainments committee. **Sports:** University sports centre. College has its own sports facilities including squash. **Hardship funds:** University hardship fund, plus many college funds. **Travel:** Easy to hitch to London. College has excellent travel grant facilities. **Work:** Study grants. Work available behind college bar.

Alumni (Editors' pick)

J R Tolkien, Sir Michael Levy, Sir Roger Bannister, Robert Robinson, Tariq Ali, Richard Burton, Martin Amis, Alan Bennett, Nevil Coghill, Ned Sherrin, Russell Harty, William Morris, John Ford, Sir Charles Lyell, J A Froude, Edward Burne-Jones, Imogen Stubbs.

CAN'T FIND WHAT YOU'RE LOOKING FOR? USE THE INDEX!

HERTFORD

Hertford College, Oxford OX1 3BW (0865 279400)

Maintenance charge 1990/91: £777 pa (average). **Accommodation available:** 200 places in college, 100 in college houses. Rent: 85% in accommodation where rent controlled by college. **Eating arrangements:** Pay as you eat. **Gate/guest hours:** All students issued with gate keys. **Admission:** Generally places are offered unconditionally either on the basis of an interview in December or, if it is preferred, the Oxford Entrance Examination in November. In either case entry is competitive with the emphasis being on promise. **Academic features:** New engineering courses; Polish and Linguistics courses. **Library:** Undergraduate and antiquarian libraries. **Hardship funds:** White, Boyd, Keasbey. **Other college facilities:** New JCR complex, lecture theatre, sports ground, boathouse, orchestra, computer, bar, rowing, squash court.

European Community: 10% first degree students take EC language as part of course and 9% spend 6 months or more in another EC country. Formal exchange links with the British Institute in Paris for modern linguists.

Undergraduates: *Men:* 221 *Women:* 137
Postgraduates: *Men:* 97 *Women:* 33

What it's like

Convivial; not the most impressive architecture or grounds in Oxford and facilities are adequate rather than extensive but it's very friendly. The pleasant atmosphere results from broad social mix of students from all regions and all backgrounds.

Accommodation is in shoe boxes in first year, in college houses or private accommodation in 2nd year, a relatively palatial room in 3rd year. Exceptionally well situated 2 minutes from town centre; 10 seconds from Kings Arms; 30 seconds from Bodleian Library.

Congenial atmosphere extends to discipline and to the attitude to overnight guests and drunkenness (barring excesses). Hertford people renowned for enjoying themselves. Numerous clubs, sports, political, social, benefit from not taking themselves too seriously and maintaining a sense of fun.

Work load averages 2 essays and tutorials a week. Pressure varies from subject to subject but is avoidable provided you keep your head above water, but pressure in finals. Generally academic work is not the dominant tenet of people's lives.

Generally people quickly develop a strong affinity to Hertford, find their niche and enjoy themselves. Very unsnobbish.

Pauper notes

Accommodation: Rooms in college for a term 1st and 3rd year. Rooms in college houses for all 2nd year. **Drink:** College bar – pint v popular. Kings Arms, White Horse, Turf, Rose and Crown, Brewhouse, all popular but not cheap. **Eats:** College cheap, not bad, veg option. Town huge variety; Sweeney Todds, Browns, Indians, Chinese etc. **Ents:** College entz – bops, videos etc. Univ entz – plays, gigs etc; very good variety. **Sports:** Free sports centres off campus; football, rugby, hockey etc; squash also rowing good facilities. **Hardship funds:** Keasby grant anyone can apply. Bursar is hot on interest free loans. **Travel:** Travel grants for linguists. **Work:** Not allowed during term (no time anyway!).

Alumni (Editors' pick)

Evelyn Waugh, John Donne, Gavin Maxwell, Thomas Hobbes, Jonathan Swift, Charles Ryder, Charles James Fox.

CAN'T FIND WHAT YOU'RE LOOKING FOR? USE THE INDEX!

JESUS

Jesus College, Oxford OX1 3DW (0865 279700)

Maintenance charge 1990/91: £660 pa for room in college, including heat and light. **Accommodation available:** All first year and all finalist undergraduates live in college accommodation. A majority of other students are accommodated. 147 rooms in college; flats to accommodate a further 233 undergraduates and graduates plus 12 flats for married graduates. **Eating arrangements:** Continental breakfast, cafeteria lunch, cafeteria dinner and set dinner in hall. **Gate/guest hours:** 8 to 2 am. **Admission:** More than half of undergraduates come to Jesus after only 2 years in sixth form. Undergraduates not admitted to fine art, oriental studies. **Scholarships:** Various scholarships and grants; Sankey scholarships to assist college members to meet expenses of being called to Bar. **Travel grants:** Charles Green Studentships for classical or other studies abroad; Dodd Benefaction for vacation travel abroad. **Other college facilities:** Library, bar, music room, 3 squash courts, sports field, computer.

European Community: 5% first degree students take EC language as part of course and 5% spend 6 months or more in another EC country. Formal exchange links with Trier, Germany.

Undergraduates: *Men:* 202 *Women:* 125
Postgraduates: *Men:* 86 *Women:* 37

What it's like

Founded by Queen Elizabeth in 1571. Compact, pretty college with 3 quads right in centre of Oxford. Handy for libraries, shops and entertainments but tends to attract tourists.

Good library, sociable common room, OK food served at convenient cafeteria, laundry facilities and a popular bar.

Accommodation is excellent and inexpensive. All first years live in as do some finalists. All third and second years live either in college or in modern self-catering college flats about 2 miles away.

Traditional Welsh connections but no admissions discrimination. Jesus people tend to come from wide range of backgrounds and schools. Politically centre/left and pretty sound.

Regular social events and wide range of college societies and sporting clubs. Sporting record rapidly improving, especially in cricket and rugby; women's rowing and hockey. College squash and tennis courts and large sports ground.

Excellent academic standards. Nearly all subjects taught in college. Work loads and timetables vary. Student/don relationships good.

No visiting restrictions. Gates close at midnight, but college members have keys.

Worst point: tends to be socially isolated. Most people know your news (or think they do) before you know it yourself.

Best point: friendly, game for a laugh, unpretentious and cheap.

Pauper notes

Accommodation: Very high standard of college accommodation guaranteed for 1st and 2nd years and finalists. **Drink:** College bar. **Eats:** College food varied and cheap. Set breakfast, cafeteria lunch and dinner or formal dinner. No evening meal served on Saturdays. Vegetarian meals are increasing on demand and improving in quality. Tea and coffee bar. **Ents:** Free weekly ent in bar or JCR – discos, bands, talent nights and game shows. Weekly video in JCR. Lots on in Oxford. **Sports:** Free sports and college facilities for rowing, football, rugby, hockey, lacrosse, tennis, cricket, squash. All nearby. Access to gym and weights. No swimming pool. **Hardship funds:** College has fund for exceptional cases of hardship. **Travel:** Travel (holiday) grants – standard. Also numerous college travel scholarships. **Work:** Vacation-study grants up to 25 days per year. Grants for study abroad. Grants to

CAN'T FIND WHAT YOU'RE LOOKING FOR? USE THE INDEX!

help fund music lessons. Book grants pay half of cost of books over the first £25 up to a maximum of £55. College doubles prizes won by undergraduates for academic achievement.

Alumni (Editors' pick)

T E Lawrence ('Lawrence of Arabia'), Lord Wilson of Rievaulx, James Burke, Magnus Magnusson, Paul Jones (Manfred Mann).

KEBLE

Keble College, Oxford OX1 3PG (0865 272727)

Maintenance charge 1990/91: Undergraduates: £811.38 per annum; Graduates: varies according to tenancy for rooms (heating inc) and cleaning (meals charged extra as taken). **Accommodation available:** 2 years in college (normally first and second) during undergraduate course. As many graduates as possible. Rent: 50% in college rooms where rent is controlled by college. **Eating arrangements:** Keble Hall (the longest in Oxford) can accommodate all who desire to eat there in one session. **Gate/guest hours:** Wicket gate keys available for all students. Visitors must leave by 1 am (guest rooms available for overnight stay). **Admission:** Pre A-level through entrance exam or conditional offer; post A-level on basis of grades achieved plus interview. Undergraduates not admitted for human sciences, oriental studies (except Japanese). **Scholarships:** Awards given for meritorious work during undergraduate course. Organ and choral awards; periodic third world scholarship. **Travel grants:** A number of study and travel grants are provided by Keble Association. **Library:** Butterfield's Victorian library was enhanced by a large extension opened 1981. **Other college facilities:** JCR, bar, music room, sports ground, boathouse, laundry, TV room, squash courts, weights room, darkroom, computer room. **Academic features:** Extension of provision for computer studies and Japanese. **Hardship funds:** There is a hardship fund for students in financial difficulty.

European Community: 7% first degree students take EC language as part of course and 7% spend 6 months or more in another EC country. No formal exchange links.

Undergraduates: *Men:* 245 *Women:* 150
Postgraduates: *Men:* 90 *Women:* 28

What it's like

Keble is one of the largest Oxford colleges both in terms of student numbers and its physically imposing Victorian structure. All undergraduates are guaranteed two years in college accommodation and college is presently considering plans to increase its housing stock. Accommodation is good: two-thirds of the rooms are sets, all have central heating and a washbasin, and hot showers and baths are plentiful. One problem is the absence of cooking facilities since, although three meals a day are provided seven days a week in hall, there is hardly any choice and the food is negative and stodgy (vegetarian alternative is okay).

Junior Common Room (small student union) itself has good facilities and provides the focus for lively activity and debate. The JCR officers provide representation on internal and external bodies, though administration is becoming increasingly intransigent. JCR offers useful information and welfare advice. The wide ranging social and geographical makeup of the students as well as the high state school intake makes Keble a friendly and open college. Post of JCR Womens' Officer created to ensure that the female perspective is considered in what has, for so long, been a predominantly male environment.

Academic performance has played an increasingly important factor in the college's self-assessment and work pressure can be high. Drop-out rate is approx 2%. Extra-curricular activity does not seem to have been unduly hindered – the

CAN'T FIND WHAT YOU'RE LOOKING FOR? USE THE INDEX!

college sporting achievements remain high; music and drama also flourish. Post-graduate unemployment rates from Keble run at between 0% and 5%.

Pauper notes

Drink: Good pubs: Lamb and Flag (2 mins walk from college); good local beer: Morrells; cheapest beer: subsidised college bars. **Eats:** Nearby pizza and kebab vans, Heroes (sandwiches), St Giles Cafe (greasy, expensive and tasty!), college shop (student run). **Ents:** Penultimate Picture Palace and Phoenix (excellent cinemas), Downtown Manhattan, The Coven (discos). Student nights vary. Numerous college drama productions within university, Oxford Venue (excellent gigs and acid-house club). **Hardship fund:** College support loan for those in extraordinary need. **Travel:** Travel scholarships available from college. Hitching not too difficult. **Work:** Pub work, local shops, language and other teaching available. Term-time work discouraged.

Alumni (Editors' pick)

Sir Peter Pears, Rev Chad Varah (father of Samaritans), Michael Croft, Imran Khan, Andreas Whittam Smith (founder of *The Independent*), Sir David Charles Wilson (Governor of Hong Kong).

LADY MARGARET HALL

Lady Margaret Hall, Oxford OX2 6QA (0865 274300)

Accommodation charge 1990/91: £891 pa plus meals as taken. **Accommodation available:** All but about 50 undergraduates live in college: single study bedrooms (some third years have private bathrooms). **Eating arrangements:** All meals in Hall on 'copytex' system. JCR kitchen/pantries on all floors. **Gate/guest hours:** Gate closed at midnight. All members of college issued with keys. Guest hours: weekdays 9 am to midnight; weekends 9 to 2 am. **Admission:** For pre A-level candidates a choice between sitting the entrance examination or interviews with a view to an offer conditional upon A-level results. For post A-level candidates interviews and, in some cases, short written tests. Undergraduates not admitted for geology, metal-lurgy. **Scholarships:** About 25 scholarships awarded to undergraduates in residence; organ scholarship; various college essay prizes. **Travel grants:** Armorel Holiday Gifts (total about £1,000 pa) to help needy undergraduates to have a good holiday. Maude Royden long vacation travelling exhibition (normally £200). Other grants in connection with academic work. **Hardship funds:** Limited grants available for unexpected hardship during course. **Library:** Open 24 hours; over 50,000 books on open shelves; law reading room; science reading room. **Other college facilities:** Bar, music practice rooms, 2 grand pianos and several upright pianos, tennis courts, croquet lawn, boathouse. Squash court, shared facilities for other sports.

European Community: Only students in modern languages and joint courses learn an EC language and spend a period in another EC country. No formal exchange links.

Undergraduates: *Men:* 194 *Women:* 188
Postgraduates: *Men:* 53 *Women:* 38

What it's like

Architecture is not glamorous but appealing; the magnificent gardens back on to the river, enabling LMH to have its own punt house. A 10-minute walk from town centre which is a welcome barrier to out of college visitors yet doesn't prevent anybody here from socialising in town. Being out of the crammed centre of town, allows excellent on-site facilities and a lack of the tourists who plague other colleges in summer. Most students live in for 3 years but 40 live out – chosen by annual ballot

CAN'T FIND WHAT YOU'RE LOOKING FOR? USE THE INDEX!

of second years. Balanced male:female ratio makes this an ideal college for women undergraduates who may feel outnumbered elsewhere.

Pauper notes
Accommodation: Very good. **Drink:** Cheap. **Eats:** Good food at LMH, reasonably priced – vegetarian options. **Ents:** Many JCR social events. **Sports:** Good but relaxed sports. **Hardship funds:** Principal's discretionary fund and a JCR living-out fund. **Travel:** Holiday fund in memory of a former undergraduate for students who have been unable to afford a good holiday in recent years.

Alumni (Editors' pick)
Benazir Bhutto, Lady Antonia Fraser, Diana Quick, Gertrude Bell, Dame Veronica Wedgwood, Dame Josephine Barnes, Elizabeth Longford, Eglantine Jebb, Baroness Warnock, Matthew Taylor MP, Andrew Q Hands.

LINCOLN
Lincoln College, Oxford OX1 3DR (0865 279800)

Maintenance charge 1990/91: £38.55 per week, inclusive of dinner (except Saturdays). **Accommodation available:** All undergraduates accommodated for two years, most for three years. Excellent purpose built block available for graduates. **Eating arrangements:** Meals in hall; also snacks in bar, teas in JCR. **Gate/guest hours:** Gate closes at midnight during term. College members have keys. **Admission:** Undergraduates admitted under uniform Oxford colleges' system. No preference between 'mode E' and 'mode N' for pre-A level applicants. No undergraduates admitted for biology, botany, geography, geology/earth sciences, human sciences, metallurgy, science of materials, economics and management, oriental studies, zoology, theology. **Scholarships:** Various, for undergraduates once in residence; graduate entrance scholarships, details on request. **Travel grants:** Up to £170 for undergraduates, £245 research grant for graduates; £155 for clinical medicals. **Hardship funds:** Grants and interest-free loans for graduates and undergraduates in financial difficulties. Commemoration Fund, Keith Murray Fund. **Library:** Especially strong in law, history, English, politics, and biological and chemical sciences. **Other college facilities:** Playing field, squash court, multigym; computing facilities; music practice rooms; JCR bar.

European Community: 10% first degree students take EC language as part of course and 10% spend 6 months or more in another EC country.

Undergraduates: *Men:* 163 *Women:* 124
Postgraduates: *Men:* 88 *Women:* 42

What it's like
Not one of the famous names of Oxford but offers a lot. One of the oldest colleges, very pretty with a striking library in the converted All Saints' Church. Ideally situated for the centre of town, with shops, pubs and the Bodleian all on the doorstep.

First and most second years live in and third years live in a road of college houses. Rooms vary from small and modern to lovely old suites of rooms. No complaints about college food; it's arguably the best in the university, with trout and duck served on normal evenings; vegetarians well catered for.

The college is one of the best endowed, shown by the sports facilities. Main ground is a good bike ride from the centre, but the pitches are in super condition with a large, modern pavilion. Nearer the centre there is a squash court and new multi-gym both in constant college use. Teams in the first division for most sports (impressive for such a small college) and there's much enthusiasm.

The social centre of college is the bar, which is a good one open till 10.30 6 nights a

CAN'T FIND WHAT YOU'RE LOOKING FOR? USE THE INDEX!

week. Several ents events a term and ball or after eights. The college is very friendly, tending towards insularity, and judges no-one on appearances.

Pauper notes
Accommodation: Accommodation very reasonable. Good 1st yr graduate accommodation also. **Drink:** Bar prices very reasonable. **Eats:** Amenable chef accommodates any nutritional needs. Exceptional value. **Ents:** Better ents – improving weekly – subsidised by JCR. **Sports:** Brilliant sports ground with new pavilion. All free. Squash courts and multi-gym; hockey, football, cricket and rugby pitches. Tennis courts. **Hardship funds:** Exist but excuses must be very good. **Travel:** 6 scholarships up to £175 pa. **Work:** Not possible under university statutes during term time. Vacation work grants readily available to all students.

Alumni (Editors' pick)
Sir Peter Parker, John Le Carré, Edward Thomas, John Wesley, Richthofen's cousin of the same name was at Lincoln.

MAGDALEN
Magdalen College, Oxford OX1 4AU (0865 276000)

Maintenance charge: Varies according to room. **Accommodation available:** All undergraduates can live in for at least 2 years. 66% in accommodation where rent controlled by college. **Eating arrangements:** Cafeteria system, with formal dinner available once or twice a week. **Gate/guest hours:** Gate keys issued. **Admission:** Entry by interview (Mode N) or by examination (Mode E). Undergraduates not admitted to geography, geology, metallurgy. **Scholarships** and prizes awarded each year. **Travel grants:** Funds for a number of purposes. **Hardship funds:** Very limited fund available. **Library:** Particularly large history and PPE sections, Daubeny science library, Denning law library; Old Library with fine collection of Renaissance and 18th century volumes. **Other college facilities:** JCR shop, wine cellar and bar; 11 tennis courts (8 grass, 3 hard), 4 squash courts, 10 college punts, sports ground in beautiful riverside setting, with probably best cricket square in Oxford. Three computers for the use of undergraduates. **Largest fields of study:** Chemistry, engineering, English, law, literae humaniores, modern history, modern languages, PPE, physics, mathematics.

European Community: 13% first degree students take EC language as part of course and 2% spend 6 months or more in another EC country. No formal exchange links.

Undergraduates: *Men:* 229 *Women:* 118
Postgraduates: *Men:* 145 *Women:* 60

What it's like
Strikingly beautiful (Great Tower and Cloisters) with extensive grounds (Addison's Walk, Deer Park, Fellows Garden etc) which give a sense of space rare in Oxford. Geography is disparate leading some to complain about lack of focus and community but new common room, bar facilities etc will hopefully combat this. Most people thrive in their freedom and independence. No image/routine is imposed upon you – you can be who you want in Magdalen.
   Modernisation programme continuing inc plumbing, central heating and more rooms meaning that increasing numbers can live in (2 yrs at least guaranteed) and that room costs are dropping to average. Accom good with some rooms palatial though most 1st years homed in infamous Waynflete Building. Sports facilities, brilliant.
   Student body: 33% women, many foreign postgraduates and increasing state school intake.

CAN'T FIND WHAT YOU'RE LOOKING FOR? USE THE INDEX!

Academically quite hot with pressure increasing but never to neurosis level. Top arts college in Norrington Table; arts better than sciences.

Music and drama societies are very active and the college choir has a worldwide reputation. Services in chapel daily and well attended.

Pauper notes
Accommodation: Married quarters easily available at Magdalen: no **really** cheap accom around. **Drink:** 90p a pint in college bar; cheap for Oxford. **Eats:** Cheap food in hall. More expensive but better in spectacular new college bar. **Ents:** College discos and bands frequently though no really 'big and classy' bands come to Oxford. Good college and univ theatre and brilliant cinema arrangements. **Sports:** Very good facilities at Magdalen plus cheap/free facilities throughout Oxford too. **Hardship funds:** Offered by both College and the University. **Travel:** Travel grants given by college (cheap travel shop for students on the High St). **Work:** Pretty standard.

Alumni (Editors' pick)
Sir Peter Medawar, Sir John Betjeman, Lord Denning, A J P Taylor, Dudley Moore, Oscar Wilde, Sir Keith Joseph, Joseph Addison, Edward Gibbon, Sir Charles Sherrington, Sir Robert Robinson, Dr Charles Daubeny, Sir Christopher McMahon, J Z Young, C S Lewis, R G Collinwood, Gilbert Ryle, Sir Peter Strawson, Kenneth Baker, Lord Gibson.

MANCHESTER

Manchester College, Mansfield Road, Oxford OX1 3TD (0865 41514)

Maintenance charge: £657 per term (including 18 meals per week). **Accommodation available:** 60 students (80%) accommodated in college houses in college precincts. **Admission:** Direct or through UCCA. Mature students (over 25) only. Undergraduates not admitted for most science courses – check prospectus. **Special features:** Became part of the University in 1990 as college for mature students. **Library:** 3 libraries: Tate (general); Carpenter (world religions); Old (books before 1800); 40,000 volumes, 30 periodicals, 40 study places. **Other college facilities:** Chaplain, JCR bar. **Largest fields of study:** English.

European Community: 1% first degree students take EC language as part of course. No formal exchange links.

Undergraduates: *Men:* 18 *Women:* 18
Postgraduates: *Men:* 1

What it's like
Shedding its slightly scruffy, comfortable feel in favour of a new smarter image, as affiliations with university grow; college now the mature students' centre of Oxford University.

Most of the students live in and accommodation is mainly situated in Holywell Street (very old, very studenty). Rooms are generally large with plenty of character and the houses are smallish and friendly.

There is a lively JCR, which is at the heart of the social life and everyone is encouraged to become involved in planning events etc. There is a bar in the JCR and a separate TV room.

One advantage of being at a small college is that you soon know everyone and there is a feeling of closeness among students not found to the same extent in larger colleges.

CAN'T FIND WHAT YOU'RE LOOKING FOR? USE THE INDEX!

Pauper notes

Drink: College bar – Sawyer Arms, cheap and awfully cheerful. **Ents:** Bursaries for college concerts. **Sports:** Croquet, punt and bursaries for sporting activities.

Alumni (Editors' pick)
Josiah Wedgwood (1750), Sir Henry Tate (1850).

MANSFIELD

Mansfield College, Oxford OX1 3TF (0865 270999)

Maintenance charge 1990/91: £775 pa plus heating and meals. **Accommodation available:** All undergraduates have a room in college for at least one year, and at least a further year in college or college house. Rent: 60% in accommodation where rent controlled by college. **Eating arrangements:** All meals available in hall, Monday to Saturday. Residents pay £25 per term in advance towards meals. Cooking facilities in all college houses and on some staircases. **Gate/guest hours:** Unrestricted. **Admission:** Entrance examination (pre-A level candidates) or interview mode of entry (pre- or post-A level candidates). Both modes of entry acceptable in most subjects. Undergraduates not accepted for modern languages, biological sciences, chemistry, medicine. **Scholarships:** Scholarships and exhibitions awarded at any stage of an undergraduate's course in recognition of high academic standards. Also a number of college prizes. **Travel grants:** 2 travelling scholarships. **Hardship funds:** An endowment plus limited provision from general funds; small grants to meet exceptional circumstances. **Library:** Spacious in relation to numbers. Strong in theology; other subjects have smaller but up-to-date collections. **Other college facilities:** Mansfield shares Merton sports grounds; has own boat club. Billiard table, croquet, table tennis, bar. Refrigerators on all staircases. **Largest fields of study:** Theology, engineering, English, geography, history, law, maths, PPE. **Academic features:** New places in engineering, metallurgy and physics available.

European Community: 4 first degree students take EC language as part of course but none spend 6 months or more in another EC country. No formal exchange links.

Undergraduates: (approx) *Men:* 106 *Women:* 41
Postgraduates: (approx) *Men:* 24 *Women:* 11

What it's like

It's often said to offer all of Oxford's advantages without many of the pitfalls. A small college on a quiet and spacious site, yet close to city centre, libraries and science area. College is maintaining its progressive stance by the imminent construction of more accommodation, the extension of resources and facilities, and a wide-ranging 'School Links Programme' designed to improve the female:male, state:independent school ratios.

Those who have found the college too small or who have wanted to extend their non-academic activities, have gone on to be prominent in university societies, music, drama and the SU. JCR and MCR (undergraduate and graduate bodies) enjoy good relations and work closely with the college authorities.
Nigel Hall

Pauper notes

Accommodation: About to be extended by new building programme. Rent equalisation scheme and small living-out grants have just been introduced. **Drink:** College bar – run by students, therefore prices are kept as low as possible. **Eats:** Food (with veg options) provided on site; kitchens and newly improved cooking facilities allow self-catering. **Ents:** Frequent college events – discos/groups/beer. Active involvement in drama etc. **Sports:** Good/extensive sports facilities shared

CAN'T FIND WHAT YOU'RE LOOKING FOR? USE THE INDEX!

with Merton College. **Hardship Funds:** An existing small fund has recently been extended in view of changing finances of students. **Travel:** A few travel scholarships awarded each year by college. **Work:** Sometimes available in vacations with conferences in college; extensive opportunities in city.

Alumni (Editors' pick)
Rev Prof G B Caird (Dean Ireland's professor of the exegesis of holy scripture, Oxford University), Rev Dr Alex Boraine (vice-president of Progressive Federal Party, South Africa), Paul Crossley (pianist), C H Dodd (theologian, chairman of New English Bible translators), Michael White (music critic), Chris Cragg (*Financial Times*), Donald MacDonald (president of university boat club during the 'mutiny' year).

MERTON

Merton College, Oxford OX1 4JD (0865 276310)

Maintenance charge 1990/91: £7.25 per day (bed-sitting room), £7.43 per day (a set). **Accommodation available:** All first and final year students guaranteed room (bedsitter or set) in or near college; half of 2nd years accommodated also. **Eating arrangements:** All meals taken in hall. **Gate/guest hours:** Gate closed at midnight during term. Guests must leave college by midnight. **Admission:** Either by examination and interview (mode E) or by interview and conditional offer (mode N). **Scholarships:** Postmasterships and Exhibitions awarded at end of first (and later) years for distinguished work. **Travel grants:** Various travel grants to 'subsidise well thought out plans for vacation travel'. **Library:** Fine Old Library (over 60,000 volumes; medieval manuscripts and chained early printed books). **Other college facilities:** Music room and organ; nearby playing fields, sports pavilion, boathouse. **Largest fields of study:** Chemistry, literae humaniores, mathematics, modern history and physics.

European Community: Number of students learning an EC language or spending time in another EC country, not known.

Undergraduates: *Men:* 160 *Women:* 92
Postgraduates: *Men:* 91 *Women:* 49

What it's like
Merton is arguably the oldest college in the university and suffers to some degree from its self-image as a 'real' Oxford college, fostered by its considerable wealth. It can afford to provide all its undergraduates with rooms for the duration of their degree course and to serve excellent food. Prices for these privileges are low, but the college does expect good academic results in return, which it invariably gets.

Nevertheless, it is easy to avoid working harder than at other colleges if you so choose. Recently students have got more capable of distracting themselves from their studies and college social life is booming with a huge number of societies and events organised by the JCR. The Christmas ball is unique among Oxford colleges and is invariably popular. Rowing, American football, croquet and women's rugby are probably the most eminent of college's sports clubs and participation is very much encouraged. Music and drama are strong with a garden show in the summer, a major event in the Oxford drama calendar. Overall, Merton is friendly and, although there is an unsatisfactorily low state school intake, it's not a Sloaney college. The only major criticism to be made is that Merton is almost too comfortable.
Damien Eames

Pauper notes
Accommodation: Very cheap college accommodation for all college members – useful as private market is expensive. **Drink:** College bar is heavily subsidised but

CAN'T FIND WHAT YOU'RE LOOKING FOR? USE THE INDEX!

lacks charm. The Turf Tavern (Bath Place) and The White Horse (Broad Street) both good. Several places (eg Brew House) do own brews. **Eats:** Best university food in Britain and very cheap. Oxford's varied assortment of eateries are all nearby. **Ents:** Cheap or often free, and improving. Penultimate Picture Palace for film classics/off beat; watch billboards for huge variety of cheap plays; concerts at various prices almost all the time. **Sports:** Swimming pool on Cowley Road; University Sports Centre on Iffley Road. Good college facilities. **Hardship funds:** College likely to help. **Travel:** Travel grants exist – but it's up to you to find out about them. **Work:** Backward college authorities prohibit working, even during vacs.

Alumni (Editors' pick)
Frank Boft, Airey Neave, Sir Patrick Wright, Conrad Russell, Henry Mayr-Harting, Jeremy Isaacs, T S Eliot, Robert Morley, Kris Kristofferson.

NEW COLLEGE

New College, Oxford OX1 3BN (0865 248541)

Maintenance charge 1990/91: £346.86 per term (bed, breakfast and dinner). **Accommodation available:** About 80% of undergraduates housed in college (all first and second year, and some third year students). **Eating arrangements:** All 3 meals provided in hall. **Gate/guest hours:** Late keys available. **Admission:** Undergraduates admitted through Oxford Colleges Admissions system for all subjects except geography. Postgraduates admitted through University's Faculty Boards. **Study grants:** About 30 a year. **Hardship funds:** Limited help available. **Library:** Over 70,000 volumes. **Other college facilities:** 10 acre sports ground 400 yards from college; college punts and boathouse.

European Community: 10% first degree students take EC language as part of course and 10% spend 6 months or more in another EC country. No formal exchange links.

Undergraduates: *Men:* 251 *Women:* 140
Postgraduates: *Men:* 125 *Women:* 45

What it's like
Despite being one of the oldest and largest of Oxford's colleges, New College provides a surprisingly relaxed and normal atmosphere. The Junior Common Room (JCR) is the name given to the collective body of students; the Common Room itself, called the Nelson Mandela Room, provides a place for students to meet, talk, watch television and read the newspapers. JCR Welfare Office provides information on welfare and benefits available to students (what's left of them) and a range of subsidised stationery.

New College is a large and relaxed place, with beautiful grounds and excellent facilities. With the library, dining hall, and JCR bar (probably the most popular student bar in Oxford) all close to each other, and with many college-based clubs and societies, it is possible to spend a great deal of time in college. The musical side is well-renowned, as are college sports, particularly rowing. Many students, however, still choose to spend much of their time getting involved in university-wide activities, and getting to know friends from other colleges.

The student body at New College is changing fast. An active Target Schools Scheme run by the students has helped to increase the number of students from state schools; the 'Sloane' is now the exception rather than the rule.

New College is not an intimidating place from the academic point of view, although it has a respectable academic record (to the amazement of the less academically-minded of its members!). Tutors tend to rely on individual interest than official sanctions, so the amount of work you do is largely up to you.

CAN'T FIND WHAT YOU'RE LOOKING FOR? USE THE INDEX!

New College, like the rest of Oxford, has its 'traditions' (wearing gowns for dinner, and calling the terms 'Michaelmas', 'Hilary' and 'Trinity'). Some find such traditions quaint, others silly. Some students come to Oxford to go out rowing early each morning and frequent Summer Balls; others do neither. New College provides an environment which allows you to get what you want out of Oxford and find your own niche to fit in – probably why most students there swear they wouldn't be anywhere else.

Pauper notes
Accommodation: Very expensive in Oxford; very limited married accommodation; New College one of cheaper in university. **Drink:** Good brews – Morlands, Wadworths, Hook Norton. You don't have to drink Pimms. **Eats:** Good Indian and Chinese on Cowley Road. **Ents:** High profile college entz, always successful. Lots of culture, some good small bands and jazz; big bands at Apollo and at Poly and CFE. **Sports:** College facilities closest of any Oxford college, and as good; swimming pool, athletics stadium and ice rink in town.

Alumni (Editors' pick)
Nigel Rees, Antony Benn MP, Lord Longford, Len Murray, John Fowles, Hugh Gaitskell.

ORIEL
Oriel College, Oxford OX1 4EW (0865 241651)

Maintenance charge 1990/91: £6.98 per day average (for room, six luncheons and seven dinners a week). **Academic features:** Joint Schools of Electronic and Structural Materials Engineering and Engineering and Computing Science. **Accommodation available:** First and second year undergraduates accommodated in college, increasingly also third year and first year graduates. **Eating arrangements:** All meals available in college. **Gate/guest hours:** Free access 24 hours a day for college members. Liberal guest rules. **Admission:** By way of mode E (Entrance Examination) or mode N (conditional or unconditional offer on the basis of extended interview). Further particulars available in the University undergraduate prospectus. College prospectus available. **Scholarships:** Oxford Colleges no longer offer Admissions awards but undergraduate members may be elected to Scholarships or Exhibitionerships on the basis of work within the College. **Travel grants:** Small grants available. **Library:** Excellent facilities (70,000 books) and liberal hours. **Other college facilities:** Facilities for all major sports; drama; music. **Largest fields of study:** Modern history, PPE, modern languages, natural sciences; Oriel admits undergraduates to read for all the degrees offered by the University except fine art and human sciences. **Structural features:** Women first admitted in 1985.

European Community: Number of students learning an EC language or spending time in another EC country, not known.

Undergraduates: *Men:* 180 *Women:* 84
Postgraduates: *Men:* 77 *Women:* 12

What it's like
One of the oldest and friendliest of the Oxford colleges, conveniently situated in town centre. First admitted women in 1985, the present ratio is approx 5:2 (not bad for Oxford as a whole).

Accommodation of a high standard is available for 1st and 2nd years, in single and shared rooms. Gates locked at 12, but overnight keys are provided (a blind eye turned to overnight guests). College hall for lunch and dinner of a reasonable standard and price; also catering for vegetarians. Good library (open 24 hours a

CAN'T FIND WHAT YOU'RE LOOKING FOR? USE THE INDEX!

day); overshadowed by the lively, popular and (cheap) beer cellar – the venue for various entertainments during term, and a good meeting point for all years. JCR shop sells cheap stationery, food etc, 2 launderettes (not so popular) and a daily tea-bar for various delicacies for hungry, overworked(?!) students. TV room with weekly video shows (seats must be booked for popular soaps such as Neighbours).

Very good sporting reputation, especially for rowing. Has been head of the river in Torpids and Eights.

Many college societies for all interests, including an excellent dramatic society which produces famous annual summer play on the steps of 1st Quad – a must for all.

Oriel is not just a place to live. There is lively interest in the JCR and its workings, ents, and possibly the strongest college identity in Oxford.

Oriel has something for everyone, and, like all Oxford colleges, has the added advantage of being situated in one of the most beautiful cities in the country.

Pauper notes

Accommodation: College accommodation reasonably priced (soon may be able to accommodate all who want to live in). Living out more expensive. Cheap launderettes. **Drink:** All college bars are very cheap – especially Oriel, 65p a pint. Pubs in town comparatively expensive, £1.30 a pint. **Eats:** Many cheap restaurants catering for all tastes. The Queens Lane coffee house, Hilo Jamaican restaurant, India Garden. College caters for vegetarians. **Ents:** Lots of cinemas, mainstream and otherwise. Millions of plays, good and bad. Good college ents. **Sports:** University Sports Centre free for all students (booking proves more difficult), and there are good facilities on a college level too. **Travel:** Lots of travel grants from college. **Work:** Work available for college services eg bar. Tutors not keen on other work in term time. Students sometimes employed in summer in library/porters' lodge. Oxford full of opportunities for temp work especially tourism – many restaurants etc.

Alumni (Editors' pick)

Sir Walter Raleigh, Cecil Rhodes, Beau Brummel, A J P Taylor, Norman Willis, Cardinal Newman, Matthew Arnold.

PEMBROKE

Pembroke College, Oxford OX1 1DW (0865 276444)

Maintenance charge 1990/91: Daily inclusive rate for living in college is £6.69 (heated room) or £6.15 (unheated). This does not include lunch (about £1.30 per day if taken in Hall) or dinner on Saturday. **Accommodation available:** About 280 rooms – all undergraduates will be able to live in college for at least 2 years. Rent: 60% in accommodation where rent controlled by college. **Eating arrangements:** Hall – formal breakfast and dinner, informal 'snack lunch'. JCR pantry for morning coffee and teas. **Gate/guest hours:** Gate closes at midnight, guests out by 2.00 am. **Admission:** For post A-level candidates on basis of interview and school reports. For pre A-level candidates admission either by entrance examination or by interview and school reports (acceptance is conditional on A-level grades). **Scholarships:** Up to 24 awards given at the end of the first year of undergraduate course based on performance in course work and examination. Any successful candidate who is qualified for an award from one of college's trusts may have his/her scholarship or exhibition named after and financed by that fund. **Travel grants:** Limited funds available for small number of grants. **Library:** Working collection of about 30,000 books covering all subjects taught; closes at 2 am. **Other college facilities:** Sports ground (1 mile from college), boathouse, bar, photographic darkroom.

CAN'T FIND WHAT YOU'RE LOOKING FOR? USE THE INDEX!

European Community: 10% first degree students take EC language as part of course and 10% spend 6 months or more in another EC country. No formal exchange links.

Undergraduates: *Men:* 207 *Women:* 114
Postgraduates: *Men:* 52 *Women:* 15

What it's like

Enjoys an excellent location, virtually adjacent to Carfax. Gardens are small but quaint. Few college stereotypes. Social diversity and gender balance is relatively good which makes for a generally unpretentious atmosphere. Academically, safely settled in the Norrington Table and though pressures are high, most find that the work gets done. As with most colleges, old rooms mean character surroundings but cold in winter. Attitude to overnight guests relaxed. College bar open 6–11 pm. Decor described as 'peeling to appealing'. Atmosphere relaxed. Offers usual music, religious, sport and dining societies. Despite a lack of amenities the consensus of opinion is that Pembroke is one of the most pleasant of Oxford's colleges.

Pauper notes

Accommodation: All first years and many of others live in. Rest in rented accommodation – sharing houses tends to be very expensive but few alternatives in Oxford. **Drink:** Most college bars cheap. Good local pubs; The Blenheim, The Gloucester Arms, Harvest 1047 and GX good brew. **Eats:** Good provision for vegetarians and ethnic food; eating out expensive. Better off self catering. **Ents:** Colleges organise own events. **Sports:** Excellent. **Hardship funds:** Vacation grants available. **Travel:** Travel in city easy; a few people hitch home, most take coach.

Alumni (Editors' pick)

Dr Samuel Johnson, Michael Heseltine MP, Lord Miles of Blackfriars (founder, Mermaid Theatre), Patrick Campbell (late broadcaster and personality), Denzil Davies MP, Charles Kempe (artist and designer), James Smithson, J Arnold MP, J Critchley MP, J Ryman MP, I Stanbrook MP, Michael Betting (Russian spy), Senator Fulbright, Senator Lugar.

QUEEN'S

The Queen's College, Oxford OX1 4AW (0865 279120)

Maintenance charge 1990/91: £818 pa. **Accommodation available:** All undergraduates have a room in college buildings for first and final years, Almost all students are accommodated for their second year. (Over 100 large rooms in main buildings; 50 rooms in modernised Queen's Lane quadrangle; 77 study bedrooms in modern and spectacular Florey Building; 39 rooms in Iffley Road building opposite university sports complex; 24 rooms in 6 self-catering houses and 12 self-catering rooms for post-graduates in a house in Banbury Road). **Eating arrangements:** Breakfast available in hall, Florey Building and Iffley Road building; lunch and dinner in hall. Meals charged at cost of materials only. **Gate/guest hours:** Undergraduates can have their own keys. **Library:** Over 140,000 volumes, including good coverage of all undergraduate subjects. **Other college facilities:** Chapel with superb modern pipe organ and concert piano; convenient sports field; boathouse with several good 'eights'; tennis courts; squash courts; beer cellar. **Travel grants:** Some vacation travel grants available. **Admission:** By the procedures common to all Oxford colleges. Information is available from the Tutor for Admissions or from the Oxford Colleges' Admissions Office. Undergraduates not admitted for English, geography, metallurgy, fine arts. **Scholarships:** Various scholarships and exhibitions offered, to students on any course, for distinguished work; College bursaries for excellence in non-academic activities (sports, etc); choral, organ or instrumental

CAN'T FIND WHAT YOU'RE LOOKING FOR? USE THE INDEX!

awards offered for distinguished performance (not restricted to students reading music).

European Community: 16.5% first degree students take EC language as part of course and 16.5% spend 6 months or more in another EC country. No formal exchange links.

Undergraduates: *Men:* 197 *Women:* 98
Postgraduates: *Men:* 47 *Women:* 17

What it's like

Centrally placed in Oxford, mainly 18th-century architecture based on designs of Hawksmoor and Wren. Further accommodation next door in modern annexe above shops facing High Street. Accommodation available to most of those who want it for all 3 years. Two modern annexes 10 mins from college which house all first-years. Strong Northern tradition, but good mix of state and public school intake. Both 'hearty' and 'arty' elements exist, so there is something for everyone. Sports teams are successful and societies cover all from drama and music to debating and wine-tasting. Academic pressure is less marked than at other colleges and results are average. College facilities are good, although those living in cannot self-cater. Food is good, and very cheap. The beer-cellar is among the best in Oxford, and entertainments are frequent and popular (including discos, cocktail parties etc). JCR is active, if politically divided. Relaxed and very friendly college.

Pauper notes

Accommodation: College rents are high, but real attempts at reduction. **Drink:** Beer cellar sells wide variety at excellent prices, main college focal point. Few feel need to drink elsewhere. Close to King's Arms and The Turf. **Eats:** Food good, catering for all tastes (incl vegetarian). Very cheap. Excellent Chinese, French, Italian and Indian restaurants nearby. **Ents:** Renowned in Oxford. Frequent and varied. Cinemas and theatres close by. **Sports:** Free facilities. Excellent football and cricket pitches plus new tennis courts and squash courts. **Travel:** Generous to those with good excuses. **Work:** Most need to work in long vac. Few seem to be badly off.

Alumni (Editors' pick)

Rowan Atkinson (comedian), Leopold Stokowski (conductor), Brian Walden (TV presenter), Gerald Kaufman (politician), Bishop of Durham.

REGENT'S PARK

Regent's Park College, Pusey Street, Oxford OX1 2LB (0865 59887)

Maintenance charge 1990/91: £1,120 pa. **Accommodation available:** for all students. **Eating arrangements:** Meals in hall. **Gate/guest hours:** All students given keys. **Admission:** By the procedures common to all Oxford colleges. Undergraduates not admitted for sciences. **Library:** 25,000 approx, 40 current periodicals, 25 study places and Angus Library of historic Baptist materials. **Scholarships:** Yes. **Other college facilities:** Kitchens on each level. Games room. TV room, JCR etc. **Travel grants:** Available. **Hardship Funds:** Some. **Largest fields of study:** Theology, but arts subjects generally.

European Community: 5% first degree students take EC language as part of course and 5% spend 6 months or more in another EC country. Special links with Bonn.

Undergraduates: *Men:* 37 *Women:* 16
Postgraduates: *Men:* 5

CAN'T FIND WHAT YOU'RE LOOKING FOR? USE THE INDEX!

ST ANNE'S

St Anne's College, Oxford OX2 6HS (0865 274800)

Maintenance charge 1990/91: £1,148 pa. **Accommodation available:** Single study-bedrooms for majority of undergraduates and first and final year students guaranteed college rooms. **Eating arrangements:** All meals available in hall but not compulsory, limited self-catering facilities in college houses. **Gate/guest hours:** No gate hours. Guests may stay overnight if signed in (under certain conditions). **Admission:** Details from Schools, the Oxford Colleges Admissions Office, or the College direct. **Scholarships:** Scholarships and Exhibitions awarded for good academic work and success in examinations. **Hardship funds:** Hardship Fund available – grants made on *ad hoc* basis. **Travel grants:** Limited funds available to undergraduates during their course but they must submit their proposed programme and have their tutor's recommendation. **Library:** Large college library with Chinese section, and law library. **Other college facilities:** Shared sports facilities with St John's; shared squash courts with St Antony's. Opportunities for rowing. **Largest fields of study:** English, history, law, mathematics, modern languages, PPE.
NB. St Anne's has tutorial fellows in the main sciences and welcomes candidates.

European Community: Number of students learning an EC language or spending time in another EC country, not known.

Undergraduates: *Men:* 232 *Women:* 168
Postgraduates: *Men:* 79 *Women:* 47

What it's like

Good male/female ratio contributes to friendly atmosphere while wide cross section of students ensures very little prejudice. Excellent college ents, (frequent discos, wine tasting, cocktail evenings etc) nightly videos. Cheap, efficient and well stocked bar open nightly provides focal centre of college social life. Various societies – drama, music, religious, political, photographic etc. Freshers encouraged to come up early – special social events arranged. Also system of student sponsors for freshers. Accommodation is generally good, most live in. All single rooms. No gate or guest restrictions. Reasonable cheap food. Alternative student-run JCR buttery open at meal times. Sports facilities shared with St Johns. College raising money to build a boathouse. One of Oxford's best college libraries, friendly staff, open 8.30–2 am during week.

Pauper notes

Accommodation: Most live in. **Drink:** College bar student run and cheap. **Eats:** Vegetarian meals available every night in college. JCR buttery. **Ents:** One college social event/week on average. Subsidised, generally well-organised and well attended. Videos shown twice nightly. Very active social committee. **Sports:** Multi-gym recently purchased. **Hardship funds:** Extant but not well publicised. **Travel:** Large availability of funds for travel abroad. **Work:** Student run bar and buttery employ student helpers. Pubs locally employ undergraduates. Library helpers employed throughout term.

Alumni (Editors' pick)

Maria Aitken, Frances Cairncross, Baroness Young, Iris Murdoch, Libby Purves, Tina Brown, Elizabeth Turner, Joanna Richardson, Naomi Mitchison, Dame Cicely Saunders, Edwina Currie.

ST CATHERINE'S

St Catherine's College, Oxford OX1 3UJ (0865 271700)

Maintenance charge 1990/91: £288 per term, without meals. **Accommodation available:** 288 rooms in college, 30 bedsits in nearby college houses. It is normal for a first year undergraduate to live in college. Rent: 66% in accommodation where rent controlled by college. **Eating arrangements:** Hall, buttery, individual staircase facilities. **Gate/guest hours:** Unrestricted. **Admission:** In line with the Oxford Entrance procedures. Undergraduates not admitted for classics, theology. **Scholarships:** Awarded for academic excellence at end of first year. **Travel grants:** Limited number for undergraduates for use in long vacation. **Other college facilities:** JCR has debating pit, bar, buttery, TV room and private dining room; Bernard Sunley Building with lecture and film theatre, outdoor and indoor theatres, music room (with harpsichord and grand piano), squash courts and 6 tennis courts, several college punts, nearby playing fields at Marston. **Largest fields of study:** Half arts/half science.

European Community: Modern language students (about 15 per year) study an EC language and spend 6 months or more in another EC country as part of their course. No formal exchange links.

Undergraduates: *Men:* 279 *Women:* 151
Postgraduates: *Men:* 90 *Women:* 31

What it's like

Catz was originally founded in the 19th century as a Society to matriculate poor students into Oxford University who could not afford the then astronomical cost of living in a college. When the government started paying for higher education, it was felt that the Society was no longer necessary in its old form, and thanks to some generous donations from various sources, St Catherine's College was founded.

It comprises a set of low buildings – angular yet graceful – and some beautiful gardens. It is about five minutes from the city centre, but surroundings are more typical of the beautiful Oxfordshire countryside than of an urban environment. The architect, Arne Jacobsen, designed everything, from bricks to SCR's cutlery.

The background of the college has led to it being one of the more liberal in Oxford – it was one of the first to go co-ed – and its open plan layout allows more freedom than at some of the older establishments. Students can live in college for two years, and the rooms are comfortable, if a little small. Self-catering facilities are also provided. It is one of Oxford's largest colleges, but has a great sense of community, despite the diversity of students' backgrounds.

The social life is lively: there are ents every other week, and a special event each term, the most popular being Catz night in November, where the entire college gets kegged on cheap cocktails. There are a number of societies, including the film soc, which screens a film each week. The college has punts, a weights room and squash, tennis and netball courts on site, and the sports field a 15-minute walk away.

Catz is strongest in sciences, but it also has a large proportion of arts students (it's just that they don't tend to work as hard).
Richard Baldry

Pauper notes

Accommodation: College owned property cheapest (£4.70 per night). Married quarters only in college houses. Quite expensive to live out. **Drink:** Catz bar is one of the cheapest college bars in Oxford Beer 70p–£1.00 per pint including Courage & Ind Coope real ales. **Eats:** Hall – 3 course evening meal except Sundays £2.20 or less with tickets, lunch £1.20, breakfast £1. Vegetarians catered for in hall. Pete's Cafe – more flexible, usually cheaper. Self-catering facilities are the best in Oxford's colleges. **Ents:** Catz has a reputation for good ents with discos, bands, etc – entry is free but restricted to JCR members and guests. Oxford theatrical productions are cheap (about £2) and frequent. **Sports:** Catz has squash courts, tennis and netball courts, weights room, punts, shared boathouse, sports field (1 mile away). **Hardship funds:** Administered by the Master (Head of College). College offers unlimited assistance in proven cases of difficulty. **Travel:** Travel scholarships are available for a wide range of projects. **Work:** Behind bar and in library during term. Available serving conference guests and gardening on campus during vacation.

Alumni (Editors' pick)
A A Milne, Sarah R Wheale, John Birt, Simon Winchester, Peter Mandellson.

ST EDMUND HALL

St Edmund Hall, Oxford OX1 4AR (0865 279000)

Maintenance charge 1990/91: £1,302 for 25 weeks (includes heating, breakfast and dinner – refunds available if meals not taken). **Accommodation available:** All undergraduates may spend at least 2 of their 3 years in college (in study bedrooms). **Eating arrangements:** Cafeteria style service, formal dinner every Sunday night; formal guest dinner three nights per term. **Gate/guest hours:** No restrictions. **Admission:** Pre A-level candidates may apply for conditional or may take the Entrance Examination. There is no quota on any mode of entrance and the majority of subjects have no preference between them. Post A-level candidates apply on basis of school record, A-level grades and interview. Undergraduates are not admitted for theology, classics, biology, zoology, human sciences. **Academic features:** New joint course in modern history and English. **Special features:** The Ruskin Master of drawing is a fellow of the college. **Scholarships:** Awards given after first year of study. **Travel grants:** Small travel grants available. **Library:** Library (restored Early English church) with some 42,000 volumes, microfilm/fiche reader, microscope; word processing facilities are available. **Other college facilities:** Boathouse, tennis courts and hockey pitches, football in university park.

European Community: 13% first degree students take EC language as part of course and 13% spend 6 months or more in another EC country. No formal exchange links.

Undergraduates: *Men:* 240 *Women:* 129
Postgraduates: *Men:* 73 *Women:* 18

What it's like
Teddy Hall is geographically small, but has one of the largest undergraduate and postgraduate intakes in Oxford. Smallness encourages friendly and intimate atmosphere. A male: female ratio of 3:2 has helped the college to lose its beer-swilling, rugby-playing image, but it's still one of the best sporting colleges in Oxford. Casual atmosphere; those who want the Brideshead style will be disappointed, although almost everyone finds their niche. The college is a strange mix of old and new, from the 16th-century quad to 1960s 4-storey towers. Accommodation for all first and third years in college, limited for 2nd years. The standard of food varies: breakfast and lunch are usually good, dinner could easily be improved. College library is in a Norman church; wonderful place for work. 24-hour access to college. JCR meetings are usually apolitical. Journalism and drama are developing a strong tradition to complement the college's sporting successes.

Pauper notes
Accommodation: First and third years assured college accommodation. Ballot for 2nd years. 2 college annexes. Married accommodation also available. **Drink:** Friendly and comparatively cheap. **Eats:** Food variable. Limited vegetarian meals. Occasional excellent guest nights. **Ents:** Regular disco/band ents. Drinks and cocktail parties. Video shows every week. **Sports:** Excellent facilities for both college and university sports. No college swimming pool. **Hardship funds:**

CAN'T FIND WHAT YOU'RE LOOKING FOR? USE THE INDEX!

Hardship funds available upon consideration of circumstances. **Travel:** Travel grants available. **Work:** Vacation grants available.

Alumni (Editors' pick)
Sir Robin Day, Terry Jones (Monty Python), Hugo MacNeill, Stuart Barnes.

ST HILDA'S

St Hilda's College, Oxford OX4 1DY (0865 276884)

Maintenance charge 1990/91: £399.33 per term. **Accommodation available:** All first year, some second, and all final year undergraduates can live in college accommodation in study/bedrooms. **Eating arrangements:** Maintenance fee includes meal tickets for a certain number of meals in hall; additional tickets can be bought as required. **Gate/guest hours:** During week, open to all 9 am–11 pm and to accompanied visitors 11 pm–2 am; overnight visitors may be signed in. **Admission:** By entrance examination and interview or by conditional offer on the basis of interview and in some cases submission of school written work. **Academic features:** The college will consider applications for any of the undergraduate courses offered in the university. **Special features:** GEC sponsorship for some engineers and physicists. **Scholarships:** Awards given annually to undergraduates in residence. Keyboard award (piano or harpsichord) open to undergraduates in any subject. Annual prizes in most subjects. **Travel grants:** About £6,000 given this year. M C Wise grants for undergraduate travel abroad and graduate research, open to all subjects: Christina Keith travel grants for classics students; K O Morgan travel grants and graduate research grants for historians. **Hardship funds:** Funds available (grants and interest-free loans). Laura Ashley bursaries for mature students. **Library:** Good range of books for most honour schools. **Other college facilities:** Small chapel, buttery, tennis court, croquet lawn, harpsichord, pianos, punts, computers and printers (with access to university computing facilities), new JCR bar, washing machines and spin dryers, cooking facilities. **Largest fields of study:** English, modern languages, history, mathematics, biological sciences.

European Community: 16% first degree students take EC language as part of course and 16% spend 6 months or more in another EC country. No formal exchange links.

Undergraduates: *Women:* 351
Postgraduates: *Women:* 35

What it's like
One of Oxford's two remaining all-women's colleges, St Hilda's lies in over six acres of gardens on the quiet River Cherwell, particularly lovely in the summer for parties, picnics, punting . . . Oxford is full enough of men for the college to be a welcome retreat; mixing with the diverse range of students in other colleges encouraged. No convent we; St Hilda's is renowned for the liveliness and friendliness of its undergraduates and boasts at least one 'Hildabeast' on the committee of most societies.

Accommodation in single furnished rooms is guaranteed for first years and finalists, and as one of the younger colleges (founded 1893) St Hilda's lacks many of the architectural and practical problems (draughts!) of older establishments. Rent includes heating, lighting and 80 meals; food is generally excellent with breakfast in unlimited supply and a formal evening meal once a week. Alternatively you can use kitchens, a college bar and buttery, or one of various nearby late night shops and takeaways (including the notorious 'deathburger vans'). On site amenities include cheap laundry facilities, subsidised college shop, common rooms, music rooms, tennis courts, croquet lawn, punts and a recently sponsored boatclub – plus everything else that the city and university have to offer, just there for the taking.

CAN'T FIND WHAT YOU'RE LOOKING FOR? USE THE INDEX!

St Hilda's takes, and gives so much, with students from every type of background making the most of the obscure and the prestigious societies, the excellent teaching and the libraries.

Academic pressure is not enormous by Oxford standards – St Hilda's suffers on the Norrington league table of Oxford colleges due to an excess of seconds rather than a lack of firsts.

Bad luck chaps, and ladies, don't miss out!
Alison Catchpole

Pauper notes
Accommodation: Reasonable but not cheap. No married quarters. **Drink:** Bar – cheapest in Oxford. **Eats:** College caters very well for vegetarians. **Ents:** Cheap ents – bands, discos etc, at the college. **Hardship funds:** College has its own hardship fund. **Travel:** Can apply to college for travel grants. **Work:** Very difficult.

Alumni (Editors' pick)
Marjory-Anne Bromhead (economist at World Bank), Nicola Le Fanu (composer), Kate Millett (feminist writer), Beryl Smalley (historian), A Bullard (vice-president, Amcon Corp, USA), Dame Helen Gardner (critic), Barbara Pym (novelist), D K Broster, Jacqueline Du Pre (cellist), Catherine Heath (writer), Hermione Lee (broadcaster).

ST HUGH'S

St Hugh's College, Oxford OX2 6LE (0865 274900)

Maintenance charge 1990/91: £1,082 in 1st year, £1,031 in subsequent years. **Accommodation available:** All undergraduates offered accommodation (study bedroom) for at least 2 years. Rent: 75% in accommodation where rent controlled by college. **Eating arrangements:** Maintenance fee includes meal tickets for certain number of meals in hall; additional tickets can be bought as required. **Gate/guest hours:** All undergraduates have keys. Visitors out by 2 am. Overnight guests at weekend by arrangement. **Admission:** Mode E: examination, interview and academic record – Pre-A level candidates only. Mode N: interview and academic record only. Pre- and post-A level candidates see University of Oxford Undergraduate Prospectus for details. College wishes to encourage more applications in mathematics and science, and welcomes applications from all kinds of school. Undergraduates not admitted for human sciences. **Academic features:** Male applicants accepted since 1987. New courses: classics & English; modern history & English. **Scholarships:** Up to 26 scholarships and exhibitions awarded annually to matriculated undergraduates; various essay prizes; organ scholarship (£100) and instrumental award. **Travel grants:** Limited amount of money available for students attending required courses. **Library:** Recently modernised; separate law and science reading rooms. **Other college facilities:** JCR bar, bar billiards, tennis, croquet, rowing, particularly large and pleasant garden, computer.

European Community: 13.5% first degree students (modern languages and joint courses) take EC language as part of course and 13.5% spend 6 months or more in another EC country. No formal exchange links.

Undergraduates: *Men:* 220 *Women:* 151
Postgraduates: *Men:* 53 *Women:* 63

What it's like
St Hugh's is now establishing itself as one of Oxford's most energetic, egalitarian, and educationally exciting colleges. Set in 14 acres of landscaped grounds in north Oxford it provides a supportive environment in which to enjoy the university as a whole.

CAN'T FIND WHAT YOU'RE LOOKING FOR? USE THE INDEX!

The atmosphere is relaxed, with both students and staff considerate and tolerant of each other. Something essential in such a small community.

Fifteen minutes' walk from town, less if you're a cyclist. Can be a bit insular, but many students very outgoing and active outside college. Admissions are evenly split between the sexes as well as the state and private school sectors. The drop-out level is low, and academic standards are rising in most departments.
David G R Young

Pauper notes
Accommodation: 310 rooms in college at £345 per term. **Drink:** Cosy and cheap college bar. **Eats:** Average food for all needs/diets in college. Lots of places to eat out in Oxford. **Ents:** Regular ents (music, live bands, jazz, comedy, etc) in college. 2 weekly videos, lots of active college societies. **Sports:** Tennis, croquet and weights all on site. Swimming pool nearby as are shared hockey/football/cricket grounds. Very active boat club. **Hardship funds:** Available in extreme cases – see Bursar. **Travel:** Lots of small (£50 – £200) grants available for summer trips. **Work:** Same as any other medium-sized city.

Alumni (Editors' pick)
Barbara Castle, Jane Glover, Catherine Johnston, Emily Davison (early suffragette), Dame Peggy Ashcroft, Mary Renault.

ST JOHN'S

St John's College, Oxford OX1 3JP (0865 277300)

Maintenance charge 1990/91: Approximately £460 per term (room + 3 meals). **Accommodation available:** Accommodation in college offered to all undergraduates for all 3 years (Jacobean, Victorian and modern rooms). **Eating arrangements:** Breakfast, lunch and early dinner self-service in hall, semi-formal dinner. Snacks available from college bar. **Gate/guest hours:** Late keys issued. **Admissions:** Conditional, pre A-level offers; by Entrance Examination; and post A-level unconditional offers. Undergraduates not admitted for geology, metallurgy. **Scholarships:** Awards offered on University examination results annually; organ scholarships and choral awards annually. **Travel grants:** Awarded annually on tutors' recommendations. Book grants open to all undergraduates. Instrumental awards. **Hardship funds:** Funds and grants occasionally available. **Library:** 12,000 older books, and working library of 30,000 volumes, many rare books and manuscripts. **Other college facilities:** Sports ground a mile from the college, tennis court, pavilion; boathouse in Christ Church meadow.

European Community: 12% first degree students take EC language as part of course and 12% spend 6 months or more in another EC country. Formal exchange links in Munich and Pisa – open to all undergraduates.

Undergraduates: *Men:* 234 *Women:* 133
Postgraduates: *Men:* 118 *Women:* 37

What it's like
Wealthy and beautiful, St John's offers perhaps the best facilities of all the Oxford Colleges. Accommodation in College available for all undergraduates (and most graduates for at least one year), almost all of a high standard. All rooms are centrally heated with a fridge nearby and kitchen facilities usually available. College food is generally very good especially formal dinner (£1.50). Facilities for students are excellent, and include a (cut-price) bar, functions rooms, TV and video, computer room, multigym and squash courts on site. A mile away is the College sports ground, with pitches for football, rugby, hockey and cricket, as well as tennis courts and a pavilion. There is a boathouse on the River Isis. The library is a particularly

attractive place to work and is especially well stocked in arts subjects, while the gardens provide a splendid setting for masterly inactivity should the library ever lose its appeal.

Recent years have seen a significant rise in the number of women students admitted, and the number of entrants from state schools is also improving, though perhaps not quite at the rate the JCR would wish. The JCR itself remains affiliated to NUS, but is not overtly political. Happily, however, noisy and entertaining caucuses do exist on both left and right. Relations between students and JCR are represented on Governing Body and several College Committees. 2 Guest Dinners held by the JCR each term are popular and verge on the glamorous; beyond these, 'organized' social life centres on discos of varying quality, a summer Garden Party, and a Ball normally every third year considered one of the best in Oxford. Otherwise, 'we makes us own fun'.

St John's remains academically strong but this does not prevent its students becoming more than visible in all areas of university life, from sport to drama to politics. Individuals may lead the life they choose, there is admirably little social pressure of any kind.

Unlike the college, St John's students are by no means universally wealthy; but they are beautiful.

Pauper notes
Accommodation: College accommodation for all undergrads – cheap by Oxford standards. Married flats ('Hart-Synot House') ¾ mile away. **Drink:** Bar subsidised and see Oxford Handbook. **Eats:** Food cheap in College. Vegetarian always available; 'bar snacks' (baked potatoes, pies, etc) an alternative. **Ents:** Lots going on in Oxford City; most student theatre – cheap. **Sports:** Sportsground 1.5 miles away. **Hardship funds:** Unlimited hardship fund on application; up to £50 a year book grant. **Travel:** Travel grants available (mostly go to 2nd years), usually £150.

Alumni (Editors' pick)
Robert Graves, Philip Larkin, John Wain, Kingsley Amis.

ST PETER'S

St Peter's College, Oxford OX1 2DL (0865 278900)

Board and lodging charge 1990/91: £1,161 pa. **Accommodation available:** All first year plus some second and third year (on a ballot) and JCR Committee and Club Secretaries in college. 75–80 more places in college houses. Rent: 60% in accommodation where rent controlled by college. **Eating arrangements:** Breakfast normally residents only. Lunch buffet-type; pay as you go or coupons. Dinner – in-residents sign out; out-residents sign in; one full sitting (7.15) and one earlier informal sitting (6.15). **Gate/guest hours:** No restrictions except as to noise and good order. The gate is locked at 12 midnight, keys available. **Admission:** Pre A-level candidates may (those for medicine must) sit an entrance examination. Post A-level candidates must (pre A-level candidates, except for medicine, may) apply instead on the basis of A-level results (known or future), school record, and interview. College welcomes applications from older candidates, especially in PPE. Undergraduates not accepted for classics, PPP, experimental psychology, human sciences, oriental studies, Russian, metallurgy. **Scholarships:** Organ scholarship and two choral awards annually at entrance. Other awards (including instrumental award) for students in residence. **Travel grants:** Grants are made annually to members of the college from the Christian Deelman Fund and by St Peter's Society. **Library:** Ample reading space, mainly undergraduate texts, with a few older and more specialist works. Separate Law Library. **Other college facilities:** Music room, usual athletics and other facilities, JCR.

CAN'T FIND WHAT YOU'RE LOOKING FOR? USE THE INDEX!

European Community: Modern linguists (some 8 per year) only take EC language as part of course and spend 6 months or more in another EC country. No formal exchange links.

Undergraduates: *Men:* 235 *Women:* 57
Postgraduates: *Men:* 77 *Women:* 23

What it's like

St Peter's is renowned throughout the university as the Lively College. Its relatively small size ensures that most students get to know everybody in the college and a strong and friendly community exists and thrives.

It's in the heart of the town centre with excellent access to all shops, restaurants and cinemas; also close to coach and railway stations.

Students guaranteed college accommodation for the first year and one further year. Food this side of average; breakfast and evening meal are included in the termly battels charges (2/3 rebate for signing out of dinner). Comprehensive library open 9am – 7am. JCR has television, video, pool and football tables, a photocopier and numerous games machines.

Recently SPC's sports clubs have come into their own; now consistently in the final stages of most competitions. Drama and music are both widely successful. College-run bar cheap and regarded as one of best of the university, always something going on.

Mixed since 1978, the male:female ratio is poor. St Peter's has informal, sociable atmosphere with complete integration of students of all backgrounds.
'Noah' Schuitemaker

Pauper notes

Accommodation: Living in guaranteed for first year and one other. New building quite luxurious, accommodation good overall. **Drink:** College bar very lively and far cheaper than local pubs. **Eats:** Food average in college. All types of food available within 100 yards of college. **Ents:** Usually free ents, from sweaty bops to local bands. **Sports:** Strong sports clubs, doing very well as of late. **Hardship funds:** Available. **Travel:** Funds available. **Work:** Available, eg waiting in restaurants, serving in bars.

Alumni (Editors' pick)

Sir Rex Hunt, Rev W Awdry, Sir Paul Reeves, Peter Wright.

SOMERVILLE

Somerville College, Oxford OX2 6HD (0865 270600)

Maintenance charge 1990/91: £1,322 pa (rent and food). **Academic features:** New degree courses in English and modern languages, English and classics, mathematics and computation, history and English. **Special features:** GEC lecturer in engineering. ICL Visiting Fellow in Computer Science. **Accommodation available:** Most undergraduates accommodated in older or modern study bedrooms (some live out for one year); small independent nursery for children of college members. **Eating arrangements:** Cafeteria system in hall. Meals paid for on ticket system (up to 50% of tickets refundable). **Gate/guest hours:** Every undergraduate is given a key. **Admission:** Candidates are considered for either mode E or mode N; Somerville has not expressed a preference for either mode. Undergraduates not admitted for geography, theology (but philosophy with theology is accepted). **Scholarships:** Various scholarships and exhibitions, both open and closed, awarded at any time in an undergraduate's career for work of especial merit, (usually worth £200 and £150 pa respectively) – also Bousfield Scholarships, open to candidates from GPDST schools, and the Dorothy McCalman Scholarship (£100) for candidates who have

CAN'T FIND WHAT YOU'RE LOOKING FOR? USE THE INDEX!

earned their living for 3 years. **Travel grants:** Various college travel grants and awards. **Hardship funds:** Limited funds available for *unexpected* financial difficulties. **Library:** Over 100,000 volumes, with strong science, history, literature, languages and philosophy collections; also a computer, electronic calculators and microfiche reader. **Other college facilities:** New JCR bar, tennis and croquet, 1 new boat, punts, organ and several pianos.

European Community: Number of students learning an EC language or spending time in another EC country, not known. One student in EC on Erasmus scheme.

Undergraduates: *Women:* 358
Postgraduates: *Women:* 67

What it's like

Somerville was founded in 1879 and is situated on St Giles and backs onto Jericho, a lovely area of Oxford. It also runs along Little Clarendon Street; expensive restaurants but some interesting ethnic shops as well as boutiques. A great mixture of buildings, old and new surround the main garden quadrangle which has beautiful lawns with lawn tennis and croquet in the summer. Atmosphere is relaxed and tranquil.

Facilities are generally good, library is not only beautiful but is also one of the best in Oxford; accessible 24 hours a day. Two laundries, sewing machine, typewriter, photocopier, ICL computer room with laser printer, plus one of Oxford's few creches. Cheap, well-run bar – newly decorated and welcomes guests. Pool table and darts. Active though ill-equipped sports clubs; rowing best for women in Oxford; very good for hockey, tennis, netball and football. Drama, arts, music societies. Varied students; a fair proportion from overseas plus mature students. No particular bias towards state or private schools but encourages applications from schools with no Oxford tradition. Academically: very good, fellows/tutors. Students pushed hard. Relations with SCR very good. Extrovert social life tending naturally towards being inter-collegiate rather than self-contained. Very relaxed attitude to overnight guests.

Practically all agree (over 90% voted for Somerville to remain single sex several years ago) that there are many benefits to its all-woman nature, feministic rather than feminist encouraging students to equip themselves for the future.

Pauper notes

Accommodation: All first years and third years guaranteed accommodation. Living out in second year is expensive, but fun. New building nearing completion. Very high standard of accommodation. Excellent kitchen/bathroom facilities. **Drink:** Very cheap bar – cheapest in Oxford – increasing in popularity. Lots of nearby pubs of different types – Eagle & Child, Jericho Tavern, Lamb & Flag. **Eats:** College food much improved and by far cheapest way to eat. Lots of restaurants in town. Browns next door. **Ents:** Excellent college events. Very popular, cheap, often free. Lively and varied, eg from bops to barn dances and very successful black-tie events. A myriad of events outside off campus. Phoenix cinema behind college, best in Oxford. **Sports:** May soon hire own sports grounds. Have access to other grounds for practice. Active hockey and best women's rowing in Oxford. **Hardship funds:** College and university funds. Sympathetic. **Travel:** Scholarships available, based on academic achievement. **Work:** Jobs quite easy to find in vacation. No time in term-time, just run into debt.

Alumni (Editors' pick)

Shirley Williams, Indira Gandhi, Iris Murdoch, Vera Brittain, Ann Oakley, Joyce Gutteridge, Victoria Glendinning, Kate Mortimer, Dr Cicely Williams, Anne Scott James, Dame Kiri Te Kanawa, Winifred Holtby, Dorothy Sayers, Dorothy Hodgkin FRS, Shirley Williams, Esther Rantzen, and of course Margaret Thatcher.

CAN'T FIND WHAT YOU'RE LOOKING FOR? USE THE INDEX!

TRINITY

Trinity College, Oxford OX1 3BH (0865 279900)

Maintenance charge 1990/91: £43.25 pw (room and dinner). **Accommodation available:** Almost all undergraduates accommodated in college for first 2 years (both old and modern rooms). New student block for remaining undergraduates. **Eating arrangements:** All meals can be taken in hall. **Gate/guest hours:** Gate keys issued to college members. **Admission:** Candidates, both pre and post A-level, admitted by Entrance Examination or conditional offers to pre A-level candidates, or unconditional offers to post A-level candidates. Undergraduates not admitted for geography, PPP, experimental psychology, human sciences, oriental studies. **Scholarships:** Various college scholarships and exhibitions, Jardine Scholarships for Hong Kong, Japanese and Bermudan students, Inlaks Scholarships for Indian students. **Travel grants:** J H Britton Travelling Bursaries; Lingen Fund (for classical studies); college funds for academically approved projects. One annual Whitehead Travelling Scholarship of £1,700 for those who have just graduated. **Hardship funds:** Keasbey Grants, Abbott's and University Hardship Fund. Some college funds. **Library:** Open 24 hours (keyholders at night). Combined arts, science and law library. **Other college facilities:** Beer cellar, darkroom, music society (organ, 2 pianos), squash court, boathouse, playing grounds and pavilion; unusually spacious lawns and gardens.

European Community: 13% first degree students take EC language as part of course and 13% spend 6 months or more in another EC country. No formal exchange links.

Undergraduates: *Men:* 177 *Women:* 86
Postgraduates: *Men:* 36 *Women:* 34

What it's like

Centrally located, architecturally attractive college in extensive gardens. Accommodation of a reasonable standard; almost all undergraduates housed for 3 years, though some second years live off-site in college houses. Complaints about lack of fridges and the fact that there is only one kitchen. Library's all-day opening; extension in bar opening hours very popular. Relatively high proportion from independent schools and a generally deserved reputation for being middle of the road – academically, politically and in sport. Small, relaxed and friendly though some complain of a certain apathy which leads them to venture outside college. On the whole traditional but most of its students find it an excellent place to spend their time at Oxford.

Alumni (Editors' pick)

Cardinal Newman, Jeremy Thorpe (former leader of Liberal Party), Sir Terence Rattigan (playwright), Lord Clark ('Civilisation'), Anthony Crosland, Miles Kington, William Pitt the Elder, A V Dicey, W Anson (both great constitutional lawyers), R Hillary (author), Sir Hans Krebs (biochemist), R Porter (immunology) – both Nobel Laureates, Lord North, Sir Arthur Quiller-Couch, Sir Angus Ogilvy, Ross and Norris McWhirter, Marmaduke Hussey, Robin Leigh-Pemberton.

UNIVERSITY COLLEGE

University College, Oxford OX1 4BH (0865 276602)

Accommodation available: Every undergraduate lives in college for his or her first 2 years; accommodation for remainder at Staverton Road site (all undergraduates can be accommodated). **Admission:** By the regular procedures for Oxford University. Undergraduates not admitted for geography, theology, human science, history

CAN'T FIND WHAT YOU'RE LOOKING FOR? USE THE INDEX!

and English; modern language combinations must include Russian. College has one of largest numbers of science undergraduates in University; it also specialises in Russian and psychology. **Hardship funds:** Small loans or grants available.

European Community: Only modern language students study EC language as part of course and may take optional year in another EC country. No formal exchange links.

Undergraduates: *Men: 267 Women: 123*
Postgraduates: *Men: 82 Women: 28*

What it's like

University College is normally painted as a rather staid institution, cold architecture, dryly academic, well respected but no place for a good time. This reputation needs an overhaul! There are few better places in Oxford and if colleges do have characters gradually perpetuated over the years then a kinder representation would be that it's down-to-earth and friendly. There's a startling level of keen intelligence, not necessarily of the intellectual kind (most people couldn't give a fig about Godard, Sartre or even Marx) but also a penetrating common sense that pervades the place. And, to be fair, although quite a serious college in attitude, there's equally a rewarding sense of fun and tolerance. Beer cellar, the envy of other colleges, can be terrifically vibrant, unintimidating even for the quiet type. Food allows students to have a moan but complaints run along the line of the old joke – 'God the food's awful – and such small portions.' Ambitious drama club, outstanding music society, active and valuable women's group, hugely successful rowing (this year, Head of the River) and rugby teams. JCR meetings have moved away from irrational, unpleasant, luddite shouting matches of old, to a more amiable atmosphere of coherent and amusing discussion. The hierarchy likes to subscribe to the motto of 'work hard, play hard', a cliche that surprisingly springs to life when acted out in the discerning, quick-witted and enlightened environment that is University College.
Andrew Klevan

Pauper notes

Accommodation: College (and the whole of Oxford) is costly. College accommodation for 3 years if wanted. **Drink:** Best beer cellar in Oxford by a long chalk – pubs very popular eg Eastgate, Wheatsheaf next door. Bullingdon Arms Cowley Road, The Cricketers Iffley Road, Star Royal Rectory Road. Cheap and unpretentious. **Eats:** College food. Go Dutch pancake house, cheap and good. Browns is the Oxford restaurant. **Ents:** College ents cheap and frequent. PPP Cinema – but very few bands in Oxford. Comedy at Apollo Theatre (eg Harry Enfield etc). **Sports:** Free college sports facilities, plus gym on Iffley Road. **Hardship funds:** Available in dire circumstances. **Travel:** NUS card, college travel grants sometimes. Keasby Bursary fund for student travel. **Work:** Lots of pubs to work in and work for college bursary/works dept in vac. Also in college beer cellar.

Alumni (Editors' pick)

V S Naipaul, Richard Ingrams, Shelley (poet), Clement Attlee, Roger Utley.

WADHAM

Wadham College, Oxford OX1 3PN (0865 277946)

Maintenance charge 1990/91: £380 per term covers all accommodation charges and dinner (breakfast and lunch extra). **Accommodation available:** All first year, few second year and 50% of third year students who want to be accommodated in college (shared sets, sets and bedsitters). **Eating arrangements:** Self-service breakfast, lunch and dinner in Hall or student refectory. **Gate/guest hours:** No restrictions. **Admission:** Follows the general pattern of Oxford entrance; for full details see the

Undergraduate Prospectus from Oxford Colleges Admissions Office, Wellington Square, Oxford OX1 2JD. Undergraduates not admitted for fine art, theology. **Scholarships:** Scholarships awarded for meritorious performance in university examinations and consistently excellent performance in tutorials. **Travel grants:** Various travel grants. **Library:** New library (1977) with space for 135 readers. **Other college facilities:** Computer room, JCR cafeteria and bar, launderette, organ and grand piano, squash court, weight-training room; sports ground 1.5 miles from college. **Hardship funds:** Some assistance with research expenses for graduates. Loans or grants available according to circumstances. Some travel grants. **Structural features:** Large modern library.

European Community: 40% first degree students take EC language as part of course and 40% spend 6 months or more in another EC country. No formal exchange links, except assistantships. Erasmus initiatives.

Undergraduates: *Men:* 240 *Women:* 170
Postgraduates: *Men:* 90 *Women:* 50

What it's like
Reasonably large and very diverse student community. Its enviable male:female ratio and enlightened admissions policy mean everyone is made to feel welcome. Wadham cliche/in-joke that it is 'an island of normality in a sea of intellectual and class snobbery' still holds true. SU dynamic and politically active: reputation for left-wing 'soundness'offset by best student bops in Oxford and almost terminal laid-backness of some members. SCR usually sympathetic and tutors generally like-able.College facilities are okay: SU subsidised launderette, stationery, TV, video, vending/games machines and own PA system! Sports ground 15 mins by bike, library open 24 hours.

Accommodation ranges from old, quaint and airy to newer, goldfishbowl-like and warm, to brand new, disinfected and well-equipped (ie kitchens). New building opening in October 1991 means all 1st years and finalists live in...although all 2nd years left to the mercy of Oxford's rapacious housing monopolies.

Graduates go on to do everything/anything/nothing: recent batch of Wadham student journos now making names for themselves in national papers.

The gardens are breathtaking; the food less so.
Chrys Meula

Pauper notes
Accommodation: No cheap accommodation. All second years forced to live out and increase overdrafts. **Drink:** SU bar for cheapish beer; Newkie Brown a bargain. Local pubs expensive. **Eats:** College lunch good value for pie/chips/beans! Restaurants overpriced. Plenty of kebab/potato vans, burger bars, Indians etc in town. **Ents:** Good cheap Indie venues; far too much low-cost student drama; excellent free SU discos. Excellent alternative cinemas: Phoenix and PPP. **Sport:** Own sports ground 1 mile; most sports catered for; public pools £1 a go. **Hardship funds:** Domestic Bursar sometimes sympathetic to rent arrears sob-stories. Wadham has a hardship fund, but is inadequate. **Travel:** Oxford well-connected by standard rail/coach/motorways. Car a nuisance as parking nonexistent and fines exorbitant. Some travel scholarships awarded each year. **Work:** College manual labour in vac. Tour guides needed in summer and A level tutoring; some pub work and waitressing.

Alumni (Editors' pick)
Christopher Wren, Michael Foot, Alan Coren, Melvyn Bragg, Sue Brown (first woman to cox Blues boat).

WORCESTER

Worcester College, Oxford OX1 2HB (0865 278300)

Maintenance charge 1990/91: Average £1,100 pa (room, breakfast and one main meal, 25 weeks). **Accommodation available:** Two years out of three accommodated in single study bedrooms in college. 65% in accommodation where rent controlled by college. **Eating arrangements:** Bar lunches available; choice of self-service or formal dinner. **Gate/guest hours:** Gates shut between 2.30 am and 6.30 am. **Admission:** College welcomes both pre and post A-level candidates, and keen to have applications from schools with no previous connection. College is building up science intake, especially in geology and biology. Undergraduates not admitted for biochemistry, electronic & structural materials engineering, human sciences, metallurgy and science of materials, metallurgy, economics and management. **Scholarships:** There are no Oxford entrance awards, apart from organ and choral awards. Scholarships and Exhibitions are awarded for exceptionally good work. **Travel grants:** About £4,000 available annually for travel with some reasonable academic purpose. Additional travel grants for geologists. **Library:** Separate law library and a number of valuable antiquarian collections. Recently-opened extension to undergraduate library, including individual reading cubicles. **Other college facilities:** Beer cellar, buttery, 26 acres of college grounds including squash courts, 7 tennis courts, playing fields; boathouse. **Largest fields of study:** Law, classics, English, modern languages, PPE, history, physics, chemistry, engineering. **Academic features:** College invites applications for new Honour Schools of Mathematics and Computation, Engineering and Computing Science, and Biological Sciences.

European Community: 11% first degree students take EC language as part of course and 11% spend 6 months or more in another EC country. No formal exchange links.

Undergraduates: *Men:* 215 *Women:* 118
Postgraduates: *Men:* 73 *Women:* 25

What it's like

West of city centre, with imposing Quad and renowned gardens. Lake and sports fields in situ. Accommodation either old, interesting and cold or new, warm and well-equipped. Washing facilities not so bad and cheap. Cooking facilities non-existent except in newly built Sainsbury Building. Students live in for first two years. Relations with SCR good. Renovated library open all night. College shop and beer cellar operates erratic hours. Food reasonable. JCR apolitical but organises social events and negotiates actively. Restrictions on overnight guests ignored. Larking very difficult. Contraceptive and pregnancy advice from college doctor (plus woman doctor). Active drama group and music society. High participation in sports. Squash courts. Top subjects: law, modern languages, maths. Courses traditional. Subject changes possible. Work-load substantial, not oppressive. Drop out rate low. Mixed from 1979, women gradually gaining growth. First woman Fellow elected 1984. Women's group recently started.

Pauper notes

Accommodation: Getting more expensive, top of range in college is not at all cheap. **Drink:** No cheap town centre pubs. Nag's Head round corner – good food. Beer cellar is cheap, as is the Union. The Brewhouse has own brews which have reputation. **Eats:** College food varies in quality, quite cheap though; vegan/vegetarian alternatives available. Formal hall offers better food with service at the same price as informal hall in return for a jacket and gown. **Ents:** Fairly regular JCR ents including hiring the ice rink. Discos very sweaty. Good choice of cinemas or video evening (weekly) for those who can't be bothered to walk to town. **Sports:** College sports facilities good – new squash courts and resurfaced tennis courts free

CAN'T FIND WHAT YOU'RE LOOKING FOR? USE THE INDEX!

to members of college. **Hardship funds:** There are measures available. **Travel:** Travel and vacation grants are available. **Work:** Very little time to work during term – vacations are long and there are opportunities in Oxford.

Alumni (Editors' pick)
Alistair Burnet, Thomas de Quincey, Richard Lovelace, John Sainsbury, Rupert Murdoch, Donald Carr, Richard Adams, Anna Markland.

PAISLEY COLLEGE

Paisley College, High Street, Paisley PA1 2BE (041-848 3000) Map A, C3

Student enquiries: Student Records and Admissions Office and Public Relations Office

Main study areas – as in What to Study section: *(First degree):* Biochemistry, biology, business studies, chemical engineering, chemistry, civil engineering, computing, electrical & electronic engineering, information technology, mathematical studies, mechanical & production engineering, physics, welfare studies. *Also:* Business economics, land economics, operational research, personnel administration and diploma in alcohol studies.

European Community: EC languages are new options in business economics and quality management and technology courses. Individual business, computing and engineering students have spent 6 months or more in another EC country supported by Comett. Formal exchange links between departments of computer science and economics and management with 3 French universities/colleges.

Application: Direct. **Special features:** Visiting professors: Professor R W Nichols (mechanical and production engineering), Professor I Macpherson (Chemistry). Alcohol Studies Centre. **Largest fields of study:** Technology, sciences and business. **Founded:** 1897. **Main awards:** BA, BSc, BEng. **Awarding body:** CNAA. **Site:** Paisley town centre. **Access:** M8 motorway, rail and air. **Academic features:** BSc electronic systems; credit accumulation transfer scheme (CATS); language options now available on certain courses. **Accommodation:** 277 places in hall (approx cost: £17.55-£18 pw). 166 college-owned flats with total of 230 places (approx cost: £10–£30 per month). 100+ rooms/digs (cost varies). **Library:** 120,000 volumes, 1,000 periodicals, up to 420 study places; recommended books reference only and overnight loan. **Welfare:** 2 student advisory officers; doctor. **Hardship funds:** Loan funds available for students in temporary difficulties. **Careers:** Personal careers counselling service; Careers Information Centre. **Amenities:** SU building with a variety of affiliated clubs and societies, sports facilities, extensive computing facilities, Educational Development Unit (incl. closed circuit TV). **Employment:** Industry, commerce, local government, HM government, multinationals.

Duration of first degree course(s) or equivalent: 3/4 years (full-time); 4/5 (sandwich); **others:** 4/5 years (Honours: mechanical and industrial, electronic product, civil engineering); **Total first degree students 1989/90:** 2,939 **Number of overseas students:** 49 **Number of mature students:** 429 **Male/female ratio 1989/90:** 2:1 **Teaching staff: full-time:** 230 **part-time:** 38 **Total full-time students 1989/90:** 3,040 **Postgraduate students:** 101 **Tuition fees, first degrees, 1990/91:** Home: £1,675 (£628 if self-financing); Overseas: £4,500.

What it's like
Paisley College is a rapidly expanding modern complex with seemingly identical

buildings. Glasgow is only five miles away and there is easy access to all travel routes. Main entertainment is supplied by SA.

SU is five minutes' walk from college and can cope with 400 students out of over 3000. Facilities include two bars, cafeteria, games room, pool tables, satellite TV and large video screen. Entertainments include regular discos till 2.00 am on Thursday, Friday and Saturday nights, plus quiz nights, pool competitions and other events now and again. There is also wide variety of sporting, religious, political and social clubs.

College and SA jointly finance creche for children of students and staff.

Accommodation ranges from cheap and nasty to expensive private sector flats as in most big towns.

College-run student advisory services offer career advice, welfare service and hardship fund information.

Pauper notes
Accommodation: From £8 upwards college accommodation. **Drink:** At the union with CAMRA beer festival each April/May. **Eats:** Union food cheapest and best in town. **Ents:** The Paisley Arts Centre for minority interests. Glasgow close to (5 miles). **Sports:** Recently opened lagoon centre with flumes, sauna etc. **Hardship Funds:** SA student advisory service for government access funds and college hardship funds. **Travel:** Glasgow is five miles away. **Work:** Local service industries.

Alumni (Editors' pick)
Gavin Hastings (Scottish/British Lions rugby football international); Douglas Druburgh (junior world curling champion).

"Small active left-wing confronts inactive reactionary majority"

PCL
Polytechnic of Central London, 309 Regent Street, London W1R 8AL (071-911 5000) Map E, B2

Student enquiries: Central Admissions/Initial Enquiries

Main study areas – as in What to Study section: *(First degree):* Accountancy, architecture, art & design, biochemistry, biology, biotechnology, building studies, business studies, chemistry, civil engineering, computing, economics, electrical & electronic engineering, English, environmental science, environmental studies,

CAN'T FIND WHAT YOU'RE LOOKING FOR? USE THE INDEX!

European studies, geography, history, industrial relations, information technology, law, linguistics, mathematical studies, mechanical and production engineering, metallurgy and materials science, microbiology, modern languages, Near Eastern & Islamic studies, physics, physiology, politics and government, psychology, sociology, speech sciences, town and country planning. *Also:* Chinese, chiropody, film studies, medical laboratory science, photography, quantity surveying.

European Community: 20% first degree students take EC language as part of course and 10% spend 6 months or more in another EC country. No formal links with EC universities/colleges known. Approved Erasmus programme 1990/91.

Application: PCAS. **Academic features:** Modern engineering foundation (1 year) and BSc software design (for Arts A-level students); BSc computer systems technology; BA housing studies; BSc in photographic and electronic imaging sciences; BA in film, video and photographic arts. **Largest fields of study:** Engineering science, built environment, business studies, languages, communication, art & design. **Founded:** 1838. **Main awards:** BA, BSc. **Awarding body:** CNAA. **Site:** 13 main sites in central London (W1/NW1) and Harrow. **Access:** All major sites within 15 minutes walk of each other, apart from Harrow site. All are on major bus and tube lines. **Accommodation:** 301 places in hall, some places in flats. Rent: 8% in accommodation where rent controlled by polytechnic. **Library:** 6 libraries, 262,000 volumes, 2,500 periodicals, 1,060 study places. Sophisticated LIBERTAS on-line catalogue system. **Welfare:** Doctor, FPA, psychiatrist, student adviser, student counsellor, chaplain, accommodation adviser. 20 place nursery. **Hardship funds:** Central fund administered by Hardship Committee. Loans, nursery bursaries and grants may be awarded to students facing unexpected financial hardship. **Careers:** Careers centre in Bolsover Street. **Amenities:** SU in Bolsover Street with staff/student bar, gymnasia, squash courts, rifle range, billiards room, table tennis room; sports ground at Chiswick.

Duration of first degree course(s) or equivalent: 3 years; 4 years (language and sandwich courses) **Total first degree students 1989/90:** 3,500 **Number of mature students:** 750 **Male/female ratio 1989/90:** 5:4 **Teaching staff: full-time:** 600 **part-time:** 400 **Total full-time students 1989/90:** 4,000 **Postgraduate students:** 600 **Tuition fees, first degrees, 1990/91:** Home: £1,675 (£651 if self-financing); Overseas: £4,500-4,750.

What it's like

PCL sites are spread throughout central London and at large faculty of Harrow. Law, languages, computing and most sciences have good reputations, as do photography and media courses run by faculty of communication.

Main advantage of studying in London is accessibility of wide range of arts and entertainment venues and cosmopolitan nature of the capital. Main disadvantage is acute housing shortage making finding a decent, affordable place to live a full-time job, especially with no housing benefit and static grants.

SU supports a wide range of political and cultural clubs and societies as well as over thirty different sports clubs. It produces a weekly magazine (McGarel), distributed free to students, that gives information on what's on and matters of interest to students. There are two union bars, one at central London site (Bolsover Street) and another at Harrow.

The Union's main campaigns are concerned with protecting and enhancing poly facilities, especially the nursery.

Pauper notes

Accommodation: PCL is bottom of league for student accommodation. Poly flats at Peckham. **Drink:** Union bar has wide selection and is cheap! **Eats:** Food generally nasty at PCL, vegetarians not generally catered for. **Ents:** Cinemas, theatres, galleries, exhibitions, markets etc. **Sports:** Union organises about 30 sports clubs.

CAN'T FIND WHAT YOU'RE LOOKING FOR? USE THE INDEX!

ULU has pool which students can use. **Hardship Funds:** Administered through student services.

Alumni (Editors' pick)
Quentin Crisp, Pink Floyd, Red Box, Pamela Armstrong, Bernard Wiltshire, Fred and Judy Vermorel, Peter Brunivels, Margaret Harker, Alexander Fleming.

PORTSMOUTH POLY

Portsmouth Polytechnic, Museum Road, Portsmouth PO1 2QQ (0705 827681) Map A, E8

Student enquiries: Assistant Registrar

Main study areas – as in What to Study section: *(First degree):* Accountancy, architecture, art & design, biology, business studies, chemistry, civil engineering, computing, economics, electrical & electronic engineering, English, environmental studies, geography, geology, history, hotel & catering management, information technology, Latin American studies, mathematical studies, mechanical and production engineering, modern languages, nursing studies, pharmacology, pharmacy, physics, politics and government, psychology, sociology, town and country planning, welfare studies. *Also:* Biomedical sciences, film studies, media studies, quantity surveying, radiography, Russian studies.

European Community: 9% first degree students take EC language as part of course and 9% spend 6 months or more in another EC country. Formal exchange links with over 50 EC universities/colleges:Belgium (1); France (17); Germany (17); Greece (1); Netherlands (2); Spain (14); many open to non-language specialists. Approved Erasmus programme 1990/91.

Application: PCAS except design (ADAR). **Academic features:** BSc in information systems; information technology & society; business information technology. BEng in manufacturing systems engineering; extended degree courses in engineering. BA in media and design. HITECC diploma engineering conversion course. **Largest fields of study:** Engineering, science. **Founded:** 1870 as Portsmouth and Gosport School of Science and Art. **Main awards:** BA, BSc, BEng, MEng. **Awarding body:** CNAA. **Site:** Main campus near town centre, Milton site 2.5 miles away (business studies, economics, education, management). **Access:** Free minibus or public transport to Milton site. **Accommodation:** 1,100 places in halls; 1,500 rooms/digs; 68 hostel places; 2,500 flats/bedsitters. Approx cost: Halls £24.91 pw (self-catering), £45.44 pw (breakfast and evening meal). **Library:** Central poly library, and branch library; total of 500,000 volumes, 3,500 periodicals, 900 study places; short loan library. **Welfare:** Head of student services; 3 student counsellors, 2 doctors and sick bay, psychiatrist, solicitor, 2 chaplains. **Hardship funds:** Paul Burrell Fund – short term loan of £80 max. **Special categories:** Residential facilities for married students, 24-place nursery (£2.50 per half day, £25.00 per week full-time). **Careers:** Information, advice and placement service, 4 careers advisers. **Amenities:** SU shop, bank, bars, travel bureau; Royal Naval Unit, Army Officer Training Corps and University Air Squadron; Chichester festival theatre; naval museum, D-Day museum, HMS Victory, HMS Warrior and Mary Rose nearby. **Sporting facilities:** Wide range of sports; excellent sailing on Solent.

Duration of first degree course(s) or equivalent: 3 years; **others:** 4 years **Total first degree students 1989/90:** 6,405 **Number of BEd students:** 56 **Number of overseas students:** 136 **Number of mature students:** 984 **Male/female ratio 1989/90:** 3:2 **Teaching staff: full-time:** 580 **part-time:** 110 **Total full-time students 1989/90:** 5,473 **Postgraduate students:** 727 **Tuition fees, first degrees, 1990/91:** Home: £1,675; Overseas: £3,500 (eg politics), £4,260 (eg physics).

CAN'T FIND WHAT YOU'RE LOOKING FOR? USE THE INDEX!

"If you come from public school, you're advised to keep quiet about it"

What it's like

Situated on two main sites around Portsmouth varying from modern tower blocks to beautiful old listed buildings to ex-army barracks. Good holiday season leads to shortage of rented accommodation: poly and SU can compensate with hostels and camp beds. Student social life is hectic with ents every night – discos, bands, theatre, folk and films. Over 150 clubs and societies offer everything from under-water hockey to instant liberalism. Water sports especially popular. Commercial Road is good shopping centre and Kings Theatre offers new play every 2 weeks; also Theatre Royal, Hornpipe Theatre – community arts centre with student conces-sions. Surveying, engineering and science courses excellent, offering good sand-wich courses. Cultural, literary and language studies homely with friendly atmosphere. Portsmouth a navy port and some pubs are services-orientated though most are full of friendly students, especially SU bars. Excellent SU is active and provides some of best student services.

Pauper notes

Accommodation: No squats; halls of residence fairly cheap; 3 housing co-ops charge about half the price of private accommodation. **Drink:** SU the cheapest. Local brews: Friarn Meux. **Eats:** SU very cheap. Some pubs, eg 'Wine Vaults' and 'Jubilee Tavern' are good value. **Ents:** SU ents hall for bands, discos. Gaiety showbar – cheap discos. Hornpipe – alternative plays, music, films. **Sports:** 46 different sports via SU. Transport to and from games arranged by SU. **Hardship funds:** Paul Burrell loans – give up to £70. **Travel:** SU travel shop offers discount for students. **Work:** Lots of summer work: ferries, fairground etc. Pub jobs during term time. Union also employs casual staff: coffee shop, bars and stewards.

CAN'T FIND WHAT YOU'RE LOOKING FOR? USE THE INDEX!

QUEEN MARGARET COLLEGE

Queen Margaret College, 36 Clerwood Terrace, Edinburgh EH12 8TS (031-317 3251) Map A, D3

Student enquiries: Admissions

Main study areas – as in What to Study section: *(First degree):* Communication studies, drama, food science & nutrition, hotel & catering management, library & information studies, nursing studies, speech sciences. *Also:* Consumer studies, health studies, media studies, occupational therapy, podiatry, physiotherapy, textiles, tourism.

European Community: Number of students learning an EC language or spending time in another EC country, not known. Approved Erasmus programme 1990/91.

Application: Direct. **Founded:** 1875, formerly Edinburgh College of Domestic Science. **Main awards:** BA, BSc. **Awarding body:** CNAA. **Academic features:** Degree courses include applied food science with marketing, health studies, speech therapy, occupational therapy and applied consumer studies. **Structural features:** Business Development Centre. **Site:** 24 acre landscaped site about 5 miles from Edinburgh city centre. **Accommodation:** 150 places in halls, 300 flats/bedsitters; most first year students from outside Edinburgh accommodated. Approx cost: £22.99 pw (self-catering), £36.06 pw (half board). **Library:** 77,799 volumes, 750 periodicals, 300 study places; books in heavy demand held in reserve only. **Welfare:** Doctor, student counsellor, accommodation officer. **Hardship funds:** Student welfare fund available. **Special categories:** Advisory interviews for students considering applying to any courses. **Careers:** Information, advice and placement service, careers adviser. **Amenities:** Students' association; licensed bar; theatre; bank; college shop, representative from Edinburgh bookshop one day a week. **Sporting facilities:** Swimming pool, tennis courts, squash court, gymnasium.

Duration of first degree course(s) or equivalent: 3 years; **others:** 4 years (dietetics, speech pathology and therapy), 4.25 years (nursing studies) **Total first degree students 1989/90:** 900 **Number of overseas students:** 50 **Number of mature students:** 350 **Male/female ratio 1989/90:** 1:4 **Teaching staff: full-time:** approx 130 **Total full-time students 1989/90:** 1,500 **Postgraduate students:** 12 **Tuition fees, first degrees, 1990/91:** Home: £1,675 (£628 if self-financing); Overseas: £4,150.

What it's like

Modern attractive and expanding college, in its own grounds, 4 miles west of Edinburgh's centre. Campus borders a residential area yet the grounds have a feeling of open space. Woodland, gardens, tennis and squash courts, swimming pool and games field; campus is very self-contained. Facilities include library, expanding information technology centre, gym, theatre, kitchens and food and science labs, drama and media studios and photography facilities, also the Students Association Union building. Student executives always available for advice and to maintain the smooth running of the Union.

More than a third of the 1,300 students live in high quality halls, amongst the cheapest in Scotland with a reputation for being the cleanest. Shopping facilities within walking distance of the campus and buses stop outside the college gates so the attractions of Edinburgh are never far away.

Pauper notes

Accommodation: Halls of various prices (half-board, self-catering, or self-contained flats – preference given to final year students). One shop on campus; small yet well-stocked, shuts at 4 pm. Laundry facilities and all halls have kitchens. Overnight guests allowed at weekends. **Drink:** SA Union bar. Lively and friendly atmosphere. **Eats:** 2 campus refectories and the Union all provide a variety of hot meals and snacks cheaply. Plenty of pubs and restaurants in Edinburgh from

CAN'T FIND WHAT YOU'RE LOOKING FOR? USE THE INDEX!

vegetarian to Mexican to Tunisian (wide price range). **Ents:** Union ents provide infrequent live bands; comedians and hypnotists from time to time. Other attractions include drink promotions, regular twice-weekly discos. Freshers lasts for 2 weeks at the beginning of term and is very cheap. Access to the numerous cinemas, theatres, pubs and clubs of Edinburgh. **Sports:** Gym, squash courts, tennis courts and swimming pool at college (equipment at a small annual fee). Various clubs from skiing to scuba diving (some affiliated with other Edinburgh colleges). New clubs budgeted for if more than 12 people are interested. **Hardship funds:** College loan system for students with good reasons. **Travel:** Edinburgh offers many student concessions on trains and buses. The numerous black cabs can work out cheaper than the bus if 4 or 5 share. **Work:** Many students have part-time work mainly in pubs and restaurants which frequently provide taxis back to campus late at night. A lot of courses involve placements in industries.

QUEEN MARY AND WESTFIELD

Queen Mary and Westfield College, University of London, Mile End Road, London E1 4NS (071-975 5555) Map D, C1

Student enquiries: Academic Registrar

Main study areas – as in What to Study section: *(First degree):* Aeronautical engineering, biochemistry, biology, biotechnology, botany, business studies, chemistry, civil engineering, classics, computing, dentistry, drama, economics, electrical & electronic engineering, English, environmental science, European studies, fine arts, geography, history, law, mathematical studies, mechanical and production engineering, medicine, metallurgy and materials science, microbiology, modern languages, physics, physiology, politics and government, zoology. *Also:* Astronomy, informatics, Rumanian, Russian.

European Community: Number of students learning an EC language or spending time in another EC country, not known but includes some science students. Formal exchange links with 25 EC universities/colleges: Belgium (1); France (2); Germany (8); Greece (1); Italy (8); Netherlands (3); Spain (2). Approved Erasmus programme 1990/91. Principal (Professor Butterworth) is pro-vice chancellor for European affairs for London University, involved in Network of European Capital Cities Universities. College library has European Documentation Centre. European chair from Jean Monnet Action Programme. Internal newsletter, Euronews. Involvement in wide range of European Commission research and development programmes and headquarters of European Centre for Pollution Research.

Application: UCCA. **Structural features:** Part of London University. **Academic features:** Italian available as a subsidiary subject and Georgian and Yiddish under the course unit system. Business studies may be combined with a variety of other subjects. **Special features:** Large number of visiting professors, including Tony Hunt, Sir Ernst Gombrich, Peter Davison, David Robinson, Terry Eagleton, Angel Vinas, Sir George Fowden, Bill Fishman, L Collins and His Honour Judge Stockdale. **Founded:** 1989, from merger of Westfield College (founded 1882) and Queen Mary College (originally founded 1887). **Main awards:** BA, MEng, BEng, BSc, BSc(Econ), BSc(Eng), LLB. **Awarding body:** London University. **Site:** Mile End Road. **Access:** Stepney Green or Mile End underground stations 5 minutes walk. Docklands Light Railway Bow Road station and bus or 10 minutes walk; buses. **Accommodation:** 700 places in halls of residence at South Woodford, other flats within 5 miles of campus, including 65 rooms in new canal-side campus residences. 460 in college self-catering accommodation. Accommodation office also deals with private sector. Rent: 20% in accommodation where rent controlled by university. **Library:** New library. 300,000 volumes, 220 periodicals, intensive use collection on 3-hour loan only. LIBERTAS computerised system for both catalogue and lending. 5 departmental libraries. **Specialist collections:** European documen-

CAN'T FIND WHAT YOU'RE LOOKING FOR? USE THE INDEX!

tation centre. **Other learning resources:** Language laboratory; LIVENET, computer facilities.**Welfare:** Health centre; chaplains, counsellors. **Hardship funds:** Small short-term loans to tide students over – further assistance might be available in extreme cases. **Special categories:** Local authority playgroup (children 2-5). **Careers:** Information, advice and placement service. **Amenities:** Bookshop and bank on site; SU building with snackbar, bar, gymnasium, squash courts, travel agency, 'Nightline' (telephone information and confidential listening service), chaplaincy (and ecumenical chapel); London University central facilities (including swimming pool) accessible; sports ground in Essex, close to central London by tube on the Central Line.

Duration of first degree course(s) or equivalent: 3 years; **others:** 4 years **Total first degree students 1989/90:** 4,757 **Number of overseas students:** 1,038 **Number of mature students:** 21% **Male/female ratio 1989/90:** 3:2 **Teaching staff: full-time:** c500 **Total full-time students 1989/90:** 5,102 **Postgraduate students:** 966 **Tuition fees, first degrees, 1990/91:** Home: £1,675; Overseas £5,208 (eg politics), £6,552 (eg physics).

What it's like (Queen Mary)

Situated in East End, 1 mile from the city; its impressive architecture dating back to 1880s is hard to miss. Easy access to centre of London, plenty of local culture. Canary Wharf 5 minutes.

New self-catering halls opened overlooking Regents Canal on the Mile End site in 1989, part of a much larger on-site residence development. Self-catering/private rented accommodation plentiful. Main halls at South Woodford (20 minutes by tube plus half-hourly night buses). Large overseas community, well integrated.

Active SU recently refurbished catering/bar facilities; expansions planned. Nightly entertainments programme. Welfare and counselling services. East London Nightline run from QMWSU. Over 100 clubs and societies, squash court, multigym and sports hall on site. New sports ground at Theydon Bois (on tube).

Renowned for science, engineering and law but many top quality smaller scale arts and social science departments. New faculty of basic medicine sciences for pre-clinical students of St Bartholomew's and the London Hospital Medical School. Course unit system provides flexibility. Language courses require a year spent abroad, usually very profitable experience. Quality of teaching varies. Work assessed by annual exams with fixed level of passes required to proceed. Generally unpopular system of having to take a year out to retake – no September resits.

Students of fairly mixed background, but noticeable tendency towards London-based students. Large numbers of American associate students. No notorious racism or sexism.

Pauper notes

Accommodation: Private rented plentiful. Some empty houses ripe for squatting. **Drink:** SU bar has wide range of drinks. Good East End pubs. 'Firkin' pubs at Hackney, Plaistow, selling the famous Dogbolter and the Barbican. **Eats:** Excellent local Indian cuisine. Cheap vegetarian wholefood at 'The Cherry Orchard', Bethnal Green. Local eel, pie & mash shops a must. **Ents:** Regular discos, weekly gigs of up and coming bands, plus cabaret slots. **Sports:** Multigym and squash courts on campus. Wide range of clubs and societies. Good local sports centres. **Hardship funds:** SU operates Hardship Fund administered by committee. **Travel:** Alice Mutta Travel Prize worth £180 for interesting project, plus expenditure fund. STA Travel branch in SU. **Work:** Work behind union bar and in union shop.

Alumni (Editors' pick)

Peter Hain, Geoffrey Drain, Sir Roy Strong, Judge Alan Lipfriend, Martin Cross, Rhys Williams, Dr Adam Neville, Lady Falkender, Ruth Prawer Jhabvala, Malcolm Bradbury, Andrea Newman, Simon Gray, Eva Figes, Christopher Holmes, Mel Gingell, Patrick Moore, Dr Paul Dean, Sir Norman Lindop, Elizabeth Andrews, Bruce Dickinson, David Sullivan.

CAN'T FIND WHAT YOU'RE LOOKING FOR? USE THE INDEX!

QUEEN'S COLLEGE GLASGOW

The Queen's College, Glasgow, 1 Park Drive, Glasgow G3 6LP
(041-334 8141) Map A, C3

Student enquiries: Student Recruitment & Publicity Office

Main study areas – as in What to Study section: *(First degree):* Health studies.

European Community: No students learn an EC language or spend time in another EC country. Informal exchange links with Netherlands. Approved Erasmus programme 1990/91.

Application: Direct. **Founded:** 1875. **Main awards:** BSc, BA. **Awarding body:** CNAA. **Site:** West end of the city. **Accommodation:** 140 places in halls of residence. Approx cost: £45 pw (meals weekdays only). **Library:** 50,000 volumes, 450 periodicals, 150 study places. **Welfare:** Student Advisory Centre; Student Representative Council; Studies Advisory Service; Overseas Students Office. **Hardship funds:** Limited funds available. **Careers:** Information, advice and milkround service. **Amenities:** Educational Development Unit, computing centre, communications studio, laboratories, students union, sports field and access to Jordanhill facilities on Southbrae campus.

Duration of first degree course(s) or equivalent: 3 years (physiotherapy and consumer & management studies); **others:** 4 years **Total first degree students 1989/90:** 570 **Male/female ratio 1989/90:** 1:6 **Teaching staff: full-time:** 79 **part-time:** small group **Total full-time students 1989/90:** 913 **Postgraduate students:** 57 **Tuition fees, first degrees, 1990/91:** Home: £1,675 (£628 if self-financing); Overseas: £4,600.

What it's like

Victorian red sandstone building with two modern wings overlooking Kelvingrove Park. Students' Residence, Gibson Hall, two miles away. Most either live at home or in flats/bedsits. Majority of students from West of Scotland; mixed backgrounds. High proportion of women due to type of courses offered. Few overseas students, quite a lot of mature students. Good relations with college authorities. Library open till 9 pm Monday–Thursday. Shop open 1½–2 hrs/week. SU becoming increasingly active – Folk Clubs and societies at the moment – basketball, badminton, volleyball, Christian Union, ski club, aerobics, Highlands connections club. Student Welfare and Careers Service run by college. Near other colleges and universities – **very** student area. Reciprocal agreements with colleges in area. Member of NUS.

No bar except at social functions, but plenty nearby.

Courses well run, with mixed methods of teaching used, most involve placement. Work assessed by exams, continual assessment and/or placement (depending on course).

Warm welcome awaits students and friends alike.

Pauper notes

Accommodation: College halls about 3 miles away – usually for first year students. Most students live in private accommodation. **Drink:** The Doublet (cheap, close to college, open all day); The Arlington Bar, Glasgow University Union (very close, very cheap). **Eats:** Refectory food reasonable but lots of great cafes and carry outs in the nearby Gibson Street. **Ents:** Grosvenor Cinema (cheap films for students). GFT student reductions. Up and coming bands at Halt bar. **Sports:** Use of swimming pool at Anniesland College, Kelvin Hall sports centre nearby. College tennis courts free for use. **Hardship funds:** Available in the form of a loan from the hardship fund. **Travel:** SRC subsidises exchange programmes to Australia, Canada and the USA. **Work:** Casual bar work in surrounding area, fast food shops, usually plenty of jobs.

CAN'T FIND WHAT YOU'RE LOOKING FOR? USE THE INDEX!

RADA

Royal Academy of Dramatic Art, 62–64 Gower Street, London WC1E 6ED (071-636 7076) Map E, C2

Student enquiries: The Registrar

Main study areas – as in What to Study section: Drama.

European Community: No students learn an EC language or spend time in another EC country.

Application: Direct. **Founded:** 1904, by Sir Herbert Beerbohm Tree; Royal Charter in 1920. **Main awards:** Diploma, Honours Diploma. **Awarding body:** RADA. **Site:** Gower Street, in heart of London University area. **Access:** Goodge Street, Euston Square, Russell Square, Tottenham Court Road or Warren Street underground stations. **Academic features:** Acting course (9 terms, autumn term intake); stage management course (6 terms, termly intake). **Access:** Central site, close to bus routes and several tube stations. **Accommodation:** No responsibility taken by Academy. **Library:** 13,000 volumes, 10 periodicals. **Specialist collections:** G B Shaw collection. **Centres of excellence:** Vanbrugh Theatre Club. **Welfare:** Access to all essential services. **Hardship funds:** Bursary Fund. **Careers:** Information, advice and placement service. **Amenities:** Three fully-equipped theatres, the Vanbrugh, the GBS and Studio 14; broadcasting studio, speech laboratory, video-tape, scenery and property workshops, design office and wardrobe, common rooms, canteen, bar. **Employment:** Theatre.

Duration of first degree course(s) or equivalent: 9 terms (acting); **others:** 6 terms (stage management) **Total first degree students 1989/90:** 120 **Number of overseas students:** 11 **Number of mature students:** 8 **Male/female ratio 1989/90:** 1:1 **Teaching staff: full-time:** 18 **part-time:** 90 **Total full-time students 1989/90:** 120 **Tuition fees, first degrees, 1990/91:** £4,410.

What it's like

You need talent, luck and determination. 2,000 apply for about 28 places: competition for female places even more intense (introduction to one of harsh realities of the theatre). Once in, pace is hectic with everybody working long hours to accommodate evening tutorials, singing lessons, rehearsals, performances, etc, etc. Timetable includes classes on voice and movement, fencing, tumbling, dialect – anything an actor is likely to need. Demanding, pressured, requires mental and physical fitness; especially for stage management students who work almost 7-day week on constant stream of productions. This course includes set design and construction, props, lighting, sound. Staff/student relations very good. Professional directors from outside work on productions in GBS or larger Vanbrugh theatres. At start of 7-term course rehearsals are evenly matched with classes but rehearsals take over by end. 2 full years of public performances – unmatched by any other drama school. When you leave there's Catch 22 situation: to get a job you need an Equity card, to get a card you have to have a job. RADA can't bend logic but it will give you best tuition and best showcase for talents in UK – if you can get in. Because of size tight student community where lasting friendships develop. Students come from large variety of backgrounds and from all over the world (GB, Ireland, NZ, USA, Canada). Excellent well-stocked library. No accommodation provided.

Pauper notes

Drink: Bar on premises not subsidised; ULU (Malet St). **Eats:** Good canteen on site. Plenty of cafes, stalls etc in the area. **Ents:** Plays are free to students on course. **Sports:** Use of ULU. **Hardship funds:** No personal loans.

CAN'T FIND WHAT YOU'RE LOOKING FOR? USE THE INDEX!

Alumni (Editors' pick)

Alan Bates, Sir John Gielgud, Dame Flora Robson, Susannah York, Sir Richard Attenborough, Glenda Jackson, Joan Collins, Ben Cross, Robert Lindsay, Lisa Eichhorn, Jonathan Pryce, Juliet Stevenson, Kenneth Brannagh, Anton Lesser, John Hurt, Richard Briers, Albert Finney, Antony Hopkins, Sir Anthony Quayle.

RAPID RESULTS COLLEGE

The Rapid Results College, Tuition House, St George's Road, London SW19 4DS (081-947 7272) Map D, B4

Student enquiries: Director of Student Services

Main study areas – as in What to Study section: *(First degree):* Law.

European Community: No students learn an EC language or spend time in another EC country.

Application: Direct. **Founded:** 1928. **Main awards:** LLB. **Awarding body:** London University (External). **Site:** Tuition House is at Wimbledon. **Access:** Wimbledon station (BR and underground). **Academic features:** Distance learning courses that are self-contained and do not require additional textbooks. Includes full tutorial service with written or telephone contact with specialist tutors. **Careers:** Information and advisory service.

Duration of first degree course(s) or equivalent: minimum of 3 years **First degree students:** No limit to entry numbers. **Tuition fees, first degrees, 1990/91:** Home: £516 (intermediate), £556 (final parts 1 and 2); Overseas: £536 (intermediate), £576 (final parts 1 and 2).

RAVENSBOURNE COLLEGE

Ravensbourne College of Design and Communication, Walden Road, Elmstead Woods, Chislehurst, Kent BR7 5SN (081-468 7071) Map D, D4

Student enquiries: Admissions Officer

Main study areas – as in What to Study section: *(First degree):* Art & design. **Also:** Television operations and engineering.

European Community: No students learn an EC language or spend time in another EC country. 2 formal exchange links in France and Netherlands. Approved Erasmus programme 1990/91.

Application: ADAR. **Founded:** 1962, ex Bromley College of Art and Beckenham School of Art. **Main awards:** BA. **Awarding body:** CNAA. **Site:** 1 mile from Chislehurst; 18 acre main site plus Wharton Road School of Television; annexe in Bromley. **Access:** British Rail from Charing Cross to Elmstead Woods for the main site, and to Bromley North for the Wharton Road, School of Television site. **Accommodation:** 105 places in hall (mixed); list of local addresses. Approx cost: £30.00 pw. 18% in accommodation where rent controlled by college. **Library:** 2, at main site and Wharton Road annexe; 20,000 volumes in total, 140 periodicals; slide library. **Other learning resources:** Desktop publishing and computer image generation laboratories. New television studios equipped to broadcast standard. **Careers:** Information and advice service. **Amenities:** All workshops necessary for art and design courses (plus process and dye labs, printing rooms, etc); SU bar;

CAN'T FIND WHAT YOU'RE LOOKING FOR? USE THE INDEX!

television studios/facilities. **Sporting facilities:** Sports centre at Crystal Palace 20–30 min bus ride away.

Duration of first degree course(s) or equivalent: 3 years **Total first degree students 1989/90:** 350 **Number of overseas students:** 26 **Male/female ratio 1989/90:** 5:4 **Teaching staff: full-time:** 40 **part-time:** 60 **Total full-time students 1989/90:** 600 **Tuition fees, first degrees, 1990/91:** Home: £1,675; Overseas: £4,912.

What it's like
Chislehurst doesn't give any clues. College nestles among expensive residences of London stockbrokers. Follow the next battered Beetle or Suzuki Jeep to get to it.

Very quiet; but Thursday night is social night. Students enjoy it, neighbours don't. Bromley also quiet. Only 15 minutes to central London though; trains about every 10 minutes. Best of both worlds really; quiet working environment near the country's social centre.

Atmosphere at college very good. Small so easy to get to know people. Everybody's familiar soon; very relaxed until you're in a studio. You're here to work, you get out what you put in. Everything's here, it's up to you.

If there's anything wrong, it's the refectory but we're working on it. Beer is a little expensive, but it doesn't seem to have stopped anyone from drinking it.

Pauper notes
Accommodation: Only two-thirds of 1st years in halls, so get to know one and crash out there. **Drink:** Fox and Firkin in Lewisham, sing along with a Dog Bolter. **Eats:** Canteen too dear and bubble and squeak too prominent. **Ents:** Film club every Tuesday. Thursday night rave – comedians, bands, discos etc. **Sports:** Aerobics every Wednesday, volleyball every Monday. Crystal Palace up the road. **Travel:** Have travel card will travel or have barrier will jump. **Work:** Plenty of part-time work servicing the Bromley big-wigs. **Shops:** Shop on campus for materials.

Alumni (Editors' pick)
Karen Franklin (Clothes Show); Maria Cornego (fashion designer).

"Lots of graduates take menial work (eg milkman) so they can continue painting"

CAN'T FIND WHAT YOU'RE LOOKING FOR? USE THE INDEX!

READING UNIVERSITY

University of Reading, Whiteknights, Reading RG6 2AH (0734 875123)
Map A, E8

Student enquiries: Sub-Dean of the Faculty in which you wish to study

Main study areas – as in What to Study section: *(First degree):* Accountancy, agriculture & horticulture, American studies, archaeology, art & design, biochemistry, biology, biotechnology, botany, business studies, chemistry, classics, computing, drama, economics, education, electrical & electronic engineering, English, environmental science, fine arts, food science and nutrition, geography, history, information technology, law, linguistics, mathematical studies, mechanical and production engineering, microbiology, modern languages, music, philosophy, physics, physiology, politics and government, psychology, sociology, speech sciences, town and country planning, welfare studies, zoology. *Also:* Building studies, crop science, estate management, medieval studies, meteorology, surveying – general practice, typography.

European Community: 10% first degree students take EC language as part of course and 9% spend 6 months or more in another EC country. Formal exchange links with over 35 EC universities/colleges: Belgium (1); Denmark (1); Eire (1); France (10); Germany (7); Italy (5); Netherlands (3); Spain (3); most open to non-language specialists. Approved Erasmus programme 1990/91.

Application: UCCA. **Special features:** Navarra String Quartet in residence. **Founded:** 1892. (Bulmershe College of HE joined the university in 1989. **Main awards:** BA, BSc, BEng, LLB, BEd. **Awarding body:** Reading University. **Site:** Whiteknights: 300 acres on Southern outskirts of Reading; also buildings in London Road and Bulmershe Court. **Access:** Easy access to M4; frequent bus service from campus to town. Good trains and buses to London and elsewhere. **Accommodation:** 4,200 students in halls of residence; all first years accommodated. Also self-catering flats. Accommodation office helps students to find flats and houses outside university. Facilities for disabled students. **Library:** Main library with 600,000 books and pamphlets, 4,000 periodicals; extra copies of course books most in demand kept in reserve collection; various faculty libraries including education. **Specialist collections:** Overstone Library (economics, literature and history); Stenton Library (history); Cole Library of Early Medicine and Zoology; Finzi Poetry Collection. **Other learning facilities:** Computer centre; university museums (English Rural Life, Greek Archaeology, and Zoology), language laboratories. **Welfare:** Counselling service and health centre (with doctors, dentists and psychiatrist), learning resource centre, tutor system, nightline, legal advice (through students' union), chaplains. **Hardship funds:** Fund available. **Careers:** Advisory service. **Amenities:** Union building with bars, shops, travel and insurance services etc; many athletic and social clubs; boathouses on Thames; sailing and canoeing on Thames and nearby gravel pits; sports hall. Reading film theatre, bookshop, banks, playing fields on the campus, playgroup, nursery.

Duration of first degree course(s) or equivalent: 3 years; 4 years (languages, art, food technology, typography) **Total first degree students 1989/90:** 5,714 **Total BEd students:** 427 **Number of overseas students:** 553 **Number of mature students:** 14% **Male/female ratio 1989/90:** 1:1 **Teaching staff: full-time:** 650 approx **part-time:** 30 approx **Total full-time students 1989/90:** 7,393 **Postgraduate students:** 2,740 **Tuition fees, first degrees, 1990/91:** Home: £1,675; Overseas: £4,560 (eg politics), £6,050 (eg physics).

What it's like

Situated on the edge of the town, mainly on the Whiteknights Park; an open, green campus. Reading's main virtue is proximity to London and Oxford, but it has good shopping facilities and excellent rail, coach and motorway connections (SU Travel

CAN'T FIND WHAT YOU'RE LOOKING FOR? USE THE INDEX!

Office supplies cheap tickets). Getting about during the rush hour is a problem.

About half the students live in one of the thirteen halls of residence. These provide good accommodation for the first year, but it's a good idea to move into a student house in the second year. Accommodation in Reading is not cheap. SU provides entertainments and services with cheap bars, shops and concerts, as well as a very thorough welfare service for all the problems students might have.

Academically, an excellent reputation in agriculture, history and, since the merger with Bulmershe College, teacher training, to name but a few. Courses allow flexibility and the FUE system allows students to change courses well into their first year. Like anything or anywhere, life at university and Reading is largely what you make it. Those who work hard and play hard tend to profit the most. Don't feel afraid to take a year out; you'll notice the benefits when you come here.

Pauper notes

Accommodation: 13 halls of residence, student houses. Student flats. Married quarters. **Drink:** All halls have a bar (cheaper than pubs, more expensive than union). SU has 2 bars. Local brews Brakespears at The Dove; Courage at The Jolly Angler; London ESB at the Butler. **Eats:** Reasonable service offered by university. Union catering expanding – cheap snacks, hot and cold plus vegetarian. Town has usual takeaways with some restaurants offering NUS discounts. **Ents:** Top name bands, cabaret, discos in union. Gigs on Tuesday in SU. Discos every Friday. Cabaret alternate Thursdays. Alternative music at the After Dark Club and Washington Heights. Theatre: Hexagon, Reading Film Theatre, South Hill Park at Bracknell. **Sports:** Sports centre on campus. Cheap sports sales in SU. Some swimming pools give NUS discount. Over 200 clubs/societies (100+ sports – football good).**Hardship fund:** University and union discretionary hardship funds. **Travel:** Easy to hitch to and from. Excellent travel office gives student fares. Good communications but very busy at peak times. **Work:** Work in SU bar. Plenty of part-time jobs available, temping during the summer.

Alumni (Editors' pick)

Andy Mackay (composer and performer, Roxy Music), Baroness Pike (chairman, Broadcasting Complaints Commission), Christine Rolfe (first known woman slaughterhouse supervisor), Sir Richard Trehane (ex-Milk Marketing Board), Steve Vines (Observer labour editor), Jim Bacon (BBC weatherman), Sue Turner (controller of children's programmes Thames TV), Gillian Freeman (novelist and biographer), Phil Vesty (Olympic walker), Richard Livesey (Liberal MP for Brecon), Clive Ponting (former civil servant), Elspeth Huxley, Sir Noel Stockdale (chairman ASDA/MFI group), Vasso Papandreou (European Commissioner), Susanne Charlton (BBC weatherperson). David Wright (arts officer for Bucks county council), Graham Ritchie (general manager, Belgrade Theatre, Coventry), Beverley Goddard (Olympic sprinter), Jennie Orpwood (wheelchair disabled Olympic swimmer).

RIPON & YORK ST JOHN

The College of Ripon & York St John, (1) The College, Lord Mayor's Walk, York YO3 7EX (0904 656771). (2) The College, College Road, Ripon HG4 2QX (0765 2691) Map A, E5

Student enquiries: Registrar (York address)

Main study areas – as in What to Study section: *(First degree):* Art and design, American studies, biology, education, English, environmental science, geography, history, modern languages, music, religious studies and theology. *Also:* Movement studies, performance arts.

CAN'T FIND WHAT YOU'RE LOOKING FOR? USE THE INDEX!

European Community: 8% first degree students take EC language as part of course and 8% spend 6 months or more in another EC country. Formal exchange links with 4 EC universities/colleges: France (1); Germany (1); Netherlands (2). Contemporary Europe studies, with semester at Grenoble University, France, or the Free University of Amsterdam available to selected students.

Application: UCCA. **Special features:** Modular degrees on semester pattern. **Academic features:** 2 year BEd for post-industrial students teaching design and technology. **Largest fields of study:** Education. **Founded:** 1975, amalgamation St John's College York and The College Ripon. **Main awards:** BA, BSc, BA/BSc (QTS). **Awarding bodies:** Leeds University/CNAA. **Site:** Campuses close to centres Ripon and York (25 miles apart). **Access:** Good road and rail links: A1, M1, M62. Regular inter-site campus buses. **Accommodation:** 420 (York) and 280 (Ripon) places in hall; 280 (York) and 60 (Ripon) places in college houses, flats; lodgings at both sites. Approx cost: Halls of residence £50 pw (incl all meals). **Library:** Library on each site; 175,000 volumes, 600+ periodicals, 330 study places, course books for reference and loan. **Specialist collections:** 19th century children's books. Local studies collection. **Other learning facilities:** Religious education centre, AV materials, slide and record library; CCTV unit and video equipment, computing facilities on both campuses. **Welfare:** Doctor, dentists, 2 chaplains. Chapel on each campus. **Special categories:** Nursery school at Ripon site. **Careers:** Information, advice and placement. **Amenities:** SU both sites – bars, coffee bars, shops, gymnasia, Olympic standard pool, squash courts, dry-slope skiing; extensive playing fields. Arts centres, galleries and museums in York. **Employment:** Education, retail management, leisure services, public service admin, social and community work, journalism, the media.

Duration of first degree course(s) or equivalent: 3 years **others:** 4 years BA/BSc (QTS) **Total first degree students 1989/90:** 1,644; **BEd students:** 601 **Male/female ratio 1989/90:** 1:3 **Teaching staff:** 134 fte **Total full-time students 1989/90:** 1,895 **Postgraduate students:** 61 **Tuition fees, first degrees, 1990/91:** Home: £1,675; Overseas: £4,180.

What it's like

Main campus in York, just outside city walls with clear view of Minster and 5 sites around the city – 3 residential. Ripon campus 25 miles away is much quieter, set in spacious grounds, good community relations. Minibus service links the two campuses 4 times daily.

All new students accommodated in halls (21 meal package included in residence fees), kitchen areas provided in all halls. College also rents other houses, but not enough. York rents rising.

Female/male 4:1 at York, less healthy at Ripon at 8:1. Mature students steadily increasing, exchange programmes to both Europe and America every year: international flavour to campus atmosphere.

Well-developed SU provides wide variety of clubs and societies, entertainments, welfare services, two shops, two bars, part and full-time staff. Focal point for social life, some political activity, much apathy. Professional counselling network on both campuses, run by staff and students. College as a whole has a very friendly atmosphere.

York has much to offer: top tourist city; 365 pubs, clubs, restaurants, two theatres, a cinema, market, art gallery, monuments, museums. London is 2 hrs by train. Ripon is very different: a quiet market town, different campus atmosphere reflects this. Has pubs, a market, restaurants, no train station, buses regularly to Harrogate.

Leeds University validated degrees. Most courses modular. High application rate – 12 for each place. Well regarded nationally, low drop-out rate. Attracts students from all over Britain, most from comprehensives or colleges of FE. Overall picture is one of healthy academic development with much social interaction.

Pauper notes

Accommodation: Internal option for all new students; external provided by college and housing agencies. Rents increasing due to house price boom and new law college. **Drink:** Yorkshire home of good beer. York – Royal Oak (Camerons), Tap & Spile (Free House), Spread Eagle (Free House), Brigadier Gerard (Sam Smiths), Black Swan; Ripon – Black Bull (Theakstons), Golden Lion, Studley Royal, King Billy. **Eats:** York – anything at any price; Ripon – Valentino's cheap Italian, Indian, Dominic's nice but pricy. Special discount in over 50 places in Ripon and York arranged by SU. **Ents:** York – Theatre Royal, cinema, Spotted Cow – live music. **Sports:** York – on campus pool, tennis courts, squash courts, 2 gymnasia 5 mins walk. Ripon – on-site gym, pool in city. Harrogate for further facilities. **Hardship funds:** SU welfare, Bursar, number of funds to help those in trouble. **Travel:** York main line intercity, 2 hrs to London. Ripon – bus to Harrogate and Leeds. **Work:** Campus vacation work and much local in Ripon and York.

Alumni (Editors' pick)
Jeff Squires, Geoff Cooke.

ROBERT GORDON'S INSTITUTE

Robert Gordon's Institute of Technology, Schoolhill, Aberdeen AB9 1FR (0224 633611) Map A, D2

Student enquiries: Assistant Registrar (Student Administration)

Main study areas – as in What to Study section: *(First degree):* Architecture, art & design, business studies, chemistry, computing, electrical and electronic engineering, food science & nutrition, hotel & catering management, information technology, library & information studies, mathematical studies, mechanical and production engineering, pharmacy, physics, public administration, welfare studies. *Also:* Building studies, European business studies, quantity surveying.

European Community: Number of students learning an EC language or spending time in another EC country, not known. 6 formal exchange links (France and Germany) all open to non-specialists, and more developing.

Application: Direct. **Special features:** 1 year exchange programmes with Oregon State University; Illinois Institute of Tech. **Academic features:** New courses in technology and business; legal and administration studies; European business administration with languages. **Largest fields of study:** Art, architecture, engineering, business studies, pharmacy. **Founded:** Designated in 1903 as one of the Scottish Central Institutions. **Main awards:** BA, BSc, BEng. **Awarding body:** CNAA. **Site:** 6 sites in or near Aberdeen city centre. **Accommodation:** 267 places for first years in halls of residence (segregated) and self-catering units; 375 self-catering flats. Approx cost: £40 pw hall; £27 pw flats. 316 private flats. Approx cost: £25–£30 per week. Rent: 25% in accommodation where rent controlled by institute. **Library:** 160,000 volumes in total, 1,600 periodicals, 410 study places. **Welfare:** Accommodation officer, student counsellors, careers officer, chaplaincy, medical advisory service. **Hardship funds:** Loan scheme from Registry. **Careers:** Information and advice service. **Amenities:** SA with bar, games room, etc; most sports (facilities available at Kepplestone).

Duration of first degree course(s) or equivalent: 3 and 4 years for honours; **others:** Business studies 4 years 1 term for honours; computer science 5 years for honours. **Total first degree students 1989/90:** 2,600 **Number of overseas students:** 160 **Number of mature students:** 150 **Male/female ratio 1989/90:** 3:2 **Teaching staff: full-time:** 310 **Total full-time students 1989/90:** 3,650 **Postgraduate students:** 300 **Tuition fees, first degrees, 1990/91:** Home: £628; Overseas: £4,400.

CAN'T FIND WHAT YOU'RE LOOKING FOR? USE THE INDEX!

What it's like

Scotland's second largest central institution spread over six sites throughout the city. Aberdeen has large student population and RGIT students mix easily with university, commerce and technical students. Increasing in size and reputation despite cutbacks at other institutes. Courses range from fine art to mechanical and offshore engineering with a highly practical slant on most, particularly attractive to employers. Relatively easy to change from degrees to honours degrees and vice versa. Assessment varies from course to course, but exams play a large part, along with lab work, practical etc.

SA building has 1 bar/disco, and a new lounge bar/art gallery, TV room, video room, hairdresser, laundry, canteen, MTV and has over 30 clubs and societies, ranging from hockey to fencing to Chinese boxing to boardgames. SA which campaigns on many political student issues, but is mainly concerned with student issues, produces 'The Review', Aberdeen's leading student newspaper. Students from all over UK, with quite large overseas contingent. Atmosphere hardworking, but lively and employment prospects are good.

Pauper notes

Accommodation: Some short life 'hard to let' flats available (further out of town – cheaper it gets). **Drink:** RGIT union, Prince of Wales (real ale), Harriet Street Bar, Caledon Bar (for architecture and art students). **Eats:** RGIT Union, Radars, Jaws (wholefood), La Lombarda (Italian). **Ents:** SA ents, Odeon/Cannon cinemas, Capitol (cheap films and bands), HM Theatre (occasional student discounts), lively student clubs, Ritzy on a Monday night, the Pelican Club. **Sports:** SA clubs and societies, RGC swimming pool, TC facilities (business studies students only). **Hardship funds:** Institute administers several funds – contact SA first. **Travel:** 'Stagecoach' cheap inter-city travel, BR railcard. **Work:** Usual part time jobs in bars, tutoring, babysitting.

"Due to oil boom private accommodation scarce and very expensive"

CAN'T FIND WHAT YOU'RE LOOKING FOR? USE THE INDEX!

ROEHAMPTON INSTITUTE

Roehampton Institute, Roehampton Lane, London SW15 5PU
(081-878 8117)
(1) Digby Stuart College, Roehampton Lane, London SW15 5PH
(081-876 8273)
(2) Froebel Institute College, Roehampton Lane, London SW15 5PJ
(081-876 2242)
(3) Southlands College, Wimbledon Parkside, London SW19 5NN
(081-946 2234)
(4) Whitelands College, West Hill, London SW15 3SN (081-788 8268)
Map D, A3

Student enquiries: Registrar (address 1 above)

Main study areas – as in What to Study section: *(First degree):* Art & design, biology, business studies, chemistry, dance, drama, education, English, environmental studies, fine arts, geography, history, mathematical studies, modern languages, music, psychology, religious studies & theology, sociology, welfare studies. *Also:* Home economics, sports studies.

European Community: 18% first degree students take EC language as part of course and 16% spend 6 months or more in another EC country. Formal exchange links with some 12 EC universities/colleges in Belgium and France (for language students only); other links being developed. Approved Erasmus programme 1990/91.

Application: UCCA. **Special features:** Degrees are combinations of 2 subjects. Over 100 possible combinations. **Largest fields of study:** Education, English, history. **Founded:** 1975, ex Digby Stuart, Froebel Institute, Southlands and Whitelands Colleges. Affiliated to the University of Surrey. **Main awards:** BA, BA(QTS), BSc. **Awarding body:** Surrey University. **Site:** 4 sites in Wimbledon/Roehampton area. **Access:** Bus, train and underground. **Accommodation:** 1,130 places in mixed and segregated halls (all first years normally accommodated; 45% of total). Rent: 45% of students housed in accommodation where rent controlled by Institute. **Library:** Library at each site; 300,000 volumes in total, 1,200 periodicals, 525 study places. **Specialist collections:** Early Childhood Archive. **Welfare:** Welfare officer, doctor, chaplains. **Careers:** Counsellor on site. **Amenities:** SU building at each site. **Sporting facilities:** Facilities in and near colleges for wide variety of sports.

Duration of first degree course(s) or equivalent: 3 years (BA/BSc), 4 years (BA(QTS)) and BA with French **Total first degree students 1989/90:** 2,565 **BA(QTS) students:** 605 **Number of overseas students:** 8 **Number of mature students:** 640 **Male/female ratio 1989/90:** 1:4 **Teaching staff:** 220 **Total full-time students 1989/90:** 2,877 **Postgraduate students:** 943 **Tuition fees, first degrees, 1990/91:** Home: £1,675; Overseas: £4,600 (eg politics), £6,100 (eg physics).

What it's like

Formed from four colleges, Digby Stuart, Southlands, Whitelands and Froebel, the size of institute offers the same academic and recreational facilities as larger universities but with the advantage of belonging to a smaller college. This can often be an advantage to students who need more support and guidance in their studies. Teaching takes place in all four colleges (a free bus service is provided to transport students).

  Digby Stuart 15% of funding comes from the Society of the Sacred Heart – a Catholic college, although you don't need to be Catholic. The Catholic ethos is apparent and Mass is available daily, but people are free to enjoy their own faith.

CAN'T FIND WHAT YOU'RE LOOKING FOR? USE THE INDEX!

A good situation geographically, close enough to central London to enjoy the benefits of city life but far enough away not to be caught up in the rat race. Close to Richmond, Putney, Kingston and Wimbledon for shopping trips, nights out and work!

SU offers range of weekly activities, discos, bands, bar games, theatre productions and lots of clubs and societies as well as information on welfare topics and talks on specific topics.

Pauper notes

Accommodation: Offered to most first years and final years; all second years live out. Help available in finding places from the accommodations officer. **Drink:** Staff/student social club. Beer prices not too bad, pretty reasonable for London. **Eats:** Food not bad in residence; lots of places to eat outside, including places that deliver free. **Ents:** Many varied societies, bands, discos, large video screen. **Sports:** Well-established field sports. Amateur sport encouraged. **Travel:** BR (Barnes Station). Good bus routes. **Work:** Noticeboards are always full of people advertising for students. 99% guaranteed of a job at Wimbledon during the championships.

Alumni (Editors' pick)

Ashley Ward (English athletics international), Vivien Leigh. Pope John Paul II visited here in 1982.

ROSE BRUFORD COLLEGE

Rose Bruford College of Speech and Drama, Lamorbey Park, Sidcup, Kent DA15 9DF (081-300 3024) Map D, D4

Student enquiries: Chief Administration Officer

Main study areas – as in What to Study section: *(First degree):* Drama. **Also:** Stage management.

European Community: No students learn an EC language or spend time in another EC country.

Application: Direct. **Academic features:** BA in theatre degree (3 years); Diploma in technical theatre arts. All courses accredited by National Council for Drama Training. **Founded:** By Rose Bruford in 1950. **Main awards:** BA and Diplomas. **Awarding body:** CNAA (degrees); College (diplomas). **Site:** Lamorbey Park, Sidcup, Kent. **Access:** British Rail (Charing Cross 30 min); easy access from A20 or M2. **Accommodation:** College is non-residential. Students live locally in flats or lodgings. Rent: no student accommodated where rent is under college control. **Library:** 24,000 books, 12,000 slides, 100 periodicals, 30 reading places; audio-visual and photocopying facilities; tuition in library use and research methods. GEAC computerised cataloguing and circulation system. **Welfare:** Accommodation officer on site; local doctors and dentists. **Careers:** Agents, theatre managers and related employers invited to College productions. Continuing placement facilities to past students. **Hardship funds:** Small funds administered by college and Student Union. **Amenities:** Barn theatre; cinemas and swimming pool locally; grass tennis courts and extensive grounds; nearby banks and shops; plus all London facilities. **Employment:** Theatre and allied fields.

Duration of first degree course(s) or equivalent: 3 years **Total first degree students 1989/90:** 182 **Number of overseas students:** 6 **Male/female ratio 1989/90:** 1:2 **Teaching staff: full-time:** 23 **part-time:** large number of visiting tutors **Total full-time students 1989/90:** 238 **Tuition fees, first degrees, 1990/91:** Home: £1,675 (£607 if self-financing); Overseas: £4,500.

CAN'T FIND WHAT YOU'RE LOOKING FOR? USE THE INDEX!

What it's like

Rose Bruford College is in the middle of an academic upheaval. The two performance courses have this year, for the first time, emerged as a unique theatre degree course. The fact that this comes at a time when the arts have suffered severe blows from the economic climate, shows a deep commitment to theatre of the future.

SU has active anti-racist/sexist, classist policies, and is designed to represent the student in all areas of concern. Because of its small size, it has none of facilities available to larger institutions, however through affiliations access is possible.

With no halls of residence of its own, students live in rented accommodation across the south-east London area. Everything is expensive, and with tremendous workload, once you graduate, you will be fully prepared for a career in theatre.

Here's to an **exciting** three years!
Jane Erridge

Pauper notes

Accommodation: College ensures suitable lodgings nearby. **Drink:** Sidcup has no cheap or interesting places, the nearest are Deptford and Lewisham. **Eats:** College has extortionate canteen – look out for Veganomics in Lewisham. **Ents:** Good location for London fringe, always something to see at college. **Sports:** Good summer sports facilities on campus, swimming baths nearby. **Hardship funds:** College has trust funds, also SU fund. **Travel:** Expensive – student rail card a must. Hitching not advisable. College welfare van – must be over 21. **Work:** Some students have to work during term; college workload means many overdrafts not repaid until holiday work!

Alumni (Editors' pick)

Freddie Jones, Tom Baker, Nerys Hughes, Angharad Rees, Barbara Kellerman, Gary Oldman, Emma Wray, Janet Dibley, Jon Iles, Diane Louise Jordan.

ROYAL ACADEMY OF MUSIC

Royal Academy of Music, Marylebone Road, London NW1 5HT (071-935 5461) Map E, B1

Student enquiries: Admissions Officer

Main study areas – as in What to Study section: *(First degree):* Music.

European Community: 15% first degree students take EC language as part of course and 1% spend 6 months or more in another EC country. Formal exchange links with Paris Conservatoire and Hochschule in Hannover, Hamburg and Freiburg (as well as, outside the EC, Vienna, Salzburg, Budapest and Warsaw); all open to all undergraduates. Other individual and group exchanges through European music education network.

Application: Direct. **Special features:** Many distinguished visiting musicians, such as the Russian violinist Zakhar Bron and the Amadeus Quartet. Five international chairs; Lynn Harrell; Anne-Sophie Mutter; Robert Tear; Hans Werner Henze; Sir Colin Davis. Annual composers festival. **Academic features:** New joint centre for Advanced Musical Studies established by Academy and King's College, London. **Founded:** 1822. **Main awards:** BMus, Certificate of Advanced Studies, MMus. **Awarding body:** Royal Academy of Music and London University. **Site:** Central London. **Access:** Baker Street or Regent's Park underground stations. **Accommodation:** 44 places in halls of residence (mixed), plus new purpose-built hostel. Rent: 9% in accommodation where rent controlled by academy. **Library:** 175,000 items in total, 40 periodicals. **Specialist collections:** Sir Henry Wood, Sullivan Archive and Otto Klemperer collections of orchestral scores. **Welfare:** Student services; SU give details of all services. **Careers:** Information and advice

CAN'T FIND WHAT YOU'RE LOOKING FOR? USE THE INDEX!

service. **Amenities:** Local music shop within a few yards; concert hall, opera theatre; 5 organs; RAM Magazine; canteen, students' club (licensed); enhanced social/sports facilities. **Hardship funds:** Substantial awards and funds available, particularly for postgraduate students.

Duration of first degree course(s) or equivalent: 4 years (performers); **others:** 3 years (GRSM and BMus) **Total first degree students 1989/90:** 344 **Number of overseas students:** 54 **Number of mature students:** 70 **Male/female ratio 1989/90:** 9:11 **Teaching staff: full-time:** 9 **part-time:** 126 **Total full-time students 1989/90:** 502 **Postgraduate students:** 158 **Tuition fees, first degrees, 1990/91:** Home: £1,675; Overseas: £6,000-£8,100.

What it's like

Housed in a pink wedding cake off busy Marylebone Road, close to Madame Tussauds, but with a little more life! Atmosphere serious but social. Practice the order of the day (every day!) for students looking to make the grade as professional musicians. Excellent personal tuition from some of the finest members of the profession and resident academic staff. Performing ability is most important but there are courses in written musical disciplines. Most musical tastes and abilities catered for: Baroque; Jazz; Big B.

ROYAL ACADEMY SCHOOLS

Royal Academy of Arts, Piccadilly, London W1V 0DS (071-439 7438) Map E, B3

Student enquiries: Secretary

Main study areas – as in What to Study section: *(First degree):* This is a postgraduate UKCPU

Main study areas – as in What to Study section *(Not at first degree level):* Art & design.

European Community: Number of students learning an EC language or spending time in another EC country, not known.

Application: Direct. **Founded:** 1768. **Main awards:** Postgraduate diploma. **Awarding body:** Royal Academy Schools. **Site:** Piccadilly. **Access:** Piccadilly underground station; various buses. **Academic features:** All courses are of 3 years' duration, with annual examinations; the majority of teaching is done by visiting tutors. All courses are postgrad. **Accommodation:** Schools secretary will advise. **Library:** 15,000 volumes, various periodicals. **Specialist collections:** Old master drawings/prints. **Welfare:** Doctor, psychiatrist, chaplain. **Careers:** Advice service. **Amenities:** St James' Church (the artists' church) opposite; National Gallery and other galleries within easy reach. **Employment:** Teaching.

Total full-time students 1989/90: 60 (postgraduate) **Tuition fees, first degrees, 1990/91:** Home/Overseas: £3,500

What it's like

Situated in the West End behind the Academy Gallery and next to the Museum of Mankind. Entrance to the College is via Burlington Gardens.

The only 3 year, full-time, postgraduate course in the country and is an independent college, not state-run. Intake of approximately 15 painters and 3–4 sculptors a year. Although these are the only basic courses offered, there is a printmaking department which is basic but covers all areas of the medium and technicians are available for help and advice.

New liberal attitude towards the individual student under the new Keeper,

Professor Norman Adams RA; students are not obliged to take up the rather more academic side of the course, ie life drawing, unless they choose to. The spaces available are getting bigger due to the cutting of the degree course and all students are guaranteed a reasonable working area. The schools have a regular turnover of Academicians who come in to tutor and outside artists also occasionally visit.

Being situated in the centre of London, access to all the large galleries is very good, and many other independent galleries such as those in Cork Street, are all a few moments away; therefore the possibilities for seeing all kinds of art work are vast.

There are links with the Royal Academy Gallery itself with at least two annual student shows in the Diploma Gallery which attract a large amount of the public. Entrance to Academy exhibitions for students is free. A small bar in the canteen and parties can be arranged.

The Royal Academy Schools are basically a set of studio spaces with regular tutoring, but being a small institution it does not operate in the same way that other colleges do. As a result of this, students are not hampered by the machinations of a larger college or university and there is more room for student influence in the running of the school.

Visiting hours are between 1.00 and 2.00 or 4.00 and 4.30.

Pauper notes
Drink: Subsidised real ale at college bar. **Eats:** Canteen very cheap by London standards. Plenty of cheap alternatives in area. **Ents:** Free admission to all RA exhibitions. **Grants:** Some DES money available for RA Schools fees. No maintenance grants. **Hardship funds:** Frequent opportunities to exhibit work in college galleries (Burlington Hse) and cash awards for outstanding work. Also able to sell work at exhibition. **Travel:** Travel scholarships to selected students. Occasional visits to far-away lands.

ROYAL COLLEGE OF ART

Royal College of Art (RCA), Kensington Gore, London SW7 2EU (071-584 5020) Map E, A3

Student enquiries: The Registrar

This is a postgraduate UKCPU

Main study areas – as in What to Study section (not at first degree level): Art and design including holography, illustration, natural history illustration, technical and scientific illustration, design management, vehicle design, tapestry, visual Islamic and traditional arts, bronze casting and history of design.

European Community: Number of students learning an EC language or spending time in another EC country, not known but college encourages student exchanges. Approved Erasmus programme 1990/91.

Special features
A postgraduate university institution with Royal Charter. **Main awards:** MA, MDes, PhD, and DrRCA. **Academic features:** Project or thesis work, following individual student proposals, forms an increasing proportion of degree work. PhD work may be carried out in any discipline provided resources exist; minimum period of study is 2 full-time equivalent years.
Application: Direct. Entry for Masters courses by competitive examination; usually about 300 places a year. Candidates normally aged 21-40 with a first degree send in portfolios of recent work. Applications for Masters by end of January; for PhD, April.

Application for state bursaries in the case of English and Welsh candidates is made through RCA but award is not automatic. Scottish candidates should apply to

CAN'T FIND WHAT YOU'RE LOOKING FOR? USE THE INDEX!

Scottish Education Department and Northern Irish candidates apply to Ministry of Education, Northern Ireland. (For addresses see *How to go about it.*)

Home students only are eligible for UK state bursaries. All financial arrangements should have been made before the student arrives.

Accommodation: College provides none. Rent: college controls no student rents.

Duration of Master's degree course(s): 2 years **Male/female ratio 1989/90:** 3:2 **Teaching staff: full-time:** 40 **part-time:** 71 **Total postgraduate degree students 1989/90:** 585 **Number of postgraduate students:** 595 **Tuition fees, 1990/91:** Home: £2,530; Overseas: £6,900.

What it's like

As a postgraduate only college, students tend to be highly motivated in their particular disciplines. They work hard, but play hard too. Being in the centre of town has advantages and disadvantages – lots to do but a real drain on the cash. Student bar is an excellent place to spend time, albeit 'cozy'; beer is cheap; regular party nights. All good fun. Then of course there is the Rector's drinkies for all first years, if you get through that unharmed then you'll survive, no problem.

Financial problems; grants often seem not to be given out to those necessarily in need, but on a less rational basis. There is a Hardship Fund though, so you won't starve.

The college has been in turmoil. It still is the best, but make the most of it while you can.

Virtually no college accommodation, and finding a room is not only hard but expensive. It can be worth waiting till college starts and getting a group so you can rent a whole house together.

There seem to be very few people for whom something doesn't work out very quickly. 'Nothing ventured, nothing gained.' So get yer boots on!

Pauper notes

Accommodation: College offers to act as a guarantor for company lets and the SU, in conjunction with the welfare officer, supplies a valuable fact sheet on housing agencies, reputable landlords etc. **Drink:** The Artbar, run by the SU is a lively place at well below pub prices. **Eats:** Canteen prices are reasonable and offer a wide selection of salads at lunchtime and at least one veggy meal at suppertime. **Ents:** The RCA is renowned for its Balls, esp Xmas, Valentines and Halloween. Film society shows a mixture of RCA produced films, oldies and biggies. **Sports:** Imperial College swimming pool and sports facilities available.

Alumni (Editors' pick)

David Hockney, Peter Blake, Ian Dury, David Gentleman, The Emmanuels, Zandra Rhodes, Kenneth Grange, Nick Butler, Len Deighton, Henry Moore, Ridley Scott, Barbara Hepworth, Edward Burra.

ROYAL COLLEGE OF MUSIC

Royal College of Music (RCM), Prince Consort Road, South Kensington, London SW7 2BS (071-589 3643; Fax: 071-589 7740) Map E, A3

Student enquiries: Admissions Tutor

Main study areas – as in What to Study section: *(First degree):* Music.

European Community: No students learn an EC language or spend time in another EC country. A number of initiatives under development.

Application: Direct. **Academic features:** MMus in performance studies (post grad). Prizes available – winners perform at public recitals in London concert halls.

CAN'T FIND WHAT YOU'RE LOOKING FOR? USE THE INDEX!

Structural features: New Britten Theatre opened 1986. College has formal relationships with many musical organisations. **Special features:** Many visiting musicians including John Williams, George Benjamin, Grigory Zhislin, Evelyn Glennie, Eileen Croxford, John Lill, Rostropovich, Dorothy DeLay (violin) and William Pleeth (cello), Geoffrey Parsons (accompaniment), visiting professors; various master classes. **Founded:** 1883, by Prince of Wales (later Edward VII). **Main awards:** BMus, GRSM, DipRCM(Perfs), MMus (RCM) in performance studies. **Awarding body:** London University, Royal Schools of Music, Royal College of Music. **Site:** South Kensington. **Access:** South Kensington and Gloucester Road underground stations; various buses. **Accommodation:** 1 hall of residence (mixed) Robert Mayer Hall; also Queen Alexandra's House (women only) has a number of places available for RCM students, accommodating majority of first year students (preference given to those living outside London). Approx cost: £680–£750 per term. **Library:** Reference and loan collections; over 250,000 volumes, including rare early printed material and manuscripts. **Specialist collections:** Portraits of musicians; Instrument Museum. **Other learning resources:** Extensive reference library and research facilities. **Welfare:** Counsellor, doctor, dentist, FPA, psychiatrist, Alexander Technique, chaplain. **Careers:** Information and advice. **Amenities:** Nearby music shop gives 10% discount to RCM students; facilities of London University (including Imperial College swimming pool). **Employment:** Orchestral; teaching; freelance playing.

Duration of first degree course(s) or equivalent: 3-4 years **Total first degree students 1989/90:** 368 **Number of overseas students:** 93 **Male/female ratio 1989/90:** 2:3 **Teaching staff: full-time:** 13 **part-time:** c160 **Total full-time students 1989/90:** 508 **Postgraduate students:** 140 **Tuition fees, first degrees, 1990/91:** Home: £1,674; Overseas: £4,470-6,480.

What it's like

Life for students at the Royal College of Music has inevitably become far more interesting and varied over the years, as college has expanded and standard of musicianship improved. The opening of new Britten Opera Theatre for example, has attracted talented singers from all over world. About 20% of students at college are from overseas, in fact there are around 35 countries represented this year. This is a great advantage as we can learn so much from our foreign counterparts, not only from a musical point of view but also about other cultures.

SA has also grown considerably over last few years. Every full-time student of college is automatically member. SA responsible for many things, is managing students' bar, arranging parties, student conductors' concerts, football matches and other social events. RCM drama association is integral part of SA; this year it will be presenting a pantomime 'The Sleeping Cutie', with large cast of 24 principals and around 15 chorus members. Everything from costumes to choreography, lighting to directing is taken on by students.

This year has also seen dreaded 'Gowrie Report' which suggested that the Royal College should merge with the Royal Academy of Music to create a 'new and better conservatoire'. In light of recent government cuts in art world, Royal College students, after holding several meetings on the subject, decided that this venture was more of a cost-cutting exercise than a true realisation of student needs. Therefore we fought unanimously against it and idea was eventually shelved. This has created a more solid and coherent attitude among students. We have pulled together and defended our rights to keep the Royal College the wonderful institution we know it to be.

I am positive that the Royal College of Music will continue to produce the high standard of musical education it always has, and I'm sure anyone would be hard pushed to find a student who was not extremely proud to be here.
Paul Keohone

Pauper notes
Accommodation: Robert Mayer Hostel, Queen Alexandra's House. **Drink:** Very

CAN'T FIND WHAT YOU'RE LOOKING FOR? USE THE INDEX!

good Merrydown Cider! **Eats:** RCM canteen very convenient, reasonable (not cheap) prices. Imperial College eating facilities very good value. **Ents:** RCM film club. Student entry to most London cinemas, theatres, etc. **Sports:** Imperial College facilities – very cheap and near RCM. **Hardship funds:** RCM Union offers interest free loans of up to £500. **Travel:** No student fares (except railcard). London Transport travel cards save money. **Work:** Various off campus; RCM Appointments Office offers lots of playing and teaching work.

Alumni (Editors' pick)

Holst, Britten, Tippett, R Vaughan Williams, Andrew Lloyd-Webber, Oliver Knussen, Rick Wakeman, Colin Davis, Peter Pears, Janet Baker, Barry Douglas, Julian Bream, James Galway, Dame Gwynneth Jones, Joan Sutherland, John Lill, Elizabeth Maconchy, Sir Neville Marriner, Sarah Walker, Sir David Willcocks.

ROYAL FREE

Royal Free Hospital School of Medicine, University of London, Rowland Hill Street, London NW3 2PF (071-794 0500) Map D, B1

Student enquiries: Registrar

Main study areas – as in What to Study section: *(First degree):* Medicine.

European Community: No students learn an EC language or spend time in another EC country.

Application: UCCA. **Structural features:** Part of London University. **Special features:** BSc course open to those who have successfully completed first 2 years of MBBS course; integration of clinical and pre-clinical teaching. **Founded:** 1874. **Main awards:** BSc, MBBS. **Awarding body:** London University. **Site:** Hampstead. **Access:** Belsize Park underground and Hampstead Heath BR stations. **Accommodation:** London University accommodation office will assist. Halls of residence plus College hall with 80 places. Rent: 20% in accommodation where rent controlled by university. **Library:** 27,000 volumes, 360 periodicals, 230 study places; reference copies of course books. **Centres of excellence:** Academic department of medicine (liver diseases and gastroenterology); department of neurological science; haematology, immunology. **Welfare:** Doctor, dentist, FPA, psychiatrist, chaplain, hospital chapel. **Amenities:** SU bar, squash courts. **Sporting facilities:** Athletics ground at Enfield. **Employment:** Some pre-registration house officer posts after graduating.

Duration of first degree course(s) or equivalent: 5 years **Other:** 6 years (including BSc) **Total first degree students 1989/90:** 510 **Number of overseas students:** 14 **Male/female ratio 1989/90:** 1:1 **Teaching staff: full-time:** 92 **part-time:** 12 **Total full-time students 1989/90:** 548 **Postgraduate students:** 98 **Tuition fees, first degrees, 1990/91:** Home: £1,675 (£665 if self-financing); Overseas: £6,500 (£11,750 for clinical course).

What it's like

All subjects taught at Royal Free Hospital in Hampstead. Pre-clinical students live in London University halls in Bloomsbury or the student house in Islington. Extremely difficult to find suitable accommodation in Hampstead. Libraries well-stocked and late study possible. SU not NUS affiliated but very active. Student facilities at hospital include 2 squash courts, 450 seat assembly hall, and bar. Also collective membership of Hospital Recreation Centre. Social events (discos, live bands, annual beer-races) held at hospital; active sports clubs, Dramsoc, orchestra and rag week. Fully confidential counselling. Continuous assessment throughout course. If 2-year pre-clinical course is successfully completed you can study for one-year intercalated BSc. Drop-out rate moderate (approx 8–10 from first year). First-time success rate for finals about 95%. Good balance between work and relaxation. One of the friendliest medical schools with good tutor/student relationships.

Pauper notes
Accommodation: SU accommodation officer. Some cheap properties on short term lease to School, but housing decidedly inadequate. **Drink:** Bar owned by medical school. **Eats:** Local trendy Hampstead restaurants. **Ents:** Good cinemas locally, Dingwalls in Camden Town and Camden Palais. **Sports:** Squash courts and recreation centre (gym and pool) on site. Sports ground at Enfield. **Hardship funds:** Some special grants/bursaries for hard-up students; apply to registry.

ROYAL HOLLOWAY AND BEDFORD

Royal Holloway and Bedford New College, University of London, Egham Hill, Egham, Surrey TW20 0EX (0784 434455) Map A, F8

Student enquiries: Schools Liaison Officer

Main study areas – as in What to Study section: *(First degree):* Biochemistry, biology, botany, classics, computing, drama, economics, English, environmental science, European studies, geography, geology, history, mathematical studies, microbiology, modern languages, music, physics, politics & government, psychology, public administration, sociology, zoology. *Also:* Electronics, operational research.

European Community: 16% first degree students take EC language as part of course and 10% spend 6 months or more in another EC country. Formal exchange links with Trieste University (open to any undergraduates) and up to 20 other links, formal or informal. New student mobility programme in music. European studies degree. Most undergraduates have access to basic language training, particularly in German.

Application: UCCA. **Structural features:** Part of London University. **Largest fields of study:** Biology, English, geography, history, maths, physics and social studies. **Founded:** 1849 Bedford College, 1886 Royal Holloway College – both as women's colleges, going co-ed in 1960s. Merged to form The New College in 1985. **Main awards:** BA, BMus, BSc. **Awarding body:** London University. **Site:** 100 acre parkland campus. Founder's building in style of Chateau of Chambord. Many newly completed buildings. **Access:** Egham station (Waterloo–Reading line); buses. Close to Heathrow airport, M3, M4 and M25. **Accommodation:** 1,700 places in halls including 200 places in self-catering houses and flats; all students in first year and most in third year offered places in residence. Rent: 60% in accommodation where rent controlled by university. **Library:** Main library; several departmental collections; 400,000 volumes in total, 1,500 periodicals, 400 study places; restricted loan collections. **Other learning resources:** 300 computer work-stations for student use. **Welfare:** Wardens, counsellor to students, doctors, FPA, psychiatrist, chaplains, interdenominational chapel. **Hardship funds:** Limited loans and grants from the Principal's Hardship Fund. **Special categories:** Residential facilities for some married students. Extra-curricular College certificate in computing and quantitative skills available by modular study. **Careers:** Information, advice and placement. **Amenities:** Purpose-built SU building; orchestra and choirs. **Sporting facilities:** Wide variety of sports (including rowing); playing fields on site.

Duration of first degree course(s) or equivalent: 3 years; **Total first degree students 1989/90:** 2,666 **Number of overseas students:** 78 **Number of mature students:** 242 **Male/female ratio 1989/90:** 1:1 **Teaching staff: full-time:** 252 **part-time:** 28 **Total full-time students 1989/90:** 3,020 **Postgraduate students:** 354

CAN'T FIND WHAT YOU'RE LOOKING FOR? USE THE INDEX!

Tuition fees, first degrees, 1990/91: Home: £1,675 (£650 if self-financing); Overseas: £5,250 (eg politics), £6,300 (eg physics).

What it's like

'London University's Country Campus', 30 minutes from central London. Housed on a campus near Windsor based on amazing Victorian 'founders' building; the result of the merger between Royal Holloway and Bedford Colleges now established as a centre of academic excellence. Geology and physics departments are both pre-eminent in their research fields and the arts faculty is one of the best in London University. A recent building programme included sciences, life sciences, maths/arts and residence buildings as well as the new SU building. One of the most popular of the new buildings is Reid Hall, where every study bedroom has a shower/toilet en suite.

SU very active, mostly social rather than political. Over 150 clubs and societies ranging from political to social, religious to sporting. It also provides a varied and enjoyable ents programme of events most days in the week, as well as an alternative comedian practically every week. Operates five bars around campus, good prices.

Pauper notes

Accommodation: Increased by 17% this year – local area expensive. Married residence 50 yards from campus. **Drink:** Best place for cheapies are union bars. Stumble Inn on campus has nice pub atmosphere and cheap prices. **Eats:** SU coffee bar – cheap and varied. 'Girovend' credit card food system on campus; vegetarian on menu. Local places – Windsor, Staines 'load of bull'. **Ents:** New cabaret venue open on campus. Drama dept does lots of plays. Very active ents. Lot of fringe theatre, 3 cinema groups, bands and alternative comedy every week. **Sports:** Campus playing field and small gymnasium. Egham Sports Centre good but expensive, Staines nearest swimming. **Hardship funds:** A few are available. **Travel:** French and ski societies do good cheapies. **Work:** College employs students during vacs, plenty of bar work etc during term with SU and local area.

Alumni (Editors' pick)

Ivy Compton-Burnett, Richmal Crompton, Felicity Lott, Janet Fookes MP, David Bellamy, Kathleen Lonsdale, Jean Rook, Marie Patterson, George Eliot.

"Most ex-students have very fond memories, as shown by attendance at ex-students' association"

REUNION PARKING

VISITING

SWANKING

CAN'T FIND WHAT YOU'RE LOOKING FOR? USE THE INDEX!

ROYAL NORTHERN COLLEGE OF MUSIC

Royal Northern College of Music, 124 Oxford Road, Manchester M13 9RD (061-273 6283) (Fax 061-273 7611) Map A, D6

Student enquiries: Secretary for Admissions

Main study areas – as in What to Study section: *(First degree):* Music.

European Community: 20% first degree students take EC language as part of course (all vocal students) but none spend time in another EC country. Formal exchange links with Conservatoires in Paris, Lyon, Copenhagen and Frankfurt (in addition to Prague and Belgrade) open to all students. Annual orchestral tours, especially to France.

Application: Direct. **Special features:** All undergraduate courses are 4 years (2 years broad musical education, 2 years specialisation); college runs a joint course with Manchester University. **Founded:** 1973, ex Northern School of Music and Royal Manchester College of Music. **Main awards:** GRNCM, GMusRNCM(Hons), PPRNCM. **Awarding body:** Royal Northern College of Music. **Site:** Fine modern buildings 1 mile south of city centre. **Access:** Buses from city centre. **Accommodation:** 176 study bedrooms (residence recommended for first year students). Approx cost: £50.00 per week (with meals). Rent: 20% (ie most first-year undergraduates) in accommodation where rent controlled by college. **Library:** Extensive reference and lending sections of books and performing material. Vast record collection with playback facilities for records, tapes, CDs and videos. Microfilm and microfiche facilities.**Specialist collections:** Henry Watson Collection of Musical Instruments; Library of Jascha Horenstein; original manuscripts of Alan Rawsthorne. **Other learning facilities:** Electronic studio, keyboard laboratory. **Welfare:** Chaplain, counsellors, instrument purchase loan scheme. **Hardship fund:** Bursaries may be awarded from College Trust Funds. **Careers:** Advisory service. **Amenities:** Opera theatre, concert hall, recital room; Junior Common Room; roof garden; refectory with bar. Full programme of public events takes place throughout the academic year. **Sporting facilities:** Tennis, football and cricket at hall of residence. **Employment:** Primarily music performance; private teaching; school teaching and music librarianship (after further study); music and arts in general.

Duration of first degree course(s) or equivalent: 4 years **Total first degree students 1989/90:** 470 **Number of overseas students:** 23 **Number of mature students:** 170 **Male/female ratio 1989/90:** 1:1 **Teaching staff: full-time:** 44 **part-time:** 72 **Total full-time students 1989/90:** 534 **Postgraduate students:** 64 **Tuition fees, first degrees, 1990/91:** Home: £1,675; Overseas: £5,000.

What it's like

It's the youngest of the four British Royal Schools of Music and boasts some of the most up-to-date facilities and opportunities for music students in Britain. Facilities include a fully staffed opera theatre, with its own workshop, concert hall, recital room, lecture theatre, comprehensive practice room facilities and its own hall of residence.

Students actively encouraged to seek external work with local orchestras and music clubs. Through its close links with BBC Philharmonic, Hallé, Liverpool Philharmonic and Camerata Orchestras, RNCM students are ideally placed to take advantage of this forward looking policy. In what is a highly competitive field, RNCM is a surprisingly friendly place, perhaps due to its large refectory area where students congregate. SU organises many social events, including two annual Balls, parties and sports.

Although the RNCM is restructuring its finances (PCFC) students and staff are confident that it will remain in the forefront of the British music scene.
Gavin Woods

CAN'T FIND WHAT YOU'RE LOOKING FOR? USE THE INDEX!

Pauper notes

Accommodation: Cheapest housing in Moss-Side, Hulme and Whalley range. Fair number of squats in Hulme. Most popular student areas are Chorlton and Withington. **Drink:** Many good locals; The Salvation (excellent Tetleys and Guinness), The Lass O'Gowrie (home brewed), SU bar (cheap) and University and Poly SUs. **Eats:** Approx 30 Indian restaurants in Rusholme (most cheap and very good), best is the Al-Noor. Good vegetarian restaurants include On The Eighth Day. **Ents:** Lots of cinemas; cheapest is The Cornerhouse (student discount). Student reductions at most theatres. Royal Exchange Theatre very good. Lots of socials at SU. **Sports:** Use of University and Poly facilities – Moss-Side Leisure Centre very cheap and convenient. **Hardship funds:** College and SU have limited resources for small loans and scholarships available. **Travel:** College fund for studying abroad. **Work:** Gigs and teaching relatively easy to find by the time you've been at college for a couple of years.

Alumni (Editors' pick)

Peter Donohoe, Jane Eaglen, Brodsky Quartet, Howard Jones.

" ....boasts curries so eerily cheap that one wonders what they put in them "

ROYAL SCOTTISH ACADEMY

Royal Scottish Academy of Music & Drama, 100 Renfrew Street, Glasgow G2 3DB (041-332 4101) Map A, C3

Student enquiries: Secretary and Treasurer

Main study areas – as in What to Study section: *(First degree):* Drama, music. *Also:* Theatre design.

European Community: No students take learn an language or spend time in another EC country.

Application: Direct. **Special features:** Many top professional concert artists and theatre directors in recitals, productions and master classes. **Academic features:** BA musical studies. **Founded:** 1847. **Main awards:** BA, BEd, DipRSAMD, Dip Dramatic Art, Dip Stage Management Studies. **Awarding body:** Glasgow University, Royal Scottish Academy of Music & Drama, CNAA. **Site:** Central Glasgow. **Accommodation:** 30 places in mixed hall (20 places for first years). Approx cost: £44.30 pw; assistance in locating private accommodation. **Library:** 80,120 music volumes, 13,750 books, 7,570 sound recordings, 26 study places, 9 listening booths. **Welfare:** Doctor, student advisor. **Hardship funds:** RSAMD Trust. **Careers:**

CAN'T FIND WHAT YOU'RE LOOKING FOR? USE THE INDEX!

Information and advice. **Amenities:** Theatre (500 seats); closed circuit TV studio; recital room; concert hall; choir (Academy Chorus); regular recitals by distinguished artistes on premises; orchestras. **Employment:** Professional orchestral musicians; members of opera companies; theatre; teaching (music and drama), solo concert artists and actors.

Duration of first degree course(s) or equivalent: 3 years; **others:** 2 and 4 years **Total first degree students 1989/90:** 267 **BEd students:** 54 **Number of overseas students:** 8 **Number of mature students:** 65 **Male/female ratio 1989/90:** 2:3 **Teaching staff: full-time:** 43 **part-time:** 115 **Total full-time students 1989/90:** 397 **Postgraduate students:** 45 **Tuition fees, first degrees, 1990/91:** Home: £1,675; Overseas: £6,000.

What it's like

Impressive orange brick building on corner of Hope and Renfrew Streets. Uninviting due to lack of windows. Used by public for performances in The New Athenaeum or the Chandler Studio Theatres, or for concerts in the Stevenson Concert Hall. Drama dept on ground floor, music on upper two floors. Extensive new library on top, complete with hi-fi, CD players and video equipment. TV studio with cameras, lighting, sound and editing. Large technical dept. Practice rooms for music and drama students. Small canteen and smaller common room. Theatre Bar – not to be used by students. Plenty of nightclubs and bars, good gay community. Lot of visiting companies and musicians in the Academy. Plenty going on in the Arts. Mayfest – Glasgow's expanding equivalent to the Edinburgh Festival during May. Large shopping centres (Sauchiehall, Buchanan Street, Argyle Street and, recently opened, exclusive Prince's Square). Academy in town centre; Glasgow Central and Queen Street rail stations nearby, also Cowcaddens Subway and Buchanan Street bus station; buses to most places in city (prices average). Easy access to parts of Scotland eg Loch Lomond only 30 minutes away. Not a high drop-out rate. Few students take a year out, especially in drama courses.

Pauper notes

Accommodation: Some music student accommodation available, prospective students given list of places for rent by office but mainly up to students themselves. Glasgow can be expensive – southside and West End popular. **Drink:** Phonograph round the corner, Art School bar where the SRC often hold events. Cheap places can be found but Glasgow is getting very trendy. **Eats:** Third Eye Centre has good wholefood cafe, Art School canteen, Fazzi's pizza place, Spud U Like potatoes, food in Academy canteen overpriced and often tasteless, Grosvenor Cafe in West End. **Ents:** Glasgow Film Theatre for alternative, one offs and popular re-runs. New 10 screen in Clydebank. Outside concerts, recitals and theatre companies perform in college. Tron and Citizens theatres cheap. Third Eye Theatre has Studio Theatre specialising in performance art and plenty of art galleries/museums. **Sports:** Kelvin Hall Sports Centre, easy to take tube. **Hardship funds:** Academy loan scheme. **Travel:** No travel scholarships as such. Hitching good on M8, students discount on trains with railcard, tube 40p anywhere. **Work:** Ushering in college, music teaching, plenty bars and restaurants.

Alumni (Editors' pick)

Hannah Gordon, Moira Anderson, Sheena Easton, Tom Conti, Sir Alex Gibson, Bill McCue, Fulton Mackay, James Loughran, Margaret Marshall, Isobel Buchanan, Ian Richardson, Victor & Barry, Bill Paterson, Christine Cairns, Kathleen Livingstone, Neil Mackie, Bryden Thomson, Judith Howarth, David Hayman, Mary Marquis, Phyllis Logan, Denis Lawson, John Cairney, John Grieve.

CAN'T FIND WHAT YOU'RE LOOKING FOR? USE THE INDEX!

ROYAL VETERINARY COLLEGE

Royal Veterinary College, University of London, Royal College Street, London NW1 0TU (071-387 2898) Map D, B1

Student enquiries: Registrar

Main study areas – as in What to Study section: *(First degree):* Veterinary studies.

European Community: No students learn an EC language or spend time in another EC country as part of their course (components of compulsory vacation work may be taken overseas). Formal exchange links with Royal Veterinary & Agricultural University Copenhagen (food hygiene) and Veterinary Faculty, Munich University (veterinary clinics). Approved Erasmus programme 1990/91.

Application: UCCA. **Structural features:** Part of London University. **Academic features:** Individual project in final year forms part of the final degree examination. **Founded:** 1791. **Main awards:** BVetMed, BSc. **Awarding body:** London University. **Site:** Pre-clinical studies at Camden Town premises, London NW1; clinical studies on 575 acre campus at Hawkshead, near Potters Bar, Herts. **Access:** Buses and tubes to Camden Town site (Camden Town, Mornington Crescent, Euston and King's Cross stations); BR stations for Hawkshead (Brookmans Park, Potters Bar) about 20 mins by train from King's Cross. **Accommodation:** London University intercollegiate halls for students at Camden campus: majority of pre-clinical students are accommodated within walking distance of the college; hall of residence at Hawkshead with 63 study bedrooms for clinical students; plus further 30 expected. **Library:** Library and reading rooms at both sites; reference copies of standard texts; public library in Camden High Street; London University library. **Other learning facilities:** Animal hospitals at Camden Town and Hawkshead. Farm Animal Practice Teaching Unit at Hawkshead. **Welfare:** Affiliated to health centre of University College London; physicians visit Camden Town and Hawkshead regularly during term. **Amenities:** ULU building in Malet Street, college refectory, and common rooms at Camden Town and Hawkshead. Playing fields and swimming pool at Hawkshead.

Duration of first degree course(s) or equivalent: 5 years **Total first degree students 1989/90:** 335 **Number of overseas students:** 14 **Number of mature students:** 30 **Male/female ratio 1989/90:** 2:3 **Teaching staff:** 70 **Total full-time students 1989/90:** 369 **Postgraduate students:** 76 (full and part-time) **Tuition fees, first degrees, 1990/91:** Home: £1,675; Overseas: £6,050 (pre-clinical); £11,150 (clinical).

What it's like

It's a split site college (part of London University) on two sites: central London at Camden Town and in Hertfordshire near Potters Bar.

The first two years of course spent in Camden Town, so providing opportunity for enjoying nightlife of London while you still have the energy. College well situated near several University Intercollegiate Halls which provide very popular accommodation and opportunity to meet people from other colleges within the university. Anybody who cannot get a place in a hall can find accommodation via the university accommodation office. It's also conveniently located near the University of London Union buildings providing easy access to their facilities. Doctor and college chaplain located in college.

In the last three years students are taught at the field station near Potters Bar. A lot of the clinical facilities are new, and it is constantly being improved. All students have access to the animals and are encouraged to take advantage of this fact.

SU very active in its social capacity and organises numerous parties at the college. Due to small size of college there is a good friendly atmosphere in which all the years mix well. There are numerous sports clubs and societies catering for a wide variety of tastes. Within these clubs there is a good social element and a convenient blend of

CAN'T FIND WHAT YOU'RE LOOKING FOR? USE THE INDEX!

competitiveness and enjoyment with opportunities for the serious and the not-so-serious sportsmen and women. The position of the college within the university provides an opportunity for regular competition with other colleges.

Pauper notes
Accommodation: Intercollegiate halls during 1st year. College hall in later 3 years. **Drink:** ULU bar plus good range of local pubs. Best range: The Sun, near International Hall, Brunswick Square. No SU bar. **Eats:** Only 20 mins from central London. **Ents:** Good and lively college social events. **Sports:** Field station has playing field, squash court, swimming pool; plus use of all ULU facilities. **Hardship Funds:** Access fund. **Work:** Not always possible especially later years, as need to do total 38 weeks of vacation study in five years.

ST ANDREWS UNIVERSITY

University of St Andrews, College Gate, St Andrews, Fife KY16 9AJ (0334 76161) Map A, D2

Student enquiries: Schools Liaison Office

Main study areas – as in What to Study section: *(First degree):* Anthropology, biochemistry, biology, biotechnology, botany, chemistry, classics, computing, economics, English, fine arts, geography, geology, history, Latin American studies, mathematical studies, medicine, microbiology, modern languages, Near East and Islamic studies, pharmacology, philosophy, physics, physiology, politics and government, psychology, religious studies and theology, zoology. *Also:* Astronomy, electronics, Hispanic studies, physical education, Scottish studies.

European Community: 6% first degree students take EC language as part of course and 3% spend 6 months or more in another EC country. Formal exchange links with some 23 EC universities/colleges: Belgium (1); France (9); Germany (3); Greece (2); Italy (2); Netherlands (3); Portugal (1); Spain (2). Approved Erasmus programme 1990/91.

Application: UCCA. **Academic features:** Many new single and joint honours courses including MA in modern languages (1, 2 or 3 languages); 4 year honours system gives great flexibility – final choice of subject(s) can be delayed until end of second year. General entrance requirements may be relaxed for mature students. **Largest fields of study:** Physical sciences, modern languages, social sciences, history. **Founded:** 1411. **Main awards:** BD, MA, BSc, MTheol. **Awarding body:** St Andrews University. **Site:** St Andrews town centre, North Haugh site half mile west of the town. **Access:** Nearest station is Leuchars (5 miles away) on main London–Aberdeen line, then bus; good road links. **Accommodation:** 1,900 places in halls; 600 student flats; 100 lodgings (all first years offered and encouraged to live in hall). **Library:** 730,000 volumes, 10,000 periodicals, 680 study areas. **Other learning facilities:** Computing laboratory, Gatty marine laboratory, language centre. **Welfare:** Doctor, FPA, chaplain, student counsellor. **Hardship funds:** Application to Hebdomadar. **Special categories:** Limited residential facilities for married and disabled students. **Careers:** Information, advice and placement service. **Amenities:** SU with coffee and snack bars, newspaper, arts and crafts area, etc; St Andrews Festival organised by town and gown. **Sporting facilities:** Modern physical education centre; excellent playing fields; 6 squash courts; 4 golf courses (including 'Old' course); local leisure complex complete with indoor swimming pool.

Duration of first degree course(s) or equivalent: 4 years Honours; **others:** 3 years Ordinary **Total first degree students 1989/90:** 3,605 **Number of overseas students:** 396 **Number of mature students:** 310 **Male/female ratio 1989/90:** 1:1 **Teaching staff:** 327 **part-time:** 12 **Total full-time students 1989/90:** 4,108

CAN'T FIND WHAT YOU'RE LOOKING FOR? USE THE INDEX!

Postgraduate students: 579 **Tuition fees, first degrees, 1990/91:** Home: £1,675; Overseas: £4,810 (eg politics), £6,300 (eg physics).

What it's like

Small university of under 4,000, in historic town on east coast of Scotland (little industry or economic activity apart from golf, university and RAF Leuchars). Town small, with good mix of historic and new. Academic departments spread over town, sciences on 1960's campus-style North Haugh site.

Cosmopolitan university – 10% overseas, 40% English, 5% Northern Irish, 45% Scottish. All first years in halls; most others in private or university-owned flats.

Flexible course structure and entry by faculty requires no honours specialisation (within reason) until third year. Exemption system means few first year students (unless they do no work) sit exams at the end of the year. Psychology and mediaeval history have excellent reputations, amongst others.

A very close-knit community. Over 150 active student societies from silly (The Tunnocks Caramel Appreciation Society) to serious (Amnesty International). Strong debating tradition and acclaimed Dramatic Society – the Mermaids. Tradition bound: Raisin Weekend, Red Gowns, Pier Walks and May Morning Dip in the North Sea.

Students' Association provides services, both social and support, for all students. Athletic Union includes excellent squash courts and playing fields.

Highlights of the social calendar are the balls: the Union Ball, the Debates Ball, residence balls and society balls, like Canmore. Easiest to crash is the Graduation Ball in July, when the college lawns are covered by marquees.

You might never leave St Andrews for good, but find yourself drawn back again and again.

Pauper notes

Accommodation: University accommodation good value, private flats vary, can be difficult to find. **Drink:** Students Association cheapest. Avoid Golfers' Lass. **Eats:** Lots of atmosphere, coffeeshops, pizzas and wholefood places. Balaka does great Indian. **Ents:** One film theatre, The Byre Playhouse very prestigious. Student productions full of imagination. Union Theatre has regular bands and smaller scale ents occur frequently in the Union bar. **Sports:** Athletic Union free to students. Local swimming pools and golf courses offer concessions. **Hardship funds:** Through the University via The Hebdomadar. **Travel:** Students Association runs cheap travel service. Nearest BR station is Leuchars (5 miles away on East Coast line). **Work:** Mostly bars and waitress service, but jobs go fast.

Alumni (Editors' pick)

Sir Hugh Cortazzi, Colin Young, Fay Wheldon, Alastair Reid, Eric Anderson, James Michener, Siobhan Redmond, Zoe Fairbairns, Michael Forsyth, Allan Stewart, Alex Salmond.

ST BARTHOLOMEW'S

The Medical College of St Bartholomew's Hospital, University of London, West Smithfield, London EC1A 7BE (071-982 6000) Map E, D2

Student enquiries: Admissions Officer

Main study areas – as in What to Study section: *(First degree):* Medicine.

European Community: No languages, exchanges or links.

Application: UCCA. **Structural features:** Part of London University. **Founded:** 1123. **Main awards:** MBBS. **Awarding body:** University of London. **Special features:** Teaching during first 2 years at Queen Mary and Westfield College, with

CAN'T FIND WHAT YOU'RE LOOKING FOR? USE THE INDEX!

new innovative curriculum, including project work and integrated teaching. Some elements of course at the Medical College Charterhouse Square site; clinical course (years 3-5) centred at St Bartholomew's Hospital. **Site:** West Smithfield, Charterhouse Square and QMW. **Access:** Barbican and St Paul's underground stations. **Accommodation:** 206 single study bedrooms in Charterhouse Square; some college flats for clinical students. Approx cost: £30. **Rent:** 60% in accommodation where rent controlled by college. Accommodation guaranteed for all first and final year students. **Library:** One on the Charterhouse Square site, clinical and media resources libraries on hospital site. **Other learning resources:** Self-teaching tape/slide programmes; computer self-teaching programmes; interactive video discs. **Amenities:** Recreational facilities in College Hall (TV lounge, bar, etc). Social club (bar, billiards room, etc) in the Robin Brook Centre for Medical Education on the Hospital site. Extensive audio-visual learning and computing facilities. **Hardship funds:** Limited funds available. **Sporting facilities:** Squash courts and gymnasium in Charterhouse Square; swimming pool in nearby nurses' home; athletic grounds in Chislehurst, Kent.

Duration of first degree course(s) or equivalent: 5 years; **others:** 6 years (with intercalated BSc) **Total first degree students 1989/90:** 580 **Number of overseas students:** 12 **Number of mature students:** 50 **Male/female ratio 1989/90:** 1:1 **Teaching staff:** 200 **Total full-time students 1989/90:** 610 **Postgraduate students:** 60 **Tuition fees, first degrees, 1990/91:** Home: £1,675 (different for self-financing); Overseas: £6,300 pre-clinical, £11,300 for clinical years.

What it's like

Beautiful, unique college, hidden in the heart of the city – allowing the best of both worlds. The hospital 200 yards away and, being in City and Hackney Health Authority, patients are the richest and poorest giving great diversity. Pre-clinical studies at Queen Mary & Westfield.

1st years guaranteed a place on campus and then you can stay in hall (lively, friendly, cheap and very convenient) or move out into Hackney/Stoke Newington which has some of the most central and cheap student digs in London. Some overseas students and 10% postgraduates. Some car parking available – usually only for finalists.

Campus library is open 9 am–10 pm 5 days/wk. SU shop open every day and nearby are all-purpose shops some open from 9 am–11 pm 7 days/wk. Nearby Smithfield allows students to take advantage of the multitude of all night cafes – great for the 4 am munchies!

Very active SU, involved in all aspects of college life, representing the students, to staff and entertainments. Welfare officer and student health officer take care of any personal/social problems confidentially – being a small college very conscious of students' welfare and not much opportunity to be lonely or isolated.

Most active societies drama and mountaineering clubs. Popular sports include rugby football (men), hockey (men/women), netball, water sports and rowing, and many more. Barbican Centre on doorstep offers huge range of drama, cinema, music and art exhibitions. Easy access to north and central London. 2 balls a year and twice weekly entertainment on campus. ULU is near, offering additional facilities. Friendly bar with unusual opening hours forms a very special social crux.

Students encouraged to comment on any problems, and generally well listened to; student reps in most areas including representation at your interviews.

Personality is important and ability to communicate. Any old medical school can churn out doctors; Barts aims to produce doctors who understand the concepts of health care. Everyone guaranteed a job after they qualify; postgraduate machinery is fairest and efficient.

Pauper notes

Accommodation: Cheap, lively hall with no petty regulations (rooms guaranteed for first years and finalists). Student-run accommodation service helps find cheap

CAN'T FIND WHAT YOU'RE LOOKING FOR? USE THE INDEX!

lodgings in N and E London. **Drink:** Real ale pubs abound. Unique and refurbished bar in hall. **Eats:** Cheap eating at college hall and hospital. Huge greasies available at all night cafes. Outstanding pub food at 'Fox and Anchor'. Wide variety of food types available locally. **Ents:** Regular discos, bands and review acts in hall bar. Regular quality productions by Drama Soc. Student reductions at next-door Barbican Centre. **Sports:** On site multigym, swimming pool, water polo. Boathouse at Chiswick. Rugby, soccer, hockey, cricket at Chislehurst. Sailing at Burnham. **Hardship funds:** Funds administered by SU and college for students in need. **Travel:** A number of college grants available for student electives. **Work:** Wide variety of jobs in hospital including some specifically reserved for particularly needy students eg graduates without grants. Jobs in city wine bars etc.

Alumni (Editors' pick)
William Harvey, John Abernethy, James Paget, Richard Gordon, Graham Chapman, Percival Pott, Thomas Vicary.

ST GEORGE'S

St George's Hospital Medical School, University of London, Cranmer Terrace, London SW17 0RE (081-672 9944) Map D, B4

Student enquiries: Registry

Main study areas – as in What to Study section: *(First degree):* Medicine.

European Community: No students learn an EC language or spend time in another EC country.

Application: UCCA. **Structural features:** Part of London University. **Founded:** 1751. **Main awards:** MB, BS, BSc. **Awarding body:** London University. **Site:** Tooting. **Access:** Tooting Broadway underground station; buses. **Accommodation:** 256 places in mixed hall of residence (all first years accommodated; 30% total). **Library:** 17,000 monographs, 30,000 journal volumes, 500 periodicals, 400 study places. **Welfare:** Student Health Service, chaplain. **Amenities:** Hospital chapel; bookshop managed by school club; bar and common rooms. **Sporting facilities:** 6 squash courts and gymnasium; Olympic standard public swimming pool just off site; playing fields.

Duration of first degree course(s) or equivalent: 5 years; 6 years (with BSc) **Total first degree students 1989/90:** 754 **Number of overseas students:** 15 **Number of mature students:** 60 **Male/female ratio 1989/90:** 4:3 **Teaching staff: full-time:** 143 **part-time:** 196 **Total full-time students 1989/90:** 804 **Postgraduate students:** 150 **Tuition fees, first degrees, 1990/91:** Home: £1,675 (£665 if self-financing); Overseas: £6,050 (pre-clinical), £11,150 (clinical).

What it's like
Large complex of buildings with all pre-clinical and approximately half clinical teaching on site. Mixed self-catering halls of residence are seven minutes' walk from the Medical School, with room for 256 students (first years are guaranteed places). Halls life is good (socially) and easy (financially and domestically). Central London is easily accessible by tube (about 20 minutes' ride).

Tooting is good for eating and drinking; theatre, film and cabaret require a short five minute bus journey.

SU has fortnightly discos held in the Medical School (featuring the longest student bar in London) with many events in between (plays, films, happy hours) and special events (Christmas revue, rag week, freshers fortnight). The bar serves the usual plus guest beers, and hot and cold food.

Most sports and leisure interests are catered for and new clubs are constantly

CAN'T FIND WHAT YOU'RE LOOKING FOR? USE THE INDEX!

becoming active, inactive and reactive (depending on demand). The sports ground is at Cobham (Surrey) and there is a sports hall on site with squash courts and multigym. Recent successful clubs are hockey, football, basketball and rowing; all clubs are remarkably active socially!

The work load in the first year is relatively light compared to the rest of the course. Failures are not by a set rate, and plenty of chances to retake are available. Once through the first year, being thrown out is unlikely. Also a third of students are offered a chance of doing an intercalated BSc at the end of the pre-clinical course. Student-staff relations are relaxed and friendly.

If you want to become a capable and caring physician, and still enjoy every moment of your five years, come to St George's.
Nic Kennedy/Brendan Dooris

Pauper notes
Drink: Tooting Tavern, Selkirk, King's Head, Corner Pin. **Eats:** Lots of Indian (many weekend buffets). **Ents:** SU events, Ritzy in Brixton for films. **Sports:** Tooting Leisure Centre next door. Centre on site. **Hardship funds:** Can sometimes be arranged by grovelling. **Work:** Work in hospital available (clerical and nursing), pizza staff at bar.

Alumni (Editors' pick)
Henry Gray, Edward Wilson, Edward Jenner, Thomas Young, John Hunter, Mike Stroud.

ST MARK & ST JOHN

College of St Mark & St John, Derriford Road, Plymouth PL6 8BH (0752 777188) Map A, C9

Student enquiries: Admissions Officer

Main study areas – as in What to Study section: *(First degree):* Art & design, education, English, geography, history, humanities, information technology, linguistics, mathematical studies, philosophy, religious studies and theology, sociology. *Also:* Film studies, public relations.

European Community: Number of students learning an EC language or spending time in another EC country, not known.

Application: UCCA. **Academic features:** Modular framework for all first degree courses, allowing full and part-time study. **Special features:** Urban Learning Foundation with teaching practice and community work opportunities in east London. Many specialist centres including for design and technology, information technology in education, primary teaching, mathematics teaching, religious education. Language studies in either European languages or English as a Foreign Language. Humanities students spend 1 term in USA. Policy of overseas visiting academics. **Founded:** St John's, Battersea, 1840; St Mark's, Chelsea 1841, amalgamation as the College of St Mark and St John in Chelsea, 1923. New location in Plymouth, 1973. **Main awards:** BA, BEd. **Awarding body:** Exeter University. **Site:** 5 miles Plymouth city centre. 53 acre site overlooking Dartmoor National Park, Plymouth Sound and City of Plymouth. **Access:** Good bus services. **Accommodation:** Priority to first and final year students for on-campus accommodation; others found approved lodgings by college accommodation officer. Rent: 70% in accommodation where rent controlled by college. **Library:** Over 100,000 volumes, 450 periodicals, plus extensive microfilm and audio-visual materials. 185 study places, plus 'out of hours' work area. **Welfare:** Careers office, chaplain, nursing officer (SRN), student welfare centre, welfare counsellors. **Special categories:** Creche during half terms. Christian Fellowship and study groups. **Careers:**

CAN'T FIND WHAT YOU'RE LOOKING FOR? USE THE INDEX!

Specialist careers adviser and information room. **Amenities:** Joint common room with bar and snack bar, games and TV rooms, SU shop, launderette, minibus, printing service, specialist bookshop, part-time banking service, chapel, drama theatre, Plymouth (arts centre, theatre, orchestras). **Sporting facilities:** Sports track and pitches; sports centre including carpeted sports halls for badminton, basketball, 5-a-side soccer, netball, tennis, volleyball etc, plus gym, weight training room, 3 squash courts, climbing wall, indoor 25-metre pool; also Dartmoor, coasts and rivers of Devon and Cornwall for sailing, canoeing, climbing etc.

Duration of first degree course(s) or equivalent: 3 years; **Other:** 4 years (BEd Hons); **Total first degree students:** 950 **Number of BEd students:** 530 **Number of overseas students:** 30 **Number of mature students:** 375 **Male/female ratio 1989/90:** 2:3 **Teaching staff:** 84 **part-time:** 30 **Total full-time students 1989/90:** 1,155 **Postgraduate students:** 50 **Tuition fees, first degrees, 1990/91:** Home: £1,675 (£651 if self-financing); Overseas: £4,450.

What it's like

New site opened in 1973 in rural, picturesque position 5 miles from city centre, within easy reach of moors, sea and Cornwall. Reasonable public transport. Modern comfortable accommodation, including recently built student village. 24 hour visiting and few regulations. Final years offered on-campus accommodation. Wide range of subjects, main ones, education, geography, English, history, recreation and community. SU active politically, socially and academically; runs shop, minibus, launderette, and magazine (Smile). Over 40 clubs and societies. New and expanding sports centre on campus with swimming pool, 2 sports halls, gymnasium, squash courts, multi-gym, plus extensive sports ground. Good shopping in city, lots of hypermarkets for good bargains; plus theatres, cinemas, pubs and Arts Centre. Good relationship with admin and teaching staff. High proportion of mature students on some courses; high proportion of overseas students. Library closed Saturday. Confidential counselling and welfare service.

Pauper notes

Accommodation: Good campus accommodation – halls and student village – off campus approved lodging system; or go private. **Drink:** Joint common rooms (JCR), bar; Lion and Lamb slightly more expensive, The George (off campus) best nearest pub – some students drive into town or Dartmoor. **Eats:** Average square meals are fairly reasonable. Other things are notoriously expensive eg fruits, yoghourt; vegetarians not well catered for on campus. **Ents:** Very good campus entertainment, bands, films, discos etc – off campus, 3 main theatres, 2 cinemas, 1 alternative film centre – lots and lots of night clubs. **Sports:** On campus very well catered for; leisure centre attached – student reductions given. **Hardship funds:** Access fund (government). **Travel:** A lot hitch from college to town (harder to do if vice-versa). Cheap fare because of competing bus companies. **Work:** Very limited on campus work – best to go in town in local pubs and shops.

Alumni (Editors' pick)

Cat Stevens, Peter Duncan.

S MARTIN'S COLLEGE

S Martin's College of Higher Education, Bowerham, Lancaster LA1 3JD (0524 63446) Map A, D5

Student enquiries: Academic Registrar

Main study areas – as in What to Study section: *(First degree):* Education, English, geography, history, nursing studies. *Also:* Social ethics, youth & community work.

CAN'T FIND WHAT YOU'RE LOOKING FOR? USE THE INDEX!

European Community: 10% first degree students take EC language as part of course and 5% spend 6 months or more in another EC country. Formal exchange links with University of Extremadura (Spain).

Application: UCCA. **Academic features:** BA nursing studies with a nurse training specialism (RGN, RMN, RMNH). BEd includes major subjects in art & design, biology, English, geography, history, maths, music, RS and minor subjects in drama, information technology and technology in contemporary society. New BA options include applications of information technology, community welfare and administration. **Other features:** Institute of Educational Computing, Moral and Social Education Resource Centre. **Founded:** 1963, as C of E college of education. Associated college of Lancaster University. **Main awards:** BA, BEd. **Awarding body:** Lancaster University. **Site:** Pleasant, single open campus 5 minutes from city centre. **Access:** Inter-city rail (London-Glasgow) or motorway (M6); frequent local bus service. **Accommodation:** All first years accommodated. 260 places in halls plus 90 places in new city centre hall. Rent: 30% in accommodation where rent controlled by college. **Library:** 160,000 volumes, 550 periodicals, 160 study places. Wide range of non-book materials. Students can use Lancaster University library. **Other learning resources:** Computer laboratories, AVA resource centre and centres for teaching resources, primary education, reading and language, science resource, religious & moral education resource, art and ceramic studios, music recital and rehearsal rooms; plus individual departmental resource facilities. **Welfare:** Doctor, resident nurse, chaplain, SU solicitor; chapel. **Careers:** Information and advice service on site, linked with University of Lancaster Careers Service. **Amenities:** Bookshop on campus, SU bar and social club; shop; new drama studio; separate Student Union building. Chapel; Medical Centre. Good art, ceramic, music and drama facilities. **Sporting facilities:** Various sports pitches (including floodlit all-weather pitch), tennis and squash courts, gymnasia, multi-gym with equipment for aerobic exercise. **Employment:** Teaching, youth and community work. All careers available to arts/humanities graduates. Nursing – general, psychiatric, mentally handicapped.

Duration of first degree course(s) or equivalent: 3 years (BA); 4 years (BEd & BA Nursing Studies) **Total first degree students 1989/90:** 950 **BEd students:** 474 **Number of mature students:** 183 **Male/female ratio 1989/90:** 2:3 **Teaching staff: full-time:** 100 **part-time:** 35 **Total full-time students 1989/90:** 1,200 **Postgraduate students:** 218 **Tuition fees, first degrees, 1990/91:** Home: £1,675; Overseas: £4,560.

What it's like

A C of E college, ¼ mile from Lancaster with a very pleasant campus. Close links with the community and much involvement with local projects. Lancaster has the usual high street stores, pubs for all tastes, restaurants for all palates, a good range of theatre, music and films. Well situated for coastal and countryside activities. Most first years can live in one of six 'warm' halls (mixed, except one all female). Meals and daily cleaning included in hall fees. Each hall has irons, kettles etc for communal use. New self-catering residence in town centre for 90 students.

Other campus facilities include medical centre, laundry, TV lounges, games room with pool table etc, refurbished coffee bar, book shop and general shop. Two bars for alcoholic and non-alcoholic drinks are linked with disco and ents.

SU Ents responsible for the weekly disco and visiting bands, also for major events like the Easter Ball.

Active SU (affiliated to NUS) strives to meet student needs in all areas, eg welfare, entertainments, clubs and societies, magazine, needs of women and minority groups. Range of sports clubs and subject related societies; others include Community Action Group, Labour Club, Video/Film. Strong links with SCAN (Student Cancer Appeal Nationwide); many students participate in a variety of events associated with this. Access to university facilities, including library, sports centre, theatre, clubs and societies.

CAN'T FIND WHAT YOU'RE LOOKING FOR? USE THE INDEX!

A place of opportunities where people can be themselves and participate in or initiate those activities which interest them.

Pauper notes

Accommodation: Well above average on campus. Provided for most first years if required. **Drink:** Social and JCR bars relatively cheap. Vast range of pubs in town. Coffee bar on campus open 8–5 weekdays. **Eats:** Refectory – full meals. Coffee bar has range of snack meals. Keen catering officer, vegetarian provision. **Ents:** Discos, local bands, films, society organised evenings. **Sports:** Adequate sports facilities plus new multi-gym. Easy access to university facilities and town sports centre. **Travel:** Trust funds and travel scholarships through the chaplaincy. **Work:** Social club, JCR discos, JCR bar, plus minibus shuttle service home from evening events.

Alumni (Editors' pick)

David Coates, Elizabeth Dent, Nicholas Rigby.

ST MARY'S COLLEGE

St Mary's College, Strawberry Hill, Twickenham TW1 4SX (081-892 0051) Map D, A4

Student enquiries: The Registrar

Main study areas – as in What to Study section: *(First degree):* Biology, chemistry, drama, education, English, geography, history, mathematical studies, religious studies and theology, sociology. **Also:** Irish studies.

European Community: No students learn an EC language or spend time in another EC country as part of their course. Formal exchange link for teaching practice in Belgium.

Application: UCCA. **Special features:** Voluntary College, Christian (RC) foundation. **Largest fields of study:** English, history, movement studies, education. **Founded:** 1850, moved 1925 to present site. **Main awards:** BA, BSc, BA (qualified teacher status). **Awarding body:** Surrey University. **Site:** 18th century 'Gothic' house built by Horace Walpole in Strawberry Hill just outside Twickenham town centre. **Access:** Bus and British Rail (Strawberry Hill Station). **Accommodation:** 450 places on campus (segregated), accommodation officer helps with rooms locally. Approx cost: £882–£948 pa or £1,316–£1,642 pa inclusive of 9 meals per week (term time only). **Library:** 136,000 volumes, 600 periodicals, 234 study places, reference copies of course books. **Other learning facilities:** TV studio, CCTV, computer centre, theatre, learning resources centre. **Welfare:** Medical centre, 1 nurse, visiting doctors; personal tutors, chaplain, wardens. **Careers:** Information and advice. **Amenities:** Campus bookshop, SU shop, bar, coffee lounge, refectory open to resident and non-resident students. **Sporting facilities:** Good sports facilities (gymnasium, dance studio, exercise physiology laboratory, sports hall, floodlit all-weather playing area).

Duration of first degree course(s) or equivalent: 3 years; **others:** 4 years **Total first degree students 1990/91:** 962; **Total BA (QTS):** 375 **Number of overseas students:** 32 **Number of mature students:** approx 200 **Male/female ratio 1990/91:** 2:3 **Teaching staff: full-time:** 93 **part-time:** 13 **Total full-time students 1990/91:** 1,465 **Postgraduate students:** 133 **Tuition fees, first degrees, 1990/91:** Home: £1,675; Overseas: £4,400; plus £321 validation examination fees, all 1st year students.

What it's like

Steeped in history and tradition, part of the college still consisting of the beautiful 18th-century mansion, St Mary's provides a classic setting for study with added

CAN'T FIND WHAT YOU'RE LOOKING FOR? USE THE INDEX!

advantage of being within half an hour's journey from central London. Spacious college grounds are 'home for a year' for vast majority of first years who choose to live in; all college accommodation no more than five minutes' walk to heart of campus. Halls of residence single sex, but opportunities abound for fruitful interractions between individuals, nowhere more so than at the thrice-weekly disco. Other SU events include Christmas and Going-Down balls and hugely popular bonfire night. Sporting facilities excellent. Movement studies, English and RS the most significant disciplines at St Mary's. Recent developments include introduction of Irish studies and environmental science.

Any attempt to define typical St Mary's student is bound to end in disappointment. They could be of British/Irish/Malaysian origin, and of any religious background, the Catholic tradition of the college being far from oppressive; they may or may not intend becoming a teacher and could be studying virtually any combination of subjects.

SU role is to ensure a fair deal for all St Mary's students as well as encouraging friendly atmosphere within college. External issues of particular interest to St Mary's students include Amnesty International and Friends of Birzeit (a West-Bank university).

St Mary's caters for students preferring the cosy ambiance of a smaller college to larger, more anonymous institutions.
Kieron O'Donovan

Pauper notes

Accommodation: 450 or more students live on campus. Others live quite close and transport is generally good – on BR and bus routes (minimum outside rents about £30). **Drink:** Cheap well stocked college bar, at least 20 pubs in walking distance. **Eats:** Richmond has many ethnic and one vegetarian restaurant. Teddington also good. 'Angelos', Twickenham excellent and 'very' cheap Italian food highly recommended. **Ents:** Excellent theatre (drama department). SU has 3 weekly discos and recent bands include Bad Manners, The Senseless Things, Dr and the Medics etc. Also local and London theatre, cinemas easy to reach. **Sports:** Excellent facilities on campus (including a new health fitness research gym). Centre of excellence in lacrosse, gymnastics. **Hardship funds:** Local banks give generous overdrafts. **Work:** Much work available in pubs, restaurants, shops and for temping agencies. Also SU deals with companies who need summer staff for Wimbledon, Henley etc. A chance to pack loads of hours into a short time.

Alumni (Editors' pick)

Robert Ackerman; Patricia Mordecai, Tom O'Connor (TV); David Bedford, Gordon Pirie (athletics); Rowena Roberts; Hon Michael Glover (Minister for Youth, Sport; Mauritius), Mick Melia (Eddie the landlord in 'EastEnders').

ST MARY'S HOSPITAL

St Mary's Hospital Medical School, University of London, Paddington, London W2 1PG (071-723 1252) Map D, B1

Student enquiries: The Admissions Secretary

Main study areas – as in What to Study section: *(First degree):* Medicine.

European Community: No students learn an EC language or spend time in another EC country.

Application: UCCA. **Structural features:** Part of Imperial College of Science, Technology and Medicine, London University. **Academic features:** Offers both pre-clinical and clinical studies and courses for intercalated BSc. Small number of clinical students admitted after pre-clinical studies at Oxford or Cambridge.

CAN'T FIND WHAT YOU'RE LOOKING FOR? USE THE INDEX!

Founded: 1854, becoming part of London University in 1900; merged with Imperial College 1988. **Main awards:** BSc, MBBS. **Awarding body:** London University. **Site:** Near Paddington station. **Access:** Paddington and Edgware Road underground stations. **Accommodation:** 240 places available in mixed hall. Approx cost: £35.00 pw (self-catering). Rent: 50% in accommodation where rent controlled by university. **Library:** 30,000 volumes, 245 periodicals, 168 study places, departmental libraries. **Welfare:** Student health service, university chaplains. **Hardship funds:** Limited endowed funds are available to assist students in financial distress. **Amenities:** SU bookshop (second-hand), nearby local bookshop specialising in medical textbooks. **Sporting facilities:** Excellent cricket, rugby, soccer and hockey at the sports ground in Teddington; swimming pool; 2 squash courts; multipurpose recreation hall. Mountain hut in Snowdonia. Access to Imperial College and University of London union facilities, eg rowing and sailing. **Employment:** Postgraduate office assists graduate students to find first 2 house officer posts and offers advice on subsequent career development.

Duration of first degree course(s) or equivalent: 5 years; **others:** 6 years (with intercalated BSc) **Total first degree students 1989/90:** 543 **Number of overseas students:** 27 **Number of mature students:** 28 **Male/female ratio 1989/90:** 8:7 **Teaching staff: full-time:** 73 **part-time:** 150 **Total full-time students 1989/90:** 574 **Postgraduate students:** 88 (inc 57 p-t) **Tuition fees, first degrees, 1990/91:** Home: £1,675 (less for self-financing students); Overseas: £6,500 (pre-clinical), £11,150 (clinical).

What it's like
Founded in 1854. Course leads to degrees of Bachelor of Medicine and Bachelor of Surgery (MB.BS), also clinical medicine courses for students from Oxbridge. 5 minutes' walk from Paddington, close to Hyde Park and central London attractions. Renowned for friendliness, one immediately feels welcome.

Pre-clinical teaching, lasting 2 years, on basis of lectures, practicals and tutorials studying basic medical sciences including anatomy (fun dissection classes), physiology, biochemistry and pharmacology. Course is intensive, a lot of work is expected. On the whole teaching is very good and most cope, sometimes organisation would help! Clinical teaching, lasting 3 years, is ward-based, it's up to the individual to gain the maximum from what is offered on your firm of medical staff.

SU very active, Nursing and Physiotherapy Schools are affiliated. Many facilities, including swimming pool, weights room and a sports ground at Teddington. About 50 clubs and societies, for a diversity of activities, ensures never a dull moment. Clubs vary from rugby, waterpolo, rifle shooting, rowing to music, photography, aerobics, wine tasting, mountaineering. Community at St Mary's is small, comprises students, doctors, nurses, physiotherapists and staff involved in research. Now the fourth constituent college of Imperial College of Science, Technology and Medicine, this community is unlikely to change and will keep its identity as always.

Pauper notes
Accommodation: Wilson House mainly 1st year and clinical, intercollegiate Halls – popular in first 2 years. **Drink:** Clubroom bar, Recreation Centre bar, The Exchange (Murphy's), 'The Flem' (Websters). **Eats:** Nurses canteen, Micky's, Just-a-Bite, Paddington Tandoori, Ganges, Old Delhi, McDonald's, Wimpy etc. **Ents:** Film Soc, fringe and pub theatres, West End etc, discos and Balls in Med School, Band nites featuring Marvis and small outside bands. **Sports:** Teddington sports ground, squash, badminton, multigym, basketball facilities on site. **Hardship funds:** Only scholarships for some mature students. **Travel:** Some SU elective grants. **Work:** Evening work in bars and in London eg auxiliary nursing, cocktail waiting. For blokes the Aid Clinics in Harley Street.

Alumni (Editors' pick)
Sir Alexander Fleming, Sir Roger Bannister, J P R Williams.

CAN'T FIND WHAT YOU'RE LOOKING FOR? USE THE INDEX!

SALFORD UNIVERSITY

University of Salford, Salford M5 4WT (061-736 5843) Map A, D6

Student enquiries: Registrar

Main study areas – as in What to Study section: *(First degree):* Accountancy, aeronautical engineering, biochemistry, biology, business studies, chemistry, civil engineering, computing, economics, electrical & electronic engineering, English, environmental science, geography, history, information technology, mathematical studies, mechanical and production engineering, metallurgy and materials science, modern languages, physics, politics and government, sociology. *Also:* Arabic, biomedical electronics, construction engineering, interpretation and translation, quantity surveying.

European Community: 17% first degree students take EC language as part of course and 15% spend 6 months or more in another EC country. Formal exchange links with some 20 EC universities/colleges: Belgium (languages); Denmark (politics); Eire (information technology); France (some engineering students, languages, information technology); Germany (languages); Greece (information technology); Italy (languages); Netherlands (politics); Portugal (information technology); Spain (languages). In addition, large number of informal links. Approved Erasmus programme 1990/91. University aims to give all undergraduates opportunity to study a foreign language.

Application: UCCA. **Academic features:** Applicants with arts or science backgrounds accepted on BEng in construction management, BSc in information technology and BSc in computer management and education. Students on special chemistry, biological sciences, business operation and control or social science degrees able to spend a year in either Lyon, France or Toledo or Wayne State, USA. New 4-year degree programmes run jointly by university and local colleges of technology; students spend 2 years at college then, if suitable, come to University for 2 years to complete degree (1 year plus 3 years for technological physics course). Over 40% of students take integrated courses which include industrial or professional training. Most degree programmes include 'student capability schemes' designed to improve skills in teamwork, verbal and written communication and presentation. **Special features:** Integrated chairs where professors work part-time in university and part-time in senior positions in their company: aeronautical and mechanical engineering (British Aerospace and Danichi-Sykes); chemistry and applied chemistry (Unilever); physics (British Nuclear Fuels); transport management (British Rail); information technology (British Telecom). **Founded:** Granted Royal charter in 1967. **Main awards:** BA, BSc, BEng, MEng. **Awarding body:** Salford University. **Site:** 34-acre campus a mile from Salford town centre, 2 miles from Manchester. **Access:** Motorway links, buses and trains from Manchester.Manchester International airport in easy reach. **Accommodation:** 540 places in halls; 2,100 self-catering flats; 100 lodgings; 800 flats/bedsitters houses (all single first year students, who accept a place by 1st September provided with accommodation and one further year guaranteed in university controlled accommodation). Approx cost: £43 pw halls, £23 pw student houses, £50 pw lodgings. 80% in accommodation where rent controlled by university. **Library:** 300,000 volumes in total, 2,000 periodicals, 750 study places, reference collection of recommended student texts. **Welfare:** Health centre, psychotherapist, 3 professional welfare officers, overseas students' adviser. **Hardship funds:** Hardship loan scheme operates. **Special categories:** Some residential facilities for married and disabled students. **Careers:** Information (excellent library of employers' material, videos and reference books), advice and placement through 'milk round'. **Amenities:** Restaurants, snackbars, bookshop, union shop and bank on campus; SU building with bar, insurance and travel bureaux; Salford City Art Gallery and Lowry Collection near campus. **Sporting facilities:** Sports hall with 6 squash courts. Outdoor playing fields at student village. **Employment:** Industry, commerce and public service.

CAN'T FIND WHAT YOU'RE LOOKING FOR? USE THE INDEX!

Duration of first degree course(s) or equivalent: 3 years; **others:** 4 years (integrated) **Total first degree students 1989/90:** 3,650 **Number of overseas students:** 350 **Male/female ratio 1989/90:** 7:3 **Teaching staff: full-time:** 350 **part-time:** 100 **Total full-time students 1989/90:** 3,950 **Postgraduate students:** 300 (f-t) **Tuition fees, first degrees, 1990/91:** Home: £1,675; Overseas: £4,570 (eg politics), £6,050 (eg physics).

What it's like

Single modern campus, a mile from Manchester and within two miles of all the university accommodation. Accommodation guaranteed for two of three years, 85% get all three. Far better accommodation than most UKCPUs.

Over 20% of students from overseas – contribute greatly to life at university. Students from all over the globe come to Salford to study. SU provides overseas secretary who gives advice and organises a welcome week and various international events. Over 15 different overseas societies. SU very active, especially social with emphasis on trading/entertainment. More than 80 different clubs or societies. Special emphasis on outdoor pursuits. Very active community services section – includes Christmas parties for senior citizens, children; English lessons for partners of overseas students; work with ex-offenders; work with the disabled.

SU has student advice centre with 3 members of staff and 4 student officers who can help with *any* problem at all: financial, legal, accommodation, visas, personal or academic; it also provides a legal adviser, overseas counsellor, student counsellor and various health campaigns.

The university is thriving, independent with a colourful history and strong links with industry. Many courses have industrial sandwich years (home and abroad). Specialising in engineering, modern languages, technology and sociology, graduates have a fine employment record, among the best in the country, mainly into industry.

Salford is small, but very friendly. People who come enjoy themselves. If you don't get in, try Manchester.

Pauper notes

Accommodation: 2,900 rooms in university accommodation, some married quarters. List of accommodation in private sector – housing advice available from SU. **Drink:** 3 main bars, 2 smaller lounges – 1 pub. Late bar till 2.00 am three nights a week at Student Village – cheaper than local pubs – range of speciality European lagers and wines and Theakstons, McEwans, Tennants, Tetley – lots of promotion nights. Local pubs a bit rough. **Eats:** 'The Cage' at Student Village – run by Union – open every night – range of cheap meals. Lots of takeaways and restaurants in Manchester. **Ents:** SU: Thurs/Sat superb video disco at Village – often have live bands, theme nights (beach party, 60s and 70s nights) and more specialised discos (Indie/House etc), many top current and classic films and special evenings on Tuesdays with cabaret/competitions etc. In town: theatre/lots of cinemas and nightclubs and gigs. **Sports:** Union runs leisure centre – weights room, sports hall, snooker room, sunbed, sports shop, video library, squash courts, outdoor play area. Good facilities – the only UKCPU with a sports policy – encouraging sports clubs to make provision of sport as large a number of students as possible a top priority. The second stage of the sports policy encourages pursuit of excellence. **Hardship funds:** Some interest-free loans from university. **Travel:** Union travel bureau on campus, offers all possibilities esp cheap air travel/train and coach. Open 9–4.30 Mon–Fri. **Work:** Union offers work on ents team – selling tickets etc and work at concerts. Also bar work. Selective library work. **Shops:** Union runs 2 shops – 1 on campus and 1 on student village. Union produces monthly magazine – Salford Student Magazine and weekly newsletter called Profile. Union also provides print shop, launderette, hairdressers and opticians.

Alumni (Editors' pick)

John Howard, Ieuan Evans, Sarah Greene.

CAN'T FIND WHAT YOU'RE LOOKING FOR? USE THE INDEX!

SANDHURST

Royal Military Academy Sandhurst, Camberley, Surrey GU15 4PQ
(0276 63344) Map A, F8

Student enquiries: (Officers' Enquiries) Careers for Army Officers, Ministry of Defence (DAR1), Empress State Building, Lillie Road, London SW6 1TR.

Main study areas – as in What to Study section: Strategic studies.

European Community: No students learn an EC language or spend time in another EC country.

Special features: All British army officers are trained at Sandhurst. **Structural features:** 3 types of course offered for different intakes: Standard Military Course for school leavers (male); Standard Graduate Course for graduates (male); Women's Standard Course for women graduates and school leavers. The Standard Military Course is three terms long with intakes each term; other two are two terms long with intakes in September and January. Graduates are commissioned officers on entry on probation; others are commissioned on successful completion of the course. After commissioning, officers usually attend specialist courses before starting a period of regimental duty. Students are organised into platoons and companies. **Academic features:** Courses are designed to teach basic military skills and develop qualities of leadership. Students on the Standard Graduate and the Women's Standard Courses may on occasions be taught together. Distinguished civilian academic staff in addition to serving officers. **Founded:** 1802 as Royal Military College Sandhurst. Womens Royal Army Corps College incorporated in 1984. **Accommodation:** 100% provided for all students. **Library:** 100,000 books, 350 periodicals. **Specialist collection:** Military history. **Other learning resources:** Audio-visual equipment; closed circuit TV recording and playback studios. **Sporting facilities:** Squash, badminton and rackets courts; playing fields; indoor swimming pool; gymnasium; physical and recreational training; adventurous training pursuits; rowing and sailing (own canoes, dinghies and sailing boats); facilities for golf, boxing, field sports; many 'indoor' clubs, flying scholarships available on merit, parachuting, caving and climbing.

Total students 1989/90: 1,000 approx of which 450 are graduate entrants **Male/female ratio 1989/90:** 9:1 **Staff:** 108 military; 35 civilian; **Total full-time students:** 825 **Number of postgraduate students:** 363

What it's like

Set in one of the most beautiful estates in the south of England. A young officer who recently 'survived' the course had this to say about his experience. 'Sandhurst dismantles you bit by bit, kicks you around for a couple of weeks, and then reassembles you in slightly more soldierlike fashion. It then goes on to teach you a great deal. In retrospect, of course, it was tremendous fun very hard, in that you can experience frustrations as well as enjoyment and real satisfaction.'

Sandhurst is not for the faint-hearted.

You will almost certainly become fitter than at any previous time of your life through physical pursuits like military exercises and adventurous training exercises. The 'physical' is, however, counter-balanced by study. You will learn about military history, organisation and military tactics, comment intelligently on world events. You will become proficient in handling weapons and cross country navigation – as well as learning how to behave as an officer. 'Behave like an officer' has been made fun of in countless films, cartoons and comedy sketches. It really means that you will be courteous and caring.

If you successfully negotiate Sandhurst and gain your commission you will then go on a 'Special to Arm' course with the Regiment or Corps of your choice. The length of this course will depend on which branch of the Army you have chosen to

CAN'T FIND WHAT YOU'RE LOOKING FOR? USE THE INDEX!

join. It is designed to give you a general appreciation of your Regiment or Corps, and the specialist knowledge you will need before taking your first command.

Alumni (Editors' pick)
Winston Churchill, General Haig, General Montgomery, King Hussein of Jordan, David Niven.

SCHOOL OF PHARMACY

The School of Pharmacy, University of London, 29/39 Brunswick Square, London WC1N 1AX (071-837 7651/8) Map E, C1

Student enquiries: The Registrar

Main study areas – as in What to Study section: *(First degree):* Pharmacology, pharmacy. *Also: Toxicology.*

European Community: No students learn an EC language or spend time in another EC country. No EC links.

Application: UCCA. **Structural features:** Part of London University. **Special features:** 3-year BPharm degree course designed to teach to honours level while equipping student vocationally for pharmaceutical profession; 4-year BSc course in toxicology and pharmacology includes 1 year industrial experience. **Founded:** 1842, instituted in 1925. **Main awards:** BPharm, BSc. **Awarding body:** London University. **Site:** Central London (between Southampton Row and Grays Inn Road). **Access:** Russell Square underground station. **Accommodation:** School is near several intercollegiate halls. Advice on other accommodation from university accommodation office. Rent: 70% undergraduates (.her than those living at home) in accommodation where rent controlled by university. **Library:** 26,000 volumes, 200 periodicals, 74 study places; recommended books in reserve collection. **Other learning facilities:** Computer centre. **Welfare:** London University health service. **Careers:** Information, advice and placement. **Amenities:** SU with shop and second-hand book service, ULU nearby; also British Museum etc. **Employment:** Pharmacists in general practice, hospitals and industrial organisations; toxicologists in industrial and government laboratories, or with environmental, regulatory and law enforcement authorities.

Duration of first degree course(s) or equivalent: 3 years (BPharm) and 4 years (BScTox) **Total first degree students 1989/90:** 337 **Number of overseas students:** 29 **Number of mature students:** 8 **Male/female ratio 1989/90:** 9:11 **Teaching staff: full-time:** 40 **part-time:** 4 **Total full-time students 1989/90:** 418 **Postgraduate students:** 81 f-t (¢ 53 p-t) **Tuition fees, first degrees 1990/91:** Home: £1,675; Overseas: £6,050

What it's like
Its academic excellence is respected throughout the world. Just as importantly it is a very friendly college so virtually everyone knows everyone else by the end of first year. All staff internal and on hand if students experience any work problems.

Social functions very popular with both internal and external students, which enables one to meet people from other institutions. SU apolitical, very active socially, and in looking after its own members' interests. Main events: annual ball, garden party, bonfire party, Christmas panto and party and, of course, the best freshers and rag weeks in the country.

The Ball is always held at a prestigious location (last year Park Lane Hotel). The garden party and bonfire party are held at the school's sports ground which is shared with the Royal Free Hospital at Myddleton House and are always superb fun. The

CAN'T FIND WHAT YOU'RE LOOKING FOR? USE THE INDEX!

Christmas panto and party produce many a laugh both for students and lecturers alike.

Rag week highlight of the second term; usual charity is Great Ormond Street Children's Hospital. A few of the functions include a bed push down Oxford Street and a three-legged pub crawl and I mean crawl!

Regular Friday night 'Bop-till-u-Drop' disco, renowned throughout London University for its atmosphere, held in student common room which has its own cheap bar, pool table, table-tennis table etc.

Many clubs and societies within the Union: football, hockey, rugby, netball, Indian, Chinese, Jewish, Christian Union and Welsh.

Successful sporty teams and the highlight of the year is when everyone travels to the BPSA sports weekend.

All societies hold their own functions in each term, such as meals, pub crawls and even trips to places such as Paris and Alton Towers! Besides having our own societies we are also affiliated to University of London Union which offers many other varied activities.

Students have a happy and enjoyable time whilst in London, making lifelong friends within their colleges and with students from other faculties as well. Being at 'The Square' is like being part of one big family where everyone helps out, so all can have three years of untroubled education and a varied and happy social life.
Steve Wells

Pauper notes

Accommodation: 6 intercollegiate halls within 5 mins walk; most 2nd and some 3rd years live out. **Drink:** Bar very cheap and cheerful. ULU bar near as well as numerous good pubs. **Eats:** Good quality cheap refectory in college – many restaurants within 5 mins walk (Chinese, Indian, Greek, Italian, hamburgers etc). **Ents:** Crowded, noisy, lively, sweaty discos every Friday night. Numerous other events including pantomime, rag week, midsessional ball etc. **Sports:** At college there are football, netball, rugby, hockey; ULU nearby with multitude of societies and sports facilities. **Hardship funds:** None available. **Travel:** No cheap fares. **Work:** Jobs in pharmacy during vacations, but not much time otherwise for work during term due to intensive nature of course.

SCOTTISH CENTRE FOR PE

The Scottish Centre for Physical Education, Movement and Leisure Studies, Moray House College of Education, Holyrood Road, Edinburgh EH8 8AQ (031-556 8455) Map A, D3

Student enquiries: Registrar

Main study areas – as in What to Study section: *(First degree):* Education. *Also:* Human movement, physical education, recreation, sports studies.

European Community: No students learn an EC language or spend time in another EC country as part of their course. Formal exchange link with University of Athens (physical education); further links developing for recreation students.

Application: Direct. **Founded:** 1905, as Dunfermline College of Education for students of physical education. Retains former campus at Cramond, but incorporated in Moray House College of Education. **Academic features:** Postgraduate courses in recreation, outdoor education and sports coaching. In-service courses for teachers and recreation professionals. **Special features:** Centre for Leisure Research, National Coaching Centre. **Main awards:** BA, BEd. **Awarding body:** CNAA. **Site:** Outskirts of Edinburgh (approx 40 acres). **Access:** Bus. **Accommodation:** 180 places in halls of residence. Accommodation provided for most first year students. Approx cost: £36.45 pw (includes 5 main meals). **Library:** 40,000

CAN'T FIND WHAT YOU'RE LOOKING FOR? USE THE INDEX!

volumes, 370 periodicals, 113 study places; short loan service for course books. **Welfare:** Medical officer, physiotherapist, counsellor. **Careers:** Advice and placement service. **Amenities:** Sports centre (gymnasia, 25m swimming pool, dance studio, games halls, playing fields). **Employment:** PE teaching, work in recreation industry.

Duration of first degree course(s) or equivalent: 4 years **Other:** 3 years **Total first degree students 1989/90:** 388 **BEd students:** 286 **Number of overseas students:** 8 **Number of mature students:** 25 **Male/female ratio 1989/90:** 2:5 **Teaching staff:** 39 **Total full-time students 1989/90:** 431 **Postgraduate students:** 43 f-t **Tuition fees, first degrees, 1990/91:** Home: £693; Overseas: £4,150.

What it's like

Situated in splendid grounds in a northern suburb of Edinburgh overlooking the Firth of Forth, the centre has well equipped residences with adequately sized rooms. Very close-knit community with excellent staff/student relations. Predominantly female. The PE teacher-trainers are still the major course on site but 4 others are available, all deal with leisure and recreation in some form. Expectations are high of good academic qualifications and career prospects generally bright, if you are prepared to travel and work anywhere in Britain or abroad.

Sports facilities include 3 gymnasia, sports hall, temp 'air-hall', finest grass playing area to be found anywhere in Britain. (Hockey pitches, football, rugby, cricket, shinty and lacrosse.)

Small, but active 'Students Committee', which the SU Bar Committee are part of, and both organise and promote an inexpensive social environment based around the Union bar on site, which is a remarkably well-kept and run service. Only 5 years old! Overall atmosphere is friendly and positive; the worst aspect of college life is that attitudes are a little reactionary/apathetic and politics is not a big issue. These are changing.

Pauper notes

Accommodation: Reasonably priced campus residences – places can be found in central Edinburgh cheaply, but it's generally expensive. **Drink:** Student pubs in town. **Eats:** Veggie restaurants available in central Edin. Plethora of Italian, Chinese and Indian places. Many cater with students in mind. **Ents:** Good/great night life. Bands of renown; choice of cinemas and theatres; discos. **Festival** Edinburgh highlight!! Free shows if you look hard enough. **Sports:** On campus sport is free. Many successful, well-organised clubs. All usual facilities except squash courts. **Travel:** Local bus group have special student card deal. **Work:** Work available on campus to students on college organised community activities programme. Kitchen work also available. College also occasionally employs students as 'Residence Wardens' (1–2 per year).

SCOTTISH COLLEGE OF TEXTILES

Scottish College of Textiles, Galashiels, Selkirkshire TD1 3HF (0896 3351) Map A, D3

Student enquiries: Academic Registrar

Main study areas – as in What to Study section: *(First degree):* Art & design, business studies, chemistry, computing, information technology, modern languages. *Also:* Clothing technology, textile technology.

European Community: No students learn an EC language; 10% spend 6 months in another EC country as part of their course.

Application: UCCA. **Structural features:** Faculty of Heriot-Watt University. **Academic features:** Degree courses in: industrial design (textiles); applied chemis-

CAN'T FIND WHAT YOU'RE LOOKING FOR? USE THE INDEX!

try (polymer and colour science and technology); textiles with clothing studies; clothing (technology, marketing, management and product design). **Largest fields of study:** Textile design, clothing studies. **Founded:** 1883, became Central Institute of HE in 1921. Joined Heriot-Watt University 1990. **Main awards:** BA, BSc. **Awarding body:** CNAA and Heriot-Watt (and Clothing Institute, Textile Institute, Clothing and Footwear Institute). **Site:** Outskirts of Galashiels. **Access:** Bus from Edinburgh (34 miles). **Accommodation:** 130 places in mixed halls, 72 places in flats on campus, 230 places in flats off-campus. All first year students accommodated in halls. Approx cost: £25.00 pw (self catering, halls of residence), £36 pw (bed & breakfast and evening meal, halls of residence), £22 pw (self-catering, off campus flats). Rent: 70% in accommodation where rent controlled by college. **Library:** 18,000 volumes, 300 periodicals, 110 study places. **Specialist collections:** Fabric samples and shawls. **Other learning facilities:** Outstanding handloom weaving workshop, extensive studios, textile and clothing workshops, IBM 4331 computer, micro-computing lab, computer-aided textile design centre. **Centres of excellence:** Textile design and technology, clothing studies. **Welfare:** Careers and welfare centre with students' counsellor; college chaplaincy; other services with local practitioners. **Hardship funds:** Small trust fund. **Careers:** Information and advice. **Amenities:** College bookshop, student/staff social club. **Sporting facilities:** Wide range of sports. **Employment:** Textile and clothing design, retail management, technology and merchandising; management, marketing, information technology, computer programming.

Duration of first degree course(s) or equivalent: 4 years **others:** 5 years **Total first degree students 1989/90:** 311 **Number of overseas students:** 7 **Number of mature students:** 30 **Male/female ratio 1989/90:** 9:11 **Teaching staff: full-time:** 40 **part-time:** 10 **Total full-time students 1989/90:** 650 **Postgraduate students:** 20 **Tuition fees, first degrees, 1990/91:** Home: £1,675; Overseas: £4,000.

What it's like

It's modern, purpose-built, on outskirts of Galashiels, 33 miles south east of Edinburgh, providing excellent facilities for study and recreation with specially designed laboratories and design studios. Very well equipped textile technology and colour chemistry departments. Specialist rooms for behavioural science, personnel management, work study; language laboratories and computer suite in management department. Design and technology departments have vast hand weaving shed, complemented by extensive modern high-speed weaving and knitting looms allowing students first-hand experience of designing commercial fabrics. Pleasant library, lecture theatre, recreation hall, refectory, licensed club room. Halls of residence on hillside near college unsegregated with full board facilities. Plenty of student flats in Galashiels. Aims of SRC: adequate facilities within college, and welfare, social and cultural facilities. Usual sports and activities including football, rugby, hockey, camera, squash, badminton, tennis, pool. Regular dances/discos and annual charities week. Employment prospects for SCOT graduates in textile industry excellent. Most courses now industrially orientated with industrial placement in 2 BSc and clothing courses.

Pauper notes

Accommodation: Halls have strict moral code and many prefer flats but accommodation difficult due to increased numbers of students. **Drink:** Student/staff club – cheap, good beer/food – Bellhaven beers. **Eats:** Halls and refectory food cheap with a large variety of choice. **Ents:** Regular discos/band in club. Cinema in town. **Sports:** Badminton, aerobics, 5-a-side football etc in college sports hall. Local swimming pool. Active football/rugby teams. **Hardship funds:** Difficult to get from college. **Travel:** Student fares on buses. Regular buses to Edinburgh etc. **Work:** Local bars and clubs. Student/staff club also uses students.

Alumni (Editors' pick)

Sir Russell Fairgrieve MP, Lord R Sanderson of Bowden, Sir Alan Smith.

CAN'T FIND WHAT YOU'RE LOOKING FOR? USE THE INDEX!

SHEFFIELD POLY

Sheffield City Polytechnic, Pond Street, Sheffield S1 1WB (0742 720911); Telex 54680 SHPOLY G; Fax 758019 Map A, E6

Student enquiries: Enquiry office

Main study areas – as in What to Study section: *(First degree):* Accountancy, art & design, business studies, chemistry, civil engineering, communication studies, computing, education, electrical & electronic engineering, English, environmental studies, European studies, fine arts, food science & nutrition, geography, geology, history, hotel & catering management, information technology, law, mathematical studies, mechanical and production engineering, metallurgy and materials science, modern languages, nursing, politics & government, physics, public administration, town and country planning, welfare studies. *Also:* Film studies, occupational therapy, physiotherapy, recreation, tourism.

European Community: Number of students learning an EC language or spending time in another EC country, not known. Approved Erasmus programme 1990/91.

Application: PCAS except art and design (ADAR). **Academic features:** New degree courses in law, tourism, financial services. Emphasis on applied and vocational courses; high proportion of sandwich courses. Access, associate student schemes and Credit Accumulation and Transfer Schemes in operation. **Special features:** Barry Hines (writer), Ian McMillan, Jane Roger and Martin Wiley on the staff. **Largest fields of study:** Technology, business and management, education, health and welfare, environmental and cultural studies. **Founded:** 1969, ex College of Technology and College of Art, joined by 3 colleges of education. **Main awards:** BA, BEd, BEng, MEng, BSc. **Awarding body:** CNAA. **Site:** 4 sites in or near Sheffield city centre. **Access:** City centre site, opposite central rail and bus stations. Good public transport and internal inter-site transport available. **Accommodation:** 1,521 places in mixed halls; 554 self-catering rooms; most first year students accommodated. Extensive register of student flats/bedsits/lodgings. Approx cost: Student residences: £21 pw (shared rooms, no meals) to £50 (single room, fully catered). Self catered, private sector: approx £28 per week per person. Rent: 15% in accommodation where rent controlled by polytechnic. **Library:** 1 library on each site; 406,547 volumes in total, 2,200 periodicals; multi-site catalogue on microfiche. 1,370 study places. Extensive short loan and reference collection. **Specialist collections:** European documentation, antique books, audio-visual statistical data, government publications, British Standards, EEC papers. **Other learning facilities:** TV and media resources centres. Microcomputing and over 250 terminals to mainframe throughout Poly. **Welfare:** 3 doctors, FPA, solicitor, 3 chaplains, 2 counsellors. **Special categories:** Day nursery (2 to 5 year olds). **Careers:** Information, advice and placement. Also sandwich training placement support. **Amenities:** Purpose-built SU in town centre; union facilities on each site; theatre, film studios, national exhibitions. Poly is close to open countryside and Peak District National Park. **Sporting facilities:** Excellent sporting resources: tennis courts, hockey pitches and running tracks, Alan Rouse Climbing Wall. Sheffield hosts World Student Games in 1991, so enormous sports complexes available. **Employment:** Due to comparatively high number of applied/vocational courses, good employment prospects.

Duration of first degree course(s) or equivalent: 3 full-time, 4 years sandwich, up to 5 years part-time; **Total first degree students 1989/90:** 9,200 **BEd students:** 881 **Number of overseas students:** 233 **Number of mature students:** 7,951 **Male/female ratio 1989/90:** 3:2 **Teaching staff: full-time:** 682 **part-time:** 45 **Total full-time students + sandwich 1989/90:** 9,851 **Postgraduate students:** 1,725 **Tuition fees, first degrees, 1990/91:** Home: £1,675 (£656 if self-financing); Overseas: £4,300 (eg politics), £5,200 (eg physics).

CAN'T FIND WHAT YOU'RE LOOKING FOR? USE THE INDEX!

What it's like

Sheffield to many people means knives and forks; still being made, but not so much now, since the recession. Sheffield is pulling itself out of the doldrums; new air of prosperity to the city. Millions of pounds of development in the City Centre and the lower Don Valley. Business is booming and Sheffield knows it. Industrial city; more than compensated by its greenness, the Peaks and the Dales are a short drive away. Sheffield has nightclubs and pubs galore – the famous Sheffield One has to be sampled to be believed; the Leadmill – a haven for those trying to get away from run-of-the-mill clubs. Fat Cat Pub in Alma Street – with its variety of real ale – one of the best, and one of the few with a no smoking section. For the hunger pangs afterwards, there's plenty of curries and kebab places, as well as the ubiquitous chippie. There are cultural delights too – the Crucible Theatre does not exist solely for the snooker tournament! Five cinemas as well as multiplex cinema, Crystal Peaks outside the city.

By the way, Sheffield is built on seven hills, like Rome.

Pauper notes

Accommodation: Lack of private accommodation as student numbers increase. **Drink:** Union bars cheapest bitter/lager; Yorkshire Grey – a must. **Eats:** Curry Centre/Latin American/Boxalls. **Ents:** The Limit/Leadmill various student nights in most discos, SU discos on sites every week, Saturday night poly 'Sheffield 1' disco. **Sports:** Most sports on sites, clubs etc well funded by union. **Hardship funds:** Access funds. **Travel:** Sheffield Union Travel Shop; near to M1, good for hitching. **Work:** Mainly in pubs in evening. Also recreation facilities/building work.

Alumni (Editors' pick)

Bruce Oldfield, David Mellor.

SHEFFIELD UNIVERSITY

University of Sheffield, Western Bank, Sheffield S10 2TN (0742 768555) Map A, E6

Student enquiries: Undergraduate Admissions Office

Main study areas – as in What to Study section: *(First degree):* Accountancy, American studies, anatomy, archaeology, architecture, art & design, biochemistry, biology, biotechnology, botany, business studies, chemical engineering, chemistry, civil engineering, computing, dentistry, economics, electrical & electronic engineering, English, environmental science, environmental studies, geography, history, information technology, law, linguistics, mathematical studies, mechanical and production engineering, medicine, metallurgy and materials science, microbiology, modern languages, music, pharmacology, philosophy, physics, physiology, politics and government, psychology, sociology, speech sciences, town & country planning, welfare studies, zoology. *Also:* Japanese, landscape, medieval studies, Slavonic studies, urban studies.

European Community: 37% first degree students take EC language as part of course and 0.5% spend 6 months or more in another EC country. Formal exchange links with 13 EC universities/colleges: Denmark (2); France (5); Germany (2); Portugal (1); Spain (3); plus Erasmus links across the EC with a number of departments. Increase in language options in all disciplines. Developing joint qualifications with EC partners. Approved Erasmus programme 1990/91.

Application: UCCA. **Academic features:** New courses in landscape design and archaeology, engineering with a modern language. **Founded:** University Charter of 1905; previously three constituent colleges (founded 1828, 1879 and 1884), then

CAN'T FIND WHAT YOU'RE LOOKING FOR? USE THE INDEX!

University College 1897–1905. **Main awards:** BA, BMus, BSc, MBChB, BDS, BMedSci, LLB, BEng, BScTech, MEng. **Accommodation:** 2,319 places in halls. Approx cost: £45 pw (includes 2 meals per day in hall). Another 1,300 places in University flats. Approx cost: up to £30. All single first year students from outside Sheffield accommodated if they wish. Rent: 3,727 students housed in accommodation where rent charged is under the control of the university. **Library:** Major branch network and most departments have their own (duplicate) libraries; 950,000 books and periodicals, **Other learning facilities:** Audiovisual and television centre, computing centre, centre for English cultural tradition and language, drama studio, English language teaching centre, language labs, computer-aided design lab. **Hardship funds:** Both SU and university run schemes to help students in financial hardship. **Sporting facilities:** Goodwin athletics centre with excellent sports complex (playing fields, 2 sports halls, 2 all-weather floodlit pitches, heated indoor swimming pool, 8 squash courts), additional 38 acres of playing fields 5 miles away; sailing at Ogston reservoir (20 miles from campus).

Duration of first degree course(s) or equivalent: 3 or 4 years; **others:** dentistry 4 or 5 years; medicine 5 or 6 years; architecture 6 years **Total first degree students 1989/90:** 7,175 **Number of first degree overseas students:** 371 **Number of mature students:** 1,197 **Male/female ratio 1989/90:** 4:3 **Teaching staff: full-time:** 823 **part-time:** 75 **Total full-time students 1989/90:** 8,513 **Postgraduate students:** 1,389 **Tuition fees, first degrees, 1990/91:** Home: £1,675 (£650 if self-financing); Overseas: £4,560 (eg politics), £6,050 (eg physics).

What it's like

It's an attractive city, which boasts more park space within its boundaries than any other major European city.

It's a non-campus university. Like Rome, it's built on seven hills; impressive Pennine peaks are mere 30 minutes' bus ride away. Main academic buildings just 10 minutes' walk from city centre and within 15 minutes' walk of each other, including halls of residence, in pleasant leafy suburbs.

City lively; local economy thriving; Sheffield fast developing reputation as media and cultural centre, with wide range of theatre, music and other entertainment. SU plays a big role; up to 20 events each week in range of venues, including multi-purpose Octagon Centre. Regular programme of major bands.

Sport increasingly important in city; SU provides more than 50 well-funded sports clubs.

Welfare services provided by SU excellent, particularly the Rights and Advice service and Nursery. 'The Times Higher Education Supplement' described the SU as 'a shining example of a union which provides excellent commercial services while placing a premium on improving welfare provision and expanding political activity'.

Relations between university and SU are generally good. Sheffield people very friendly; SU has good relationship with local organisations; many students involved in community projects.
Helen Pitts

Pauper notes

Accommodation: Decent university accommodation – hall fees average. Most first years are provided with place; late entrants may have difficulty. **Drink:** SU runs a variety of excellent bars, and a pub the 'Fox and Duck' in nearby Broomhill. Plenty of local pubs, including 'Frog and Parrot' which brews the strongest beer in UK brewed on premises. **Eats:** Variety of cheap and pleasant outlets on campus; city offers Italian, Indian, Chinese, Turkish and a growing number of vegetarian restaurants. **Ents:** Varied programme on campus, including 4 films a week in SU's own cinema (only purpose-built student cinema in UK). The Crucible Theatre enjoys a good reputation, and Lyceum is about to re-open for ballet, opera etc. Plenty of cinemas: Anvil offers best range. **Sports:** Free facilities at University

CAN'T FIND WHAT YOU'RE LOOKING FOR? USE THE INDEX!

Sports Centre – one of best swimming pools (union) in country. Over 50 sports clubs. **Hardship funds:** Run by university. SU offers interest-free loans for abortions. **Travel:** Excellent SU travel shop. Local transport relatively cheap. **Work:** Occasional pub work – high youth unemployment.

Alumni (Editors' pick)
David Blunkett, Amy Johnson, Jane Irving, Tony Miles, Willy Hamilton MP, Tim Robinson, Sir Peter Middleton, Jack Rosenthal, Carol Barnes, Roger Humm.

SHRIVENHAM (Faculty of Cranfield)

Royal Military College of Science Shrivenham, Swindon SN6 8LA (0739 782551) Map A, E8

Student enquiries: Academic Registrar, RMCS

Main study areas – as in What to Study section: *(First degree):* Aeronautical engineering, civil engineering, electrical and electronic engineering, information technology, mechanical engineering. **Also:** Command control, information systems engineering.

European Community: No students learn an EC language or spend time in another EC country.

Application: UCCA. LEA places and Shrivenham scholarships for civilian students. **Academic features:** BEng degree in information systems engineering. **Founded:** 1946. Became a Faculty of Cranfield Institute of Technology in 1984. **Main awards:** BEng, BSc. **Awarding body:** Cranfield Institute of Technology. **Site:** Campus at Shrivenham. **Access:** A420. **Accommodation:** 370 single rooms in halls plus annexe. Rent: 100% in accommodation where rent controlled by college. **Library:** 50,000 volumes, 35,000 textbooks, 40,000 reports, 900 periodicals. **Welfare:** Resident nurse in medical centre; doctor in Shrivenham village. Resident student services co-ordinator. C of E and RC churches on site. Each student has own academic adviser. **Amenities:** Heated outdoor swimming pool, stables, small theatre, range of sports facilities including squash courts and golf course in excellent grounds; a wide range of recreational social clubs and societies.

Duration of first degree course(s) or equivalent: 3 years; **others:** 4 years **Total first degree students 1989/90:** 430 **Number of overseas students:** 13 **Male/female ratio 1989/90:** 20:1 **Teaching staff:** 104 **Total full-time students 1989/90:** 673 **Postgraduate students:** 243

What it's like
Main function of college is to run undergraduate courses for the army, RAF and civilians in equal proportions. Officers selected to read degrees at college do so after completing period of regimental duty following attendance and commissioning at Sandhurst. Also masters and specialist courses for the army and defence industry. Many other courses open to all.

BSc courses cover engineering (civil, mechanical and electrical) and applied science. A number of scholarships can be awarded annually to civilians for these courses; they are worth approximately the same as maximum LEA grant, with no means test, and only prior condition is willingness to consider applying to join Scientific Civil Service on graduation. Also a number of vacancies available for students on normal LEA grants. BSc courses eminently suitable for civilians as well as army, and for women as well as men. No overseas students other than military officers sponsored by their governments are accepted on courses.

RMCS has most of facilities of other colleges and universities – full civilian

CAN'T FIND WHAT YOU'RE LOOKING FOR? USE THE INDEX!

academic staff, library (no need for any student to buy books), tutoring and counselling, nuclear physics chemistry teaching facilities not commonly met within university laboratories, and so on. On-site accommodation available for all students, and those with cash to spare can look for living-out accommodation after first year.

Extra-mural facilities excellent and cheap: resident doctor, CofE and RC churches, heated outdoor swimming pool, stables, small theatre, golf course, beagles and so on. Students who can't find club or society that caters for their particular interest will very likely find money available to start one.

Disadvantages? Nearest towns are Swindon (7 miles) and Oxford (23 miles), and students who cannot use any on-site facilities and cannot afford car may get bored. Civilians must be prepared to live in a service-oriented environment with older students, even if 'military influence is subdued'.

SILSOE COLLEGE (Faculty of Cranfield)

Silsoe College, Silsoe, Bedford MK45 4DT (0525 60428) Map A, F7

Student enquiries: Student Recruitment Executive

Main study area – as in What to Study section: *(First degree):* Agriculture, business studies, environmental studies. *Also:* Agricultural engineering, environmental engineering.

European Community: 100% first degree students take EC language as part of course and 20% spend 6 months or more in another EC country. Formal exchange links with 2 French universities/colleges: (Le Havre, Montpellier). Approved Erasmus programme 1990/91.

Application: UCCA. **Academic features:** Preparatory year to BEng (if required); European language included in BSc. **Founded:** Silsoe College in 1962 (formerly National College of Agricultural Engineering). Now forms Faculty of Agricultural Engineering, Food Production and Rural Land Use of Cranfield Institute of Technology. **Main awards:** BEng, BSc. **Awarding body:** Cranfield Institute of Technology. **Site:** Silsoe, midway between Luton and Bedford (20km south of Cranfield). **Access:** A6 and M1. **Accommodation:** 258 places in halls of residence (all first year students are offered place on campus). **Library:** 37,000 books and pamphlets, 300 periodicals, 49 study places. **Other learning resources:** Language unit, college farm, computer facilities, workshop areas, teaching laboratories. **Welfare:** Doctor, dentist, nurse, student services adviser. **Hardship fund:** Douglas Bomford Trust Education Awards, Merricks Trust, Whitworth Scholarship, AFRC Engineering Scholarships, Elizabeth Nuffield Educational Fund. **Careers:** Careers information and advice given by Head of Student Services. **Amenities:** SU with bar, vehicle repair shop, TV, shop, etc; many societies including Motor Club, Brewing and Ploughing Clubs, sailing, shooting, parachuting etc. **Sporting facilities:** Wide range on campus (eg soccer, cricket, rugby, tennis and squash). **Employment:** At home and overseas within rural sector, local authorities, food and agricultural industries: research and teaching institutes: engineering and agricultural consultants.

Duration of first degree course(s) or equivalent: 4 years **Others:** 3 years **Total first degree students 1989/90:** 130 **Number of overseas students:** 5 **Number of mature students:** 20 **Male/female ratio 1989/90:** 7:1 **Teaching staff: full-time:** 50 **part-time:** 4 **Total full-time students 1989/90:** 480 **Postgraduate students:** 340 **Tuition fees, first degrees, 1990/91:** Home: £1,675; Overseas: £5,700.

What it's like

It's in mid-Bedfordshire in pleasant village of Silsoe, typical rural environment. Bedford and Luton both 10 miles away. Of 300 students about half are under-

graduates. Social life good and varied; many exchanges with Bedford girls' colleges. Excellent sporting facilities, clubs and societies, different religions provided for. Undergraduates guaranteed accommodation in halls (self-catering at weekends). College food quite acceptable. Course based on engineering core, supplemented by agricultural subjects. No specialisation until final year of BSc, so first degree students have plenty of time to find out what appeals to them. Academic staff very pleasant and approachable; most have wealth of world-wide experience.
Robert Curtis

Pauper notes
Accommodation: 50% live on-campus; halls quite expensive, self-catering cheaper with high demand, so apply early. Off-campus the area is becoming more expensive. College off-campus service not very good, so start early. **Drink:** Best pub is Ye Three Fyshes, Turvey (on the A428 about 5 miles from Bedford). Local brewer is Charles Wells, most famous as UK licensee for Red Stripe Jamaican lager. **Eats:** The Magna Tandoori, Tavistock Street, Bedford is good and quite cheap. Sunflower Wholefoods, Castle Road, Bedford is a good shop. **Ents:** The Point, 10 screen cinema complex in Milton Keynes, does student reductions and is very comfortable with good projection and screens. **Hardship funds:** Apparently one is being set up. **Travel:** Campus is not far from M1 – good for hitching. **Work:** Social Club bar work, department workshops on campus. Warehouses, supermarkets etc, off campus – not too hard to find.

SLADE

Slade School of Fine Art, University College London, Gower Street, London WC1E 6BT (071-387 7050 ext 510) Map E, C1

Student enquiries: The Secretary

Main study areas – as in What to Study section: *(First degree):* Art & design, fine arts. *Also:* Film, media, theatre design.

European Community: 1% first degree students take EC language as part of course and 4% spend 6 months or more in another EC country. Formal exchange links with 2 German universities/colleges (Dusseldorf, Frankfurt).

Application: UCCA. **Structural features:** Part of University College, London University. **Special features:** All staff are practising artists. **Academic features:** 4 year degree courses composed mainly of studio work plus history of art as a mandatory subject (at University College) and one other subject from a list of options. **Founded:** 1871; part of University College, London. **Main awards:** BA. **Awarding body:** London University. **Site:** Gower Street, Bloomsbury. **Access:** Warren Street or Euston Square underground stations; buses. **Accommodation:** Apply to University College London accommodation office for hostel places. Rent: 60% undergraduates in accommodation where rent controlled by university. **Library:** Donaldson Library of University College; 4,500 periodicals and 60 study places; Slade/Duveen fine art reference library; slide collection of University College. **Welfare:** Professional welfare officer; all other facilities from student health association. **Careers:** Information and advice service. **Amenities:** Automatic membership of University College SU which has own premises with bar, television, music rooms, etc; also central collegiate building with theatre, indoor sports facilities; Slade itself maintains a close relationship with all major galleries in London. **Employment:** Artists and related fields.

Duration of first degree course(s) or equivalent: 4 years **Total first degree students 1989/90:** 98 **Number of overseas students:** 5 **Number of mature**

CAN'T FIND WHAT YOU'RE LOOKING FOR? USE THE INDEX!

students: 11 **Male/female ratio 1989/90:** 1:1 **Teaching staff: full-time:** 10 **part-time:** 25 **Total full-time students 1989/90:** 190 **Postgraduate students:** 100 **Tuition fees, first degrees, 1990/91:** Home: £671; Overseas: £6,995.

What it's like

Small art college within a large university. Reputation on international level: all tutors/lecturers are successful practising artists, working alongside rather than teaching their students. The structure is peculiar to the Slade. Undergraduate students from all years work together, in 5 separate studios which tend to become inward looking groups; these are (1) the F studio traditionalist, re: Coldstream; (2) Bruce's studio: experimental and contemporary; (3) Tess' studio: artistic; (4) Ron's studio: narrative; (5) Sculpture: hard to define. Postgraduate studios for painting, sculpture, printing, theatre design and media. Facilities for sound recording, computer graphics and general workshops. Access to all members of the Slade to all facilities.

Atmosphere and work are at times exciting, and in spite of traditional reputation there are few constraints. Tutors very willing to discuss problems. Shortage of space, but the setting within the quadrangle of University College London and the West End more than make up for any of the college's disadvantages.

Pauper notes

Accommodation: Extremely difficult if you aren't in halls. Squats increasingly temporary. Halls epitome of studentum. However this should not put you off. **Drink:** UCL union and ULU very cheap for London. Slade lunchtime drink a pint of Guinness or bottle of Pils. Tequila slamming is becoming an increasingly popular pastime. **Eats:** Food is very bad in college. UCL union is best. Otherwise the whole of London is open to you – very cheap places. **Ents:** You'd have to be boring to be bored in London. **Sports:** Very good sporting societies, outside college probably a bit expensive, swimming pool at ULU. **Hardship funds:** Don't count on them, but there is money available if you really need it. **Travel:** Scholarship abroad available on a termly basis. **Work:** Plenty of work available, many people work in art galleries. There is at present £50 per year materials grant.

Alumni (Editors' pick)

Augustus John, Stanley Spencer, Gwen John, Derek Jarman.

SOAS

School of Oriental & African Studies, University of London, Thornhaugh Street, Russell Square, London WC1H 0XG (071-637 2388) Map E, C1

Student enquiries: Registrar

Main study areas – as in What to Study section: *(First degree):* African studies, anthropology, archaeology, Asian studies, economics, fine arts, geography, history, law, linguistics, music, Near East and Islamic studies, politics and government, religious studies and theology.
Also: Unique range of African and Asian languages/studies, eg Bengali, and Burmese to Sanskrit, Swahili and Urdu.

European Community: No students learn an EC language or spend time in another EC country at present.

Application: UCCA. **Structural features:** Part of London University. **Largest fields of study:** Geography, law, history, Far Eastern languages, Arabic, anthropology, economics, politics. **Founded:** 1916. **Main awards:** BA, LLB. **Awarding body:** University of London. **Site:** Central London university site. **Access:** Russell

CAN'T FIND WHAT YOU'RE LOOKING FOR? USE THE INDEX!

Square, Goodge Street underground stations; buses. **Accommodation:** Inter-collegiate halls; self-catering flats. 5% in accommodation where rent controlled by university; further 20% in university halls. **Library:** 700,000 items, 600 study places; reserve and short loan collections. **Specialist collections:** Regional libraries on Africa, Far East, South and South-East Asia, Near and Middle East; subject collections on art, law, geography, social sciences. **Welfare:** Doctors, dentists, FPA, psychiatrist, chaplains, counsellor, optician, behavioural psychologist; free legal advice centre. **Careers:** London University careers advisory service. **Amenities:** All facilities of ULU union building (including swimming pool); University church and prayer room; Percival David collection of Chinese art. **Sporting facilities:** Sports ground at Greenford; boat house at Chiswick and sailing club; squash courts, gymnasium.

Duration of first degree course(s) or equivalent: 3 years; 4 years for some languages **Total first degree students 1989/90:** 671 **Number of overseas students:** 73 **Number of mature students:** 130 **Male/female ratio 1989/90:** 3:4 **Teaching staff:** 200 **Total full-time students 1989/90:** 718 **Postgraduate students:** 296 **Tuition fees, first degrees, 1990/91:** Home: £1,675; Overseas: £5,400.

What it's like

SOAS has an international reputation in its field – though little known in rest of country. Founded in 1916, in order to train administrators for the empire, it is unique in western world in combining fields of Asian and African studies.

Unfortunately, college doesn't seem to have completely thrown off its past and there have been complaints that some courses and departments are Eurocentric in their approach.

Student population is a mixture. There are students from all over the world, many pursuing postgraduate courses, but 80% of undergraduates are British. In addition FCO and MOD staff take crash courses in languages and politics, and business types do college's new diploma in Japanese and Japanese economy. It would seem that such courses are seen as the future by the college's authorities – profit rules!

For a time in mid-80s, SOAS's existence seemed threatened by Thatcher's cuts, but having survived that, numbers are rising and it seems likely that college will expand.

SOAS is now housed in original building (mainly now used for administration), attached to a new (late 70s) building of lecture rooms and staff offices which surrounds the college's five-storey library (open six days a week). It's located in a surprisingly pleasant area of central London, off Russell Square, where students laze and the rugby team train. All handy for the British Museum and Library and a short walk from Oxford Street and Tottenham Court Road.

Work mainly assessed by end of year exams – though some courses are partially or wholly graded on essays and/or dissertations. Teaching is by a combination of lectures and seminars with regular tutorials. Staff are quite approachable for help!

SU small but active – and has a radical reputation. There is very little in way of faction-fighting and bureaucracy which can dog other unions. If you're willing to get involved there's a chance for individuals to shine. Largest societies are Labour club (which combines left-oriented people, not necessarily Labour party supporters, also Greens, anarchists and fellow-travellers), Palestine Society and Africa Society. Understandably, union has a reputation for supporting liberation campaigns in Asia and Africa – though it's also active in national and local campaigns.

Asian and African bands and discos take place in college, as well as more off-beat ents with reduced prices for SOAS students.

Pauper notes

Accommodation: Lots of students squat and will help others out. College accommodation in intercollegiate halls (close to college) and flats in Colindale (30 mins away). **Drink:** SOAS bar cheap and friendly. Plenty of other student bars around.

CAN'T FIND WHAT YOU'RE LOOKING FOR? USE THE INDEX!

You can get very drunk very cheaply at ULU beer festival (Autumn term) and plenty of CAMRA festivals throughout year. Bruces Firkin pubs across capital popular with students – Dog Bolter is an acquired taste but very good and strong. **Eats:** Food in college not brilliant or particularly cheap. Greenhouse restaurant local; very good vegetarian food in nice atmosphere. LSE cafe (half-mile away), good veggie; School of Hygiene & Tropical Medicine (across road) lunches (meat, veggie and salads) – lots of people but quick service and nice food. **Ents:** Scala cinema, programme changes every day, £2.50 to students before 4.30pm weekdays. All-nighters (Sat 11.30pm) 4 or 5 related films for £5. Gigs in college 3 times/term (mainly world music) also at ULU most Thursday/Friday nights. **Sports:** Pool, gym, jacuzzi, sauna, weights etc at ULU. Small gym in SOAS. Lots of sports clubs – football, hockey, rugby, squash, cricket teams in college – surprisingly successful for small college. Successful professional teams – but all very expensive to go and see. **Hardship funds:** Some – but very hard to get hold of – not specifically for people going bust either, so don't count on it. **Travel:** London Transport very expensive, so bike it – worth checking to see if you can get a BR train instead of underground, *much* cheaper than tube if you've got railcard. Easy to get anywhere if you're willing to pay. If travelling by rail be aware it's often cheaper to start your journey outside London, ie if you're travelling home and intend to return within a month it's worth buying a return when setting out – starting off in London is often a few quid more. **Work:** Loads available. Cloakroom, bar and shop in college and some gig work. Outside college – bars, shops, restaurants – anything really – keep your eyes peeled and avoid agencies who'll get you work but rip you off.

Alumni (Editors' pick)
Enoch Powell.

SOUTH BANK POLY

South Bank Polytechnic, Borough Road, London SE1 0AA
(071-928 8989) Map E, D3

Student enquiries: Central Registry

Main study areas – as in What to Study section: *(First degree):* Accountancy, architecture, biology, biotechnology, business studies, chemical engineering, chemistry, civil engineering, computing, education, electrical & electronic engineering, environmental science, European studies, food science & nutrition, hotel and catering management, information technology, law, mathematical studies, mechanical and production engineering, modern languages, nursing studies, politics and government, sociology, town and country planning. *Also:* Construction management, energy studies, estate management, home economics.

European Community: Number of first degree students taking EC language as part of course not known. Students on language degrees (with international studies/ business) spend 6 months or more in another EC country. Formal exchange links with 11 EC universities/colleges: France (6); Germany (4); Spain (1). Approved Erasmus programme 1990/91. Language tuition is an option on a number of courses. European studies available with various engineering specialisms.

Application: PCAS. **Academic features:** Education route (leading to additional award of Cert. Ed) available on some BEng courses. 4-year BA in home economics and resource management, available with industry route (sandwich) or teaching route (full-time). New courses in: engineering with European studies; educational studies for health care professionals; fire safety engineering and risk management; radiography. **Founded:** 1970, ex 4 colleges of further education, joined in 1976 by Battersea and Rachel McMillan Colleges of Education. **Main awards:** BA, BEd, BEng, BSc, LLB. **Awarding body:** CNAA. **Site:** 2 main locations in central South

CAN'T FIND WHAT YOU'RE LOOKING FOR? USE THE INDEX!

London. **Access:** Elephant & Castle, London Bridge and Waterloo stations. **Accommodation:** Approx 370 places in halls (priority to first year students), list of private lodgings. Apply to accommodation officer early. Rent: 11% in accommodation where rent controlled by polytechnic. **Library:** 2 main libraries, 280,000 volumes and other catalogued items; 29,500 bound volumes of periodicals and some 2,225 subscriptions to periodicals. GEAC advanced software system on ICDN computer for sophisticated cross referencing. **Other learning facilities:** Courses, individual tuition or supervised self-pacing language laboratory sessions in language centre (programmed tapes, video-cassettes, direct reception of foreign broadcasts and audio-interactive microcomputers). Computing facilities include DEC system 1091; VAX 8650 clustered with 2 VAX 11/785 computers; VAX 11/750 for general purpose computing; microcomputers in departmental computing labs. **Welfare:** Student services unit: housing service, counselling, visiting medical officers, nursery facilities for children under 5, chaplaincy, careers service. **Hardship funds:** Limited hardship funds available. **Careers:** Information and counselling. **Amenities:** Active students union; new union building. 2 sports halls and gymnasia on main sites, 21 acre sports ground at Dulwich, nearby South Bank arts complex.

Duration of first degree course(s) or equivalent: 3 or 4 years **Total first degree students 1989/90:** 5,872 **Number of BEd students:** 330 **Number of overseas students:** 288 **Male/female ratio 1989/90:** 2:1 **Teaching staff: full-time:** 526 part-time: 500-700 **Total full-time students 1989/90:** 5,859 **Postgraduate students:** 1,239 **Tuition fees, first degrees, 1990/91:** Home: £607; Overseas: £4,500.

What it's like

Mixmatch of split sites: three main ones are Borough Road (science, engineering, school of bakery), London Road (social studies, languages, law), and Wandsworth Road (built environment). Public transport provides easy access with the exception of Wandsworth Road, a bit more isolated. London Road is in style of neighbouring Technopark, Borough Road has town hall cakey appearance, Wandsworth is more of an architectural oddity. Polytechnic accommodation is limited, so apply early. Otherwise it's digs or bedsits which vary in quality and can be pricey. SU facilities are scruffy but adequate with usual range of sports activities and numerous culturally based societies. Sports at both main sites, playing fields at Dulwich quite a trek away. Courses are practical, including industrial placements and studies abroad. Lots of access courses; many mature students. Excellent library services. New SU building coming. Ents programmes are in hand.

Pauper notes

Accommodation: Students sharing can find cheap houses, squats are a possibility. **Drink;** SU has cheapest booze, Goose and Firkin is popular (landlord brews own potent beer, and live ents most nights). **Eats:** Poly plat-du-jour best value, Castello Pizza and variety of choices. SU grub reasonable. **Ents:** Society socials most nights of week, plus bands and cabarets. Films most Wednesday afternoons. Drama Society active at local fringe theatre. **Hardship fund:** Arranged by poly. **Travel:** Not unknown for London Transport's prices to encourage fare-dodging on tube (take stairs at Elephant & Castle rather than lift). **Work:** Always part-time jobs going in town.

CAN'T FIND WHAT YOU'RE LOOKING FOR? USE THE INDEX!

SOUTH WEST POLY

Polytechnic South West, (1) Drake Circus, Plymouth PL4 8AA (0752 600600)
(2) Faculty of Arts & Design, Earl Richards Road North, Exeter EX2 6AS (0392 412211)
(3) Rolle Faculty of Education, Exmouth, EX8 2AT (0395 265344)
(4) Seale-Hayne Faculty of Agriculture, Food & Land Use, Newton Abbot TQ12 6NQ (0626 52323)
Map A, C9

Student enquiries: Admissions Registry at appropriate campus

Main study areas – as in What to Study section: *(First degree):* Accountancy, agriculture, architecture, art & design, biology, business studies, chemistry, civil engineering, computing, drama, economics, education, electrical & electronic engineering, English, environmental science, fine arts, food science and nutrition, geography, geology, history, hotel & catering management, law, maritime studies, mechanical and production engineering, mathematical studies, physics, politics and government, psychology, sociology, welfare studies. *Also:* Astronomy, media studies, ocean sciences, personnel management, podiatry, surveying, oceanography, performance arts.

European Community: 8% first degree students take EC language as part of course and 1% spend 6 months or more in another EC country. Formal exchange links with 17 EC universities/colleges: Eire (1); France (5); Germany (4); Greece (2); Netherlands (2); Spain (3). Approved Erasmus programme 1990/91. Courses in international business and business studies with a language involve work and/or study in EC. Agriculture students can study French.

Application: PCAS; except fine art and design, ADAR. **Largest fields of study:** Technology, biological sciences, geography, business studies. **Founded:** 1970 as Plymouth Poly. Merged with Rolle College and Exeter College of Art (1988), and Seale-Hayne College (1989). **Main awards:** BA, BSc, BEd, BEng. **Awarding body:** CNAA (and University of Exeter). **Site:** Main campus in Plymouth city centre, three faculty campuses located in Exeter, Exmouth and outskirts of Newton Abbot, each with its own academic welfare support services and social amenities. **Access:** Road and rail links to all sites good. Cheap coach fares to London and other major cities. **Special features:** Navigation simulator, computer aided engineering facilities, diving school. Extensive participation in European Space Agency satellite communication and broadcasting programme. **Academic features:** Participation in International Student Exchange Programme. Wide-ranging combined honours scheme (science/social science/marine studies/arts/agriculture, food and land use). **Accommodation:** approx 700 places in hall on Plymouth campus (self-catering); 314 places in hall on Exmouth campus; 150 full board and 48 self-catering places on Newton Abbot campus. Priority given to first years. Approx cost: £23-£27 pw (Plymouth campus); £23-£26 pw, plus catering contract £70 per term (Exmouth campus); £25-£52 pw (Newton Abbot campus); payable termly in advance. Assistance given in finding private accommodation for those not allocated places in halls. Rent: 16% in accommodation where rent controlled by polytechnic. **Library:** 330,000 volumes, 2,200 journals, 820 study places; short loan collection, inter-library loans, film hire. Computer-based on-line information services. **Other learning facilities:** Study skills course, comprehensive computing service, audio-visual workshop and TV studio. **Welfare:** Counselling, chaplaincy, medical and other welfare services on each campus. **Careers:** Careers education programme; careers fair; information rooms; computer-assisted guidance system. **Amenities:** SU main building and offices on Plymouth site with facilities on other campuses including bars, shops, welfare and support services. Weekly campus newspaper. **Sporting facilities:** Sports halls and facilities for outdoor sports at Plymouth

CAN'T FIND WHAT YOU'RE LOOKING FOR? USE THE INDEX!

(including squash courts) and Newton Abbot. 13-acre playing field at Exmouth for soccer, rugby, hockey, netball and tennis. **Employment:** Good record of graduate employment (most courses vocational).

Duration of first degree course(s) or equivalent: 3 years; **others:** 4 years (BEd/ sandwich courses) **Total first degree students 1989/90:** 6,100 **BEd students:** 580 **Number of overseas students:** 146 **Number of mature students:** 1,420 **Male/ female ratio 1989/90:** 4:3 **Teaching staff: full-time:** 568 **part-time:** not available **Total full-time students 1989/90:** 7,730 **Postgraduate students:** 350 **Tuition fees, first degrees, 1990/91:** Home: £1,675 (£651 if self-financing); Overseas: £4,950.

What it's like – Exeter

Once upon a time it was Exeter College of Art and Design but these days its known as Polytechnic South West, Exeter Faculty of Art and Design: one site in the new 4-site poly. While it is the smallest of the four sites, (SU-wise) it's done well so far. Changes come thick and fast round here.

Exeter SU has a full-time sabbatical officer, an office, a union steward and aspirations to greatness. Facilities include a common room, which doubles as a bar in the evening, laundry room, showers, pool table and some gaming machines. All are heavily used during the day; bar is enjoying increasing success in evenings.

Academically, the college offers mainly degree courses. With foundation and BTEC courses available, a number of students under 18. Approximately 70% female students. Work loads, especially for design students, can be heavy. All courses require self-motivation, some more than others. Majority of students quite keen; failing on a degree course not really possible – you get thrown off first. Drop out rate about 5%. Graduates go on to anything – from dustmen to designing the animatronics for Spitting Image.

SU represents students' views on faculty committees and to new poly directorate: staff/student relationship good, but not always effective.

SU run on tight budget; input and enthusiasm from students important for it to survive. Entertainments based around site bar small, popular; complemented occasionally by hire of local nightclub. Fluctuating number clubs/societies: the longstanding ones are women's group, Christian union, sports society.

It's a modern building with good-ish bus links to town. Exeter's student population is quite large (approx 7,000); students quite well catered for; there's a four-screen cinema, a couple of theatres, good sporting facilities, quite a few tasty pubs and nightclubs – all available if you can be bothered.

Pauper notes

Accommodation: £30-35 (average cost of room), squats are hard to find. There is no faculty accommodation. **Drink:** Barts, Double Locks, Bowling Green. Far too many local brews but 'Old Bastard' sticks in the mind. **Eats:** On campus food quite good/cheap. Herbies for vegetarians and Harleys for huge, cheap fry-ups. **Ents:** Low budget on site. Univ has big bands. 2 cinemas, 2 theatres, both off campus. **Sports:** Limited sports resources currently, shortly to be upgraded with an afternoon dedicated to the union. **Hardship funds:** £50 max loan on application to union in writing, concessions to amount given. **Travel:** Hitching is easy, straight up M5. Occasional scholarships (US mainly) and good European exchange system. **Work:** All usual stuff, including bar work, cleaning etc; an abundance of agencies – none much cop.

Alumni (Editors' pick)

Anna Tait (art editor of Photographic Journal), Chris Cook, Steve Mattheson (artists), Dave Sawyer, Pam St Clements ('Pat' in EastEnders).

What it's like – Exmouth

Attractive location. Friendly, relaxed working environment. Near Exmouth beach and cliff walks to other small Devon towns. Campus now part of Poly South West –

CAN'T FIND WHAT YOU'RE LOOKING FOR? USE THE INDEX!

was Rolle College. One of largest polys in country. Access to other/better facilities on other sites, eg watersports centre in Plymouth. SU part of Poly South West SU, therefore stronger union than before. Site rag raised £4,100 last year.

Site has large BEd faculty and BA dept. Good reputations. Excellent pass rates, good records of employment. It's great.
S Taylor, Site President

Pauper notes
Accommodation: All 1st years in halls of residence, plus catering contract. Rest in town. **Drink:** Refurbished bar; good range of alcoholic/non-alcoholic drinks. Many good pubs in town, Exeter and in between. **Eats:** Campus refectory good value. Reasonably priced restaurants in town, including vegetarian, pizza, Chinese etc. **Ents:** SU social and rag very active all year. Cinema in town and theatre in Exeter. Regular student productions (part of BA and BEd courses). Also light operatic society. **Sports:** Good facilities on site. Sports officer (full-time) to co-ordinate activities over 4 sites of poly. Sports centre in town. **Hardship funds:** SU in desperate cases lend students £50. **Travel:** Near M5. Good for hitching. Buses and trains to Exeter. **Work:** SU bar and local pubs, other part-time work, also vacation work.

What it's like – Plymouth
Situated in the very centre of town on a fairly compact campus, 5 mins walk from BR and coach stations and main shopping centre. Halls of residence are fairly close (two on campus) but cater for small proportion of students. Accommodation is starting to get harder to find and often poor quality. Three times more male than female students and few overseas students. Large number of mature students who are mostly local. Lesbian and gay social and political activities are on increase. Very good poly student services centre with counsellors, career, chaplaincy etc. Doctors on campus. Severe lack of NHS pregnancy advice, voluntary testing and advice service run from local women's centre. Polytechnic library extremely inadequate, suffering from lack of space and resources like rest of poly. SU small but active with 3 bars, travel centre, 2 shops etc. Good academic and welfare advice centre. Plenty of opportunity to get involved in wide spectrum of political groupings both SU and town centred. Lots of social life – SU bands nights, lots of nightclubs, restaurants, theatre. Plymouth well situated by sea – lots of water sports. Union has myriad of sporting and non-sporting clubs.

Pauper notes
Accommodation: SU noticeboards; Western Evening Herald (Thurs).Getting hard to find, grotty, expensive, approx £30-35. Few squats.**Drink:** Approx £1.05 a pint. Lots of scrumpy ciders. Local real ales - Plympton. The Woodside, King's Head, Thistle Park Tavern, The Swan. Dartmoor pubs: Elephant's Nest, Who'd Have Thought It. Much cheaper at union bars. **Eats:** Captain Jasper in the Barbican fish market, the Arts Centre, Crepes, Unity (pub), The Bank (pub), Kurbari Tandoori, Ganges Indian.**Ents:** Union lounge Thurs night bands free; Ritzy – bands. The Breakwater, Swan and King's Head; Barbican Theatre; Arts Centre films. **Sports:** Ernesettle sports complex some way out – free bus on Weds and Sats run by SU, squash courts on campus. **Hardship funds:** SU for needy only. **Travel:** Poor bus/train service in Plymouth. Good hitching from Marsh Hills roundabout. Free women's minibus run by union twice nightly. **Work:** SU bar, local pubs, seasonal tourism, some temp work but getting harder to find.

CAN'T FIND WHAT YOU'RE LOOKING FOR? USE THE INDEX!

SOUTHAMPTON UNIVERSITY

University of Southampton, Southampton SO9 5NH (0703 595000)
Map A, E8

Student enquiries: Academic Registrar (0703 592379)

Main study areas – as in What to Study section: *(First degree):* Accountancy, aeronautical engineering, archaeology, biochemistry, biology, botany, business studies, chemistry, civil engineering, computing, economics, education, electrical & electronic engineering, English, environmental science, European studies, food science and nutrition, geography, geology, history, industrial relations, Latin American studies, law, linguistics, marine technology, mathematical studies, mechanical and production engineering, medicine, modern languages, music, nursing studies, pharmacology, philosophy, physics, physiology, politics and government, psychology, public administration, sociology, welfare studies, zoology. *Also:* Actuarial studies, Iberian studies, operational research, oceanography, space.

European Community: 2% first degree students take EC language as part of course and 2% spend 6 months or more in another EC country. Formal exchange links with Frankfurt University plus some 10 links with EC universities/colleges under Erasmus. Approved Erasmus programme 1990/91. New courses in LLB (European studies) and MEng with Tripartite Diploma.

Application: UCCA. **Academic features:** New degree courses in business economics and languages; marine sciences; oceanography with marine biology/geography; geology with computer science; nutrition and biochemistry/physiology; LLB (European studies); industrial applied mathematics; environmental engineering; economics with actuarial studies. **Special features:** Concert hall, theatre and art gallery on campus. **Founded:** 1952. **Main awards:** BA, BEng, BM, BN, BSc, BSc(Social Sciences), LLB, MEng. **Awarding body:** University of Southampton. **Site:** 2 miles from Southampton City centre. **Accommodation:** 1,200 places in halls; 1,600 places (self-catering). 90% first year students accommodated. Approx cost (30 weeks): £1,119 pa (full board), £645 pa (self catering). Rent: 40% in accommodation where rent controlled by university. **Library:** Main library with 3 subsidiary subject libraries; 83,000 volumes in total, 1,600 study places; short-loan collection. **Specialist collections:** Agriculture to 1900, local history, parliamentary papers, history of relations between Jewish and non-Jewish peoples, Wellington papers, Mountbatten papers. **Other learning facilities:** IBM 3090/150 (one of largest in any UK university); over 800 workstations for students' use. Advanced network being installed. **Welfare:** Doctor, education and welfare office, FPA, psychiatrist, chaplain, university counsellors, legal advice centre. **Special categories:** Residential facilities for married and disabled students, 44 place nursery (£2.90 per half day for students). **Careers:** Information, advice and placement service. **Amenities:** SU shop, travel agency, launderette, banks, concert hall, theatre, art gallery etc. **Sporting facilities:** Excellent playing fields and sailing facilities, 6 squash courts and sports hall. **Employment:** Comparatively high proportion of graduates enter industry and commerce.

Duration of first degree course(s) or equivalent: 3 years; **others:** 4 years (language courses, engineering with foundation year, double honours courses, nursing, sociology and social policy); 5 years (medicine, MEng with Tripartite Diploma) **Total first degree students 1989/90:** 5,878 **Number of overseas students:** 248 **Number of mature students:** 182 **Male/female ratio 1989/90:** 3:2 **Teaching staff:** full-time: 715 part-time: 60 **Total full-time students 1989/90:** 6,983 **Postgraduate students:** 1,105 **Tuition fees, first degrees, 1990/91:** Home: £1,675 (£650 if self-financing); Overseas: £4,600 (eg politics), £6,060 (eg physics), £11,150 (clinical).

CAN'T FIND WHAT YOU'RE LOOKING FOR? USE THE INDEX!

What it's like

Campus is a mixture of modern and traditional buildings set in rolling pastures and trickling brook, three miles out of city centre. It is in the residential area, shops nearby, centre is 10 mins bus ride away.

Most academic buildings on campus; medical sciences building (preclinical medics and biochemists) is 8 mins walk away. Other campus facilities include theatre, concert hall, art gallery and banks.

Halls all off campus, within walking distance. Nearly all first years offered a place in halls (choice of self-catering or fully catered) usually in single study/bedrooms. All halls have good facilities (bars, shops, launderette) and are cheap.

All courses/facilities are of high standard, in particular the pioneering medical course and the prestigious engineering department. Students represented on all faculty boards and most other university committees. Hartley Library has just been extensively altered giving more space and easier access to its resources.

SU provides for social, cultural and fun interests of its members through over 200 clubs and societies, discos, bands and talks. Welfare service is of exceptional standard with advice, help and campaigning on student (finance/housing) and more general issues (AIDS, anti-racism etc). Politics present but not overwhelming, lying somewhere between left and right.

Pauper notes

Accommodation: Halls for 1st years; private rented accommodation has good choice of price/standard/area. **Drink:** SU and hall bars cheap (members only), wide variety of local pubs. **Eats:** SU coffee bar. Many take-aways near campus and in centre. Cheap veggie/ethnic shops/restaurants in town. **Ents:** SU discos, bands, cabarets, films. Discount for students at campus theatre. Rest of town variable. **Sports:** Union has use of good sports grounds 2 miles from campus. Squash, sports hall and multi-gym on site. No swimming pool yet. **Hardship funds:** SU/University hardship fund. **Travel:** SU Travel Centre has all mod cons. **Work:** Depending on season there is some.

Alumni (Editors' pick)

Jon Potter, T G Thomas, John Nettles, Baroness Hooper, Lord Tonypandy, Jenny Murray, Chris Packman, Kathy Tayler.

SPURGEON'S COLLEGE

Spurgeon's College, South Norwood Hill, London SE25 6DJ (081-653 0850) Map D, C4

Student enquiries: Registrar

Main study areas – as in What to Study section: *(First degree):* Religious studies and theology.

European Community: No students learn an EC language or spend time in another EC country.

Application: Direct. **Special features:** Theological college; a small denominational college, devoted primarily to the training of men and women to serve as ordained Baptist ministers. Strong vocational bias. The college does not accept applicants straight from school, but mature men and women supplied by the churches. Small numbers of students seeking theological training for purposes other than the Baptist ministry are accepted. A part-time degree course in theology is also available to applicants who have already received some theological education. **Main awards:** BA. **Awarding body:** CNAA.
Accommodation: Mainly for single students though some available for married couples and families. Rent: 33% in accommodation where rent controlled by

college. **Library:** 35-40,000 volumes. **Other learning resources:** Extensive audio-visual equipment.

Duration of first degree course(s) or equivalent: 3 years; **others:** 4-5 years (part-time) **Total first degree students 1989/90:** 57 **Number of overseas students:** 5 **Number of mature students:** 57 (21+) **Male/female ratio 1989/90:** 56:1 **Teaching staff: full-time:** 9 **part-time:** 6 **Total full-time students 1989/90:** 70 **Postgraduate students:** 14 (part-time) **Tuition fees, first degrees, 1990/91:** Home and Overseas: £3,100.

What it's like

A theological college for the training of Baptist ministers and other Christian workers. Situated in South London so all the facilities of central London are close. Crystal Palace National Sports Complex is five minutes away by car. 30 students in hall of residence; another 40 live locally. In addition many part-time training courses are available. Unmarried students live in. Food and living expenses included in fees. All students are mature: school leavers not generally accepted. Some overseas students, but few female students. Social activities are organised for students and their spouses. There is a well-stocked computer catalogued library and a bookshop on site; sports facilities include: tennis, snooker and table-tennis. Football, cricket and rugby matches are arranged against other colleges.

Pauper notes

Accommodation: College tries to assist in finding accommodation. Rooms automatically available on campus for single students. **Drink:** Not on campus!! **Eats:** Available on site, included in maintenance fee. The economically/gastronomically astute may be able to provide for themselves more cheaply. **Ents:** Student rates at Fairfield Halls/Warehouse Theatre in Croydon. **Sports:** Tennis court and croquet lawn on site. Crystal Palace sports stadium. **Hardship funds:** Students operate their own fellowship fund. **Travel:** Buy student railcard. **Work:** Some vacation work available on campus, otherwise local shop work.

SSEES

School of Slavonic & East European Studies, University of London, Senate House, Malet Street, London WC1E 7HU (071-637 4934) Map E, C1

Student enquiries: Registrar

Main study areas – as in What to Study section: *(First degree):* European studies, history, modern languages. *Also:* Finnish studies, Hungarian, Polish, Rumanian, Russian, Serbo-Croat, Bulgarian.

European Community: 14% first degree students take EC language as part of course and 7% spend 6 months or more in another EC country. Formal exchange links with Cologne University. Possibility of German studies degree.

Application: UCCA. **Structural features:** Part of London University. **Special features:** Visiting lecturers teach each language; Soviet television by satellite. **Academic features:** 4 year courses for students without an A- or A/S-level in particular language; first year is then intensive language year. Language students and some social sciences students spend a period of study abroad. **Largest fields of study:** Russian, East European studies, history. **Founded:** 1915, becoming a university institute in 1932. **Main awards:** BA. **Awarding body:** London University. **Site:** Heart of London University area. **Access:** Goodge Street, Tottenham Court Road, Russell Square underground stations; buses. **Accommodation:** London University accommodation office and intercollegiate halls of residence.

CAN'T FIND WHAT YOU'RE LOOKING FOR? USE THE INDEX!

School has none of its own. **Library:** 280,000 volumes, 1,200 periodicals, 70 study places; reference facilities for course books. **Specialist collections:** Rumanian and Hungarian literature; pre-1800 Russian and Church Slavonic books. **Other learning resources:** Language laboratory. **Welfare:** London University health service. **Careers:** Information, advice and placement; careers computer. **Amenities:** Student common room, bar and canteen. All facilities of ULU in Malet Street.

Duration of first degree course(s) or equivalent: 4 years (languages); **others:** 3 years (history and contemporary East European studies) **Total first degree students 1989/90:** 298 **Number of overseas students:** 26 **Number of mature students:** 32 **Male/female ratio 1989/90:** 1:1 **Teaching staff: full-time:** 45 **part-time:** 9 **Total full-time students 1989/90:** 324 **Postgraduate students:** 72 **Tuition fees, first degrees, 1990/91:** Home: £1,675 (£675 if self-financing); Overseas: £4,860.

What it's like

Yes, SSEES is indeed one of the smallest colleges within the London University. It is also one of the very few that is classified as an 'institute' rather than a 'school', though you wouldn't think it looking at its name. This difference means nothing to the average SSEES student. However, our 'smallness' (c320 students) means a great deal. Our facilities, predictably, are not boundless but with ULU just a stagger away they are, surprisingly, sufficient. Also, it is very difficult not to get to know/be known by everybody here and SSEES camaraderie is infamous.

Lecture loads vary from just 3–4 hours a week for history finalists to well over 20 for Russian first year 'intensives'. Those of us studying even more esoteric languages (Bulgarian, Polish, Hungarian) often find ourselves with very little company apart from the tutor during lectures while some history courses (open to history students throughout the university) seem to need Wembley Stadium to seat everybody. Postgraduates don't tend to hide from undergraduates here, socially as well as academically, and our new(-ish) Social Science Department is evidence that the rumour that we're expanding is true.

Our bar has also expanded and been repainted and it remains the presumed centre of SSEES social life. It's certainly the focus of post-match revelry for sports teams. Most popular societies: mountaineering, drama, East European, history and Russian (not necessarily in that order); rising high alongside our college magazine, 'Ceasefire', is our monthly monitor of East European affairs, 'Eurus', both produced entirely by students. Last year our Russian Society took two plays to Russia, our hockey team toured in Holland and no-one escaped participation in our November Rag Week. Few other colleges have such reputations (and names) which stun inquirers into silence.

Pauper notes

Accommodation: No college accommodation, but good intercollegiate halls nearby can be used for up to 2 years of a course. **Drink:** SSEES bar, run by students, has short hours, but good parties and promotions which should not be missed. Many college and hall bars nearby; bars in ULU building. Some very pleasant pubs in the vicinity. **Eats:** SSEES canteen for tea, coffee, sandwiches and a limited selection of hot meals, including vegetarian dishes. Wider selection at ULU or other nearby college canteens. **Ents:** Near the West End; best selection of clubs, theatres, cinemas, concerts in the country, but tend to be expensive. Cheaper entertainments in outer London. SSEES throws good parties. **Sports:** Despite small size, fields teams, competing with some success in football, hockey, cricket, badminton and athletics. Shares a rugby team with SOAS. **Social societies:** (current list): Drama, Russian, Polish, Balkan, History and Mountaineering societies. Labour and Conservative clubs. **Work:** Bar work in SSEES enjoyable but not financially very rewarding. Some work in ULU, or in shops nearby.

Alumni (Editors' pick)

Professor T G Masaryk, Jonathan Ross.

CAN'T FIND WHAT YOU'RE LOOKING FOR? USE THE INDEX!

STAFFS POLY

Staffordshire Polytechnic, College Road, Stoke-on-Trent ST4 2DE (0782 744531) Map A, D6

Student enquiries: Academic Registrar (Admissions)

Main study areas – as in What to Study section: (*First degree*): American studies, art & design, biology, business studies, chemistry, computing, economics, electrical and electronic engineering, English, environmental science, European studies, fine arts, geography, geology, history, information technology, law, mathematical studies, mechanical and production engineering, modern languages, philosophy, physics, politics and government, psychology, sociology, welfare studies. *Also:* Ceramic technology, estate management, humanities, sports studies, surveying.

European Community: Number of students learning an EC language or spending time in another EC country, not known. Approved Erasmus programme 1990/91.

Application: PCAS except Art and Design (ADAR). **Academic features:** New extended engineering degrees for students with A-levels in subjects other than maths and physics. **Largest fields of study:** Business studies, computing, design, law. **Founded:** 1970, ex Stoke-on-Trent College of Technology, Stoke-on-Trent College of Art and Stafford College of Technology. **Main awards:** BA, BSc, BEng, LLB. **Awarding body:** CNAA. **Site:** Split on 2 sites. **Access:** Easy access to both sides by road (M6) and rail (Stoke-on-Trent and Stafford stations both on main line routes to London). **Accommodation:** Over 1,100 poly places, majority single study bedrooms. Extensive stocks of approved private housing locally. Rents from £20 pw. **Library:** Large libraries on each site. **Other learning resources:** Extensive computing facilities, language, science and engineering laboratories, design and fine art studios. Study skills support. **Welfare:** Counsellors, nurses and chaplaincy service. Local GPs visit each site weekly. **Amenities:** SU with office on each site, snack bars, shops, minibus service, travel company; banking facilities on Stafford site; cinema and art gallery on Stoke campus and Victoria Theatre close. **Sporting facilities:** New sports hall on Stoke site, together with playing fields. Stafford students have concessionary access to new local leisure centre complex.

Duration of first degree course(s) or equivalent: 3 years; **others:** 4 years (sandwich and extended engineering degrees); 5 years (sandwich extended engineering degrees) **Total first degree students 1989/90:** 5,100 **Number of overseas students:** 180 **Number of mature students:** 800 **Male/female ratio 1989/90:** 3:2 **Teaching staff: full-time:** 460 **part-time:** 30 **Total full-time students 1989/90:** 5,600 **Postgraduate students:** 700 **Tuition fees, first degrees, 1990/91:** Home: £1,675; Overseas: £4,500 (eg politics), £4,900 (eg physics).

What it's like

Stoke is the larger site both in student numbers and size of the premises; humanities course moving there from Stafford, so will put even more pressure on inadequate SU facilities in Stoke. An industrial town based around the Potteries and what's left of mining and steel industries. Easy to get out into countryside Peak District and to major cities, particularly if you can afford a car; railway station right next to poly.

Stafford is a market town 17 miles south of Stoke. Very pleasant; more up-market than surrounding areas. Move of humanities to Stoke means a male-dominated student body will be left in Stafford.

Much accommodation in Stoke is in long, terraced streets in urban renewal area. Stafford is better but costs more. Some halls in Stoke are a long way from poly, though poly provides limited bus service to them (best to make sure of a floor to kip on in Stoke on Monday nights, which is student night at the local night spots and no bus).

SU offers facilities from banking to launderettes and minibuses for student societies. Regular comedy, gigs and a disco – students come from all over the UK

CAN'T FIND WHAT YOU'RE LOOKING FOR? USE THE INDEX!

and overseas. Staffordshire can be a good place to see the world from – it's cheap. Poly is on the up.

Pauper notes

Accommodation: Up to 1500 places-hall share. Some good, some hideous. Local accommodation is good in Stoke but hard to come by in Stafford. **Drink:** SU 92p Kronenburg. Good, cheap bars and local pubs. Banks, Marstons Pedigree. **Eats:** Campus food not brilliant. Few local places offer discount; local vegetarian and vegan foods as well as good Italian, Indian etc. **Ents:** Regular live music at both SUs; thriving local music scene in Stoke. Plenty of theatres, cinemas and gig venues. **Sports:** Sports centre at Leek Road, swimming pool nearby – local facilities represent good value for money. Local authority offers students 'recreation key' for £1, allowing cheap/free use of local recreation facilities. **Hardship funds:** Government access funds only – poly has no known criteria. **Travel:** Good access: London 1 hr 40 mins, Manchester and Birmingham less than 1 hr, so possible for nights out. **Work:** Some student work in pubs, cinemas, nightclubs etc.

STIRLING UNIVERSITY

The University of Stirling, Stirling FK9 4LA (0786 67043) Map A, C2

Student enquiries: Schools Liaison Oficer/Student Recruitment Officer

Main study areas – as in What to Study section: *(First degree):* Accountancy, biochemistry, biology, botany, business studies, communication studies, computing, economics, education, English, environmental science, environmental studies, history, industrial relations, mathematical studies, microbiology, modern languages, philosophy, politics & government, psychology, religious studies and theology, sociology, welfare studies. *Also:* Film studies, Japanese, personnel administration, Scottish studies.

European Community: 30% first degree students take EC language as part of course and 5% spend 6 months or more in another EC country. Formal exchange links with 15 EC universities/colleges: Belgium (2); France (6); Germany (3); Italy (1); Netherlands (2); Spain (1); most open to non-language specialists. Approved Erasmus programme 1990/91. Number of exchanges increasing each year. European-orientated course options being introduced.

Application: UCCA. **Special features:** Semester system (2 semesters, 15-weeks per academic year); concurrent education (teacher training) courses; continuous assessment policy. **Academic features:** BSc in aquaculture; BA in Japanese language. Range of combined degrees. **Founded:** 1967. **Main awards:** BA, BSc, BAcc. **Awarding body:** Stirling University. **Site:** 300 acre site c. 2 miles north-east of Stirling. **Access:** A9; buses from Stirling direct to campus. **Accommodation:** 1,140 places in halls of residence; 600 flats. First years accommodated. Rent: 80% in accommodation where rent controlled by university. **Library:** 400,000 volumes, 2,400 periodicals, 800 study places; reference collection. Computerised catalogue and issue system. **Specialist collections:** Rare books (19th century); government publications. **Welfare:** Doctor, chaplains, counsellors and academic advisers on site; other services available locally. **Hardship fund:** Some funds usually available. **Special categories:** Limited residential facilities for married and disabled students. **Careers:** Information and advice. 2 careers advisers. **Amenities:** Bookshop on campus, chaplaincy centre, students' association with shop and travel service; bank, supermarket, chemist, post office; MacRobert Arts Centre; particularly good facilities for disabled students (wheelchair routes, paraplegic toilets). **Sporting facilities:** Gannochy sports centre with wide range of indoor and outdoor sports; swimming pool and golf course on campus.

CAN'T FIND WHAT YOU'RE LOOKING FOR? USE THE INDEX!

Duration of first degree course(s) or equivalent: 4 years (honours); **others:** 3 years (general) **Total first degree students 1989/90:** 2,700 **BEd students:** 43 **Male/female ratio 1989/90:** 1:1 **Teaching staff: full-time:** 262 **part-time:** 32 **Total full-time students 1989/90:** 3,800 **Postgraduate students:** 700 **Tuition fees, first degrees, 1990/91:** Home: £637; Overseas: £4,780-£6,280.

What it's like

Stirling University campus – wild, woolly and well populated by wildlife and students alike. So close to Stirling town you can walk if you're the lively type. In fact if you are the lively type you can clamber over miles of wooded hills and mountains or spend hours working out in our incredibly well-equipped gym. The Union has everything and does everything (well everything it can afford). Ents are getting better, clubs are improving – in fact the Union is on the up and up.

Academically – interesting, stimulating, good library, flexible degree programme. International selection of students.
Arline Import

Pauper notes

Accommodation: Reasonable cost, campus study rooms – single/double/family. **Drink:** Students Association cheap beer (up to 5p/pint cheaper). **Eats:** Robbins student centre – coffee bar all day and meals lunch and evening. Vegetarian food. **Ents:** Varied and excellent. New bands and established as well as musicians, hypnotists, comedy etc. **Sports:** Excellent sports facilities. Very cheap for students. **Hardship funds:** Necessitous student fund – more and more stretched, but with loans from university etc. **Travel:** Private travel shop on campus. **Work:** Some local and Student Union.

Alumni (Editors' pick)

Tommy Sheridan, Dr John Reid MP, Stewart Hepburn.

STRATHCLYDE UNIVERSITY

The University of Strathclyde, Glasgow G1 1XQ (041-552 4400) Map A, C3

Student enquiries: Registry

Main study areas – as in What to Study section: *(First degree):* Accountancy, architecture, biochemistry, biology, biotechnology, business studies, chemical engineering, chemistry, civil engineering, computing, economics, education, electrical & electronic engineering, English, environmental science, food science & nutrition, geography, history, hotel & catering management, industrial relations, information technology, law, marine technology, mathematical studies, mechanical and production engineering, metallurgy and materials science, microbiology, modern languages, pharmacology, pharmacy, physics, politics and government, psychology, public administration, sociology, town and country planning, welfare studies. *Also:* Building technology, forensic chemistry, horticulture, laser physics, offshore engineering, operational research, prosthetics, Scottish studies, tourism.

European Community: Number of students learning an EC language or spending time in another EC country, not known. Erasmus exchange links with 30+ EC universities/colleges: Belgium (2); Denmark (2); Eire (1); France (7); Germany (6); Greece (2); Italy (8); Portugal (1); Spain (2). Approved Erasmus programme 1990/91.

Application: UCCA. **Academic features:** BA in international business and modern languages. Flexible credit-based system for all classes. Student's performance assessed by course work as well as final examination; practical training and experience are features of many degree courses (aided by the University's

Engineering Applications Centre). **Founded:** 1964. Applied scientific education on present campus since 1796. **Main awards:** BA, BArch, BSc, BEng, BEd, LLB, MEng. **Awarding body:** Strathclyde University. **Site:** Glasgow city centre. **Accommodation:** 25% students live in halls of residence (both mixed and segregated). Apply as soon as possible to Residence and Catering Services. (Many students live at home). **Library:** 400,000 volumes, 1,500 study places, short loan collection. **Specialist collections:** Business information centre, rare books and manuscripts in Andersonian Library. **Centres of excellence:** Centre for academic practice with media section; computer centre. **Welfare:** Health clinics on site; consultant psychiatrist; chaplaincy centre; student adviser. **Hardship funds:** A fund available. **Special categories:** Limited number of flats for married students; playgroup run by students' association. **Careers:** Information and advice service. **Amenities:** Students' association with internal TV service. **Sporting facilities:** Sports centre with large twin-court games hall; gymnasium, swimming pool; 7 football pitches; artificial grass floodlit pitch for hockey, soccer and club training; athletics club has over 40 sections covering most indoor and outdoor sports.

Duration of first degree course(s) or equivalent: 4 years (Honours); **others:** 5 years (MEng) 3 years (Ordinary) **Total first degree students 1989/90:** 6,595; **Number of overseas students:** 453 **Number of mature students:** 300 **Male/female ratio 1989/90:** 7:5 **Teaching staff: full-time:** 590 **part-time:** 57 **Total full-time students 1989/90:** 7,987 **Postgraduate students:** 1,388 **Tuition fees for first degrees 1989/90:** Home: £1,675; Overseas: £4,660 (eg politics), £6,150 (eg physics).

What it's like

Attractively landscaped city centre campus lying between George Square and magnificent Glasgow cathedral. Modern, sought after residencies on campus. Further residencies and other university accommodation off campus. University located on a series of hills though not all buildings accessible by wheelchair. Well served by all forms of public transport. SA has purpose-built union building with 10 levels. 5 distinct bars/lounges selling wide variety of snacks and meals; games room; major band venue on level 8 capable of holding 800 people; film society; debating chamber; suites available for hire; bank and shopping mall in building; launderette and child care facility organised by Association. Over 150 different sports and non-sports clubs boasting over 6,000 members.

Students from west of Scotland mix well with high proportion of overseas students. Very high numbers of mature students add character to student mix. Elective classes available; university is proud of its technological eminence though arts and other faculties also strong.

Pauper notes

Accommodation: Halls competitively priced but otherwise limited amount of accommodation, price of which has increased dramatically in recent years in keeping with new yuppie image of city. **Drink:** SU bars, Press bar in Albion St, Ingram Bar Queen St and Chambers bar at George Sq. **Eats:** Union bars, wide range of food to suit most tastes available throughout city centre. **Ents:** Best ents are at Union. Reasonably priced theatre in town. **Sports:** Sports centre on campus complemented by excellent facilities off campus including many all-weather surfaces. **Work:** Bars and many new tourist-orientated businesses.

Alumni (Editors' pick)

John Logie Baird, Sir Monty Finniston, Bobby McGregor, Frank Clement. Also Manager of the Great Wall Hotel in Peking; Geologist with British Antarctic Survey; Computer Manager with Burroughs Ltd, Melbourne, Australia; Architect in Qatar; David Livingstone, John Reith, Sir Ian McGregor, Sir Adam Thompson; Malcolm Bruce, Douglas Henderson, Dick Douglas, Maria Fyfe, Clive Soley (MPs); James Kelman (writer).

CAN'T FIND WHAT YOU'RE LOOKING FOR? USE THE INDEX!

SUNDERLAND POLY

Sunderland Polytechnic, Edinburgh Building, Chester Road, Sunderland SR1 3SD (091-515 2000) Map A, E4

Student enquiries: Admissions Officer
(International students contact International Office, Unit 4, Technology Park, Chester Road, Sunderland SR2 7PS; Tel: (44) 91 510 9460; Fax: (44) 91 510 0990)

Main study areas – as in What to Study section: *(First degree):* Accounting, American studies, art & design, biochemistry, biology, biotechnology, business studies, chemistry, civil engineering, communication studies, computing, economics, education, electrical and electronic engineering, English, environmental studies, fine arts, geography, geology, history, information technology, mathematical studies, mechanical and production engineering, metallurgy and materials science, microbiology, modern languages, pharmacology, pharmacy, philosophy, physics, physiology, politics and government, psychology, religious studies and theology, sociology, strategic studies, welfare studies. *Also:* Chiropody, media studies, medical laboratory science, sports studies, urban studies, Victorian studies.

European Community: 20% first degree students take EC language as part of course and 15% spend 6 months or more in another EC country. Links with over 60 universities/colleges across the EC – including student exchanges. Approved Erasmus programme 1990/91.

Application: PCAS except art and design (ADAR). **Academic features:** New BA in health studies. **Special features:** Main library and life sciences building are accessible to mobility-impaired students. **Largest fields of study:** Science (including pharmaceutical science), humanities, engineering. **Founded:** 1969. **Main awards:** BA, BEd, BSc, BEng. **Awarding body:** CNAA. **Site:** 4 town centre sites within 10 min walk. **Accommodation:** 872 places in halls, including 800 in poly houses, priority given to first and final years students; most first years accommodated. Approx cost: From £25.00 pw (self-catering units); £40.00 pw (single room in hall, part board), shared rooms (2 and 3) at lower prices. Rent: 33% in accommodation where rent controlled by polytechnic. **Library:** Main central, art and design; 180,000 volumes in total, 1,350 periodicals, 750 study places. **Other learning resources:** Art Gallery; well-equipped language laboratories; media resources unit; computer network run by computer centre providing operators, programmers and advice allowing access to mini-computers and to main computer. **Welfare:** Professional welfare officer; solicitor through SU; chaplain; nursing sister on call for first aid. Creche facilities. **Hardship funds:** Some funds available from SU. **Careers:** Information, advice and placement. **Amenities:** SU with numerous societies (including ski club) and shop; bookshop on site; Sunderland arts centre; Crowtree leisure centre; poly swimming pool.

Duration of first degree course(s) or equivalent: 3 years; 4 years sandwich **Other:** 4–5 years part-time **Total first degree students 1989/90:** 4,378 full-time, 811 part-time **BEd students:** 607 full-time, 204 part-time **Number of overseas students:** 305 **Male/female ratio 1989/90:** 3:2 **Teaching staff: full-time:** 400 **part-time:** 40+ **Total full-time students 1989/90:** 5,387 **Postgraduate students:** 223 full-time, 370 part-time **Tuition fees, first degrees, 1990/91:** Home: £1,675; Overseas: £3,000 (eg politics), £5,000 (eg physics).

What it's like

It's a splinter-site campus with over 40 buildings scattered over Sunderland, all within walking distance. Student numbers increasing yearly; proportions of men to women about 6:4; large number of overseas students (from over 50 different countries); also large number of local and mature students. All in all it's a very varied student population.

The standard of poly buildings varies immensely in terms of age, size and facilities, but poly is still expanding. Academically the poly is under-rated at a national level – it's strong in most areas, particularly in pharmacy, business and education. Modular degrees give students a lot of choice and flexibility.

SU very active. It has 5 sabbatical officers and 7 non-sabbaticals. SU services include 2 bars (very cheap!), shop and travel office (both also cheap), entertainments, welfare services, nightline, and late night transport for women. SU subsidises activities of over 80 clubs and societies (sporting, political, cultural). It campaigns on many issues.

The town is very much orientated towards students – with a few exceptions in the form of non-recommended pubs. Most nightclubs offer cheap student nights, and some shops and restaurants offer student discount. The cheap cost of living in the North East is a definite bonus, making the paltry student grant stretch a little further.

Though Sunderland suffers the unfortunate reputation of being 'the place students go when they fail their A-levels and nowhere else will have them', this image does not do it justice. Most develop a fierce loyalty to both the polytechnic and the town, and many choose to stay here on completion of their degree.
Jayne Deeley

Pauper notes
Accommodation: Over 800 places in halls of residence, large increase in student numbers this year has left private housing in short supply and forced prices higher. **Drink:** Union bars cheapest. Good locals include Museum Vaults, Saltgrass, Kings Arms, Tap and Spile (good for real ale). Local brews: Newcastle Brown and Vaux beers. **Eats:** Town has plenty of kebab/pizza/Chinese/chippy takeaways. Good cheap sit-down Italians and Indian. Many on campus eating places. **Ents:** Poly biggest venue – weekly discos, regular balls, bands, rag events etc. Local theatre/cinema but more variety in Newcastle (30 mins away). **Sports:** Poly sports facilities are poor, but include a swimming pool and 3 gyms. Local facilities include Crowtree Leisure Centre and Silksworth Sports Complex. **Hardship fund:** Limited hardship fund. **Travel:** Poly sites all within walking distance. Union travel office offers cheap travel anywhere. **Work:** Poor choice of work during term time or vacation but bar work is always available and limited shop/factory work.

SURREY UNIVERSITY

The University of Surrey, Guildford, Surrey GU2 5XH (0483 571281)
Map A, E8

Student enquiries: Undergraduate Admissions Office

Main study areas – as in What to Study section: (*First degree*): Biochemistry, biology, biotechnology, chemical engineering, chemistry, civil engineering, computing, dance, economics, electrical & electronic engineering, European studies, food science & nutrition, hotel & catering management, information technology, law, linguistics, marine technology, mathematical studies, mechanical and production engineering, metallurgy and materials science, microbiology, modern languages, music, nursing, physics, psychology, sociology. *Also:* Offshore engineering, toxicology, Russian studies.

European Community: 19% first degree students take EC language as part of course and 6% spend 6 months or more in another EC country. Formal exchange links with 8 EC universities/colleges: France (4); Germany (4). Approved Erasmus programme 1990/91. European language teaching centre established with aim of providing language teaching to all students.

CAN'T FIND WHAT YOU'RE LOOKING FOR? USE THE INDEX!

Application: UCCA (except for some industrial-sponsored applicants). **Academic features:** 3 year engineering courses; 4-year courses including professional training. New BEng/MEng in civil engineering with computing; BSc mechanical engineering with industrial automation/power engineering/offshore and maritime engineering; BSc chemistry for Europe (France/German); physics with environmental protection; retail management; BSc French/German/Russian with economics with international business law/European and Soviet studies. **Special features:** Most first degree courses offer periods of industrial/professional training in UK or abroad. Applications from mature students are welcomed. **Founded:** 1966, from Battersea College of Technology. **Main awards:** BMus, BSc, BA, BEng, MEng. **Awarding body:** Surrey University. **Site:** 1 mile outside Guildford. **Access:** 10 mins' walk from station, bus from Guildford, A3. **Accommodation:** 2,294 segregated places in halls. Most first years accommodated. Approx cost: £25 pw (single). Rent: 60% in accommodation where rent controlled by university. **Library:** 366,000 volumes, 2,300 current periodicals, 550 study places. **Other learning resources:** Computing facilities include UNIX based multi-access system, PRIME service and high computational machine, accessed from 1000 terminals across campus (simple VDUs to sophisticated work stations and local area networks). Ratio of terminals/students highest for any UK university. **Welfare:** 2 student counsellors, doctor, FPA, psychiatrist, welfare officer, chaplain. **Hardship funds:** Available only in exceptional circumstances, in final year of course. **Special categories:** Limited residential facilities for married and disabled students. **Careers:** Information, advice and placement. **Amenities:** SU house with sewing-room, print-room, games-room, restaurants, bars, canteen; bookshop, grocer, post office, launderette, bank, restaurants, hairdresser on campus.

Duration of first degree course(s) or equivalent: 3 years; **others:** 4 years (including professional training) **Total first degree students 1989/90:** 3,169 **Number of overseas students:** 263 **Number of mature students:** 412 **Male/female ratio 1989/90:** 4:3 **Teaching staff: full-time:** 323 **part-time:** 63 **Total full-time students 1989/90:** 3,875 **Postgraduate students:** 1,482 **Tuition fees, first degrees, 1990/91:** Home: £1,675 (£665 for some self-financing students); Overseas: £4,610 (classroom courses), £6,100 (lab-based).

What it's like

It's a medium sized campus university built on the grassy cathedral hillside, overlooking Guildford. Fifteen minutes' walk to railway station (only 35 minutes to London), 20 minutes to bus station. It's built on a hill – not ideal for disabled students.

First, final and overseas students accommodated on campus. Standard OK to very good; most rooms have a sink, 10-28 share a kitchen; single and mixed floors. A good community. Also separate residence site 3 miles from university.

Campus has expensive launderette (handwashing common), small shop plus bookshop, hairdresser, post office, NatWest Bank. Large library, open until 10.00 pm; so is sports hall. Three catering outlets, excellent entertainments (some free), society entertainments and nightly discos. Surrey University is 'on the ball' with increasing NUS activity. Weekly student magazine, campus radio station.

No visiting restrictions, and few student cars. University gives social advice and support, plus university health and family planning centre, confidential counselling service and a student run 'night-help line'.

Guildford expensive, not offering much for students; relationships with students fragile. Good number of pubs, a theatre, cinema, concert hall and lovely countryside. University is the social centre – an easy place to make friends.

Basically a technological university with linguistics, music and dance the only balancing arts. Courses are generally 'up-to-date', most having a year in industry, often abroad, offering valuable experience. Workload varies from OK to hard – generally combining yearly exams with assessed coursework.

CAN'T FIND WHAT YOU'RE LOOKING FOR? USE THE INDEX!

Pauper notes

Accommodation: Campus for all 1st/final/overseas students. Few married/family flats. Practically no provision for single parents. Off campus expensive (£25–£40) and in short supply. Forget squats! Also little 'cheap' rented. **Drink:** 3 out of the 5 university bars inexpensive with wide range of beers and spirits. Most pubs expensive. Good local brew – Galse HSB. **Eats:** University-run catering cheapest; vegetarian catered for. Town: good choice but expensive. **Ents:** Very good on site, with cabaret, free Sunday night band, lunchtime concerts, discos, balls and annual festivals. Town offers theatre, cinema and concert hall. **Sports:** Very good facilities; friendly and competitive. Town pool. **Hardship funds:** University hardship fund. SU has fund for home and EC students. **Travel:** SU office offering student fares; hitching to London easy. **Work:** Plenty on and off site during term and vacation.

Alumni (Editors' pick)

Alan Wells (sprinter).

SUSSEX UNIVERSITY

University of Sussex, Falmer, Brighton, Sussex BN1 9RH (0273 606755) Map A, F8

Student enquiries: Admissions Office, Sussex House

Main study areas – as in What to Study section: *(First degree):* African studies, American studies, anthropology, Asian studies, biochemistry, biology, biotechnology, botany, business studies, chemistry, civil engineering, computing, economics, electrical & electronic engineering, English, environmental science, fine arts, geography, history, information technology, law, linguistics, metallurgy and materials science, mathematical studies, mechanical and production engineering, modern languages, music, philosophy, physics, politics and government, psychology, sociology, welfare studies. *Also:* Astrophysics, conservation, media studies, Soviet and East European studies.

European Community: 14% first degree students take an EC language as part of course and 5% spend 6 months or more in another EC country. Formal exchange links (including ECTS) in Belgium (3); Denmark (2); Eire (1); France (25); Germany (18); Greece (1); Italy (8); Netherlands (5); Portugal (2); Spain (6). Approved Erasmus programme 1990/91. Maths, science and law may be combined with European studies.

Application: UCCA. **Academic features:** Combinations of science and engineering with a European language, or with management studies available. **Largest fields of study:** English, engineering, computing, mathematics, physics, biology, chemistry, history, economics, law, psychology, French. **Founded:** 1961. **Main awards:** BA, BSc, BEng, MEng. **Awarding body:** Sussex University. **Site:** 4 miles from Brighton town centre. **Access:** Bus, train. **Accommodation:** Accommodation office will assist all first year students to find accommodation, usually on campus. **Library:** 500,000 volumes, 3,500 periodicals, 1,000 study places, short loan collection, audio-visual section. **Welfare:** Health service, sick bay on campus, personal counselling unit. **Hardship funds:** Special funds for disabled. **Special categories:** Residential facilities for disabled students; creche and nursery. **Careers:** Information and advice (also for vacation work). **Amenities:** SU with concert hall, bar, vegetarian restaurant, shop, television studio, campus student radio station; Gardner Arts Centre. **Sporting facilities:** Sports centre for most indoor sports; playing fields, tennis courts, etc adjoining campus, sports injury clinic. **Employment:** Research, teaching, central and local government, welfare, financial, commercial, communications, manufacturing, media.

CAN'T FIND WHAT YOU'RE LOOKING FOR? USE THE INDEX!

Duration of first degree course(s) or equivalent: 3 years; **others:** 4 years **Total first degree students 1989/90:** approx 4,100 **Male/female ratio 1989/90:** 5:4 **Teaching staff: full-time:** approx 395 **part-time:** approx 100 **Total full-time students 1989/90:** approx 4,500 **Postgraduate students:** approx 1,200 **Tuition fees, first degrees, 1990/91:** Home: approx £607; Overseas: £5,000-£7,000.

What it's like

Award-winning red brick architecture amidst trees and beautiful South Downs, 3 miles from Brighton centre. Many arts taught with pro-feminist, left emphasis, challenging established ideas. Interdiscipline system means varied (if sometimes superficial) education without excessive role learning. Emphasis on independent research. Euro and American Studies students have third year abroad. Science more formal, structured and conservative; excellent reputation for attracting research grants. Still one of Britain's more radical universities. Active SU with large, well-attended meetings, many vibrant campaigns against student loans, poll tax etc. Campaigning societies (eg anti-apartheid, women's group and lesbian and gay) very active. Radical, anti-racist and anti-sexist atmosphere predominates. Union societies representing *all* political affiliations. 13% mature students and many from overseas. Good facilities for disabled students, constantly under review. Link-Up (Student Community Action Group) connects students to outside world through community-based projects. Aids Campaign based at Sussex. Brighton: excellent student town, lively 'alternative' social scene. Has many antique and junk shops, plus all the delights of a posh seaside town. Major problems for average student: finding somewhere to live.

Pauper notes

Accommodation: Campus: mainly single self-catering, but some doubles and family flats. No petty regulations on visitors. Local: appalling housing Brighton area; rents expensive; big trouble. **Drink:** Rose Hill Tavern university union owned or poly's basement club. 6 campus bars. Many and varied watering holes in Brighton. **Eats:** Plenty of choice in all price ranges. Veggie, canteen and snacks on campus. Brighton has many good cheap places. **Ents:** Good 'alternative' circuit in Brighton. Off campus Duke of York's cinema recommended, many alternative pubs and clubs. Campus known to be boring at weekends but has regular bands, films and own Gardner Arts Centre. **Sports:** Plenty of facilities, wide range of activities for all levels of participation. Competitive and non-competitive sports. **Hardship funds:** Government access funds hopelessly inadequate; union has little money. **Travel:** Buses very expensive; buses/trains to Brighton/Lewes. Student travel shop good. Hitching on and off campus OK in pairs. **Work:** Good in summer – but wages too low to sustain decent standard of living.

Alumni (Editors' pick)

Ian McEwan, Bernard Coard, Howard Brenton, Brendan Foster, Neil from 'The Young Ones', Virginia Wade, Kathy Foster, Howard Barker, Julia Somerville, Peter Jones, Brian Behan.

SWANSEA

University College of Swansea, University of Wales, Singleton Park, Swansea SA2 8PP (0792 205678) Map A, C8

Student enquiries: Registrar

Main study areas – as in What to Study section: *(First degree):* American studies, anthropology, biochemistry, biology, botany, business studies, chemical engineering, chemistry, civil engineering, classics, computing, economics, education, electrical & electronic engineering, English, environmental studies, geography, history, mathematical studies, mechanical and production engineering, metallurgy

CAN'T FIND WHAT YOU'RE LOOKING FOR? USE THE INDEX!

and materials science, microbiology, modern languages, philosophy, physics, politics and government, psychology, sociology, zoology. *Also:* marine biology, mediaeval studies, Welsh studies.

European Community: Number of students learning an EC language or spending time in another EC country, not known. Formal exchange links with 9 EC universities/colleges: France (3); Germany (2); Italy (4). Approved Erasmus programme 1990/91. European Business Management School.

Application: UCCA. **Structural features:** Part of Wales University. **Academic features:** 4-year engineering degree for students with arts-based A-levels; range of schemes involving modern languages with business studies. **Special features:** School of Postgraduate Medical Studies. Mass Spectrometry Research Unit; Institute of Numerical Analysis; Hayter Centre for Russian and East European studies. **Largest fields of study:** Arts and pure science. **Founded:** 1920. **Main awards:** BA, BSc, BSc(Econ), BEng, MEng. **Awarding body:** University of Wales. **Site:** 2 miles to west of Swansea, near Gower Peninsula (designated area of outstanding natural beauty). **Access:** Bus from Swansea city centre. **Accommodation:** 1,100 places in halls (both segregated and mixed); 1,000 places in self-catering flats and houses; 1,200 flats/bedsitters; all first year students accommodated. Approx cost: From £17 pw shared self-catering to £48 pw halls. Rent: 55% in accommodation where rent controlled by university. **Library:** Main library plus departmental libraries; 500,000 volumes in total, 3,600 periodicals, 1,100 study places in library complex + 150 in maths/physics/applied science buildings. **Welfare:** Doctor, dentist, chaplains; legal and financial advice through students' union. Student Counsellor. **Hardship funds:** Cases of financial hardship treated on individual merit. **Special categories:** Resident welfare facilities for married and disabled students. **Careers:** Information, advice and placement. **Amenities:** SU building with shop, launderette, dark room, radio station, etc; closed circuit television unit; large arts centre on campus; access to recently opened Swansea leisure centre. **Sporting facilities:** Modern indoor sports centre; gymnasia, swimming pool, rifle range; wide range of sports especially soccer and rugby; surfing and canoeing on Gower beaches. **Employment:** Industry, commerce, education and public service.

Duration of first degree course(s) or equivalent: 3 years; **others:** 4 years (MEng, BA philosophy, languages/European business and management studies) **Total first degree students 1989/90:** 4,362 **Number of overseas students:** 315 **Number of mature students:** 654 **Male/female ratio 1989/90:** 3:2 **Teaching staff:** 500 **Total full-time students 1989/90:** 5,083 **Postgraduate students:** 721 **Tuition fees, first degrees, 1990/91:** Home: £1,675 (£670 if self-financing); Overseas: £4,560 (eg politics), £6,050 (eg physics).

What it's like

Very accessible sixties campus, set in between Singleton Park and sea. Walkable campus encompasses all faculties except teacher training centre (20 mins' walk). 6 halls of residence (3 on campus, 3 off, about 20 mins' walk away), with meals provided. Hendrefoilan Student Village houses 1,300 (30 minutes walk from campus) a self-catering complex with facilities including a shop, massively renovated SU-owned bar, launderette, tennis courts and car park. Nearly 50% of students in fairly unrestricted college accommodation. Rented accommodation reasonable. Over 500 overseas students, plus mature students. Very mixed backgrounds reflected in relaxed atmosphere at college.

SU very active, excellent welfare service including cheap, full-time creche, counselling service, first sabbatical women's officer in University of Wales and only sabbatical overseas officer in the country. Union services include: shop, bar, launderette, coffee bar and travel office. Over 100 societies, Labour club, film society, RAG, community action volunteers, women's group, overseas societies, music societies topping the bill.

CAN'T FIND WHAT YOU'RE LOOKING FOR? USE THE INDEX!

Semi-student city, very friendly – lots of pubs, clubs, cinemas, theatres. Very easy to meet other students. Gower peninsula only 7 miles away for picturesque walks or outdoor pursuits such as surfing, windsurfing, rock climbing etc. Ents programme getting much better over last few years with many big name bands now playing.

Quite easy to change courses in first year as often made up of three chosen subjects. Language and American studies get a year abroad but not many sponsored or sandwich course students. Easy to get a year out (University of Wales five year rule). Work assessed differently from course to course, can be course work, single or split finals. Work rate reasonable – you have to be a real slacker to fail. Excellent quality of degrees coupled with a comprehensive careers back up make for high graduate employment.

Pauper notes

Accommodation: Bedsit land in Uplands, Brynmill, Mumbles. OK generally – average rent £28. Student village best all round value for money. **Drink:** Student Village again – renovated bar. Local pubs very varied and friendly and cheap; no London prices! Lowenbrau 1664, Brains Beer, Felinfoel and Directors in abundance. **Eats:** College refectory reasonable. Usual fastfood joints – about 30 Indian/Chinese restaurants on one street. Plenty of variety for all tastes, vegetarian, vegan, ethnic. **Ents:** Clubs cheap – student nights in most of big ones. 14 cinemas plus film society – reasonable. Blues, jazz, folk and acid scene in town, but requires investigation. Swansea fringe festival annually. Theatres provide excellent mix of well-known and new productions. Outdoor and indoor markets. **Sports:** Leisure centre good and cheap – wave machine etc. Very cheap campus sports centre. All very easy to get to. **Hardship funds:** Some joy from college but proximity to death's door is a requirement. **Travel:** Reasonably priced extensive local bus and train services. **Work:** Plenty casual/seasonal work.

Alumni (Editors' pick)

Donald Anderson MP, John Morgan, Lamin Mbye, Mark Wyatt, Paul Thorburn, Gwynne Howell, Mavis Nicholson, Alun Richards, Sir Ieuan Maddock FRS, Terence Hedley Matthews, John Ormond, Paul Russell, Steve Alexander, Gwyn Evans.

TEESSIDE POLY

Teesside Polytechnic, Middlesbrough, Cleveland TS1 3BA
(0642 218121) Map A, E4

Student enquiries: Admissions Officer

Main study areas – as in What to Study section: *(First degree):* Accountancy, architecture, art & design, biochemistry, biotechnology, business studies, chemical engineering, chemistry, civil engineering, communication studies, computing, electrical & electronic engineering, English, history, information technology, law, mathematical studies, mechanical and production engineering, metallurgy & materials science, modern languages, nursing studies, philosophy, politics and government, psychology, public administration, sociology, welfare studies. *Also:* Building & construction, footwear, leisure studies, operational research, physiotherapy.

European Community: 3% first degree students take EC language as part of course and 0.5% spend 6 months or more in another EC country. Formal exchange links with 10 EC universities/colleges: France (4); Germany (1); Greece (3); Netherlands (1); Spain (1) – mostly open to all students. Approved Erasmus and Comett programmes 1990/91. Internationally orientated courses eg international business information technology.

CAN'T FIND WHAT YOU'RE LOOKING FOR? USE THE INDEX!

Application: PCAS, except art and design (ADAR). **Academic features:** New courses in quantitative methods in business, applied science and forensic measurement, history of design, psychology, law. **Largest fields of study:** Business studies, humanities, social studies, computer science, engineering. **Founded:** 1930. **Main awards:** BA, BSc, BEng, LLB. **Awarding body:** CNAA. **Site:** Middlesbrough city centre and Flatts Lane, Normanby (4 miles away). **Access:** Nearby bus and railway stations; A19 road; Teesside international airport. **Accommodation:** 389 places in mixed and segregated halls of residence, approx cost: £32 pw b&b; £30 pw self-catering; 191 places in self-catering houses (approx cost: £27 pw).146 places in self-catering self-contained high rise block of flats (approx cost: £16.50 pw plus electricity). 70% all places in halls reserved for first years. Help in finding lodgings and self-catering furnished properties in the private sector; 1200 registered places, rents negotiated annually. **Library:** Main site and Flatts Lane centre; 210,000 volumes; plus 10,000 annually. 2,000 periodicals; 500 study places (main site), 65 (Flatts Lane). **Other learning facilities:** Computer centre with networks of Prime mainframe computers and Apollo CAD workstations, and assorted microcomputer facilities. **Welfare:** Medical counsellor, accommodation officer, disabled counsellor, welfare officer, student counsellor, chaplains. **Special categories:** Limited residential facilities for the disabled; 40-place nursery (enquire when applying). **Careers:** Information and guidance on vocations, jobs and further courses. **Amenities:** Recreation unit, amenities block with SU bar, coffee bar, refectory (meals and cultural activities organised by Poly and SU).

Duration of first degree course(s) or equivalent: 3 years; 4 years sandwich **Total first degree students 1989/90:** 2,600 **Number of overseas students:** 115 **Number of mature students:** 1,400 **Male/female ratio 1989/90:** 2:1 **Teaching staff:** full-time: 320 part-time: 20 **Total full-time students 1989/90:** 4,580 **Postgraduate students:** 160 **Tuition fees, first degrees, 1990/91:** Home: £1,675 (£651 if self-financing); Overseas: £3,500-£4,000.

What it's like

It's on two sites the main one in central Middlesbrough, the other, Flatts Lane, five miles away at the foot of the Eston Hills. The poly library is not huge but better than others, always a rush around every deadline time.

There is a lack of purpose built accommodation for first years; the private sector seems saturated. The accommodation situation worsens every year; and the poly expects to expand to 8,000 students by 1994. Some first years end up on camp beds for the first few weeks. Don't expect the situation to get better. Avoid problems if you can, look for accommodation as soon as possible when you know you are coming.

The poly does not have very good access for disabled students.

Some excellent courses, in particular computing, mathematics, business studies and Flatts Lane management courses.

Teesside is not a cultural desert, it has cinemas, amateur/professional theatre, music co-operatives, arts centre and bingo.

SU employs 36 full-time staff, 120 casual staff and runs many services for its membership including 2 shops, 3 bars, 3 minibuses, a pizzeria, print shop, insurance agent, welfare officer, women's minibus service and the largest nursery of any higher education college (but demand still high, get your application in early).

Middlesbrough, with its Transporter Bridge, gothic Town Hall, its history in Yorkshire, its present in Cleveland, is on the bank of the Tees. See it and believe it.
Toren Smith

Pauper notes

Accommodation: Massive problems. Lack of purpose-built accommodation. Private sector saturated. If you want to avoid camp beds in first year, come early. **Drink:** SU cheapest in town: 85p per pint.Local pubs £1.10p per pint. Nightclubs £1.50+ per pint. **Eats:** Cheap pizza, burger/chip breakfast places available. Ethnic

CAN'T FIND WHAT YOU'RE LOOKING FOR? USE THE INDEX!

tends to be wide range quality/price. Indian food often excellent and expensive Chinese restaurants. **Ents:** SU ents tend to be varied and cheap. 3 cinema screens. Amateur theatre and arts centre films/plays at Stockton. Teeside not cultural desert. **Sports:** Variety sports clubs and various local facilities available to students. **Hardship funds:** SU runs a welfare loan system and has a hardship fund. **Travel:** Coach journey from London 5 hours and BR getting ever more expensive. **Work:** Could be a problem, Teesside has highest unemployment rate in England.

Alumni (Editors' pick)
David Bowe MEP, Stephen Hughes MEP.

THAMES POLY

Thames Polytechnic, Wellington Street, London SE18 6PF (081-316 8000) Map D, D2

Student enquiries: Assistant Registrar (Admissions)

Main study areas – as in What to Study section: *(First degree):* Accountancy, architecture, biochemistry, biology, business studies, chemistry, civil engineering, computing, economics, education, electrical & electronic engineering, environmental science, environmental studies, European studies, geography, geology, information technology, mathematical studies, mechanical and production engineering, metallurgy and materials science, physics, politics and government, religious studies and theology, sociology. *Also:* Building surveying, estate management, horticulture, landscape architecture, quantity surveying.

European Community: 2.5% first degree students take EC language as part of course and 2.5% spend 6 months or more in another EC country. Formal exchange links with 6 EC universities/colleges: Eire (Limerick); France (Paris); Germany (Berlin & Stuttgart); Greece (Athens); Spain (Madrid). EC study available with chemistry, biological sciences, business studies, architecture and landscape architecture. Approved Erasmus programme 1990/91.

Application: PCAS. **Special features:** Mature students may be admitted without normal entry requirements, if poly satisfied they suit the course. Considerable transferability between courses allowed. **Largest fields of study:** Business, social sciences, humanities, education, computing and surveying. **Founded:** 1970, ex Woolwich Polytechnic and part of Hammersmith College of Building and Art; joined by Dartford College of Education (1976), Avery Hill College (1985) and Garnett College (1987). **Main awards:** BA, BSc, BEd, BEng. **Awarding body:** CNAA. **Site:** 7 sites (Woolwich, Dartford, Eltham, Wapping, Roehampton, Deptford and Shadwell). **Accommodation:** Over 1,200 places in own halls or affiliated halls; wide range of private sector rented accommodation close to Poly. 'First years first' policy. **Library:** 7 libraries; 400,000 volumes, 2,000 periodicals, 850 study places; short loan for course texts; photocopying; on-line information services. **Other learning facilities:** Computer centre, microcomputer facilities on all sites. **Welfare:** 2 counsellors, nursing officer and nurses, medical officers and consultant psychiatrist, Anglican and RC chaplains. **Careers:** Information, advice and placement. **Amenities:** Students' union, stationery and bookshop; dance and drama hall; creche on Woolwich campus. **Sporting facilities:** Gymnasia, heated indoor swimming pool, playing fields including all weather surfaces, tennis, netball and squash courts.

Duration of first degree course(s) or equivalent: 3 years, 4 years (sandwich) **Total first degree students 1989/90:** 5,690 **BEd students:** 872 **Number of overseas students:** 244 **Male/female ratio 1989/90:** approx 4:3 **Teaching staff:** 488 **Total**

CAN'T FIND WHAT YOU'RE LOOKING FOR? USE THE INDEX!

full-time students 1989/90: 9,382 **Postgraduate students:** 1,007 **Tuition fees, first degrees, 1990/91:** Home: £1,675 (£607 if self-financing); Overseas: £4,700

What it's like

Spread over 6 sites, Thames stretches from Wapping (just east of the City of London) in fast-growing yuppy docklands area, to Dartford in Kent. Each site specialises in different types of courses – Wapping: accountancy, Shadwell: geology & earth sciences, Deptford: environmental, Woolwich: arts & sciences, Avery Hill: teacher training, and Dartford: architecture & surveying.

Poly accommodation reasonable, all rooms are single; poly guarantees accommodation for all first years.

Poly and highly active SU strictly enforce policies of equality of opportunity, which give rise to a pleasant, friendly, cosmopolitan community. Thames is a lively, fun and safe place to study, live and meet interesting people from a large cross-section of the community.
Stephen F Thompson

Pauper notes

Accommodation: Poly accommodation office does all it can, but it's still a little expensive. Some good squats around; no married quarters. **Drink:** SU bars are the only place to be. SU opening new bar at Eltham – cheap, fun and friendly. **Eats:** Refectories on all sites and some reasonably priced restaurants around. **Ents:** Bands and cabaret at SU regularly. SU film society shows a film every Monday night. New ents manager promises bigger and better things than before. **Sports:** Excellent sporting facilities incl squash courts, tennis courts, swimming pool, football, hockey, lacrosse and rugby pitches. **Work:** Some SU bar work – loads of p-t off campus work available.

Alumni (Editors' pick)

Hale & Pace (TV comedians), Brian Jacks (Olympic judo medallist), Ann Packer (Olympic athletics medallist), Rachel Heyhoe Flint (cricketer), Prof Ian McAllister (Prof of politics, Univ of New South Wales), Graham Ingham (BBC2 economics correspondent – Newsnight).

THAMES VALLEY COLLEGE

Thames Valley College, Wellington Street, Slough, Berkshire SL1 1YG (0753 34585) Map: A, F8

Student enquiries: The Registrar

Main study areas – as in What to Study section: *(First degree):* Accountancy, business studies, hotel and catering management.

European Community: Number of students taking EC languages and spending 6 months of more in another EC country, not known.

Application: PCAS. **Largest fields of study:** Business and management. **Founded:** 1989 – previously Slough College. **Main award:** BA and BSc. **Awarding body:** CNAA. **Site:** Single campus in centre of Slough, near to Windsor, London and Heathrow Airport. **Access:** Easily reached by road and British Rail. **Accommodation:** No residential accommodation. Student services hold a computerised listing for student rooms, houses and flats. Approx cost: £35-£40, without meals. **Library:** 65,600 volumes, 550 periodicals, 100 study places. **Specialist collections:** Computer terminals give access to national and international databases. Over 2,000 video and audio tapes. **Careers:** Information and advice available. **Welfare:** Counsellor; occupational nurses. **Hardship funds:** Access funds (for UK full-time students over 19 years, who otherwise would be unable to undertake a course). **Amenities:**

CAN'T FIND WHAT YOU'RE LOOKING FOR? USE THE INDEX!

Purpose-built SU complex organises 5 major functions/year; plus several large gigs. Numerous small events arranged, plus several clubs and societies. **Sports facilities:** Well-equipped fitness centre on campus.

Duration of first degree course(s) or equivalent: 3 years **Total first degree students 1989/90:** 481 **Number of overseas students:** 55 **Male/female ratio 1989-90:** 7:3 **Teaching staff:** Number not known **Total full-time students 1989/90:** 930 **Postgraduate students:**462 **Tuition fees, first degrees, 1990/91:** Home: £1,675; Overseas £4,563.

TRINITY & ALL SAINTS

Trinity & All Saints College, Brownberrie Lane, Horsforth, Leeds LS18 5HD (0532 584341) Map A, E5

Student enquiries: Deputy Registrar

Main study areas – as in What to Study section: *(First degree):* Business studies, communication studies, dance, economics, education, English, geography, history, mathematical studies, modern languages, psychology, public administration, religious studies and theology, sociology. *Also:* Physical education, public media, recreation studies.

European Community: 11% first degree students take EC language as part of course and 11% spend 6 months or more in another EC country. Formal exchange links with 5 EC universities/colleges: France (3); Germany (1); Spain (1). Approved Erasmus programme 1990/91.

Application: UCCA. **Structural features:** College of the University of Leeds, R.C. **Academic features:** Courses designed to lead to specific career outcomes – all students combine an academic and a professional subject. Two six-week attachments for non initial teacher training students. **Largest fields of study:** Public media, business management and administration, education. **Founded:** 1966. **Main awards:** BA, BSc, BA (with QTS), BSc (with QTS) **Awarding body:** Leeds University. **Site:** Single campus in semi-rural surroundings. **Access:** Bus stop at door (direct services Leeds & Bradford); rail station 10 mins walk (Leeds to Harrogate line). **Accommodation:** 8 halls of residence; 330 study bedrooms. Plentiful private accommodation nearby. Approx cost: £41.75 pw (incl 3 meals/day). Rent: 25% (all first years) in accommodation where rent controlled by college. **Library:** 100,000 volumes, 800 periodicals, 170 study places. **Other learning facilities:** Computer labs, sound radio studio, video editing suite, TV studio, photography dark rooms, science labs, primary and secondary education bases. **Welfare:** College counsellor (half-time); sick bay, local GP visits. Special coordinator for mature/access students. **Special facilities:** Nursery – run for students as part of early years education course. **Hardship funds:** Scholarships committee disburses about £5,000 to needy students each year. **Careers:** Information and advice available. **Amenities:** Self-contained SU building/performing centre/2 bars/ coffee bar. Recreational and cultural activities, including performing arts, golf, car maintenance, modern languages, keep fit etc. **Sporting facilities:** Double gym, 5 squash courts, all-weather pitch, rugby & soccer, cricket, fitness centre. Very successful sporting record. **Employment:** Teaching, management, marketing, journalism, broadcasting, recreation, finance.

Duration of first degree course(s) or equivalent: 3 years **others:** 4 years (BA/BSc with QTS) **Total first degree students 1989/90:** 1,150 **Number of BA/BSc (education) students:** 534 **Number of overseas students:** 12 **Number of mature students:** not known **Male/female ratio 1989/90:** 5:2 **Teaching staff: full-time:** 89 **part-time:** 30 **Total full-time students 1989/90:** 1,250 **Postgraduate students:** 100. **Tuition fees, first degrees, 1990/91:** Home: £1,675; Overseas: £3,600.

CAN'T FIND WHAT YOU'RE LOOKING FOR? USE THE INDEX!

What it's like
It was built in the sixties and fairly modern in design. Accommodation good, as is the food. Each first year is offered a chance to live in hall but the numbers involved mean that some might have to share or live in locality. Halls of residence mixed; each room fitted with a wash basin, wardrobe, cupboard, a desk, easy chair and bed.

Atmosphere on campus that of a small community, where everyone knows everyone else; relationship between staff, both domestic and academic, and students is good. Social life good, with activities taking place on campus. It's within the bounds of Leeds and Bradford, both university cities, with a number of student orientated events.

Travel good; 5 bus services pass college gates. Horsforth BR station 15-20 mins walk away. Leeds/Bradford airport 2 miles away. (College good for plane spotters.)

Pauper notes
Drink: College bar; wide selection of beers, lagers and ciders at cheap prices. Local pubs good – geared to younger generation. **Eats:** Cheap eats: The Outside Inn, Horsforth, good food, big portions and very reasonably priced. **Ents:** Cinemas in and around Leeds give discounts, also Bradford Museum of Film & Photography. Most nightclubs have student nights. **Travel:** West Yorkshire metro system operates cheap off-peak fares on bus and rail: you can travel round all west Yorkshire for approx 50p. **Hardship Funds:** Apply through Dean of Students.

TRINITY COLLEGE CARMARTHEN

Trinity College, Carmarthen SA31 3EP (0267 237971/2/3) Map A, C7

Student enquiries: Registrar

Main study areas – as in What to Study section: *(First degree):* Education. *Also:* Humanities, rural environment studies.

European Community: No students learn an EC language or spend time in another EC country as part of their course. Formal exchange links with Eire (Limerick).

Application: PCAS. **Special features:** Conference centre. 50 USA students follow special course as part of their degree programme. **Academic features:** BEd in bilingual education in Wales. **Founded:** 1848 Church Voluntary College. **Main awards:** BEd, BA. **Awarding body:** University of Wales. **Site:** On outskirts of West Wales market town of Carmarthen (administrative centre of Dyfed). Within easy reach of the Pembrokeshire and Brecon Beacons National Parks. **Accommodation:** Hostels on campus for all first, third and fourth-year students. **Learning resources:** Microcomputers; film cameras and closed circuit TV; new biology and rural science labs; 130 acre farm. Modernised language lab; 2 modern theatres. **Careers:** Guidance given. **Sporting facilities:** Heated swimming pool, 2 well-equipped gymnasiums; multi-purpose floodlit all-weather playing surfaces; strong rugby tradition.

Duration of first degree course(s) or equivalent: BEd 4 years; BA 3 years **BEd students:** 456 **Number of overseas students:** 60 **Number of mature students:** 80 **Male/female ratio 1989/90:** 1:2 **Teaching staff: full-time:** 70 **part-time:** 20 **Total full-time students 1989/90:** 830 **Postgraduate students:** 60 **Tuition fees, first degrees, 1990/91:** Home: £1,685; Overseas: £4,568.

What it's like
Bilingual (English/Welsh) college in West Wales close to climbing, hill walking, rivers, forests and sea. East Dyfed School of Nursing on campus. New SU bar. Daily religious services (voluntary). Excellent sporting facilities – 2 gymnasia, indoor heated swimming pool, rugby, soccer and hockey pitches, athletics track,

CAN'T FIND WHAT YOU'RE LOOKING FOR? USE THE INDEX!

tennis and netball courts, all-weather match cricket as well as grass wickets and five concrete practice wickets. Active drama societies, orchestra, choir, folk groups, brass and woodwind ensembles. Opportunities for learning Welsh.

Small college so everyone knows everyone else. Live music every weekend in SU. Disco, Twmpaths (Welsh folk dancing).

A must for anyone who knows how to have a good time.

Pauper notes
Accommodation: Campus hostels. Digs in town. **Drink:** Cheap in SU bar. 56 pubs in town. **Eats:** Good food on campus and veg food. **Ents:** Excellent groups videos, discos on campus. **Sports:** Good gyms, weights, pool. Outdoor pursuits. Huge local leisure centre. **Travel:** Railway station and buses. **Work:** Not that much.

Alumni (Editors' pick)
Barry John, Carwen James.

TRINITY COLLEGE OF MUSIC

Trinity College of Music, Mandeville Place, London W1M 6AQ (071-935 5773) Map E, B2

Student enquiries: Registrar

Main study areas – as in What to Study section: *(First degree):* Music.

European Community: No students lean an EC language or spend time in another EC country.

Application: Direct. **Academic features:** Jazz and electronic, IT and early music departments. DipTCL for teachers and performers; MMus (performance and related studies); specialist short courses for overseas students. **Special features:** College was founded to provide training in church music, but is a conservatoire for training teachers and performers for a variety of careers in music. Arthur Davison CBE and Malcolm Layfield, Simon Bainbridge, Bobby Lamb (jazz) visit. **Largest fields of study:** Piano, singing and orchestral instruments. **Founded:** 1872. **Main awards:** GTCL, DipTCL, FTCL, LTCL, BMus. **Awarding body:** Trinity College; London University for BMus. **Site:** Just off Manchester Square, central London. **Access:** Bond Street underground station; buses. **Accommodation:** 30 places in mixed hall (priority to those outside London area); registrar's assistant will help first years. Approx cost: £500–£640 per term in hall. **Rent:** no student accommodated where college controls rent. **Library:** 4,000 volumes, 12 periodicals, 30 study places. **Other learning resources:** Recording studio. **Specialist collections:** Barbirolli Collection of scores. **Welfare:** Doctor, FPA, psychiatrist, physiotherapist, solicitor, welfare officer. **Careers:** Information, advice and placement. **Employment:** Music teaching and performing.

Duration of first degree course(s) or equivalent: 3 years; **others:** 4 years **Total first degree students 1989/90:** 117 **Number of overseas students:** 52 **Male/female ratio 1989/90:** 1:2 **Teaching staff: full-time:** 8 **part-time:** 104 **Total full-time students 1989/90:** 396 **Postgraduate students:** 76 **Tuition fees, first degrees, 1990/91:** Home: £1,675; Overseas: £5,100.

What it's like
Trinity is a small but perfectly formed friendly college with around 400 students who study all aspects of music. Although student population is on the whole made up of British nationals, there is a strong overseas contingent from countries as diverse as Iceland and Indonesia.

Trinity has long history of music education. It started life as a conservatoire for church music in 1872 and has expanded rapidly ever since. It has pioneered practical music exams, an early music department, and a junior department. The college itself consists of two buildings a couple of minutes walk from each other in heart of the West End.

Regular public concerts are given by the symphony orchestra and chamber groups at various venues in and around London. 'See press for details'!

Student facilities leave a lot to be desired, in fact they are all but non-existent. There is a common room with a coffee machine, pool table and a couple of video games and that's just about it. Plenty of sandwich shops nearby, and the union sells food two days a week.

Active SU has two representatives on the governing body. It supports several clubs and societies as well as dealing with welfare problems.

Pauper notes

Accommodation: Henry Wood House has places for 28 students, other accommodation found in a number of other Church run hostels otherwise students find their own digs. **Drink:** Bar facilities at College, however most students go to Angel where they drink Samuel Smith's Ale. **Eats:** Stockpot (Italian run) and Alpino's Snack bar. **Ents:** Social societies such as RATS, The Pork Pie Society, a curry appreciation club and a Video Club. Students often get in cheap to a number of Concert halls etc. **Sports:** Football team, sailing, nearest sports complex ULU. **Hardship funds:** Students in desperate need are lent £25. **Travel:** Day trips and other continental trips arranged by SU. **Work:** Part-time shop work etc is readily available as well as part-time teaching. Students also supplement their grants by playing gigs.

Alumni (Editors' pick)

Heather Harper, Margaret Price, John Hancorn, Manoug Parikian.

ULSTER UNIVERSITY

University of Ulster, Cromore Road, Coleraine, County Londonderry, Northern Ireland BT52 1SA (0265 44141) Map A, B4

Student enquiries: Admissions Officer

Main study areas – as in What to Study section: *(First degree):* Accountancy, American studies, art & design, Asian studies, biochemistry, biology, business studies, civil engineering, communication studies, computing, drama, economics, education, electrical & electronic engineering, English, environmental science, European studies, fine arts, food science & nutrition, geography, history, hotel & catering management, mathematical studies, mechanical and production engineering, modern languages, music, nursing studies, philosophy, politics & government, psychology, sociology, speech sciences, welfare studies. *Also:* Interpretation and translation, Irish studies, media studies, medical laboratory science, physiotherapy, sports studies, surveying, tourism.

European Community: 10% first degree students take EC language as part of course and 1.5% spend 6 months or more in another EC country. Formal exchange links with 13 EC universities/colleges in France, Germany and Spain. Approved Erasmus programme 1990/91; participating in 17 Erasmus exchange programmes, of which 11 are not intended for language specialists. Year in EC country available, with additional diploma, on courses in geography, environmental science and regional analysis and development.

Application: UCCA; but direct for BSc Nursing for registered nurses (professional development in nursing) and Bachelor of Technology; ADAR for art and design. **Academic features:** New courses in radiography, theatre studies. **Founded:** 1984. Merger of the New University of Ulster and the Ulster Polytechnic. **Main awards:**

CAN'T FIND WHAT YOU'RE LOOKING FOR? USE THE INDEX!

BA, BEd, BSc, BMus, BEng, MEng, BTech. **Awarding body:** University of Ulster.
Site: Main campuses at Jordanstown, 7 miles NE of Belfast, and Coleraine, 55 miles
N of Belfast. Also campuses in Belfast and Londonderry; close to the heart of the
city in both cases. **Access:** All campuses have road and rail connections. Air and sea
routes from UK. **Accommodation:** 680 residential places at Jordanstown, majority
allocated to first year students at Jordanstown: 310 places at Coleraine; also
residential places at Magee College. Other students live at home, in rented
accommodation or accommodation provided by Student Housing Association.
Library: Library on each site; main libraries at Coleraine and Jordanstown; 540,000
volumes in total; 5,600 periodicals. **Other learning resources:** Education Technology Unit; Computer Services; Social Skills Training Centre. **Welfare:** Counsellors;
doctors, chaplains. **Special categories:** Residential facilities for married and
disabled students (Jordanstown); creche and day nursery (Coleraine, Jordanstown
and Magee College). **Careers:** Information, advice and placement. **Amenities:** SU
with extensive leisure facilities; Belfast museums and galleries; Ulster Orchestra
concerts; Riverside Theatre at Coleraine. **Sporting facilities:** Sports centres on
Coleraine and Jordanstown sites with full facilities including swimming and diving
pools at Jordanstown.

Duration of first degree course(s) or equivalent: 3 years; **others:** four years (eg
sandwich; courses including period study/work abroad); 5 years for MEng **Total
first degree students 1989/90:** 6,570 **BEd students:** (Part-time only) 205 **Number
of overseas students:** 161 **Number of mature students:** 20% of full-time degree
students **Male/female ratio 1989/90:** 8:9 **Teaching staff:** 800 **Total full-time
students 1989/90:** 8,635 **Postgraduate students:** 475 (f-t) **Tuition fees, first
degrees, 1990/91:** Home: £1,675; Overseas: £3,370 (eg politics), £4,495 (eg
physics).

What it's like
4 campuses. Belfast has all the advantages of the city's wide ranging services.
Students work in bright, airy buildings of ex art college. Atmosphere relaxed,
facilities adequate; art and design subjects dominant in the academic programme.
Almost 20% of students on foundation (pre-entry programmes). Jordanstown, 7
miles north of Belfast, is the largest campus (4,326 ft/2,829 pt). High reputation for
industry. Very high proportion of part-time students. Facilities good. Student
village with 760 places attractive but for N Ireland, pricey. Business management
and science and technology most important courses. Campus well integrated with
European, American/Canadian and Far East students.
  Coleraine is university headquarters. Campus of the 60s situated close to 2 of N
Ireland's main holiday resorts, Portstewart and Portrush, much favoured by
students for accommodation outside the summer months. Student facilities have
markedly improved. All major faculties present at Coleraine, which has a high
reputation in sports and excellent facilities. Academic courses strongly favour
continuous assessment. Magee campus transferred over 5 years. New buildings now
surround the 19th century college, which has proved a major success in attracting
mature students to foundation, degree and postgraduate courses. Commitment
through new buildings at Magee has marked a considerable departure from current
education policy and is a sign of the confidence held for Magee and Derry in the
future.

Pauper notes
Accommodation: South side of city holds large student population with good
services but rents high for only fair accommodation. **Ents:** Good social life on
campus. Wide range univ ents. Good bars in the city. **Hardship funds:** Union loans
approx. £50. **Travel:** Cheap taxis from city to Jordanstown site, morning and
afternoon. **Work:** Union employs 70–80 students part-time, mainly from hardship
list.

CAN'T FIND WHAT YOU'RE LOOKING FOR? USE THE INDEX!

UMIST

The University of Manchester Institute of Science & Technology
PO Box 88, Sackville Street, Manchester M60 1QD (061-236 3311)
Map A, D6

Student enquiries: Registrar

Main study areas – as in What to Study section: *(First degree):* Biochemistry, biology, business studies, chemical engineering, chemistry, civil engineering, computing, electrical & electronic engineering, environmental studies, linguistics, mathematical studies, mechanical and production engineering, metallurgy and materials science, microbiology, modern languages, physics. *Also:* Building, biochemical engineering, computational linguistics, ophthalmic optics, operational research, textiles.

European Community: 6% first degree students take EC language as part of course and 6% spend 6 months or more in another EC country. Formal exchange links with 15 EC universities/colleges: Belgium (1); Denmark (1); France (7); Germany (2); Greece (1); Italy (1); Portugal (2). Approved Erasmus programme 1990/91. Languages may be combined with paper science, biochemistry, chemical engineering, chemistry, maths, physics, management, textiles.
Application: UCCA. **Academic features:** BEng (3-year) and MEng (4-year) courses in major engineering disciplines. Large and prestigious school of management. Many joint courses including languages, environmental studies and management. Only UK first degree in paper science, with management and language options. **Largest fields of study:** Science and technology, management sciences. **Founded:** 1824, faculty of Manchester University since 1905, charter awarded 1956. **Main awards:** BSc, BEng, BScMEng, MEng. **Awarding body:** Manchester University. **Site:** Centre of Manchester. **Access:** Bus and train. **Accommodation:** Over 6,600 places in halls and university self-catering residences (shared with Manchester University). Approx cost: £1,200 pa (halls), £750 pa (self-catering). Rent: 36% in accommodation where rent controlled by university. **Library:** Over 170,000 volumes; also resources of main university library and public libraries. **Centres of excellence:** John Rylands University Library at Manchester, Nuffield Radio Astronomy labs at Jodrell Bank. **Welfare:** Services include doctors, dentists, psychiatric adviser, clinical psychologist, counsellors and nurses. Purpose built chapel for all denominations. **Hardship funds:** UMIST Student Hardship Loan Fund, Access funds. **Careers:** Information, advice and placement. **Amenities:** SU building with bar, shop, travel bureau, halls, lounges, and welfare office; wide range of clubs and societies; sports centre; students may also join Manchester University SU.

Duration of first degree course(s) or equivalent: 3 years; **others:** 4 years **Total first degree students 1989/90:** 3,491 **Number of overseas students:** 449 **Number of mature students:** 327 **Male/female ratio 1989/90:** 5:2 **Teaching staff: full-time:** 430 **part-time:** 18 **Total full-time students 1989/90:** 4,687 **Postgraduate students:** 1,359 **Tuition fees, first degrees, 1990/91:** Home: £1,675; Overseas: £4,560 (eg arts), £6,050 (eg science & technology).

What it's like

Campus university, in the heart of Manchester. 2 mins walk from all the record stores, fast food shops and department stores you'll ever need. Pubs (The Old Garratt, Lass O'Gowrie) and SU bars all no more than 60 seconds away from campus. But perhaps the most visible thing about student life is UMIST Union politics, unlike any other Manchester-based educational establishment. Parties such as Slightly Choclatey, Drunken Slob and Apathetics Unanimous have all been elected to Council and sabbatical executive positions.

　SU facilities range from dark room, bar etc to the Copyshop with computer

CAN'T FIND WHAT YOU'RE LOOKING FOR? USE THE INDEX!

typesetting facilities and four-colour photocopying. SU Travel Bureau among the most popular in Manchester, offering special student discounts. Popular Coffee Shop packed every lunchtime, sells mega-dobber sandwiches which are very popular. SU fortnightly newspaper, *Grip*, written, produced, composed and arranged by students who also develop the photographs and typeset the text. SU disco (Sharansky's) has eclectic selection of music night to night, Acid House to Heavy Metal catered for. Regular bar promotions ensure that UMIST SU has cheapest bars in Manchester. All entertainment organised by students who DJ, set up lighting rigs, act as roadies for bands, mix and publicise.

About 21% overseas students, 25% women and 24% post-graduates. World-wide reputation for science research. A separate university with its own campus and Union; students can also take full advantage of the facilities of Manchester University, concerts, societies, sports facilities and halls.

Pauper notes
Accommodation: University halls offer to UMIST and univ students, Hulme flats. **Drink:** Lass O'Gowrie (Charles St), Robin Hood (Moss Side), The Clarence (Irish pub on Wilmslow Rd), King's Arms (Chorlton-on-Medlock, brews Dobbins beer in cellar). **Eats:** Chicago Diner (East Didsbury), Chinese restaurants in Chinatown (loads of them), massive Asian quarter in Rusholme has all manner of dishes at wildly varying prices. **Ents:** Free concert and movie tickets if reviewing for SU newspaper, 7 theatres, 7 cinemas, 5 art galleries, Cornerhouse is trendy but not expensive, free SU disco on Thursday. **Sports:** McDougall Sports Centre, Armitage centre, Sugden centre featuring squash, pool etc. **Hardship funds:** Institute fund and SU welfare loans. **Travel:** SU travel office open to enquiries.

Alumni (Editors' pick)
Sir John Cockroft, Sir Alan Veale, Gary Bailey, Sir William Barlow, David Clark MP, Keith Oates.

UNITED MEDICAL SCHOOLS

United Medical & Dental Schools of Guy's & St Thomas's Hospitals, Lambeth Palace Road, London SE1 7EH (071-922 8013) Map E, D3, C4

Student enquiries: Undergraduate Admissions Officer

Main study areas – as in What to Study section: *(First degree):* Dentistry, medicine.

European Community: No students learn an EC language or spend time in another EC country as part of their course. Approved Erasmus programme 1990/91.

Application: UCCA. **Structural features:** Part of London University. **Special features:** Students admitted for both pre-clinical and clinical studies (some places for students who have completed pre-clinical studies at Oxbridge). Dental students taught at Guy's and medical students on both 2 sites. **Main awards:** MBBS, BDS. **Awarding body:** London University. **Founded:** 1982 from Guy's and St Thomas's Medical Schools. **Site:** St Thomas's Hospital (south of Westminster Bridge) and Guy's Hospital (south of London Bridge). **Accommodation:** School accommodation for 435 students; university halls of residence also available for first year students (all first-years are guaranteed a room). Rent: 25% in accommodation where rent controlled by university. **Library:** Substantial libraries housed on both sites along with computer-video and audio-visual learning facilities. **Welfare:** Doctor, dentist, counsellor, chaplain, student advisers. **Careers:** Various pre-registration posts reserved for UMDS students at hospitals in or near London. **Sporting facilities:** The school has ample sporting facilities including swimming pools,

CAN'T FIND WHAT YOU'RE LOOKING FOR? USE THE INDEX!

gymnasium, squash courts and 2 sports grounds. Site: playing fields 10 mins by train from London Bridge.

Duration of first degree course(s) or equivalent: 5 years **Total first degree students 1989/90:** 1,500 **Number of overseas students:** 45 **Number of mature students:** 120 **Male/female ratio 1989/90:** 3:2 **Teaching staff: full-time** 200 **part-time:** 400 **Total full-time students 1989/90:** 1,800 **Postgraduate students:** 300 **Tuition fees, first degrees, 1990/91:** £1,675 (£670 if self-financing); Overseas: £6,050 (pre-clinical), £11,150 (clinical).

What it's like

UMDS was formed from two of London's most prestigious medical schools: Guy's and St Thomas's. Now in our second year of complete amalgamation we are reaping the benefits of union and most of the hatchets and rivalry have been buried.

St Thomas's is very attractively situated opposite Westminster and only 10 minutes away from the West End. Guy's is a short bus journey away at London Bridge and has peaceful gardens and courtyards.

Teaching is evenly split between the campuses both being well equipped with lecture theatres and boasting between them brand new anatomy and physiology departments. UMDS has four libraries, two student bars, shops, laundries, canteens and two playing fields and the historic Gordon Pathology Museum (one of the largest in the country).

The course is traditional in structure; however clinical experience (including GP and nursing attachments) is becoming an increasing part of preclinical years. Dental school is situated on the Guys campus and contains most of its own teaching facilities. Pastoral guidance is provided throughout the course by a tutor/guidance scheme. Clinical teaching is provided by two of London's largest and well-respected hospitals.

Sport is inevitably strong following amalgamation and successes at university level are matched by the variety on offer (from polo to korfball).

The schools have a very active drama society with regular shows and an appearance at Edinburgh Festival. Music is also strong and college bands and concert groups are provided with rehearsal rooms and a PA system.

UMDS hosts one of the largest summer balls in London and the annual Snowflake and Valentine's balls are always eagerly anticipated. There are social events on at least one campus every week and if that doesn't keep you happy, then London also has plenty to offer in entertainment.

London has never been a great place for student accommodation but UMDS has campus halls for students and nearly everyone finds somewhere they're happy with.

London is the most exciting and dynamic city in the country and a training at UMDS not only gives you the opportunity to enjoy the capital but also to receive a high-quality medical education in modern surroundings.
Richard Simcock

Pauper notes

Accommodation: Student halls at both campuses. Most are pleasant, modern and cheap. **Drink:** Guys new bar one of cheapest in London. **Eats:** Two subsidised restaurants, also cheap hospital canteens (if you dare!). **Ents:** Very active SU. Hops every week, 3 annual balls, West End in easy reach, regular shows. **Sports:** Two gyms, swimming pool, squash courts, two playing fields, mountaineering hut, boat club on Thames. **Hardship funds:** Some scholarships available. **Travel:** Biking between campuses quick, easy and cheap. Anywhere in London in easy reach by bus. **Work:** Some do nursing work in hospital but plenty of part-time work available in London. **European Community:** 2 delegates for European Medical Students' Association (EMSA) in Brussels, 1991; night classes in French (and maybe German).

CAN'T FIND WHAT YOU'RE LOOKING FOR? USE THE INDEX!

" True Dickensian atmosphere at a snip..... "

Alumni (Editors' pick)

Dr David Owen MP, Somerset Maugham, John Keats, Geoffrey Tate (conductor), Lord Butterfield, Addison (as in disease), Florence Nightingale, Sir William Gull (possibly Jack the Ripper).

UNIVERSITY COLLEGE LONDON

University College London, Gower Street, London WC1E 6BT (071-387 7050) Map E, C1

Student enquiries: Registrar

You can look up Institute of Archaeology, National Hospitals College and Slade separately.

Main study areas – as in What to Study section: *(First degree):* Anatomy, anthropology, archaeology, architecture, biochemistry, biology, biotechnology, botany, business studies, chemical engineering, chemistry, civil engineering, classics, computing, economics, electrical and electronic engineering, English, environmental studies, European studies, fine arts, geography, geology, history, Latin American studies, law, linguistics, marine technology, mathematical studies, mechanical and production engineering, medicine, microbiology, modern languages, Near East and Islamic studies, pharmacology, philosophy, physics, physiology, psychology, speech sciences, town and country planning, zoology. *Also:* Biosocial science, Egyptology, neuroscience, Rumanian, Scandinavian studies.

European Community: Number of students learning an EC language or spending time in another EC country, not known. Formal exchange links with numerous EC universities/colleges including Denmark (Copenhagen); Italy (Venice, Pisa); plus universities of Aix-Marseille III (law with French law), Cologne (law with German law) and Florence (law with Italian law). Approved Erasmus programme 1990/91. BA modern European studies.

CAN'T FIND WHAT YOU'RE LOOKING FOR? USE THE INDEX!

Application: UCCA. **Structural features:** Part of London University. **Academic features:** 3- or 4- year LLB course available. MEng (4 yrs) in chemical engineering, biochemical engineering, electronic and electrical engineering. **Special features:** School of medicine offers clinical studies to students who have completed pre-clinical studies at Oxbridge. **Founded:** 1828; merged with Middlesex Hospital Medical School and Institute of Archaelogy. **Main awards:** BA, BSc, BSc(Econ), BSc(Eng), MBBS, LLB, BEng, MEng. **Awarding body:** London University. **Site:** Heart of London University area in Bloomsbury. **Access:** Warren Street, Euston Square, Goodge Street underground stations, buses. **Accommodation:** 713 places in halls, more than 1,700 in other accommodation; London University Accommodation Office deals with rooms, digs, flats, bedsits, lodgings. **Library:** Main library in ten departments – 900,000 volumes, 7,000 periodicals, 1,162 study places; special reference facilities for some course books; extensive specialist collections. **Centres of excellence:** UCL and its school of medicine (formerly University College Hospital School of Medicine) both have national and international reputations. **Welfare:** Doctor, dentist, psychiatrist, solicitor, chaplain, student counselling service. **Hardship funds:** Funds available but not for first year students. **Careers:** Information, advice and placement service. **Amenities:** Central London. **Sporting facilities:** 60 acre athletic ground at Shenley.

Duration of first degree course(s) or equivalent: 3 years; **others:** 4 years **Total first degree students 1989/90:** 6,295 **Number of overseas students:** 954 **Male/female ratio 1989/90:** 5:4 **Teaching staff:** 750 **Total full-time students 1989/90:** 8,000 **Postgraduate students:** 2,431 **Tuition fees, first degrees, 1990/91:** Home: £1,675; Overseas: £5,365 (eg economics), £6,995 (eg physics).

What it's like
The portico is the centrepiece of the college and can be viewed from the Gower Street entrance. The main campus is situated on Gower Street; much of it is unsuitable for students with disabilities. UCL's academic reputation ranks second only to Oxbridge, many of our departments being on a par with their Oxbridge counterparts. UCL has over 60 departments and 9,000 students.

UCL has both purpose-built and converted halls of residence and student houses. It tries to accommodate all first years and as many third years as possible. Although UCL rents are increasing, still lowest of any London college.

Union housed in small building which was intended only to be a temporary home. Despite lack of space, the union provides a full range of services, bars and catering. Many active societies and sports club funded by union.

UCL is a cosmopolitan environment in the heart of a cosmopolitan environment – London. Standards are generally very high in all aspects of college life, but particularly in terms of research. Over 50% of students attain first or upper second class degreees. Around a quarter of students are postgraduates. The heart of Bloomsbury is one of the best places to study. Students come from all backgrounds, although those from private school sector may be in a slight majority. Easy to integrate into UCL life.

Pauper notes
Accommodation: Housing rights and advice pack produced by union. Good student halls, cheaper than the rest of London University. **Drink:** The Bricklayers Arms (very comfy armchairs and sofas). Also new union cafe-bar. **Eats:** Lots of good, cheap food if you look around. 3rd floor food bar in SU. Very good veggie. **Ents:** Film soc get many of latest films which are still in West End. **Sports:** University of London pool in Bloomsbury precinct, massive sports ground at Shenley, Herts and at Chiselhurst in Kent. New fitness centre with very cheap rates for students. **Hardship funds:** New access funds for both postgraduates and undergraduates to help with accommodation costs. **Travel:** Many departments award travel scholarships for long vacation. Most students use the tube. **Work:** Lots of work in union.

CAN'T FIND WHAT YOU'RE LOOKING FOR? USE THE INDEX!

Alumni (Editors' pick)

David Lodge, David Storey, Clare Francis, Jonathan Miller, Lloyd Cole (Commobins) lasted 1 term, Jonathan Dimbleby, David Gower, Carol Thatcher, Goeffrey Dear (Chief Constable of West Midlands Police), David Johnson (Features editor, Daily Telegraph).

WALES COLLEGE OF MEDICINE

University of Wales College of Medicine, Heath Park, Cardiff CF4 4XN (0222 755944) Map A, D8

Student enquiries: Registrar and Secretary

Main study areas – as in What to Study section: *(First degree):* Dentistry, medicine, nursing studies.

European Community: No students learn an EC language or spend time in another EC country as part of their course. Formal exchange links with Hanover and Munster.

Application: UCCA. **Structural features:** Part of Wales University. **Special features:** Offers 6-year medical and 5-year dental courses (students usually admitted direct to second year); pre-clinical studies at Cardiff. 3- and 4-year courses in nursing. **Founded:** 1931. **Main awards:** MBBCh, BDS, BN. **Awarding body:** University of Wales. **Site:** Part of complex shared with University Hospital of Wales, 2 miles from city centre. **Access:** By road. **Accommodation:** 213 places in hall, 23 study bedrooms in hostels, 18 flatlets 2 miles from campus. Accommodation available from Warden for all clinical students. Approx cost: £19 pw halls, £30.50–£33 pw flatlets. **Library:** Main and dental libraries; 65,000 volumes, 850 current periodicals, 190 study places, audio-visual facilities. **Centres of excellence:** Tenovus Institute for Cancer Research; Institute of Nephrology; Department of Medical Genetics. **Welfare:** Doctor, dentist, psychiatrist, chaplain, 2 student counsellors, international development officer. **Special categories:** Some residential facilities for married students; creche at University of Wales College of Cardiff. **Careers:** Information and advice (pre-registration house officer posts in Welsh hospitals virtually automatic). **Amenities:** Medical bookshop on campus, music and drama societies. Staff and students' social club. **Sporting facilities:** Athletics facilities College of Cardiff.

Duration of first degree course(s) or equivalent: 5/6 years MB, BCh; 3/4 years BN, 5 years BDS **Total first degree students 1989/90:** 726 Number of overseas students: 34 **Number of mature students:** 5 **Male/female ratio 1989/90:** 8:9 **Teaching staff: full-time:** 260 **part-time:** 35 **Total full-time students 1989/90:** 726 **Postgraduate students:** 284 **Tuition fees, first degrees, 1990/91:** Home: £1,675; Overseas: £6,050 (BN), £11,150 (MBBCh, BDS).

What it's like

Situated on a 53-acre purpose-built (1970) campus some two and a half miles north of the city centre, UWCM provides teaching facilities for students in medicine, dentistry and bachelor of nursing courses. The campus is easily accessible and is on most main bus routes.

The pre-clinical course is at nearby University of Wales College Cardiff (UWCC) and therefore most 1st year pre-clinical, and some 2nd year pre-clinical students are accommodated by UWCC halls of residence, which include self-catering or full-board facilities. Accommodation is provided for approximately one-third of clinical students on campus, offering single-study bedrooms with shared catering and laundry facilities. There is a small number of places for married students. Other students usually choose to find lodgings, which are plentiful in the neighbourhood.

SU and bar (Med Club) are located on ground floor of the 'on-site' hall of residence. SU is essentially apolitical but very active socially, and fields teams in most major sports (not just rugby!). It enjoys exceptionally good relations with college authorities and unlike many other medical student associations it is an autonomous body within the NUS. Students are also able to make full use of the fine facilities offered at UWCC.

UWCM is highly regarded nationally and internationally with an excellent teaching record and a high pass rate. It has over 200 academic staff, and teaching takes the form of lectures, seminars and tutorials, with an emphasis on clinical skills. Free transport for students is provided to hospitals around the Cardiff area. Most students have opportunity to study in hospitals throughout Wales, as well as undertaking an elective period either abroad or in UK. Examinations take the form of traditional and multiple choice papers as well as vivas. Students are assessed by course work before presentation for degree exams. Resits are possible, but there is no fixed failure rate. Medically trained members of staff act as student counsellors, who treat all information confidentially.

The city has a large student population, and has much to offer. Cardiff is the cultural and sporting centre of Wales, boasting the National Stadium at the Arms Park, the National Sports Centre for Wales, National Museum of Wales, and the headquarters of Welsh National Opera. It has a fine castle, and superb civic buildings as well as seven cinemas and four theatres including the 2,000-seat St David's Hall. Cardiff is an excellent shopping centre and has numerous pubs, clubs and restaurants.

Students come from a wide variety of backgrounds: 40% Welsh students, 50% from other UK countries and 10% overseas students (1989), with a male:female ratio of 1:1. There is no discrimination of any description.

The Students' Club has recently contacted medical student associations at Charles University in Prague and the Albet Szent Gyorgy Medical University in Szeged, Hungary. As Eastern Europe becomes more accessible to the West, it is hoped that we will be able to send students to visit these countries in the near future. *Richard H Evans*

Pauper notes

Accommodation: Campus hall £19/week, others pay £20 - £35/week in rented houses. Small number of houses/flats for married students. **Drink:** Med Club cheapest prices in Cardiff. Brains is local brew, but many other excellent local beers. **Eats:** Excellent variety of restaurants in town, now with many vegetarian and ethnic eateries. Many offer 10% student discount. **Ents:** New 9-screen cinema due to open. Wed afternoons half-price for students at all cinemas. Student stand-by tickets at reduced cost for most theatres. **Sports:** All SU sports clubs free; National Sports Centre very reasonable. Sports and Social Club on campus has membership fee, but also reasonable. **Travel:** Free transport to hospitals in Cardiff area. Scholarships available to help fund electives. **Work:** Preclinical students have similar holidays to other students; clinical students have little/no time to supplement grants with outside work due to long academic terms.

Alumni (Editors' pick)

Dr Gareth Crompton, J N Parry, John Peters, Doreen Vermeulen-Cranch, Professor B Knight.

WALES POLY

The Polytechnic of Wales, Pontypridd, Mid Glamorgan CF37 1DL (0443 480480) Map A, D7

Student enquiries: Admissions Officer

Main study areas – as in What to Study section: *(First degree):* Accountancy, biology, biotechnology, business studies, chemical engineering, chemistry, civil engineering, communication studies, computing, drama, electrical & electronic engineering, English, environmental science, fine arts, geography, geology, history, information technology, law, mathematical studies, mechanical and production engineering, philosophy, psychology, public administration, religious studies and theology, sociology. *Also:* Energy studies, estate management, pollution, Welsh studies.

European Community: 12% first degree students take EC language as part of course and 12% spend 6 months or more in another EC country. Formal exchange links with 9 EC universities/colleges: Eire (1); France (2); Germany (2); Italy (2); Netherlands (1); Spain (1). Approved Erasmus programme 1990/91.

Application: PCAS. **Main awards:** BA, BSc, BEng, MEng. **Awarding body:** CNAA. **Site:** Single campus situated in Treforest, Pontypridd. **Access:** Good road and rail links. **Academic features:** BSc in technology & business studies; combined sciences with options in geological science and biological science & technology); surveying for research development; BEng manufacturing systems engineering. **Accommodation:** 500 single study bedrooms; 114 self-catering/shared accommodation. Approx cost: £45 pw single study, £23 self-catering. Rent: 13% in accommodation where rent controlled by polytechnic. **Library:** Over 150,000 volumes, 1,700 serial publications, 520 study places. **Specialist collections:** Law library, statistics. **Other learning facilities:** Computer centre, media resources unit. **Welfare:** Medical centre, 3 chaplains. **Hardship funds:** None, but sympathetic consideration given to individual cases of genuine hardship. **Careers:** Information, advice and placement. **Amenities:** SU with discos, films, etc, sports fields, tennis courts, multi-gym, campus general shop, bookshop.

Duration of first degree course(s) or equivalent: 3 and 4 years **Total first degree students 1989/90:** 3,792 **Number of overseas students:** 315 **Number of mature students:** 565 **Male/female ratio 1989/90:** 5:2 **Teaching staff: full-time:** 365 **part-time:** 50 **Total full-time and sandwich students 1989/90:** 4,752 **Postgraduate students:** 240 **Tuition fees, first degrees, 1990/91:** Home: £1,675; Overseas: £4,563.

What it's like

It's the only polytechnic in Wales, situated in the south Wales valleys on the outskirts of Pontypridd, a valleys market town, half-way between Merthyr Tydfil and Cardiff (approx 12 miles to each). Trefforest has own valley line train service, with station just off campus. Campus pleasant, green and built very much on the side of a hill, which may pose access problems for people with disabilities. It's the only campus with resident sheep.

On campus halls of residence accommodate approx 500 out of 4,500 full-time students. A smaller number of places available in off-campus self-catering halls. Majority of students live in local private rented accommodation. Some live in Cardiff, a better centre, only 30 mins train journey away. Growing number of overseas students, currently around 10%. Students come from all over Britain, but obviously fairly high percentage are Welsh.

SU provides the main focal point. It has many facilities: the shop (stationery, confectionary, essentials) incorporates travel shop and insurance office. The SU houses 'Suds' (launderette), 'The Green' fast food eatery, 'The George Knox' recently refurbished tavern bar and 'Shafts' live music venue and club. There's a

CAN'T FIND WHAT YOU'RE LOOKING FOR? USE THE INDEX!

varied entertainments programme, with something on every night of the week; also a host of sporting and non-sporting clubs and societies. The SU executive committee consists of eight annually elected members, including 3 sabbaticals (full-time officers) – the President, Deputy President Finance & Services and Deputy President Education and Welfare.

Pauper notes
Accommodation: Fairly good campus halls of residence, some self-catering off-campus halls. Majority in private rented accommodation in surrounding area or commuting from Cardiff.**Drink:** SU 'George Knox' bar is cheapest. Plenty of good local pubs. Local(ish) brews incl. Brains, Buckleys, Felinfoel, Hancock's, Crown. **Eats:** SU 'The Green' fast food eatery caters for vegetarians. Two on campus refectories. Surrounding area not brilliant. Plenty in Cardiff. **Ents:** SU nightclub/disco 'Shafts'; varied arts programme with regular bands, discos, cabaret and films. **Sports:** Excellent on-campus new sports centre. 3 local swimming pools. Very active SU sports. **Hardship funds:** SU hardship loans system for when you hit rock bottom. Visit the Welfare Office. **Travel:** Good train service to Pontypridd and Cardiff. Buses locally. SU travel shop.

WALES UNIVERSITY

This is a federal university consisting of 6 UKCPUs: Aberystwyth, Bangor, Cardiff, Lampeter, Swansea and Wales College of Medicine. All select and teach their first degree students themselves. You can look up the profiles in *Where to Study*.

Trinity College, Carmarthen and the Welsh College of Music and Drama both offer Wales University degrees.

WARWICK UNIVERSITY

The University of Warwick, Coventry CV4 7AL (0203 523523) Map A, E7

Student enquiries: Academic Registrar

Main study areas – as in What to Study section: *(First degree):* Accountancy, American studies, biochemistry, biology, business studies, chemistry, civil engineering, classics, computing, drama, economics, education, electrical & electronic engineering, English, European studies, fine arts, geography, history, Latin American studies, law, mathematical studies, mechanical and production engineering, microbiology, modern languages, music, philosophy, physics, politics and government, psychology, religious studies and theology, sociology, welfare studies. *Also:* Caribbean studies, comparative literature, film studies, medicinal chemistry, operational research, theatre studies, virology.

European Community: 9% first degree students take EC language as part of course and 5% spend 6 months or more in another EC country. Formal exchange links with some 29 EC universities/colleges: Belgium (3); Denmark (1); Eire (1); France (10); Germany (5); Greece (1); Italy (4); Netherlands (3); Spain (1). All are open to non-language specialists. Approved Erasmus programme 1990/91.

Application: UCCA. **Academic features:** New BA degree courses in ancient history, classical archaeology; English & Spanish-American literature; French with film studies; philosophy with classical civilisation; chemistry with medicinal chemistry. **Special features:** High percentage of mature students. University provides adult and continuing education courses locally and validates an Open Access scheme; range of part-time degrees by day and/or evening study. Resident German writer, many visiting professors; quartet in residence. Successful science park; close links with industry. **Founded:** 1964. **Main awards:** BA, BA with qualified teacher status, BSc, LLB, BEng, MEng. **Awarding body:** University of Warwick. **Site:** 2.5 miles southwest of Coventry city centre. **Access:** Buses from Coventry and Leamington Spa to campus. **Accommodation:** 2,173 places in mixed and segregated halls; 1,331 places in campus flats; 20 in student houses; 1,400 places in 300 privately-owned off-campus houses available through University's property leasing scheme. Majority of first year students accommodated. Approx cost: £31 pw halls; £23.20 pw for periods of 30 weeks and 39 weeks. Rent: 53% in accommodation where rent controlled by university. **Library:** 3 libraries; nearly 700,000 volumes in total, 4,000 periodicals, 1,200 study places in central library; short-term loan period for books in heaviest demand. **Specialist collections:** Business Information Service; Modern Records Centre. **Other learning resources:** Computing centre; language centre. **Welfare:** Doctors, dentists, psychiatrist, chaplains, law centre (in School of Law), 2 student counsellors and personal tutor system. **Special categories:** Creche with 20 places. **Careers:** Careers library, individual counselling, employers' recruitment visits. **Amenities:** Modern SU building, newspaper, travel and insurance offices; refectory; university arts centre (theatres, concert hall, music centre, cinema, art gallery, sculpture court, bookshop, restaurant and bars); shops and services on campus; facilities of Coventry (Belgrade Theatre, international 50m swimming pool). **Hardship fund:** Small fund administered by Vice-Chancellor. **Sporting facilities:** Extensive playing fields, tennis courts, dri-pla floodlit area, running track, trim track, sports centre (25m pool, squash courts, etc). **Employment:** Significant proportion of graduates enter financial areas.

Duration of first degree course(s) or equivalent: 3 years **others:** 4 years (BEng/MEng; BA (QTS); languages); **Total first degree students 1989/90:** 5,626; **Total BA(QTS) students:** 774 **Number of overseas students:** 1,101 **Number of mature students:** 714 **Male/female ratio 1989/90:** 1:1 **Teaching staff:** 580 **Total full-time students:** 8,031 **Postgraduate students:** 3,554 **Tuition fees, first degrees, 1990/91:** Home: £1,675 (eg politics), £2,500 (eg physics); Overseas: £4,560 (eg politics), £6,050 (eg physics).

What it's like

University is very keen on its external appearance with a variety of different types of building. Tries to blend in with rural surroundings. Currently building a second lake.

Definitely a campus university, situated 4 miles from Coventry which is easily accessible by bus throughout the day and 8 miles from Leamington, although less frequent bus service there is a hitching system in operation. Car parking hard during daytime – recently ban on students living on campus from parking cars on campus with few exceptions.

Accommodation generally good. Has high proportion of students in residence on campus although nearest housing is several miles away. About fifth of rooms now with ensuite bathrooms. All first years and 60% of finalists on campus. All second years off campus. Large proportion of off campus students in Leamington, where many student pubs and good shopping.

Relationship between university admin and union has improved considerably recently. Most facilities open for reasonable hours, having recently changed.SU very active, although not all political. Received block grant rise for welfare expansion. Over 200 clubs and societies. Runs entertainments programme 6 days a week with new multi-purpose venue ('nightclub'). Has 6 bars, 5 food outlets including vegetarian, pasta restaurant and dial-a-pizza, union shop, Endsleigh Insurance, Warwick Study (an academic resource outlet), travel shop and launderettes. Mixed union executive and 'No Politics' (a new venture), campaigning more on student issues.

Comprehensive welfare service offered via 2 full-time welfare officers, 1 sabbatical officer and rights and advice service. Counselling totally confidential. Half-term creche run.

CAN'T FIND WHAT YOU'RE LOOKING FOR? USE THE INDEX!

Largest society: film soc. Most active: Rag, over 600 members, over £33,000 to charity, good link with local towns. 63 sports societies, most tastes catered for, eg even Clint Eastwood Society.

Top subjects include maths, history, law and business studies. All with very high reputations. Some courses include years/time abroad. Some workloads heavy, most examined at end of year, although some assessments. Some departments pushing for anonymous marking.

Entertainment programme includes free discos, comedy/cabaret, raves, bops and balls. Also is Warwick's unique Whipround with small bands playing on Saturday nights, many who become big later, eg Roachford, Del Amitri, the event being free to students. Warwick balls often include big bands such as De La Soul, Tom Robinson and the Pogues.

Successful Southern African scholarship scheme currently funding one scholar, soon to finance a second. High proportion of graduates enter employment often after a year off.

Overall, Warwick University is a great campus university with a great SU for a great 3-4 years of your life.
Ian Bradley

Pauper notes
Accommodation: Average on campus £25 to £30 for ensuite bathroom. Rents off campus upwards of £25/week excluding bills and transport. **Drink:** SU good price and variety (Bass, S&N, Courage). Local brews include M&B, Ansells. **Eats:** Snack bar, Harvey's, pasta restaurant, vegetarian outlet and pizzas in Union, all good price. University has several restaurants/refectories. **Ents:** SU runs all student entertainment including film society. University has big Arts Centre including small cinema. **Sports:** Union runs sports clubs; univ run 2 sports centres including pools and running track. **Hardship funds:** Union and university (VC) have small funds. Still to sort out access funds and how to distribute. **Travel:** 40p hitch to Leamington (8 miles); approx 50p to Coventry, 90p Leamington by bus. **Work:** Vacation work with conferences, bars and catering on campus throughout year. Some off campus casual work.

Alumni (Editors' pick)
Sting (for 1 term), Steve Heighway, Dave Nellist (Militant MP), David Davis MP, Jeff Rooker MP, Timmy Mallett (TV personality), Stephen Pile (journalist), Simon Mayo (DJ).

WATFORD COLLEGE

Watford College, Hempstead Road, Watford, Herts WD1 3EZ (0923 57500) Map A, F8

Student enquiries: Department of Printing and Packaging (0923 57661)

Main study areas *(first degree):* Management, packaging technology, printing, publishing.

European Community: Languages are optional for first degree students; number taking up options not known. 10% spend 6 months or more in another EC country. No formal exchange links with EC universities/colleges, although many international links.

Application: PCAS. **Special features:** Postgrad publishing diploma. **Largest fields of study:** Printing and packaging technology. **Founded:** 1874. **Main awards:** BSc. **Awarding body:** CNAA. **Site:** Watford town centre and 3 other sites. **Access:** Watford Junction station (British Rail). **Accommodation:** Welfare officer will assist in finding lodgings in and around Watford. None provided by college. **Library:** Main library, plus 2 site libraries; 45,000 volumes in total, 350 periodicals,

100 study places. **Specialist collections:** Printing technology library. **Other learning facilities:** Computer unit; reprographic unit. **Welfare:** Medical advisory service, counselling service. **Careers:** Information, advice and informal placement service. **Amenities:** On site: social centre and bar, gymnasium, tennis courts, bookshop. Watford: Concert hall, live theatre, cinemas; Division 2 football, harriers. London facilities 20 minutes away. **Employment:** Printing and packaging industries, their suppliers and customers.

Duration of first degree course(s) or equivalent: 4 years sandwich **Total first degree students 1989/90:** 85 **Number of overseas students:** 8 **Number of mature students:** 7 **Male/female ratio 1989/90:** 12:1 **Teaching staff: full-time:** 20 **part-time:** 4 **Total full-time students 1989/90:** 1,250 **Postgraduate students:** 120 **Tuition fees, first degrees, 1990/91:** Home: £1,750; Overseas: £5,000

What it's like

It's made up of six sites, all near town centre, although only one of these is really concerned with higher education courses. There is no college accommodation but there is a welfare/housing officer to help you out. There is also a YMCA and YWCA. Town's entertainment is pretty standard: one nightclub – Paradise Lost – a general release cinema and loads of pubs. Rag week is best week in the year. Print department is one of best in world and attracts many overseas students. Relations between different nationalities very friendly. Employment easy to come by, especially after print courses.

Pauper notes

Accommodation: None. All private housing expensive (£40-£45 per week). **Drink:** College bar cheapest in town with good real ales though it shuts early. The Horns and Blakes are good student places. Benskins and Greene King good local brews. **Eats:** Cheap food at student snack bar in college; lots of kebabs, Greek, Chinese, curry and burgers in town. **Ents:** Live bands at college, Pump House Theatre. Not much else in Watford. **Sports:** Lots of swimming-pools and golf centres (pitch + putt course) locally. **Hardship Funds:** See welfare officer. **Travel:** Good hitching to most parts of the UK on the M1, A1 and M4. SU experts on cheap travel. **Work:** Part-time jobs often available – details from Association Office.

WELSH COLLEGE OF MUSIC AND DRAMA

Welsh College of Music and Drama, Castle Grounds, Cathays Park, Cardiff CF1 3ER (0222 342854/6) Fax: (0222 237639) Map A, D8

Student enquiries: Chief Administrative Officer

Main study areas – as in What to Study section: *(First degree):* Drama, music. **Also:** Stage management design.

European Community: No students learn an EC language or spend time in another EC country.

Application: Direct. **Special features:** Visiting Professors: Sir Geraint Evans, Christopher Adey, Anthony Hopkins, Janet Price, Elizabeth Vaughan, John Mitchison. **Academic features:** 4-year BEd in music and drama in conjunction with Cardiff Institute; considerable emphasis is laid on practical studies. BA Performing Arts (music). Graduate diploma course for drama. **Founded:** 1949, as Cardiff College of Music, gaining its present title in 1971. **Main awards:** BA, BEd. **Awarding body:** Wales University. **Site:** Cardiff city centre. **Access:** Site close to main bus and railway station. **Accommodation:** Apply to Student Accommodation Service, (University College, 58 Park Place, Cardiff CF1 3AT, tel: 0222 874000). Rent: no students in accommodation where rent controlled by the college. **Library:** 10,000 volumes, 35 periodicals, 34 study places. **Welfare:** Doctor, chaplain.

CAN'T FIND WHAT YOU'RE LOOKING FOR? USE THE INDEX!

Careers: Information, advice and placement service. **Amenities:** Theatre on site; studios and workshops, television studio, refectory; recreational facilities of Cardiff (eg national sports centre). Concert and opera ticket concessions; strong practical association with BBC, WNO. **Employment:** Teaching and professional work.

Duration of first degree course(s) or equivalent: 3 years; **others:** 4 years BEd **Total first degree students 1989/90:** 80; **Total BEd students:** 38 **Male/female ratio 1989/90:** 1:3 **Teaching staff: full-time:** 16 **part-time:** 11 **Total full-time students 1989/90:** 304 **Postgraduate students:** 63 **Tuition fees, first degrees, 1990/91:** Home: £1,675; Overseas: £4,563.

What it's like

Situated in grounds of Cardiff Castle, short walk to city centre, emphasis on performance. Students perform to the public in the college's Bute Theatre, St David's Hall, Sherman Theatre, Llandaff Cathedral and other city venues. The Bute Theatre has a workshop, design, rehearsal and dance studios, and a bar regularly used for SU bar nights, discos and other social activities. College has recital and orchestral rooms, and practice rooms for students' use. TV Studio where production as well as performance is encouraged. SU enjoys excellent relations with college staff, and encourages students to perform in social activities and to participate in the variety of societies available. No halls of residence, but many bedsitters, flats, etc near by.

Students have unique opportunity to develop fully in academic and practical fields, and leave college to work in all areas of musical and dramatic art.

Pauper notes

Accommodation: Information on digs, shared houses readily available from UC Cardiff accommodation board – loads of accommodation under £25. **Drink:** Brains bitter, Brains S A – Skull Attack, no end of Welsh drinking traditions to be upheld. **Eats:** Campus canteen with large selection. **Ents:** As drama and music college, entertainments in varied and plentiful supply and often free/very cheap. U C Cardiff affiliated for Big Bands. **Sports:** College teams and access to Cardiff facilities. **Hardship funds:** No problem – support from Union and College. **Travel:** Good train access, M4 to west Wales and Southern England. **Work:** Refer to U C Cardiff Work and Vacation Office.

Alumni (Editors' pick)

Anthony Hopkins, Sir Geraint Evans, Hugo E Blick, Victor Spinetti, Peter Gill, Hywell Gwyfryn, Geraint Morris, Jane Freeman, Maldwyn Davies, Caryl Thomas, Sioned Williams, David Gwesyn Smith, Kenneth Smith, Iris Williams.

WEST GLAMORGAN INSTITUTE

West Glamorgan Institute of HE, Townhill Road, Swansea SA2 0UT (0792 203482) Map A, C8

Student enquiries: Registry

Main study areas – as in What to Study section: *(First degree):* Accountancy, business studies, computing, economics, education, electrical & electronic engineering, English, fine arts, information technology, law, nursing studies. *Also:* Behavioural science, media studies, urban studies.

European Community: 2.5% first degree students take EC language as part of course and 2% spend 6 months or more in another EC country. No formal exchange links with EC universities/colleges.

Application: PCAS. **Founded:** 1976, ex Colleges of Art, Technology and Education. **Main awards:** BA, BEd, BEng, BNursing. **Awarding body:** Wales Univer-

CAN'T FIND WHAT YOU'RE LOOKING FOR? USE THE INDEX!

sity; London University; CNAA. **Site:** 3 main campuses, 1 in town centre; 2 outside. **Access:** Public transport. **Accommodation:** 260 places in mixed halls of residence. 70% of students are home based. **Library:** 3 libraries (Mount Pleasant and Townhill sites); 70,000 volumes in total; 611 periodicals, 100 study places, reserved copies of course books. **Specialist collections:** Salmon collection of 18th and 19th century books. **Other learning facilities:** Visual aid centre, print room and resources centre. **Welfare:** Student counsellor, doctor, chaplains. **Careers:** Careers counsellor. **Amenities:** SU bar and coffee bar, gymnasia, Swansea leisure centre. **Employment:** Teaching, business, nursing, accountancy, engineering, computing, law, vocational art.

Duration of first degree course(s) or equivalent: 3 years **Other:** 4 years **Total first degree students 1989/90:** 755; **Total BEd students:** 350 **Number of overseas students:** 10 **Number of mature students:** 309 **Male/female ratio 1989/90:** 1:2 **Teaching staff: full-time:** 75 **part-time:** 8 **Total full-time students 1989/90:** 1,828 **Postgraduate students:** 10 **Tuition fees, first degrees, 1990/91:** Home: £1,675; Overseas: £4,563.

What it's like

4 sites, Townhill and Mount Pleasant are main campuses; Alexandra Road and Penybryn are annexes. All close to each other. Wide range of courses, business studies, education, stained glass, ceramics and technology most popular. Extensive range of Diploma courses. Recreational facilities poor. Townhill campus has a gymnasium but few other facilities; compensated by free use of Swansea Leisure Centre for WGIHE students during the day. Halls only cater for 240 students so apply really early. SU very active but not very political. Provides many facilities including two coffee bars, materials and stationery shops. Private accommodation difficult because of close proximity of University. Libraries at Townhill and Mount Pleasant open 9.00 am–9.00 pm, closed at weekends, limited vacation hours. All sites close to town centre and the famous Gower Peninsula is only a 15 minute bus ride away. SU has about 35 societies including rock-climbing, watersports, Christian Union, rugby. Confidential counselling services provided by Institute which is small but very friendly. Good relationships between staff and students are a priority. Degree courses are CNAA or Welsh University validated. Overseas students encouraged, students from all ethnic minorities. Students from all over GB, Europe, China, Nigeria, America, etc. Drop-out rate is very low. A close-knit atmosphere as students tend to live close to each other.

Pauper notes

Accommodation: Halls relatively cheap but definitely not the Ritz. Bed-sits, flats etc, moderate but very scarce; grab places before the univ do. **Drink:** SU bar at Townhill. Juke box, pool tables. Quite cheap – plastic glasses. Loads of local pubs. Some welcome students, others ban them. Waterside's (in the marina) happy hour recommended. Majority are student dominated. **Eats:** College refectories not bad in general. SU coffee bars for snacks and drinks. Chinese, Indian, Cantonese and Greek food in abundance. Vegetarian in Emma's community bookshop. Local chippies very good, cheap and everywhere. Many health food shops and restaurants. **Ents:** Different ents each Wednesday. Cinema discount with SU card. **Sports:** Free use of Swansea Leisure Centre with SU card. **Hardship funds:** None to speak of. Rare occasions money can be obtained from the college but fund is small. Grovel to understanding bank managers. Abundance of tight-fisted cashpoint machines. **Travel:** M4 express hitch route to the East. Good overall communication including coach and train services. Shared lifts always advertised. **Work:** Local department stores, bar/restaurant work. Summer jobs plentiful, apply early.

Alumni (Editors' pick)

Mervyn Davies.

CAN'T FIND WHAT YOU'RE LOOKING FOR? USE THE INDEX!

WEST LONDON INSTITUTE

West London Institute of Higher Education, Gordon House, 300 St Margaret's Road, Twickenham, Middlesex TW1 1PT (081-891 0121) Map D, A3

Student enquiries: Co-ordinator, Academic Registry

Main study areas – as in What to Study section: *(First degree):* American studies, drama, education, English, geography, geology, history, music, religious studies and theology. *Also:* Physical education, physiotherapy, sports studies.

European Community: No students learn an EC language or spend time in another EC country as part of their course. Approved Erasmus programme 1990/91.

Application: PCAS. **Academic features:** BA/BSc/BEd part of modular scheme with business studies, computer studies, leisure management, minor subjects scheme; BSc physiotherapy. **Special features:** Preparatory 'return to study' course for mature students; access links with further education and adult education institutes. **Founded:** 1976, ex Borough Road College (1798), Chiswick Polytechnic (1850), Maria Grey College (1878) and West Middlesex School of Physiotherapy (1987). **Main awards:** BA, BEd, BSc. **Awarding body:** CNAA; Brunel University (physiotherapy). **Site:** 2 campuses, Lancaster House in Isleworth, Gordon House in Twickenham. **Access:** BR and underground; close to Heathrow, M25, M4 and M3; free inter-campus transport. **Accommodation:** 300+ places in halls; college list of approved lodgings. Priority accommodation for first year students (10–15% first degree students home-based). Approx cost: £36.00 pw halls (incl. part-board) £30–35 pw lodgings. **Library:** 2 libraries; 160,000 volumes in total, 960 periodicals, 400+ study places, restricted loan facilities. **Other learning facilities:** Media resources centre with CCTV, VTR; computer service. Micro computer laboratories; learning resource areas. **Welfare:** 2 doctors, 3 chaplains, 2 nurses, 4 (part-time) counsellors. **Hardship funds:** Student Union and other funds available; staged payments possible for fees. **Careers:** Careers officer and library. **Amenities:** SU shops, club bars; bookshops, orchestras, studio opera, choir, student societies, recreation officer. **Sporting facilities:** New sports hall, incorporating 2 international size basketball courts, 8 badminton courts etc; 3 rugby pitches, 2 football pitches, 2 hockey pitches and additional floodlit training facilities; cricket pitch, lacrosse pitch, tennis courts, athletics track (tartan) and associated facilities.

Duration of first degree course(s) or equivalent: 3 years; 4 years (BEd) **Total first degree students 1989/90:** 1,177; **Total BEd students:** 360 **Number of overseas students:** 16 **Number of mature students:** 130 **Male/female ratio 1989/90:** 2:3 **Teaching staff:** full-time: 168 part-time: 60 **Total full-time students 1989/90:** 2,100 **Postgraduate students:** 137 **Tuition fees, first degrees, 1990/91:** Home: £1,675; Overseas: £4,563.

What it's like

Split-site campus – approx 1 mile apart. River Thames flows past the Gordon House campus; Borough Road campus on Great West Road (easy access Heathrow and London) but noise caused by jet aircraft can be problem, especially during summer term.

5 halls of residence house approx 300 students – mainly first years. Rented accommodation outside halls very expensive and scarce, especially Richmond and Twickenham areas. Hounslow cheaper but distinctly less pleasant. Libraries on both sites scarcely adequate.

Despite excellent reputation for sports studies and high class sports teams, lack of actual pitches for football, rugby and hockey quite startling.

Usual social life – discos and bands – organised regularly by SU. SU has never been particularly political; sees itself as funding body for many diverse clubs and societies. Union staff: 3 annually elected sabbatical officers; 2 full-time staff: an admin officer and secretary.

CAN'T FIND WHAT YOU'RE LOOKING FOR? USE THE INDEX!

With London/West End being so close (via Hounslow and Richmond stations) there are plenty of distractions from academic side of student life. Loadsa pubs, wine bars, restaurants, theatres, cinemas and horse and dog tracks provide scope for frittering away grant cheques. Staff-student relationships generally very amicable but, of course, there have been exceptions over the years. It's not a bad place to get a degree.

Pauper notes

Accommodation: Very difficult to find cheap accommodation in Richmond and Twickenham environs; some less expensive digs in Hounslow area. **Drink:** Fullers Brewery is just up the road in Chiswick. ESB (Extra Special Bitter) is not the weakest tipple known to man! **Eats:** College catering facilities expensive but range of food good; Maria Grey campus superior. **Ents:** Closeness to London ensures plenty of cheap entertainment, ie pub bands/cabaret etc. **Sports:** Two swimming pools close to campus/sports hall on Borough Road campus. Large leisure centre at Brentford. **Hardship funds:** One Institute run welfare fund; one run by the Union. Small short-term loans. **Travel:** Rail and coach cards available with NUS cards. **Work:** Increasingly difficult to find vacation work although some on campus, ie portering and cleaning staff.

Alumni (Editors' pick)

M Naylor, Kathy Cook, B C Rose, P Stimpson, Brian Hooper, Alan Pascoe, Dave Otley, Martin Cross, Phil Bainbridge.

WEST SURREY COLLEGE

West Surrey College of Art & Design, Falkner Road, The Hart, Farnham, Surrey GU9 7DS (0252 722441) Map A, E8

Student enquiries: Admissions Officer

Main study areas – as in What to Study section: *(First degree):* Art & design, fine arts. *Also:* Animation, film studies.

European Community: No students learn an EC language or spend time in another EC country. Formal exchange links with 5 EC universities/colleges in Belgium, France, Germany and Netherlands. Comett exchanges with computer animation industry in Europe.

Application: ADAR. **Academic features:** Unique full time BA Animation. Part time BA Fine Art. **Largest fields of study:** Fine art, audio-visual studies, crafts. **Founded:** 1969, ex Farnham and Guildford schools of art. **Main awards:** BA. **Awarding body:** CNAA. **Site:** Within walking distance of Farnham town centre. **Special features:** Most academic staff are practising artists, designers, film makers and crafts people. Many students major award winners in animation (eg BBC, National Film Theatre), film and video (eg London International Film Festival, Dutch TV), textiles (eg Young Designers of the Year, Victoria and Albert Museum). Commissioned work included Coat of Arms for the Worshipful Company of Ironmongers and students' work featured in BBC Clothes Show and Vogue Magazine. **Accommodation:** 148 hostel places; assistance in finding lodgings. Rent: 13% in accommodation where rent controlled by college. **Library:** 42,000 volumes, 325 specialist periodicals. **Welfare:** Doctor, professional welfare officer. **Careers:** Information, advice and informal placement. **Amenities:** Redgrave Theatre at Farnham and Yvonne Arnaud Theatre at Guildford. **Sporting facilities:** Games hall on site; sports centres at Farnham, Guildford and Alton.

Duration of first degree course(s) or equivalent: 3 years; **others:** 5 years (part-time BA fine art) **Total first degree students 1989/90: 639 Number of overseas students: 26 Number of mature students: 472 (over 21) Male/female ratio**

CAN'T FIND WHAT YOU'RE LOOKING FOR? USE THE INDEX!

1989/90: 4:7 Teaching staff: full-time: 31 part-time: 63 Total full-time students 1989/90: 827 Postgraduate students: 6 Tuition fees, first degrees, 1990/91: Home: £1,675; Overseas: £4,917.

What it's like

WSCAD is near the town centre of Farnham (50 mins by BR from London). Very good reputation, especially in Audio Visual Dept (Animation recently won many awards, including a BAFTA award). Three Dimensional Design Dept has a very good reputation and offers one of the few glass degree courses in the country. Most courses offer limitless expression within your work and a chance to experiment with media other than that on your chosen course. Due to the size (only 750+ students) there's a good community feeling but apathy is sometimes a problem. Farnham's a small, middle-class town in pleasant surroundings but limited entertainments for young people. SU provides bands, discos, parties, films, cabarets, sports clubs etc, with limited financial support. Accommodation can be a problem (hard to find and quite pricey). 3 college hostels, the Main Hostel (behind the college), West Street Hostel (about 2 mins away), Shortheath Hotel (1.5 miles away). International exchange programmes yearly, the number of foreign and mature students is increasing. Good complementary studies dept; very low failure and drop-out rate. Well stocked and expanding library. Students tend to be politically aware and sensitive to a huge variety of issues. Local transport is terrible, hence the need for bikes; Farnham well served by trains, coaches and major roads.

Pauper notes

Accommodation: Hostels/shared rooms for 1st years. Some single rooms in 3rd year. Student houses, bedsits and landlady type lodgings. **Drink:** SU bar (Grapes Club) – cheap. Large selection of spirits, beers, real ales and lagers. In student pubs change every year. **Eats:** Lots of restaurants around town – Indian, Chinese, Italian, Nepalese. College canteen open 3 times a day – expensive. **Ents:** SU bops, discos, bands, cabarets, films etc. **Sports:** Farnham has well equipped sports centre. No student reductions. Sports clubs at college. **Hardship funds:** SU welfare fund lends money to tide over. **Travel:** Regular exchange programme with European colleges. STA at Surrey Univ (Guildford). **Work:** Vacation work in restaurants, supermarkets and cleaning.

Alumni (Editors' pick)

Adrian Knowles (picture editor, Amateur Photographer), Terence Hudson (animator), Lindsey Hullen, Poni Amin (lecturer, Malaysia), Annabelle Jankel (cucumber animation – Max Headroom), Dave Banks (editorial photographer – Face, etc), Jankel and Morton (Max Headroom), Mark Bauer (Grand Prix, Annely).

WEST SUSSEX INSTITUTE

West Sussex Institute of Higher Education, The Dome, Upper Bognor Road, Bognor Regis, West Sussex PO21 1HR (0243 865581) Map A, F8

Student enquiries: Assistant Director (Academic Services)

Main study areas – as in What to Study section: (First degree): Art & design, dance, education, English, geography, history, music, religious studies and theology, welfare studies. Also: Performance arts, sports studies.

European Community: No first degree students take EC language as part of course; a few spend a term in another EC country. Formal exchange links with 11 EC universities/colleges: Belgium (1); France (1); Germany (1); Portugal (3); Spain (5). Approved Erasmus programme 1990/91.

CAN'T FIND WHAT YOU'RE LOOKING FOR? USE THE INDEX!

Application: PCAS.**Founded:** 1977, ex Bishop Otter College Chichester and Bognor Regis College. **Main awards:** BA, BEd, BSc. **Awarding body:** CNAA, Southampton University. **Site:** 2 sites (Chichester and Bognor Regis). **Access:** Both sites within walking distance of respective town centres. **Accommodation:** All first and fourth year students have opportunity of living in halls. Rent: 31% in accommodation where rent controlled by institute. **Library:** Library on each site. 125,000 volumes in total, 550 periodicals, 230 study places; restricted loan collections. **Specialist collections:** Gerard Young local history collection, art collection. **Welfare:** Doctor, psychiatrist, chaplain, professional welfare officer. **Hardship funds:** Co-ordinator of Student Services can give short term loans for students in temporary need. **Careers:** Information, advice and placement. **Amenities:** SU with many societies, travel and insurance bureaux. Chaplaincy, art collection. **Sporting facilities:** Sports hall and pitches.

Duration of first degree course(s) or equivalent: 3 years; 4 years BEd **Total first degree students 1989/90:** 1,480; **BEd students:** 613 **Number of overseas students:** 84 **Number of mature students:** not known **Male/female ratio 1989/90:** 1:4 **Teaching staff: full-time:** 92 **part-time:** 23 **Total full-time students 1989/90:** 1,636 **Postgraduate students:** 36 **Tuition fees, first degrees, 1990/91:** Home: £1,675 (£630 approx if self-financing); Overseas: £4,600.

What it's like
It's made up of two colleges, The Bognor Regis College and the Bishop Otter College in Chichester. All first years and some final year students live in halls of residence, others find accommodation in town. Very friendly atmosphere for study and a good social life. Selection of BA and BEd degrees. Many overseas students.

Ideally placed for the south coast countryside, but parking is a problem. Many clubs and societies provided by SU for a wide range of sporting and cultural activities. A small, friendly college which offers a good alternative to the larger establishments around the country.

Pauper notes
Accommodation: Hall accommodation all 1st and some final years (often in shared rooms). **Drink:** SU bar on each site for cheap drinks, nice pubs in both Chichester and Bognor although expensive. **Eats:** Food at college is not the highest quality. Several good eating places in town – especially Chichester. **Ents:** Ents at colleges with regular bands performing. Chichester town lacks alternative entertainments and Bognor has a couple of night clubs. **Sports:** Sports at college very good, both towns have leisure centre. Chichester has access to swimming pool. **Hardship funds:** Little provision. **Travel:** Little. Hitching difficult. **Work:** Some bar work easily available, summer work on nurseries also possible.

WESTMINSTER COLLEGE
Westminster College, Oxford OX2 9AT (0865 247644) Map: A, E7

Student enquiries: The Registrar

Main study areas – as in What to Study section: *(First degree):* Education, religious study and theology.

European Community: 10% first degree students take EC language as part of course but none spend 6 months in another EC country. Approved Erasmus programme 1990/91.

Application: PCAS. **Structural features:** Academic association with Oxford University. **Special features:** Visiting professors from USA. **Largest fields of study:** Education (primary school teachers). **Founded:** 1851. **Main award:** BA, BEd. **Awarding body:** CNAA. **Site:** Single site with 100 acres overlooking Oxford.

CAN'T FIND WHAT YOU'RE LOOKING FOR? USE THE INDEX!

Access: Just off Oxford ring road; Oxford rail station. **Accommodation:** 420 places on site: approx cost £49 per week (room + 12 meals). Plenty private accommodation in neighbourhood (accommodation officer helps). Rent: 50% in accommodation where rent controlled by college. **Library:** 60,000 volumes, 450 periodicals, 100 study places. **Specialist collections:** Archives of Methodist education. **Other learning facilities:** TV studio, drama area, primary classrooms, information technology facilities. **Careers:** Information, advice and placement service. **Employment:** Mainly teaching, social services, pastoral work. **Welfare:** Nurse and sick bay. **Special facilities:** Playgroup one afternoon/week. **Hardship funds:** Samaritan fund available.

Duration of first degree course(s) or equivalent: 3 years (standard) 4 years (other). **Total first degree students 1989-90:** 680 **Total number of BEd students:** 600 **Mature students:** 20 **Male/female ratio 1989-90:** 7:3 **Teaching staff: full-time:** 45; **part-time:** 10 **Total full-time students 1989/90:** 700 **Postgraduate students:** 120 **Tuition fees, first degrees, 1990/91:** Home: £1,675 Overseas: £4,150.

WIMBLEDON SCHOOL OF ART

Wimbledon School of Art, Merton Hall Road, London SW19 3QA (081-540 0231) Map D, B4

Student enquiries: Registrar

Main study areas – as in What to Study section: *(First degree):* Art & design.

European Community: No students learn an EC language or spend time in another EC country.

Application: ADAR. **Academic features:** 3 year BA courses in fine art and theatre. All include mandatory courses in history of art and complementary studies. Normally students must have completed foundation course. **Special features:** Programme of visiting lectures by professional artists and designers. **Largest fields of study:** Theatre. **Founded:** 1890. **Main awards:** BA. **Awarding body:** CNAA. **Site:** Main site plus annexe for foundation course. **Access:** Wimbledon station or bus for main site; South Wimbledon or Merton Park stations + 77a bus for annexe. **Accommodation:** None provided by college. Approx cost locally: £35–£45 pw. Rent: no student in accommodation where rent is under control of the school. **Library:** 26,000 books, 100 periodicals, 57 study places; slide collection, video tapes. **Welfare:** Trained student counsellor, accommodation assistant and information held on all other services. **Careers:** Departmental advice service. **Amenities:** SU with common rooms, shop, etc; workshop theatre.

Duration of first degree course(s) or equivalent: 3 years **Total first degree students 1989/90:** 291 **Number of overseas students:** 33 **Number of mature students:** 25 **Male/female ratio 1989/90:** 2:3 **Teaching staff: full-time:** 27 **part-time:** 26 **Total full-time students 1989/90:** 459 **Postgraduate students:** 41 **Tuition fees, first degrees, 1990/91:** Home: £1,675 (£651 if self-financing); Overseas: £4,912; £65 registration and conferment fee added to all fees.

What it's like

Situated in quiet, leafy suburbia, 5 minutes walk from Wimbledon Chase station; 15/20 minutes from Wimbledon or South Wimbledon. Far enough out of London for a small town feeling yet close enough for galleries etc or going out at night (10 minutes to Waterloo).

Foundation course in the annexe in Palmerston Road Wimbledon; some facilities are shared. The staff on all courses are very experienced and helpful, some are well known and respected in the art world. One of the largest regular part time staffs in the country and occasional visiting artists and lecturers with fresh views and a great

CAN'T FIND WHAT YOU'RE LOOKING FOR? USE THE INDEX!

deal of energy. Facilities generally excellent; sculpture dept is well equipped to do large scale works in stone, steel, wood or plaster and a life room of its own. The painting dept has large studio spaces, a well equipped film and video room, a photography dept with full time technical staff and part time specialist tutors. Facilities open to other depts. Preparation and woodwork rooms for making stretchers, stretching canvas, grinding paint etc, a painting seminar room bookable in advance for large scale works, exhibitions, discussions and a permanent life room with usually three models. Print dept has two large areas which together can cater for all major fine art printing methods – and these facilities can be used freely by BA painting students. Theatre dept also very well equipped; own theatre, bang up to date facilities for lighting and sound. Individual studio spaces for students, a model making workshop, large props workshop and in theatre wardrobe, in addition to usual facilities, there are a number of industrial sewing machines and separate areas for pattern cutting, fitting etc. Palmerston Road site is a large building equipped to give students a grounding in almost all aspects of painting, sculpture and design.

Well stocked library with friendly and efficient staff, comprehensive slide library, video collection with viewing facilities available to any student on request, 2 complementary studies seminar rooms, lecture theatre/projection room space in the foyer for exhibitions and a well stocked school shop with good discounts. Materials are not free but many of them are covered by a levy which is paid once a year.

Canteen not bad; a bit plain and uncomfortable. Student common room small and a bit grubby, however the college is undertaking a large building project with SU which involves getting an architect to redesign these 2 areas to make them more inviting. Common room contains a pool table, darts board and a video game but no tea or food machines and no bar. SU social evening on Thursdays proved so popular it may be run on other evenings too. Social life at Wimbledon very much up to the students. Pub down the road packed with students. 2 or 3 parties a term, organised by SU in the theatre, often with bands, touring theatre and ballet companies perform there at the start of tours because of work done for them by the design and wardrobe depts, these evenings tend to be free. Only other entertainment is film and video club which tries to put on a film every week. Essentially a place for working, however atmosphere is very friendly; large number of private parties which all students are usually invited to.

Almost no student housing provided, but housing officer is useful for finding houses and generally people have no problem getting somewhere reasonable. But look as soon as you get the housing list and if you're using a housing agency find out just what you'll get for your money.

Pauper notes
Accommodation: 2 college properties. **Drink:** Leather Bottle and Prince of Wales student pubs. **Eats:** Vegetarian cafe; Greek, Italian, Chinese, Indian and MacDonalds. **Ents:** Theatre, cinema and central London 10 min; SU film soc, and parties. **Sports:** YMCA. **Shops:** School shop for materials. **Work:** Plenty of restaurants and bar work in Wimbledon in the summer if you can get it.

Alumni (Editors' pick)
Louise Belson (freelance designer with RSC), Rolf Langenfass (designer, Vienna Opera), Iona McLeish (freelance designer, Pal Joey), John Pascoe, James Acheson (Oscar winner 1988), Raymond Briggs, Raymona Brooks.

CAN'T FIND WHAT YOU'RE LOOKING FOR? USE THE INDEX!

WINCHESTER SCHOOL OF ART

Winchester School of Art, Park Avenue, Winchester SO23 8DL (0962 842500) Map A, E8

Student enquiries: Admissions Officer

Main study areas – as in What to Study section: *(First degree):* Art & design, fine arts.

European Community: All first degree students take EC language and go on exchanges as part of course; all exchanges are of 3 months' duration and almost all are to EC. Formal exchange links with 7 EC universities/colleges: France (4); Netherlands (1); Spain (2). Approved Erasmus programme 1990/91.

Application: ADAR. **Special features:** Teaching staff are practising painters, sculptors, designers. **Academic features:** Normally entrants must have completed foundation course or appropriate BTEC course; change of course possible during first year between fine art and textiles. **Founded:** 1870 to provide training for local Winchester craftsmen. **Main awards:** BA. **Awarding body:** CNAA. **Site:** Winchester town centre. **Accommodation:** 56 hostel places. Approx cost: from £30.00 pw. Rent: 10% in accommodation where rent controlled by college. **Library:** 13,000 volumes, 100 periodicals, 35 study places; slide collection, BBC micro-computer. **Careers:** Information service by library/academic staff. **Amenities:** Second-hand bookshops nearby; excellent learning facilities including shed for spray painting; SU; recreation centre and park adjacent to college.

Duration of first degree course(s) or equivalent: 3 years **Total first degree students 1989/90:** 260 **Number of overseas students:** 5 **Number of mature students:** 25 approx **Male/female ratio 1989/90:** 1:2 **Teaching staff: full-time:** 25 **part-time:** 100 **Total full-time students 1989/90:** 380 **Postgraduate students:** 20 **Tuition fees, first degrees, 1990/91: Home:** £1,675; **Overseas:** £5,250.

What it's like

Small but expanding college in beautiful surroundings on the banks of the river Itchen, very close to town centre. A 60's style building with 80's additions. Car parking is limited to those who live out of Winchester. Accommodation is expensive, a few student houses remaining. Roughly equal numbers of students in flats, houses, halls and lodging houses. SU provides washing facilities; most places are self-catering.

The main buildings house BA and postgraduate courses. Many part-time tutors have good links with London studios and are working artists. Good work placements for textile students, and lots of opportunities to study in European colleges on an exchange basis. All BA students travel to foreign lands ie Paris, Barcelona, Florence, Milan, Russia – fine art also have access to a cottage in Cornwall for drawing excursions during the summer term.

SU provides regular parties and occasional bands, cheap beer and pool room! There are lots of pubs in Winchester, some famous, others infamous. Live music regularly at the Railway Inn. Easy access to Southampton clubs etc. SU has one sabbatical officer and a committee of students who are always open to suggestions and voluntary help.

Remember – Winchester School of Art is relatively small and everyone knows everything on the grapevine!

Pauper notes

Accommodation: Good when you can find it! Few student houses, only 2 hostels, mostly rented accommodation, very expensive. **Drink:** City full of pubs, many of distinctive individual character and good food, out of town especially, good country pubs. Local brew, Marstons. SU Allied Breweries. Good places – The Willow Tree, The Bush, The Mash-Tun, Prince of Wales, Railway Inn, Vine, Eclipse, etc. **Eats:**

CAN'T FIND WHAT YOU'RE LOOKING FOR? USE THE INDEX!

Refectory, pub grub, Pizza Express, Muswells, New York Pizza, various Chinese and Indian restaurants and take-aways, 2 chip shops, Blue Dolphin and Olivers; cheap health food from the Grainstore (Parchment Street – close to college). **Ents:** SU only alternative night-out in Winchester, plus cinema, 3 theatres (one of which shows films regularly), Tower Arts Centre. 1 nightclub – tries to cater for students, Jesters. Many sports clubs and societies. SU tries to cater to all these, speciality bands. 3 theatres, one of which shows films regularly. Tower Arts Centre. Southampton bigger and better. **Sports:** College next to recreation centre, recently greatly expanded. Large new leisure pool. Competitive/fun football team. Group and individual sport available, cheapest on day-user ticket or with SU. **Hardship funds:** None as yet. **Travel:** Courses comprise many compulsory European study visits; exchanges with New York, Barcelona, Paris, Moscow, Holland, Germany, Italy etc. One hour from Waterloo. **Work:** Lots of jobs going especially in pubs, also life modelling pays well, cleaning, shops.

Alumni (Editors' pick)
Brian Eno.

WOLVERHAMPTON POLY

Wolverhampton Polytechnic, Wulfruna Street, Wolverhampton WV1 1SB (0902 321000) Map A, D6

Student enquiries: Academic Registrar

Main study areas – as in What to Study section: *(First degree):* Agriculture, American studies, art & design, biochemistry, biology, biotechnology, business studies, chemistry, civil engineering, communication studies, computing, drama, economics, education, English, environmental science, European studies, fine arts, geography, history, hotel and catering management, information technology, law, mathematical studies, mechanical and production engineering, microbiology, modern languages, nursing studies, philosophy, physics, politics and government, psychology, sociology. *Also:* Building, photography, physiotherapy, surveying.

European Community: Target of 5% first degree students take EC language as part of course and 5% spend 6 months or more in another EC country. Formal exchange links with over 30 EC universities/colleges: France (9); Germany (10); Greece (3); Italy (1); Netherlands (3); Spain (6). Exchanges open to students on most courses. Approved Erasmus programme 1990/91. Member of Text Consortium (for student exchange and transfer in Europe); student mobility encouraged. Languages available to study as part of any course.

Application: PCAS, except art and design (ADAR). **Academic features:** Credit Accumulation and Transfer Scheme, and BA/BSc combined studies enable students to negotiate individually-tailored programmes of study; virtually all courses are modular (leading to CertHE, DipHE and BA/BSc). Work placements encouraged. Strong emphasis on continuing education and the development of international links. **Largest fields of study:** Business and social science. **Founded:** 1969, ex former Colleges of Technology and Art, merged subsequently with 4 teacher training institutions. **Main awards:** BA, BEd, BSc, BEng. **Awarding body:** CNAA. **Site:** Main Wolverhampton site plus 3 other sites. **Access:** Public transport, special arrangements made when necessary, daily coaches between sites. **Accommodation:** 1,350 hostel places, priority to first years. Approx cost: £45 pw (part board), £30 pw (self-catering). Rent: 8% in accommodation where rent controlled by polytechnic. **Library:** Main library and 4 branch libraries; over 350,000 books and 3,000 journals in total; over 1,200 study places, computerised databases. **Specialist collections:** Regional history of West Midlands, company and legal reports, European Documentation Centre Collection. **Other learning**

CAN'T FIND WHAT YOU'RE LOOKING FOR? USE THE INDEX!

resources: Computer centre; resource based learning provision. **Welfare:** Advice on all sites, networked with other agencies and health consultancy service; access to dentist, FPA, psychiatrist, professional welfare officer, overseas student counsellor, chaplains, industrial relations officer; financial adviser, academic counselling based on Higher Education Shop which also advises applicants. **Careers:** Information and advice service. **Amenities:** SU premises on each site (coffee bar, TV rooms, sports facilities (including swimming pool at Walsall), bank, stationery and travel, shops, bars); Wolverhampton sports stadium (Olympic standard); art gallery, museums, cinema at Dudley and Wolverhampton, theatre and concert hall in Wolverhampton, arboretum at Walsall.

Duration of first degree course(s) or equivalent: 3 years; **others:** 4 years **Total first degree students 1989/90:** 6,448 (inclusive of p-t) **BEd students:** 1,079 **Number of overseas students:** 117 **Male/female ratio 1989/90:** 1:1 **Teaching staff: full-time:** 450 **part-time:** 10 **Total full-time students 1989/89:** 6,809 **Postgraduate students:** 476 **Tuition fees, first degrees, 1990/91:** Home: £1,675 (+ registration fee £65 CNAA); Overseas: £4,395.

What it's like

It's now on 5 sites, main one in centre of Wolverhampton; Compton Park 1.5 miles away; Dudley site 7 miles away; Walsall site 9 miles away; smallest, newest site at Telford, 15 miles away. Travel between sites should be provided by poly – not always reliable. Accommodation a problem; not enough to go around; much substandard private sector accommodation.

Largest intake from local area. Social life centred around SU – town is lacking in certain facilities. SU very cheap. Wide range of discos and bands every week cater for all tastes. Many clubs and societies: sporting, political, cultural. Sports clubs always fare reasonably well; political and cultural societies fairly active.

SU advice unit open every weekday – free, confidential advice on all matters. Newspaper called 'Sheep's Clothing' published fortnightly.

Strong in languages, law, business, computing. Local work placements for sandwich courses. Staff/student liaison generally good; reps on all poly committees.

Pauper notes

Accommodation: Not all freshers get into halls. Lots of private housing of varying price and quality. Poly has block of old council flats. Some cheap houses but often damp and in poor condition. **Drink:** SU prices very low: lager 90p. Excellent bar facilities on all sites. Long opening hours. Some local pubs OK. SU deals with Scottish and Newcastle. **Eats:** Poly catering sub-standard. SU does snacks on couple of sites. Wealth of OK cheap restaurants in vicinity. **Ents:** Varied, cheap and good value. Comedy, live bands, discos, promotions, free nights. No decent venues nearby. **Sports:** Facilities OK but not special. Now have to pay. Sports halls and playing fields on various sites. Swimming pool at Walsall. **Hardship funds:** At discretion of VP Internal Affairs; must be genuine. **Travel:** SU has travel shop catering for most needs. Not bad for hitching – M6 nearby. **Work:** Part-time bar work in SU and town. Pay isn't good. Local unemployment high.

WORCESTER COLLEGE

Worcester College of HE, Henwick Grove, Worcester WR2 6AJ (0905 748080) (Fax: 0905 748162) Map A, D7

Student enquiries: Academic Registrar

Main study areas – as in What to Study section: *(First degree):* Art and design, biology, computing, drama, economics, education, English, environmental science, geography, history, mathematical studies, music, psychology, sociology. *Also:* Home economics, physical education, urban studies.

CAN'T FIND WHAT YOU'RE LOOKING FOR? USE THE INDEX!

European Community: No students learn an EC language or spend 6 months or more in another EC country, but some exchange visits.

Application: PCAS. **Special features:** Primary Teaching Centre. Opportunity for 2nd year students to spend term in USA. Sponsorship/bursary scheme for BA/BSc students. **Academic features:** BA English studies, geographical studies, historical studies, social sciences; BSc biological sciences, environmental sciences. **Founded:** 1946. **Main awards:** BA, BSc, BEd. **Awarding body:** CNAA. **Site:** 55 acre campus 2 miles from Worcester town centre. **Access:** Bus service from Worcester. **Accommodation:** 580 places in mixed and single sex halls of residence. Approx cost: £45 pw. New self-catering hall for 200 students. **Library:** 100,000 volumes, 500 periodicals, 280 study places. **Other learning resources:** Media Services Primary Centre. **Welfare:** Medical and health centre (doctor, FPA), chaplain, counselling service, advisory tutor system. **Careers:** Information and advice service. **Amenities:** SU bar, shops, newspaper, dance studios, drama studio, computer centres. **Sporting facilities:** Playing fields, tennis courts, gymnasia, floodlit hard playing area on site. **Employment:** Teaching, commerce, industry, public service, administration, buying/marketing, management services, information and library work, personnel and welfare.

Duration of first degree course(s) or equivalent: 3 years; 4 years (BEd) **Total first degree students 1989/90:** 1,300; **BEd students:** 600 **Number of mature students:** 200 **Male/female ratio 1989/90:** 2:3 **Teaching staff: full-time:** 100 **part-time:** 30 **Total full-time students 1989/90:** 1,250 **Postgraduate students:** 250 **Tuition fees, first degrees, 1990/91:** Home: £1,675; Overseas: £4,563 plus in both cases £65 registration fee in first year

What it's like

It's a single site college in mature grounds of shrubs and playing fields. Short walk from banks of Severn and city centre. Most first years and many finalists live on campus in halls – some modern flats, generally relaxed attitude to friends staying overnight. On-site facilities include shops – cheap laundry, TV and video rooms and medical centre. Typical but picturesque smallish provincial city; many shops, nightclubs, theatre, cinema, restaurants and a multitude of pubs to suit all tastes.

BEd courses recognised as some of the best in the country, female dominated. For further details of course apply to SU for Alternative Prospectus. Academic study travel opportunities exist mainly to Europe but as far afield as The Shetlands and Tunisia. Exchange programmes to Hungary, Finland and the USA.

Good staff-student relationships – students seen as individuals not just one of the crowd. Tutors only too willing to help if you need it. Trained counsellors can help with any problems you may have – sympathetically and confidentially – active and approachable SU will also help in any way they can.

SU bar – 'The Dive' – is the 'Mecca' of our universe. SU organises many ents – great Freshers and Rag Week. Wide range of clubs and societies. Students come from all over the country – all types of background – slight Northern bias – no typical student here.

On the whole a very relaxed and friendly place. Most students are happy socially and academically. Who knows, you may even get a good degree out of it – a great many do.

As for breaking the ice…What ice?
Geoff Stoves, Derrin Kent, Mick Hornby

Pauper notes

Accommodation: 10 meal licence in rooms in halls of residence. Some shared rooms. Self-catering flats only available to final year students. **Drink:** SU bar cheapest place in a city full of pubs. World's strongest beer brewed at 'The Brewery Tap'. 'Little Pub Company' pubs surround us. **Eats:** Canteen and snack bar on campus. Lots of various restaurants with veggie options. 'Desperate Dan Cow-Pies' sold at 'The Little Sauce Factory'. **Ents:** Theatre, cinema, nightclubs, live bands in

CAN'T FIND WHAT YOU'RE LOOKING FOR? USE THE INDEX!

pubs; but the best ents are always right here at college. **Sports:** County cricket ground, racecourse (horses), rowing and canoe clubs on river, banger racing circuit, rugby and football clubs, leisure centres. **Hardship funds:** SU helps with financial difficulties. **Travel:** Good train and bus services all over the country. **Work:** Fair amount of local jobs available, particularly in pubs.

Alumni (Editors' pick)
Derrin Kent.

WRITTLE

Writtle College, Chelmsford, Essex CM1 3RR (0245 420705)
Map: A, F7

Student enquiries: Student Registration Officer

Main study areas – as in What to Study section: *(First degree):* Agriculture horticulture and forestry, business studies.

European Community: No students take EC languages as part of course, 2% spend 6 months of more in another EC country. Formal exchange links with 6 EC colleges. Some BSc (horticulture) do work experience in EC.

Application: PCAS. **Academic features:** Modular courses; flexible learning methods. **Structural features:** Partners with Hatfield Poly (BSc Hort); Anglia (BSc Hons Rural Res Dev); Essex University (BSc Ag). **Founded:** 1893. **Main award:** BSc. **Awarding body:** CNAA. **Site:** Single campus. **Access:** Just off A414 at Writtle. Chelmsford railway station 2 miles. **Accommodation:** On-site for 200; approx cost: £50/week single room, all meals. 300 places in cottage/flat lodgings; approx cost £30/week, no meals. **Rent:** 45% in accommodation where rent controlled by college. **Library:** 40,000 volumes, 300 periodicals, 50 study places. **Specialist collections:** Agriculture, horticulture and rural resources. **Other learning facilities:** 500-acre estate including 3 farms; separate fruit farm, commercial glass, equestrian centre, amenity centre, farm shop, engineering workshops, labs. **Careers:** Information, advice and placement service. **Employment:** Management in horticulture, leisure, agriculture etc. **Welfare:** Health centre, counselling. **Amenities:** Bar and recreation centre. New bar/disco/social centre soon. **Sports:** Sports hall, squash, tennis, fitness centre on site.

Duration of first degree course(s) or equivalent: 4 years 3 years (rural resources). **Total first degree students 1989/90:** 120 **Number of overseas students:** 10 **Number of mature students:** 20 **Male/female ratio 1989/90:** 3:1 **Teaching staff: full-time:** 12 **Part-time:** 4 **Total full-time students 1989/90:** 600 **Postgraduate students:** 4 **Tuition fees, first degrees, 1990/91:** Home: £1,675; Overseas: £4,600.

WYE COLLEGE

Wye College, University of London, Ashford, Kent TN25 5AH (0233 812401) Map A, G8

Student enquiries: The Registrar

Main study areas – as in What to Study section: *(First degree):* Agriculture, horticulture and forestry, biotechnology, business studies, environmental science, horticulture and forestry, botany, economics, environmental studies, zoology. *Also:* Agricultural business management, agricultural economics, soils and plant nutrition.

CAN'T FIND WHAT YOU'RE LOOKING FOR? USE THE INDEX!

European Community: No students learn an EC language or spend 6 months or more in another EC country as part of their course. Formal exchange links with Denmark (Copenhagen), France (Montpellier, Toulouse) and Spain (Barcelona) as well as ad hoc links with a number of others/. Approved Erasmus programme 1990/91.

Application: UCCA. **Structural features:** Part of London University. **Academic features:** Courses in agriculture and the environment, countryside management, business studies, environmental science, plant biotechnology. **Special features:** Research into the impact of human activity in the environment eg recycling organic waste, channel tunnel; and into aspects of food production in developed and developing countries. **Largest fields of study:** Agriculture, business management, rural environment studies and agricultural economics. **Founded:** 1945, ex South Eastern Agricultural College and the Swanley Horticultural College for Women. 1900 admitted to London University as a constitutional 'School'. **Main awards:** BSc. **Awarding body:** London University. **Site:** Combination of medieval and modern buildings in Wye town centre. **Access:** Wye station; A20 from London, A28 from Ashford. **Accommodation:** 280 places in mixed and segregated halls of residence (all new undergraduates expected to live in hall for their first year). Approx cost: £1,350 pa (breakfast and evening meal 5 days pw). Rent: 65% in accommodation where rent controlled by college. **Library:** 39,000 books, 600 periodical titles, 120 study places. **Specialist collections:** Library of the Centre for European Agricultural Studies, including European Documentation Centre within main library. **Other learning resources:** Labs, glasshouses, field laboratories; 300 hectares of arable and grassland, 30 hectares horticultural crops and orchards. **Welfare:** College medical officer, resident nursing sister, counselling service, college chaplain: Directors of Study, Wardens (halls of residence and hostels). **Hardship funds:** Principal's Fund is available should hardship arise once the course has started. **Special categories:** Limited accommodation for married students; 3 undergraduate rooms with wheelchair access. **Careers:** Information and advice service through both London University Careers Advisory Service and Wye College. **Amenities:** SU building with bar, music room, photographic facilities and many active clubs and societies; cultural facilities of Canterbury 11 miles away; situated in an area of outstanding natural beauty. **Sporting facilities:** Tennis courts, playing fields, college beagle pack, swimming pool, squash courts. **Employment:** Agricultural and horticultural industries; civil service; local government; scientific research establishments; conservation and resource management.

Duration of first degree course(s) or equivalent: 3 years **Total first degree students 1989/90:** 389 **Number of overseas students:** 8 **Number of mature students:** 42 **Male/female ratio 1989/90:** 1:1 **Teaching staff: full-time:** 60 **part-time:** 6 **Total full-time students 1989/90:** 632 **Postgraduate students:** 243 **Tuition fees, first degrees, 1990/91:** Home: £1,675; Overseas: £5,532 (classroom-based), £6,389 (lab-based).

What it's like

It's unique being situated in rural Kent, and a college of London University. Wye is small, jolly friendly and full of character. Typically it attracts 600 students with similar attitudes, yet there are varied backgrounds and everyone gets along harmoniously. Students derive from a wide geographical area but a fair number tend to come from the home counties.

Student population comprises two-thirds undergrads and one-third postgrads. Half of postgrads from overseas. Relationship between students and staff is superb, tutors often maintaining links over dinner.

College's appearance is very traditional with quadrangles, cloisters and gardens. Some parts date back to 1447. It has been described as the agricultural equivalent of a mini Oxford college. All buildings are close in proximity with never far to walk. College farm and research facilities are used extensively. Wye is set in idyllic surroundings on the Downs with magnificent views. Established village shops serve

CAN'T FIND WHAT YOU'RE LOOKING FOR? USE THE INDEX!

the college well – there's even a small take-away. Although separated from main university by some 60 miles, there are links, mainly on sports field. Nearest towns Ashford (4-5 miles) and Canterbury (12 miles); many students have own cars but bus and train services are good.

All 1st year students accommodated in either college or Withersdane building (5 minutes up the road). Every room is served with a cleaner and the residence is safe day and night with 24-hour porters.

Canteen at lunchtime and evening. Pubs serve reasonably priced good food.

Courses based on unit system, so flexibility in choosing courses and exams are taken at the end of every year. Some coursework is assessed. Failure rates very low.

SU is reasonably active but not politically. It sponsors about 50 clubs and societies. Many tastes catered for. Easy to create your own.

Wye courses well reputed internationally and may lead to a wide range of careers whether it be on the land, in industry or in government office. Most student aspirations: to own land, to enjoy life. Essential accessories: dinner jacket/ballgown, Barbour and wellies.
Rupert Steiner

Pauper notes

Accommodation: Excellent standard, reasonable price. Meals included in price of college accommodation. Plenty of decent houses locally for 2nd and 3rd years. Limited married quarters. **Drink:** Cheap drinks in SU, fantastic pubs all around – Ushers, Fremlins, Flowers, Marstons, Ruddles etc. **Eats:** Canteen okay. Two formal meals/week (gowns & smart dress). Best meal breakfast. **Ents:** Most ents arranged by Union society. Wide range of tastes. Cinema and theatre in Canterbury. **Sports:** Good sport on campus incl swimming pool, squash and tennis court, gym. Riding and shooting popular. One of 4 universities to have a beagle pack. **Hardship funds:** In *exceptional* cases college is known to be considerate. **Travel:** Close to south coast – trips to seaside and day trips/duty free runs to France and Europe. **Work:** Local farms and odd jobs; fruit picking; pub jobs.

Alumni (Editors' pick)

Sir Peter Mills, MP; Professor Chris Baines; Professor Bill Hill FRS.

YORK UNIVERSITY

University of York, Heslington, York YO1 5DD (0904 430000)
Map A, E5

Student enquiries: Undergraduate Admissions Office (0904 433535)

Main study areas – as in What to Study section: *(First degree):* Archaeology, biochemistry, biology, chemistry, computing, economics, education, electrical and electronic engineering, English, environmental science, history, linguistics, mathematical studies, modern languages, music, pharmacology, philosophy, physics, physiology, politics and government, psychology, sociology. *Also:* Chinese, Hindi, Swahili.

European Community: 5% first degree students take EC language as part of course and 8% spend 6 months or more in another EC country. Formal exchange links with 9 EC universities/colleges: France (3); Germany (3); Italy (2); Spain (1). Most open to non-language specialists. Approved Erasmus programme 1990/91.

Application: UCCA. **Academic features:** BEng (sandwich) in electronic engineering; 3/4 year BEng physical electronics; BA linguistics and Chinese/Hindi/Swahili; 4 year BSc biology with 1 year in Germany; 4 year BSc (sandwich) in biology and biochemistry; 3 year BA in English/history of art (equal combination). **Special**

CAN'T FIND WHAT YOU'RE LOOKING FOR? USE THE INDEX!

features: College system. Recently established Institute for Applied Biology, Centre for Women's Studies. Resident quartet – the Sorrell Quartet. **Main awards:** BA, BEng, BSc, MEng. **Awarding body:** York University. **Site:** 86 hectare site about 2 miles from city centre. **Access:** Bus from York; signposted turnings off A64. **Accommodation:** Approx 3,000 places on or near campus. Seventh college recently opened. Approx cost: £680 pa (all meals extra). 75% in accommodation where rent controlled by university. **Library:** 440,000 volumes, 2,200 periodicals; 725 reading places (university library) + 390 (college libraries); multiple copies of course books; reserve collection. **Open learning facilities:** Audiovisual centre, computing service, language teaching centre. **Amenities:** Over 100 student societies; social functions, discos, community action projects; student newspaper, television and radio; 3 studios for pottery, printmaking and painting for use of all students; open air chess board and 'Boules' terrain; children's nursery; all colleges have rooms adapted for disabled students. **Sporting facilities:** 40 acres of playing fields on site; 400 metre 7-lane athletics track; boathouse on the River Ouse for rowing; York's 3-swimming pool complex half mile away. **Hardship funds:** Bursary scheme for self-financing students.

Duration of first degree course(s) or equivalent: 3 years; **others:** 4 years **Total first degree students 1989/90:** 3,354 **Number of overseas students:** 183 **Number of mature students:** 13% **Male/female ratio 1989/90:** 11:9 **Teaching staff: full-time:** 334 **part-time:** 16 **Total full-time students 1989/90:** 4,142 **Postgraduate students:** 788 (f-t) 496 (p-t) **Tuition fees, first degrees, 1990/91:** Home: £1,812 (£807 if self-financing); Overseas: £4,560 (eg politics), £6,050 (eg physics).

What it's like

York, the city, is beautiful, picturesque, historic etc but a bit small, and has not the facilities or business of other northern cities.

York University is also small. It's all on one site with students divided into 7 colleges (6 mixed, 1 graduate only) which can be a bit claustrophobic but makes it easy to make friends and means that help is never far away. Also there is something to do or someone to talk to almost all the time.

York is very much an academic university, with no main concert hall, relatively poor sports facilities, no SU building and a very 'boarding school' like atmosphere a lot of the time. However, there is loads to do and most people seem happy, comfortable and secure.

A nursery has opened on campus providing cheap child care for 2-5 year-olds. Entertainment facilities look to be improving with promises of a new concert hall and increased budget for student services a possibility.

The town is busy, full of tourists, but has a good atmosphere with little antagonism between students and locals. Pub scene is excellent, and if you want to get out you can get a train to anywhere from York.

A good place to do a degree, with a good reputation and nice atmosphere.
James Minton

Pauper notes

Accommodation: Campus still very cheap and available to all first years. Houses in town for second years £30 pw, but nice(!). **Drink:** Best place to drink in north of England. Pubs are brilliant. Clubs improving. John Smiths, Tetley, Bass and loads of guest foreign beers. **Eats:** Food on campus dreadful (with one or two exceptions). Loads of choice in town; often expensive and caters for tourists. **Ents:** Not much in town or on campus – not a large city, no major hall. **Sports:** University sports centre not the best. New centre opening in town (15 mins from campus) next year. Small swimming pool in town. **Hardship funds:** Union will help. University can also loan money. **Travel:** Travel shop on campus. Standard discounts offered. Sponsored hitch to Paris each year. **Work:** Loads of pub jobs in town. No jobs on campus outside vacations. **European Community:** There is a '92 Society' on campus which

CAN'T FIND WHAT YOU'RE LOOKING FOR? USE THE INDEX!

has links with Belgium and France and EC headquarters. Very active, well-organised society – student run.

Alumni (Editors' pick)

Tony Banks MP, Harriet Harman MP, Michael Brown MP, Harry Enfield, Victoria Lewis-Smith (broadcaster), Moray Welsh (cellist), Paul Roberts (pianist), Genista McIntosh (Director of National Theatre).

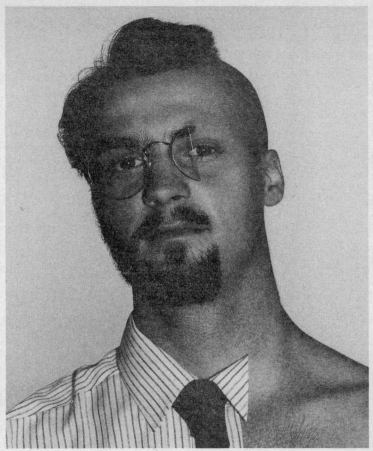

Don't forget, a Young Persons Railcard trims a third off.

If you are aged 16-23 it's worth remembering that a Young Persons Railcard cuts a third off most rail fares for a year. It's just the job for getting to interviews or for visiting friends. Pick up a leaflet for conditions of use at main BR Stations or Rail Appointed Travel Agents. It's a snip.

YOUNG PERSONS RAILCARD

Maps

This section has — you'll never believe this — *maps*. First there is a list of all the UKCPUs in the *Where to Study* section and their map references.

UKCPUs

Aberdeen University *Map A, D2*
Aberystwyth *Map A, C7*
ALRA *Map D, B3*
Anglia *Map A, F7*
Architectural Association *Map E, C2*
Aston University *Map A, E7*
Bangor *Map A, C6*
Bangor Normal College *Map A, C6*
Bath College *Map A, D8*
Bath University *Map A, D8*
Bedford College *Map A, F7*
Belfast University *Map A, B4*
Birkbeck College *Map E, C1*
Birmingham Conservatoire *Map A, E7*
Birmingham Poly *Map A, E7*
Birmingham University *Map A, E7*
Bolton Institute *Map A, D5*
Bournemouth Poly *Map A, E9*
Bradford & Ilkley *Map A, E5*
Bradford University *Map A, E5*
Bretton Hall *Map A, E5*
Brighton Poly *Map A, F8*
Bristol Old Vic *Map A, D8*
Bristol Poly *Map A, D8*
Bristol University *Map A, D8*
British Institute in Paris
British School of Osteopathy
  Map E, C3
Brunel University *Map A, F8*
Buckingham University *Map A, E7*
Buckinghamshire College *Map A, E8*
Buckland *Map A, E7*
Camberwell College of Arts
  Map D, C2
Camborne School of Mines
  Map A, B9
Cambridge University *Map A, F7*
  Christ's
  Churchill
  Clare
  Corpus Christi
  Downing
  Emmanuel
  Fitzwilliam
  Girton
  Gonville & Caius
  Jesus
  King's
  Lucy Cavendish
  Magdalene
  New Hall
  Newnham
  Pembroke
  Peterhouse
  Queens'
  Robinson
  St Catharine's

  St Edmund's
  St John's
  Selwyn
  Sidney Sussex
  Trinity
  Trinity Hall
  Wolfson
Cardiff *Map A, D8*
Cardiff Institute *Map A, D8*
Central St Martin's *Map E, C2*
Central School of Speech and Drama
  Map D, B1
Charing Cross and Westminster
  Map D, A2
Chelsea *Map E, B4*
Cheltenham & Gloucester College
  Map A, D7
Chester College *Map A, D6*
Christ Church College *Map A, G8*
Cirencester *Map A, D7*
City Poly *Map E, D2*
City University *Map E, D1*
Colchester Institute *Map A, F7*
Courtauld Institute *Map E, B2*
Coventry Poly *Map A, E7*
Cranfield *Map A, F7*
Cranwell *Map A, F6*
Crewe & Alsager *Map A, D6*
Dartington *Map A, C9*
Dartmouth *Map A, C9*
Derbyshire College *Map A, E6*
Duncan of Jordanstone *Map A, D2*
Dundee Institute *Map A, D2*
Dundee University *Map A, D2*
Durham University *Map A, E4*
Ealing College *Map D, A2*
East Anglia University *Map A, G6*
East London Poly *Map D, D1*
Edge Hill *Map A, D5*
Edinburgh College of Art *Map A, D3*
Edinburgh University *Map A, D3*
Essex University *Map A, F7*
European Business School *Map E, B1*
Exeter University *Map A, D9*
Falmouth School of Art *Map A, B9*
Glasgow College *Map A, C3*
Glasgow College of Building
  Map A, C3
Glasgow School of Art *Map A, C3*
Glasgow University *Map A, C3*
Goldsmiths' College *Map D, C3*
Guildhall School *Map E, D2*
Harper Adams *Map A, D6*
Hatfield Poly *Map A, F7*
Heriot-Watt University *Map A, D3*
Heythrop College *Map E, B2*
Holborn College *Map D, B2*

Homerton *Map A, F7*
Huddersfield Poly *Map A, E5*
Hull University *Map A, F5*
Humberside Poly *Map A, F5*
Imperial College *Map E, A3*
Institute of Archaeology *Map E, C1*
Institute of Education *Map E, C1*
Jews College *Map A, F8*
Keele University *Map A, D6*
Kent Institute *Map A, F8*
Kent University *Map A, G8*
King Alfred's College *Map A, E8*
King's College London *Map E, C2*
King's College School of Medicine
   Map D, C3
Kingston Poly *Map D, A4*
La Sainte Union *Map A, E8*
Laban Centre *Map D, C3*
Lampeter *Map A, C7*
Lancashire Poly *Map A, D5*
Lancaster University *Map A, D5*
Leeds Poly *Map A, E5*
Leeds University *Map A, E5*
Leicester Poly *Map A, E6*
Leicester University *Map A, E6*
Liverpool Institute *Map A, D6*
Liverpool Poly *Map A, D6*
Liverpool University *Map A, D6*
London Bible College *Map A, F8*
London Business School *Map E, B1*
London College of Dance *Map A, F7*
London College of Music *Map E, B2*
London College of Printing
   Map E, D4
London Contemporary Dance School
   Map E, C1
London Hospital *Map D, C2*
London International Film School
   Map E, C2
London University
Loughborough College of Art
   Map A, E6
Loughborough University *Map A, E6*
LSE *Map E, C2*
Luton College *Map A, F7*
Manadon *Map A, C9*
Manchester Business School
   Map A, D6
Manchester Poly *Map A, D6*
Manchester University *Map A, D6*
Middlesex Poly *Map A, F8*
Napier Poly *Map A, D3*
National Extension College
   Map A, F7
National Film School *Map A, E8*
National Hospitals College *Map E, C1*
Nene College *Map A, E7*
Newcastle Poly *Map A, E4*
Newcastle University *Map A, E4*
Norfolk Institute *Map A, G6*

North Cheshire College *Map A, D6*
North East Wales Institute
   Map A, D6
North London Poly *Map D, B1*
Northern School of Contemporary
   Dance *Map A, E5*
Nottingham Poly *Map A, E6*
Nottingham University *Map A, E6*
Oak Hill College *Map A, E8*
Open University
Oxford Poly *Map A, E7*
Oxford University *Map A, E7*
   Balliol
   Brasenose
   Christ Church
   Corpus Christi
   Exeter
   Hertford
   Jesus
   Keble
   Lady Margaret Hall
   Lincoln
   Magdalen
   Manchester
   Mansfield
   Merton
   New College
   Oriel
   Pembroke
   Queen's
   Regent's Park
   St Anne's
   St Catherine's
   St Edmund Hall
   St Hilda's
   St Hugh's
   St John's
   St Peter's
   Somerville
   Trinity
   University College
   Wadham
   Worcester
Paisley College *Map A, C3*
PCL *Map E, B2*
Portsmouth Poly *Map A, E8*
Queen Margaret College *Map A, D3*
Queen Mary & Westfield *Map D, C1*
Queen's College Glasgow *Map A, C3*
RADA *Map E, C2*
Rapid Results College *Map D, B4*
Ravensbourne College *Map D, D4*
Reading University *Map A, E8*
Ripon & York St John *Map A, E5*
Robert Gordon's Institute *Map A, D2*
Roehampton Institute *Map D, A3*
Rose Bruford College *Map D, D4*
Royal Academy of Music *Map E, B1*
Royal Academy Schools *Map E, B3*
Royal College of Art *Map E, A3*

Royal College of Music *Map E, A3*
Royal Free *Map D, B1*
Royal Holloway and Bedford
  Map A, F8
Royal Northern College of Music *Map
  A, D6*
Royal Scottish Academy *Map A, C3*
Royal Veterinary College
  Map D, B1
St Andrews University *Map A, D2*
St Bartholomew's *Map E, D2*
St George's *Map D, B4*
St Mark & St John *Map A, C9*
S Martin's College *Map A, D5*
St Mary's College *Map D, A3*
St Mary's Hospital *Map D, B1*
Salford University *Map A, D6*
Sandhurst *Map A, F8*
School of Pharmacy *Map E, C1*
Scottish Centre for PE *Map A, D3*
Scottish College of Textiles
  Map A, D3
Sheffield Poly *Map A, E6*
Sheffield University *Map A, E6*
Shrivenham *Map A, E8*
Silsoe College *Map A, F7*
Slade *Map E, C1*
SOAS *Map E, C1*
South Bank Poly *Map E, D3*
South West Poly *Map A, C9*
Southampton University *Map A, E8*
Spurgeon's College *Map D, C4*
SSEES *Map E, C1*
Staffs Poly *Map A, D6*
Stirling University *Map A, C2*
Strathclyde University *Map A, C3*

Sunderland Poly *Map A, E4*
Surrey University *Map A, E8*
Sussex University *Map A, F8*
Swansea *Map A, C8*
Teesside Poly *Map A, E4*
Thames Poly *Map D, D2*
Thames Valley College *Map A, F8*
Trinity & All Saints *Map A, E5*
Trinity College Carmarthen
  Map A, C7
Trinity College of Music *Map E, B2*
Ulster University *Map A, A4 & B4*
UMIST *Map A, D6*
United Medical Schools
  Map E, D3 & C4
University College London
  Map E, C1
Wales College of Medicine *Map A, D8*
Wales Poly *Map A, D7*
Wales University
Warwick University *Map A, E7*
Watford College *Map A, F8*
Welsh College of Music and Drama
  Map A, D8
West Glamorgan Institute *Map A, C8*
West London Institute *Map D, A3*
West Surrey College *Map A, E8*
West Sussex Institute *Map A, F8*
Westminster College *Map A, E7*
Wimbledon School of Art *Map D, B4*
Winchester School of Art *Map A, E8*
Wolverhampton Poly *Map A, D6*
Worcester College *Map A, D7*
Writtle *Map A, F7*
Wye College *Map A, G8*
York University *Map A, E5*

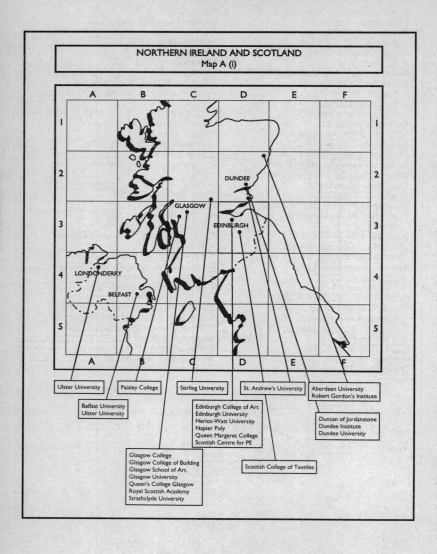

NORTHERN IRELAND AND SCOTLAND
Map A (i)

DUNDEE

GLASGOW

EDINBURGH

LONDONDERRY

BELFAST

Ulster University

Belfast University
Ulster University

Paisley College

Stirling University

St. Andrew's University

Aberdeen University
Robert Gordon's Institute

Edinburgh College of Art
Edinburgh University
Heriot-Watt University
Napier Poly
Queen Margaret College
Scottish Centre for PE

Duncan of Jordanstone
Dundee Institute
Dundee University

Glasgow College
Glasgow College of Building
Glasgow School of Art
Glasgow University
Queen's College Glasgow
Royal Scottish Academy
Strathclyde University

Scottish College of Textiles

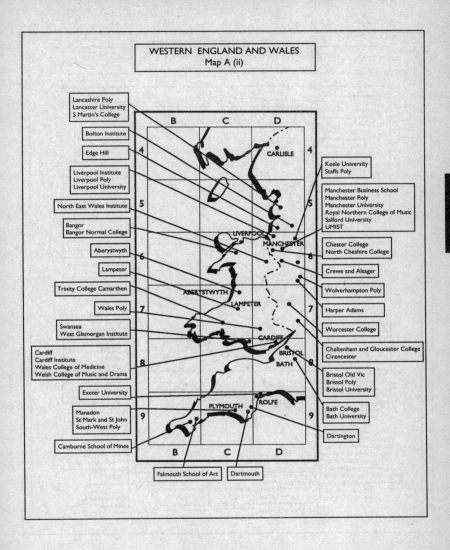

WESTERN ENGLAND AND WALES
Map A (ii)

Lancashire Poly
Lancaster University
S Martin's College

Bolton Institute

Edge Hill

Liverpool Institute
Liverpool Poly
Liverpool University

North East Wales Institute

Bangor
Bangor Normal College

Aberystwyth

Lampeter

Trinity College Camarthen

Wales Poly

Swansea
West Glamorgan Institute

Cardiff
Cardiff Institute
Wales College of Medicine
Welsh College of Music and Drama

Exeter University

Manadon
St Mark and St John
South-West Poly

Camborne School of Mines

Falmouth School of Art   Dartmouth

Keele University
Staffs Poly

Manchester Business School
Manchester Poly
Manchester University
Royal Northern College of Music
Salford University
UMIST

Chester College
North Cheshire College

Crewe and Alsager

Wolverhampton Poly

Harper Adams

Worcester College

Cheltenham and Gloucester College
Cirencester

Bristol Old Vic
Bristol Poly
Bristol University

Bath College
Bath University

Dartington

B   C   D

CARLISLE

LIVERPOOL
MANCHESTER

ABERYSTWYTH
LAMPETER

CARDIFF

BRISTOL
BATH

PLYMOUTH   ROLFE

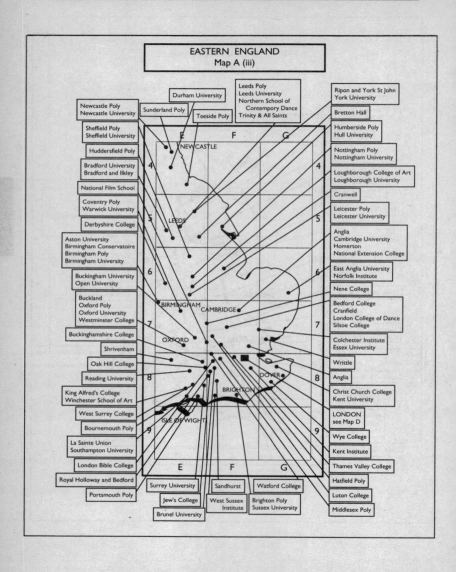

EASTERN ENGLAND
Map A (iii)

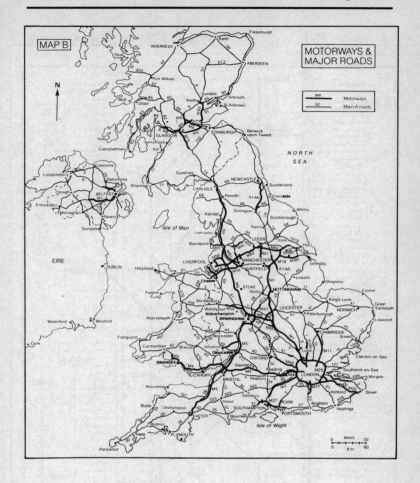

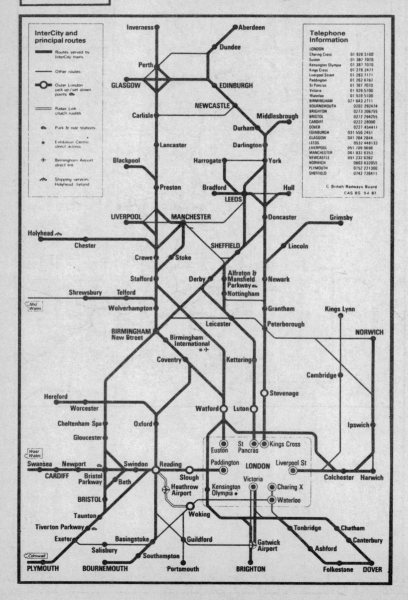

MAP C

Inter-City Services

InterCity and principal routes

- Routes served by InterCity trains
- Other routes
- Outer London pick up/set down points
- Radan Link coach routes
- Park & ride stations
- Exhibition Centre direct access
- Birmingham Airport direct link
- Shipping services Holyhead Ireland

Telephone Information

LONDON
Charing Cross	01 928 5100
Euston	01 387 7070
Kensington Olympia	01 387 7070
Kings Cross	01 278 2477
Liverpool Street	01 283 7171
Paddington	01 262 6767
St Pancras	01 387 7070
Victoria	01 928 5100
Waterloo	01 928 5100
BIRMINGHAM	021 643 2711
BOURNEMOUTH	0202 292474
BRIGHTON	0273 206755
BRISTOL	0272 294255
CARDIFF	0222 28000
DOVER	0227 454411
EDINBURGH	031 556 2451
GLASGOW	041 704 2844
LEEDS	0532 448133
LIVERPOOL	051 709 9696
MANCHESTER	061 832 8353
NEWCASTLE	091 232 6262
NORWICH	0603 632055
PLYMOUTH	0752 221300
SHEFFIELD	0742 726411

C British Railways Board

CAS 85 54 87

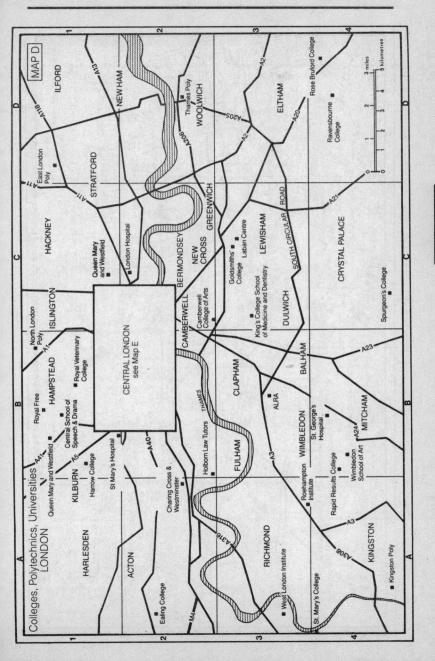

Colleges, Polytechnics, Universities
LONDON

MAP D

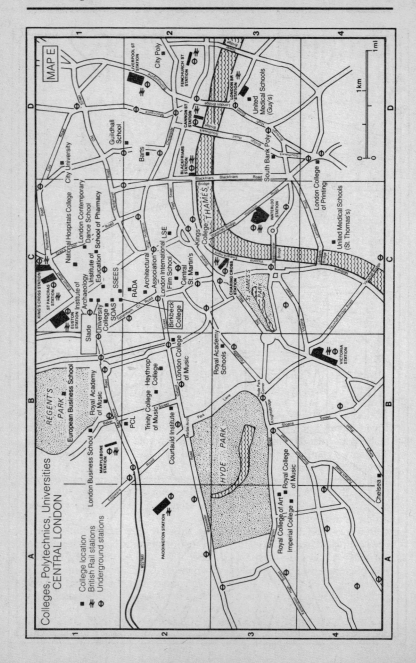

MAP E

Colleges, Polytechnics, Universities
CENTRAL LONDON

■ College location
╫ British Rail stations
Ⓤ Underground stations

Subject and Places Index

If you already know the subjects you are interested in studying and want to make a shortlist of prospectuses worth getting hold of – **START HERE**. This index spotlights the subjects offered by UKCPU's as all (or a major part) of a first degree course.

If you would like to know more about the subjects that interest you, you can **ALSO START HERE**. This index shows you if your subject is described in the **WHAT TO STUDY** section eg French refers you to the article on Modern Languages.

Beware. UKCPU's often hide the subjects they teach under fancy course titles or, more confusingly, create bureaucratic conglomerations of subjects with grandiose names eg School of .... Don't be put off. If you persevere you can usually find which UKCPU's teach your subject; remember, each UKCPU labels its own courses as it chooses and you will probably have to identify your subject under a variety of different names. Which makes it all the more important not to rely on secondary sources but to **GET HOLD OF THE PROSPECTUS** AND **FIND OUT FOR YOURSELF**.

A

Accountancy
Possible prospectuses: Aberdeen Univ, Aberystwyth, Anglia, Aston Univ, Bangor, Belfast Univ, Birmingham Poly, Birmingham Univ, Bournemouth Poly, Brighton Poly, Bristol Poly, Bristol Univ, Buckingham Univ, Cardiff, Cheltenham & Gloucester Coll, Cirencester, City Poly, City Univ, Coventry Poly, Derbyshire Coll, Dundee Inst, Dundee Univ, Ealing Coll, East Anglia Univ, East London Poly, Edinburgh Univ, Essex Univ, European Bus Sch, Exeter Univ, Glasgow Coll, Glasgow Univ, Hatfield Poly, Heriot-Watt Univ, Holborn College, Huddersfield Poly, Hull Univ, Humberside Poly, Kent Univ, Kingston Poly, Lancashire Poly, Lancaster Univ, Leeds Poly, Leeds Univ, Leicester Poly, Liverpool Poly, Liverpool Univ, LSE, Loughborough Univ, Luton Coll, Manchester Poly, Manchester Univ, Middlesex Poly, Napier Poly, Nene Coll, Newcastle Poly, Newcastle Univ, North London Poly, Nottingham Poly, Nottingham Univ, Oxford Poly, PCL, Portsmouth Poly, Reading Univ, Salford Univ, Sheffield Poly, Sheffield Univ, South Bank Poly, South West Poly, Southampton Univ, Stirling Univ, Strathclyde Univ, Sunderland Poly, Teesside Poly, Thames Poly, Thames Valley Coll, Ulster Univ, Wales Poly, Warwick Univ, West Glamorgan Inst. *See also: **Business studies**.*
Study area: Accountancy.

Acoustic engineering
Possible prospectuses: Cambridge Univ, Salford Univ, Southampton Univ.*See also: **Electrical engineering**.*
Study areas: Electrical & electronic engineering; mechanical & production engineering.

Acoustics
*See: **Acoustic engineering; electronic engineering; music; physics; speech sciences**.*

Acting
Possible prospectuses: ALRA, Manchester Poly, RADA, Welsh Coll Music/Drama. *See also: **Drama**.*
Study area: Drama and Theatre arts.

Actuarial studies
Possible prospectuses: City Univ, Glasgow Coll, Heriot-Watt Univ, Kent Univ, LSE, Southampton Univ. *See also: **Mathematics; social sciences; statistics**.*
Study area: Mathematical studies.

Administration
*See: **Business administration; estate management; housing administration; personnel administration; public administration**.*

Advertising design
*See: **Graphic design**.*

Aerodynamics
Possible prospectuses: Cambridge Univ, Coventry Poly, Kingston Poly, Manchester Univ.
Study area: Aeronautical engineering.

Aeronautical engineering
Possible prospectuses: Bath Univ, Belfast Univ, Birmingham Univ, Bristol Poly, Bristol Univ, Cambridge Univ, City Univ, Coventry Poly, Cranwell, Glasgow Univ, Hatfield Poly, Imperial Coll, Kingston Poly, Loughborough Univ, Manadon, Manchester Univ, North East Wales Inst, Queen Mary & Westfield, Salford Univ, Southampton Univ.
Study area: Aeronautical engineering.

Aesthetics
See: Fine arts; philosophy.

African studies
Possible prospectuses: Birmingham Univ, Coventry Poly, Kent Univ, Liverpool Univ, SOAS, Sussex Univ. *See also: Archaeology; Asian studies; Near East studies.*
Study area: African studies.

Afro-Asian studies
See: African studies; Asian studies.

Agricultural botany
Possible prospectuses: Aberystwyth, Bangor, Belfast Univ, Cirencester, Imperial Coll, Leeds Univ, Newcastle Univ, Nottingham Univ, Reading Univ, Wye Coll. *See also: Agriculture; botany.*
Study area: Agriculture, horticulture and forestry.

Agricultural chemistry
See: Chemistry; agriculture.
Study area: Chemistry; agriculture, horticulture and forestry.

Agricultural economics
Possible prospectuses: Aberdeen Univ, Aberystwyth, Bangor, Belfast Univ, Cirencester, Edinburgh Univ, Exeter Univ, Glasgow Univ, Manchester Univ, Newcastle Univ, Nottingham Univ, Reading Univ, Silsoe Coll, Wye Coll.
See also: Economics; agriculture.
Study area: Agriculture, horticulture and forestry; economics.

Agricultural engineering
Possible prospectuses: Anglia, Harper Adams, Newcastle Univ, Silsoe Coll, Wolverhampton Poly, Writtle.

Agriculture

Possible prospectuses: Aberdeen Univ, Aberystwyth, Anglia, Bangor, Belfast Univ, Cirencester, Edinburgh Univ, Glasgow Univ, Harper Adams, Newcastle Univ, Nottingham Univ, Reading Univ, Silsoe Coll, South West Poly, Wolverhampton Poly, Writtle, Wye Coll. *Study area:* Agriculture, horticulture and forestry.

Agronomy

See: Agriculture.

Aircraft engineering

See: Aeronautical engineering; air transport engineering.

Air force

Possible prospectus: Cranwell.

Air transport engineering

Possible prospectuses: City Univ, Cranwell, Loughborough Univ, Queen Mary & Westfield.

Akkadian

Possible prospectuses: Cambridge Univ, Liverpool Univ, Manchester Univ, SOAS, University Coll London. *See also: **Near East studies.*** *Study area:* Near East and Islamic studies.

American studies

Possible prospectuses: Aberystwyth, Belfast Univ, Birmingham Univ, Crewe & Alsager, Derbyshire Coll, Dundee Univ, Ealing Coll, East Anglia Univ, Essex Univ, Exeter Univ, Hull Univ, Keele Univ, Kent Univ, King Alfred's Coll, Lancashire Poly, Lancaster Univ, Leeds Univ, Leicester Univ, Liverpool Inst, Liverpool Univ, Manchester Univ, Middlesex Poly, Nottingham Univ, Reading Univ, Ripon & York St John, Sheffield Univ, Staffs Poly, Sunderland Poly, Sussex Univ, Swansea, Ulster Univ, Warwick Univ, West London Inst, Wolverhampton Poly. *Study area:* American studies.

Amharic
See: Asian studies.

Analogues
See: Computing; electrical engineering; electronic engineering.

Analytical
See: Individual subjects, eg *chemistry.*

Anatolia
See: Archaeology.

Anatomy
Possible prospectuses: Aberdeen Univ, Belfast Univ, Birmingham Univ, Bristol Univ, Cambridge Univ, Cardiff, Dundee Univ, Glasgow Univ, King's Coll London, Leeds Univ, Manchester Univ, Newcastle Univ, Sheffield Univ, University Coll London. *See also: Medicine; human biology.*
Study area: Anatomy.

Ancient history
Possible prospectuses: Belfast Univ, Birkbeck, Birmingham Univ, Bristol Univ, Cambridge Univ, Cardiff, Edinburgh Univ, Exeter Univ, Keele Univ, Kent Univ, King's Coll London, Lampeter, Leicester Univ, Liverpool Univ, Manchester Univ, Newcastle Univ, Nottingham Univ, Oxford Univ, Reading Univ, Royal Holloway & Bedford, St Andrews Univ, Swansea, University Coll London, Warwick Univ. *See also: Classics; history.*
Study area: History; classics.

Anglo-Saxon
Possible prospectus: Cambridge Univ.

Animals
See: Agriculture; animal science; veterinary science; zoology.

Animal science
Possible prospectuses: Aberdeen Univ, Aberystwyth, Brunel Univ, Cirencester, East Anglia Univ, East London Poly, Edinburgh Univ, Glasgow Univ, Imperial Coll, Leeds Univ, Newcastle Univ, Nottingham Univ, Open Univ, Reading Univ, Royal Vet Coll, Wolverhampton Poly, Writtle, Wye Coll.
Study area: Zoology.

Animation
Possible prospectuses: Edinburgh Coll Art, Royal Coll Art, West Surrey Coll. *See also: Film studies.*

Anthropology
Possible prospectuses: Brunel Univ, Cambridge Univ, Durham Univ, East Anglia Univ, Edinburgh Univ, Goldsmiths' Coll, Hull Univ, Keele Univ, Kent Univ, LSE, Manchester Univ, Oxford Poly, SOAS, Swansea, University Coll London. *See also: Social anthropology.*
Study area: Anthropology.

Applied
See: Individual subjects, eg *Biology.*

Arabic
Possible prospectuses: Aberdeen Univ, Cambridge Univ, Durham Univ, Edinburgh Univ, Exeter Univ, Glasgow Univ, Leeds Univ, Manchester Univ, Oxford Univ, PCL, St Andrews Univ, Salford Univ, SOAS.
Study area: Near East and Islamic studies.

Aramaic
*See: **Near East studies**.*

Archaeology
Possible prospectuses: Bangor, Belfast Univ, Birmingham Univ, Bournemouth Poly, Bradford Univ, Bristol Univ, Cambridge Univ, Cardiff, Durham Univ, East London Poly, Edinburgh Univ, Exeter Univ, Glasgow Univ, Inst Archaeology, King Alfred's Coll, King's Coll London, Lampeter, Leicester Univ, Liverpool Univ, Manchester Univ, Newcastle Univ, Nottingham Univ, Reading Univ, SOAS, Sheffield Univ, Southampton Univ, University Coll London, York Univ. *See also: **Anthropology**.*
Study area: Archaeology.

Architecture
Possible prospectuses: Architectural Association, Bath Univ, Belfast Univ, Birmingham Poly, Brighton Poly, Cambridge Univ, Cardiff, Duncan of Jordanstone, Dundee Univ, East London Poly, Edinburgh Coll Art, Edinburgh Univ, Glasgow Univ, Heriot-Watt Univ, Huddersfield Poly, Humberside Poly, Kent Inst, Kingston Poly, Leeds Poly, Leeds Univ, Leicester Poly, Liverpool Poly, Liverpool Univ, Manchester Poly, Manchester Univ, Newcastle Univ, North London Poly, Nottingham Univ, Oxford Poly, PCL, Portsmouth Poly, Robert Gordon's Inst, Royal Coll Art, Sheffield Univ, South Bank Poly, South West Poly, Strathclyde Univ, Teesside Poly, Thames Poly, University Coll London.
Study area: Architecture

Army
Possible prospectuses: Sandhurst.

Art & design
*See: **Fine art; graphic design; photography; silversmithing; textiles; three-dimensional design**.*

Art history
*See: **Fine arts**.*

Artificial intelligence
See: Computer science.

Asian studies
Possible prospectuses: Cambridge Univ, Edinburgh Univ, Leicester Poly, Liverpool Univ, Manchester Univ, Newcastle Univ, North London Poly, Oxford Univ, SOAS, Sussex Univ, Ulster Univ. *See also: Near East studies; South East Asian studies.*
Study area: Asian studies.

Assyriology
See: Archaeology; Near East studies.

Astronautics
See: Aeronautics.

Astronomy
Possible prospectuses: Cambridge Univ, Cardiff, Edinburgh Univ, Glasgow Univ, Hatfield Poly, Lancashire Poly, Leicester Univ, Manchester Univ, Newcastle Univ, Queen Mary & Westfield, St Andrews Univ, Sheffield Univ, South West Poly, Southampton Univ, University Coll London.
Study area: Physics.

Astrophysics
Possible prospectuses: Aberystwyth, Birmingham Univ, Cambridge Univ, Cardiff, Edinburgh Univ, Imperial Coll, Kent Univ, King's Coll London, Lancashire Poly, Leeds Univ, Leicester Univ, Manchester Univ, Newcastle Univ, Queen Mary & Westfield, Royal Holloway & Bedford, St Andrews Univ, Sussex Univ, University Coll London.
Study area: Physics.

Audio-visual communication
See: Communication studies; electronics engineering; fine art.

Automotive engineering
Possible prospectuses: Birmingham Univ, Brunel Univ, Coventry Poly, Hatfield Poly, Loughborough Univ.
Study area: Mechanical & production engineering.

Avionics
Possible prospectuses: Glasgow Univ, Queen Mary & Westfield. See also: *Aeronautical engineering.*

B

Bacteriology
Possible prospectuses: Birmingham Univ, Brunel Univ, Edinburgh Univ, Glasgow Univ, Manchester Univ, Reading Univ.
Study area: Microbiology.

Banking
Possible prospectuses: Bangor, Birmingham Poly, Birmingham Univ, Buckingham Univ, Cardiff, Cheltenham & Gloucester Coll, City Poly, City Univ, Ealing Coll, Glasgow Coll, Liverpool Poly, Loughborough

Univ, Napier Poly, Teesside Poly, Trinity & All Saints, Ulster Univ.
*See also: **Business studies; economics.***
Study area: Business studies.

Bantu Language
Possible prospectus: SOAS.
Study area: African studies.

Behavioural science
Possible prospectuses: Brunel Univ, Ealing Coll, Huddersfield Poly,
Manchester Univ, Nottingham Univ, Open Univ, PCL, Reading Univ,
Teesside Poly, Ulster Univ, Wales Poly, West Glamorgan Inst. *See also:*
Psychology; zoology.
Study areas: Psychology; zoology.

Bengali
Possible prospectus: SOAS. *See also: **Asian studies.***
Study area: Asian studies.

Biblical studies

HAVE YOU EVER
CONSIDERED
THE POWER
OF PRAYER?

Biblical studies
Possible prospectuses: Aberdeen Univ, Bangor, Belfast Univ,
Birmingham Univ, Cambridge Univ, Edinburgh Univ, Glasgow Univ,
Heythrop Coll, Jews' Coll, King's Coll London, London Bible,
Manchester Univ, National Extension Coll, Oak Hill Coll, St Andrews
Univ, Sheffield Univ, Spurgeon's Coll. *See also: **Religious studies;
theology.***
Study area: Religious studies & theology.

Biochemical engineering
Possible prospectuses: Birmingham Univ, Bradford Univ, Heriot-Watt
Univ, Imperial Coll, Luton Coll, Surrey Univ, Swansea, Teesside Poly,
University Coll London, UMIST. *See also: **Biochemistry;
biotechnology; chemical engineering.***
Study areas: Biochemistry; biotechnology; chemical engineering.

Biochemistry
Possible prospectuses: Aberdeen Univ, Aberystwyth, Bangor, Bath
Univ, Belfast Univ, Birmingham Univ, Bradford Univ, Bristol Univ,
Brunel Univ, Buckingham Univ, Cambridge Univ, Cardiff, Cirencester,
Coventry Poly, Dundee Univ, Durham Univ, East Anglia Univ, East
London Poly, Edinburgh Univ, Essex Univ, Glasgow Coll, Glasgow
Univ, Heriot-Watt Univ, Huddersfield Poly, Imperial Coll, Keele Univ,
Kent Univ, King's Coll London, Lancashire Poly, Lancaster Univ,
Leeds Univ, Leicester Univ, Liverpool Poly, Liverpool Univ, Luton

Coll, Manchester Poly, Manchester Univ, Newcastle Univ, North London Poly, Nottingham Univ, Open Univ, Oxford Univ, Paisley Coll, PCL, Portsmouth Poly, Queen Mary & Westfield, Reading Univ, Royal Holloway & Bedford, St Andrews Univ, Salford Univ, Sheffield Univ, Southampton Univ, Stirling Univ, Strathclyde Univ, Sunderland Poly, Surrey Univ, Sussex Univ, Swansea, Teesside Poly, Thames Poly, Ulster Univ, University Coll London, UMIST, Warwick Univ, Wolverhampton Poly, York Univ.
Study area: Biochemistry.

Biological chemistry
Possible prospectuses: Aberystwyth, Essex Univ, Glasgow Coll, Heriot-Watt Univ, Hull Univ, Imperial Coll, Kent Univ, King's Coll London, Lancashire Poly, Leicester Univ, Manchester Univ, Nottingham Univ, Queen Mary & Westfield, Stirling Univ, Warwick Univ. *See also:* ***Biotechnology.***
Study area: Biochemistry.

Biology
Possible prospectuses: Aberdeen Univ, Aberystwyth, Anglia, Aston Univ, Bangor, Bath Univ, Belfast Univ, Birkbeck, Birmingham Univ, Bolton Inst, Brighton Poly, Bristol Poly, Bristol Univ, Brunel Univ, Buckingham Univ, Cambridge Univ, Cardiff, Cardiff Institute, Chester Coll, Cirencester, Coventry Poly, Crewe & Alsager, Derbyshire Coll, Dundee Inst, Dundee Univ, Durham Univ, East Anglia Univ, East London Poly, Edinburgh Univ, Essex Univ, Exeter Univ, Glasgow Coll, Glasgow Univ, Hatfield Poly, Heriot-Watt Univ, Homerton, Hull Univ, Humberside Poly, Imperial Coll, Keele Univ, Kent Univ, King's Coll London, La Sainte Union, Lancashire Poly, Lancaster Univ, Leeds Univ, Leicester Poly, Leicester Univ, Liverpool Inst, Liverpool Poly, Liverpool Univ, Luton Coll, Manchester Poly, Manchester Univ, Napier Poly, Newcastle Univ, North London Poly, Nottingham Poly, Nottingham Univ, Open Univ, Oxford Poly, Oxford Univ, Paisley Coll, PCL, Portsmouth Poly, Queen Mary & Westfield, Reading Univ, Ripon & York St John, Roehampton Inst, Royal Holloway & Bedford, St Andrews Univ, St Mary's Coll, Salford Univ, Sheffield Univ, South Bank Poly, South West Poly, Southampton Univ, Staffs Poly, Stirling Univ, Strathclyde Univ, Sunderland Poly, Sussex Univ, Swansea, Thames Poly, Ulster Univ, University Coll London, Wales Poly, Warwick Univ, Wolverhampton Poly, Worcester Coll, York Univ. *See also: eg* ***Botany, zoology.***
Study area: Biology.

Biomedical electronics
Possible prospectuses: Kent Univ, Lancashire Poly, Salford Univ.
Study area: Electrical & electronic engineering.

Biophysics
Possible prospectuses: Aberdeen Univ, Cambridge Univ, East Anglia Univ, East London Poly, Imperial Coll, King's Coll London, Leeds Univ, Liverpool Poly, Luton Coll, Portsmouth Poly.
Study area: Biology.

Biosocial science

Possible prospectus: University Coll London. *See also: **Human sciences.***
Study areas: Biology; sociology.

Biotechnology

Possible prospectuses: Aberdeen Univ, Birmingham Univ, Bristol Poly, Cardiff, Dundee Inst, East London Poly, Edinburgh Univ, Imperial Coll, Kent Univ, King's Coll London, Lancashire Poly, Leeds Univ, Leicester Poly, Leicester Univ, Liverpool Univ, Luton Coll, Nottingham Univ, PCL, Queen Mary & Westfield, Reading Univ, St Andrews Univ, Sheffield Univ, South Bank Poly, Strathclyde Univ, Sunderland Poly, Surrey Univ, Sussex Univ, Teesside Poly, University Coll London, Wales Poly, Wolverhampton Poly, Wye Coll. *See also: **Biochemical engineering; biochemistry.***
Study area: Biotechnology.

Botany

Possible prospectuses: Aberdeen Univ, Aberystwyth, Bangor, Belfast Univ, Birkbeck, Birmingham Univ, Bristol Univ, Brunel Univ, Cambridge Univ, Cardiff, Dundee Univ, Durham Univ, East Anglia Univ, East London Poly, Edinburgh Univ, Exeter Univ, Glasgow Univ, Imperial Coll, King's Coll London, Leeds Univ, Leicester Univ, Liverpool Univ, Manchester Univ, Newcastle Univ, Nottingham Univ, Oxford Univ, Queen Mary & Westfield, Reading Univ, Royal Holloway & Bedford, St Andrews Univ, Sheffield Univ, Southampton Univ, Stirling Univ, Swansea, University Coll London, Wye Coll. *See also: **Agriculture; biology; horticulture.***
Study area: Botany.

Brewing
Possible prospectus: Heriot-Watt Univ. *See also: Microbiology.*
Study area: Microbiology.

Building and construction
Possible prospectuses: Bath Univ, Bolton Inst, Brighton Poly, Bristol
Poly, Coventry Poly, Dundee Inst, Glasgow Coll, Glasgow Coll
Building, Heriot-Watt Univ, Lancashire Poly, Leeds Poly, Liverpool
Poly, Loughborough Univ, Luton Coll, Napier Poly, Nene Coll,
Newcastle Poly, Nottingham Poly, Oxford Poly, Paisley Coll, PCL,
Reading Univ, Salford Univ, Sheffield Poly, South Bank Poly, Teesside
Poly, UMIST, Wales Poly, Wolverhampton Poly. *See also:
Architecture; building surveying; building technology; civil
engineering.*

Building studies
Possible prospectuses: Anglia, Bolton Inst, Brunel Univ, Cirencester,
Coventry Poly, Dundee Univ, Glasgow Coll, Glasgow Coll Building,
Lancashire Poly, Liverpool Poly, Luton Coll, Napier Poly, National
Extension Coll, Newcastle Poly, Nottingham Poly, PCL, Reading
Univ, Robert Gordon's Inst, Sheffield Poly, South Bank Poly, Ulster
Univ, University Coll London, UMIST, Wolverhampton Poly. *See also:
Architecture; building surveying; building technology; civil
engineering.*

Building surveying
Possible prospectuses: Birmingham Poly, Brighton Poly, Bristol Poly,
Cirencester, Glasgow Coll, Glasgow Coll Building, Heriot-Watt Univ,
Lancashire Poly, Leicester Poly, Liverpool Poly, Luton Coll, Napier
Poly, Newcastle Poly, Nottingham Poly, Reading Univ, Robert
Gordon's Inst, Salford Univ, Sheffield Poly, South Bank Poly, South
West Poly, Thames Poly, Wales Poly, Wolverhampton Poly.

Building technology
Possible prospectuses: Coventry Poly, Glasgow Coll, Glasgow Coll
Building, Heriot-Watt Univ, Lancashire Poly, Liverpool Univ,
Loughborough Univ, Luton Coll, Napier Poly, Nottingham Poly,
Reading Univ, Robert Gordon's Inst, South Bank Poly, Strathclyde
Univ, Ulster Univ, UMIST, Wolverhampton Poly.

Bulgarian
Possible prospectus: SSEES.
Study area: Modern languages.

Burmese studies
Possible prospectus: SOAS. *See also: Asian studies.*
Study area: Asian studies.

Business
*See: Accountancy; business administration; business studies;
economics; law; mathematics.*

Business administration
Possible prospectuses: Aberystwyth, Anglia, Aston Univ, Bath Univ,
Belfast Univ, Birmingham Univ, Brighton Poly, Bristol Poly, Brunel
Univ, Buckinghamshire Coll, Cardiff, Cardiff Institute, Cirencester,

Coventry Poly, Ealing Coll, European Bus Sch, Glasgow Coll, Harper Adams, Heriot-Watt Univ, Huddersfield Poly, Humberside Poly, Kingston Poly, Lancashire Poly, Leeds Poly, Liverpool Poly, London Business Sch, Loughborough Univ, Luton Coll, Manchester Business Sch, Manchester Poly, Middlesex Poly, North Cheshire Coll, Nottingham Poly, Reading Univ, Robert Gordon's Inst, Salford Univ, Scottish Coll Textiles, Sheffield Poly, Staffs Poly, Stirling Univ, Strathclyde Univ, Trinity & All Saints, Wales Poly, West Glamorgan Inst, Wolverhampton Poly.
Study area: Business studies.

Business economics
Possible prospectuses: Aberystwyth, Anglia, Birmingham Univ, Brunel Univ, Buckingham Univ, Cardiff, Coventry Poly, Durham Univ, Ealing Coll, European Bus Sch, Glasgow Coll, Heriot-Watt Univ, Hull Univ, Leicester Univ, Liverpool Univ, Luton Coll, Manchester Univ, Middlesex Poly, Nottingham Poly, Paisley Coll, PCL, Queen Mary & Westfield, Reading Univ, Salford Univ, Scottish Coll Textiles, Southampton Univ, Staffs Poly, Surrey Univ, West Glamorgan Inst, Wolverhampton Poly.
Study areas: Business studies; economics.

Business studies
Possible prospectuses: Aberystwyth, Anglia, Aston Univ, Birmingham Poly, Birmingham Univ, Bolton Inst, Bournemouth Poly, Bradford Univ, Brighton Poly, Bristol Poly, Brunel Univ, Buckingham Univ, Buckinghamshire Coll, Cardiff, Cheltenham & Gloucester Coll, Cirencester, City Poly, City Univ, Coventry Poly, Derbyshire Coll, Dundee Inst, Ealing Coll, East Anglia Univ, East London Poly, Edinburgh Univ, European Bus Sch, Exeter Univ, Glasgow Coll, Hatfield Poly, Heriot-Watt Univ, Holborn College, Huddersfield Poly, Hull Univ, Humberside Poly, Kent Univ, King's Coll London, Kingston Poly, Lancashire Poly, Leeds Poly, Leeds Univ, Leicester Poly, Liverpool Poly, London Business Sch, London Coll Printing, Loughborough Univ, Luton Coll, Manchester Business Sch, Manchester Poly, Middlesex Poly, Napier Poly, Nene Coll, Newcastle Poly, North East Wales Inst, North London Poly, Nottingham Poly, Oxford Poly, PCL, Portsmouth Poly, Queen Mary & Westfield, Reading Univ, Robert Gordon's Inst, Roehampton Inst, Salford Univ, Scottish Coll Textiles, Sheffield Poly, Sheffield Univ, South Bank Poly, South West Poly, Staffs Poly, Stirling Univ, Strathclyde Univ, Sunderland Poly, Sussex Univ, Swansea, Teesside Poly, Thames Poly, Thames Valley Coll, Trinity & All Saints, Ulster Univ, University Coll London, UMIST, Wales Poly, Warwick Univ, West Glamorgan Inst, Wolverhampton Poly, Wye Coll.
Study area: Business studies.

Byzantine studies
See: Classics; history.

C

Canadian studies
See **American studies.**

Carbon dating
See **Archaeology.**

Caribbean studies
Possible prospectuses: Kent Univ, North London Poly, Warwick Univ.

Caring
See: Education; medicine; nursing; social administration.

Carpet design
Possible prospectus: Wolverhampton Poly. *See also: Textiles.*
Study area: Art and design.

Catalan
Possible prospectuses: Cardiff, Liverpool Univ, Southampton Univ. *See also: Spanish.*
Study area: Modern languages.

Catering
Possible prospectuses: Birmingham Poly, Bournemouth Poly, Ealing Coll, Huddersfield Poly, Lancashire Poly, Manchester Poly, Middlesex Poly, Napier Poly, Oxford Poly, Queen Margaret Coll, Robert Gordon's Inst, Sheffield Poly, South Bank Poly, Surrey Univ, Thames Valley Coll, Ulster Univ, Wolverhampton Poly.
See also: Dietetics; hotel & catering management.
Study area: Hotel & catering management.

Cell biology
Possible prospectuses: Aberdeen Univ, Aberystwyth, Birmingham Univ, Brunel Univ, Cambridge Univ, East Anglia Univ, Essex Univ, Glasgow Coll, Glasgow Univ, Imperial Coll, Keele Univ, Kent Univ, King's Coll London, Kingston Poly, Leicester Univ, Liverpool Univ, Manchester Univ, Open Univ, Oxford Poly, PCL, St Andrews Univ, Sheffield Univ, Surrey Univ, University Coll London, UMIST, York Univ. *See also: Microbiology.*
Study areas: Biology; microbiology.

Cellular pathology
Possible prospectuses: Bradford Univ, Bristol Univ, Glasgow Coll, Reading Univ. *See also: Pathology.*
Study areas: Microbiology; dentistry; medicine.

Celtic studies
Possible prospectuses: Aberdeen Univ, Aberystwyth, Belfast Univ, Cambridge Univ, Edinburgh Univ, Glasgow Univ, Manchester Univ.
See also: Irish studies; Scottish studies; Welsh studies.

Central European studies
See: European studies.

Ceramic science
*See: **Chemistry***.

Ceramics
Possible prospectuses: Bath Coll, Birmingham Poly, Bretton Hall,
Brighton Poly, Bristol Poly, Buckinghamshire Coll, Camberwell Coll,
Cardiff Institute, Central St Martins, Coventry Poly, Crewe & Alsager,
Duncan of Jordanstone, Edinburgh Coll Art, Glasgow Sch Art,
Goldsmiths' Coll, Heriot-Watt Univ, Leeds Univ, Leicester Poly,
Liverpool Inst, Loughborough Coll, Manchester Poly, Middlesex Poly,
PCL, Portsmouth Poly, Robert Gordon's Inst, Royal Coll Art, Sheffield
Univ, Staffs Poly, Sunderland Poly, Ulster Univ, West Surrey Coll,
Wolverhampton Poly. *See also: **Three-dimensional design***.
Study area: Art and design.

Chemical engineering
Possible prospectuses: Aston Univ, Bath Univ, Belfast Univ,
Birmingham Univ, Bradford Univ, Cambridge Univ, Edinburgh Univ,
Exeter Univ, Heriot-Watt Univ, Huddersfield Poly, Humberside Poly,
Imperial Coll, Leeds Univ, Loughborough Univ, Newcastle Univ,
Nottingham Univ, Paisley Coll, Sheffield Univ, South Bank Poly,
Strathclyde Univ, Surrey Univ, Swansea, Teesside Poly, University
Coll London, UMIST, Wales Poly.
Study area: Chemical engineering.

Chemical physics
Possible prospectuses: Bristol Univ, East Anglia Univ, Edinburgh
Univ, Glasgow Univ, Imperial Coll, Kent Univ, Liverpool Univ,
Manchester Univ, Open Univ, Sheffield Univ, Southampton Univ,
Sussex Univ, University Coll London, UMIST.
Study area: Physics; chemistry.

Chemistry

Possible prospectuses: Aberdeen Univ, Anglia, Aston Univ, Bangor, Bath Univ, Belfast Univ, Birkbeck, Birmingham Univ, Bradford Univ, Brighton Poly, Bristol Univ, Brunel Univ, Cambridge Univ, Cardiff, Coventry Poly, Crewe & Alsager, Derbyshire Coll, Dundee Inst, Dundee Univ, Durham Univ, East Anglia Univ, Edinburgh Univ, Essex Univ, Exeter Univ, Glasgow Coll, Glasgow Univ, Hatfield Poly, Heriot-Watt Univ, Homerton, Huddersfield Poly, Hull Univ, Humberside Poly, Imperial Coll, Keele Univ, Kent Univ, King's Coll London, Kingston Poly, Lancashire Poly, Lancaster Univ, Leeds Poly, Leeds Univ, Leicester Poly, Leicester Univ, Liverpool Poly, Liverpool Univ, Loughborough Univ, Manchester Poly, Manchester Univ, Napier Poly, Newcastle Poly, Newcastle Univ, North East Wales Inst, North London Poly, Nottingham Poly, Nottingham Univ, Open Univ, Oxford Poly, Oxford Univ, Paisley Coll, PCL, Portsmouth Poly, Queen Mary & Westfield, Reading Univ, Robert Gordon's Inst, Roehampton Inst, St Andrews Univ, St Mary's Coll, Salford Univ, Scottish Coll Textiles, Sheffield Poly, Sheffield Univ, South Bank Poly, South West Poly, Southampton Univ, Staffs Poly, Strathclyde Univ, Sunderland Poly, Surrey Univ, Sussex Univ, Swansea, Teesside Poly, Thames Poly, University Coll London, UMIST, Wales Poly, Warwick Univ, Wolverhampton Poly, York Univ.
Study area: Chemistry.

Chinese

Possible prospectuses: Cambridge Univ, Durham Univ, Edinburgh Univ, Leeds Univ, Oxford Univ, PCL, SOAS, York Univ. *See also: Asian studies.*

Chiropody

Possible prospectuses: Birmingham Poly, Brighton Poly, Cardiff Institute, Derbyshire Coll, Huddersfield Poly, Nene Coll, PCL, Queen Margaret Coll, Queen's Coll Glasgow, South West Poly, Sunderland Poly.

Church history

Possible prospectuses: Aberdeen Univ, Cambridge Univ, Edinburgh Univ, Lampeter, London Bible, Manchester Univ, National Extension Coll, Oak Hill Coll, Spurgeon's Coll.
Study area: History.

Civil engineering
Possible prospectuses: Aberdeen Univ, Aston Univ, Belfast Univ, Birmingham Univ, Bolton Inst, Bradford Univ, Brighton Poly, Bristol Univ, Cambridge Univ, Cardiff, City Univ, Coventry Poly, Dundee Inst, Dundee Univ, Durham Univ, East London Poly, Edinburgh Univ, Exeter Univ, Glasgow Coll, Glasgow Univ, Hatfield Poly, Heriot-Watt Univ, Imperial Coll, King's Coll London, Kingston Poly, Leeds Univ, Liverpool Poly, Liverpool Univ, Loughborough Univ, Manchester Univ, Middlesex Poly, Napier Poly, Newcastle Univ, Nottingham Poly, Nottingham Univ, Oxford Poly, Oxford Univ, Paisley Coll, PCL, Portsmouth Poly, Queen Mary & Westfield, Salford Univ, Sheffield Poly, Sheffield Univ, Shrivenham, South Bank Poly, South West Poly, Southampton Univ, Strathclyde Univ, Sunderland Poly, Surrey Univ, Swansea, Teesside Poly, Thames Poly, Ulster Univ, University Coll London, UMIST, Wales Poly, Warwick Univ, Wolverhampton Poly. *See also: Engineering*.
Study area: Civil engineering.

Classical studies
Possible prospectuses: Aberystwyth, Bristol Univ, Durham Univ, Edinburgh Univ, Keele Univ, Kent Univ, King's Coll London, Lampeter, Liverpool Univ, North London Poly, Nottingham Univ, Open Univ, Queen Mary & Westfield, Reading Univ, Royal Holloway & Bedford, St Mary's Coll, Warwick Univ.
See also: Individual subjects, eg Arabic.

Classics
Possible prospectuses: Belfast Univ, Birkbeck, Birmingham Univ, Bristol Univ, Cambridge Univ, Central Sch Speech/Drama, Durham Univ, Edinburgh Univ, Exeter Univ, Glasgow Univ, Kent Univ, King's Coll London, Lampeter, Leeds Univ, Liverpool Univ, Manchester Univ, Newcastle Univ, North London Poly, Nottingham Univ, Oxford Univ, Reading Univ, Royal Holloway & Bedford, St Andrews Univ, Swansea, University Coll London, Warwick Univ.
Study area: Classics.

Climate
See: Geography; meteorology.

Clothing
See: Fashions; textiles.

Coastal engineering
See: Civil engineering.

Commerce
Possible prospectuses: Birmingham Univ, Cirencester, Dundee Inst, Ealing Coll, Edinburgh Univ, Glasgow Coll, Napier Poly, Robert Gordon's Inst, Scottish Coll Textiles, Wales Poly. *See also: Business studies*.
Study area: Business studies.

Communication engineering
Possible prospectuses: Bath Univ, Birmingham Univ, Bradford Univ, Coventry Poly, Essex Univ, Heriot-Watt Univ, Hull Univ, Imperial

Coll, Kent Univ, Leeds Poly, Liverpool Poly, Manchester Univ, Napier Poly, Newcastle Poly, North London Poly, Ravensbourne Coll, Salford Univ, Sheffield Univ, Shrivenham, South West Poly, Southampton Univ, Strathclyde Univ, Sunderland Poly, Teesside Poly, Thames Poly. *Study area:* Electrical & electronic engineering.

Communication studies
Possible prospectuses: Bangor Normal Coll, Birmingham Poly, Bournemouth Poly, Bradford Univ, Bristol Poly, Brunel Univ, Cardiff, Coventry Poly, Duncan of Jordanstone, Ealing Coll, Glasgow Coll, Goldsmiths' Coll, Huddersfield Poly, Humberside Poly, Kent Inst, Kent Univ, Lancaster Univ, Liverpool Univ, Middlesex Poly, Napier Poly, North Cheshire Coll, North London Poly, Nottingham Poly, Open Univ, Queen Margaret Coll, Sheffield Poly, Stirling Univ, Sunderland Poly, Teesside Poly, Trinity & All Saints, Ulster Univ, Wales Poly, Wolverhampton Poly. *See also: **Media studies.***
Study areas: Communication studies; art and design.

Community arts
Possible prospectuses: Bretton Hall, Dartington, Kent Inst.
Study area: Art and design.

Community studies
*See: **Public administration; social work; sociology; town planning; urban studies; youth and community work.***

Comparative literature
Possible prospectuses: Bradford Univ, Buckingham Univ, East Anglia Univ, Essex Univ, Kent Univ, Manchester Univ, Warwick Univ.

Computer engineering
Possible prospectuses: Bangor, Birmingham Univ, Bolton Inst, Bournemouth Poly, Bristol Univ, Brunel Univ, Coventry Poly, Dundee Inst, European Bus Sch, Glasgow Coll, Heriot-Watt Univ, Huddersfield Poly, Hull Univ, Kent Univ, Liverpool Poly, Loughborough Univ, Napier Poly, Nottingham Poly, PCL, Queen Mary & Westfield, Sheffield Poly, Sheffield Univ, South Bank Poly, Staffs Poly, Strathclyde Univ, Sussex Univ, Teesside Poly, Thames Poly, Wales Poly, West Glamorgan Inst, York Univ.
*See also: **Computer technology.***

Computer science
Possible prospectuses: Aberdeen Univ, Aberystwyth, Aston Univ, Belfast Univ, Birmingham Univ, Bradford Univ, Brighton Poly, Bristol Poly, Bristol Univ, Brunel Univ, Buckingham Univ, Cambridge Univ, Cardiff, City Univ, Coventry Poly, Dundee Inst, Dundee Univ,

Durham Univ, East Anglia Univ, East London Poly, Edinburgh Univ, Essex Univ, Glasgow Coll, Glasgow Univ, Goldsmiths' Coll, Hatfield Poly, Heriot-Watt Univ, Hull Univ, Imperial Coll, Keele Univ, Kent Univ, King's Coll London, Kingston Poly, Lancashire Poly, Lancaster Univ, Leeds Univ, Leicester Poly, Liverpool Poly, Liverpool Univ, LSE, Loughborough Univ, Luton Coll, Manchester Poly, Manchester Univ, Napier Poly, Newcastle Univ, Nottingham Poly, Nottingham Univ, Open Univ, Oxford Poly, Paisley Coll, PCL, Portsmouth Poly, Queen Mary & Westfield, Reading Univ, Robert Gordon's Inst, Royal Holloway & Bedford, St Andrews Univ, Salford Univ, Scottish Coll Textiles, Sheffield Poly, Sheffield Univ, Shrivenham, South Bank Poly, Southampton Univ, Staffs Poly, Stirling Univ, Strathclyde Univ, Sunderland Poly, Surrey Univ, Sussex Univ, Swansea, Teesside Poly, Thames Poly, Ulster Univ, University Coll London, UMIST, Wales Poly, Warwick Univ, West Glamorgan Inst, Wolverhampton Poly, York Univ. *See also:* **Computing**.
Study area: Computing.

Computer technology
Possible prospectuses: Aberystwyth, Anglia, Bath Univ, Birmingham Univ, Bradford Univ, Brighton Poly, Bristol Univ, Brunel Univ, City Univ, Coventry Poly, Dundee Inst, Ealing Coll, Essex Univ, Glasgow Coll, Heriot-Watt Univ, Imperial Coll, Kent Univ, Leicester Poly, Liverpool Univ, Loughborough Univ, Manchester Univ, Napier Poly, Nottingham Poly, Open Univ, Paisley Coll, PCL, Salford Univ, Scottish Coll Textiles, Sheffield Univ, Staffs Poly, Sunderland Poly, Surrey Univ, Teesside Poly, Warwick Univ. *See also:* **Computer science**.
Study area: Computing.

Computing
Possible prospectuses: Aberdeen Univ, Aberystwyth, Anglia, Aston Univ, Bangor, Bath Univ, Bedford Coll, Birkbeck, Birmingham Poly, Bolton Inst, Bournemouth Poly, Bradford Univ, Brighton Poly, Bristol Poly, Brunel Univ, Buckinghamshire Coll, Cambridge Univ, Cardiff, Cheltenham & Gloucester Coll, Chester Coll, City Poly, Coventry Poly, Derbyshire Coll, Dundee Inst, Dundee Univ, Ealing Coll, East Anglia Univ, East London Poly, Essex Univ, Exeter Univ, Glasgow Coll, Hatfield Poly, Heriot-Watt Univ, Huddersfield Poly, Imperial Coll, Kent Univ, King's Coll London, Lancashire Poly, Leeds Poly, Leeds Univ, Leicester Poly, Leicester Univ, Liverpool Inst, Liverpool Poly, Liverpool Univ, Loughborough Univ, Luton Coll, Manchester Poly, Manchester Univ, Middlesex Poly, Napier Poly, Newcastle Poly, Newcastle Univ, North East Wales Inst, North London Poly, Nottingham Poly, Open Univ, Oxford Poly, Oxford Univ, PCL, Queen Mary & Westfield, Reading Univ, Robert Gordon's Inst, Royal Coll Art, St Andrews Univ, Salford Univ, Scottish Coll Textiles, Sheffield Poly, South Bank Poly, South West Poly, Staffs Poly, Stirling Univ, Sunderland Poly, Surrey Univ, Sussex Univ, Teesside Poly, Thames Poly, University Coll London, UMIST, Wales Poly, Warwick Univ, Wolverhampton Poly, Worcester Coll. *See also:* **Computer science**.
Study area: Computing.

Conflict
See: War studies.

Conservation
Possible prospectuses: Bournemouth Poly, Cardiff, Cheltenham &
Gloucester Coll, Cirencester, Edinburgh Coll Art, Royal Coll Art,
Sussex Univ, Writtle, Wye Coll.
See also: Archaeology; biology; ecology.

Construction
See: Building and construction.

Control engineering
Possible prospectuses: Aberdeen Univ, Birmingham Univ, Bolton Inst,
Brunel Univ, City Univ, Coventry Poly, Glasgow Coll, Glasgow Univ,
Huddersfield Poly, Hull Univ, Imperial Coll, Loughborough Univ,
Napier Poly, National Extension Coll, Open Univ, PCL, Reading Univ,
Robert Gordon's Inst, Salford Univ, Sheffield Poly, Sheffield Univ,
Staffs Poly, Strathclyde Univ, Sunderland Poly, Sussex Univ, Teesside
Poly.
Study areas: Computing; electrical & electronic engineering.

Corrosion
See: Materials science.

Cosmetic technology
See: Chemistry.

Counselling
See: Social work.

Criminology
See: Law; sociology.

Crop Technology
Possible prospectuses: Aberystwyth, Cirencester, Edinburgh Univ,
Reading Univ, Writtle.
Study areas: Agriculture, horticulture and forestry.

Cultural studies
Possible prospectuses: Aberdeen Univ, Birmingham Univ, Cheltenham
& Gloucester Coll, Ealing Coll, East London Poly, Lancaster Univ,
Liverpool Poly, Middlesex Poly, Portsmouth Poly, Sheffield Poly,
Sussex Univ, Thames Poly, Trinity & All Saints, Warwick Univ,
Wolverhampton Poly.

Cuneiform studies
See: Near East studies.

Cybernetics
Possible prospectuses: Coventry Poly, Loughborough Univ, Reading
Univ. *See also: Computing; control engineering.*

Czech/Slovak
Possible prospectuses: Cambridge Univ, Glasgow Univ, SSEES.
Study area: Modern languages.

D

Dance
Possible prospectuses: ALRA, Bedford Coll, Birmingham Univ,
Bretton Hall, Brighton Poly, Cardiff Institute, Crewe & Alsager,
Dartington, Laban Centre, Leicester Poly, London Coll Dance,
London Contemp Dance Sch, Loughborough Univ, Middlesex Poly,
Northern Sch Cont Dance, Roehampton Inst, Surrey Univ, Trinity &
All Saints, West Sussex Inst. *See also:* **Drama; movement;
performance arts.**
Study area: Dance.

Danish
Possible prospectus: East Anglia Univ, Edinburgh Univ, Hull Univ,
University Coll London. *See also:* **Scandinavian studies.**
Study area: Modern languages.

Data processing
Possible prospectuses: Bolton Inst, Bradford Univ, Bristol Poly, City
Univ, Ealing Coll, Glasgow Coll, Leeds Univ, Manchester Univ, Napier
Poly, Nene Coll, Open Univ, Oxford Poly, Scottish Coll Textiles,
Sheffield Univ, Staffs Poly, Ulster Univ, UMIST, Wales Poly.
See also: **Computing.**
Study area: Computing.

Decision theory
Possible prospectuses: Brunel Univ, Ealing Coll, Hatfield Poly,
Manchester Univ, Open Univ. *See also:* **Business studies; economics;
politics.**

Demography
See: **Geography; sociology.**

Dentistry
Possible prospectuses: Belfast Univ, Birmingham Univ, Bristol Univ,
Dundee Univ, Glasgow Univ, King's Coll London, King's Coll Sch
Medicine, Leeds Univ, Liverpool Univ, London Hospital, Manchester
Univ, Newcastle Univ, Queen Mary & Westfield, Sheffield Univ,
United Medical Sch, Wales Coll Medicine.
Study area: Dentistry.

Design
See: Individual subjects, eg **interior design, industrial design.**

Developmental
*See: Individual subjects, eg **biology**.*

Deviance
*See: **Psychology; sociology; statistics.***

Dietetics
Possible prospectuses: Cardiff Institute, King's Coll London, Leeds
Poly, North London Poly, Queen Margaret Coll, Queen's Coll
Glasgow, Robert Gordon's Inst, Surrey Univ.
*See also: **Nutrition**.*
Study area: Food science & nutrition.

Digital microelectronics
Possible prospectuses: Birmingham Univ, Dundee Inst, Dundee Univ,
Edinburgh Univ, Glasgow Coll, Heriot-Watt Univ, Imperial Coll, Kent
Univ, Liverpool Poly, Open Univ.*See also: **Computing; electronic
engineering**.*

Divinity
*See: **Theology; religious studies**.*

Docks
*See: **Civil engineering**.*

Drama
Possible prospectuses: Aberystwyth, ALRA, Bangor Normal Coll,
Bedford Coll, Birmingham Univ, Bretton Hall, Brighton Poly, Bristol
Univ, Central Sch Speech/Drama, Chester Coll, Crewe & Alsager,
Dartington, Derbyshire Coll, East Anglia Univ, Exeter Univ, Glasgow
Univ, Goldsmiths' Coll, Guildhall, Homerton, Huddersfield Poly, Hull
Univ, Kent Univ, King Alfred's Coll, Lancaster Univ, Leeds Univ,
Leicester Poly, Liverpool Inst, Liverpool Poly, Loughborough Univ,
Manchester Poly, Manchester Univ, Middlesex Poly, Nene Coll,
Newcastle Poly, Nottingham Poly, Queen Margaret Coll, Queen Mary
& Westfield, Reading Univ, Roehampton Inst, Rose Bruford Coll,
RADA, Royal Holloway & Bedford, Royal Scottish Academy, St
Mary's Coll, South West Poly, Ulster Univ, Wales Poly, Warwick
Univ, Welsh Coll Music/Drama, West London Inst, Wolverhampton
Poly, Worcester Coll. *See also: **Dance; performance arts**.*
Study area: Drama and theatre arts.

Dutch
Possible prospectuses: Cambridge Univ, Hull Univ, Liverpool Univ,
National Extension Coll, University Coll London.
Study area: Modern languages.

E

Earth sciences
Possible prospectuses: Aberystwyth, Birmingham Univ, Cambridge
Univ, Derbyshire Coll, East Anglia Univ, Hull Univ, Imperial Coll,
Kingston Poly, Leeds Univ, Liverpool Poly, Liverpool Univ,
Manchester Univ, Nene Coll, Open Univ, Oxford Poly, Oxford Univ,
Royal Holloway & Bedford, Sheffield Univ, Stirling Univ, Thames

Poly, University Coll London, West London Inst, Wolverhampton Poly. *See also:* **Geology.**
Study area: Geology; environmental science.

Ecology
Possible prospectuses: Aberdeen Univ, Bedford Coll, Cardiff, Cirencester, City Poly, Derbyshire Coll, Durham Univ, East Anglia Univ, East London Poly, Edinburgh Univ, Harper Adams, Huddersfield Poly, Hull Univ, Imperial Coll, King's Coll London, Lancaster Univ, Leeds Univ, Leicester Univ, Liverpool Poly, Loughborough Univ, Luton Coll, Manchester Univ, Open Univ, Royal Holloway & Bedford, St Andrews Univ, Sheffield Univ, Stirling Univ, Sunderland Poly, Sussex Univ, Ulster Univ, University Coll London, Wolverhampton Poly, Worcester Coll, Writtle, York Univ.
See also: eg **Botany; biology; zoology.**
Study area: Biology; environmental science.

Econometrics
Possible prospectuses: Birmingham Univ, Brunel Univ, Essex Univ, Heriot-Watt Univ, Kent Univ, Leeds Univ, Liverpool Univ, LSE, Loughborough Univ, Manchester Poly, Manchester Univ, Nottingham Univ, Reading Univ, Sheffield Univ, Southampton Univ, Staffs Poly, Surrey Univ, Warwick Univ, York Univ. *See also:* **Economics; mathematics.**
Study area: Economics.

Economic history
Possible prospectuses: Aberdeen Univ, Aberystwyth, Belfast Univ, Birmingham Univ, Bristol Univ, Cambridge Univ, Ealing Coll, East Anglia Univ, Edinburgh Univ, Essex Univ, Exeter Univ, Glasgow Coll, Glasgow Univ, Hull Univ, Kent Univ, Leeds Univ, Leicester Univ, Liverpool Univ, LSE, Manchester Poly, Manchester Univ, Newcastle Univ, Nottingham Univ, PCL, Portsmouth Poly, Queen Mary & Westfield, Reading Univ, Royal Holloway & Bedford, St Andrews Univ, Salford Univ, SOAS, Sheffield Univ, Southampton Univ, Staffs Poly, Strathclyde Univ, Sussex Univ, Swansea, University Coll London, Warwick Univ, York Univ. *See also:* **History.**
Study area: History.

Economics
Possible prospectuses: Aberdeen Univ, Aberystwyth, Anglia, Bangor, Bath Univ, Belfast Univ, Birkbeck, Birmingham Poly, Birmingham Univ, Bradford Univ, Brighton Poly, Bristol Poly, Bristol Univ, Brunel Univ, Buckingham Univ, Cambridge Univ, Cardiff, Cirencester,

City Poly, City Univ, Coventry Poly, Dundee Inst, Dundee Univ, Durham Univ, Ealing Coll, East Anglia Univ, East London Poly, Edinburgh Univ, Essex Univ, European Bus Sch, Exeter Univ, Glasgow Coll, Glasgow Univ, Goldsmiths' Coll, Hatfield Poly, Heriot-Watt Univ, Holborn College, Hull Univ, Keele Univ, Kent Univ, Kingston Poly, Lancashire Poly, Lancaster Univ, Leeds Poly, Leeds Univ, Leicester Poly, Leicester Univ, Liverpool Poly, Liverpool Univ, LSE, Loughborough Univ, Manchester Poly, Manchester Univ, Middlesex Poly, Nene Coll, Newcastle Poly, Newcastle Univ, North London Poly, Nottingham Poly, Nottingham Univ, Open Univ, Oxford Poly, Oxford Univ, PCL, Portsmouth Poly, Queen Mary & Westfield, Reading Univ, Royal Holloway & Bedford, St Andrews Univ, Salford Univ, SOAS, Sheffield Univ, South West Poly, Southampton Univ, Staffs Poly, Stirling Univ, Strathclyde Univ, Sunderland Poly, Surrey Univ, Sussex Univ, Swansea, Thames Poly, Trinity & All Saints, Ulster Univ, University Coll London, Warwick Univ, West Glamorgan Inst, Wolverhampton Poly, Worcester Coll, Wye Coll, York Univ.
Study area: Economics.

Education
Possible prospectuses: Aberystwyth, Anglia, Bangor, Bangor Normal Coll, Bath Coll, Bath Univ, Bedford Coll, Belfast Univ, Birmingham Poly, Birmingham Univ, Bolton Inst, Bradford & Ilkley, Bretton Hall, Brighton Poly, Bristol Poly, Brunel Univ, Cambridge Univ, Cardiff, Cardiff Institute, Central Sch Speech/Drama, Cheltenham & Gloucester Coll, Chester Coll, Christ Church Coll, Crewe & Alsager, Derbyshire Coll, Durham Univ, East Anglia Univ, East London Poly, Edge Hill, Exeter Univ, Glasgow Univ, Goldsmiths' Coll, Hatfield Poly, Homerton, Huddersfield Poly, Hull Univ, Inst Education, Jews' Coll, Keele Univ, King Alfred's Coll, King's Coll London, Kingston Poly, La Sainte Union, Lancashire Poly, Lancaster Univ, Leeds Poly, Liverpool Inst, Liverpool Poly, Liverpool Univ, Loughborough Univ, Manchester Poly, Manchester Univ, Middlesex Poly, Nene Coll, Newcastle Poly, North East Wales Inst, North London Poly, Nottingham Poly, Open Univ, Oxford Poly, Reading Univ, Ripon & York St John, Roehampton Inst, St Mark & St John, S Martin's Coll, St Mary's Coll, Sheffield Poly, South Bank Poly, South West Poly, Southampton Univ, Stirling Univ, Strathclyde Univ, Sunderland Poly, Swansea, Thames Poly, Trinity & All Saints, Trinity Coll Carmarthen, Ulster Univ, Warwick Univ, West Glamorgan Inst, West London Inst, West Sussex Inst, Westminster Coll, Wolverhampton Poly, Worcester Coll, York Univ.
Study area: Education.

Egyptology
Possible prospectus: University Coll London.
*See also: **Archaeology; history; Near East studies.***

Electrical engineering
Possible prospectuses: Aberdeen Univ, Aston Univ, Bangor, Bath Univ, Belfast Univ, Birmingham Univ, Bradford Univ, Brighton Poly, Bristol Poly, Bristol Univ, Brunel Univ, Cambridge Univ, Cardiff, City Univ, Coventry Poly, Derbyshire Coll, Dundee Inst, Durham Univ, East Anglia Univ, East London Poly, Edinburgh Univ, Essex Univ,

Exeter Univ, Glasgow Coll, Glasgow Univ, Hatfield Poly, Heriot-Watt Univ, Huddersfield Poly, Humberside Poly, Imperial Coll, King's Coll London, Kingston Poly, Lancashire Poly, Leeds Univ, Leicester Univ, Liverpool Poly, Liverpool Univ, Loughborough Univ, Manadon, Manchester Poly, Manchester Univ, Middlesex Poly, Napier Poly, National Extension Coll, Newcastle Poly, Newcastle Univ, North East Wales Inst, Nottingham Poly, Nottingham Univ, Oxford Poly, Oxford Univ, Paisley Coll, PCL, Portsmouth Poly, Queen Mary & Westfield, Robert Gordon's Inst, Salford Univ, Sheffield Poly, Sheffield Univ, South Bank Poly, South West Poly, Southampton Univ, Staffs Poly, Strathclyde Univ, Sunderland Poly, Surrey Univ, Sussex Univ, Swansea, Teesside Poly, Thames Poly, Ulster Univ, University Coll London, UMIST, Wales Poly, Warwick Univ. *See also:* **Electronic engineering; engineering.**
Study area: Electrical & electronic engineering.

Electromechanical engineering
Possible prospectuses: Aston Univ, Dundee Inst, Glasgow Coll, Imperial Coll, Lancaster Univ, Loughborough Univ, Manchester Poly, Manchester Univ, Southampton Univ, Strathclyde Univ, UMIST.
See also: **Engineering.**
Study area: Mechanical & production engineering.

Electronic engineering
Possible prospectuses: Aberdeen Univ, Aberystwyth, Aston Univ, Bangor, Bath Univ, Belfast Univ, Birmingham Poly, Birmingham Univ, Bolton Inst, Bournemouth Poly, Bradford Univ, Brighton Poly, Bristol Univ, Brunel Univ, Cambridge Univ, Cardiff, City Univ, Coventry Poly, Derbyshire Coll, Dundee Inst, Dundee Univ, Durham Univ, East Anglia Univ, East London Poly, Edinburgh Univ, Essex Univ, Exeter Univ, Glasgow Coll, Glasgow Univ, Hatfield Poly, Heriot-Watt Univ, Huddersfield Poly, Hull Univ, Imperial Coll, Kent Univ, King's Coll London, Kingston Poly, Lancashire Poly, Lancaster Univ, Leeds Poly, Leeds Univ, Leicester Poly, Leicester Univ, Liverpool Poly, Liverpool Univ, Loughborough Univ, Luton Coll, Manadon, Manchester Poly, Manchester Univ, Middlesex Poly, Napier Poly, Newcastle Poly, Newcastle Univ, North East Wales Inst, North London Poly, Nottingham Poly, Nottingham Univ, Open Univ, Oxford Poly, Oxford Univ, Paisley Coll, PCL, Portsmouth Poly, Queen Mary & Westfield, Ravensbourne Coll, Reading Univ, Robert Gordon's Inst, Salford Univ, Sheffield Poly, Sheffield Univ, Shrivenham, South Bank Poly, South West Poly, Southampton Univ, Staffs Poly, Strathclyde Univ, Sunderland Poly, Surrey Univ, Sussex Univ, Swansea, Teesside Poly, Thames Poly, Ulster Univ, University Coll London, UMIST, Wales Poly, Warwick Univ, West Glamorgan Inst, York Univ. *See also:* **Electrical engineering, engineering.**
Study area: Electrical & electronic engineering.

Electronics

Possible prospectuses: Aberystwyth, Anglia, Aston Univ, Bangor, Birmingham Univ, Bolton Inst, Bradford Univ, Brighton Poly, Bristol Poly, Brunel Univ, Cardiff, City Univ, Coventry Poly, Dundee Inst, Dundee Univ, Durham Univ, Edinburgh Univ, Essex Univ, Glasgow Coll, Glasgow Univ, Hatfield Poly, Heriot-Watt Univ, Huddersfield Poly, Imperial Coll, Keele Univ, Kent Univ, King's Coll London, Kingston Poly, Lancashire Poly, Lancaster Univ, Leeds Univ, Liverpool Poly, Liverpool Univ, Loughborough Univ, Manchester Univ, Middlesex Poly, Napier Poly, Newcastle Poly, Nottingham Poly, Nottingham Univ, Open Univ, Oxford Poly, Paisley Coll, PCL, Queen Mary & Westfield, Reading Univ, Robert Gordon's Inst, Royal Holloway & Bedford, St Andrews Univ, Salford Univ, Sheffield Univ, Southampton Univ, Staffs Poly, Sussex Univ, Ulster Univ, UMIST, Wales Poly, Warwick Univ, West Glamorgan Inst, York Univ.
Study area: Physics.

Embroidery

Possible prospectuses: Birmingham Poly, Edinburgh Coll Art, Glasgow Sch Art, Loughborough Coll, Manchester Poly, Royal Coll Art. *See also:* **Textiles**.
Study area: Art and design.

Embryology

See: **Biology; medicine**.

Energy engineering

Possible prospectuses: Heriot-Watt Univ, Imperial Coll, Leeds Univ, Napier Poly, PCL, South Bank Poly, Wales Poly.

Energy studies
Possible prospectuses: Brunel Univ, Glasgow Coll, Heriot-Watt Univ, Leeds Univ, Manchester Univ, Newcastle Univ, South Bank Poly.
Study area: Chemical engineering.

Engineering (General)
Possible prospectuses: Aberdeen Univ, Anglia, Aston Univ, Birmingham Poly, Bolton Inst, Bournemouth Poly, Brighton Poly, Bristol Poly, Brunel Univ, Camborne Sch Mines, Cambridge Univ, Cardiff, Coventry Poly, Durham Univ, East London Poly, Edinburgh Univ, Exeter Univ, Glasgow Coll, Heriot-Watt Univ, Hull Univ, Humberside Poly, Imperial Coll, Kingston Poly, Lancashire Poly, Lancaster Univ, Leicester Poly, Leicester Univ, Liverpool Poly, Liverpool Univ, Loughborough Univ, Manadon, Manchester Poly, Manchester Univ, Middlesex Poly, Napier Poly, National Extension Coll, Newcastle Poly, Newcastle Univ, North East Wales Inst, Nottingham Poly, Nottingham Univ, Open Univ, Oxford Poly, Oxford Univ, PCL, Portsmouth Poly, Queen Mary & Westfield, Reading Univ, Robert Gordon's Inst, Sheffield Poly, Shrivenham, Silsoe Coll, South Bank Poly, Southampton Univ, Staffs Poly, Sunderland Poly, Surrey Univ, Sussex Univ, Teesside Poly, Thames Poly, Ulster Univ, UMIST, Wales Poly, Warwick Univ, Wolverhampton Poly.
See also: eg **Electrical engineering, mechanical engineering**.

Engineering mathematics
Possible prospectuses: Aberdeen Univ, Bristol Univ, Brunel Univ, Glasgow Coll, Heriot-Watt Univ, Loughborough Univ, Napier Poly, National Extension Coll, Queen Mary & Westfield, Swansea.
See also: **Mathematics**.

English
Possible prospectuses: Aberdeen Univ, Aberystwyth, Anglia, Bangor, Bangor Normal Coll, Bedford Coll, Belfast Univ, Birkbeck, Birmingham Poly, Birmingham Univ, Bolton Inst, Bretton Hall, Brighton Poly, Bristol Poly, Bristol Univ, Buckingham Univ, Cambridge Univ, Cardiff, Central Sch Speech/Drama, Cheltenham & Gloucester Coll, Chester Coll, Christ Church Coll, Crewe & Alsager, Derbyshire Coll, Dundee Univ, Durham Univ, Ealing Coll, East Anglia Univ, Edge Hill, Edinburgh Univ, Essex Univ, Exeter Univ, Glasgow Univ, Goldsmiths' Coll, Hatfield Poly, Homerton, Huddersfield Poly, Hull Univ, Humberside Poly, Keele Univ, Kent Univ, King Alfred's Coll, King's Coll London, Kingston Poly, La Sainte Union, Lampeter, Lancashire Poly, Lancaster Univ, Leeds Univ, Leicester Poly, Leicester Univ, Liverpool Inst, Liverpool Poly, Liverpool Univ, Loughborough Univ, Luton Coll, Manchester Poly, Manchester Univ, Middlesex Poly, National Extension Coll, Nene Coll, Newcastle Poly, Newcastle Univ, North East Wales Inst, North London Poly, Nottingham Poly, Nottingham Univ, Open Univ, Oxford Poly, Oxford Univ, PCL, Portsmouth Poly, Queen Mary & Westfield, Reading Univ, Ripon & York St John, Roehampton Inst, Royal Holloway & Bedford, St Andrews Univ, St Mark & St John, S Martin's Coll, St Mary's Coll, Salford Univ, Sheffield Poly, Sheffield Univ, South West Poly, Southampton Univ, Staffs Poly, Stirling Univ, Strathclyde Univ, Sunderland Poly, Sussex Univ, Swansea, Teesside Poly, Trinity & All Saints, Ulster Univ, University Coll London, Wales Poly, Warwick

Univ, West Glamorgan Inst, West London Inst, West Sussex Inst, Wolverhampton Poly, Worcester Coll, York Univ.
Study area: English.

Entomology
See: Biology; zoology.

Environmental archaeology
Possible prospectuses: Inst Archaeology, Lampeter, Luton Coll, Sheffield Univ.
Study area: Archaeology.

Environmental engineering
Possible prospectuses: Bath Univ, Cardiff, City Univ, Imperial Coll, Liverpool Univ, Loughborough Univ, Luton Coll, Middlesex Poly, Silsoe Coll, South Bank Poly, Southampton Univ, Strathclyde Univ, Sunderland Poly, University Coll London.
Study area: Environmental science.

Environmental health
Possible prospectuses: Bristol Poly, Cardiff Inst, King's Coll London, Leeds Poly, Luton Coll, Manchester Poly, Nottingham Poly, Open Univ, Salford Univ, South Bank Poly, Strathclyde Univ, Thames Poly, Ulster Univ.

Environmental science
Possible prospectuses: Aberdeen Univ, Aberystwyth, Birkbeck, Bradford Univ, Brunel Univ, Cirencester, City Poly, Coventry Poly, Crewe & Alsager, Dundee Univ, East Anglia Univ, East London Poly, Edinburgh Univ, Essex Univ, Exeter Univ, Hull Univ, Keele Univ, Kent Univ, King's Coll London, Kingston Poly, Lancashire Poly, Lancaster Univ, Liverpool Poly, Loughborough Univ, Luton Coll, Manchester Poly, Middlesex Poly, Nene Coll, Newcastle Univ, North London Poly, Nottingham Univ, Open Univ, Oxford Poly, PCL, Queen Mary & Westfield, Reading Univ, Ripon & York St John, Royal Holloway & Bedford, Salford Univ, Sheffield Univ, South Bank Poly, South West Poly, Southampton Univ, Staffs Poly, Stirling Univ, Sussex Univ, Thames Poly, Ulster Univ, Wales Poly, Wolverhampton Poly, Worcester Coll, Wye Coll, York Univ.
Study area: Environmental science.

Environmental studies
Possible prospectuses: Aberdeen Univ, Aberystwyth, Anglia, Bangor Normal Coll, Bedford Coll, Belfast Univ, Bretton Hall, Buckinghamshire Coll, Cardiff, Crewe & Alsager, Derbyshire Coll, East Anglia Univ, Edinburgh Coll Art, Hatfield Poly, Humberside Poly, Leicester Poly, Liverpool Inst, Luton Coll, Manchester Poly, Manchester Univ, Newcastle Poly, North East Wales Inst, North London Poly, Open Univ, Oxford Poly, PCL, Portsmouth Poly, Queen Mary & Westfield, Roehampton Inst, Sheffield Poly, Sheffield Univ, Silsoe Coll, South Bank Poly, Stirling Univ, Sunderland Poly, Swansea, Thames Poly, University Coll London, UMIST, Wolverhampton Poly, Wye Coll. *See also:Environmental archaeology*.
Study area: Environmental studies.

Equine studies
Possible prospectus: Coventry Poly.

Ergonomics
Possible prospectuses: Aston Univ, Loughborough Univ.

Estate management
Possible prospectuses: Aberdeen Univ, Birmingham Poly, Bristol Poly, Cambridge Univ, Cirencester, City Univ, Coventry Poly, East London Poly, Edinburgh Coll Art, Heriot-Watt Univ, Kingston Poly, Leicester Poly, Liverpool Poly, Luton Coll, Newcastle Poly, Newcastle Univ, Nottingham Poly, Oxford Poly, PCL, Reading Univ, Sheffield Poly, South Bank Poly, South West Poly, Staffs Poly, Thames Poly, Ulster Univ, Wales Poly, Writtle. *See also: **Urban estate management**.*

Ethics
See: Philosophy; theology.

European business studies
Possible prospectuses: Anglia, Birmingham Univ, Brighton Poly, Bristol Poly, Buckingham Univ, Buckinghamshire Coll, Cardiff Inst, Cirencester, City Poly, Coventry Poly, Derbyshire Coll, Ealing Coll, East London Poly, European Bus Sch, Glasgow Coll, Hatfield Poly, Heriot-Watt Univ, Hull Univ, Humberside Poly, Kent Univ, Kingston Poly, Lancashire Poly, Lancaster Univ, Leeds Poly, Liverpool Poly, Luton Coll, Manchester Poly, Middlesex Poly, Nene Coll, Newcastle Poly, North London Poly, Nottingham Poly, PCL, Reading Univ, Robert Gordon's Inst, Sheffield Poly, South Bank Poly, South West Poly, Strathclyde Univ, Sunderland Poly, Swansea, Thames Poly, Ulster Univ, Wolverhampton Poly, Writtle.
Study area: Business studies; European studies.

European studies
Possible prospectuses: Aberdeen Univ, Aberystwyth, Anglia, Aston Univ, Bath Univ, Bedford Coll, Bradford Univ, Brunel Univ, Buckingham Univ, Cambridge Univ, Cardiff, Dundee Univ, Ealing Coll, East Anglia Univ, Edge Hill, Edinburgh Univ, Essex Univ, Hull Univ, Keele Univ, Kent Univ, King's Coll London, La Sainte Union, Lancashire Poly, Leicester Univ, Loughborough Univ, Manchester Poly, Manchester Univ, North London Poly, Nottingham Poly, Open Univ, PCL, Queen Mary & Westfield, Royal Holloway & Bedford, SSEES, Sheffield Poly, South Bank Poly, Southampton Univ, Staffs Poly, Surrey Univ, Sussex Univ, Thames Poly, Ulster Univ, University Coll London, Warwick Univ, Wolverhampton Poly.
*See also: eg **Scandinavian studies**.*
Study area: European studies.

Exploration

MENU
Prunes

I AM JUST GOING OUTSIDE, AND I MAY BE SOME TIME

Exploration
Possible prospectuses: Camborne Sch Mines, Cardiff, University Coll London. *See also: **Mining; geology**.*
Study area: Geology.

F

Fashion
Possible prospectuses: Birmingham Poly, Bretton Hall, Brighton Poly, Bristol Poly, Central St Martins, Cheltenham & Gloucester Coll, East London Poly, Edinburgh Coll Art, Heriot-Watt Univ, Kingston Poly, Lancashire Poly, Leicester Poly, Liverpool Poly, Manchester Poly, Middlesex Poly, Newcastle Poly, Nottingham Poly, PCL, Ravensbourne Coll, Royal Coll Art, Ulster Univ. *See also: **Textiles**.*
Study area: Art and design.

Fermentation
*See: **Biochemistry; microbiology**.*

Film making techniques
*See: **Film studies**.*

Film music
Possible prospectuses: London Int Film Sch, National Film Sch.

Film studies
Possible prospectuses: Central St Martins, Coventry Poly, Derbyshire Coll, Ealing Coll, East Anglia Univ, Glasgow Univ, Humberside Poly, Kent Inst, Kent Univ, London Coll Printing, London Int Film Sch, Manchester Poly, Middlesex Poly, Napier Poly, National Film Sch, Newcastle Poly, North London Poly, PCL, Portsmouth Poly, Reading Univ, Royal Coll Art, St Mark & St John, Sheffield Poly, Staffs Poly, Stirling Univ, Warwick Univ, West Glamorgan Inst, West Surrey Coll.
Study area: Art and design.

Finance
Possible prospectuses: Aberystwyth, Aston Univ, Bangor, Birmingham Poly, Bournemouth Poly, Buckingham Univ, Cardiff, Cheltenham & Gloucester Coll, Cirencester, City Poly, City Univ, Coventry Poly, Dundee Inst, Dundee Univ, Ealing Coll, East London Poly, European Bus Sch, Heriot-Watt Univ, Huddersfield Poly, Humberside Poly, Lancashire Poly, Lancaster Univ, Liverpool Poly, Loughborough Univ, Luton Coll, Nottingham Poly, Paisley Coll, PCL, Salford Univ, Scottish Coll Textiles, Sheffield Poly, South Bank Poly, Staffs Poly,

Strathclyde Univ, Teesside Poly, Thames Valley Coll, Ulster Univ, West Glamorgan Inst. *See also:* **Accountancy; business studies; economics.**
Study area: Business studies.

Fine art
See: **Painting; printmaking; sculpture; photography.**

Fine arts (art history)
Possible prospectuses: Aberdeen Univ, Aberystwyth, Birkbeck, Birmingham Poly, Birmingham Univ, Bretton Hall, Brighton Poly, Bristol Univ, British Institute in Paris, Camberwell Coll, Cambridge Univ, Cardiff Inst, Central St Martins, Cheltenham & Gloucester Coll, Chester Coll, Courtauld Institute, Coventry Poly, Derbyshire Coll, Dundee Univ, Ealing Coll, East Anglia Univ, Edinburgh Coll Art, Edinburgh Univ, Essex Univ, Exeter Univ, Glasgow Univ, Goldsmiths' Coll, Hull Univ, Humberside Poly, Kent Inst, Kent Univ, Kingston Poly, Lancashire Poly, Leeds Poly, Leeds Univ, Leicester Poly, Leicester Univ, Liverpool Poly, Manchester Poly, Manchester Univ, Middlesex Poly, Newcastle Poly, Newcastle Univ, Nottingham Poly, Nottingham Univ, Open Univ, Oxford Poly, Oxford Univ, Queen Mary & Westfield, Reading Univ, Roehampton Inst, St Andrews Univ, SOAS, Scottish Coll Textiles, Sheffield Poly, Slade, South West Poly, Staffs Poly, Sunderland Poly, Sussex Univ, Ulster Univ, University Coll London, Wales Poly, Warwick Univ, West Glamorgan Inst, West Surrey Coll, Winchester Sch Art, Wolverhampton Poly.
Study area: Fine arts.

Finnish studies
Possible prospectus: Hull Univ, National Extension Coll, SSEES.
See also: **Scandinavian studies.**
Study area: European studies.

Fishery science
Possible prospectuses: Aberdeen Univ, Cirencester, Edinburgh Univ, Humberside Poly, South West Poly.

Flying
Possible prospectus: Cranwell. *See also:* **Aeronautical engineering.**

Food science
Possible prospectuses: Belfast Univ, Bournemouth Poly, Cardiff, Ealing Coll, Harper Adams, Humberside Poly, King's Coll London, Leeds Univ, Manchester Poly, North London Poly, Nottingham Univ, Oxford Poly, Queen Margaret Coll, Reading Univ, Robert Gordon's Inst, Sheffield Poly, South Bank Poly, South West Poly, Strathclyde Univ, Surrey Univ, Ulster Univ.
See also: **Nutrition.**
Study area: Food science and nutrition.

Footwear
Possible prospectus: Leicester Poly, Scottish Coll Textiles, Teesside Poly. *See also:* **Textiles.**
Study area: Art and design.

Forensic science
See: **Chemistry.**

Forestry
Possible prospectuses: Aberdeen Univ, Bangor, Cirencester, Edinburgh Univ.
Study area: Agriculture, horticulture and forestry.

French
Possible prospectuses: Aberdeen Univ, Aberystwyth, Anglia, Aston Univ, Bangor, Bath Univ, Bedford Coll, Belfast Univ, Birkbeck, Birmingham Poly, Birmingham Univ, Bradford Univ, Bristol Poly, Bristol Univ, British Institute in Paris, Brunel Univ, Buckingham Univ, Cambridge Univ, Cardiff, Central Sch Speech/Drama, Chester Coll, City Poly, Coventry Poly, Crewe & Alsager, Derbyshire Coll, Durham Univ, Ealing Coll, East Anglia Univ, East London Poly, Edinburgh Univ, Essex Univ, European Bus Sch, Exeter Univ, Glasgow Coll, Glasgow Univ, Goldsmiths' Coll, Heriot-Watt Univ, Huddersfield Poly, Hull Univ, Humberside Poly, Keele Univ, Kent Univ, King's Coll London, Kingston Poly, La Sainte Union, Lampeter, Lancashire Poly, Lancaster Univ, Leeds Poly, Leeds Univ, Leicester Univ, Liverpool Inst, Liverpool Poly, Liverpool Univ, Loughborough Univ, Luton Coll, Manchester Poly, Manchester Univ, Middlesex Poly, National Extension Coll, Nene Coll, Newcastle Poly, Newcastle Univ, North London Poly, Nottingham Poly, Nottingham Univ, Oxford Poly, Oxford Univ, PCL, Portsmouth Poly, Queen Mary & Westfield, Reading Univ, Ripon & York St John, Roehampton Inst, Royal Holloway & Bedford, St Andrews Univ, Salford Univ, SSEES, Scottish Coll Textiles, Sheffield Poly, Sheffield Univ, South Bank Poly, Southampton Univ, Staffs Poly, Stirling Univ, Strathclyde Univ, Sunderland Poly, Surrey Univ, Sussex Univ, Swansea, Teesside Poly, Trinity & All Saints, Ulster Univ, University Coll London, UMIST, Warwick Univ, Wolverhampton Poly, York Univ.
Study area: Modern languages.

Freshwater biology
See: Marine biology.

Fuel science
See: Chemistry; energy studies.

Furniture design
Possible prospectuses: Birmingham Poly, Buckinghamshire Coll, City Poly, Edinburgh Coll Art, Goldsmiths' Coll, Heriot-Watt Univ, Kingston Poly, Leeds Poly, Leicester Poly, Loughborough Coll, Middlesex Poly, Nottingham Poly, Ravensbourne Coll, Royal Coll Art.
Study area: Art and design.

Furniture production
Possible prospectus: Heriot-Watt Univ.

G

Genetics
Possible prospectuses: Aberdeen Univ, Aberystwyth, Belfast Univ, Birmingham Univ, Cambridge Univ, Cardiff, Cirencester, East Anglia

Univ, Edinburgh Univ, Glasgow Univ, Leeds Univ, Leicester Univ, Liverpool Univ, Manchester Univ, Newcastle Univ, Nottingham Univ, Open Univ, St Andrews Univ, Sheffield Univ, Sussex Univ, Swansea, University Coll London, York Univ. *See also: **Biology**.*
Study area: Biology.

Geochemistry
Possible prospectuses: Aberystwyth, Cambridge Univ, Imperial Coll, Leicester Univ, Manchester Univ, Open Univ, Reading Univ, Royal Holloway & Bedford, St Andrews Univ, Thames Poly.
*See also: **Geology; chemistry**.*
Study area: Geology.

Geography
Possible prospectuses: Aberdeen Univ, Aberystwyth, Anglia, Bedford Coll, Belfast Univ, Birkbeck, Birmingham Univ, Bradford Univ, Brighton Poly, Bristol Poly, Bristol Univ, Cambridge Univ, Cheltenham & Gloucester Coll, Chester Coll, Christ Church Coll, City Poly, Coventry Poly, Crewe & Alsager, Derbyshire Coll, Dundee Univ, Durham Univ, Ealing Coll, East Anglia Univ, Edge Hill, Edinburgh Univ, Exeter Univ, Glasgow Coll, Glasgow Univ, Homerton, Huddersfield Poly, Hull Univ, Humberside Poly, Keele Univ, Kent Univ, King's Coll London, Kingston Poly, La Sainte Union, Lampeter, Lancashire Poly, Lancaster Univ, Leeds Univ, Leicester Univ, Liverpool Inst, Liverpool Poly, Liverpool Univ, LSE, Loughborough Univ, Luton Coll, Manchester Poly, Manchester Univ, Middlesex Poly, National Extension Coll, Nene Coll, Newcastle Poly, Newcastle Univ, North London Poly, Nottingham Univ, Open Univ, Oxford Poly, Oxford Univ, PCL, Portsmouth Poly, Queen Mary & Westfield, Reading Univ, Ripon & York St John, Roehampton Inst, Royal Holloway & Bedford, St Andrews Univ, St Mark & St John, S Martin's Coll, St Mary's Coll, Salford Univ, SOAS, Sheffield Poly, Sheffield Univ, South West Poly, Southampton Univ, Staffs Poly, Strathclyde Univ, Sunderland Poly, Sussex Univ, Swansea, Thames Poly, Trinity & All Saints, Ulster Univ, University Coll London, Wales Poly, Warwick Univ, West London Inst, West Sussex Inst, Wolverhampton Poly, Worcester Coll.
Study area: Geography.

Geology
Possible prospectuses: Aberdeen Univ, Aberystwyth, Anglia, Belfast Univ, Birkbeck, Birmingham Univ, Bristol Univ, Camborne Sch

Mines, Cambridge Univ, Cardiff, Cheltenham & Gloucester Coll, Derbyshire Coll, Durham Univ, East Anglia Univ, Edinburgh Univ, Glasgow Univ, Hatfield Poly, Imperial Coll, Keele Univ, Kingston Poly, Leeds Univ, Leicester Univ, Liverpool Poly, Liverpool Univ, Luton Coll, Manchester Univ, Middlesex Poly, North London Poly, Open Univ, Oxford Poly, Oxford Univ, Portsmouth Poly, Queen Mary & Westfield, Royal Holloway & Bedford, St Andrews Univ, Sheffield Poly, South West Poly, Southampton Univ, Staffs Poly, Sunderland Poly, Thames Poly, University Coll London, Wales Poly, West London Inst.
Study area: Geology.

Geophysics
Possible prospectuses: Aberystwyth, Bath Univ, Camborne Sch Mines, Cambridge Univ, Durham Univ, East Anglia Univ, Edinburgh Univ, Imperial Coll, Lancaster Univ, Leeds Univ, Leicester Univ, Liverpool Univ, Manchester Univ, Newcastle Univ, Open Univ, Southampton Univ, University Coll London. *See also: **Geology; physics**.*
Study area: Geology.

German
Possible prospectuses: Aberdeen Univ, Aberystwyth, Anglia, Aston Univ, Bangor, Bath Univ, Belfast Univ, Birkbeck, Birmingham Poly, Birmingham Univ, Bradford Univ, Bristol Poly, Bristol Univ, Brunel Univ, Buckingham Univ, Cambridge Univ, Cardiff, Central Sch Speech/Drama, City Poly, Coventry Poly, Durham Univ, Ealing Coll, East Anglia Univ, East London Poly, Edinburgh Univ, Essex Univ, European Bus Sch, Exeter Univ, Glasgow Univ, Goldsmiths' Coll, Heriot-Watt Univ, Hull Univ, Humberside Poly, Keele Univ, Kent Univ, King's Coll London, Kingston Poly, La Sainte Union, Lampeter, Lancashire Poly, Lancaster Univ, Leeds Poly, Leeds Univ, Leicester Univ, Liverpool Poly, Liverpool Univ, Loughborough Univ, Luton Coll, Manchester Poly, Manchester Univ, Middlesex Poly, National Extension Coll, Newcastle Poly, Newcastle Univ, North London Poly, Nottingham Poly, Nottingham Univ, Oxford Poly, Oxford Univ, PCL, Portsmouth Poly, Queen Mary & Westfield, Reading Univ, Royal Holloway & Bedford, St Andrews Univ, Salford Univ, SSEES, Sheffield Poly, Sheffield Univ, South Bank Poly, Southampton Univ, Staffs Poly, Strathclyde Univ, Sunderland Poly, Surrey Univ, Sussex Univ, Swansea, Trinity & All Saints, Ulster Univ, University Coll London, UMIST, Warwick Univ, Wolverhampton Poly, York Univ.
Study area: Modern languages.

Glass
Possible prospectuses: Birmingham Poly, Buckinghamshire Coll, Edinburgh Coll Art, Heriot-Watt Univ, Manchester Poly, Royal Coll Art, Sheffield Univ, Staffs Poly, Sunderland Poly, West Surrey Coll, Wolverhampton Poly. *See also: **Three dimensional design**.*
Study area: Art and design.

Goldsmithing
*See: **Silversmithing**.*

Government
*See: **Politics**.*

Graphic design
Possible prospectuses: Aberystwyth, Anglia, Bath Coll, Birmingham Poly, Bournemouth Poly, Brighton Poly, Bristol Poly, Camberwell Coll, Cardiff Inst, Central St Martins, Coventry Poly, Derbyshire Coll, Duncan of Jordanstone, Dundee Univ, Ealing Coll, Edinburgh Coll Art, Falmouth, Glasgow Sch Art, Goldsmiths' Coll, Heriot-Watt Univ, Humberside Poly, Kent Inst, Kingston Poly, Lancashire Poly, Leeds Poly, Leicester Poly, Liverpool Poly, London Coll Printing, Luton Coll, Manchester Poly, Middlesex Poly, Newcastle Poly, Norfolk Inst, Nottingham Poly, PCL, Portsmouth Poly, Ravensbourne Coll, Reading Univ, Robert Gordon's Inst, Royal Coll Art, South West Poly, Staffs Poly, Ulster Univ, West Surrey Coll, Wolverhampton Poly.
Study area: Art and design.

Greek, Ancient/classical
Possible prospectuses: Aberystwyth, Belfast Univ, Birkbeck, Birmingham Univ, Bristol Univ, Cambridge Univ, Durham Univ, Edinburgh Univ, Glasgow Univ, Kent Univ, King's Coll London, Lampeter, Leeds Univ, London Bible, Manchester Univ, Newcastle Univ, Nottingham Univ, Oxford Univ, Reading Univ, Royal Holloway & Bedford, St Andrews Univ, Swansea, University Coll London. *See also: Classics.*
Study area: Classics.

Greek, Modern
Possible prospectuses: Birmingham Univ, Cambridge Univ, Edinburgh Univ, King's Coll London, National Extension Coll, Oxford Univ.
Study area: Modern languages.

Gujarati
Possible prospectus: SOAS. *See also: Asian studies.*
Study area: Asian studies.

H

Harbours
See: Civil engineering.

Hausa
Possible prospectus: SOAS. *See also: African studies.*
Study area: African studies.

Health
Possible prospectuses: Aberdeen Univ, Anglia, Bangor, Bournemouth Poly, Chester Coll, Coventry Poly, Crewe & Alsager, Derbyshire Coll, East London Poly, Hull Univ, Humberside Poly, Lancashire Poly, Leeds Poly, Liverpool Poly, Liverpool Univ, North London Poly, Open Univ, PCL, Queen Margaret Coll, Queen's Coll Glasgow, Robert Gordon's Inst, Sheffield Poly, Sunderland Poly, West Sussex Inst, Wolverhampton Poly.

Hebrew
Possible prospectuses: Aberdeen Univ, Belfast Univ, Cambridge Univ, Cardiff, Edinburgh Univ, Glasgow Univ, Jews' Coll, Liverpool Univ, London Bible, Manchester Univ, Oxford Univ, St Andrews Univ, SOAS, University Coll London. *See also: **Near East studies; religious studies**.*
Study area: Near East & Islamic studies.

Hellenistic studies
*See: **Classics; Greek, Ancient**.*

Highway/traffic
*See: **Civil engineering; town planning; transport studies**.*

Hindi
Possible prospectuses: Cambridge Univ, SOAS. *See also: **Asian studies**.*
Study area: Asian studies.

Hindustani
*See: **Asian studies**.*

Hispanic studies
Possible prospectuses: Aberdeen Univ, Belfast Univ, Birmingham Univ, Bristol Univ, Cardiff, Ealing Coll, Edinburgh Univ, Glasgow Univ, Hull Univ, King's Coll London, Leeds Univ, Liverpool Univ, Manchester Univ, North London Poly, Portsmouth Poly, Queen Mary & Westfield, St Andrews Univ, Salford Univ, Sheffield Univ, Southampton Univ, Swansea, Wolverhampton Poly. *See also: **Iberian studies; Portuguese; Latin American studies**.*
Study areas: European studies; Latin American studies; Spanish.

History
Possible prospectuses: Aberdeen Univ, Aberystwyth, Anglia, Bangor, Bangor Normal Coll, Bedford Coll, Belfast Univ, Birkbeck,

Birmingham Univ, Bolton Inst, Bradford Univ, Brighton Poly, Bristol Poly, Bristol Univ, Buckingham Univ, Cambridge Univ, Cardiff, Cheltenham & Gloucester Coll, Chester Coll, Christ Church Coll, Coventry Poly, Crewe & Alsager, Derbyshire Coll, Dundee Univ, Durham Univ, Ealing Coll, East Anglia Univ, Edge Hill, Edinburgh Univ, Essex Univ, Exeter Univ, Glasgow Univ, Goldsmiths' Coll, Hatfield Poly, Homerton, Huddersfield Poly, Hull Univ, Humberside Poly, Keele Univ, Kent Univ, King Alfred's Coll, King's Coll London, Kingston Poly, La Sainte Union, Lampeter, Lancashire Poly, Lancaster Univ, Leeds Poly, Leeds Univ, Leicester Poly, Leicester Univ, Liverpool Inst, Liverpool Poly, Liverpool Univ, LSE, Luton Coll, Manchester Poly, Manchester Univ, Middlesex Poly, Nene Coll, Newcastle Poly, Newcastle Univ, North East Wales Inst, North London Poly, Nottingham Poly, Nottingham Univ, Open Univ, Oxford Poly, Oxford Univ, PCL, Portsmouth Poly, Queen Mary & Westfield, Reading Univ, Ripon & York St John, Roehampton Inst, Royal Holloway & Bedford, St Andrews Univ, St Mark & St John, S Martin's Coll, St Mary's Coll, Salford Univ, SOAS, SSEES, Sheffield Poly, Sheffield Univ, South West Poly, Southampton Univ, Staffs Poly, Stirling Univ, Strathclyde Univ, Sunderland Poly, Sussex Univ, Swansea, Teesside Poly, Trinity & All Saints, Ulster Univ, University Coll London, Wales Poly, Warwick Univ, West London Inst, West Sussex Inst, Wolverhampton Poly, Worcester Coll, York Univ.
See also: **eg Economic history; social history**.
Study area: History.

History of art
See: **Fine arts.**

History of Science
Possible prospectuses: Belfast Univ, Cambridge Univ, Edinburgh Univ, Keele Univ, Kent Univ, King's Coll London, Lancaster Univ, Leeds Univ, Leicester Univ, Open Univ, St Andrews Univ.
Study area: History.

Home economics
Possible prospectuses: Bath Coll, Bradford & Ilkley, Cardiff, Duncan of Jordanstone, Ealing Coll, Leeds Poly, Liverpool Poly, Manchester Poly, Middlesex Poly, North London Poly, Queen Margaret Coll, Robert Gordon's Inst, Roehampton Inst, Sheffield Poly, South Bank Poly, Trinity & All Saints, Ulster Univ, Worcester Coll.

Horticulture

Possible prospectuses: Bath Univ, Cirencester, Hatfield Poly, Lancashire Poly, Nottingham Univ, Reading Univ, Strathclyde Univ, Thames Poly, Writtle, Wye Coll.
Study area: Agriculture, horticulture and forestry.

Hotel and catering management

Possible prospectuses: Birmingham Poly, Bournemouth Poly, Brighton Poly, Buckingham Univ, Cardiff, Cheltenham & Gloucester Coll, Duncan of Jordanstone, Dundee Univ, Ealing Coll, Huddersfield Poly, Lancashire Poly, Leeds Poly, Manchester Poly, Middlesex Poly, Napier Poly, North London Poly, Nottingham Poly, Oxford Poly, Portsmouth Poly, Queen Margaret Coll, Queen's Coll Glasgow, Robert Gordon's Inst, Sheffield Poly, South Bank Poly, South West Poly, Strathclyde Univ, Surrey Univ, Thames Valley Coll, Ulster Univ, Wolverhampton Poly.
Study area: Hotel & catering management.

Hotel & Catering Management

Housing administration

Possible prospectuses: Bristol Poly, Edinburgh Coll Art, Edinburgh Univ, Heriot-Watt Univ, Humberside Poly, PCL, Salford Univ, Sheffield Poly, South Bank Poly, Stirling Univ, Ulster Univ.
See also: Estate management.

Human biology

Possible prospectuses: Aberdeen Univ, Aston Univ, Cambridge Univ, East London Poly, Hatfield Poly, King's Coll London, Liverpool Univ, Loughborough Univ, Manchester Univ, Nene Coll, Nottingham Poly, Oxford Poly, PCL. *See also: Anatomy; physiology.*
Study area: Anatomy; biology; physiology.

Human communication

Possible prospectuses: Coventry Poly, Kent Univ, Lancaster Univ, Queen Margaret Coll, Ulster Univ, Wales Poly.

See also: **Communications studies; psychology.**
Study areas: Communication studies; psychology.

Human movement
See: Movement studies.

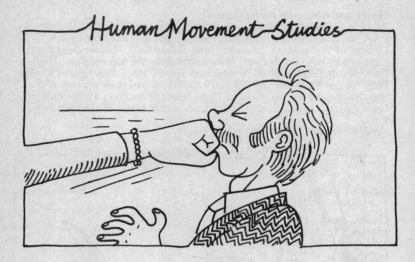

Human sciences
Possible prospectuses: Bradford Univ, Brunel Univ, East London Poly, King's Coll London, Loughborough Univ, Nottingham Poly, Oxford Univ, Reading Univ, Surrey Univ, Sussex Univ, University Coll London. *See also:* **Biosocial science.**

Humanities
Possible prospectuses: Bangor Normal Coll, Birkbeck, Bolton Inst, Bradford Univ, Bretton Hall, Brighton Poly, Bristol Poly, Cambridge Univ, Crewe & Alsager, Derbyshire Coll, Ealing Coll, East London Poly, Edge Hill, Hatfield Poly, Humberside Poly, Kent Univ, King's Coll London, Kingston Poly, Leicester Poly, Liverpool Poly, Manchester Poly, Newcastle Poly, North London Poly, Nottingham Poly, Open Univ, Oxford Poly, Royal Coll Art, St Mark & St John, South West Poly, Southampton Univ, Staffs Poly, Sunderland Poly, Teesside Poly, Thames Poly, Trinity Coll Carmarthen, Ulster Univ, Wales Poly, West Glamorgan Inst, Wolverhampton Poly.

Hungarian
Possible prospectuses: Cambridge Univ, SSEES.
Study area: Modern languages.

Hydraulic engineering
See: Civil engineering.

I

Iberian studies
Possible prospectuses: Manchester Univ, Southampton Univ, University Coll London. *See also: **Hispanic studies; Portuguese; Spanish.***
Study area: European studies.

Icelandic
Possible prospectus: University Coll London.
*See also: **Scandinavian studies.***
Study area: Modern languages.

Illustration
*See: **Graphic design.***

Immunology
Possible prospectuses: Aberdeen Univ, Brunel Univ, Edinburgh Univ, Glasgow Univ, King's Coll London, Strathclyde Univ, University Coll London. *See also: **Bacteriology; microbiology.***
Study area: Microbiology.

Indian studies
*See: **Asian studies.***

Indonesian studies
Possible prospectus: SOAS.
Study area: Asian studies.

Industrial design
Possible prospectuses: Birmingham Poly, Bournemouth Poly, Brunel Univ, Cardiff Inst, Central St Martins, Coventry Poly, East London Poly, Glasgow Sch Art, Glasgow Univ, Heriot-Watt Univ, Huddersfield Poly, Imperial Coll, Leeds Poly, Leicester Poly, Manchester Poly, Napier Poly, Newcastle Poly, Open Univ, Ravensbourne Coll, Royal Coll Art, Scottish Coll Textiles, Sheffield Poly, South Bank Poly, Teesside Poly. *See also: **Three dimensional design.***
Study area: Art and design.

Industrial engineering
Possible prospectuses: East London Poly, Hatfield Poly, Heriot-Watt Univ, Imperial Coll, Manchester Univ, Napier Poly, Nottingham Poly, Paisley Coll, Royal Coll Art, Surrey Univ, Wales Poly, Wolverhampton Poly.
Study area: Mechanical & production engineering.

Industrial relations
Possible prospectuses: Brunel Univ, Cambridge Univ, Cardiff, Coventry Poly, Kent Univ, Lancaster Univ, Leeds Univ, LSE, PCL, Scottish Coll Textiles, Southampton Univ, Stirling Univ, Strathclyde Univ. *See also: **Business studies; economics; law; sociology.***
Study area: Industrial relations.

Industrial studies
Possible prospectuses: Aberdeen Univ, Birmingham Poly, Loughborough Univ, Napier Poly, Nottingham Poly, Nottingham Univ, Paisley Coll, Sheffield Poly.

Informatics
Possible prospectuses: Heriot-Watt Univ, Lampeter, Queen Mary & Westfield, South West Poly.

Information design
See: Graphic design.

Information science
Possible prospectuses: Aberystwyth, Buckinghamshire Coll, Cambridge Univ, Ealing Coll, Hull Univ, Imperial Coll, Luton Coll, North London Poly, Open Univ, Portsmouth Poly, South Bank Poly, Staffs Poly, Strathclyde Univ, UMIST.

Information studies
Possible prospectuses: Aberystwyth, Belfast Univ, Birmingham Poly, Ealing Coll, East London Poly, Leeds Poly, Liverpool Poly, Loughborough Univ, Luton Coll, Manchester Poly, Newcastle Poly, North London Poly, Queen Margaret Coll, Robert Gordon's Inst, Scottish Coll Textiles, Sheffield Univ. *See also: Library studies.*
Study area: Library & information studies.

Information technology
Possible prospectuses: Aberystwyth, Aston Univ, Belfast Univ, Birmingham Poly, Bradford Univ, Brighton Poly, Bristol Poly, Brunel Univ, Cheltenham & Gloucester Coll, City Poly, Coventry Poly, Derbyshire Coll, Ealing Coll, Edinburgh Univ, European Bus Sch, Glasgow Coll, Heriot-Watt Univ, Huddersfield Poly, Humberside Poly, Imperial Coll, Kingston Poly, Lancashire Poly, Lancaster Univ, Leicester Poly, Loughborough Univ, Luton Coll, Manchester Poly, Manchester Univ, Middlesex Poly, Napier Poly, Newcastle Poly, North Cheshire Coll, North London Poly, Nottingham Poly, Open Univ, Paisley Coll, PCL, Portsmouth Poly, Reading Univ, Robert Gordon's Inst, St Mark & St John, Salford Univ, Scottish Coll Textiles, Sheffield Poly, Sheffield Univ, Shrivenham, South Bank Poly, Staffs Poly, Strathclyde Univ, Sunderland Poly, Surrey Univ, Teesside Poly, Thames Poly, Wales Poly, West Glamorgan Inst, Wolverhampton Poly.
Study area: Information technology.

Instrumentation
Possible prospectuses: Glasgow Coll, Luton Coll, Manchester Poly, Open Univ, Teesside Poly.

Insurance
See: Actuarial studies; business studies.

Interior design
Possible prospectuses: Birmingham Poly, Brighton Poly, Buckinghamshire Coll, Cardiff Inst, City Poly, Duncan of Jordanstone, Dundee Univ, Edinburgh Coll Art, Glasgow Sch Art, Heriot-Watt Univ, Kingston Poly, Leeds Poly, Leicester Poly, Manchester Poly, Middlesex Poly, Napier Poly, North London Poly, Nottingham Poly, Ravensbourne Coll,Royal Coll Art, Scottish Coll Textiles, Teesside Poly.
Study area: Art and design.

International relations
Possible prospectuses: Aberdeen Univ, Aberystwyth, Birmingham
Univ, Bradford Univ, Coventry Poly, Ealing Coll, Keele Univ, Kent
Univ, Lancaster Univ, LSE, Nottingham Poly, Open Univ, Reading
Univ, St Andrews Univ, Scottish Coll Textiles, South Bank Poly,
Southampton Univ, Staffs Poly, Surrey Univ, Sussex Univ, Ulster
Univ, Warwick Univ. *See also: Politics; war studies.*
Study area: Politics & government.

Interpretation and translation
Possible prospectuses: British Institute in Paris, Ealing Coll, Heriot-
Watt Univ, Salford Univ, Scottish Coll Textiles, Ulster Univ.
Study area: Modern languages.

Investment
See: Business studies.

Iranian studies
See: Near East studies.

Irish studies
Possible prospectuses: Aberystwyth, Belfast Univ, Liverpool Univ,
Manchester Univ, North London Poly, St Mary's Coll, Ulster Univ.
See also: Celtic studies.
Study area: European studies.

Islamic studies
Possible prospectuses: Durham Univ, Edinburgh Univ, Exeter Univ,
Lampeter, Manchester Univ, Newcastle Univ, Oxford Univ, St
Andrews Univ, SOAS.
Study area: Near East and Islamic studies.

Italian
Possible prospectuses: Aberystwyth, Anglia, Belfast Univ, Birmingham
Univ, Bristol Univ, Cambridge Univ, Cardiff, Durham Univ,
Edinburgh Univ, European Bus Sch, Exeter Univ, Glasgow Univ, Hull
Univ, Kent Univ, Lancashire Poly, Lancaster Univ, Leeds Univ,
Leicester Univ, Luton Coll, Manchester Univ, National Extension Coll,
Oxford Univ, PCL, Reading Univ, Royal Holloway & Bedford, Salford
Univ, SSEES, Scottish Coll Textiles, Sheffield Poly, Strathclyde Univ,
Sussex Univ, Swansea, University Coll London, Warwick Univ.
Study area: Modern languages.

J

Japanese
Possible prospectuses: Cambridge Univ, Cardiff, Edinburgh Univ,
Glasgow Coll, Leeds Univ, Luton Coll, Oxford Univ, SOAS, Sheffield
Univ, Stirling Univ. *See also: Asian studies.*
Study area: Asian studies.

Jewellery
Possible prospectuses: Birmingham Poly, Buckinghamshire Coll, Central
St Martins, City Poly, Crewe & Alsager, Duncan of Jordanstone,

Dundee Univ, Edinburgh Coll Art, Glasgow Sch Art, Heriot-Watt Univ, Loughborough Coll, Middlesex Poly, Robert Gordon's Inst, Royal Coll Art, Sheffield Poly, Ulster Univ. *See also: **Three dimensional design**. Study area:* Art and design.

Jewish studies
Possible prospectuses: Jews' Coll, Manchester Univ, SOAS, University Coll London. *See also: **Hebrew**. Study areas:* Religious studies & theology.

Journalism
*See: **Communication studies**.*

Jurisprudence
*See: **Law**.*

L

Labour
*See: **Business studies; economics; industrial relations; law; politics; sociology**.*

Land administration
*See: **Estate management**.*

Land economy
Possible prospectuses: Aberdeen Univ, Cambridge Univ, Cirencester, Harper Adams, Hull Univ, Paisley Coll, Wye Coll.

Land surveying
*See: **Quantity surveying**.*

Landscape architecture
Possible prospectuses: Cheltenham & Gloucester Coll, Edinburgh Coll Art, Heriot-Watt Univ, Leeds Poly, Manchester Poly, Manchester Univ, Sheffield Univ, Thames Poly.

Landscape studies
Possible prospectuses: Edinburgh Coll Art, Heriot-Watt Univ, Kingston Poly, Manchester Univ, Reading Univ, Sheffield Univ, Writtle. *See also: **Architecture; geography; horticulture**.*

Languages
*See: **Individual languages** (eg **French**) or **regional studies*** (eg African studies).

Laser
*See: **Physics**.*

Latin
Possible prospectuses: Aberystwyth, Belfast Univ, Birkbeck, Birmingham Univ, Bristol Univ, Cambridge Univ, Durham Univ, Edinburgh Univ, Exeter Univ, Glasgow Univ, Hull Univ, Kent Univ, King's Coll London, Lampeter, Lancaster Univ, Leeds Univ, Manchester Univ, Newcastle Univ, Nottingham Univ, Oxford Univ, Reading Univ, Royal Holloway & Bedford, St Andrews Univ, Swansea, University Coll London, Warwick Univ. *See also: **Classics**.*
Study area: Classics.

Latin American studies
Possible prospectuses: Aberdeen Univ, Bristol Univ, Cambridge Univ, Ealing Coll, Essex Univ, Glasgow Univ, King's Coll London, Leeds Univ, Liverpool Univ, Manchester Univ, Newcastle Univ, North London Poly, Portsmouth Poly, St Andrews Univ, Southampton Univ, University Coll London, Warwick Univ. *See also: **Hispanic studies; Iberian studies; Portuguese; Spanish**.*
Study area: Latin American studies.

Law
Possible prospectuses: Aberdeen Univ, Aberystwyth, Anglia, Belfast Univ, Birmingham Poly, Birmingham Univ, Bournemouth Poly, Bristol Poly, Bristol Univ, Brunel Univ, Buckingham Univ, Buckland, Cambridge Univ, Cardiff, City Poly, City Univ, Coventry Poly, Dundee Univ, Durham Univ, Ealing Coll, East Anglia Univ, East London Poly, Edinburgh Univ, Essex Univ, Exeter Univ, Glasgow Univ, Hatfield Poly, Holborn Coll, Huddersfield Poly, Hull Univ, Keele Univ, Kent Univ, King's Coll London, Kingston Poly, Lancashire Poly, Lancaster Univ, Leeds Poly, Leeds Univ, Leicester Poly, Leicester Univ, Liverpool Poly, Liverpool Univ, LSE, Manchester Poly, Manchester Univ, Middlesex Poly, Napier Poly, National Extension Coll, Nene Coll, Newcastle Poly, Newcastle Univ, North London Poly, Nottingham Univ, Oxford Poly, Oxford Univ, PCL, Queen Mary & Westfield, Rapid Results Coll, Reading Univ, SOAS, Sheffield Poly, Sheffield Univ, South Bank Poly, South West Poly, Southampton Univ,

Staffs Poly, Strathclyde Univ, Surrey Univ, Sussex Univ, Teesside
Poly, University Coll London, Wales Poly, Warwick Univ, West
Glamorgan Inst, Wolverhampton Poly.
Study area: Law.

Leisure studies
Possible prospectuses: Anglia, Bournemouth Poly, Ealing Coll,
Humberside Poly, Leeds Poly, North London Poly, Teesside Poly,
Writtle.

Levant
*See: **Archaeology.***

Library studies
Possible prospectuses: Aberystwyth, Birmingham Poly, Brighton Poly,
Ealing Coll, Leeds Poly, Liverpool Poly, Loughborough Univ,
Manchester Poly, Newcastle Poly, North London Poly, Robert
Gordon's Inst. *See also: **Information studies.***
Study area: Library & information studies.

Life science
*See: **Biology.***

Linguistics
Possible prospectuses: Bangor, Brighton Poly, Cambridge Univ,
Durham Univ, East Anglia Univ, Edinburgh Univ, Essex Univ, Exeter
Univ, Hatfield Poly, Kent Univ, Lancashire Poly, Lancaster Univ,
Leeds Univ, Manchester Univ, Newcastle Univ, Nottingham Univ,
PCL, Reading Univ, St Mark & St John, SOAS, Sheffield Univ,
Southampton Univ, Surrey Univ, Sussex Univ, University Coll
London, UMIST, York Univ.
*See also: Individual languages, eg **French**.*
Study area: Linguistics.

Literature
*See: Individual languages, eg **Chinese**.*

Logic
*See: **Mathematics; philosophy.***

M

Malay studies
Possible prospectus: SOAS.
Study area: Asian studies.

Management
Possible prospectuses: Aberdeen Univ, Aston Univ, Birmingham Univ,
Bradford Univ, Bristol Poly, Brunel Univ, Cambridge Univ, Cardiff,
Cirencester, City Univ, Dundee Inst, Ealing Coll, East London Poly,
Edge Hill, Glasgow Coll, Glasgow Univ, Hatfield Poly, Heriot-Watt
Univ, Holborn Coll, Hull Univ, Humberside Poly, Keele Univ, Kent
Univ, King's Coll London, Kingston Poly, Lancashire Poly, Lancaster
Univ, Leeds Poly, Leeds Univ, Liverpool Univ, London Business Sch,
LSE, Loughborough Univ, Luton Coll, Manchester Business Sch,

Manchester Univ, Newcastle Univ, Nottingham Poly, Nottingham
Univ, Oxford Poly, Oxford Univ, PCL, Reading Univ, Royal Holloway
& Bedford, St Andrews Univ, Salford Univ, Sheffield Univ, Silsoe Coll,
South Bank Poly, Southampton Univ, Stirling Univ, Strathclyde Univ,
Sunderland Poly, Sussex Univ, Swansea, Teesside Poly, Trinity & All
Saints, Ulster Univ, UMIST, Warwick Univ, Writtle, Wye Coll. *See
also:* ***Business studies; economics; estate management; hotel &
catering management; public administration.***
Study area: Business studies.

Manufacturing engineering
Possible prospectuses: Aberdeen Univ, Aston Univ, Bath Univ, Belfast
Univ, Birmingham Poly, Birmingham Univ, Bolton Inst, Bradford
Univ, Bristol Poly, Bristol Univ, Brunel Univ, Cambridge Univ,
Cardiff, Coventry Poly, Derbyshire Coll, Dundee Univ, East London
Poly, Exeter Univ, Glasgow Coll, Hatfield Poly, Heriot-Watt Univ,
Huddersfield Poly, Hull Univ, Imperial Coll, Kingston Poly, Leeds
Poly, Leeds Univ, Liverpool Poly, Liverpool Univ, Loughborough
Univ, Luton Coll, Manchester Univ, Newcastle Poly, North East Wales
Inst, Nottingham Poly, Open Univ, Paisley Coll, PCL, Portsmouth
Poly, Salford Univ, Sheffield Poly, South West Poly, Staffs Poly,
Sunderland Poly, Ulster Univ, UMIST, Warwick Univ,
Wolverhampton Poly. *See also:* ***Production engineering.***
Study area: Mechanical and production engineering.

Marathi
Possible prospectus: SOAS. *See also:* ***Asian studies.***
Study area: Asian studies.

Marine architecture
Possible prospectuses: Newcastle Univ, Strathclyde Univ, University
Coll London. *See also:* ***Naval architecture; naval engineering.***
Study area: Marine technology.

Marine biology
Possible prospectuses: Aberdeen Univ, Bangor, Heriot-Watt Univ, Hull
Univ, Liverpool Univ, Newcastle Univ, Portsmouth Poly, St Andrews
Univ, Southampton Univ, Stirling Univ, Swansea. *See also:* ***Maritime
studies.***
Study area: Biology.

Marine engineering
Possible prospectuses: Liverpool Poly, Liverpool Univ, Manadon,
Newcastle Univ, Surrey Univ.
Study area: Marine technology.

Maritime studies

Registration 10.00
Sick bag distribution 10.30
Lunch 12.00-13.00
Sick bag collection 14.00

Maritime studies
Possible prospectuses: Cardiff, Liverpool Poly, Manadon, South West Poly, Southampton Univ, Surrey Univ.
Study area: Maritime studies.

Marketing
Possible prospectuses: Aberystwyth, Aston Univ, Bournemouth Poly, Cheltenham & Gloucester Coll, Cirencester, City Poly, Coventry Poly, European Bus Sch, Glasgow Coll, Harper Adams, Hatfield Poly, Huddersfield Poly, Humberside Poly, Kingston Poly, Lancashire Poly, Lancaster Univ, Leicester Poly, Loughborough Univ, Luton Coll, Manchester Poly, Newcastle Univ, Paisley Coll, PCL, Salford Univ, Silsoe Coll, South West Poly, Staffs Poly, Stirling Univ, Strathclyde Univ, Sunderland Poly, Teesside Poly, Thames Poly, Ulster Univ, UMIST, Writtle. *See also: **Business studies**.*
Study area: Business studies.

Materials science
Possible prospectuses: Bath Univ, Birmingham Univ, Cambridge Univ, Dundee Univ, Imperial Coll, Leeds Univ, Liverpool Univ, Loughborough Univ, Manchester Poly, Manchester Univ, Nottingham Poly, Nottingham Univ, Open Univ, Oxford Univ, PCL, Queen Mary & Westfield, Robert Gordon's Inst, Sheffield Poly, Sheffield Univ, Shrivenham, Strathclyde Univ, Sunderland Poly, Surrey Univ, Swansea, Thames Poly, UMIST, Wolverhampton Poly. *See also: **Chemistry; engineering**.*
Study area: Metallurgy & materials science.

Materials technology
Possible prospectuses: Birmingham Univ, Brunel Univ, Coventry Poly, Imperial Coll, Leeds Univ, Loughborough Univ, Manchester Univ, Nottingham Poly, Open Univ, Sheffield Poly, Sheffield Univ, South West Poly, Surrey Univ, Swansea, UMIST.
Study area: Metallurgy & materials science.

Mathematics
Possible prospectuses: Aberdeen Univ, Aberystwyth, Aston Univ, Bangor, Bangor Normal Coll, Bath Univ, Belfast Univ, Birkbeck, Birmingham Univ, Bolton Inst, Bradford Univ, Brighton Poly, Bristol Univ, Brunel Univ, Buckingham Univ, Cambridge Univ, Cardiff, Cheltenham & Gloucester Coll, Chester Coll, Christ Church Coll, City Poly, City Univ, Coventry Poly, Crewe & Alsager, Dundee Inst, Dundee Univ, Durham Univ, East Anglia Univ, East London Poly, Edinburgh Univ, Essex Univ, Exeter Univ, Glasgow Coll, Glasgow Univ, Goldsmiths' Coll, Hatfield Poly, Heriot-Watt Univ, Homerton, Hull Univ, Imperial Coll, Keele Univ, Kent Univ, King's Coll London, Kingston Poly, La Sainte Union, Lancashire Poly, Lancaster Univ, Leeds Univ, Leicester Poly, Leicester Univ, Liverpool Inst, Liverpool Poly, Liverpool Univ, LSE, Loughborough Univ, Luton Coll, Manchester Poly, Manchester Univ, Middlesex Poly, Napier Poly, Nene Coll, Newcastle Poly, North London Poly, Nottingham Poly, Nottingham Univ, Open Univ, Oxford Poly, Oxford Univ, Paisley Coll, PCL, Portsmouth Poly, Queen Mary & Westfield, Reading Univ, Robert Gordon's Inst, Roehampton Inst, Royal Holloway & Bedford,

St Andrews Univ, St Mark & St John, St Mary's Coll, Salford Univ, Sheffield Poly, Sheffield Univ, South Bank Poly, South West Poly, Southampton Univ, Staffs Poly, Stirling Univ, Strathclyde Univ, Sunderland Poly, Surrey Univ, Sussex Univ, Swansea, Teesside Poly, Thames Poly, Trinity & All Saints, Ulster Univ, University Coll London, UMIST, Wales Poly, Warwick Univ, Wolverhampton Poly, Worcester Coll, York Univ.
Study area: Mathematical studies.

Mechanical engineering
Possible prospectuses: Aberdeen Univ, Aston Univ, Bath Univ, Belfast Univ, Birmingham Univ, Bradford Univ, Brighton Poly, Bristol Poly, Bristol Univ, Brunel Univ, Cambridge Univ, Cardiff, City Univ, Coventry Poly, Derbyshire Coll, Dundee Inst, Dundee Univ, Durham Univ, Edinburgh Univ, Exeter Univ, Glasgow Coll, Glasgow Univ, Hatfield Poly, Heriot-Watt Univ, Huddersfield Poly, Hull Univ, Humberside Poly, Imperial Coll, King's Coll London, Kingston Poly, Lancashire Poly, Lancaster Univ, Leeds Univ, Leicester Poly, Leicester Univ, Liverpool Poly, Liverpool Univ, Loughborough Univ, Luton Coll, Manadon, Manchester Poly, Manchester Univ, Middlesex Poly, Newcastle Poly, Newcastle Univ, Nottingham Poly, Nottingham Univ, Open Univ, Oxford Poly, Oxford Univ, Paisley Coll, PCL, Portsmouth Poly, Queen Mary & Westfield, Reading Univ, Robert Gordon's Inst, Salford Univ, Sheffield Poly, Sheffield Univ, Shrivenham, South West Poly, Southampton Univ, Staffs Poly, Strathclyde Univ, Sunderland Poly, Surrey Univ, Sussex Univ, Swansea, Teesside Poly, Thames Poly, Ulster Univ, University Coll London, UMIST, Wales Poly, Warwick Univ, Wolverhampton Poly.
See also: **Engineering.**
Study area: Mechanical & production engineering.

Media and production
See: **Graphic design.**

Media studies
Possible prospectuses: Birmingham Poly, Birmingham Univ, Bournemouth Poly, Brunel Univ, City Univ, Coventry Poly, Durham Univ, Ealing Coll, Edge Hill, Huddersfield Poly, Kent Inst, Leicester Poly, Liverpool Poly, London Coll Printing, Luton Coll, Manchester Poly, Newcastle Poly, North Cheshire Coll, Nottingham Univ, PCL, Portsmouth Poly, Queen Margaret Coll, St Mark & St John, Slade, South West Poly, Staffs Poly, Stirling Univ, Sunderland Poly, Sussex Univ, Trinity & All Saints, Ulster Univ, Wales Poly, West Glamorgan Inst, Wolverhampton Poly.
See also: **Communication studies.**
Study area: Communication studies.

Medical laboratory science
Possible prospectuses: Bradford Univ, Cardiff Inst, Leeds Poly, Leicester Poly, Manchester Poly, PCL, Sunderland Poly, Ulster Univ.

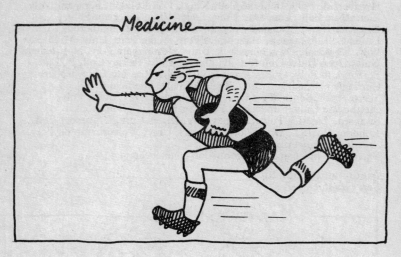

Medicine

Medicine
Possible prospectuses: Aberdeen Univ, Belfast Univ, Birmingham Univ, Bristol Univ, Cambridge Univ, Charing Cross & Westminster, Dundee Univ, Edinburgh Univ, Glasgow Univ, Imperial Coll, King's Coll London, King's Coll Sch Medicine, Leeds Univ, Leicester Univ, Liverpool Univ, London Hospital, Manchester Univ, Newcastle Univ, Nottingham Univ, Oxford Univ, Queen Mary & Westfield, Royal Free, St Andrews Univ, St Bartholomew's, St George's, St Mary's Hospital, Sheffield Univ, Southampton Univ, United Medical Sch, University Coll London, Wales Coll Medicine.
Study area: Medicine.

Medicinal chemistry
Possible prospectuses: Dundee Univ, Exeter Univ, Loughborough Univ, University Coll London, Warwick Univ.

Medieval studies
Possible prospectuses: Birmingham Univ, Cambridge Univ, Cardiff, Edinburgh Univ, Lancaster Univ, Liverpool Univ, Manchester Univ, Oxford Univ, Reading Univ, St Andrews Univ, Sheffield Univ, Southampton Univ, Swansea. *See also:* **History**.
Study area: History.

Mediterranean studies
Possible prospectuses: Birmingham Univ, Bristol Univ, Queen Mary & Westfield. *See also:* **Archaeology**.
Study area: Archaeology.

Mesopotamia
See: **Archaeology**.

Metallurgy
Possible prospectuses: Birmingham Univ, Brunel Univ, Camborne Sch Mines, Cambridge Univ, Imperial Coll, Leeds Univ, Liverpool Univ, Loughborough Univ, Manchester Poly, Manchester Univ, Newcastle Univ, Oxford Univ, Salford Univ, Sheffield Univ, Strathclyde Univ, Surrey Univ, Swansea, Teesside Poly, Thames Poly, UMIST.
See also: **Materials science**.
Study area: Metallurgy & materials science.

Metaphysics
See: **Philosophy**.

Meteorology
Possible prospectuses: Imperial Coll, Reading Univ, South West Poly.
See also: **Geography**.
Study area: Geography.

Microbiology
Possible prospectuses: Aberdeen Univ, Aberystwyth, Belfast Univ, Birmingham Univ, Bradford Univ, Bristol Univ, Brunel Univ, Cambridge Univ, Cardiff, Cirencester, Dundee Univ, Durham Univ, East Anglia Univ, East London Poly, Edinburgh Univ, Glasgow Coll, Glasgow Univ, Heriot-Watt Univ, Imperial Coll, Kent Univ, King's Coll London, Lancashire Poly, Leeds Univ, Leicester Univ, Liverpool Univ, Manchester Poly, Manchester Univ, Newcastle Univ, North London Poly, Nottingham Univ, PCL, Queen Mary & Westfield, Reading Univ, Royal Holloway & Bedford, St Andrews Univ, Sheffield Univ, Strathclyde Univ, Sunderland Poly, Surrey Univ, Swansea, University Coll London, UMIST, Warwick Univ, Wolverhampton

Poly. *See also:* **Bacteriology; biochemistry; biology; genetics; virology.**
Study area: Microbiology.

Microelectronics
See: **Electronics; computer science.**

Middle East studies
See: **Near East studies; Asian studies.**

Mineral processing technology
Possible prospectuses: Birmingham Univ, Camborne Sch Mines, Imperial Coll, Leeds Univ. *See also:* **Geology; mining.**

Mineralogy and petrology
See: **Geology.**

Mining
Possible prospectuses: Camborne Sch Mines, Imperial Coll, Leeds Univ, Leicester Univ, Nottingham Univ.

Modern languages
See: Individual languages (eg **French**) *or regional studies (eg* **Scandinavian studies**).

Moral philosophy
See: **Philosophy.**

Movement studies
Possible prospectuses: Brighton Poly, Bristol Old Vic, Cardiff Inst, Christ Church Coll, Dartington, Laban Centre, Leeds Poly, Liverpool Univ, Middlesex Poly, Ripon & York St John, St Mary's Coll, Scottish Centre for PE, Thames Poly. *See also:* **Dance; drama; physical education.**

Music
Possible prospectuses: Aberdeen Univ, Anglia, Bangor, Bangor Normal Coll, Bath Coll, Belfast Univ, Birmingham Conservatoire, Birmingham Poly, Birmingham Univ, Bretton Hall, Brighton Poly, Bristol Univ, Cambridge Univ, Cardiff, Christ Church Coll, City Univ, Colchester Inst, Crewe & Alsager, Dartington, Derbyshire Coll, Durham Univ, Ealing Coll, East Anglia Univ, Edinburgh Univ, Essex Univ, Exeter Univ, Glasgow Univ, Goldsmiths' Coll, Guildhall, Homerton, Huddersfield Poly, Hull Univ, Keele Univ, King's Coll London, Kingston Poly, Lancaster Univ, Leeds Univ, Leicester Poly, Liverpool

Inst, Liverpool Univ, London Coll Music, Manchester Univ, Middlesex Poly, Newcastle Poly, Newcastle Univ, Nottingham Univ, Open Univ, Oxford Poly, Oxford Univ, Reading Univ, Ripon & York St John, Roehampton Inst, Royal Academy Music, Royal Coll Music, Royal Holloway & Bedford, Royal Northern Coll Music, Royal Scottish Academy, SOAS, Sheffield Univ, Southampton Univ, Surrey Univ, Sussex Univ, Trinity Coll Music, Ulster Univ, Warwick Univ, Welsh Coll Music/Drama, West London Inst, West Sussex Inst, Worcester Coll, York Univ.
Study area: Music.

Mycology
See: Botany.

Mythology
See: Anthropology; classics; psychology.

N

Nautical studies
See: Maritime studies.

Naval architecture
Possible prospectuses: Glasgow Univ, Newcastle Univ, Southampton Univ, Strathclyde Univ, University Coll London.
See also: Marine architecture; naval engineering.
Study area: Marine technology.

Naval engineering
Possible prospectus: Dartmouth, Manadon, University Coll London.
See also: Marine engineering.
Study area: Marine technology.

Navy
Possible prospectuses: Dartmouth, Manadon.

Near East studies
Possible prospectuses: Birmingham Univ, Cambridge Univ, Durham Univ, Manchester Univ, Oxford Univ, St Andrews Univ, SOAS.
See also: Asian studies.
Study area: Near Eastern & Islamic studies.

Neurobiology
See: Biology; physiology; psychology.

Neuroscience
Possible prospectuses: Cardiff, Edinburgh Univ, Glasgow Univ, Lancashire Poly, St Andrews Univ, University Coll London.

Norse
See: Anglo Saxon.

Norwegian
Possible prospectus: East Anglia Univ, Edinburgh Univ, Hull Univ, University Coll London.
See also: Scandinavian studies.
Study area: Modern languages.

Nuclear science
Possible prospectuses: Manchester Univ, PCL.
Study area: Physics.

Nuclear technology
Possible prospectus: Imperial Coll, Manchester Univ.
Study area: Physics.

Nursing
Possible prospectuses: Anglia, Birmingham Poly, Birmingham Univ,
Bradford Univ, Bristol Poly, Buckinghamshire Coll, Cardiff Inst, City
Univ, Coventry Poly, Crewe & Alsager, Derbyshire Coll, Dundee Inst,
East London Poly, Edinburgh Univ, Glasgow Coll, Glasgow Univ, Hull
Univ, King's Coll London, Lancashire Poly, Leeds Poly, Liverpool
Poly, Liverpool Univ, Luton Coll, Manchester Poly, Manchester Univ,
Middlesex Poly, Newcastle Poly, North East Wales Inst, Nottingham
Univ, Oxford Poly, Portsmouth Poly, Queen Margaret Coll, S Martin's
Coll, Sheffield Poly, South Bank Poly, Southampton Univ, Surrey
Univ, Teesside Poly, Ulster Univ, Wales Coll Medicine, West
Glamorgan Inst, Wolverhampton Poly.
Study area: Nursing studies.

Nutrition
Possible prospectuses: Bradford Univ, Cardiff Inst, Ealing Coll,
Huddersfield Poly, King's Coll London, Lancashire Poly, Leeds Poly,
Newcastle Univ, North London Poly, Nottingham Univ, Oxford Poly,
Queen Margaret Coll, Queen's Coll Glasgow, Robert Gordon's Inst,
South Bank Poly, Southampton Univ, Surrey Univ, Ulster Univ.
Study area: Food science & nutrition.

Occupational psychology
See: Psychology.

Occupational therapy
Possible prospectuses: Coventry Poly, Derbyshire Coll, Liverpool Inst,
Nene Coll, Newcastle Poly, Queen Margaret Coll, Queen's Coll
Glasgow, Sheffield Poly, Ulster Univ.

Oceanography
Possible prospectuses: Aberdeen Univ, Bangor, East Anglia Univ,
Liverpool Univ, Open Univ, South West Poly, Southampton Univ.
Study areas: Geography; maritime studies.

Office organisation
Possible prospectuses: Buckinghamshire Coll, Ealing Coll, Humberside
Poly, Lancashire Poly, Luton Coll, Newcastle Poly. *See also: Business
studies.*
Study area: Business studies.

Offshore engineering
Possible prospectuses: Heriot-Watt Univ, Imperial Coll, Strathclyde
Univ, Surrey Univ.
Study area: Marine technology.

Operational research
Possible prospectuses: Belfast Univ, Cambridge Univ, Coventry Poly,
Essex Univ, Exeter Univ, Hull Univ, Kent Univ, Lancaster Univ,
Leeds Univ, Loughborough Univ, Manchester Univ, Nottingham Poly,
Paisley Coll, PCL, Royal Holloway & Bedford, Salford Univ, South
West Poly, Southampton Univ, Staffs Poly, Strathclyde Univ, Teesside
Poly, UMIST, Warwick Univ.

Ophthalmic optics
Possible prospectuses: Aston Univ, Bradford Univ, Cardiff, City Univ,
Glasgow Coll, UMIST.

Organisational behaviour
Possible prospectuses: City Poly, Ealing Coll, European Bus Sch,
Luton Coll.
Study areas: Business studies; psychology.

Organisational studies
Possible prospectuses: Bradford & Ilkley, Ealing Coll, Lancashire Poly,
Lancaster Univ, Luton Coll, Reading Univ.

Oriental studies
See: Asian studies.

Ornithology
See: Zoology.

Orthoptics
Possible prospectus: Queen's Coll Glasgow.

Osteopathy
Possible prospectus: British Sch Osteopathy.

P

Packaging technology
Possible prospectus: Hatfield Poly, Watford Coll, West Surrey Coll.

Painting
Possible prospectuses: Aberystwyth, Anglia, Bath Coll, Birmingham
Poly, Bretton Hall, Brighton Poly, Bristol Poly, Camberwell Coll,
Cardiff Inst, Central St Martins, Chelsea, Cheltenham & Gloucester
Coll, Coventry Poly, Duncan of Jordanstone, Dundee Univ, East
London Poly, Edinburgh Coll Art, Falmouth, Glasgow Sch Art,

Goldsmiths' Coll, Heriot-Watt Univ, Humberside Poly, Kent Inst, Kingston Poly, Lancashire Poly, Lancaster Univ, Leicester Poly, Liverpool Inst, Liverpool Poly, Loughborough Coll, Manchester Poly, Middlesex Poly, Newcastle Poly, Newcastle Univ, Norfolk Inst, Portsmouth Poly, Reading Univ, Ripon & York St John, Robert Gordon's Inst, Roehampton Inst, Royal Academy Sch, Royal Coll Art, Sheffield Poly, Slade, Staffs Poly, Ulster Univ, West Surrey Coll, West Sussex Inst, Wimbledon Sch Art, Winchester Sch Art, Wolverhampton Poly.
Study area: Art and design.

Parasitology
Possible prospectus: Cirencester, Glasgow Univ, Imperial Coll, King's Coll London.
Study area: Biology.

Pathology
Possible prospectuses: Aberdeen Univ, Belfast Univ, Bristol Univ, Cambridge Univ, Dundee Univ, Edinburgh Univ, Glasgow Univ, Leeds Univ, Manchester Univ, Reading Univ, St Andrews Univ.

Peace studies
See: **War studies**.

Performance arts
Possible prospectuses: Birmingham Univ, Bretton Hall, Brighton Poly, Bristol Old Vic, Dartington, Glasgow Univ, Kent Univ, Laban Centre, Leicester Poly, Middlesex Poly, North Cheshire Coll, Nottingham Poly, Ripon & York St John, RADA, South West Poly, Welsh Coll Music/Drama, West Sussex Inst. *See also:* **Dance; Drama.**

Persian
Possible prospectuses: Cambridge Univ, Edinburgh Univ, Manchester Univ, Oxford Univ, SOAS. *See also: **Near East studies***.
Study area: Near East & Islamic studies.

Personnel administration
Possible prospectuses: Anglia, Aston Univ, Ealing Coll, Keele Univ, Luton Coll, Napier Poly, Paisley Coll, South West Poly, Strathclyde Univ, Teesside Poly.

Petroleum engineering
Possible prospectuses: Aberdeen Univ, Imperial Coll, Luton Coll, Strathclyde Univ. *See also: **Energy studies***.
Study area: Chemical engineering.

Pharmacology
Possible prospectuses: Aberdeen Univ, Bath Univ, Bradford Univ, Bristol Univ, Cambridge Univ, Cardiff, Dundee Univ, East London Poly, Edinburgh Univ, Glasgow Univ, King's Coll London, Lancashire Poly, Leeds Univ, Liverpool Univ, Loughborough Univ, Manchester Univ, Portsmouth Poly, St Andrews Univ, School Pharmacy, Sheffield Univ, Southampton Univ, Strathclyde Univ, Sunderland Poly, University Coll London, York Univ. *See also: **Pharmacy***.
Study area: Pharmacology.

Pharmacy
Possible prospectuses: Aston Univ, Bath Univ, Belfast Univ, Bradford Univ, Brighton Poly, Cardiff, King's Coll London, Leicester Poly, Liverpool Poly, Manchester Univ, Nottingham Univ, Portsmouth Poly, Robert Gordon's Inst, School Pharmacy, Strathclyde Univ, Sunderland Poly. *See also: **Pharmacology***.
Study area: Pharmacy.

Philosophy
Possible prospectuses: Aberdeen Univ, Anglia, Belfast Univ, Birkbeck, Birmingham Univ, Bolton Inst, Bradford Univ, Bristol Univ, Cambridge Univ, Cardiff, Cheltenham & Gloucester Coll, City Univ, Crewe & Alsager, Dundee Univ, Durham Univ, East Anglia Univ, Edinburgh Univ, Essex Univ, Glasgow Univ, Hatfield Poly, Heythrop Coll, Hull Univ, Jews' Coll, Keele Univ, Kent Univ, King's Coll London, Lampeter, Lancaster Univ, Leeds Univ, Liverpool Univ, London Bible, LSE, Manchester Poly, Manchester Univ, Middlesex Poly, National Extension Coll, North London Poly, Nottingham Univ, Open Univ, Oxford Univ, Reading Univ, St Andrews Univ, St Mark &

St John, S Martin's Coll, Sheffield Univ, Southampton Univ, Staffs
Poly, Stirling Univ, Sunderland Poly, Sussex Univ, Swansea, Teesside
Poly, Ulster Univ, University Coll London, Wales Poly, Warwick
Univ, Wolverhampton Poly, York Univ.
Study area: Philosophy.

Philosophy of science
see: History of science.

Phonetics
See: Linguistics.

Photography
Possible prospectuses: Bradford & Ilkley, Coventry Poly, Derbyshire
Coll, Edinburgh Coll Art, Falmouth, Glasgow Sch Art, Heriot-Watt
Univ, Humberside Poly, Kent Inst, London Coll Printing, Manchester
Poly, Middlesex Poly, Napier Poly, Nottingham Poly, PCL, Royal Coll
Art, Sheffield Poly, Slade, Staffs Poly, West Surrey Coll,
Wolverhampton Poly.
Study area: Art and design.

Physical education
Possible prospectuses: Bangor, Bangor Normal Coll, Bedford Coll,
Birmingham Univ, Brighton Poly, Cardiff Inst, Cheltenham &
Gloucester Coll, Chester Coll, Crewe & Alsager, Leeds Poly, Leeds
Univ, Liverpool Inst, Liverpool Poly, Liverpool Univ, Loughborough
Univ, Nottingham Poly, Reading Univ, St Mark & St John, Scottish
Centre for PE, Sunderland Poly, Thames Poly, Trinity & All Saints,
Warwick Univ, West London Inst, West Sussex Inst, Worcester Coll.
See also: Sports studies.

Physical science
See: Individual sciences (eg Chemistry).

Physics
Possible prospectuses: Aberdeen Univ, Aberystwyth, Aston Univ, Bath
Univ, Belfast Univ, Birkbeck, Birmingham Univ, Brighton Poly,
Bristol Poly, Bristol Univ, Brunel Univ, Cambridge Univ, Cardiff,
Coventry Poly, Crewe & Alsager, Dundee Inst, Dundee Univ, Durham
Univ, East Anglia Univ, Edinburgh Univ, Essex Univ, Exeter Univ,
Glasgow Univ, Hatfield Poly, Heriot-Watt Univ, Homerton, Hull Univ,
Imperial Coll, Keele Univ, Kent Univ, King's Coll London, Lancashire
Poly, Lancaster Univ, Leeds Univ, Leicester Univ, Liverpool Poly,
Liverpool Univ, Loughborough Univ, Manchester Poly, Manchester
Univ, Napier Poly, Newcastle Poly, Newcastle Univ, North London
Poly, Nottingham Univ, Open Univ, Oxford Poly, Oxford Univ,
Paisley Coll, PCL, Portsmouth Poly, Queen Mary & Westfield,
Reading Univ, Robert Gordon's Inst, Royal Holloway & Bedford, St
Andrews Univ, Salford Univ, Sheffield Poly, Sheffield Univ, South
West Poly, Southampton Univ, Staffs Poly, Strathclyde Univ,
Sunderland Poly, Surrey Univ, Sussex Univ, Swansea, Thames Poly,
University Coll London, UMIST, Warwick Univ, Wolverhampton
Poly, York Univ.
Study area: Physics.

Physiology
Possible prospectuses: Aberdeen Univ, Belfast Univ, Birmingham Univ, Bristol Univ, Cambridge Univ, Cardiff, Crewe & Alsager, Dundee Univ, East Anglia Univ, East London Poly, Edinburgh Univ, Glasgow Univ, King's Coll London, Lancashire Poly, Leeds Univ, Leicester Univ, Liverpool Univ, Loughborough Univ, Manchester Poly, Manchester Univ, Newcastle Univ, Oxford Univ, PCL, Queen Mary & Westfield, Reading Univ, Royal Holloway & Bedford, St Andrews Univ, Sheffield Univ, Southampton Univ, Sunderland Poly, University Coll London, York Univ.
Study area: Physiology.

Physiotherapy
Possible prospectuses: City Univ, Coventry Poly, East London Poly, King's Coll London, Leeds Poly, Manchester Univ, Newcastle Poly, PCL, Queen Margaret Coll, Queen's Coll Glasgow, Sheffield Poly, Teesside Poly, Ulster Univ, West London Inst, Wolverhampton Poly.

Planetary physics
See: Astrophysics.

Plant science
See: Botany.

Plastics
See: Polymers.

Polish
Possible prospectuses: Cambridge Univ, Glasgow Univ, National Extension Coll, SSEES.
Study area: Modern languages.

Political economy
See: Economics.

BEING IN POLITICS MEANS NEVER HAVING TO SAY YOU'RE SORRY

Politics
Possible prospectuses: Aberdeen Univ, Aberystwyth, Aston Univ, Bath Univ, Belfast Univ, Birkbeck, Birmingham Poly, Birmingham Univ, Bradford Univ, Bristol Poly, Bristol Univ, Brunel Univ, Buckingham Univ, Cambridge Univ, Cardiff, City Poly, Coventry Poly, Dundee Univ, Durham Univ, Ealing Coll, East Anglia Univ, Edinburgh Univ, Essex Univ, Exeter Univ, Glasgow Coll, Glasgow Univ, Goldsmiths' Coll, Huddersfield Poly, Hull Univ, Keele Univ, Kent Univ, Kingston

Poly, Lancashire Poly, Lancaster Univ, Leeds Poly, Leeds Univ,
Leicester Poly, Leicester Univ, Liverpool Poly, Liverpool Univ, LSE,
Loughborough Univ, Manchester Poly, Manchester Univ, Middlesex
Poly, Newcastle Poly, Newcastle Univ, North London Poly,
Nottingham Univ, Open Univ, Oxford Poly, Oxford Univ, PCL,
Portsmouth Poly, Queen Mary & Westfield, Reading Univ, Royal
Holloway & Bedford, St Andrews Univ, Salford Univ, SOAS, Sheffield
Poly, Sheffield Univ, South West Poly, Southampton Univ, Staffs Poly,
Stirling Univ, Strathclyde Univ, Sunderland Poly, Sussex Univ,
Swansea, Teesside Poly, Thames Poly, Ulster Univ, Warwick Univ,
Wolverhampton Poly, York Univ.
Study area: Politics & government.

Pollution
Possible prospectus: Luton Coll, Wales Poly.
See also: Ecology; environmental science; environmental studies.

Polymers
Possible prospectuses: Brunel Univ, Heriot-Watt Univ, Lancaster
Univ, Loughborough Univ, Manchester Poly, Manchester Univ,
Napier Poly, North London Poly, Queen Mary & Westfield, Sheffield
Univ, Sunderland Poly, Sussex Univ, UMIST. *See also: Chemistry;
materials science.*
Study areas: Chemistry; chemical engineering; metallurgy & materials
science.

Portuguese
Possible prospectuses: Aberystwyth, Belfast Univ, Cambridge Univ,
Cardiff, Edinburgh Univ, Glasgow Univ, King's Coll London, Leeds
Univ, Liverpool Univ, Manchester Univ, National Extension Coll,
Oxford Univ, Salford Univ, Southampton Univ. *See also: Hispanic
studies; Iberian studies; Latin American studies.*
Study area: Modern languages.

Printing and typography
Possible prospectuses: Ealing Coll, Edinburgh Coll Art, Hatfield Poly,
Kent Inst, Liverpool Inst, London Coll Printing, Manchester Poly,
Napier Poly, Reading Univ, Watford Coll, Wolverhampton Poly.
Study area: Art and design.

Printmaking
Possible prospectuses: Birmingham Poly, Bretton Hall, Brighton Poly,
Bristol Poly, Camberwell Coll, Central St Martins, Chelsea,
Cheltenham & Gloucester Coll, Coventry Poly, Duncan of Jordanstone,
Edinburgh Coll Art, Falmouth, Glasgow Sch Art, Heriot-Watt Univ,
Kent Inst, Kingston Poly, Lancashire Poly, London Coll Printing,
Loughborough Coll, Manchester Poly, Middlesex Poly, Newcastle
Poly, Norfolk Inst, Portsmouth Poly, Reading Univ, Ripon & York St
John, Robert Gordon's Inst, Royal Coll Art, Sheffield Poly, Slade,
South West Poly, Staffs Poly, Watford Coll, West Surrey Coll,
Winchester Sch Art, Wolverhampton Poly.
Study area: Art and design.

Probation
See: Social work.

Production engineering
Possible prospectuses: Aston Univ, Birmingham Poly, Birmingham Univ, Brighton Poly, Brunel Univ, Coventry Poly, East London Poly, Heriot-Watt Univ, Imperial Coll, Kingston Poly, Leicester Poly, Liverpool Poly, Loughborough Univ, Luton Coll, Manchester Poly, Manchester Univ, Middlesex Poly, Newcastle Univ, Nottingham Poly, Nottingham Univ, Paisley Coll, PCL, Portsmouth Poly, Sheffield Poly, South Bank Poly, Staffs Poly, Strathclyde Univ, Sunderland Poly, Teesside Poly, UMIST, Wales Poly, Warwick Univ, Wolverhampton Poly.
Study area: Mechanical & production engineering.

Programming
See: Computing; computer science.

Psychology
Possible prospectuses: Aberdeen Univ, Aston Univ, Bangor, Belfast Univ, Birkbeck, Birmingham Univ, Bolton Inst, Bradford Univ, Bristol Univ, Brunel Univ, Buckingham Univ, Cambridge Univ, Cardiff, Cardiff Inst, Chester Coll, City Poly, City Univ, Crewe & Alsager, Dundee Univ, Durham Univ, Ealing Coll, East London Poly, Edinburgh Univ, Exeter Univ, Glasgow Coll, Glasgow Univ, Goldsmiths' Coll, Hatfield Poly, Huddersfield Poly, Hull Univ, Keele Univ, Kent Univ, Lancashire Poly, Lancaster Univ, Leeds Poly, Leeds Univ, Leicester Univ, Liverpool Inst, Liverpool Poly, Liverpool Univ, LSE, Loughborough Univ, Luton Coll, Manchester Poly, Manchester Univ, Middlesex Poly, Newcastle Poly, Newcastle Univ, Nottingham Univ, Open Univ, Oxford Poly, Oxford Univ, PCL, Portsmouth Poly, Reading Univ, Roehampton Inst, Royal Holloway & Bedford, St Andrews Univ, Sheffield Univ, South West Poly, Southampton Univ, Staffs Poly, Stirling Univ, Strathclyde Univ, Sunderland Poly, Surrey Univ, Sussex Univ, Swansea, Teesside Poly, Trinity & All Saints, Ulster Univ, University Coll London, Wales Poly, Warwick Univ, Wolverhampton Poly, Worcester Coll, York Univ.
Study area: Psychology.

Public administration
Possible prospectuses: Aston Univ, Birmingham Univ, Brunel Univ, Durham Univ, Essex Univ, Glasgow Coll, Hull Univ, Kent Univ, Leeds Univ, Leicester Poly, Liverpool Poly, LSE, Luton Coll, Manchester Poly, Manchester Univ, Nottingham Poly, Open Univ, Robert Gordon's Inst, Royal Holloway & Bedford, Sheffield Poly, Southampton Univ, Strathclyde Univ, Teesside Poly, Trinity & All Saints, Wales Poly.*See also: Social administration.*
Study area: Public Administration.

Public health
Possible prospectuses: Luton Coll, Sunderland Poly.
See also: Environmental health.

Public relations
Possible prospectuses: Bournemouth Poly, Leeds Poly, Luton Coll, PCL, St Mark & St John.

Publishing
Possible prospectuses: Ealing Coll, London Coll Printing, Napier Poly, Oxford Poly, Watford Coll.

Q

Quality control
See: Production engineering.

Quantity surveying
Possible prospectuses: Birmingham Poly, Bristol Poly, Dundee Inst, Glasgow Coll, Glasgow Coll Building, Heriot-Watt Univ, Kingston Poly, Leeds Poly, Liverpool Poly, Loughborough Univ, Luton Coll, Napier Poly, Newcastle Poly, PCL, Portsmouth Poly, Reading Univ, Robert Gordon's Inst, Salford Univ, Sheffield Poly, Staffs Poly, Thames Poly, Ulster Univ, Wales Poly, Wolverhampton Poly.

R

Radar
See: Electronic engineering.

Radio
See: Electronic engineering.

Radiography
Possible prospectuses: Derbyshire Coll, Portsmouth Poly, Queen's Coll Glasgow, South Bank Poly.

Recreation
Possible prospectuses: Birmingham Univ, Cheltenham & Gloucester Coll, Ealing Coll, Luton Coll, North Cheshire Coll, St Mark & St John, Sheffield Poly, Staffs Poly, Trinity & All Saints, Writtle.
See also: Sports studies; tourism; town planning.

Religious studies
Possible prospectuses: Aberdeen Univ, Aberystwyth, Bangor, Bangor Normal Coll, Birmingham Univ, Bristol Univ, Cambridge Univ, Cardiff, Cheltenham & Gloucester Coll, Chester Coll, Christ Church Coll, Crewe & Alsager, Derbyshire Coll, Edinburgh Univ, Exeter Univ, Homerton, Hull Univ, King's Coll London, Lampeter, Lancaster Univ, Leeds Univ, Liverpool Inst, Liverpool Univ, London Bible, Manchester Univ, Middlesex Poly, National Extension Coll, Newcastle Univ, Oak Hill Coll, Open Univ, Oxford Univ, Ripon & York St John, Roehampton Inst, St Andrews Univ, St Mark & St John, St Mary's Coll, SOAS, Spurgeon's Coll, Stirling Univ, Sunderland Poly, Trinity & All Saints, Wales Poly, Warwick Univ, West London Inst, West Sussex Inst. *See also: Biblical studies; theology.*
Study area: Religious studies & theology.

Renaissance studies
See: History.

Risk
See: Actuarial studies.

Rumanian
Possible prospectuses: Birmingham Univ, SSEES, University Coll London.
Study area: Modern languages.

Rural environment studies
Possible prospectuses: Aberdeen Univ, Anglia, Cheltenham & Gloucester Coll, Cirencester, Coventry Poly, Edinburgh Univ, Reading Univ, Silsoe Coll, South West Poly, Trinity Coll Carmarthen, Writtle, Wye Coll.
Study area: Environmental studies.

Russian
Possible prospectuses: Bangor, Belfast Univ, Birmingham Univ, Bradford Univ, Bristol Univ, Cambridge Univ, Durham Univ, Ealing Coll, Edinburgh Univ, Essex Univ, Exeter Univ, Glasgow Univ, Heriot-Watt Univ, Keele Univ, King's Coll London, Leeds Univ, Liverpool Poly, Manchester Univ, National Extension Coll, Newcastle Poly, Nottingham Univ, Oxford Univ, PCL, Portsmouth Poly, Queen Mary & Westfield, St Andrews Univ, SSEES, Sheffield Univ, Strathclyde Univ, Surrey Univ, Sussex Univ, Swansea, Wolverhampton Poly. *See also: Russian studies; Slavonic studies.*
Study area: Modern languages.

Russian studies
Possible prospectuses: Belfast Univ, Birmingham Univ, Cambridge Univ, East Anglia Univ, Edinburgh Univ, Essex Univ, Glasgow Univ, Leeds Univ, Liverpool Univ, Manchester Univ, Portsmouth Poly, St Andrews Univ, SSEES, Sheffield Univ, Sunderland Poly, Surrey Univ, Sussex Univ, Swansea. *See also: Russian; Slavonic studies.*
Study areas: Modern languages; European studies.

S

Safety
See: Environmental health.

Sanskrit
Possible prospectuses: Cambridge Univ, Edinburgh Univ, Oxford Univ, SOAS. *See also: Near East studies.*
Study area: Near East & Islamic studies.

Scandinavian studies
Possible prospectuses: East Anglia Univ, Edinburgh Univ, Hull Univ, University Coll London. *See also: Individual languages (eg Danish).*

Scientific and technical graphics
Possible prospectus: Falmouth.
See also: Graphic design.

Scottish studies
Possible prospectuses: Aberdeen Univ, Edinburgh Univ, Glasgow Univ, St Andrews Univ, Strathclyde Univ. *See also: Celtic studies.*

Sculpture
Possible prospectuses: Bath Coll, Bretton Hall, Brighton Poly, Bristol Poly, Camberwell Coll, Central St Martins, Chelsea, Cheltenham & Gloucester Coll, Coventry Poly, Duncan of Jordanstone, Dundee Univ, East London Poly, Edinburgh Coll Art, Falmouth, Glasgow Sch Art, Goldsmiths' Coll, Heriot-Watt Univ, Humberside Poly, Kent Inst, Kingston Poly, Lancashire Poly, Leicester Poly, Liverpool Inst, Loughborough Coll, Manchester Poly, Middlesex Poly, Newcastle Poly, Newcastle Univ, Norfolk Inst, Portsmouth Poly, Reading Univ, Robert Gordon's Inst, Royal Academy Sch, Royal Coll Art, Sheffield Poly, Slade, South West Poly, Staffs Poly, West Surrey Coll, West Sussex Inst, Wimbledon Sch Art, Winchester Sch Art, Wolverhampton Poly.
Study area: Art and design.

Secretarial studies
See: Office organisation.

Seismology
See: Geology.

Semiconductors
See: Electronic engineering.

Semitic languages
Possible prospectuses: Manchester Univ, SOAS. *See also: Individual languages (eg Arabic).*
Study area: Near East & Islamic studies.

Serbo-Croat
Possible prospectuses: Cambridge Univ, Nottingham Univ, SSEES. *See also: Yugoslav studies.*
Study area: Modern languages.

Shipbuilding
See: Naval architecture; marine architecture.

Silversmithing
Possible prospectuses: Birmingham Poly, Buckinghamshire Coll, Camberwell Coll, City Poly, Crewe & Alsager, Duncan of Jordanstone, Dundee Univ, Edinburgh Coll Art, Glasgow Sch Art, Heriot-Watt Univ, Leicester Poly, Loughborough Coll, Royal Coll Art, Ulster Univ, West Surrey Coll. *See also: Three dimensional design.*
Study area: Art and design.

Sinhalese
Possible prospectus: SOAS. *See also: Asian studies.*
Study area: Asian studies.

Slavonic studies
Possible prospectuses: Cambridge Univ, Glasgow Univ, Hull Univ, Manchester Univ, Nottingham Univ, SSEES, Sheffield Univ.
Study area: European studies.

Social administration
Possible prospectuses: Bangor, Bangor Normal Coll, Birmingham Univ, Brighton Poly, Bristol Univ, Brunel Univ, Cardiff, Dundee Univ, Durham Univ, East London Poly, Edinburgh Univ, Essex Univ, Glasgow Univ, Goldsmiths' Coll, Hatfield Poly, Hull Univ, Kent Univ, Lancashire Poly, Lancaster Univ, Leeds Poly, Leeds Univ, LSE, Loughborough Univ, Luton Coll, Manchester Poly, Manchester Univ, Middlesex Poly, Newcastle Univ, Nottingham Poly, Nottingham Univ, Open Univ, Paisley Coll, PCL, Portsmouth Poly, Roehampton Inst, Sheffield Poly, Sheffield Univ, South West Poly, Southampton Univ, Stirling Univ, Strathclyde Univ, Sussex Univ, Teesside Poly, Ulster Univ, Warwick Univ, York Univ.
Study area: Welfare studies.

Social anthropology
Possible prospectuses: Belfast Univ, Brunel Univ, Cambridge Univ, East Anglia Univ, Edinburgh Univ, Goldsmiths' Coll, Hull Univ, Keele Univ, Kent Univ, LSE, Manchester Univ, St Andrews Univ, SOAS, Sussex Univ, Swansea, University Coll London. *See also:*
Anthropology.
Study area: Anthropology.

Social biology
Possible prospectus: Roehampton Inst.
See: **Biosocial science; Human sciences.**

Social history
Possible prospectuses: Aberdeen Univ, Aberystwyth, Belfast Univ, Birmingham Univ, East Anglia Univ, Edinburgh Univ, Exeter Univ, Glasgow Coll, Hull Univ, Kent Univ, Lancashire Poly, Lancaster Univ, Leicester Univ, Liverpool Univ, Luton Coll, Manchester Poly, Manchester Univ, Newcastle Univ, Nottingham Univ, Open Univ, Reading Univ, St Andrews Univ, Sheffield Univ, Staffs Poly, Strathclyde Univ, Sussex Univ, Swansea, York Univ. *See also:*
Economic history; history.
Study area: History.

Social psychology
See: **Psychology.**

Social science
Possible prospectuses: Aberdeen Univ, Belfast Univ, Bradford & Ilkley, Bradford Univ, Bristol Univ, Cambridge Univ, City Univ, Coventry Poly, Derbyshire Coll, Ealing Coll, East Anglia Univ, East London Poly, Edge Hill, Edinburgh Univ, Essex Univ, Goldsmiths' Coll, Hatfield Poly, Hull Univ, Humberside Poly, Keele Univ, Kent Univ, Kingston Poly, Liverpool Poly, Liverpool Univ, Loughborough Univ, Luton Coll, Manchester Poly, Manchester Univ, Middlesex Poly, Newcastle Univ, North London Poly, Nottingham Poly, Open Univ, Oxford Poly, Paisley Coll, PCL, Reading Univ, Robert Gordon's Inst, Royal Holloway & Bedford, Salford Univ, Sheffield Poly, South West Poly, Southampton Univ, Staffs Poly, Stirling Univ, Sunderland Poly, Sussex Univ, Swansea, Teesside Poly, Ulster Univ, Wales Poly, Wolverhampton Poly.
See also: Individual subjects (eg **economics, politics, sociology***).*

Social statistics
See: Statistics; sociology.
Study area: Mathematical studies.

Social studies
Possible prospectuses: Birmingham Univ, Bradford Univ, Bretton Hall,
East London Poly, Hatfield Poly, Lancashire Poly, Liverpool Poly,
Liverpool Univ, Luton Coll, Manchester Poly, Nottingham Poly,
Paisley Coll, Robert Gordon's Inst, Sheffield Poly, South Bank Poly,
Staffs Poly, Stirling Univ, Strathclyde Univ, Sussex Univ, West
Glamorgan Inst. *See also: Social science.*

Social work
Possible prospectuses: Anglia, Birmingham Poly, Birmingham Univ,
Bradford Univ, Buckinghamshire Coll, Cardiff, Cardiff Inst, Coventry
Poly, East Anglia Univ, East London Poly, Edge Hill, Hatfield Poly,
Hull Univ, Humberside Poly, Kingston Poly, Lancashire Poly,
Lancaster Univ, Liverpool Poly, Liverpool Univ, Luton Coll,
Manchester Poly, Manchester Univ, Middlesex Poly, Newcastle Univ,
North London Poly, Oxford Poly, Paisley Coll, Portsmouth Poly,
Queen's Coll Glasgow, Reading Univ, Robert Gordon's Inst, Sheffield
Poly, South West Poly, Southampton Univ, Staffs Poly, Stirling Univ,
Sunderland Poly, Teesside Poly, Ulster Univ, West Sussex Inst.
Study area: Welfare studies.

Sociology
Possible prospectuses: Aberdeen Univ, Anglia, Aston Univ, Bangor,
Bath Univ, Bedford Coll, Belfast Univ, Birmingham Poly, Birmingham
Univ, Bradford Univ, Bristol Poly, Bristol Univ, Brunel Univ,
Buckinghamshire Coll, Cambridge Univ, Cardiff, City Poly, City Univ,
Crewe & Alsager, Durham Univ, Ealing Coll, East Anglia Univ, East
London Poly, Edinburgh Univ, Essex Univ, Exeter Univ, Glasgow
Coll, Glasgow Univ, Goldsmiths' Coll, Huddersfield Poly, Hull Univ,
Keele Univ, Kent Univ, Kingston Poly, Lancashire Poly, Lancaster
Univ, Leeds Poly, Leeds Univ, Leicester Univ, Liverpool Inst,
Liverpool Poly, Liverpool Univ, LSE, Loughborough Univ, Luton
Coll, Manchester Poly, Manchester Univ, Middlesex Poly, Newcastle
Poly, Newcastle Univ, North London Poly, Nottingham Univ, Open
Univ, Oxford Poly, PCL, Portsmouth Poly, Reading Univ,
Roehampton Inst, Royal Holloway & Bedford, St Mark & St John, St
Mary's Coll, Salford Univ, Sheffield Univ, South West Poly,
Southampton Univ, Staffs Poly, Stirling Univ, Strathclyde Univ,
Sunderland Poly, Surrey Univ, Sussex Univ, Swansea, Teesside Poly,
Thames Poly, Trinity & All Saints, Ulster Univ, Wales Poly, Warwick
Univ, Wolverhampton Poly, Worcester Coll, York Univ.
Study area: Sociology.

Soil science
Possible prospectuses: Aberdeen Univ, Aberystwyth, Bangor,
Cirencester, Edinburgh Univ, Hull Univ, Luton Coll, Manchester
Univ, Newcastle Univ, Nottingham Univ, Reading Univ, South Bank
Poly, Writtle, Wye Coll.

Solid state electronics
See: Electronics.

Solid state physics
See: Physics.

South America
See: Latin American studies.

South East Asian studies
Possible prospectuses: Hull Univ, Kent Univ, Newcastle Univ, SOAS.
See also: Asian studies.
Study area: Asian studies.

Soviet studies
See: Russian studies.

Space
Possible prospectuses: Aberystwyth, Leicester Univ, Open Univ,
Southampton Univ. *See also: Astronomy.*
Study area: Physics.

Spanish
Possible prospectuses: Aberdeen Univ, Aberystwyth, Anglia, Belfast
Univ, Birkbeck, Birmingham Poly, Birmingham Univ, Bradford Univ,
Bristol Poly, Bristol Univ, Buckingham Univ, Cambridge Univ,
Cardiff, Central Sch Speech/Drama, Coventry Poly, Durham Univ,
Ealing Coll, Edinburgh Univ, Essex Univ, European Bus Sch, Exeter
Univ, Glasgow Univ, Heriot-Watt Univ, Hull Univ, Humberside Poly,
King's Coll London, Kingston Poly, Leeds Univ, Liverpool Poly,
Liverpool Univ, Luton Coll, Manchester Poly, Manchester Univ,
Middlesex Poly, National Extension Coll, Newcastle Poly, Newcastle
Univ, North London Poly, Nottingham Univ, Oxford Univ, PCL,
Portsmouth Poly, St Andrews Univ, Salford Univ, Sheffield Poly,
Sheffield Univ, Southampton Univ, Staffs Poly, Strathclyde Univ,
Sussex Univ, Swansea, Trinity & All Saints, University Coll London,
Wolverhampton Poly. *See also: Hispanic studies; Iberian studies;
Latin American studies.*
Study area: Modern languages.

Spanish studies
Possible prospectuses: Manchester Univ, Stirling Univ.
*See: Hispanic studies; Iberian studies; Latin American studies;
Spanish.*
Study area: European studies.

Speech sciences
Possible prospectuses: Central Sch Speech/Drama, City Univ,
Manchester Univ, National Hospitals Coll, Newcastle Univ, Reading
Univ, Sheffield Univ, University Coll London.
Study area: Speech sciences.

Speech therapy
Possible prospectuses: Birmingham Poly, Cardiff Inst, Central Sch
Speech/Drama, Glasgow Univ, Leeds Poly, Leicester Poly, Manchester
Poly, Manchester Univ, National Hospitals Coll, PCL, Queen Margaret

Coll, Reading Univ, Sheffield Univ, Ulster Univ.
See also: **Speech sciences.**
Study area: Speech sciences.

Sports studies
Possible prospectuses: Bangor, Bedford Coll, Birmingham Univ, Brighton Poly, Cheltenham & Gloucester Coll, Chester Coll, Crewe & Alsager, Glasgow Univ, Leeds Poly, Liverpool Poly, Loughborough Univ, Newcastle Poly, North Cheshire Coll, Nottingham Poly, Roehampton Inst, Scottish Centre for PE, Staffs Poly, Sunderland Poly, Ulster Univ, West London Inst, West Sussex Inst. *See also:* **Physical education.**

Stage management
Possible prospectuses: ALRA, Guildhall, Queen Margaret Coll, Rose Bruford Coll, RADA, Welsh Coll Music/Drama.

Statistics
Possible prospectuses: Aberdeen Univ, Aberystwyth, Bath Univ, Belfast Univ, Birkbeck, Birmingham Univ, Bradford Univ, Brighton Poly, Bristol Univ, Brunel Univ, Cardiff, Cheltenham & Gloucester Coll, City Poly, City Univ, Coventry Poly, Dundee Inst, Dundee Univ, Durham Univ, Ealing Coll, East London Poly, Edinburgh Univ, Essex Univ, Exeter Univ, Glasgow Univ, Goldsmiths' Coll, Hatfield Poly, Heriot-Watt Univ, Hull Univ, Imperial Coll, Keele Univ, Kent Univ, Lancashire Poly, Lancaster Univ, Leeds Univ, Leicester Univ, Liverpool Poly, Liverpool Univ, LSE, Loughborough Univ, Luton Coll, Manchester Univ, Middlesex Poly, Newcastle Poly, Newcastle Univ, North London Poly, Nottingham Univ, Open Univ, Paisley Coll, PCL, Portsmouth Poly, Queen Mary & Westfield, Reading Univ, Royal Holloway & Bedford, St Andrews Univ, Salford Univ, Sheffield Poly, Sheffield Univ, South West Poly, Southampton Univ, Staffs Poly, Strathclyde Univ, Surrey Univ, Sussex Univ, Swansea, Teesside Poly, Thames Poly, Ulster Univ, University Coll London, UMIST, Wales Poly, Warwick Univ, York Univ. *See also:* **Mathematics.**
Study area: Mathematical studies.

Surveying – general practice
Possible prospectuses: Bristol Poly, Camborne Sch Mines, Cirencester, East London Poly, Harper Adams, Heriot-Watt Univ, Kingston Poly, Lancashire Poly, Liverpool Poly, Loughborough Univ, Luton Coll, Napier Poly, Newcastle Univ, PCL, Reading Univ, South West Poly, Staffs Poly, Thames Poly, Wales Poly. *See also:* **Quantity surveying.**

Swahili
Possible prospectuses: SOAS, York Univ. *See also:* **African studies.**
Study area: African studies.

Swedish
Possible prospectuses: East Anglia Univ, Edinburgh Univ, Hull Univ, Lampeter, Surrey Univ, University Coll London. *See also:* **Scandinavian studies.**
Study area: Modern languages.

Systems analysis
Possible prospectuses: Bristol Poly, Cardiff, City Univ, East London

Poly, Imperial Coll, Kent Univ, Luton Coll, Manchester Univ, North London Poly, PCL, Sheffield Poly, South Bank Poly, Staffs Poly, UMIST. *See also: Computer science; Computing.*
Study area: Computing.

T

Talmud
See: Jewish studies.

Tamil
Possible prospectus: SOAS.
See also: Asian studies.
Study area: Asian studies.

Teaching
See: Education.

Telecommunications engineering
Possible prospectuses: Anglia, Birmingham Univ, Bradford Univ, Essex Univ, Heriot-Watt Univ, Imperial Coll, Luton Coll, Napier Poly, Open Univ, Queen Mary & Westfield.
Study area: Electrical and electronic engineering.

Television
See: Communication studies; film studies.

Textile technology
Possible prospectuses: Bolton Inst, Heriot-Watt Univ, Huddersfield Poly, Leeds Univ, Leicester Poly, Nottingham Poly, UMIST, Wolverhampton Poly.
Study area: Chemical engineering.

Textiles
Possible prospectuses: Birmingham Poly, Bolton Inst, Bretton Hall, Brighton Poly, Cardiff, Central St Martins, Coventry Poly, Crewe & Alsager, Derbyshire Coll, Duncan of Jordanstone, Dundee Univ, East London Poly, Edinburgh Coll Art, Glasgow Sch Art, Goldsmiths' Coll, Heriot-Watt Univ, Huddersfield Poly, Leeds Univ, Leicester Poly, Liverpool Inst, Liverpool Poly, Loughborough Coll, Manchester Poly, Middlesex Poly, Queen Margaret Coll, Robert Gordon's Inst, Royal Coll Art, Teesside Poly, Ulster Univ, UMIST, West Surrey Coll, Winchester Sch Art, Wolverhampton Poly, Worcester Coll.
Study area: Art and design.

Thai studies
Possible prospectus: SOAS.
Study area: Asian studies.

Theatre design
Possible prospectuses: Birmingham Poly, Bristol Old Vic, Central St Martins, Crewe & Alsager, Nottingham Poly, RADA, Royal Scottish Academy, Slade, Welsh Coll Music/Drama, Wimbledon Sch Art.
Study areas: Art and design; drama and theatre arts.

Theology
Possible prospectuses: Aberdeen Univ, Aberystwyth, Bangor, Belfast Univ, Bristol Univ, Cambridge Univ, Cardiff, Durham Univ, Edinburgh Univ, Exeter Univ, Glasgow Univ, Heythrop Coll, Hull Univ, Kent Univ, King's Coll London, La Sainte Union, Lampeter, Lancaster Univ, Leeds Univ, Liverpool Univ, London Bible, Manchester Univ, Newcastle Univ, Nottingham Univ, Oak Hill Coll, Oxford Univ, St Andrews Univ, St Mark & St John, St Mary's Coll, Spurgeon's Coll, Thames Poly, Trinity & All Saints, West Sussex Inst, Westminster Coll. *See also: **Religious studies**.*
Study area: Religious studies & theology.

Third World
Possible prospectuses: Open Univ, St Mark & St John.

Three dimensional design
Possible prospectuses: Birmingham Poly, Bradford & Ilkley, Brighton Poly, Bristol Poly, Buckinghamshire Coll, Coventry Poly, Crewe & Alsager, Edinburgh Coll Art, Kingston Poly, Lancashire Poly, Leeds Poly, Leicester Poly, Loughborough Coll, Loughborough Univ, Manchester Poly, Middlesex Poly, Newcastle Poly, Open Univ, PCL, Ravensbourne Coll, Reading Univ, Ripon & York St John, St Mark & St John, Sheffield Poly, South West Poly, Staffs Poly, Sunderland Poly, Teesside Poly, West Surrey Coll, Wolverhampton Poly, Worcester Coll.
Study area: Art and design.

Topographical science
Possible prospectus: Glasgow Univ, Luton Coll, Swansea.

Tourism
Possible prospectuses: Bournemouth Poly, Brighton Poly, Cardiff Inst, Ealing Coll, Hatfield Poly, Luton Coll, Newcastle Poly, North Cheshire Coll, North London Poly, Oxford Poly, PCL, Queen Margaret Coll, Sheffield Poly, Staffs Poly, Strathclyde Univ, Ulster Univ, Wolverhampton Poly, Writtle.

Town and country planning
Possible prospectuses: Aston Univ, Birmingham Poly, Birmingham Univ, Bristol Poly, Cardiff, Cheltenham & Gloucester Coll, Cirencester, Coventry Poly, Duncan of Jordanstone, Dundee Univ, Edinburgh Coll Art, Heriot-Watt Univ, Luton Coll, Manchester Univ, Newcastle Univ, Oxford Poly, PCL, Portsmouth Poly, Reading Univ, Sheffield Poly, South Bank Poly, Strathclyde Univ, University Coll London.
*See also: **Environmental studies**.*
Study area: Town & country planning.

Toxicology
Possible prospectuses: Bradford Univ, Hull Univ, King's Coll London, Luton Coll, School Pharmacy, Surrey Univ.
Study area: Pharmacology.

Transport studies
Possible prospectuses: Aston Univ, Cardiff, City Poly, Coventry Poly, Hatfield Poly, Huddersfield Poly, Loughborough Univ, Napier Poly, South West Poly, Ulster Univ.

Turkish
Possible prospectuses: Cambridge Univ, Edinburgh Univ, Manchester
Univ, Oxford Univ, SOAS. *See also: Near East studies.*
Study area: Near East & Islamic studies.

U

United States
See: American studies.

Urban estate management
Possible prospectuses: Heriot-Watt Univ, Leicester Poly, Liverpool
Poly, Luton Coll, Oxford Poly, PCL, Portsmouth Poly, Sheffield Poly,
South Bank Poly, Wales Poly, Writtle. *See also: Estate management.*

Urban studies
Possible prospectuses: Aberdeen Univ, Aston Univ, Bristol Poly,
Coventry Poly, Ealing Coll, Edge Hill, Edinburgh Coll Art, Kent Univ,
Leeds Poly, Liverpool Poly, Liverpool Univ, Loughborough Univ,
Manchester Univ, Middlesex Poly, North London Poly, Open Univ,
Oxford Poly, Portsmouth Poly, Reading Univ, Sheffield Poly, Sheffield
Univ, Sunderland Poly, Sussex Univ, Wales Poly, West Glamorgan
Inst, Worcester Coll.

Urdu
Possible prospectuses: Luton Coll, SOAS.
See also: Asian studies.
Study area: Asian studies.

V

Valuation
See: Estate management; quantity surveying; surveying.

Veterinary studies
Possible prospectuses: Bristol Univ, Cambridge Univ, Edinburgh Univ,
Glasgow Univ, Liverpool Univ, Royal Vet Coll.
Study area: Veterinary studies.

Victorian studies
Possible prospectuses: Lampeter, Open Univ, Sunderland Poly.

Vietnamese studies
Possible prospectus: SOAS.
See also: Asian studies.
Study area: Asian studies.

Virology
Possible prospectuses: Glasgow Univ, Manchester Univ, Reading Univ,
Warwick Univ.
Study area: Microbiology.

Visual communication
See: Graphic design.

W

War studies
Possible prospectuses: Bolton Inst, Bradford Univ, Cranwell, Dartmouth, King's Coll London, Manchester Univ, Open Univ, Sandhurst, Sunderland Poly. *See also:* ***History; international relations; politics.***
Study area: Strategic studies.

Water resources
Possible prospectuses: Luton Coll, Napier Poly, Writtle.

Welfare studies
See: ***Social administration; social work.***

Welsh studies
Possible prospectuses: Aberystwyth, Bangor, Bangor Normal Coll, Cardiff, Lampeter, Manchester Univ, Swansea, Wales Poly. *See also:* ***Celtic studies.***

Wildlife and fisheries management
Possible prospectus: Cirencester, Edinburgh Univ.

Wood technology
Possible prospectus: Buckinghamshire Coll, Luton Coll.

Y

Youth and community work
Possible prospectuses: Bradford & Ilkley, Brunel Univ, Crewe & Alsager, Humberside Poly, Luton Coll, Reading Univ, St Mark & St John, S Martin's Coll, South West Poly, Sunderland Poly, Thames Poly, Ulster Univ.
Study area: Welfare studies.

Yugoslav studies
Possible prospectuses: Cambridge Univ, SSEES, Sussex Univ. *See also:* ***Serbo-Croat; Slavonic studies.***

Z

Zoology
Possible prospectuses: Aberdeen Univ, Aberystwyth, Bangor, Belfast Univ, Birkbeck, Birmingham Univ, Bristol Univ, Cambridge Univ, Cardiff, Cirencester, Dundee Univ, Durham Univ, East Anglia Univ, East London Poly, Edinburgh Univ, Glasgow Univ, Imperial Coll, King's Coll London, Leeds Univ, Leicester Univ, Liverpool Univ, Manchester Univ, Newcastle Univ, Nottingham Univ, Oxford Univ, PCL, Portsmouth Poly, Queen Mary & Westfield, Reading Univ, Royal Holloway & Bedford, St Andrews Univ, Sheffield Univ, Southampton Univ, Swansea, University Coll London, Wye Coll. *See also:* ***Animal science.***
Study area: Zoology.

Zulu
See: ***African studies.***

What to Study

Here over 70 teachers in higher education define their own study areas and outline how they are taught in UK Colleges, Polytechnics and Universities (UKCPUs). Try browsing. Then list the Study Areas that interest you, and turn to the *Where to Study* section to check whether the UKCPUs you might want to shortlist teach in your study area. Remember that each UKCPU labels its own courses as it chooses, so get hold of the prospectus to check directly that what you want to study is in fact taught there.

The articles in this section are:

About Study Areas, Subjects and Subject Mixes,
Professor Sir Graham Hills, Strathclyde University
Accountancy, Professor M Bromwich, LSE
Aeronautical Engineering, Professor Donald McLean,
    Southampton University
African Studies, Richard Rathbone, SOAS
Agriculture, Horticulture and Forestry, Professor W Holmes,
    Wye College
American Studies, Dr Michael Dunne, Sussex University
Anatomy, Professor Anthony Firth, St Mary's Hospital Medical
    School, London
Anthropology, Professor Adam Kuper, Brunel University
Archaeology, Dr S W Hilson, University College London
Architecture, Sandra Morris, Architectural Association School
    of Architecture
Art and Design, Bernard Gay
● Fine Art ● Graphic Design ● Photography
● Textiles/Fashion ● Three Dimensional Design
Asian Studies, Dr Ian Brown, SOAS
Biochemistry, Dr R B Freedman, Kent University
Biology, Dr N Maclean, Southampton University
Biotechnology, Dr J H Parish, Leeds University
Botany, Professor D M Moore, Reading University
Business Studies, Alan Munro, City of London Polytechnic
Chemical Engineering, Dr J R Backhurst, Newcastle University
Chemistry, Dr L D Pettit, Leeds University
Civil Engineering, Emeritus Professor Sir Alan Harris, Imperial
    College
Classics, Dr Oswyn Murray, Balliol College, Oxford University
Communication Studies, Robert Ferguson, Institute of
    Education
Computing, Professor D Conway, Leicester Polytechnic
Dance, Dr Richard Ralph, London Contemporary Dance
    School
Dentistry, Jane R Goodman, Eastman Dental Hospital
Drama and Theatre Arts, Malcolm Griffiths, Nottingham
    Polytechnic
● Acting, Malcolm Griffiths ● Drama, John Marshall, Bristol
University ● Theatre design, Malcolm Griffiths
Economics, Professor David W Pearce, University College
    London
Education, Dr David Bridges, Homerton College, Cambridge
    University
Electrical and Electronic Engineering, Dr J C Earls
English, Professor Patrick Parrinder, Reading University

Environmental Sciences, Dr Ian F Spellerberg, Southampton
University
Environmental Studies, Emeritus Professor A D G Smart,
University College, London
European Studies, Dr Juliet Lodge, Hull University
Fine Arts, Dr Alex Potts, East Anglia University
Food Science and Nutrition, Professor R A Lawrie,
Nottingham University
Geography, Professor M D I Chisholm, Cambridge University
Geology, Professor T R Owen, Swansea, University of Wales
History, Dr Maurice Keen, Balliol College, Oxford University
Hotel and Catering Management, J O'Connor, Oxford
Polytechnic
Industrial Relations, Professor K F Sisson, Warwick University
Information Technology, R S Burgess, Newcastle Polytechnic
Latin American Studies, Dr Simon Collier, Essex University
Law, Professor Geoffrey Wilson, Warwick University
Library and Information Studies, Dr Margaret Evans,
Loughborough University
Linguistics, Dr Michael Garman, Reading University
Marine Technology, Professor J B Caldwell, Newcastle
University
Maritime Studies, Alston Kennerley, South West Polytechnic
Mathematical Studies, R Daniel Hirsch, City of London
Polytechnic
Mechanical and Production Engineering, Emeritus Professor
M W Thring, Queen Mary & Westfield College London
Medicine, Dr David Sturgeon, University College and
Middlesex School of Medicine
Metallurgy and Materials Science, Vernon John, City
University
Microbiology, Professor John Postgate, Sussex University
Modern Languages, Professor Dennis Ager, Aston University
Music, Professor Brian Trowell, Oxford University
Near Eastern and Islamic Studies, Professor H T Norris,
SOAS
Nursing Studies, Professor Penny Prophit, Edinburgh
University
Pharmacology, Dr Robin Hoult, King's College London
Pharmacy, Dr Robin Hoult, King's College London
Philosophy, Professor Antony Flew, Reading University
Physics, Dr P E Hodgson, Oxford University
Physiology, Dr D J Begley, King's College London
Politics and Government, Peter Dawson, LSE
Psychology, Professor Keith Oatley, Glasgow University
Public Administration, Barry J O'Toole, Loughborough
University

Religious Studies and Theology, Professor John R Hinnells, Manchester University

Sociology, Dr Jason Ditton, Glasgow University

Speech Sciences, Dr Jane Maxim & Dr Sheila Wirz, National Hospitals College of Speech Sciences

Strategic Studies, Dr Gerald Segal, Bristol University

Town and Country Planning, Professor Margaret Roberts

Veterinary Studies, Professor E J L Soulsby, Cambridge University

Welfare Studies, Professor Olive Stevenson, Nottingham University

Zoology, Professor R McNeill Alexander, Leeds University

About Study Areas, Subjects and Subject Mixes:

Professor Sir Graham Hills, Strathclyde University

To enter university, college or polytechnic is to step on to a new stage, a higher platform of opportunity and attainment. It is a world of greater challenges which, when overcome, lead to greater achievements. It is a world in which the undergraduate takes a giant step towards the confident, likeable, knowledgeable, skilful person that he or she must become to live a fruitful life. The ensuing journey is the same whatever subjects are studied and whatever courses are followed. At the end of your course you will be on your own. You will swim without being held. Real life will have begun.

So whilst the context in which all this happens is nevertheless important, it is not vitally so. Some classicists eventually become computer linguists. A surprising number of engineers become accountants. Occasionally even a medical doctor becomes something else, for example, an author. It is a fact that most graduates quickly find employment in subject areas far from those they studied so diligently. It is in that sense, therefore, that it is less important what you study than how you do it and how it enables you to blossom into that gifted person you, your parents and your friends wish you to become.

Many undergraduates will nevertheless enter higher education with firm intentions to undertake specialised study, say of chemistry, politics or accounting. They may well have gained entry to higher education on the basis of success already obtained in areas of scientific or other specialisations. Those intending to become medical doctors, veterinary or dental surgeons, electronic engineers and so on will not have much choice in the matter. Their courses will be laid out in front of them, although, even here, there is likely to be some scope for variations in the later years.

It is in relation to this issue that the intending undergraduate will need to study in detail what is on offer in the wide range of courses offered by universities, polytechnics and colleges. Some of the courses will reflect some seemingly haphazard combination of disparate courses and subjects. Others will reflect a deeply held view that most young people should not specialise before they have to. Keeping one's options open seems sensible and it is common practice in many other countries. It enables the student to shed some of the experiences and prejudices of school. It enables the student to explore new subjects not encountered before. It also enables the student to consider what jobs are likely to be available and to target his or her courses accordingly.

One famous example of this is the Oxford course, which combines philosophy, politics and economics (PPE), a combination of subjects which has attracted large numbers of students who have subsequently gone on into government, law, administration and business. In earlier times there was a general degree which, as its name implies, requires prowess in more than one subject, often three subjects, after which the student then proceeded to the honours degree. That degree is still commonly found in Scotland. It is generally unclassified (no honours) but even it could be taken with honours, thereby preserving the breadth to the very end. This tendency towards breadth in Scottish higher education is encouraged by an equivalent breadth in the secondary schools. The argument between breadth and depth will continue for some time. It is my belief that breadth will win.

In higher education, the extent of breadth varies from one subject grouping to another or, in administrative terms, from faculty to faculty. A faculty is a collection of similar (cognate) subjects which enjoy similar outlooks and similar methods (for example the use of laboratories). Thus the family of sciences will normally contain mathematics, physics, chemistry, bioscience, geology, perhaps computing science, pharmacy and pharmacology. These subjects mix well but they also tend to specialise further in themselves, for example, into theoretical chemistry, particle physics, or immunology. The tendency to ever greater specialisation and fragmentation can be a problem for scientists. It may need to be compensated by an insistence on general, foundation courses at the level of first or second year where the essentials of the neighbouring sciences can be brought into the course. This is the case at MIT or Stanford in the United States. At both these institutions early specialisation is frowned upon.

In the arts and humanities the same attitudes prevail. English, history, modern languages are often the basis of single separate degrees. But many institutions will now expect, indeed insist, that a range of subjects are studied in the early years. The same is true for the social sciences and business studies.

For engineers, doctors, vets and the like the arrangements are different again. Their students would also benefit from a breadth of outlook but the professional bodies which control and validate the degrees and grant the graduates chartered status often insist on specified courses which cramp the students' ability to range widely and to choose freely. Even here, things are changing and it should be possible for intending students to enjoy more choice in their professional subjects. In the even more vocational subjects, such as music, nursing or architecture, great emphasis is placed on specialised performance. Whether this is ultimately good or bad is not yet clear and will continue to be debated.

There is a view that all students should read a general degree before going on to specialise in anything. That would mean that most specialised professional courses would be the basis of a second degree. It would then be impossibly to be an undergraduate student in say law or medicine. That is the case in other countries now but not yet so in Britain.

One of the questions to be answered by all intending undergraduates in Britain is therefore 'Do I want to keep my options open or would I like to specialise?' If you want to do research you will have to specialise but not necessarily at the beginning. It is worth remembering that premature specialisation may cut you off from other careers yet to be encountered. On the other hand, if you are keen to be an astrophysicist then no-one should stop you from being one. Somewhere you will find an undergraduate course in it.

These remarks therefore have to do with the shape of your undergraduate course. Is it to be broadly based? Is it to be a flat pyramid? Or is it to be a tall spike of achievement? Most experienced educators would wish it to be all of these things and it usually can be. Even the broadest courses will end up with a project the extent and depth of which will be up to you.

To mention options is to consider choice and there are administrative penalties to pay for wide varieties. Nowadays most institutions of higher education offer their courses in modular form on a common timetable so that in principle at least, any combination of courses can be taken. Academic guidance is invariably offered to those who need it or want it but ultimately the choice is yours. This arrangement of course options is progressive by nature. As each module is assessed the examination successes are accumulated as credits. Credit accumulation then leads to your degree and, in Britain, to the class of your degree.

This matter of classes of degree is largely a British phenomenon. All honours degrees in Britain are classified into first, upper second, lower second and third class honours and there may be a pass degree also. Much is made of the need to get a first or at least an upper second. A double first, in say, politics and economics is the sort of success that a good career could be launched on. This arrangement reflects an elitist view of education in which excellence is everything. One must not belittle achievement but there are those who note that this kind of attitude reflects primarily academic prowess and leaves other qualities unrecognised and unrewarded. Whilst, therefore, it is immensely worthwhile to obtain a first, it is not a disaster to get a third.

What do employers think? They will inevitably be guided by the performance indicators of the examinations at universities and colleges. But, in time, the results of these examinations dim. It is said that you get your first job entirely on the basis of your initial qualifications but that you get your last job entirely on the basis of your personality. It is a fact of life that most men and women are highly intelligent but with a variable capacity to succeed in academic examinations. To use their intelligence is a life-long characteristic dependent on many other qualities. These qualities are therefore encouraged during undergraduate study, especially by many of the extra curricular, non-academic activities available at most universities and colleges.

When considering your higher education you will therefore be confronted with a seemingly limitless range of choices of subjects and subject mixes. You may be bewildered by that choice but you will have some idea of what you like and what you are good at. What you do not study now can perhaps be studied later. It is a poor person who once educated does not stay a student all of his or her life.

You will be pleasantly surprised at what you discover you can do. Remember to build on success – nothing is so successful at motivating you to do more. In the end you will emerge as a clever, gifted and, I would hope, confident and charming personality.

I want to stress the word confident. To be under-confident is almost as dangerous as being over-confident. Confidence is bred from achievement and from the strengthening by that achievement of your regard for yourself. To like yourself is not to be a latter-day Narcissus but to be someone who knows their potential as well as their shortcomings. The three or four years as an undergraduate will have an important part to play in this business of building you up (or building you down).

In the worst case, a diffident undergraduate can be confronted by a seemingly unscalable wall of knowledge. The professors seem to find it easy but you find it impossibly difficult. This kind of encounter is inevitable but should not be too frequent. The respect (one could say awe) in which knowledge is held does not help. There are knowledge-mongers who perpetuate the idea that the more difficult the knowledge or the concept appears to be the more valuable or important it is. Many text books are written more to impress the author's peers than to help the ordinary reader. So one must be wary of the people and circumstances that belittle or discourage the beginner.

In short, knowledge is not everything. It too has its defects. It wears out or degrades with time. Nowadays it can be as conveniently stored in a computer's database as stuffed into the head. A lot of mathematics and science takes abstract, and at first obscure, forms because that was once the only way of expressing the complexities of the real world. These forms should be differentiated from the simpler concepts they are intended to describe. It is the concepts that matter. They stimulate the imagination and allow the human mind to enter the scene of science. Unless that happens, these subjects will wither away. Again most experienced educators are aware of the dangers of over-emphasising the knowledge-base or the content as it is called. In selecting your courses and institutions you will have regard for the way in which these fundamental issues are dealt with. Too many demands on the knowledge base is the way of demotivation and a denting of that confidence.

Using the knowledge is the way to differentiate between what is useful and what is not, what is valuable and what is not. A sense of values is an essential part of good judgement which is another plank on which confidence is built. Using knowledge is applying it to useful purposes. It is usually an enjoyable experience in which mistakes are made from which you will learn. The process of learning belongs to the human side of education. It is a skill to be acquired and when acquired is likely to last a lifetime. The acquisition of this skill and others like it is part of the permanent development of the individual. It is therefore the most valuable part of the experience of higher education.

Subjects, courses and institutions vary in the way they approach these matters. If you find learning an easy process then perhaps it doesn't matter where you go or what you do. But for many students this will not be so. They should be careful in their choice of options. However, in my opinion, for all students it is at least as important for them to become skilled as to become knowledgeable. Skills add to competence and that is yet another basis for the confidence which I believe all young people should strive to develop.

So bear these things in mind when you approach your higher education.

Do you want to be a specialist or a generalist? Do you want to develop your personality as well as your knowledge-base? Think carefully about those needs and ask yourself quite selfishly 'What is best for me?'.

Accountancy
Prof M Bromwich, LSE

For well over two decades the accountancy profession has been growing very rapidly and this growth shows little evidence of any slow down. There is an especially great demand for newly qualified accountants. Recently the major growth has been in management accounting, which seeks to help management make decisions and control these decisions, in consultancy, where the skills offered by the accounting firms extend far beyond accountancy and tax.

Much of accounting is concerned with providing financial information to those who make decisions and who wish to monitor their existing plans. Thus, accounting is useful to almost everyone from those planning household expenditure, investors, the trade unions for wage negotiation to senior managers evaluating a vast capital project like a new factory or a new car model. This does not mean that the better known aspects of accounting are no longer of importance. One of accounting's major contributions to society is its ability to handle and summarise large amounts of data. The mechanics of this – book-keeping – used to be tedious but this work is now done by computer, thereby freeing accountants to concentrate on analysing the meaning of the accounting figures so produced. That book-keeping is the foundation of accountancy means that those who wish to take up the subject as a career need to be fairly comfortable with figures. More important necessary abilities are to be able to discern what accounting figures mean, to perceive the trends implicit in them and to be able to communicate persuasively with others. Thus, in the present environment the ability to ensure adequate cash is flowing into the business is at a premium.

These abilities are needed in full strength in the auditing sphere of what is known as financial accounting. The objective of auditing is to ensure that organisations have kept their accounts properly, that these contain the information they are required to produce, that they have not been subject to fraud and are likely to be able to continue in operation in the future. Efficiency audits which go further than this and attempt to consider organisational effectiveness are likely to be an important task of auditors in the future.

There are some very difficult problems to be solved with regard to the other major areas of financial accounting, the production of accounting reports for the general public. First, as these reports are used by many different people for many different purposes, should there be special reports for special purposes or should the accountancy profession attempt to provide a general purpose set of accounts for use to all? A second problem is how should the effects of inflation be reflected in accounts?

Among the large number of other problems which remain to be solved is that of attempting to say what published financial reports should contain for this is still a matter of substantial choice by their preparers.

The other major area of activity of accountants is that of management accounting which is concerned with providing information to help organisations make decisions and to monitor those already made. Many of the problems of financial accounting (such as allowing for the effects of inflation) plague its internal variant, but there are many problems which are of especial urgency to management accountants. How, for example, does one modify management accounting to reflect the major trend towards automating and computerising both manufacture and planning for manufacture?

That many of these problems have, as yet, no entirely satisfactory solutions is one reason why many accounting degrees concentrate on the basic disciplines underlying accounting such as economics, elementary statistics, behavioural studies, law and the more theoretical aspects of accounting. The objective of this is to give students the theoretical foundations which will help them to understand these problems and aid them in finding and understanding their solutions. Another reason why accounting degrees and their alternative one-year foundation courses in polytechnics concentrate on the more theoretical aspects of the subject is that after graduating from accounting courses those who wish to make their career in the subject have to study in some depth the existing techniques of accounting and to take professional examinations (after approximately 3 years for graduates and 4 years for foundation course students). It would be a misallocation of resources for degree studies to cover the same ground. The professional examinations cover a wide range of subjects with the contemporary emphasis being especially on management subjects. There is also a strong trend away from part-time study for these examinations toward block release from work for such studies. Reflecting the wide range of disciplines covered in accounting degrees, there is usually no restriction on the A-levels required of potential accounting students.

This ability to understand future developments in the subject provided by accounting degrees and the opportunities to study other related disciplines such as law in some depth is what attracts many to accounting degrees. The unsolved problems of accounting provide plenty of intellectual excitement and ensure the development of reasoning and independent judgement. Most courses have a similar core of economics, elementary statistics, law and accounting. Operations research, which is the use of quantitative techniques to help in decision making, usually forms part of this core. Given the wide range of disciplines which impact on decisions, different accountancy degrees specialise in exploring the interaction of accounting with various disciplines. Many degrees stress the relation between accounting and economics. Indeed some would say that accounting is mainly microeconomics writ large. Some courses attempt to integrate accounting and business studies. Others concentrate on the sociological and psychological aspects of accounting, others combine computing and accounting and yet others explore the interaction between law and accounting. It is of importance for potential students to bear this in mind when selecting an accounting course.

There still seems to be a high demand for accountants of all varieties. It is possible to specialise in financial accountancy either within an organisation or within the auditing profession. Management accounting makes a good alternative career whether in industry or the public sector. Most areas of the accounting profession offer opportunities for foreign travel and the ability to specialise in one area of accounting, such as tax advice. Often accountants, after success in their chosen branch of accounting, move on to become Managing Directors or Chairmen of large companies reflecting the necessary wide experience of all aspects of the business acquired by senior accounting personnel.

Aeronautical Engineering
Professor Donald McLean,
Southampton University

Telling anyone about aeronautical engineering is about as easy as defining an elephant: you can recognise it when you see it, but you can't describe it. The reason why it is so difficult is that aeronautical engineering is a very big subject. A large number of specialised technical disciplines go to make up the subject, but each of those disciplines can become a lifetime study for some of us. Yet to be any good at aeronautical engineering means that you must have an understanding of all of them. You must learn about the physical principles involved when anything flies, or when it moves through space where there is no real atmosphere. You have to learn the techniques needed to analyse and design aerospace vehicles. But it is that very variety and the great complexity of these vehicles which gives aeronautical engineering its special grand dimension: as an engineering subject it calls forth the greatest imagination and enthusiasm from everyone who works in it. The kind of vehicles you may be lucky enough to deal with can range from those which operate in the earth's atmosphere, to those which go beyond it. Such atmospheric vehicles are called aircraft and they range in type from the helicopter, which is slow in the air (sometimes even stationary), to Concorde, which is fast (but never hovers). Some spacecraft travel at super high speeds and operate outside earth's atmosphere, but often in the atmosphere of some other planet. In between the helicopter and Concorde there are the single-engined and twin-engined general aviation aircraft which don't fly very fast, very far, or very high, but which are the most common aircraft type in the world: in total, they fly ten times the number of hours flown by all the commercial passenger and large transport aircraft operating in the world, and by the fighters, the bombers, and the strike aircraft of all the military air forces. These commercial jet transports fly millions of people daily in safety and comfort over millions of miles at affordable cost. And then there are all the different types of military aircraft whose performance is evidently a function of their intended missions. Although each of these aircraft types has its special problems, because each operates in a different speed regime, and although research is carried out continuously on them in industrial design offices, university laboratories, and military research establishments, each type is linked by a common core of technical specialisations and disciplines which are used as the basic subjects of any British aeronautical degree. Typically, degrees have a first year devoted to subjects like mathematics, mechanics, computing, elasticity, thermodynamics, fluid mechanics, properties of materials and basic electricity which are common to all engineering subjects. In the second year all the aeronautical subjects, like aerodynamics, aircraft structures, propulsion system dynamics and stability and control, which every aeronautical engineer should know something of, are dealt with. And the final year is usually devoted to optional subjects and a project which are chosen by the student to help him specialise in his or her chosen branch of aeronautical engineering.

If you study a supersonic passenger aircraft, such as Concorde, you will find that such very high speed flight can only be achieved if it has been arranged for the air to flow over the wing, the fuselage, and the vertical fin, in a fashion which causes the efficient creation of forces and moments. But at such very high speeds, the air reacts chemically with the metal surface of the aircraft which then begins to heat up. Arranging for that heat to be dissipated before the aircraft's structure is affected, and before the passengers and crew are caused discomfort, is a major technical problem. In Concorde it was solved by using the engines' fuel as a coolant for the aircraft's surface. When we study how and why the shape of an aircraft can be arranged so that these forces and moments are produced satisfactorily by the air flow we are concerned with **aerodynamics**. From aerodynamics, for example, we learn why high speed aircraft must have swept wings. To study aerodynamics effectively means that you have to be able to get access to a wind tunnel in which a model aircraft or an airfoil can be used to obtain good measurements which apply to a real aircraft. For a good understanding of aeronautical engineering, a knowledge of aerodynamics is indispensable, and familiarity with wind tunnel techniques is most helpful in learning about aerodynamics. So, try to study where there are plenty of wind tunnels but be warned; such facilities are expensive, so they are heavily used for laboratory classes, projects and even for staff research. In the future it may be possible to obtain the same data from computer simulation using computational fluid dynamics.

You may wonder why it is so important to know such forces and moments in such detail: the answer is that the aircraft's motion and, therefore, its flight path will be governed by them. Whenever we study aircraft motion, and the corresponding aircraft trajectory which occurs as a consequence of such forces and moments, we are then dealing with flight dynamics. Here we are concerned with the aircraft's performance, how fast it will fly, how high it will climb, how long it can fly, and how far it can fly. But in the atmosphere the air is never still, so the motion of the aircraft is always being disturbed by the very air through which it flies. Thus, the aircraft has to be controlled at every moment of its flight if it is to maintain its desired path. That continuous control can be provided by a human pilot or by an automatic flight control system. (Never call it an autopilot: that was the trade name – like Hoover – of the automatic flight control system used in the Zeppelin airships.) Whenever such human or automatic control is being studied it is necessary to know the degree of stability of the aircraft. This property is often indicated by means of the measured flying qualities of the aircraft, but with many modern aircraft, the aircraft simply cannot be designed with flying qualities which will allow a pilot to fly it safely and, as a result, automatic flight control systems have to be fitted so that the aircraft can be flown. This important topic, **stability** and **control**, is an essential part of all aeronautical engineering degree courses, although the design of the automatic control systems may be dealt with separately under Avionics. Very few aeronautical departments have a test aircraft, but even if they had it would be prudent to use **simulation**, nearly always carried out on a digital computer. You must expect to use digital computers as routinely as using a pencil. All UK courses provide a one-week test flight course.

Of course, when an aerospace vehicle is moving around it has to be structurally sound: its frame and surface must be strong enough to withstand the stresses which result from the very great forces to which a vehicle is subject whenever it is manoeuvred, or whenever it meets atmospheric turbulence. Even spacecraft orbiting outside the earth's atmosphere can be subjected to torque disturbances caused by gravity gradients and solar pressure. Thus, the study of the behaviour of materials, the stresses and strains within that material, the study of vibration, and the deflection and twisting of the structural elements, are referred to as **structural analysis**. It is an important subject for every aeronautical engineer and it is taught in every aeronautical engineering course. Equally important is the study of how a vehicle is accelerated: **propulsion**. Every engine is governed by the laws of thermodynamics and every course will give a brief introduction to propulsion, including reciprocating petrol engines and their associated propellers, the turbojet, the ramjet and, perhaps, the rocket motor. Some courses have specialised option subjects in Propulsion which are particularly useful if you want to work with aircraft or spacecraft engines.

Aircraft and spacecraft carry a considerable amount of systems equipment for auxiliary power, heat exchanging, life support, fire extinguishing, communication, navigation, and flight control not to mention the wide variety of weapons systems fitted to military aircraft. Some of these systems are described by the neologism: **avionics** (a compound word from *aviation electronics*). How such systems work, and how aerospace vehicles depend upon them, are usually covered in degree courses but there are also specialist courses in avionics systems or aerospace systems engineering. The core subjects of an aerospace systems course are likely to include mathematics, computation, communication theory, electromagnetism, system dynamics, signal analysis, power and actuator systems, as well as aerodynamics, propulsion, and structural design.

Avionics systems courses involve the five principal areas of modern aeronautical engineering, namely: aerodynamic and structures, propulsion, communication and guidance, flight control systems, and information systems. If you understand that a little more than half the cost of a modern military aircraft (and sometimes as much as a third of the cost of a commercial passenger aircraft) is spent on such systems you will be able to appreciate how important such new courses are going to be in helping provide British industry with the well-educated aeronautical engineers it needs to successfully respond to the great challenges of aerospace in the future.

HELPFUL READING: O G Sutton, *Mastery of the Air* (Hodder and Stoughton, 1965); this is an up-dated version of an earlier book published by Penguin books in 1948. It was then called 'The Science of Flight'. J D Anderson, *An Introduction to Flight* (McGraw-Hill, 1978); R Shevell, *Fundamentals of Flight* (Prentice-Hall, 1983); both these books are elementary text-books, but each provides a good introduction to aeronautical engineering. C H Gibbs-Smith, *Aviation* (HMSO, Science Museum, 1985); an excellent historical account of the development of aeronautical engineering; B Sweetman, *Aircraft 2000* (Hamlyn Publishing, 1984); a good look at what present research in aeronautical engineering will accomplish.

African Studies
Richard Rathbone,
School of Oriental and African Studies

You have to be *exceptionally* boring to find Africa dull. African art, music and literature, all more and more available in the West, convey some of the excitement of this huge continent. Africa isn't like anywhere else. Understanding even a little of the lives of Africans demands imaginative minds that don't think that Britain is the centre of the universe. First of all you will have to cope with a *continent* not a country. Africa is massive and the historical experiences of its peoples have been immensely different. Africa boasts a virtually uncountable number of cultures, languages and styles of life. Second, you will be presented with a set of populations whose lives have changed more dramatically in the last two hundred years than any other large collection of people. Travelogue films on TV always harp on the vanishing world of the Bushmen or the herders of the encroaching Sahara. Romantic stuff; but romance always ignores the fact that such rural people are ruled from cities with motorways, fax machines and stock exchanges. When rural people look at the sky they see not only fire-crowned bishop birds, but 747s coming in to land at the nearest international airport. Not many people carry spears when there are no tourists about. People your age are more likely to wear personal stereos and 501s than loincloths.

That doesn't mean that Africa is becoming a sort of tropical Croydon. The challenge of African studies is understanding how 500 million people have retained their cultural, spiritual and personal individuality in the midst of rapid change. Just about everything is relevant to that understanding. Geography helps us to grasp the immensity of the task the ancestors of modern Africans undertook when they progressively colonised often unpromising eco-systems like rain-forests or desert fringes. It also helps us to imagine the developmental possibilities of this potentially rich continent. The history of Africa, the birthplace of all our *homo sapiens* ancestors, forces us to think about how states emerged, and perhaps even more challengingly, why some African peoples set their faces against such political organisation. It also forces us to think about why African historical development has been so unlike that of Europe. Even before the intervention of Islam and then Europe into Africa, it's clear that African political, social and economic organisations had their own striking individuality. Looking at Africa before the slave trade and colonialism allows us to tease out which elements of the dramatic changes were imposed upon Africa and which are the results of Africa's own robust initiatives.

Some of the answers to those questions will emerge from a concentration on social anthropology. This discipline helps us to get to grips with extremely varied but always original forms of African social organisation, the centrality of family relationships in their widest sense and, no less importantly, with how Africans have understood both the visible and invisible world. Understanding the root of African thought is crucial. A keen student of Africa wants more than descriptions, however good. What would you think about an African student studying Britain without learning English? Trying to learn, however basically, one of Africa's major languages equips you with the tools to begin to understand some of the words and concepts which shape African thought. The languages are not as difficult as you might think.

Many of you are interested in modern Africa because its sad problems are all that British press sensationalism is interested in. If you look at Africa through the discipline of political science you will again find a huge kaleidoscope of contrast. African states have emerged through exciting and sometimes bloody opposition to colonialism. Some are grim, repressive states like South Africa or Zaire, others are relatively democratic and open like Senegal or Tanzania. Why do we hear so little about the success stories? Again the economists will surprise you with a continent in which Sudanese famine plays much less of a role than hard-won development and the improvement in people's standards of living of the sort that has been evident in Botswana and Zimbabwe. It's certainly true that studying modern Africa will help you understand some of the great problems of today like the north–south divide, the population and resource crises, military intervention and South Africa, but it's not all gloomy. It's an environment, after all, from which an African novelist has recently won the Nobel prize for literature, in which the Bhundu Boys and all the musical innovators from Mali we've been enjoying in Britain recently and some of the greatest athletes in the world have developed their skills.

African Studies is usually approached through a combined studies format. You'll get advice about good combinations from the teachers at individual colleges and universities. Be warned we are all fanatics. We've all worked in Africa and can't put it down. Studying Africa makes for a kind of commitment which is unusual in higher education. Students get infected too and there is no known cure. Why is it so infectious? Firstly there are few better opportunities to embark on comparative, multi-disciplinary studies which use some of the skills you've acquired at school but demand you use them in a totally different environment. Secondly Africa comes to matter a lot to those who study it. It's not a place, but an excitingly varied collection of populations. And these people are exciting, warm and original. The more you learn about the things they think are important, the more you wonder about your own society's values and styles. Above all, as with all study, there is a lot to learn and a lot of it is hard, but the slog is always accompanied by the availability of Africa's art, its music, its literature. If any of this begins to sound interesting, read some of the novels I have suggested. If it stops being interesting then you are, as I suggested in the beginning, exceptionally boring.

HELPFUL READING: Fiction. Chinua Achebe, *Things Fall Apart* (Heinemann, 1958); Chinua Achebe, *Anthills of the Savanna* (Heinemann, 1987); M Dikobe, *The Marabi Dance* (Heinemann, 1973); Bessie Head, *A Collector of Treasures* (Heinemann, 1977). Non-fiction. S E Akpabot, *Football in Nigeria* (Macmillan, 1985); D Coplan, *In Township Tonight! South Africa's black city music and theatre* (Longman, 1985); John Dunn (ed), *West African States* (CUP, 1978); Paulin J Hountondji, *African Philosophy, Myth and Reality* (Hutchinson, 1983); John Mack, *Madagascar. Island of the Ancestors* (British Museum, 1986); Ali A Mazrui, *The Africans. A triple heritage* (BBC Publications, 1986); P Richards, *Indigenous Agricultural Revolution: ecology and food production in West Africa* (Hutchinson, 1985); Landeg White, *Magomero* (CUP, 1987); John Iliffe, *The African Poor: a History* (CUP, 1987).

Agriculture, Horticulture and Forestry
Professor W Holmes, Wye College

The study of natural resources, and their management to provide food, fibre and other materials is of major importance throughout the world. The current emphasis on the environment makes it even more important that the physical, biological and economic principles underlying the production of crops, trees, and animals, and their interactions with the environment, are well understood.

Agriculture, horticulture and forestry and related subjects studied at degree level deal with these subjects in a very effective way. General courses give a broad training and open the way to many careers. There are also specialist courses in sciences (agricultural botany, agricultural bio-chemistry, agricultural zoology, animal science, horticultural science, wood science); courses emphasising economics (such as agricultural economics, agricultural business management, agricultural and food marketing); environmental courses (agriculture and environmental science, forestry and natural resources, terrestrial ecology) and in agricultural engineering.

Before you start, you must of course have a genuine interest in the subject. You might have grown up on a farm but this is certainly not essential. The subject may appeal because you like the growing of plants or you like working with animals. Or, you may wish to apply your skills and interests in biology, or chemistry, or economics, or geology, or mathematics, or physics to the real life situation. Or you may just like the countryside and country pursuits. Whatever your motivation, evidence of a keen interest and that you have read something about the subject will help to impress the selectors; a vague sentimental interest in nature and the open air is not enough.

For most courses, it is preferred that you spend at least one year after school, gaining practical experience on a farm, a horticultural holding or an agricultural research station before you start. Even farmers' sons and daughters are encouraged to gain experience away from home. The majority of students find it enjoyable and rewarding to learn some of farming's manual skills and to live through the annual cycle of events. Moreover many employers consider such experience to be essential. As an alternative, a few courses provide for the student to take a sandwich year to gain his practical experience in the middle rather than before the course begins.

Courses in the UK normally last 3 or 4 years, in addition to the practical year, with a progression from basic studies in the first year to more applied studies in the later years. For example, a course in agriculture will probably include the study of biology, biochemistry and economics together with introductory aspects of agriculture and statistics in the first year. Soil science, crop production, animal production, farm mechanisation and farm management would be second-year courses. Advanced aspects of crop and animal production, and of farm management together with selections from more specialist topics (eg animal breeding, marketing, plant pathology or intensive horticultural cropping) might occupy the final years. In addition most final year courses include a project, in which the student pursues a particular interest in some detail and submits a report or dissertation as part of the final examination.

Courses in horticulture, plant science and agricultural botany concentrate on plants. The horticultural courses include production and amenity horticulture, economics, management and marketing as well as the sciences of plant nutrition, plant physiology and plant pathology. Courses in plant science and agricultural botany are more science oriented: they omit management and devote the additional time to experimental techniques and frequently to the conduct of small scale investigations.

Similarly, courses in animal science and agricultural zoology provide for more detailed study of the anatomy, physiology and biochemistry of farm animals and of the parasites and insects of agricultural importance but omit some of the more practical aspects of animal husbandry and management. Since some of the work is conducted with smaller organisms, practical laboratory projects may be included.

Courses in agricultural economics are intended primarily for planners or consultants rather than for farm or estate managers whose needs are usually met by courses in agriculture, agricultural business management or horticulture. These courses therefore start from a base of economics, mathematics and statistics and progress to advanced economics, agrarian development, agricultural policy, economic statistics, management and marketing with relatively brief reference to agricultural technology. Courses in agricultural business management and land economy depend more heavily on economics, management techniques and legal aspects and they give less emphasis to scientific subjects.

Of course it is not all work. The faculties of agriculture are usually small communities of from 400–800 students, sometimes in a rural setting. They usually have a strong community spirit with good sports facilities, a wide range of other student activities and excellent staff/student relationships.

A good degree gained in this wide field of study opens a remarkable variety of career opportunities. Some graduates are soon running their own business in farming or horticulture, many are managing businesses for larger organisations or estates. A further large proportion is involved in advisory work either with state or EC organisations or with commercial companies. Education, research and government posts at home or overseas also provide many opportunities.

These subjects lead to a wide range of interesting and useful careers in Britain, Europe and in the tropics. Indeed if you wish to apply science to the benefit of mankind, what better opportunity, apart from medicine, than in the oldest technology, agriculture.

HELPFUL READING: Books which give a general description of British agriculture include *Freams Agriculture* (John Murray, 1983); and Michael Haines, *An Introduction to Farming Systems* (Longman, 1982), *Farming UK* (HMSO, 1987). There are weekly journals like *The Farmers Weekly* and *The Grower*, while serious newspapers have many articles on agricultural topics such as the Common Agricultural Policy and agricultural development overseas.

American Studies
Dr Michael Dunne, Sussex University

The term, American studies, is somewhat misleading; for though the adjective American can be applied to the whole of the Western Hemisphere, in this country American studies denotes primarily the investigation of the past and present society of the USA. Canada, the USA's northern neighbour, is not normally included in American studies syllabuses and more usually appears as part of British Imperial and Commonwealth history and relations. As for the huge and populous areas of South and Central America, including the Caribbean, these are most often grouped into Latin American studies. In the latter case a number of separate departments or institutions of Latin American studies exist; alternatively, the study of Latin America is pursued in departments of Hispanic or Romance language and literature as part of the dispersion of the Spanish and Portuguese-speaking peoples.

One consequence of this academic map-drawing is that most American (ie USA) studies departments emphasize the British roots of contemporary United States society. If, therefore, you are seeking non-Anglo perspectives on today's United States you would be well advised to investigate the options provided by colleges, polytechnics and universities which give instruction in Spanish, Portuguese and French (the latter for Canada and the Caribbean). Additionally, if your concern is to study the indigenous, non-European (pre-Columbian) peoples and languages of the Americas, then you should survey the opportunities provided by departments of anthropology and ethnology.

From this it is clear that geographical considerations and limitations merge into chronological ones; and American studies is no exception. Here the concentration is upon events and issues since the War for Independence (1776–1783); and while many American studies departments provide general and specialist options in British North American culture and society, if your main concerns are with the pre-Independence period or imperial relations, then you may be better served in the more traditional straight history departments.

These geographical and chronological axes help to explain one of the most striking characteristics of American studies, namely its concern (preoccupation might be a better word) with definitions of national identity. 'What is an American?' was a question posed by an observer of the newborn United States, the Frenchman Crevecoeur; and the early decades of American studies after World War II echoed with the rephrasing and inconclusive answering of that conundrum. Nor has its resonance faded: women's studies, ethnic studies, black studies are, in the United States, conscious and vigorous movements to re-direct academic as well as popular concern to the presumptions and values which have informed the traditional analyses of American history and literature. That such fields of intellectual study and social activity have not been institutionalized to the same extent in this country as they have in the United States is one measure of the differences between the British and American cousins. At the same time the elasticity of American studies in this country does offer room for exploring such important subjects by combining long-established disciplines such as history, literary analysis, sociology and anthropology with the newer tools fashioned from structuralism and semiology.

These comments should not be taken to mean that American studies departments provide instruction in every branch of social enquiry! Rather they are intended to point to the possibilities of combining area and interdisciplinary studies. For the simple truth is that American studies still retains its links with long-established modes of academic investigation – what we call the disciplines. In most American studies departments academic interests will cluster around one of three nuclei: literature, history and (increasingly) a number of the social sciences, especially politics, sociology and economics. This means that students are trained to become experts in particular disciplines through the application of those disciplines to American materials. But the theory is by no means exclusively American: literature specialists must be prepared to grapple with the classics of continental structuralism; historians with the techniques of the Annales school; and social scientists with Marx, Weber and Durkheim.

From these perspectives it may be easily seen that American studies need be no more outlandish than studying European history, English literature or international relations. Conversely American studies does distinguish itself by the strength and success of its efforts to relate the study of history, literature, politics and so forth to one another. Thus you will find courses on Gender in American Society, on the South and the West, on Black Culture and Black Consciousness, on Class and Social Mobility – in all of which the diachronic and synchronic methods of structuralism are employed in redrawing conceptual and disciplinary boundaries. The West is not merely California, even Hawaii of today; it is also the West in the imagination of the eighteenth century enlightenment; gender is not merely the definition of contemporary women and men but of the ideologies of equality and freedom at the time of the Revolution. So too with racism and class: similarities and dissimilarities are explored across time and place by examining people's lives, their social relations and their artefacts.

Much of the material (or data, evidence) of American studies reflects its concern with questions of social formation and reproduction. How does the mass media operate? What is the social function of the leisure industry? What are the preconceptions and dangers in basing academic enquiry upon printed (and predominantly book-form) sources? These sorts of theoretical questions explain why American studies embraces film and broadcasting; the press and journalism; oral history and folklore; music and the visual and plastic arts.

Not all departments of American studies treat every one of these subjects in equal depth. When consulting school and college advisers, reading through prospectuses and syllabuses, questioning interviewers and admissions officers you should look out for the teaching and resource strengths in particular areas. Try to find out the possibilities for research in depth *and* for bridging traditional gaps (say between high and popular culture; between painting and photography; between economic or legislative history and sociological theory). In this way you will be making your own contribution to the shape and advance of American studies.

HELPFUL READING: Lawrence W Levine, *Black Culture and Black Consciousness* (OUP, 1977); Linda K Kerber and Jane de Hart-Mathews, eds, *Women's America: Refocusing the Past* (OUP, 1987); S Fender, *Plotting the Golden West: American Literature and the Rhetoric of the California Trail* (Cambridge, 1981); W Issel, *Social Change in the United States 1945–1983* (Macmillan, 1985).

Anatomy
Professor Anthony Firth, St Mary's Hospital Medical School, London

Anatomy does not form a body of knowledge clearly distinct from other biomedical sciences such as physiology or biochemistry, for all of these concern themselves with the problem of how living things work. However, anatomy takes a distinctive approach to investigation of this problem. The word 'anatomy' means 'cutting apart'; the anatomical approach is to explore the structure of living organisms as a way of getting at how they work. Anatomists tend to think in terms of shapes and relationships in space as the most striking and exciting aspects of living things – their imagination tends to be visual and spatial rather than abstract.

The earliest anatomists relied on dissection of dead organisms ('dissection' is another word meaning 'cutting apart') as their main method of study, and dissection of the dead bodies of people or of domestic animals still forms the core of anatomy courses in medical, dental or veterinary science. Research in anatomy has more or less exhausted all but the small print of this 'gross anatomy' and has largely moved on to other things, although each generation of medical students still discovers anew the fascination of exploring the elegant intricacy of the human body.

Most students of biology outside the health sciences do not come across anatomy as a formal subject in their courses, but nonetheless they use the methods of structural study which typify the anatomical approach to biology. These now range from naked-eye observations during dissection to high-resolution microscopic examination of cells and their components. The first effective use of the electron microscope on biological materials in the 1950s both emphasise the power of the visual approach and also underline its limitations. With these instruments it is possible to reveal the organisation not only of cell interiors but also of the large molecules such as DNA and proteins which characterise living tissue, but until quite recently this ability to see fine structural detail has been offset by the maddening difficulty of finding out anything precise about the chemical nature of the structures so revealed. For example, despite the hundreds of articles which have been published about the structure of the seamlike junctions between cells of the surface-covering sheets called epithelia, there is a spectacular lack of hard evidence as to whether the main chemical component of these junctions is protein or lipid.

This kind of problem is rather akin to that which once confronted astronomers who could see stars very clearly through telescopes but could say nothing about their chemical composition. The astronomers made headway against this problem by recognising that particular elements leave tell-tale absorption lines at characteristic frequencies in the spectrum. Over the last generation, and particularly in the last ten years, biologists have learned to characterise the molecular composition of microscopic structures by a range of methods which allow the presence of specific molecules to be revealed by light or electron microscopy. This hybrid science of histochemistry is an extraordinarily powerful tool, for it has allowed specific chemical information to be obtained with all the precision about structure and spatial relationships which characterises microscopic science. At first this could only be exploited for a fairly limited number of biologically interesting chemicals which were sufficiently distinctive for them to be stainable by chemical reactions which failed to stain other substances: starch and neutral fats are good examples. The most interesting molecules of living systems, the nucleic acids and proteins, could be identified as classes but it seemed impossible to label selectively a single species of protein or a single gene in a chromosome.

Something could be done with those proteins which happened to be catalysts, the enzymes, as they could often be manipulated to yield a visible and insoluble reaction product which could be recognised by light or electron microscopy. Enzyme histochemistry has been with us for about thirty years and grows in subtlety and usefulness every year; it can show us not only where enzymes are within a cell, but also which reactions they can catalyse and even how fast they can do it.

However, the real explosion of biological microscopy in the last decade owes its existence to a group of methods collectively and repulsively described as 'specific ligand binding histochemistry'. These exploit the ability of certain classes of molecules to recognise and bind very selectively to other molecules of biological interest. For example, the group of proteins called antibodies, made by cells of the immune system, are characterised by the ability of a particular antibody type to bind very selectively to a particular site on a specific protein or some other molecule of moderate complexity. A wide range of methods can be used to label this antibody so that it can be used as a visible probe. In light microscopy a spectacular result is obtained by using labels such as fluorescein which glow brilliantly when exposed to ultraviolet light of the correct wavelength; cells or other structures which have bound the fluorescein-labelled antibody literally 'light up'. Similar stratagems using labels such as colloidal particles of gold allow the extension of these immunohistochemical methods to electron microscopy. Our ability to culture clones of antibody-making cells derived from a single original cell now allows us to make single-specificity antibodies against single components of complex and unpurifiable mixtures of molecules, ability to make these monoclonal antibodies being only limited by practical considerations of time and expense. Similarly, another family of specific probes can be directed against the genes themselves; genetic engineering methods allow single genes or groups of genes to be grown in bacterial cells, and these mass-produced 'cloned DNA' molecules can be labelled and used to light up matching gene sequences within cells. Short sequences of synthetic DNA can be used in a similar way.

This fusion of microscopy with the 'new biology' of cloned DNA and monoclonal antibodies has revolutionised biomedical research in just a few years. If anatomy is defined as 'what anatomists do', then most biologists are becoming anatomists as labelled probes and microscopes become ubiquitous tools of experimental biology. Good anatomy has always been concerned with the relationship between form and function rather than with the sterile description of form for its own sake, and these new histochemical methods enable us to paint our maps of the body in functionally defined and vivid colours.

For students entering biology these are exciting times. Those training for medicine and allied professions meet both the traditional and the new anatomy. They study the human body by dissecting the dead, by examining pictures generated by an ever-growing range of non-invasive imaging methods such as x-radiographs, computerised tomography, ultrasound and magnetic resonance imaging. They explore living anatomy by examining their own bodies and those of other students. They study the mature and the developing body by microscopic means which increasingly depend on the chemically specific and functionally informative methods of histochemistry. For all biologists form and function are becoming unified by new methods in microscopy. Whether we work on the unfolding of the genetic program of development, the functional organisation of the brain, the subtly disordered biology of cancer cells, or the means by which Amoeba achieves the extraordinarily complex task of crawling across a piece of glass, our approach leans heavily on the central insight of anatomy: that form is the visible aspect of invisible functions and so can serve as a road to understanding them.

HELPFUL READING: Edited B Alberts et al, *Molecular Biology of the Cell* (New York, Garland, 1989 (2nd edition)); edited C F Graham & P F Wareing, *Developmental Control in Animals and Plants* (Oxford, Blackwell, 1984 (2nd edition)).

Anthropology
Professor Adam Kuper, Brunel University

Anthropologists have a romantic image. They are pictured camping in an Amazonian rain forest, or sailing on a frail barque between two little Pacific islands, accompanying a picturesquely attired party intent on some exotic ritual exchange. In Germany, students are flocking to study anthropology, apparently because they believe it is the Green Party of the social sciences. But it is true that not everyone finds the romance irresistible. My mother believed that anthropologists were driven crazy by isolation in the bush. When I began working in the Kalahari Desert she suffered gloomy forebodings – and who shall say she was wrong? But few people have much idea what anthropologists are really up to, and they are surprised to discover that we may also do field studies rather closer to home, in Greek islands, Irish villages, or even Midlands factories.

Anthropology is about the evolution, unity and diversity of the human species. One branch of anthropology, physical anthropology, is concerned largely with the biological evolution of human beings. However, the main differences between human communities over the past 100,000 years at least have been cultural rather than biological, and the other main branches of anthropology concern themselves with the study of cultural development and variation. Archaeologists drive deep shafts back in time, reconstructing cultural processes in the distant past. Social or cultural anthropologists study contemporary human communities, charting their customs and practices and attempting to explain them.

The central experience of anthropologists is always fieldwork. Ideally they spend one or two years alone in an exotic community, participating as far as possible in the life of the people, speaking their language and forging bonds of friendship and trust. This sometimes trying, often inspiring, always important experience of immersion in a totally strange way of life is then laboriously relived at home, and translated into a formal analysis either of the community or, more usually today, of an aspect of its life. (But a number of anthropologists do slip the academic restrictions and produce lively impressionistic and personal accounts of their experience, such as Nigel Barley's humorous reminiscences of fieldwork in West Africa and Indonesia.)

Fieldwork – ethnography – is only one aspect of the anthropologist's work. The challenge to field-workers is not only to make sense of their observations, but to relate what they have seen to studies made of similar institutions elsewhere. The ultimate goal is to further our understanding of social and cultural processes at large.

Social anthropology is a comparative social science, living on particularly intimate terms with history and sociology, though there are also fecund links with other disciplines. It can often be studied in association with another subject, sometimes in the traditional company of physical anthropology and archaeology, but otherwise together with ancient history, linguistics, African or Asian languages, psychology or sociology.

First-year students are sometimes shocked by their sudden, unjudging exposure to the variety of ways in which people think it proper and sensible to order their lives but this is itself a profoundly educational experience and the discipline provides rich insights into other cultures. Students are also given a training in social science approaches and techniques, which often provides a basis for further independent academic development or opens the way to a career in the media, market research, social work, teaching or, in some cases, to the adventure of anthropological research.

Applied anthropology is a growing field. Government departments or development agencies are the usual employers but in the USA today more than half of professional anthropologists are employed by the private sector. Anthropologists advise on problems of development abroad and are often to be found on teams of planners associated with development projects. Others have come to specialise in community relations at home, particularly in multi-cultural environments and they may contribute to policy-making in fields as diverse as medical or educational services and town planning.

For some anthropologists, the ultimate justification of our studies is a moral one. Lévi-Strauss has suggested that the study of anthropology offers two advantages:

> First, they encourage us to take a level-headed and unbiased view of customs and ways of life remote from our own – without, however, attributing to them absolute merits such as no society can claim to possess. Second, they dissuade us from taking for granted the 'right-ness' or 'naturalness' of our own customs, as can easily be the case if we know of no others, or know of them only partly and with bias.

HELPFUL READING: Claude Lévi-Strauss, *Triste Tropiques* (Harmondsworth: Penguin, 1976); Adam Kuper, *Anthropology and Anthropologists: the Modern British School* (London: Routledge and Kegan Paul, 1983). The Royal Anthropological Institute publishes a lively bi-monthly magazine, *Anthropology Today*. Subscription is £8 (£15 for libraries), payable to the Royal Anthropological Institute, 50 Fizroy Street, London W1P 5HS.

Archaeology

Dr S W Hillson, University College London

Lost cities, great ancient works of art in gold and precious stones, the sumptuous tombs of forgotten kings. If you study archaeology, you can certainly learn about such exciting and exotic things, but most archaeologists spend most of their time dealing with much more mundane objects such as broken pottery and bones – the accumulated waste of ordinary households, farms and towns. What keeps us fascinated is the light that archaeology can shed on everyday life in ancient communities, rather than the lives and works of the great and powerful. This is one of the major differences between archaeology and history. Written history is mostly about rulers and the nobility, military and religious life. Archaeology is based on physical remains rather than records and the great bulk of the material which survives from the past represents the common people. Most ancient objects, even those which may seem to us to be ugly, poorly made or badly damaged, have a story locked up in them. There is a real thrill in taking a small, broken fragment out of the ground, and bringing this story out with careful detective work. If you want to find out how people live, a good way is to look in their household refuse, and much of archaeology is tied up with the recovery and sophisticated analysis of ancient domestic rubbish.

Archaeology is an unusually broad subject, bridging the arts and the sciences. It ranges throughout the world, wherever people have lived, and extends from the earliest artifacts made by our extinct relatives some two and a half million years ago, through the period of historical records, including the industrial revolution and up to the present day. The basic approach is scientific, because objects must be excavated and studied in as methodical and objective a manner as possible, but there is also room for the artistic appreciation of beautiful artifacts and for interpretations which involve history, philosophy and sociology. An expanding field is 'science-based archaeology'; applying techniques which originated in the more traditional sciences. Physics is used to date objects and to locate buried sites. Chemistry helps to discover ancient methods of manufacture and trade routes. Biology is applied in the study of health, hygiene and diet in ancient communities. With all these different strands to archaeology, it can be difficult to define the core of the subject.

If you apply to study archaeology, you will find a bewildering range of degree courses and options. Some courses are highly specialised, such as classical archaeology, medieval archaeology, Egyptology, Near Eastern archaeology and archaeological conservation (the restoration and preservation of artifacts). These are really for people who already know the area of archaeology in which they would like to concentrate. The majority of people are less sure and apply for general archaeology courses, but the coverage of these also varies considerably. The subject is so wide that very few UKCPUs have the staff to cover the full range, or even a substantial part of it. Look very carefully at what options are available before you apply. The majority of courses deal with the archaeology of Europe,

Mediterranean and Middle Eastern countries. It is much harder to find course options on the archaeology of Africa, eastern Asia and Australasia, and the Americas. Some departments specialise in prehistory, whilst others concentrate on the classical or medieval periods. Relatively few UKCPUs have specialist options in the various science-based archaeology subjects but some departments concentrate on them and several BSc degrees in archaeology are offered. Because of all these variations, it is a good idea to visit archaeology departments in good time before you apply. Most departments will be very pleased to arrange this. I certainly see many people each year in this way.

Despite the rather exotic nature of the material, much of an archaeology course follows the traditional pattern of classes but one of the distinctive features of the subject is practical work. You are likely to do a lot of fieldwork because it is the basis of all archaeology. Fieldwork is one of the main attractions for most professional archaeologists and students, ranging from a regional field survey to full excavation of a particular site. Depending on the course, you may travel widely with your fieldwork. There may also be a lot of practical work in the drawing office and laboratory. You could be identifying and piecing together sherds of pottery, learning to interpret aerial photographs, practising drawing site plans, learning to sort and identify animal bone fragments, or using a microscope to identify pollen grains. Archaeological conservation involves a specialised training with a great deal of laboratory work, learning various treatments and restoration techniques. Most students enjoy handling ancient objects very much. The fieldwork and practical content of courses varies, and it is well worth finding out what facilities are available in a particular department and how much hands-on experience of artifacts and other remains there is.

What kinds of people do archaeology? Archaeology is at present rarely taught at A and AS level, so school or college leavers come with all sorts of different combinations of subjects including both arts and sciences. There is no 'best' combination and most subjects are relevant to some aspect of archaeology. Some students have had little or no previous experience of archaeology, whilst others have been helping on excavations for years. Thousands of people are actively involved as amateurs on archaeological projects, either in their own local societies or as volunteers on professionally run excavations. If you are thinking of studying archaeology you would be well advised to try a little excavation beforehand. The archaeology bug can bite at any age and, although some students started digging in their early teens, an increasing number of people are well established in another career before they decide that their real interests lie in archaeology. You will certainly meet people from a wide variety of backgrounds, age groups and nationalities.

HELPFUL READING: Kevin Greene *Archaeology: an introduction* (Batsford, 1983); Keith Branigan (Ed.) *The Atlas of Archaeology* (Macdonald & Co, 1982); Andrew Sherratt (Ed.) *The Cambridge Encyclopedia of Archaeology* (Cambridge University Press, 1980).

Architecture

Sandra Morris, Architectural Association School of Architecture

Architecture is the world around us. It is the room in which we live, the house across the road, the city in which we walk each day. It is equally the Dogong village carved into the rock, the Bedouin tent, the Eskimo igloo, another world of architecture in which architects have had no hand. The urge to build a shelter, to create a personal space, we are dependent on the architect and his team to provide us with an environment in which we can feel comfortable, happy and relaxed.

The development of any city is a history of complex issues. Buildings do not simply emerge fully fledged from the mind of an architect, but reflect the social economic and aesthetic issues of their day. To walk round a Georgian square is to experience a certain lifestyle. An understanding of the predominant issues that have determined form, structure and materials is essential to any criticism of architecture.

An architect is not just a skilled technician but a highly creative person whose skills enable him or her to communicate intentions and aspirations through drawings, and to organise the various components of a building into an integrated whole. At best the architect is still an artist, in the same way that Brunelleschi or Alberti were artists of the Renaissance.

There are many ways of approaching architecture and as many ways of teaching it. No-one expects a student beginning a course to be able to 'draw a building'. What every school looks for are the students with an eye and a lively imagination, who know how to select from among the myriad images with which we are bombarded every day of our lives what is important for them. Drawing skills can be acquired, but ideas are more difficult to come by. It is the quality of the ideas that will finally distinguish the architect from the draughtsman.

Most architectural schools – and there are over thirty to choose from in the UK – operate a selection system based on a personal interview. Once a student has fulfilled the academic requirements, a place will be offered on the basis of suitability for the course. A portfolio of drawings, paintings, photographs is the surest way of convincing a panel that you have the motivation and commitment to undertake a five year full-time course and another two years of practical training in an architect's office.

Architecture is not a subject that can be spoon-fed or learned from books – although books on architecture and by architects should certainly be an important feature of any architect's life. From day one a student can expect to be looking at things in a new and spatial way, to be making associations with art, cinema and literature, to be solving simple three dimensional problems. But architecture is not an abstract art. Although like the artist, the architect uses form mass and colour, his art is functional. He is also responsible for choosing structures and materials which other people will assemble in order to create the building he has designed. So the student must discover how different materials behave in particular circumstances and respond to stress and tension. He will work on the technical aspects of his design and perhaps build a detail of it in steel, concrete, glass, whatever is appropriate. The workshop can become an important place for acquiring technical knowledge and a feel for materials. An understanding of what a specific material will do in certain conditions, of how sunlight will hit a wall or lie across a floor at a certain time of day, can be the key to experiencing a building.

Looking at End of Year Exhibitions in architectural schools can be both inspiring and overwhelming. It is a very important way of helping a student to select the right school, but it is sometimes hard for a beginner to believe that he or she will one day be capable of making drawings as beautiful as those on the walls. It is always important to remember that the drawing is only a tool, the real significance of which lies in its ability to communicate with clarity.

The architect must always understand the needs of those who will inhabit his spaces, and ensure that his building is sympathetic to its context, whether urban or rural. In the Dogon village, the villagers themselves build according to their needs. The architect still has a great deal to learn from the techniques of other cultures, which is why it is so important for every student to have access through lectures and exhibitions to work that is being done by other architects all over the world. But he can never assume that what has been right for one set of people will be appropriate for another. Today in Britain architecture is once again the subject of popular concern. But will the architecture of tomorrow be something to remember or will it be merely a nostalgic reminder of a bygone age? This is what you, the architectural students of tomorrow, will determine. It is a responsible and challenging role to undertake.

HELPFUL READING: Kenneth Frampton: *Concise History of Modern Architecture*; Stein Eiler Rasmussen: *Experiencing Architecture*; Rayner Banham: *Theory & Design in the First Machine Age*; Robert Harbison: *Eccentric Spaces*.

Art and Design
Bernard Gay

Academically able and talented young people who can dedicate themselves to a future concerned with influencing and improving the quality of life through design or who can contribute to the cultural ethos of society through the visual arts will find rewarding and interesting careers in the world of art and design.

Many academically able applicants who have a desire to be makers and doers as well as thinkers embark on careers of study in art and design despite the education system in Britain rather than because of it. No gifted young person at school should allow themselves to be dissuaded from the idea of such a career if they feel their abilities, interests and inclinations lie in that direction. It is often the case that the most gifted sixth formers will be discouraged from considering courses in art and design and persuaded to consider what are regarded as more academically respectable subject areas. In fact art and design requires high intellectual ability combined with visual awareness and the capacity to translate ideas into material form.

The term art and design embraces five separate areas of study and practice: they are fine art, graphic design, textiles/fashion, three dimensional design, photography. These umbrella titles give no idea of the diversity of courses of study which they embrace. The majority of courses are pursued in the public sector of education in schools and colleges of art and in the polytechnics, the remainder may be found in certain universities. The information here refers to the public sector of education where degrees are awarded by The Council for National Academic Awards (CNAA). The duration of the degree courses is either of three years full time study or four years on sandwich courses when a substantial period is spent in industry or in a related professional practice. There are a number of routes of entry to degree courses, at present the CNAA preferred route is the foundation course.

As an alternative to the degree applicants may embark on vocational courses which now are also nationally validated by the Design and Art Committee of the Business and Technician Education Council (BTEC). This recently introduced pattern of courses is equivalent to the Ordinary and Higher National Diploma. BTEC awards a diploma and a higher diploma, the higher diploma course attracts a mandatory grant. (For more details on the above see *How to Go About It*, Art and design.)

TABLE: ART & DESIGN DEGREE COURSE STUDY AREAS AND SPECIALISATIONS

Study area	Area of specialisation
Fine art	**includes** painting; printmaking; sculpture; some photography, film and in some courses other media studies
Graphic design	**includes** visual communication; graphic design; typography; illustration; advertising design; media and production; information design; scientific and technical graphics
Photography	**includes** photographic arts; applied photography; film and television; visual communication; photographic sciences (this last does not require a foundation course)
Textiles/ fashion	**includes** woven and printed textiles; fashion; contour fashion; design of carpets and related textiles; embroidery; footwear design; fashion administration and marketing; knitwear
Three dimensional design	**includes** ceramics; furniture; glass; industrial design (engineering); industrial design (transportation); interior design; jewellery; silver and metal; silversmithing; theatre design; and wood, metal, ceramics and plastics

Fine Art

Fine art is an infinitely more variable study than used to be the case. Painting, sculpture and printmaking remain as hitherto the principal areas of practice, but fine art can now embrace film, photography, video, animation, elements of sound and movement, performance, and a large range of other media and practice. The nature of a particular course will be determined by the teaching staff many of whom are likely to be visiting part-time teachers who are successful practising artists. The content and structure of a course of study will reflect their interests and professional practice.

There are such important differences in content and approach in fine art courses that students will be well advised to investigate carefully the nature and philosophy of any course before committing themselves to it.

The majority of courses have in common a firmly structured beginning but will allow and encourage increasing freedom as study progresses, offering students the opportunity through practice to discover their personal language and direction and the media through which their ideas can be best expressed.

The initial stages of a course are likely to be exploratory; students will be confronted with a wide range of approaches and methods of working though they will not be required to acquire predetermined specific skills to any high degree. In fact the development of a particular skill or technique as an end in itself is likely to be discouraged. While in recent years there has been less concern with training in established disciplines and techniques, there has recently been a re-emergence of more traditional attitudes. The majority of courses, however, remain open-ended and will encourage students to discover those areas of visual art most appropriate to their particular talent and inclinations.

After the initial stages of the course have been completed, where work is likely to have been based on projects and assignments, it is usual for students to opt for a particular area or studio and for the teaching to be carried forward by means of tutorials and by means of a personal critical dialogue between the student and usually several individual members of staff. All courses contain an academic element of study broadly related to the history of art and design and it is usual for each student to complete a thesis on an agreed subject of their own choice. These studies are separately assessed and contribute to the grade of the final degree. Final assessment is usually conducted through a display of the work carried out during the course of study.

Graphic Design

No one can be unaware of the sustained impact of the mass media in our society. We are daily bombarded with visual and verbal messages. This is the world of the graphic designer who through the whole range of communication media will engage in art form to persuade, manipulate, transform, and educate the public.

A large number of degree and vocational courses is available for the student who wants to work in the graphic/communication design field. Courses are different in emphasis from each other. Some concentrate on illustration, the drawn image, print making and fine printing, others will specialise in film, photography, video, and animation. The majority will be concerned with the graphic image and typography in advertising; some will concentrate more on the visual image, others more on typography and the printed image. All will be concerned with the development of original and personal solutions to communication design problems.

Some graphic designers, those who specialise in the illustration of books, for example, will be engaged in private practice, freelancing, working with an author or a publisher as commissioned. The majority are likely to work in an organisation or agency designing and operating within constraints set by a client. For such a designer creative identity is concerned with problem solving within the parameters set by the particular project. The designer will be required to practise to a high level of ability over a wide range of techniques, methods, and media.

Graphic design, the title which has traditionally covered the work of designers in mass media, is now often referred to as communication design which better explains the technology including computer based printing and image making and television which, with other photo-based imagery, now dominates the graphic design world. Students who engage in this form of study need a good visual sense, a command of the spoken and written word, creative flair, and the ability to visualise ideas and images.

A good course will familiarise the aspiring designer with the technologies, techniques and methods employed by other designers while nourishing and promoting the natural aptitudes and abilities of the individual student.

Photography

Recently photography has grown in scale and importance. It has always been recognised as a science, a technical skill and a craft. It is now increasingly regarded as a significant art form in its own right. Courses at degree and vocational level are available to accommodate those students who see their futures in one of the numerous specialist areas of professional photographic practice.

As in other areas of art and design education, the content and orientation of courses will depend to some extent upon the special interests of the staff and the nature and level of specialist resources available. Photographic technology, photographic sciences, medical and technical photography, photographic journalism, fashion photography, film and photographic arts, applied photography, visual communication photography, film and television, and holography are some of the many major study areas covered by existing courses. They are also likely to cover the history of photo graphy, the history of art, communication studies and other appropriate contextual studies such as the literary arts, the history of ideas, and social studies. Courses will certainly contain studies in the technical theory of photography. The balance between theoretical and practical work will vary between one course and another.

Employment opportunities for graduates are wide, ranging from employment in the photographic industry, in large photographic and film units in industry, or in medical illustration departments in hospitals. Careers can also be made as a professional photographer, film maker, sponsored photographic artist, teacher, film critic, archivist, researcher, or film librarian.

Students with an interest in the photographic arts who are not certain that they want to pursue a course dedicated only to photography will, if they read the notes on other art and design degree and vocational courses (or study individual college prospectuses), recognise that some fine art and graphic design courses offer a major option in some combination of photography, film and television.

Textiles/Fashion

For those considering a career in textiles or fashion design there is plenty of choice in the number and nature of courses at degree and vocational level. Courses vary in the emphasis they place on different aspects of the subject. Aspiring textile designers can specialise in printed, woven or knitted textiles. Some courses combine the study of textiles with fashion while others specialise in fashion. Most courses will ensure that students gain experience in more than one particular area before they commit themselves to a single specialisation. It will be found that these courses provide a broad and varied experience leading to interesting careers.

Fashion courses will provide opportunities to design for men and children as well as for women. Some teach fashion illustration or accessory design and there are courses which provide an emphasis on business studies and management. Students will learn to cut and make garments as a means to realise ideas. Many courses help develop considerable drawing skills. Some experience in the fashion industry is often part of the course and there is sometimes the opportunity to travel to fashion centres in other countries such as Paris, Florence, Frankfurt and New York.

Textile courses are equally as varied in character; the approach of some is near to fine art while others are closely linked to industry. A good colour sense, drawing ability and some interest in machinery, especially if weave or knit is seen as a specialism, are all necessary to the successful textile designer. Professional textile designers frequently freelance, often working from home, so personal motivation, integrity, tenacity and a good business sense are all important. Textile and fashion designers need lively and creative minds balanced by common sense, and they need the ability to work as part of a team.

Three Dimensional Design

This umbrella title covers a wide range of design practice embracing jewellery, ceramics, glass, furniture, interior design, product, and industrial design; everything from Concorde to a paperclip. Every man-made thing is designed by someone and there are a substantial number of courses in schools and colleges of art and polytechnics to train designers in all the varied disciplines.

Product and industrial design is concerned with the functional, ergonomic, and aesthetic qualities of manufactured products. Designers in this field are required to have an understanding of technological developments, manufacturing processes, professional practice and management in industry. They must also have a good visual understanding and awareness and an open mind uncluttered by conventional solutions to design poblems. Drawing ability and the capacity to explain ideas visually and verbally are necessary for success. Additionally such designers should be endowed with an acute social and environmental awareness and must be able to work as part of a highly trained team of industrial specialists all of whom will have a contribution to make to a design solution.

Interior designers have a similar social and environmental base to their professional practice. In this field the designer must be able and willing to temper creative ideas with the mundane but necessary understanding of structures and building regulations. As well as having a good visual sense and drawing ability, the interior designer must be able to project ideas by means of working and presentation drawings.

Furniture designers often work in an industrial situation and much that applies to product and interior designers applies to them though the furniture designer might also be a designer craftsman and so bridge the area between industrial and craft practice, which is the area relating to the jeweller, silversmith, and the practitioner in glass and ceramics.

In these specialist fields study will help students towards a critical awareness and sensitive response to the materials of their art. They will need to develop a creative appreciation of form and function and to master the manipulative skills and techniques to fashion the artefacts which they design.

Graduates may find themselves in industry but more usually will find themselves in individual workshop practices determining for themselves the nature of the work they produce and selling it through exhibitions or retail outlets, though on occasions they may work to commissions (silversmiths especially). These art and design based craft practices at their highest level demand dedication, highly developed sensibilities, imagination and a limitless appreciation of colour, line, scale, three dimensional form, two dimensional surface design, as well as technical knowledge, highly developed craft abilities and a personal understanding of the value and significance of the objects produced.

Other Opportunities. Art and Design

The above is an outline of the major areas of study in art and design but does not exhaust all possibilities. In three dimensional design no mention has been made of a study such as wrought iron work, but there are courses concerned with the design and fabrication of wrought iron at both degree and vocational levels. No mention has been made either of picture restoration or the restoration of prints and drawings though courses in these studies are available. Finally, the history of art and design has had only passing mention. This has increased in availability in the public sector in recent years, one example being a degree in the history of prints and drawings. There are also combined degrees which have a major option in some aspect of the visual arts, eg a major option in history, criticism and appreciation through the study and practice of fine art.

It is important that applicants, once they have some idea of the kind of study they want to pursue seek appropriate advice. There are many sources including school or college staff, careers advisers, the local education authorities, regional advisory councils and the department of education and science. Agencies such as the Design Council, The Crafts Council and the validating bodies, such as CNAA and BTEC, can greatly assist. Do seek advice, visit courses, discuss their content, and then decide.

Asian Studies
Dr Ian Brown, SOAS

To read for a degree in Asian Studies in practice means following a particular discipline or combination of disciplines – for example anthropology, economics, geography, history, languages, philosophy, politics or religious studies – with reference to one or more of the four major regions of Asia, that is the Far East (China, Japan, Taiwan and the Koreas); South East Asia (Vietnam, Thailand, Burma, Malaysia, Indonesia, the Philippines); South Asia (India, Pakistan, Bangladesh, Sri Lanka); and the Middle East (see *Near East and Islamic Studies*). The number and variety of courses subsumed under Asian Studies is therefore very great indeed. They include the study of subjects as diverse as the economic problems of contemporary India; ritual and religion in Indonesia; environmental problems in the rapidly expanding urban centres of Asia; the rise of anti-colonial movements in India, Vietnam or Indonesia in the first half of the twentieth century; Japanese language and literature; Buddhist thought; or contemporary political problems in the Middle East.

But why study Asia at all? To many people such courses may seem rather exotic or even esoteric fields of study that will provide the graduate with little or no introduction to a particular career. Whilst a few graduates from Asian Studies do in fact find employment in areas where their knowledge of Asia can be put to practical use – as diplomats, in certain branches of journalism, in overseas commerce or banking, with international organisations – it is true that the numbers involved are comparatively small. A degree in some aspect of Asian Studies is not primarily a vocational degree. But this is true of virtually all arts and social science degrees. Therefore the question posed at the beginning of this paragraph should perhaps be rephrased: why study, for example, the modern history of India rather than the modern history of Britain; why pursue a course in economics that in its orientation concerns itself with the contemporary problems of Asia rather than those of the western world; why study Japanese rather than French? Two answers may be offered to this question. First, I would suggest that the most important reason for undertaking an arts or social science degree is to train yourself to think critically and imaginatively, while developing a greater understanding of yourself and of the world in which we live. This can be achieved through close study of, for example, a particularly complex historical problem, or an area of literary criticism, or a field of political thought. The study of Asia provides a particularly rich and varied opportunity to train your mind in this way, partly because of the great cultural and historical diversity of the region, but more importantly because it involves achieving an understanding of societies and civilisations which are clearly and profoundly different from those of Europe. Brief examples may make the argument clear. To achieve an understanding of the thinking of an Indian peasant under British colonial rule or of a Chinese Emperor of the Ming dynasty; to appreciate the intricacies of contemporary Japanese politics; to comprehend fully the social, economic and political barriers to economic development in present-day India, in each case requires a student to work in cultures, societies and historical traditions outside his or her own experience. This provides a fascinating and exhilarating challenge. Once this challenge is met – and it is by no means an impossible one to surmount despite Rudyard Kipling's dictum concerning the east and west – a student will then be acquiring not only the trained and disciplined mind referred to above but also greater insight into his or her own culture, society and history. Intellectual horizons will be widened; invaluable and unique understandings acquired. The second important reason for studying Asia can be dealt with much more briefly. Asia is a region of great and increasing significance in world affairs. It need only be noted that almost 60% of the world's population live in Asia. Over 20% of the people on this planet live in China. In an increasingly volatile and interdependent world we all need to acquire a much greater understanding of Asia.

There are two final points. The first concerns languages. In some degrees in Asian Studies there is a strong emphasis on mastering the language and literature of a particular region as the entrance to understanding its culture. However, where the approach to Asia is through a discipline or combination of disciplines such as economics, history or politics, rarely is language training required at the undergraduate level, though it is possible to combine those disciplines with a language, as for example in a joint degree in Japanese and Far East history. For those who wish to undertake a single subject Asian language degree no previous knowledge of the language is required, although evidence of linguistic interest and competence is sought, and for this reason A-level language or languages are often necessary for admission. The second point is that only a small proportion of the applicants for degrees in some branch of Asian Studies have had substantial previous experience of Asia. For the large majority of applicants, previous knowledge of the region is usually slight and indirect, arising, for example, from school-level geography, from those parts of the British and European A-level history syllabus which touch on European involvement in Asia, from a reading of Asian literature in translation, or most usually from an interest in contemporary world affairs, particularly the problems of poverty and underdevelopment. If in any of these ways you have had an initial contact with Asian Studies, and that contact has stimulated your interest, then the reading suggested below should enable you to explore further. And, of course, those offering courses in Asian Studies will be pleased to provide additional detailed guidance.

HELPFUL READING: Edgar Snow, *Red Star over China* (Harmondsworth: Penguin, 1972); Milton Osborne, *Southeast Asia: an introductory history* (Sydney: George Allen and Unwin, 1979); Dilip Hiro, *Inside India Today* (London: Routledge and Kegan Paul, 1976); Bernard Lewis, *The Arabs in History* (London: Hutchinson, 1968).

Biochemistry
Dr R B Freedman, Kent University

If you decide to study biochemistry, you will be observing and taking part in what many historians of science believe to be one of the major intellectual achievements of the century – the interpretation of living organisms and the phenomena of life in terms of the properties, activities and interactions of the molecules of which they are made. Biochemistry (the word and the science both date from this century) is essentially a search for an understanding of life in chemical terms. This makes it both an exciting and a demanding subject for study. Exciting, because biochemistry is now the central biological science, as ideas and techniques from biochemistry are now the basis of research in medicine, agriculture, biotechnology and the pure biological sciences. Demanding, because biochemistry involves the use of a wide range of techniques (many of them physical techniques) to understand biological phenomena in terms of chemical and molecular principles. So a student of biochemistry needs a good knowledge of chemistry, some aptitude for quantitative physical thinking, and an interest in a broad range of biological phenomena from cell structure and physiology, to genetics and evolution. Biochemistry graduates play an important part in the pharmaceutical, agrochemical, food, cosmetics and fine chemical industries and in the laboratories of hospitals, police forces, public health authorities etc. Biochemists in all these professions read textbooks and journals, and buy equipment and specialised chemicals, and so there is a further set of careers in 'service' areas. Work in scientific publishing and scientific instruments combines closeness to the cutting edge of the science with a flavour of the commercial world.

Biochemistry deals with four kinds of questions, of increasing depth and complexity. The first question is simply, 'Of what kinds of molecules are living things made? What are the detailed structures of these molecules?' A century ago this led to the recognition of proteins, carbohydrates, fats and later nucleic acid as the major ubiquitous components of all living things. But questions of this kind are still being asked as biochemists probe the detailed three-dimensional structures of molecules containing hundreds of thousands of atoms, or when they try to establish the identities of newly discovered powerful hormones and other transmitters which the body manufactures in only tiny amounts. In the last few years it has become possible to isolate and purify proteins which, in trace amounts, act as key messengers in the immune system, produced by one set of cells to switch on others. From very limited structural information on these 'cytokines' it is now possible to track down the genes coding for them, to isolate these genes and transfer them to other cells where they can be 'overexpressed' so that a research scientist can rapidly generate more of the pure protein in a test-tube than could ever be produced from the natural source. Most of what we now know about the structure of interferon and its anti-viral and anti-cancer properties is derived from studies on material produced in this way.

The second question follows on from the first. If you know the nature of the molecules making up living things, it is natural to ask what the chemical reactions are which lead to the construction of these molecules. How exactly do green plants convert CO_2 and water into carbohydrates? How do cows convert grass into beef and milk? How do some bacilli sour milk by converting milk sugars into acids, while other micro-organisms perform the welcome task of turning sugars into CO_2 and ethanol? These questions deal with the area known as 'metabolism' and much of bio-chemistry concerns the establishment of 'metabolic pathways' – route maps explaining all the chemical interconversions which take place in an organism. The whole network is immensely complex, but after a while you will be able to pick out the main highways; the catabolic pathways by which foodstuffs are broken down into a small number of simple units, the downtown interchanges such as the Krebs tricarboxylic acid cycle which links many of the central metabolites, and the anabolic or biosynthetic pathways which lead to the formation of new complex materials for the simpler building blocks. Much of metabolism was worked out in the period from 1910 to 1960 but there is still exciting exploration going on in this area even if there are no 'dark continents' left. We introduce hundreds of tons of new chemical pesticides and industrial wastes into the environment each year; how are these new molecules metabolised by the plants and micro-organisms in rivers, sea and land? We develop new drugs, cosmetics and food additives; what changes do these undergo in the body? Are they converted into harmless waste products or into toxic metabolites? All these problems provide new and pressing questions for metabolic research.

Biochemistry's third question arises from the second. If we know the myriad chemical processes going on in a living organism, can we understand how these reactions are catalysed, how the energy-requiring processes are harnessed to the energy-yielding processes, how all the reactions in a single cell are regulated and controlled and how all the cells in a complex organism are integrated with each other? This question opens up the whole field of enzymes and their regulation, of hormones, like insulin and the steroids, of the molecular changes involved in physical work and exercise, and the molecular basis of nerve and brain function. As you will recognize, in this area biochemical knowledge is brought to bear on all the central questions of physiology.

Biochemical questions of the fourth kind are essentially old biological questions asked in a new way. If we know all about the composition of a living thing, and the reactions going on within it, and the way in which these are regulated and integrated, how is the information for all this stored and passed on to that organism's progeny? Thirty years ago this question could hardly be answered at all – now our knowledge is so extensive that the Sunday papers regularly record successes not just in understanding the molecular basis of heredity, but in altering it through 'genetic engineering'. In late 1989, it was announced that the defect in cystic fibrosis, the most common 'genetic' disorder in Britain, had been traced to a change in a specific gene, and that the properties of the protein product of this gene could now be studied. This breakthrough will certainly generate new possibilities for therapy. A more difficult question to answer is how it is that all the cells in an individual organism, which share the same genetic blueprint nevertheless turn out as very different specialised cells; this question of development and differentiation is occupying biochemists increasingly. And in similar ways, biochemical modes of thinking and experimenting are being applied in every area of biology, to answer questions in evolution and taxonomy for example, or to extend ecological knowledge by studying how organisms survive and flourish in extreme environments of high temperature, high acidity or high salt concentrations.

As a biochemistry student you will look at questions of all these kinds. Wherever you go you will study the central aspects of the structures of biological molecules, metabolism, enzymology and molecular biology. But beyond that the emphasis of your study will vary with the nature and context of the institution. In a university or polytechnic with major industrial connections the advanced aspects of the course may have a strong applied flavour. Where a biochemistry department is part of a medical school, it will also be teaching medical students and the course may reflect their interests. In other institutions biochemistry comes under a larger biological sciences umbrella; in others again there is a strong link to physiology or to microbiology. So the precise emphasis of the course will depend on the context in which it runs, and this variation will be most marked in the final year.

It is possible to combine biochemistry with other subjects, or to extend a degree with a year of quite different experience. Some courses offer biochemistry with a related science (eg microbiology, physiology, pharmacology); others offer biochemistry with industrial training as 'sandwich' degrees. Some offer a bigger contrast eg biochemistry with management science, or biochemistry with a language and a year in Europe.

The teaching of biochemistry inevitably involves a lot of practical work. This is partly professional training in specific skills, but its main purpose is to give you some sense of the way in which biochemical knowledge is acquired, questioned and revised, by careful and critical experimentation. So you will spend much of your timetabled time at the lab bench in addition to lectures and teaching in small groups. Frequently the practical work develops from rather standardised exercises into more open-ended work, and at many places you will be encouraged to do an individual research project in your final year. You will not be studying biochemistry only, of course. Early on you will do a good deal of chemistry, some more general biology and probably some maths too.

Most students say they are attracted to biochemistry because they like both biology and chemistry (which makes sense), but it is clear that a broad science background is invaluable, and the best preparation is probably three sciences at A-level, such as chemistry and biology with either maths or physics.

A course in biochemistry should 'train your mind' so that you can tackle problems, recall, organize and express knowledge. But the same can probably be argued for any degree course. The best reason for choosing to study biochemistry is because you really enjoy finding out about an exciting, fundamental and wide-ranging subject.

Biology

Dr N Maclean, Southampton University

Biology, the study of life and living things, occupies a unique position in the spectrum of human interest and knowledge. Although undoubtedly a science, it has much in common with the arts, partly because nature appeals to our aesthetic as well as our rational senses, also because we ourselves are part of nature. For this reason many people who would not otherwise choose to study science finally settle on biology. On the other hand, with the rapid growth of molecular biology over the last decade, some who would previously have chosen to study physical sciences are now considering biology as a possible and challenging alternative. It should also be emphasised that many departments offer a choice of degree options in biology, botany, zoology, cell biology and applied biology, the choice of degree title depending on courses chosen for study.

Thus if you find yourself subscribing to any of the following categories then it may mean that biology should be your prime choice of subject. (1) Your interests straddle the two cultures of science and arts, (2) you are very keen on natural history, birds, plants, insects or whatever, (3) your greatest passion is conservation of the planet and its natural resources, (4) you are not at all keen about natural history or conservation, but you are intrigued by problems of living systems and how they work, (5) you are interested in medicine but don't want to become a 'doctor'.

Biology is often taken to represent 'soft' science rather than 'hard' science, that is a science where the number of variables in any one situation may be so great that the construction of an equation or formula is impossible. Although with the recent growth of molecular biology and biotechnology this is much less true than it once was, it is still sufficiently true to mean that biology may appeal to those with limited expertise in the physical sciences. But do not be beguiled into thinking that the softer science indicates a softer option. Ability to analyse and understand complex situations such as arise, for example, in evolutionary genetics, requires a sharp mind as well as considerable breadth of knowledge.

But the complex nature of many biological situations does have a significance for the career prospects of those who study this discipline. It is accepted by many experienced industrialists and management consultants that a training in biology is a good, perhaps even an ideal, preparation for a career in management. This follows from the realisation that most situations involving people are, by their nature, complex, and relatively difficult to define with precision. Someone who has been trained in the physical sciences may find their new skills of rather limited usefulness in tackling complex industrial decision making. On the other hand an entirely arts-based course of study may not provide the necessary training in analysis and directional strategy. So biology is not solely beneficial to those who proceed to a science-orientated career.

Let me now try and impart to you the flavour of modern biology in terms of what topics you might expect to study in depth. The central core in most departments would consist of cell biology, genetics, ecology, and the form and function of living organisms; students will often be encouraged or compelled to study computation and statistics on the one hand and biochemistry and physiology on the other. From this basic groundwork will stem a range of optional specialisations, for example, parasitology, taxonomy, evolution, cell and molecular biology, developmental biology, immunology, applied ecology, and advanced courses in genetics or comparative physiology. You will notice that the emphasis in biology has substantially shifted in the last decade or so from a direct focus on the organism to a focus on the nature of life and living systems. So instead of courses emphasising entomology, reptile biology or flowering plant families, there is much more importance attached to understanding cell structure and function on the one hand and ecological interactions on the other. Of course many departments have their own special areas of research expertise, but these are reflected more in higher degree course structures than in undergraduate ones. When you visit a department as a prospective student, you can do worse than enquire as to the areas in which the research strength of a department lies. It may not coincide at all with the area in which you would want to specialise.

A second way of imparting flavour is to describe to you two activities which all first year students experience in the department in Southampton. In the Easter vacation of their first year, all our undergraduates participate in a field course, either in Southern France or Southern Spain. In springtime in Spain the fields are ablaze with flowers and the sky often filled with migrating storks and eagles. Even students who have previously found taxonomy boring (probably the majority) find new excitement in identifying beetles, birds, or plants both in the field and in the laboratory. There is no better way to appreciate the strategies of evolution, the elaborate networks of ecology, or the problems of biological classification than to see and work with organisms in the field.

The second location is a genetics laboratory in which my students study the regulation of genes in bacterial cells. In the course of an afternoon we are able to carry through an experiment, involving the induction of beta galactosidase enzyme in mutant strains of *E. coli*, for which two eminent French scientists, Jacob and Monod, shared the Nobel Prize in 1965. One's belief in the molecular organisation of an operon is greatly strengthened by finding that one can manipulate it oneself in the laboratory.

Many of the key questions facing mankind now and in the future are essentially biological. How can we control our own population, avoid war, cure disease, conserve nature? To my mind one of the most exciting things about being a student of biology is that one learns so much more about oneself. You learn to understand your own anatomy, physiology, behaviour and evolution, but you also come to see yourself in the context of nature, as one amongst many other species, as a member of an evolved and evolving population of organisms, interacting at all times and levels with the other diverse organisms with which we share the planet. Whether you are managing staff in Marks and Spencer's or running field trials of agricultural crops, there is much to be gained from the bracing sense of perspective, both evolutionary and ecological, available to those who have learned to think deeply about biology.

HELPFUL READING: Ralph Buchsbaum, *Animals without backbones* (Chicago University Press, 1987 (3rd edition)); *The Molecules of Life* – Readings from *Scientific American* (W H Freeman, 1986); Christian de Duve, *A Guided Tour of the Living Cell* (W H Freeman, 1985); R Dawkins, *The Selfish Gene* (Oxford University Press, revised edition 1989); J D Watson, *The Double Helix* (Penguin, 1981 (revised edition)).

Biotechnology
Dr J H Parish
Leeds University

Biotechnology is concerned with the application of the biological sciences to manufacturing processes. Some of the processes themselves (especially those concerned with the food and drink industries) are thousands of years old but the analysis of the processes by the application of scientific method and the use of scientific enquiry to expand the variety of biological products is relatively recent – largely because biological science, as opposed to natural history, is a relatively recent academic discipline. In order to try and specify modern biotechnology, a person who makes homebrew beer is not a biotechnologist but biotechnologists are employed by commercial breweries in order to optimise the performance of these companies by applying such subjects as fermentation technology and the molecular genetics of yeast to the brewing process.

There are four major academic foundations of biotechnology. (1) Biochemistry: the subject emphasises a certain unity among living organisms. All organisms have energy-yielding metabolism whereby substrates are converted to products and energy is trapped by the synthesis of ATP, a chemical that represents the energy currency of a cell. Energy-yielding metabolism invariably involves oxidation/reduction (in our species reduced substrates such as cream cakes and fish and chips are oxidised to carbon dioxide and water) but the variety in different forms of life is considerable. All organisms convert substrates to the chemicals required for growth by processes that involve expenditure of ATP. All these chemical conversions are catalysed by enzymes. Finally the role of DNA in inheritance is common to all forms of life. (2) Genetic engineering: classical genetics is limited by the 'breeding barrier' (you can cross barley and rye, horses and donkeys, but not diverse species – such as carrots and elephants). However there are techniques for introducing a gene or a few genes (ie a bit of DNA) from one organism into cells of a totally unrelated host. The hosts are commonly microbes but can be animal or plant cells. The value of doing this seemingly exotic experiment is explained a little later. (3) Cell culture: traditionally, bacteria, yeasts and moulds have been the organisms used in industrial fermentations. To these can now be added cells of animals and plants and specialised examples of these are used for production of vaccines, antibodies and natural products. Additionally photosynthetic microbes (including algae) suggest an alternative (yet to be realised commercially) for the large scale fixation of CO_2. (4) Fermentation engineering and reactor design: these are specialised engineering subjects and biotechnology presents engineers with problems concerned with sterilisation, stirring, heat exchange and downstream processing of large volumes of aqueous materials.

The applications of biotechnology are varied so the following examples are necessarily incomplete. Let us just consider the biotechnology that follows from two of the foundation subjects. Genetic engineering allows the construction of microorganisms and animal and plant cells in culture that contain cloned genes from a variety of sources. Further manipulation allows the expression of these genes. We can thus construct a bacterial or fungal strain that will produce proteins of animal origin and which is of established value. Examples are chymosin (an enzyme used in cheese manufacture obtained otherwise from calves) and several human proteins (such as insulin, tissue plasminogen activator and blood clotting factor VIII) of medical importance. The benefits of using fermentation technology (rather than material from the slaughterhouse, human post mortem remains or a blood bank) vary between the economic, humanitarian and medically desirable: in the case of a source for factor VIII, there is no danger of a microbe being infected by the AIDS virus. The implications of the ability to introduce and express foreign genes into plant and animal cells are rather different. If these cells are used to generate whole plants or if their genetic information is introduced into embryonic animals we obtain 'transgenic' higher organisms. A transgenic plant might have (for example) properties of resistance to pests, diseases or herbicides to improve agricultural productivity. Transgenic animals might be used to generate recombinant proteins in their milk. However the applications of genetic engineering mentioned so far do not define the limits of biotechnological potential. The ability to manipulate DNA in the laboratory either by altering the structure of cloned DNA or by synthesising the sequence chemically provides a method for altering or improving the performance of a protein for specific purposes. Such activities are referred to as 'protein engineering'. The starting points for a protein engineer are the cloned gene(s) involved and a knowledge of the structure and function of the protein(s) in question. One example of protein engineering is the modification of the enzyme present in biological washing powders to allow it to perform better at the relatively high temperatures used in washing machines. Examples that might have rather more importance for the human race involve the modification of proteins for medical use. One example is the development of hybrid interferons; another is the production by recombinant bacteria of antibody molecules with either improved specificity or smaller size that are likely to lead to dramatic improvements in the treatment of viral infections and possibly in the treatment of cancer. The generalisation that follows from all these examples from the sharp end of biotechnological research is that although the science of molecular biology has followed a progressive development over the past several years, it has generated a technological revolution. Just as the subject of synthetic organic chemistry generated novel chemicals, such as dyestuffs and plastics, that came to dominate parts of the chemical industry, molecular biology has entered a synthetic or creative phase that is leading to a domination of parts of the fermentation, pharmaceutical and agricultural industries.

Our second group of examples comes from the large scale use of cells or enzymes derived from them for industrial conversions. A sickly sweet goo called fructose syrup is used in the USA to sweeten soft drinks: this material is made from corn starch by using microbial enzymes. Fuel alcohol (obtained by fermentation) is another example of a biotechnological alternative to a chemical process. More generally the production of 'biomass' (a word much loved by biotechnologists) from simple cheap sources (such as the example of algae in the last paragraph) represents a biological option for a renewable energy resource.

How do you become a biotechnologist? For a school leaver there are two alternative routes. One is to apply for a BSc degree in biotechnology or applied molecular biology. You will find from the university and college prospectuses that different institutions give emphasis to different aspects of the subject. These reflect the fields of research expertise in the relevant department(s). For general guidance, it is more important to end up with a good degree than to worry about the fine tuning of the curriculum but any worthwhile course should certainly contain individually supervised practical research projects because the ability to plan and execute such a project is an essential skill for a biotechnologist. Biotechnology students must become familiar with the use of computers which are used routinely in analysis of genes, the interrogation of databases of protein and DNA sequence and structure as well as in automated instrumentation and control. The alternative route into biotechnology is to do a BSc degree in one of the foundation subjects or a combination of these. In some universities the biotechnology course will share a substantial amount of teaching with 'pure' molecular biology teaching. The graduate biochemist/geneticist/microbiologist has opportunities to obtain further training and experience in biotechnology either through a specialised MSc degree or by experience gained during industrial training or a PhD in an applied biological subject.

HELPFUL READING: *A Revolution in Biotechnology* edited by J L Marx (1989, Cambridge University Press) is up-to-date, comprehensive and comprehensible to an A-level scientist.**New Scientist** and *Trends in Biotechnology* both carry regular articles on current developments in Biotechnology.

Botany
Professor D M Moore, Reading University

This study area deals with plants. It has beginnings in the distant past, when primitive man learned to distinguish edible from inedible plants and in the middle ages, when *Materia Medica* summarised knowledge on the healing properties of plants – reflected until relatively recently in the requirement that medical students attend courses in botany. The need to identify useful plants gave rise to the field of taxonomy, which is concerned with describing the great diversity of plants in the world, assessing their relationships and evolution, and ordering them in some utilisable system of classification. External morphological features are still important in taxonomy but it is now very broadly based, using information on the chromosomes, chemistry, internal structure, physiology etc, as can be appreciated by reading V H Heywood, **Plant Taxonomy** (London: Arnold, 1976).

Of course the mosses, algae and fungi, ferns, conifers and flowering plants that inhabit the world today (see P Bell and C Woodcock, **The Diversity of Plants** (London: Arnold, 1971)) are the only survivors of the myriad forms that have arisen and become extinct during the 630 million years since plant life first appeared. The remains of some of these plants have been preserved in the rocks as fossils, the study of which – palaeobotany – provides our only direct observations on the changes which have taken place in plants through the long course of evolution.

It is part of our common experience that different species of plants live together in communities, that is in various kinds of forest, grassland, heathland etc. The plant communities, which are each characterised by a particular structure and species-composition, are determined by the ability of the available species both to live together and to cope with the prevailing conditions of light, temperature, rainfall, soil etc. This study of the interactions of plants with each other, with the physical environment and with animals is the concern of ecology (see B D Collier, G H Cox, A W Johnson and P C Miller, **Dynamic Ecology** (London: Prentice-Hall International, 1974)). As your knowledge of this field improves, you will increasingly appreciate its fundamental relevance to matters of current public concern such as conservation and environmental planning. Information on the present habitats of plants permits identification of the plant remains (particularly pollen) preserved in peat deposits and lake muds and this is a powerful tool for finding out about changes in climates and vegetation during at least the last 15–20,000 years (see R G West, *Studying the Past by Pollen Analysis* (Oxford University Press, 1971)).

Apart from the study of plant populations, ecology is also concerned with evolutionary genetics, that is with the numbers of individuals having various inherited characteristics within a population, the extent to which they are adapted to the local environments and the degree to which the numbers are maintained, decreased or increased from one generation to the next. These factors, which are considered important in the evolution of the species, are affected by, for example, competition and plants' breeding systems; the latter frequently depend upon the relationship between plants and their pollinators (insects, bats, birds etc), providing a link with zoology.

Anatomy deals with both the diverse and the constant features of the internal structure of plants. As noted earlier, these characteristics are important in determining the taxonomic relationships between plant groups. The advent of the light microscope permitted the careful description of cells and tissues of plants, and the relatively recent use of scanning and transmission electron microscopes has not only provided more information but has also permitted study of the fine structure of cells, including the membranes and organelles which are involved in operating and controlling living functions. Your anatomical studies, therefore, can range from the minute structural features of plant tissues, as utilised in taxonomy and, for example, in forensic science and archaeology (see D F Cutler, *Applied Plant Anatomy* (London: Longman, 1978), to features of cells which are fundamental to plant functions and to all living organisms.

The structures and mechanisms involved in such basic processes as metabolism and reproduction will show you the strong link between plants and other living things. At this point you will need a knowledge of chemistry. There is a common biochemical basis in plants and animals, bacteria and viruses relating to such universal life activities as respiration (dependent upon the proper functioning of series of enzymes) and inheritance (largely dependent upon the nucleic acids DNA and RNA). Helpful books about this are E E Coon and P K Stumf, *Outlines of Biochemistry* (New York, London: Wiley, 1967) and W S Klug and M R Cummings, *Concepts of Genetics* (Columbus: Merrill, 1986).

An understanding of these fundamental properties of living organisms will enable you to tackle the study of plant physiology, which is largely concerned with metabolic processes that can only be carried out by plants. Paramount among these is photosynthesis, by which the sun's energy is harnessed by green plants to synthesise the food. It is utilised by most living organisms and without it life on this planet as we know it would be impossible (see D O Hall and K K Rao, *Photosynthesis* ed.4, (London: Arnold, 1988)). The uptake of water and mineral salts by plants – vital to their nutrition and their effect on the soil – and the movement of solutions and chemicals within the plant are other important concerns of plant physiology (F B Salisbury and C M Ross, *Plant Physiology* ed.3 (Belmont: Wadsworth, 1985). Through its interest in the production and distribution of auxins (plant hormones), physiology links with morphogenesis. This deals with the mechanisms controlling the orderly growth and development of the plant from a single cell to a fully-fledged flowering individual (see, for example, F A L Clowes, *Morphogenesis of the Shoot Apex* (Oxford University Press, 1972).

During your botany course you will be introduced to many facts and concepts. They will range from understanding the fundamental part played by plants in producing the world's food, whether cabbages or steak, to the diversity of plants and vegetation and the means by which they arose. Each of the fields within botany impinges upon and assists in understanding and interpreting the others. There are also strong links with other study areas. Furthermore, from the level of the cell through that of the individual to that of the community, plants interrelate with all other sorts of living organisms. At the end of your degree course you should appreciate this more clearly. To start your course, the most suitable A-levels are botany or biology, and preferably chemistry.

Business Studies
Alan Munro, City of London Polytechnic

What is Business Studies? Is it **about** business or **for** business? Is it academically respectable and intellectually demanding? These were popular questions in the late 1960s when undergraduate education in business studies started to take off. Even today for some considering the wide choice available in higher education the questions still remain. For most, however, courses in business studies are perceived to afford an educationally attractive and vocationally relevant experience as preparation for a successful business career. Potential applicants should not underestimate either the competition for places or the challenges they will face when embarking on courses available at UKCPUs.

Business studies, as a field of enquiry, is concerned with understanding business and its changing environment. In advancing our knowledge about business it is necessary to address problems and issues relevant to the manager of today and the future. These problems if not fully understood and resolved can, for the small firm, lead to insolvency or for the larger firm, a hostile 'takeover'. The factors that have been identified as significant for **successful** British companies are discussed by Walter Goldsmith and David Clutterbuck in *The Winning Streak* (Penguin 1984). Some of these factors relate for example to the personal characteristics of leadership and an ability to understand people, other factors relate to technical skills in finance, marketing, production control and communication. For these firms considerable emphasis is placed on improving the quality and availability of their products/services. The business must therefore be prepared for change and successful firms adapt and evolve over time. Today business is experiencing technological progress of a radical kind, with the most fundamental developments occurring in information technology and transportation. The implications for future managers are not obvious although it is generally accepted that the rapidly changing environment presents great opportunities.

Clearly then the scope, variety of business problems is immense, more importantly managers have to make decisions (to make no decision is a decision in itself!) ranging from future plans to current operating details. It is this scope which allows for both specialist and generalist studies of business and which creates problems for some of subject definition but real intellectual challenges to those who enter the field. As might be expected an understanding of business and its problems can be achieved by careful analysis of activities undertaken within business, and acquisition of relevant techniques. These activities normally include marketing, finance, distribution and production, also general management. In most courses an opportunity to specialise in at least one of these areas is normally available. Many business studies graduates continue this specialisation by taking relevant professional qualifications, eg in accounting, marketing etc.

To undertake the analysis special knowledge and familiarity with a number of disciplines is required. These disciplines provide what are essentially building blocks. They normally include economics, at both the micro and macro levels, since not only business efficiency and competitive market situations are involved but also the general economic environment and government policy in relation to it. The study of the behavioural sciences of psychology and sociology is essential. In business, individual and group decision-making is involved. The formation of attitudes including attitudes to risk as well as questions of motivation clearly affect the successful implementation of such decisions. More widely it is necessary to understand the nature and direction of social change externally and its influence within the firm on organisational structures. The complex nature of business, its evolution and interaction with its environment frequently requires expression in mathematical form. Statistics, mathematics and logical analysis are also building blocks which are relevant for forecasting market changes for a more sophisticated analysis of risk, and many other business operations. Many decisions within business take place within a framework of law, which sets constraints on action and decisions. All large businesses are multi-national in scale and therefore the studying of language and different cultures frequently forms a contribution to business studies courses. These building blocks are then further developed to provide insights into the main activities within business, discussed earlier. For the student this often involves the selection of appropriate disciplines and a reconciliation of their different perspectives in relation to real problems faced by business. In this sense business studies is considered to be one of the best examples of an interdisciplinary field of enquiry.

Thus the ability to perform well in business requires an awareness of social, economic and industrial conditions, and the pressures associated with them in addition to special skills and knowledge. This awareness is not one which can be gained simply by studying, to ensure facility with techniques, or by even paying close attention to the results of detailed research. Direct involvement with industry and commerce is necessary. This involvement is an essential element in all undergraduate business studies courses and normally extends over the period of one year. It aims to provide you with a critical edge on your studies as well as an understanding of business, and the opportunity to assess your own personal abilities within a business context to aid you to plan for career development.

The opportunity to combine academic and vocational elements and the closeness of the world of work has meant that for many, business studies courses are the first stage in the development of a successful career. However the variety of courses offered means that you must examine carefully the content and structure of your selected course to see if it matches your own interests and career expectations. Remember it is **your** investment.

Chemical Engineering
Dr J R Backhurst, Newcastle University

> 'Well, I'm not bad at maths and physics and quite interested in chemistry so chemical engineering seemed a good idea.'

These words first appeared in an early edition of *The Student Book* and the quotation is heard just as often now, 10 years later. The reply is so familiar to those who interview prospective students that any response showing a more informed opinion is likely to come as a great surprise. The reason for the apparent ignorance of the subject is easy to understand since very few professional engineers find their way into schoolteaching and the media persist with their image of oily rags and spanners. What then is chemical engineering and why should anybody consider it for a future career?

The Institution of Chemical Engineers produced a definition: 'Chemical engineering is the science of processes in which materials undergo a change, changes which can be chemical and/or physical.' This sort of statement can hardly be expected to fire enthusiasm into the hearts of those deciding upon their chosen paths, however factually correct it may be. The name 'chemical engineering' itself is rather misleading as it implies that it is only concerned with chemicals. Many university departments have incorporated the word 'process' into their names and this gives a much better impression of the subject. It is the engineering of processes with which the chemical engineer is concerned and the bold definition above gives no idea of the challenges which will be encountered and the excitement of a life being involved with the production of anything ranging from North Sea oil through chemicals and synthetic fibres to cosmetics and frozen foods. The scope of processes is very wide and a chemical engineer can, for example, be instrumental in both creating, developing and running a process to meet the demand of a world market.

Chemical engineering is an international discipline. The raw materials for industry have to be extracted from where they occur naturally. As resources are used at an ever-increasing rate, the search for new supplies is spread further, often to remote and ecologically hostile parts of the world. Oil, gas and uranium for energy supplies are familiar examples.

The UK chemical industry has an economic record of which it can be justly proud. Its products are not produced solely for the demands of a consumer society. Two of the major problems facing the world at present – problems which will assume even greater importance in the future – are the supply of food and energy. By means of modern fertilisers, herbicides and pesticides, large areas of previously barren land are now able to support food production. The expertise of our own industry is being offered to developing countries in the form of complete plants, which bring the additional benefits of employment and technology. The challenge of energy in the face of dwindling supplies of oil is attracting the attention of chemical engineers. Whilst atomic power must provide the bulk of the immediate solution, the possibilities of harnessing solar energy, wind power and energy from the waves of the sea are both technically difficult and exciting. Chemical engineers through the training they receive, are uniquely equipped to offer new processes and better techniques to the problems encountered in the important field of conservation of energy and raw materials.

Chemical plants are not noted for their great beauty but new plant complexes, often costing many millions of pounds, are certainly impressive and great efforts are taken to ensure that they have a negligible effect in terms of pollution. Indeed, many new plants return their effluent in a cleaner condition than the river water to which it is discharged – incidentally the traditional place of the civil engineer in effluent treatment has now largely been assumed by the chemical engineer because of his unique ability to consider all the problems involved. Capital investment in chemical plant is high and safety requirements rigorous. The lessons learned from a disaster like the tragic explosion at Flixborough some years ago are incorporated into both design methods and safety legislation. The safety record of the chemical industry is excellent, though the very small number of accidents do receive abnormally high publicity. This in turn tends to further improve the safety measures possibly, however, to the detriment of a good public image.

How do you become a chemical engineer? Training is usually, and preferably, undertaken in the form of a full-time degree course at university or polytechnic, although it is possible to become professionally qualified whilst working in industry and studying on a part-time basis. The problem in deciding which UKCPU is helped by the choice between three- or four-year courses, honours or ordinary degrees, sandwich course or not – all information available in the prospectuses.

Normally the first two years of a chemical engineering course include an introduction to chemical process operations, heat and mass transfer, fluid flow, material and energy balances, fuel science, control, computing and further mathematics and chemistry. Most of these subjects will be new to you, though your A-level studies are an essential background. Laboratory work will probably be on a larger scale from anything you have encountered previously – though not on the industrial scale. Your first contact with the industrial world, apart from works visits, is likely to be during the long summer vacation when most departments arrange a period of industrial experience for students. Whilst this period is short, it does provide a valuable insight into the outside world and most students enjoy this part of the course.

The final year is likely to contain a design and research project as well as lecture courses on all aspects of chemical engineering. The projects are usually carried out by small teams of students supervised by a member of staff. Working as part of a team is a facet of industrial life and it is as well to realise the inherent difficulties at an early stage. The design project will introduce you to the flavour of the industrial design situation and will encourage you to apply the theoretical knowledge acquired earlier in the course. The research project enables you to demonstrate your initiative and originality in a practical way. Both of these projects are a challenge which students enjoy and find useful to their professional career.

Life as a chemical engineer is never mundane and a position can always be found which can offer everything demanded of a satisfying career. Do not imagine that all plants are designed and controlled by computers; important they may be, but it is people that make them work and it is dealing with people that makes life interesting. Research, development, design, production, sales, marketing, finance and even teaching are some of the possibilities. There is responsibility, opportunity for travel, and financial security. The demand for chemical engineers has been maintained throughout the 1980s and is likely to exceed the output of new graduates before too long and and a recent survey showed that starting salaries are amongst the highest of all the engineering disciplines. The economic health of the country tends to move in cycles and as you read this, you will be at least three years away from graduation by which time the employment situation could be even better than it is now.

Traditionally, A-level subjects suitable for a chemical engineering course are mathematics, physics and chemistry, though other combinations are possible. Mathematics and chemistry are essential though entrance requirements and the courses available are flexible. Biology is sometimes offered instead of physics at A-level and it can provide a useful foundation for a course which includes biochemical engineering – a fast expanding area of industry. If you chose to take different A-levels at the start of your 6th-form career and now wish to become a chemical engineer, several UKCPUs offer a Foundation Year course designed to not only make good deficiencies in your knowledge, but to provide you with a genuine engineering course while you are doing it. You do not need to be a genius at all your A-level subjects to be a successful engineer. Sound common-sense is often more important than brilliance in the examination room, though if you do succeed in eventually attaining a first-class degree the world will be at your feet. Engineering is a challenge. The problems are real and often urgent, but remember that however desirable a project may be it must always make economic sense. If you feel that you can rise to the challenge, consider chemical engineering and enjoy the experience.

HELPFUL READING: available from the Institution of Chemical Engineers, 165-171 Railway Terrace, Rugby CV21 3HQ.

Chemistry
Dr L D Pettit, Leeds University

Chemistry is an area of study which touches human life at innumerable points. It is the science which forms a bridge between physics and biology as well as between earth sciences and life and medical sciences. It is therefore a **central science** which holds the key to an appreciation and understanding of life-cycles on the one hand through to man-made processes on the other.

The development of chemistry as a science has taken place at an increasingly rapid rate over the last two centuries, and has depended upon **quantitative** reasoning. Chemists of the nineteenth century could not have anticipated the contribution which their research would make to the applications of chemistry today – applications which range from micro-circuits and developments in solid state devices to the use of hormones as a new generation of pesticides, and which even give a glimmering of understanding of the chemical basis of life itself. In many cases this rapid progress in the application of chemistry has itself created new crises for man (eg some forms of pollution; the effect of some pesticides on the environment, or the side effects of some pharmaceuticals), but chemists have immediately led the search for an answer to the resulting problems so that the advances could be controlled or harnessed to the benefit of man.

Superficially it is fairly easy to visualise the earth in terms of basic chemical concepts – it is an apparent equilibrium between solid, liquid and vapour phases surrounded by space and supplied with energy from the sun. However, the apparent position of the equilibrium is continually moving and small changes have profound effects on the processes of life. For our survival in anything approaching an 'advanced state of civilisation' we must exploit the energy content of as much of our environment as possible, while minimising the effect on the equilibrium of that environment. In all aspects of this interaction chemistry plays a key role. In agriculture, for example, in our attempt to use the sun's energy in the way most beneficial – and palatable – to our present populations, we use fertilizers and pesticides and these lead on to problems of nitrogen fixation, the possibility of genetic engineering, and the applications of hormones and similar chemicals to control specific species. On another front, that of our demands for energy, our use of fossil and of nuclear fuels is fundamentally linked to their chemistry. Pollution that results from their use can itself be controlled only by a detailed knowledge of their chemistry and the application of chemical principles. We have inherited problems resulting from past attempts to harness energy resources, and we in our turn must be ever aware of the inheritance that we are leaving succeeding generations.

How are we to understand the 'energy crisis'? If the energy of the universe is conserved (the well known first law of thermodynamics), why are we in danger of running out of energy? The answer lies in the less well understood second law which relates to useful work which can be obtained from available energy. An understanding of these basic concepts of thermodynamics is essential to an understanding of the problems of our material needs and their possible solution. Hence, a sound grounding in mathematics and, to a lesser extent, physics is necessary if we are to grasp the fundamental quantitative concepts of chemistry, and to apply them in the service of mankind.

Because of our numbers and aspirations we consume vast quantities of chemicals, usually intentionally but often unintentionally. We thus have to live with the waste of our endeavours and adapt our lifestyles to the resulting shortages when scarce resources are depleted. Our environment and, on a more personal level, our metabolism is vulnerable to the corrupting results of so many of our endeavours, and the answer can only lie in the careful and responsible application of our knowledge of chemistry. What is more, we are continually needing new materials to replace those no longer available in sufficient quantities, or to take advantage of the advance of the frontiers of knowledge. We have seen an explosion in the use of plastics and synthetic organic polymers. The petrochemical industry is a particularly important industrial application of chemistry since petroleum products are too valuable as sources of organic molecules to be simply burnt for heat and advances in this field are far from exhausted. Inorganic polymers are also likely to become more important and the development of solid state technology is, in all probability, barely out of its infancy. Biological polymers, in particular proteins and nucleic acids, will continue to be an expanding topic. Already studies in this field have contributed enormously to our understanding of the chemical basis of life, of genetic diseases and of heredity. Through a study of biological systems we are beginning to understand the molecular mechanism for the production and transfer of energy within the living cell, and so to open the door to new methods of exploiting solar energy. This will lead to new sources of food supply at a time when existing sources are becoming overstrained.

For all these daunting tasks and exciting prospects chemistry is a key subject. However, the importance and fascination of chemistry goes beyond purely material applications of the science. In chemistry we make and study beautiful crystalline compounds and we are introduced to theoretical concepts and ideas which are both elegant and interesting from a philosophical point of view. A chemist is one who studies both the practical synthesis and reactions of substances and also the underlying theories which unite and classify such a wide variety of compounds.

Chemistry is therefore a fund of knowledge which can open up the whole field of related technologies. The preferred A-level subjects are chemistry with one or both of mathematics and physics. In general three science-based A-levels are required, although many institutions will consider students with two science and one arts-based A-level, or with only two good A-levels.

Amidst the rapid advances of today, science students are wise to choose a course that will **open** rather than **close** doors to them. They need to choose a starting point which is equally suited to continued specialisation or continued diversification, depending on the developing interest of the individual. Chemistry provides a basis upon which either more chemistry, or another science or technology can be built. It is also increasingly recognised as a sound training for an eventual career in management, administration or some other field completely outside science. As a quantitative science a study of chemistry can therefore prove to be a means of enriching the life of the recipient and also the basis for a rewarding and satisfying career.

Civil Engineering
Emeritus Professor Sir Alan Harris,
Imperial College

The job of the civil engineer is the world – making it habitable, enabling it to support human life.

First the provision of clean water and the disposal of human and industrial waste – this more than anything else has permitted the increase of the world's population this last century. For food, the civil engineer acts indirectly except where irrigation is economic, but his role in satisfying the world's need for energy is central and ever expanding – engineering offshore is a new field. He builds the infrastructure needed for transport by land, sea and air, without which there would be little food and little energy. He is the servant of every sort of manufacture and finally he provides the structure of the shelter within which people may carry on their lives.

His activity is the application of the practical intelligence to constructing things which serve these ends. This makes of civil engineering an art and by art is to be understood the right making of what needs making. As an art it has certain peculiarities.

It has an insatiable appetite for exact knowledge, but only for such knowledge as clarifies or facilitates the task and that at a given time and place – information delivered in London on Thursday might be of value; in Edinburgh on Friday week, none. Its concern with knowledge is thus utilitarian, serving a practical need, as opposed to that of science which seeks knowledge for its own sake. It is nevertheless not helpful to see engineering as 'applied science'; there are as many branches of science founded by the quest of engineers for knowledge as the reverse – the steam engine preceded thermodynamics, aircraft flew before there was a science of aerodynamics. In both, the practice of the art profited hugely from the science which it instigated.

This need for exact knowledge requires that the typical civil engineer must master sophisticated intellectual techniques which he will use either in determining what is to be constructed, in checking its adequacy, in pursuing minimum cost, or in managing its construction. These techniques develop continuously; new ones are always being invented. He may not suppose that with a degree he is equipped for life.

None of the works of man incorporates more material than do those of civil engineering. A moon rocket may cost more in human labour, but for bulk of material an earth-fill dam has few rivals since the pyramids. The sheer magnitude of civil engineering works in terms of the material, labour and plant needed in their execution profoundly affects the nature of the art – it makes it anonymous, communal, a twentieth century folk-art. It is not without charm that there are several hundred men who can pass by even quite a small job and say to his family 'Do you see that job? That's my job; I did that.'

The civil engineer is in servitude to the purpose of the work and to the practicalities of construction; his cannot be an expressive art and it is fatuous for a designer to see his work as self-expression – if he does, he is playing the fool with his clients' money and is mocking the efforts of the men on site. To ask an engineer who has just finished a bridge, 'What were you trying to say?' will not prompt a coherent reply.

Among the arts, then, civil engineering is perhaps the most useful, the most learned, the most substantial, the most servile, the most impersonal and the least expressive. Let us not forget that it sometimes achieves beauty, even a certain majesty, though the incidence of such is not less capricious than in any other category of the works of human hands. (This beauty has inspired contemporary architecture with, it has to be admitted, results which are often good and sometimes less good.)

The field is broad; there are firms, both designers and constructors, who deal with it all, but not many. But in any part, however narrow, of the field there is a wide range of functions needing different talents – research, design, analysis, detailing, costing, construction – and none of these can succeed without management. Whilst no one can hope to be expert in all, the well-rounded engineer will know something about each. The education of the civil engineer will thus be broad, as will be his early practical experience but, according to his talents and character he can choose from this diversity a function in which to specialise, within which he may still deal with a wide range of types of work.

A hierarchy exists in the profession, as organised by the Institution, between three levels known, in the jargon of the day, as the chartered engineer, the technician engineer and the technician. The chartered engineer is a professional, capable of original thought and judgement and of accepting major responsibilities; the title will be conferred at about 27–28 years of age by the Institution. The technician engineer is an executive, fully understanding what he is asked to do and capable of carrying it out with little supervision. Engineers in both these categories will normally have a degree; there are paths between them. The technician is a practical man with the knowledge, skill and understanding needed to carry out the intentions of the chartered and technician engineers.

The classic group of A-level subjects seen as a proper preliminary to a civil engineering degree is mathematics, physics and chemistry. Mathematics is desirable and physics and chemistry are useful but many civil engineers see attractions in such subjects as economics, English or a foreign language as part of the mix.

The number of women in the profession is still small but is increasing. Experience shows that there is no need to distinguish between the sexes in the practice of civil engineering, where women have distinguished themselves right across the field, including running a site. Are there matters of ecology where the sensitivity of women engineers is irreplaceable?

One of the attractions of civil engineering as a career is that positions at the very top are open to members. Firms of civil engineering consultants are, of course, run by civil engineers; contractors have civil engineer directors and government ministries, municipalities, nationalised corporations, have large civil engineering departments under the direction of civil engineers. Another attraction is that the civil engineer may be concerned with works anywhere in the world.

There is a small but significant tendency to see a civil engineering degree as a liberal education in itself – the intellectual discipline, numeracy and sense of physical reality which it instils are beginning to be seen as a desirable basis for management and administration.

HELPFUL READING: CONSULT: *Civil Engineering – A Career Guide*, Institute of Civil Engineers, Great George Street, London SW1.

Classics
Dr Oswyn Murray, Balliol College, Oxford University

Classics, the study of the cultures of Greece and Rome, is the oldest non-vocational university subject; it was the original course in 'humanities' (the study of man rather than God) and is still a central arts discipline at most major UK universities. This long tradition raises two questions: firstly what is the justification of the classics in the modern world, and secondly what are its strengths and weaknesses, both now and for the future?

The justification of classics lies in the nature of the Western cultural tradition. The essential characteristic of our culture, what the sociologist Max Weber called its 'formal rationality', is a creation of the Greeks. It was transmitted to the whole of Europe through that first institution of European unity, the Roman Empire, and diffused through the rest of the world by the colonial expansion of Europe after the Renaissance, to become the basis of the first world civilisation. The Greeks were the first to separate clearly the three great functions of social civilisation – politics, religion and culture – as defined by the nineteenth century historian Jacob Burckhardt in his *Reflections on History*. In all essential aspects they set out the major branches of human investigation: biology, physics (atomic and field), medicine and mathematics in science; metaphysics, ethics, politics and logic (formal and informal) in philosophy; sociology, psychology and anthropology in the social sciences; sculpture, pottery, architecture and the concept of representation in the arts; tragedy, comedy, epic, personal lyric, pastoral, history, biography and the divide between truth and fiction in literature – to mention only the obvious areas. Where the Greeks were lacking, Rome often filled the gap, as in law and constructional engineering. Of course many of these activities (though not all) have transcended their beginnings, but the study of their classical origins reveals the interconnection between such different subjects and so the fundamental nature of Western man.

For obvious reasons, therefore, the Western world has always looked back to the Greco-Roman past as an ideal and often sought to restore it in the present. One recurrent phenomenon in our culture is the creative importance of the renaissance or rebirth. The renewal of classical influences has marked every major new departure in culture from the fourth century AD to at least the nineteenth century. We cannot of course know the future. We may wonder if the chain has been broken, but even so its existence in the past is a fact, so that in the arts no major area of Western thought or literature can be understood without some knowledge of the classics.

This explains the existence of classics courses in the majority of universities, both new and old, for some access to the classics is presupposed for any serious arts studies: hence, too, the great popularity of foundation courses and of options covering classical history and literature in translation. Recently, at a level, involving linguistic knowledge, joint courses such as the school of classics and modern languages at Oxford and the joint English/Latin degree at Warwick have been successful, particularly in opening up opportunities for graduate research.

Language requirements vary between courses and universities. For literary studies prior knowledge of Latin or Greek is an obvious advantage; but all universities make provision for beginners in one or both languages; What is necessary is a keenness to learn. All universities teach in varying degrees in translation, often exclusively in translation for history and philosophy while in literature a combination of survey in translation with in-depth study in the original is typical. Many universities also now offer courses in Classical Studies, in which the thought, literature, art, history and archaeology of the classical world play a dominant role. But there are two warnings. Firstly, willingness to learn the language of any foreign culture is an essential part of understanding it. Secondly, even with subjects studied in translation, the standards of attainment and understanding are ultimately set in relation to those who know the languages (your teachers and the past scholars in your subject); if you become really interested in your course you will want to learn the languages in order to continue the dialogue with the past. It follows that the best A-level preparation for classics at university lies in Latin and, if possible, Greek; the various ancient history and classical civilisation A-level courses are also useful. If there is no provision for language work at your school, get in touch with the *Joint Association of Classical Teachers*, 31–34 Gordon Square, WC1, for information on the many residential and non-residential courses for beginners in both languages: do it early, because they are very popular and great fun.

The strengths and weaknesses of classics lie in its self confidence and the existence of a set of professional standards – which must be mastered in order to be manipulated, or they will become a prison-house of irrelevant conservatism. Classics is a European discipline; many of the books and articles you read will have been translated into English from French, German or Italian, or written by scholars who were not English-speaking by birth, and classics teaching in the UK is still dominated by the work of the refugees who came over from Germany and Italy in the 1930s. Increasingly you will meet students from other EC countries studying classics in England and you will undoubtedly travel to Greece and Italy during your time at university. In the past classics pioneered major techniques in the arts – for example textual criticism in literature, the critical study of history, and many of the early theories in anthropology and sociology. Today the situation is reversed and classicists need to be aware of advances in disciplines outside their own. Only classical archaeology still maintains something of its past supremacy as one of the most advanced areas of archaeology, with its enviable precision in stratigraphic techniques, dating by style, aerial photography, area surveys and underwater archaeology.

One last point: traditionally classics divides both into the two cultures of Greece and Rome and also into four major areas – literature, history, philosophy and archaeology. It is important to decide how you want to mix these various subjects and to choose your university accordingly.

HELPFUL READING: *The Oxford History of the Classical World* (Oxford University Press, 1986); E R Dodds, *The Greeks and the Irrational* (Cambridge University Press, 1951); Gordon Williams, *The Nature of Roman Poetry* (Oxford University Press, 1970); M I Finley, *Aspects of Antiquity*, 2nd edn (Pelican, 1977); E Panofsky, *Renaissance and Renascences in Western Art* (London: Paladin, 1970); John Boardman, *The Greeks Overseas* (London: Thames and Hudson, 1980).

Communication Studies
Robert Ferguson, Institute of Education

Communication is a fundamental factor in all our lives. At the very least, we have to communicate to live. Whether we are going to the shops or getting on a bus or sitting in a school or college classroom, we are engaged in the process of communication as a regular and continuing part of our existence. Much of this communication takes place through the spoken word and a lesser part of it takes place through reading and writing. But we also communicate through what we wear, the way we stand or sit and our attitude towards those with whom we communicate. All this is to do with us as individual senders of messages. But, of course, we are all also part of groups of various kinds. There is the family for some. For others there is the football team or the local club. Even the street corner where we meet our friends can be a place where groups communicate. And all this involves different kinds of language – different forms of communication.

Just as we all spend a great deal of our lives communicating with others, or sending messages, so we all spend a great deal of time receiving messages. Many of these messages come from outside our immediate circle of friends or family. They may come from institutions such as the school or the employment office, but by far the largest number of messages that we receive come to us from the mass media. These media include hoardings, the radio, the cinema, magazines, comics, pop records, videos, newspapers and overwhelmingly from the television set.

Communication studies is about the ways in which all these messages are sent and received. It is also about all the different theories which have been put forward to explain how the communication process works. Once we set about studying the communication process, we find out that what seemed a simple and clear issue becomes difficult and clouded. Communication on an interpersonal basis and communication via a mass medium such as television often involves misunderstandings and raises issues about whether those doing the communicating are trying to tell us something clearly or 'pull the wool over our eyes'. Communication studies is, in part, about trying to unravel some of these mysteries, especially in relation to the mass media.

There have been theorists of communication dating back as far as Aristotle and before, but the birth of communication studies as we now understand it is usually linked with the names of Shannon and Weaver and their model of communication. This dates from 1949, and it represents an approach to communication which is one-way and rather basic. They suggested that in every communication process there was a sender, a receiver and a message. The sender would transmit the message and the receiver would receive it, provided no 'noise' got into the system. By 'noise' they meant anything which stopped the receiver from getting that message in its pure form. But it did not take long before this model of communication and others like it were seen to be very inadequate. One of the main reasons for this was that messages were also about meaning, and this was an altogether more slippery concept to handle. It led to theories of communication which looked at the ways in which meanings could be produced by one group of people who had some influence over another group of people. Communication was perceived by some theorists as a political act.   So communication studies is about the ways in which communication processes, from writing to speech, from dress to music, help to sustain or break with patterns of authority and control. It is about the ways in which messages are designed to communicate or to reassure, to sustain relationships of power or to question them. Thus we may look at the ways in which communication takes place between international powers as they negotiate for peace, or the way in which communication takes place between an interviewer and a contestant in the *Miss World* Competition. Or we may analyse the kinds of messages which are given to us in an advertisement which have less to do with the product itself than a *dream* which we are being offered if we buy the product.

Communication studies is also about the way in which communication is organised and structured through major media organisations. It is concerned with patterns of control and responsibility in broadcasting and in the press. It is concerned with the ways in which information does or does not pass from one part of the world to another. In the coming years it will be increasingly concerned with satellite broadcasting and the laws which will or will not regulate the messages which are sent and received around the world.

Above all, Communication studies is a critical activity. It is a means whereby the various theories about communication can be scrutinised. It involves the detailed study of various forms of communication, from the personal to the international. This in turn requires the development of skills in the various fields associated with other disciplines such as sociology, linguistics, anthropology, social theory and literary studies. It is essentially a synthetic field which cannot be tied down to any one discipline. This is both an attraction and a potential pitfall for those who wish to be involved in its study. For it requires a will to take on board a whole range of skills and disciplines. But it also means that it is difficult to keep a clear and structured perspective on a vast field whilst immersed in one or other of its many facets.

It should also be noted that many communication studies courses are about *making* messages as well as studying them. Practical work in video, film, sound and graphic communication are amongst the many activities which are offered. Students for such courses come from a whole range of subject fields. These would normally include English and may require a modern foreign language at A-level. But it would be unwise to generalise, and would-be students of communication should check the specific entry requirements of the place where they hope to study. A-level communication studies, for instance, is *not* a requirement in many institutions offering communication studies degrees!

HELPFUL READING: A good overview of the field which is relatively easy to understand is *Introduction to Communication Studies* by John Fiske (Methuen, 1982). This is a paperback and it contains constructive suggestions for further reading and work at the end of each chapter.

Computing
Professor D Conway, Leicester Polytechnic

The computer and the microprocessor have become an integral part of all aspects of modern life. Society's information needs continue to grow at an alarming rate and our desire to harness IT in business and industry far outstrips the availability of skilled workers. Computing is still a relatively new area of study. The subject is developing rapidly and as a discipline available for study at degree level it has come of age – the first courses started over 21 years ago. Innovations in the subject continue to emerge with breathtaking rapidity, thus ensuring the discipline has the vigour and enthusiasm expected in a youthful subject. The present era has been referred to by many as the new 'industrial revolution'. Modern computers increasingly provide users with more and more power to process information with, surprisingly, associated reductions in cost. This provides mankind with the ability to extend the use of the mind, just as the industrial revolution provided the power to extend the use of the muscle.

What do computing professionals do?

Although the range of specific activities is great it is possible to describe the tasks as satisfying society's information needs. These are almost exclusively problem solving activities which frequently involve a high level of interaction with other people. Many problems still involve the creation of new solutions and workers gain great satisfaction from the implementation of their own ideas. The tasks vary from generalised solutions with a wide range of applications to highly specific solutions. For example the generation of a word processing system on a PC has to provide an interface suitable for general users in both the home and office environment. This can then be specially tailored to make the facility available to blind workers, hence requiring a totally new approach to designing the interface with the user. Alternatively, you may be building a system to enable fashion knitwear designers to create garments for immediate distribution to sales outlets.

Who can do it?

There are few restrictions and with the wide range of application areas, computing can enable you to encompass many other special interests. Because of its creative content it places a high premium on intellectual capabilities. The emphasis on 'information' makes precision and logic an important feature of the work. Usually, because of the 'human' aspects, it is important to be good at communicating. It is not an area with inbuilt prejudices though, at present, women (who generally possess all the appropriate characteristics) tend not to take advantage of the opportunities, hence denying the UK a valuable source of skilled workers. With the high level of demand for professionals, work in this area normally involves a high level of commitment and most people find they work very hard.

There are now a wide range of courses available at degree level and, generally, computing professionals are expected to be of graduate calibre. (Although as supply is still well short of demand, about a third of these have taken non-computer orientated degrees.) Most relevant courses bear the title 'computer science', but there are others, eg information technology, systems analysis, software engineering, computing and business, information systems. Sometimes you can combine computing with law, accounting, physics etc. Even courses with similar titles can be quite different and you should examine the curriculum carefully and make sure the courses you apply for reflect the sort of emphasis you want, eg software, business orientated, industrially orientated, theoretical, computer technology. Some courses require prescribed studies at A-level, others just want intelligent applicants with good A-level grades. Almost all assume you know little about computers and start from scratch but assume all the students are literate, numerate and hard working.

The discipline has attracted much support from successive governments because the skilled manpower produced can make a significant contribution to the economic wealth of the nation. The courses provided are still leaders world wide and graduates are able to compete in the multi-national arena with those from the US and Japan. In spite of the highly vocational emphasis placed on the courses, there are, as well, clear avenues for personal development of other kinds. The use of computing in the medical field has enabled great achievements to be made in, for example, learning systems for the deaf, expert systems for diagnosis, automated artificial limbs. The present interest in 'artificial intelligence' poses problems relating to mankind's thought processes and the challenging goal of amplifying our brain power.

Finally, one must stress the responsibilities involved. Just as bulldozers enable us to make bigger holes more quickly, computers enable us to make more mistakes (in information) faster than ever before – for example, a large firm paid everyone twice one month! Power brings with it responsibility.

What will you study?

You will, of course, have to acquire skills and knowledge. It is important to know how the computer functions and to develop skills in programming, but the real interest lies in situations where you have to design your own 'information processing system'. This is a creative activity where the solutions are reflections of your style and precision. When the system is put to work you can participate in its testing and see it in action at first hand. It will be your responsibility to put it right and eventually you will experience great satisfaction when you feel you have a flawless system. The context of this design will vary considerably. There are three main areas. At the very applied end of the spectrum you could be designing a system for the users of a railway timetable which answers enquiries posed by travellers. Alternatively, you might be devising a system that allows programmers to manipulate objects on a graphical display, eg create the graphic image seen at the beginning of television programmes. In contrast the problem might be to devise an algorithm that enables you to specify the most likely diagnosis of an illness for a patient whose symptoms have been established by a doctor. In such a system subsequent events should be used to modify the algorithms so that the system 'learns' about the patients. The real excitement is in that the computers you use should give you the power to crack problems you previously felt were beyond your capabilities.

HELPFUL READING: *The Information Technology Revolution* Ed. Tom Forester (Blackwell); *Computer Studies through Applications* Kennewell (Oxford).

Dance
Dr Richard Ralph,
London Contemporary Dance School

One of my own favourite questions to students coming to audition for my School goes as follows: 'Is there anything else you could possibly be happy doing as a career?' If the answer is 'yes' I tell the student to do that, as without any doubt it would be easier than a training and subsequent career in dance. For dancing – like a religious vocation, with which it has many parallels – chooses you rather than you choosing it. Young people suddenly discover that they need to move their bodies, to reach deep into their reserves of stamina, strength and courage – and to dance. It can come upon you at the advanced age of sixteen or seventeen or it might be something you wanted to do since infancy. But these days you are likely to have had the chance to study part-time, if only for a short period.

The basis of most professional dance courses is the learning of dance technique (this is usually either ballet or contemporary dance technique; other forms include jazz). This takes at least three hours of every day always following the same pattern and gives you a basic movement alphabet – the building bricks with which a choreographer will be able to express his or her art through you, or with which you will be able to communicate with others through movement.

Technique is a bit like doing scales, if you are a musician, or press-ups, if you are an athlete. It is a daily routine which stays with you as a dancer and which keeps the body fit, supple and responsive to the instructions your brain gives it. Of itself it is not necessarily artistic, but it makes art possible: for the choreographer will paint and compose with the dancers' bodies. It is important to emphasize the place of technique in a dance school because it consumes many of the dance student's waking hours.

As the body is trained painstakingly and methodically to master the full range of dance technique, it changes shape as the muscle is developed appropriately and as all spare tissue is reduced. (This is the process known as 'changing the body'.) The way that the movement is timed and phrased gracefully and beautifully in relation to music will also be learned and the inner ideas or 'feeling tones' and muscular habits connected with certain sequences will become second nature. But learning to dance is no automatic business of idle repetition and following the lead of the teacher; rather, it is a mental and physical activity requiring ferocious concentration and considerable endurance. It tests commitment severely and many fall by the wayside. In any professional dance course the main credit will be given on the basis of progress made in technique classes.

Physical aptitude is important to any dance student; your body has got to be strong, but people with less-than-ideal or 'difficult' bodies can work wonders, especially if they undertake an appropriately supervised course of corrective strengthening exercises with a physiotherapist, qualified osteopath or body conditioning expert. But there are certain weaknesses which carry the risk of injury and which rule out rigorous training. So a proportion of students are not accepted at audition for physical reasons. In ballet the stereotyped look is more necessary than in contemporary dance, which tends to be more individual with less emphasis on the *corps de ballet*.

As I hinted before, the most important qualification and the secret of eventual success in dance is an 'appetite' for movement: the burning need to express yourself physically. Even in an untrained body this can show itself unmistakably in the height of the leap, the length or depth of an extension, the follow through of a movement or exercise, or in a general sense of joy or even ecstasy. However, facial and physical beauty are of themselves not enough. The body as a whole must need to speak out in movement.

What I have described is a study in itself: a full-time job. But a course of theoretical studies as provided by most dance schools (especially those with degree courses) can actually speed your development as a dancer. Such subjects as music, anatomy and costume are obviously relevant, dealing as they do with the essential elements of the professional dancer's craft, but increasingly the dancer is being required to operate part-time as a community worker and teacher. Few companies do not include such work in their annual programme and some preparation for teaching is necessary at dance school. It also helps future dancers to know a little of the problems to be found in modern urban social life.

Equally important to most high-level professional dance courses is an emphasis upon personal and cultural development. All the best dance schools have good libraries, record and video collections. It is vital that young dance students know something of the history of dance – how it came to be as it is – and about other art forms. Students need to go to museums, theatres, concerts and films, preferably with some guidance from the School. All of these art forms provide vital resources for any dancer. Without some emphasis on developing the whole person the student could end up with a marvellous technique and nothing to say; developing interpretative artists must feed their mind and spirit.

A powerful sense of identity and considerable self confidence are necessary to dance generally and contemporary dance in particular. The dancer is saying 'Here I am; this is what I am doing; look at me'. And the 'I' is vitally important. There has to be somebody interesting to look at. All too often the hothouse intensity of the dance school produces a cold obsessiveness and a narrowing of horizons which ends up by actually threatening artistic values. So resolve to keep your mind active and your interest in the world around you alive.

Any good dance school will give prominence to the creative and interpretative aspects of dance. Choreography, or dance composition, is usually taught from an early stage. Of course it is mainly a matter of individual ability, but there is a basic craft which can be taught to all, and which will help dancers to understand the choreographers who will work with them in their professional careers, even if they are not destined to become established choreographers themselves. Even modest compositions can help dance students to develop as interpretative performers and to move creatively. For this reason it is encouraged. It is an excellent preparation for professional life for students to work with other dancers on group pieces and to find ways of working through the inevitable artistic and personal tensions that arise.

Repertory is a very popular subject, consisting in the learning of a dance which has already been performed. Once students have mastered the steps they learn how to perform it in front of other students and sometimes a public paying audience. It is important that students should always remember that they are studying a theatrical art form which is designed to be performed; although too much performance too early in the course is usually seen as inappropriate. The technical groundwork must be laid before it can be absorbed into interpretation.

In summary, the dancer's training is very tough and requires much dedication and there are already many good and fully trained dancers pursuing too few professional jobs. But such warnings are useless to those who have decided they must dance. And should you not achieve your ambition of dancing professionally, there is now a range of interesting dance-related careers open to the well-trained dancer. But here, too, commitment and love of dance are essential; and careful course selection when you are applying for your dance course can keep a range of career options open.

Dentistry
Jane R Goodman, Eastman Dental Hospital

Conversation at social gatherings often turns to how you earn a living. 'I'm a dentist' brings a response ranging from curiosity to horror, followed by compliments or complaints about their own practitioner, and details of recent dental experiences.

Dentistry for many patients is still an ordeal, which they undergo with some trepidation, and during which they may feel anxious and vulnerable. The dental surgeon has to reassure the patient while carrying out intricate work on what is probably the most sensitive area of the body.

A desire to work with people and an ability to communicate with them are therefore essential qualifications for dentistry. Manual dexterity, which may prove difficult to assess initially becomes highly developed during training. In the majority of cases a scientific training to A-level is necessary, although exceptions can be made to this. Family connections within the profession are strong, and maintaining this tradition, and that of the hospital where trained, is still considered by some to be important.

Dentistry as a university degree bears little resemblance to any others save perhaps medicine. Because of the nature of the subject, the course of five years is very structured. At the end of this time, however, one is able to start practising without any further period of study or apprenticeship, unlike other professions such as medicine, law or accountancy.

The degree of Bachelor of Dental Surgery (BDS) is divided into three parts – 1st, 2nd and 3rd BDS. A-levels in physics, chemistry and biology give exemption from 1st BDS. However, a few medical schools will offer this course to arts students and mature students, who having pursued other careers wish to retrain. These students would at interview have to show that, despite lack of scientific training, they had the interest and ability to study dentistry.

The first year of basic medical sciences – anatomy, physiology and biochemistry, with the addition of dental histology – is tightly packed with lectures and practicals, culminating in the 2nd BDS examination, usually held in June. The anatomy concentrates on the head, neck and thorax regions and the histology deals with the structure of teeth and related tissues. Wherever possible the application of these subjects to the clinical work encountered in the following years is stressed, making the subjects more relevant and integrated. Having survived the first year – and at this stage there are some who drop out – one starts clinical training and treatment of patients under close supervision. One learns all the different aspects of operative dentistry: prosthetics (false teeth), conservation (fillings, crowns and bridges), periodontology (gums), orthodontics (correct positioning of teeth with braces), children's dental problems, and oral surgery (extraction etc). The practice of preventive dentistry for the community and individual is also encouraged. The theory of pharmacology and pathology, as well as a basic grounding in medicine and surgery, are taught during this period. Most schools will encourage students to have an elective period during which they can visit other units in this country or abroad.

In the final months of training the questions of how and where to practise raise themselves. The choice is varied. Although the majority of newly qualified dentists go straight into practice, there are openings in hospital and community services. Vocational training courses in general practice and community dentistry have been started in many centres throughout the country. Here trainees, on a day release basis from a chosen practice or clinic, attend lectures or seminars to improve their awareness of the possibilities within the service in which they have chosen to work. A few graduates, particularly those with an interest in science or basic medical subjects and with less of an interest in clinical work, may turn immediately to research.

In dental practice, whether as an associate member, with fewer management responsibilities, or a full partner of a group, one can pursue and develop particular interests and ideas. Although there is still a general lack of concern by the public in dental health, and routine treatment is necessary, more people are expressing an interest in and demanding advice on preventive dentistry. There is the satisfaction of having responsibility for patients attending one's practice and getting to know and interest them. At the same time one is running a business unit and administering the day-to-day workings of a group of personnel. There are, of course, good financial rewards in return for hard work, although these may decrease with middle age if one is unable to maintain the pace of work. Probably the main advantage of practice over the other branches of dentistry is personal independence, which is partly true of the National Health Service and even more so in the growing private sector.

To specialise in one of the branches of dentistry will involve climbing the career ladder in university or to a consultant post in a hospital. Oral surgery ranges from extractions under local anaesthesia to cosmetic surgery and treatment of head and neck cancer. Orthodontics, restorative dentistry and paediatric dentistry are other specialities for which the diploma of Fellowship of Dental Surgery (FDS) is necessary, but for oral surgery and oral medicine a medical degree is also required. One of the rewards of hospital work is the challenge of particularly difficult procedures, which with time, technical assistance and expertise one is able to perform. In paediatric dentistry one may be consulted about a patient with, for example, an unusual hereditary condition. This requires long-term treatment planning which takes into consideration the growth and development of the child, and alterations in the dentition. Restorative dentistry involves conservation of teeth, treatment of gum conditions and advanced crown and bridge work combined with removable prostheses, which includes precision dental engineering. The orthodontist, by means of removable or fixed appliances, moves teeth to provide better function and improved aesthetics. The community dentist will consider the provision of care on a wider population, taking into account the epidemiology of disease and changing health patterns. Recently training programmes for specialists have been established in this field. Specialisation enables one to develop new approaches to problems, to inform colleagues of innovations, and to influence people concerned with health services, both consumers and administrators. This ensures that the care available is of a high standard, and continues to improve.

Both in hospital and practice, as well as community dentistry, where the service is directed towards the special groups, the handicapped and the elderly, dentistry is basically a practical career. Preparing cavities and filling them, repositioning teeth, cutting soft tissue and bone all require manual dexterity accompanied by good communication skills. Major technological changes in the past two decades have led to more efficient equipment and the development of new materials. These wide ranging changes have greatly increased the scope of the work, and have made treatment easier for the patient and more interesting for the dentist.

Drama and Theatre Arts
Malcolm Griffiths, Nottingham Polytechnic

Theatre is an uniquely challenging art form and an equally challenging study. It combines personal exploration with social purpose, individual experimentation with collective responsibility, research with performance, images with words. The past decade has seen a marked increase in the number of applications for drama and theatre arts courses. This is partly the result of the successful development of theatre studies at A-level, partly the result of the growth of youth theatre activities throughout the country but chiefly because live performance now plays an important role in people's cultural and social lives. The interest in theatre in all its forms is increasing with the result that the demand for places has rocketed. Rock bands and West End musicals have harnessed technological wizardry to provide audiences with visual spectacles matching the impact of their sound systems. Theatre-in-Education companies and community theatre groups have brought exciting and relevant theatre to less traditional theatre spaces. High standard opera productions tour the country and attract audiences of all ages. Contemporary playwrights explore important aspects of today's world in innovative ways. Add to these the crucial contributions theatre makes to television, film and video and you will begin to capture the vitality and potency of theatre and the wide range of opportunities it offers. Whilst you may be aware of the controversies surrounding funding for the arts and the anger being increasingly felt at the way in which they are being devalued in political circles, it is important to recognise that the art of theatre in Britain is thriving.

Having decided to study drama or theatre arts, you will have begun your search for the most appropriate and attractive course and will have discovered that the situation is at best confused, if not downright daft. A galaxy of institutions in both the public and private sectors of higher education promote a bewildering range of degree and diploma courses. Some are widely recognised and acclaimed. Some are simply shady. With so many young people wanting to enter this area of study there are many opportunities for unscrupulous operators to take advantage of people's aspirations. The Business and Technician Education Council, the Conference of Drama Schools, the Council for National Academic Awards and the Standing Council of University Drama Departments represents the best available in their different areas. You should ensure that an institution you are thinking of applying to is recognised by one of these organisations.

If you have sought advice on how best to make a career in theatre you will have encountered two conflicting points of view. On the one hand people argue that a degree course provides an all-round education, that you should not specialise too soon, that many of our foremost theatreworkers never took any formal training but progressed through student drama societies and that, as theatre work is so precarious, you should ensure that you do not narrow down your career choices too far. Others argue that theatre has now emerged from the dark ages when people drifted into it with a kind of inspired amateurism, that vocationally-orientated courses can best help you acquire the skills and insights necessary to survive and build a successful career and that a professionally-rigorous course provides you with creative, intellectual and inter-personal challenges which are in themselves an all-round education. All, however, will agree that theatre is an exacting art form and that any drama or theatre arts course worth the candle will stretch your capabilities to the full – artistically, intellectually, technically and socially. This may make for a tough education but, provided you are determined, also makes for a rewarding one.

Whatever aspect you choose to study the following points should be considered before making your application:

There is no uniformity of courses. Each has its strengths and weaknesses, principles and eccentricities. It is important to find out about these before committing yourself. Comparing prospectuses is useful but they are, of course, a form of advertising. Try to visit courses and form a first-hand idea of how they work. This takes time and money, but you owe it to your own future to make the right decision. Most courses have nothing to hide and welcome arranged visits. But don't turn up unannounced and expect the red carpet treatment. Above all, talk with current students. They are at the cutting edge and know what the course is really like.

Contact your local regional theatre, arts association, youth drama groups and drama advisors to see whether they can help you with information.

Check carefully with your local education authority about grants. Some courses carry only discretionary awards and these are becoming more and more difficult to obtain.

Check the entry requirements carefully and what is expected in the way of interviews, auditions, portfolios of work etc. Some places charge a non-returnable audition fee.

Try to discover the employment record of graduates. This information is generally available so think twice if you are being fobbed off with evasive replies.

Acting

The image of the successful actor or actress projected by the media and magazines is one of often far-fetched glamour. Real success can mean being able to afford to choose between work in theatre, films or television or to remain with a company over a number of years developing a particular form of theatre. The majority of performers, however, face a harsher reality where stretches of unemployment are broken by the occasional television engagement, promotional video or short repertory season. A career in acting requires a special toughness and determination in addition to real talent. If you succeed, it will be very rewarding. Should you fail, nobody else will shed a tear.

Drama schools are a comparatively recent phenomenon and have largely replaced the actor's traditional apprenticeship on the job with opportunities for developing skills, learning techniques, making mistakes and acquiring self-confidence before trying to survive in a highly competitive market. Although there will always be room for people with irrepressible natural talent, the importance of drama schools in nurturing ability and improving standards is now recognized. Schools are acutely aware that a professional actor needs to be adaptable to all kinds of theatre – compelling a pub audience in cabaret, projecting the nuances of a character's psyche in a large auditorium, devising a show with disabled children etc. Each school will try to prepare students to meet the exceptional range of responses and skills required, but each will have evolved its particular philosophy and style. It is here that care needs to be taken in selecting a course. All drama schools provide tution in voice, movement and acting but how these three fundamentals are taught will differ widely. Movement teaching, for example, can vary from exercises drawn from gymnastics or acrobatics to precise schooling in dance. One school may place great emphasis on a highly individualistic approach focussing on students' technical and expressive proficiency and on the production of playtexts in order to give the student the experience to develop as a flexible and disciplined instrument of interpretation. Another will stress the essential collaborative aspect of theatre and develop work from a basis of group improvisation in order to increase students' creative responsiveness and social awareness. No drama school would claim to be able to turn you into a great actor but it can help you further your ambition by providing a thorough grounding, expertise and time.

Before deciding which course to apply to, you should consider what facilities the school has and how much work is done in radio, television and film as these will become a crucial source of your future livelihood. Also find out whether the school employs visiting professionals for projects or productions and whether it covers both past and contemporary theatre forms. *Going on the Stage* – a report to the Calouste Gulbenkian Foundation – is still a useful background book to consult and should be available through your local library.

In addition to drama schools there are a number of performing and creative arts courses which offer opportunities for more experimental approaches to performance in conjunction with, for example, dance, music and visual arts studies. These courses do not claim to provide the kind of training found at drama schools but to encourage students to create their own performance events and to learn through both practice and the wider debate on the arts.

Drama

John Marshall, Bristol University

Of all the arts, drama is perhaps the most public and popular. In the various forms of live theatre, film and television, more drama is seen now than ever before. Although this popularity may, in part, be attributed to the greater accessibility afforded by television it cannot disguise the very real significance of performed drama to society. Why should this be so? What made London audiences flock to the public playhouses in Elizabethan England? Why do millions of people watch *Eastenders*? How did Shakespeare ensure that the audience not only watched and listened to his plays but also returned to see his next one? How do soap operas work in terms of character, story line, dialogue, subject matter, setting, camera angles, editing and so forth? The serious asking of these questions and the rigorous thinking, exploring and analysis required to answer them is, in very simple terms, what constitutes the study of drama. To be able to comprehend fully the role of drama in society and to engage critically with text and performance it is necessary to gain knowledge and experience in a number of theoretical and practical areas which contribute to the informed study of drama. In the pursuit of textual analysis and practical criticism students may find themselves drawing on aspects of such diverse disciplines as art, architecture, history, religion, politics, physics, philosophy, psychology, sociology etc. This wide range of contributing knowledge is one of the exciting qualities of drama study at undergraduate level which places it deservedly within the area of liberal arts education and distinguishes it from the more specialised and specific actor training with which it is sometimes confused. For the most part drama degrees are not vocational, they are not designed to train students for particular professional posts in the theatre or television and should not be regarded as a fail-safe alternative to drama school. The candidate at interview who professes a yearning to act but wants a degree to 'fall back on' is unlikely to impress. It is rewardingly true that many drama graduates do proceed professionally but in most cases this follows an additional period of appropriate training.

The number of degree courses available in the subject has grown considerably since the first, forty years ago; and although many may have 'drama' in the title the courses may be very different in content and approach. It is, therefore, extremely important that candidates read course outlines very carefully in order to select the type of course which best suits their interest. For example, many departments acknowledge the significant contribution of television and film to the drama of the twentieth century and may incorporate not only the theoretical study necessary for the critical analysis of text and screening but also a complementary element of practical film or video making. Other courses may concentrate entirely on the process and products of the theatre and yet both degrees may be listed in handbooks as BA(Hons) Drama. Similarly, the variety of courses reflects the variety of approaches available to the study of drama and while most will combine a number of these the emphasis on the historical, critical, sociological and generic approach may be different in each case.

What courses will have in common, however, and what distinguishes drama from other apparently similar disciplines such as English, is the essential emphasis attached to performance. Although the printed text may represent the most tangible object for study it is only the written record of what the author intended the actors to say and, in a very limited way, to do. As such it qualifies as a piece of dramatic literature but it cannot record the effect in performance of the interpretative contributions of the actors, the director and the designer. Nor can it indicate such things as the influence of the audience or the venue or the means of finance and administration on the experience of performance. The analysis of these elements which make up the dramatic performance requires the acquisition and application of a vocabulary and methodology which is part of the undergraduate study of drama.

One of the methods which particularly characterises the study of drama is the practical exploration of aspects of performance and production. In most UKCPUs this is designed to enhance students' experience and understanding of the ways in which the practical, technical and interpretative skills of the theatre, film and television contribute to the production of drama. As such these activities, be they workshops or full productions, are as much part of the study methods necessary to the discipline of drama as those that may be regarded as traditionally academic. It is for this reason that most departments consider the division of drama study into 'practical' and 'academic' areas as artificial and misleading, for it seems to imply that some methods are more proper to degree study than others. The relationship between these study methods should perhaps be seen as equivalent to that of theory and experiment in the laboratory sciences where one informs upon the other.

It would be wrong, however, not to acknowledge that it is the opportunity to approach a subject through practice as well as theory that attracts very many students. Often the earliest interest in drama develops from the enjoyable participation in the school play or local youth theatre. In some schools this interest can be encouraged further by directing it towards GCSE-level drama and A-level theatre studies. Success in and enjoyment of these courses can be a good indication of whether a degree in drama would be a valid option. Not all students, of course, have the opportunity to take these subjects and it is important to realise that this in no way penalises candidates in their chances of acceptance. What admission tutors will be looking for, in addition to academic ability and suitability, will be a committed interest in the subject which is commensurate with local opportunity. In other words, a demonstrable and critical interest in theatre going, cinema and television viewing as well as an active involvement in some area of theatre performance (not necessarily acting) or film/video making will be as important as A-level choice.

Drama study, in common with its professional relations, theatre, television and film, is apparently glamorous but in reality extremely hard work, not only intellectually but physically and emotionally as well. It is demanding in terms of time as well as effort but it is also sociable and pleasurable and to the outsider enjoyment can sometimes be confused with easiness. Don't be confused; be prepared to work long hours at reading as well as rehearsing and to give a great deal of yourself, not merely for your own benefit but for the collective advantage and development of others.

HELPFUL READING: A useful introduction to the subject is Martin Esslin's *An Anatomy of Drama* (London, Temple Smith, 1976).

Theatre Design

Malcolm Griffiths, Nottingham Poly

Once the cinema had supplanted the theatre's meagre capacity for spectacle with visual splendour, fantasy and glamour and television had created a detailed authenticity which exposed the theatre's efforts as clumsy and unconvincing, it became necessary to rethink the purpose and aesthetics of design in the theatre. It has taken the sustained efforts of two generations of designers to achieve this new understanding and to demonstrate that theatre design is neither a poor derivative of fine art nor a slap-happy version of industrial design but a complex creative discipline in its own right.

Changes in theatre over recent decades – the building of new and different theatres throughout the country, the extensive growth of touring companies, the creation of the Theatre-in-Education movement, the new technology available, the new languages of performance explored by dance and experimental companies etc – have heightened the importance design plays in theatre production and in the audience's enjoyment. British theatre design is internationally renowned and the development of theatre design courses closely related to professional practice has meant that an undervalued area of theatre arts has now emerged as a major consideration in performance events. *British Theatre Design – the Modern Age* (published in 1989) will give you some idea of the artistic challenges faced by a theatre designer.

There are many qualities needed to make a good theatre designer – a feeling for space, mass, colour and texture; the ability to analyse playtexts, operas etc and imagine the performance they embody; an interest in research and social background; an understanding of lighting design; a knowledge of costume construction and of the development of fashion and morality in dress; an awareness of the qualities and possibilities of different materials; and an ability to collaborate, delegate, organise and manage a budget without losing sight of one's own creative purpose. Above all it requires a good eye, a good mind and a good pair of hands.

Although some drama schools and departments offer options in design, the major courses are situated in schools of art and design and normally expect applicants to have successfully completed an art and design Foundation course.

Economics

Professor David W Pearce, University College London

You may not have thought of economics as the sort of subject that is relevant to organised crime or whether it is worth taking a postgraduate degree, or even to explaining just why one in four American men and women have extra-marital affairs. That is the beauty of economics. It creeps in everywhere and for a very simple reason. Basically, there is nothing (well, nearly nothing) you can do that does not imply an economic decision. Consider the petty thief and whether we should allocate the much overstrained resources of the police force to catching him. Say he has stolen £1,000. He is better off by £1,000 and his victim is worse off by £1,000. Society as a whole is no worse off – we have merely redistributed money from one person to another. Now, if we set the police on him, we have all the costs of catching the thief. And if he is caught, it gets worse. Then we have the costs of criminal proceedings and, worse still, if he is imprisoned, we have the (substantial) costs of looking after him and hopefully rehabilitating him for re-entry into society. We can be fairly sure it will all cost more than £1,000. So is it worth catching the marginal criminal? It may look like a moral problem and it is, but the example shows you that it is also an economic problem. There aren't enough police to go round and we can't afford to give them all the resources they would need to capture all the villains. So some crimes must go unsolved for want of resources.

Of course, you wouldn't want economics alone to decide issues like this (though some would). But you'll begin to see that dry statements like 'economics is about the allocation of resources' imply a rather dull and turgid subject, whereas some of its aspects are a little more exciting. Take the issue of taking a postgraduate degree or a professional qualification. Is it worth it to you? Count the cost of being without work while you secure the qualification, then work out the difference between what you would have earned with the qualification and what you would have earned without it. (You can find the statistics to do this, so long as you know you are going to be a brain surgeon or a car park attendant.) On the basis that you won't care too much now about what you will earn when you are sixty-five, apply a factor which 'discounts' future earnings in each case.

Compare the sum of these discounted earnings with what you forgo by taking the course. If you are thinking about an undergraduate degree, the answer will come out in favour of taking the qualification in most cases. If your intended PhD is in Transylvanic gravestone inscriptions of the fourteenth century, you may well find a negative rate of return (there isn't very much demand for that sort of person). There is even a good chance you are investing badly if you take an economics doctorate, but check carefully.

So now you've done your very own personal 'cost-benefit analysis'. You have even learnt a piece of economic jargon fairly painlessly. Of course, you might want to justify your staying on at school to society. What you now do is to point out that your extra earnings are some sort of measure of your extra worth to society (debatable that one, but begin that way) and then point to the enormous benefits other people will gain from having you around (you'll be able to answer the four year old's questions on the relative size of dinosaurs and man, or exactly what a balanced budget multiplier is, and so on). If you win this argument (you might not) you have demonstrated that you are an 'external benefit' to society (they benefit at your cost) and you've gained a bit more jargon.

We'll leave the one on extra-marital affairs since you might prefer to worry about the pre-marital ones first. But it is true that economists have sought to explain why they take place (something one had always thought psychology was concerned with). Not that the glamour should be exaggerated. Before you decide whether to criticise the health board for buying an expensive body scanner instead of buying more dialysis machines for kidney patients, you'll have to find out about marginal costs and programme budgets.

Moreover, you might find yourself dealing with a textbook that denies economics has anything to do with any of this. That would be a shame, but some economists are purists and think we can only answer questions about fact and prediction. They are the 'positivists'. That is they say we can only talk about what would happen if something else happened. Well, we can disagree and we often do (though not as much as those silly jokes about economists suggest), but there is a richer field of prescriptive economics to be mined and, at the end of the day, you cannot divorce economics from what is desirable. Indeed, just think about it. If economics is about how best to allocate resources, what does 'best' mean? It could mean give it all to me. Or it could mean that we should make as many products as we can from the resources we've got. Or it could mean we should do the last thing, but allow for the 'quality of life'. The 'best' allocation can only be defined by reference to some moral principle.

Economists are into everything. The only catch if you want to join us is that you have to take a short course in how to think in economic terms. That probably means a textbook. Hopefully you'll stay with the textbook for a year or two but you may be able to insist to your teacher that there are some everyday issues – crime, environment, health care, education – to which even the most rudimentary economics can be applied.

HELPFUL READING: Guy Routh, *The Origin of Economic Ideas* (London: Macmillan, 1975).

Education
Dr David Bridges, Homerton College, Cambridge University

With a few exceptions the study of education in undergraduate courses is associated with a preparation for a career in teaching, and typically it is in the context of a four year BEd programme (though some universities are re-designating these courses as BA or BA Ed). You don't have to teach at the end of a BEd course – some 15% to 20% of BEd graduates use the qualification as a stepping stone into advertising, accountancy, the professional theatre, banking and everything else that graduates of non-vocational courses enter by way of employment. A head hunter for management trainees from Marks and Spencers once told some of my students that they like BEd graduates because the experience they had working with other adults and taking responsibility for children gave them an extra maturity. However, degrees in education involve a lot of practical work in schools, and if you are really unexcited by teaching or if you turn pale at the sight of a writhing mass of young humanity, then perhaps this is not the subject for you.

There are usually four main components to undergraduate courses in education. Let me say a little about each.

Main subject study   Degrees in education are effectively combined subject degrees in which the equivalent of two years of undergraduate study has to be devoted to a main academic subject, such as maths, English, music, science to be found in the school curriculum. You will not be able for this purpose to take eg sociology, business studies or law. Your main subject will be studied in much the same way as it would be studied in any other purely academic degree course. Indeed in most cases you will be studying it alongside other undergraduates in the same subject area.

Teaching methodology   If you are preparing to teach in a secondary school this part of the course will concentrate on the teaching of your main subject with perhaps some attention to a subsidiary area of teaching. You will look at the requirements of the national curriculum and the newly developing system of assessment. You will become familiar with teaching resources – books, packages, videos, information technology, etc – and with a wide repertoire of teaching and learning styles including eg games and simulations, collaborative group work and field visits as well as 'chalk and talk'.

If you are preparing to teach in a primary school, the demands of this part of the degree are of course much wider, and you will have to gain some familiarity at your own level with a reasonable range of the subjects you will be expected to teach. Maths, science and English will be required components of the training of all primary teachers, but it will not end there. You will also have to take a selection of courses from eg expressive arts, history, geography, technology, religious studies and physical education. So be prepared to tackle some pretty diverse experiences!

Education theory or Education studies   These elements of a degree in education look two ways. In one direction they seek to root the study and practice of education in the academic discourse appropriate to a degree programme. In this regard the study of education looks in particular to the research and scholarship to be found in writing in the disciplines of psychology, sociology, philosophy and history. Indeed the study of education can provide an interesting inroad into the study of the social sciences in their own right. You will typically explore elements of child development, learning theory, motivation, the sociology of education (including eg school and community studies and investigations of ethnicity and education) ethics, theory of knowledge and the history of education. You will be expected to bring the same kind of demands for evidence, the same questioning and critical stance and the same discipline to this study as you would expect to bring to your main academic study – though, frankly, in the time available in the undergraduate course you will only be able to lay the foundations of study which, hopefully you may be able to extend in an MA or MEd after you have had a few years in teaching.

At the same time however the study of education has to look to the real world of schools and classrooms and the practical concerns – your practical concerns – which it is reasonably expected to inform. The study of education in this context is an applied study which should help you to do your job better – not 'better' in the most crudely practical sense that you can for example write more clearly on the blackboard, but better in the sense that you have a wider understanding of what you are about, that you have thought out a defensible rationale for what you are doing, that you are capable of articulating and reflecting on your practice, discussing it with others and modifying it in the light of experience and changing circumstances. For many of us, these demands which arise from practice, far from undermining the purely intellectual appeal of the study of education add a special excitement and piquancy to its engagement.

School experience/teaching practice This is the really practical end of the course where you will be working directly with children. To begin with you will probably work with individual children or pairs alongside other students and under the supervision of a teacher or one of your tutors. Gradually you will take responsibility for larger groups and have more of a role in planning the work you will do with them. Some of your teaching methods course may be school-based. You will probably have two substantial teaching practices: my own students, for example, have a five week practice in the second year of their programme and ten weeks in the fourth year. By the end of the course you should have experience of taking a whole class (primary) or whole classes (secondary) for a reasonably sustained period by yourself.

It is this last ingredient – the practice of teaching – which makes the degree in education a somewhat different experience from other purely academic degrees. Undoubtedly it confronts you with extra challenges. I don't think anyone faces their first class alone without some doubts as to whether they are going to be able to cope.

But it also has its satisfactions. It does take you out of what you can sometimes feel is a rather precious and inward looking undergraduate environment into the local community and into a position of real responsibility in which teaching colleagues, children – and often their parents too

– need you and are depending upon your skill, imagination and resourcefulness. For some students, the exercise of that responsibility provides an important balance to other elements of their undergraduate experience.

Electrical and Electronic Engineering
Dr J C Earls

To reflect upon the profession of electronic and electrical engineers after thirty years of involvement is curiously difficult. One can stress the very considerable contribution of the profession to society through developments in energy supply, communications, medical electronics, computers, automatic control systems etc, etc. I suppose it is true that many present-day electronic and electrical engineers had in mind the relevance of our profession to the well-being of humanity when they decided on such a career. But was that the primary force which influenced their decision? It is difficult to speak for others, but I would judge that many of us decided upon our career path for many other reasons – we had some involvement with electronics or electrical engineering as schoolchildren and found electronic or electrical devices interesting; or we assumed that 'being good' at physics and mathematics was a helpful indicator that we would make good engineers. Certainly there is an elegance about the study of electronic and electrical engineering which readily appeals to those who find mathematics and the natural sciences interesting subjects. Another force in our choice might well have been the obvious rapid technological change taking place within our profession (and this continues at an even greater pace now) which gave it an excitement and a challenge.

The origins of our profession go back centuries to the early observations on the phenomena of electricity and magnetism. It was not however until the 19th century that these phenomena were well understood and a collection of laws and theories could be systematically deployed in the creation of apparatus and machinery that we would now recognise. Early pioneers could be cited – Ohm, Faraday, Wheatstone, Kirchhoff etc, etc; they, with many others, laid the foundations of engineering principles upon which many modern developments are based – radio, radar, energy generation and transmission etc. In the early 20th century the profession was concerned with communication (telegraphy and radio) and with electrical energy generation and its use (lighting and transport). Up until the second world war (1939) there were very few undergraduate courses in electronic and electrical engineering, these subjects were usually part of general courses in engineering which embraced mechanical engineering and, in some cases, civil engineering. The 1939–45 war promoted a heightened interest in electronics and developments took place rapidly – the refinement of radar systems, and the creation of a whole new range of electronic circuits – based of course on the vacuum valve. The latter part of the war and the immediate years following saw the early precursors of the modern computer – though the principles had been first enunciated in the 17th century by Pascal and by Babbage in the early 19th century.

The transistor, the integrated electronic circuit, and the microprocessor in turn have revolutionised electronic and electrical engineering (and our lives) in the past thirty years. All the time new phenomena are being applied and the revolution continues – for example superconductivity is set to lead to new types of computer, and magnetic levitation is the basis of new forms of transport. Robots are in the factory and will soon be in our homes. It is an exciting time for engineers and for those they serve.

What sort of people are electronic and electrical engineers? Well you cannot tell by looking at them and it will not necessarily be easy to judge by talking to them. The evidence is best taken from the things they do and create. Some are in research and development – looking at fundamental electronic processes, investigating new materials and circuits, assessing new applications of systems already proved; others will be associated with the design of systems to meet particular commercial or industrial needs. All will have some form of management role, and the ability to be creative and resourceful will be important to their success. Because of the rapid rate of change in technology, all will require to be resilient and be prepared to learn and develop throughout their professional careers.

Clearly the form and style of courses for electronic and electrical engineers have necessarily reflected the changes and pressures within the profession. In 1979 the Committee of Enquiry into the Engineering Profession published its very thorough report 'Engineering our Future'. This resulted in the creation of the Engineering Council which maintains an overview of standards in the engineering profession. The report also had a significant influence upon all courses in engineering. Particular among these were the increased emphasis upon students gaining insight into real engineering problems during their study and a generally heightened stress upon undergraduates establishing individually, and collectively, links with industry. How is this manifest? Well there is much more attention paid to design, to project work and to case studies. Problems set are much more likely to be open-ended, solutions requiring the exercise of creativity and of judgment. Knowledge and the skills of analysis remain important but are now accompanied by the skills of communication and of group activity. The old-fashioned mould (if incorrect) of the introspective backroom-boy has been well and truly broken; the electronic and electrical engineers of today must not only be academically able but must be innovative, resourceful and be effective as a part of a team and as managers of people.

Because of rapid changes in the past and the continued rate of change there are a very wide range of courses in electronic and electrical engineering. In outline structure they are similar – three years duration for full-time courses, and four years for sandwich courses, most leading to the award of BEng or BSc (there are some new extended courses leading to an MEng, though comparatively speaking these are few). The variety exists in their content and level of specialisation – some remain fairly general and embrace a wide range of subjects, others are quite specialised, concentrating on such aspects as communications or computer technology. Most courses will be accredited by the Institution of Electrical Engineers and/or by the Institution of Electronic and Radio Engineers. Accreditation means that upon completion of the course the graduate will be exempt from the academic part of the requirements to be met for Chartered Engineer.

Earlier I used the expression 'backroom-boy'; I was not intending to be sexist but it is true that few girls have chosen engineering as a career. Happily the situation is changing and the number of girls on engineering courses is rising quickly. Electronic and electrical engineering offers particularly attractive prospects for girls because of the nature of the work (see Helpful Reading).

Since I graduated in 1953 I have witnessed, and happily I have been part of, many changes in the profession. Most of these changes have been technical – the dramatic development of the power of computers, the many new forms of communication, the transistor, then the integrated circuit, lasers, automation, the widespread use of electronics in medicine, vast increases in the power capacity of single generators, nuclear power and the harnessing of new power sources (wind and wave) etc, etc. Many of the changes have led to higher standards of living and have led to products that enrich our lives. They are the products of a society which seeks change, which is concerned for people and which recognises the value of technical expertise and innovation. Electronic and electrical engineers have made their contribution and will continue to do so. I have certainly found it to be fun and to be rewarding.

HELPFUL READING: *What is Different About Being a Woman in Electrical Engineering? Have You Got What it Takes?* (Both these can be obtained free from the Schools Liaison Service, Institution of Electrical Engineers, Michael Farady House, 6 Hills Way, Stevenage, Herts SG1 2AY; telephone 0438 313311.)

English
Professor Patrick Parrinder,
Reading University

The study and teaching of imaginative literature is as old as recorded history. In British education this function was for long fulfilled by Greek and Latin literature, so that English did not come into its own until the twentieth century. English remains in many respects a young subject, combining the study of a well-loved body of texts with a tradition of engagement in wider cultural issues and a style of sharp, lively and sometimes volatile debate.

For the student, the initial attraction of an English course is likely to be the opportunity to immerse oneself in the most exciting, and most exacting, works of poetry, fiction and drama in the language. Some of our motives for studying literature are quite properly introspective – a desire to know ourselves and to explore our cultural and psychic identity. But literary study is outward- as well as inward-looking. Central to the discipline is the concept of literary criticism, as developed in the writings of such intellectual precursors as S T Coleridge, Matthew Arnold, T S Eliot and F R Leavis. Current criticism offers a daunting variety of principles and methods, and the concept itself has been challenged by the growth of a more philosophically-demanding corpus of 'literary theory'. Critics and theorists are united in the belief that the literary work (and the material out of which it is constructed) offers a key to the nature of human experience. It is a presupposition of literary study that literature is not mere entertainment and that the impulses to make poetry, to tell stories and to act out our feelings in words play a central part in our lives. Whatever the claims that the other arts and non-literary forms of communication make on us today, literary study remains one of the more ambitious forms of intellectual enterprise.

In Joyce's *Dubliners* we learn – among other things – that there are two ways of opening a corked bottle of stout. You can use a corkscrew, or you can warm the bottle on the hob until the glass expands, the pressure inside builds up and the cork flies out. What really matters is the liquid inside. Traditionally, the fires of the critic's appreciative prose were supposed to warm up the bottle. Modern techniques of literary analysis often seem like patent corkscrews useful for opening large numbers of bottles in a hurry. Many literary theorists, on the other hand, would deny that poems or novels are given objects like this imaginary bottle of stout; we ourselves may be said to 'construct' the texts as we read them. Yet reading and re-reading can be a lifelong process; no single reading or act of interpretation is final. An English degree must always be to some extent a crash course which risks leaving the liquid overheated or peppered with pieces of cork.

The reason why some kinds of writing are considered more literary than others is, at bottom, a question of language and form. But since virtually any literary text can evoke moral, psychological, historical, religious and political as well as aesthetic responses, the number of valid critical approaches is very considerable. You are likely to be introduced to several approaches – some of them perhaps strongly imprinted with the personality of a particular lecturer – and you will have the opportunity to find out others for yourself. The range of authors and texts studied, however, is often quite predictable. Chaucer, Shakespeare and his contemporaries, Donne, Milton, Pope, Swift, the romantic poets, the Victorian novelists and the major early twentieth-century writers are likely to feature heavily in at least two of the three years. The core of compulsory papers is often less adventurous, though much more thorough, than the A-level syllabus. In addition, most departments provide a number of optional courses in fields from Anglo-Saxon to contemporary popular fiction, television and film. Occasionally the study of some literature in another language is required, and in fields such as medieval studies and the twentieth century the 'comparative' element, drawing on other European literatures, is sometimes strong. The study of the English language, after many years of relative decline, has been given special emphasis by the reports of the Kingman and Cox Committees on the teaching of English in schools. Aspects of linguistic science with a bearing on English may be made compulsory in a number of courses. The position of English as a core subject, in the national curriculum, is leading to a reassessment of the subject at undergraduate level, as well as in teacher training.

Many English courses for single honours students aim to provide at least an outline of the whole literary tradition from Chaucer and Spenser to the present. The (near) complete works of Shakespeare and some other 'canonical' texts – the *Canterbury Tales*, *The Faerie Queene*, *Paradise Lost*, *The Prelude* – or the major novels of Dickens and George Eliot – are likely to be studied in depth. At the same time an English degree course aims to develop versatility of response and skills of attentive reading, critical analysis, argument and evaluation. Many courses begin with 'practical criticism' – or the exercise of discussing and responding to unseen passages of verse and prose – and in the final year you are likely to be given the opportunity of writing a dissertation or series of extended essays on subjects of your own choice. Creative writing and literary composition as such are very rarely part of the syllabus. English in the UK is firmly regarded as an intellectual discipline, less abstract than philosophy, less factual than history, yet closer to these subjects than to the creative and performing arts. The creative atmosphere which a good English department can succeed in nurturing is a precious asset, but an English degree is only one (and not always the best) course of study open to a future novelist or poet.

The most recent developments in English studies have reflected the wider cultural changes of the times in which we live. While the English language has continued to spread, Britain's world power and influence has declined, and Britain itself has become a multicultural society; so that it is now becoming necessary to distinguish between traditional 'English literature' and the current plurality of literatures in English. Individual courses differ widely in their coverage of these new literatures. Broad intellectual movements such as feminism, structuralism and semiotics (ie theories of sign and symbol) have also had a marked impact on the way the subject is taught. The idea of the 'canon' or agreed tradition of major authors is the focus of continuing debate. The generic approach, which stresses the inherent structure and potentialities of such forms as tragedy, the lyric poem and the novel, has been supplemented (and in some cases more or less supplanted) by the contextual approach which involves studying the social and literary background to the texts concerned. Other new developments may be on the way, for English remains a vigorous, argumentative and open-ended discipline.

English graduates are able to follow the full range of careers open to those with an arts degree, with a bias towards journalism, teaching, publishing and the media.

HELPFUL READING: P D Roberts, *How Poetry Works* (Harmondsworth: Penguin, 1986); F R Leavis, *The Common Pursuit* (London: Hogarth Press, 1984); R Selden, *A Reader's Guide to Contemporary Literary Theory* (Brighton: Harvester Press, 1985).

Environmental Sciences
Dr Ian F Spellerberg, Southampton University

An exciting, recent development in higher education has been the establishment of courses which cut across the traditional boundaries of the well known and more traditional single disciplines. Environmental sciences is an example of a comparatively new and refreshing interdisciplinary science which is based on various aspects of the traditional science subjects such as biology, geography, chemistry, geology and oceanography. Environmental sciences and environmental studies are concerned with both the natural and built environments but whereas environmental sciences has a sound science component, environmental studies incorporates aspects of the social sciences and the arts.

If you study environmental sciences, you will find that it is interdisciplinary and not multidisciplinary. In other words, environmental sciences, like environmental studies, is not made up of randomly chosen bits of different subjects which have been 'cellotaped' together. In all the traditional science subjects there are topics which are of practical relevance to our understanding of the environment and the processes which take place in the environment. Such topics can be brought together in an integrated fashion and so provide the all-important interdisciplinary basis for environmental sciences. For instance, studies of water pollution in rivers and estuaries requires an interdisciplinary approach, incorporating relevant aspects of environmental biology, physical geography, environmental chemistry and biological aspects of oceanography. Similarly, studies of alternative land use strategies will require a sound knowledge of carefully selected aspects of geography, geology, environmental biology and possibly some subjects outside science such as environmental engineering and environmental law.

Environmental sciences deal with current issues about the natural environment and the built environment and is thus an attractive option for a wide range of students. But clearly any such interdisciplinary studies and training is not a soft option or an easy way to get a degree. Although the component parts of environmental sciences are generally the same as those taken by students specialising in single subject degree courses, environmental sciences students have to think about the integral links between subjects and have to draw upon resources provided by more than one subject when tackling interdisciplinary assignments. Environmental sciences therefore appeals to highly motivated and enthusiastic students who are able to face the challenge of becoming familiar with various aspects of more than one science subject.

One of the many attractions of environmental sciences is that you may have the opportunity either to specialise in one of the many areas, while retaining the interdisciplinary background or to retain a more general approach. You might specialise in waste resource management, economic geology, coastal management, nature conservation, hydrology, public health engineering, urban planning, ecological chemistry, land management, biological and chemical aspects of pollution or the economic aspects of sustainable development. Alternatively, many students choose environmental sciences because they simply want a good grounding in a broad variety of environmental topics. The value of such a grounding is obvious at a time when environmental education is becoming recognised as important and relevant to all walks of life.

Although environmental sciences is comparatively new, it is now a scientific discipline well recognised by industry, by the European Community and by international organisations such as UNESCO. It's not unusual nowadays to see advertisements by industry, local authorities and conservation agencies seeking 'an environmental scientist'. Further evidence for this recognition can be found in the growing amount of literature; there are now many books and scientific journals with titles incorporating the words environment and environmental sciences.

An interdisciplinary approach to the study of the natural and the built environments has increasing practical relevance because of the growing impact of human activities upon environmental resources and environmental processes. Thus, concern about many environmental issues (such as global warming, deforestation, spread of desert conditions, disposal of toxic wastes and extinction of plants and animals) has prompted the need for more research and better ways of managing our resources. The increasing awareness of environmental problems is resulting in a greater participation in environmental organisations and in the creation of more environmental legislation, which must be based on a sound knowledge of environmental processes. For example environmental impact assessments (assessing the likely impact of proposed major developments) are comparatively new but have already stimulated the need for people trained to manage interdisciplinary problems. Those engaged in assessing environmental impacts of motorways, electricity generating stations, marinas, or petroleum installations will be required to communicate effectively with biologists, geologists, geographers, or oceanographers and others who can contribute to the understanding of environmental impacts of urban, industrial and other developments.

Environmental sciences has a central theme but depending on where you study, there are different and unique components to the way it is taught as the bias or structure will, in part, reflect the research interests of the teaching staff. This is an added bonus but makes it important to find out all you can about the different degree courses. All of them offer a friendly information service about the teaching, research projects, field courses, entry requirements and careers of their graduates. Ask for a reading list or have a look at any of the books mentioned below.

There is no doubt there is something special about environmental sciences students. Perhaps it's their enthusiasm, interest and concern in the many and varied environmental issues which brings them together in a friendly and cooperative manner. Environmental sciences provides an agreeable and stimulating atmosphere for exercising the mind, enjoying debates and above all learning about a better approach to the management of our natural and built environments. The environmental scientists of the future will be playing a very important role in bringing about a sustainable way of life and a wiser use of the world's resources.

HELPFUL READING: The World Commission on Environment and Development, *Our Common Future* (Oxford University Press, 1987); I G Simmons, *The Ecology of Natural Resources,* (London: Edward Arnold, 1974, 1981); P R Ehrlich, A H Ehrlich, J P Holdren, *Ecoscience: Population, Resources, Environment,* (San Francisco: W H Freeman, 1970, 1977).

Environmental Studies

Emeritus Professor A D G Smart, University College, London

Environmental studies, environmental science, environmentalism. Environment is not a precise term. What do we mean by it? Probably its most frequent use is to describe the habitat of a living species, but even here the context ranges widely – an anthill or a city, a microclimate or a weather system.

Thus the study of environment is potentially a huge subject, involving science, social science and the arts. You'll find aspects of it in many long-standing disciplines, for example in biology. But there are two developing areas – environmental studies and environmental science – in which the relationship between species (including man) and environment is treated more comprehensively, although the very complexity of the systems and the links between them inevitably leads to some specialisation. One division, broad as it is, focuses on the 'man-made environment' (sometimes equated with the built environment or, more appropriately, the urban and rural environment). This tends to be called environmental studies, whereas environmental science is more often concerned with the natural environment.

Why study the man-made environment? It is of the utmost social and political importance, an area of frequent controversy, where decisions have tended in the past to be made without adequate analysis and where mistakes can be costly in human and financial terms. Everybody has views about it and wants to be involved, but the buck has to stop somewhere. Policy-making and design for the man-made environment is a heavy responsibility, a true vocation.

Imagine a city of about one million people. Its population is growing slowly and the activities within it are quickly being dispersed as employment, housing and, to some extent, shopping move out to peripheral sites. The city's nineteenth century core is being depopulated, and there are decreasing numbers of suitable jobs for those whose circumstances force them to remain. Even though the local council long ago gave up building tall blocks of flats and is encouraging modernisation of housing instead, progress is disappointingly slow. The general surroundings in which people live in this core are deteriorating all the time, contrasting sharply with the more wealthy and leafy outer suburbs.

In the city's hinterland, farming is subject to more and more disturbance from people, especially at weekends, and from changes in ownership as landowners put their land up for sale in hopes of more profitable uses. The landscape is becoming shabby and derelict. Small towns and villages within commuting distance are growing quickly, their local communities swamped and their individual character at risk of being lost in a featureless suburbia.

Despite all this dispersal, the city centre thrives during the day-time, drawing in workers to the new office blocks there. But the approach roads are choked twice a day, there is a serious noise problem, pedestrians are at risk, and public transport is sometimes giving up the unequal struggle.

All in all, it is a well known situation. But there are some bright spots. The local authority is providing, against great odds, well designed community schools, playspaces, traffic-free areas and extra greenery, and voluntary groups are helping out with many kinds of community activities. There is new inner city housing, a new district centre and some workshops for small firms, inspired by far-sighted politicians, entrepreneurs and professionals. A polluted canal and the valley through which it runs is being reclaimed as a country park, a village green has been preserved, and a face-lift to an old market place is attracting shoppers back.

Anyone who is involved in helping to shape the future of our cities and countryside needs to understand the forces at work – social, economic and physical – and the issues to which they give rise: whether, for example, to devote scarce money to rebuilding old housing areas to modern standards (with long-term benefits) or to renovating them (with less disturbance to communities, but only short-term economies); whether to improve public transport and deter car commuters, with the risk that the city centre will become less attractive to car users, thus aiding and abetting more dispersal; whether to reduce pollution, possibly making it more costly for industry to operate in the inner core where jobs are so badly needed; whether to spend a lot on preserving historic buildings for which new uses are hard to find; and whether to save agricultural land despite this making housing sites more costly.

The people who help to make these key decisions may be planners, architects or other professionals whose education has been concerned with the planning, design and management of the man-made environment. Their degree courses will have included environmental studies and project work attuned to their special interests – humanities (history, geography, economics, sociology, social administration) and technology (design and construction processes, at the scale of the city or of its individual components). They will have found it an exacting education and if they had entered upon it under the impression that it was about the birds and the bees, they soon had to come to a point of decision.

Thus be sure that you understand the purpose of environmental studies courses. These aim to analyse the factors (social, economic and aesthetic) which make for quality in the man-made environment, and to promote good environmental planning, design and management. Preliminary reading will help you in this. And so will the sections of this book which deal more fully with some of the basic disciplines involved, such as architecture and landscape, town and country planning, geography, other social sciences, land management and building studies. As for course entrance requirements, most places tend to go for good A-level results rather than particular subjects.

HELPFUL READING: J B Cullingworth, **Town & Country Planning in Britain** (Allen & Unwin, 1985); N Fairbrother, **New Lives, New Landscapes** (Architectural Press, 1970); Peter Hall, **Urban and Regional Planning** (Allen & Unwin, 1985); HMSO series on careers in planning, architecture, building, etc; N Pevsner, **Pioneers of Modern Design from William Morris to Walter Gropius** (Harmondsworth: Penguin, 3rd revised ed 1977); *The Construction Team* (Building (Publishers) Ltd, 1983); *Building, a Professional Career* (Careers Consultants Ltd); R A Burgess & G White, *Building Production and Project Design* (Construction Press, 1979); also: S E Rasmussen, *Experiencing Architecture*, (1962).

European Studies
Dr Juliet Lodge, Hull University

On the surface, the term 'European studies' seems self-explanatory. In reality, it covers a vast range of options. All the hype over 1992 and the realisation of the single market has spawned renewed interest in Europe in general and in the European Community in particular. Do not be discouraged! Your future lies in Europe. Employers are increasingly keen to employ people who have knowledge about Europe and the European Community.

European studies exposes you to the many facets of life that have gone into producing the Europe of today. European studies involves a broad examination of Europe's history, geography, culture, economics, philosophies, literature, politics and society.

European studies normally involves gaining fluency in at least one and usually two European languages besides your mother tongue. French, German and Spanish are the most popular but it is also possible to study Italian, Dutch, Russian etc. Language courses that form part of European studies degrees are increasingly practical in their orientation. Modern languages rather than linguistics or the literature of the 17th century are stressed, although you would also gain an appreciation of the literature of the country(ies) whose language(s) you were acquiring.

European society in all its ramifications tends to be studied both at a general level and in greater detail with reference to key European states. Western Europe, broadly conceived, and often the USSR tends to be studied in greater detail than Eastern Europe.

Comparative politics and political economy or economic history rather than econometrics often form components of European studies degrees. The states most often studied include: Germany, France, the USSR, the UK and possibly Italy, Spain and Sweden. You would normally learn about American and international politics as well.

You could not do a European studies degree without learning about the history, politics and economic origins of the European Community, and the origins, development and changing nature of East-West relations.

European studies degrees also normally involve a study of political philosophy from Plato, Machiavelli, and Hobbes to Locke, Marx and Marcuse, for example. Major contemporary political trends – liberalism, socialism, communism, totalitarianism, fascism, feminism, etc – may also be studied from a variety of perspectives: literary, philosophical, historical, economic or political, for example.

It is now possible to take degree courses in subjects like chemistry or maths, for instance, that have a European studies component in them. You can also combine European studies with languages, or with law, history, art history, environmental studies, business studies, management, sociol-· ogy, economics or politics.

Most European studies degrees offer you the chance to study relevant European elements from a number of different disciplines. You are likely to get a basic grounding in the history, politics and economic history of Europe whatever European studies course you follow.

Normally, you also spend a period of time in Europe either at a European university or polytechnic or working. Some courses sandwich two periods abroad into a four-year programme. During this time, you would be expected to write a dissertation of around 8,000 words (in English or one of your other European languages) on a topic relevant to your studies. Reasonable language proficiency needed if you are to make the most of this. All European studies courses help you with your language before you go. On your return, you should be fluent in the language in which you have worked or studied.

Some of the most exciting courses in European Studies are now offered by departments in the field of social science. These very often have a vocational component to them and they let you get right to the heart of European affairs.

If you are keen on politics, lobbying, trade, international affairs and business, for example, you can now take courses which build in a 'stage' at the European Parliament, for example. (A stage is the European term commonly used to refer to a period of unpaid internship.) This means that while continuing your studies in Brussels, you may also have working links with Members of the European Parliament. You get to see how Europe ticks. Periods working in Europe or as 'stages' or in partner European universities and polytechnics are highly illuminating, socially and person- ally rewarding. In addition, they are fun. As you become an active part of the·trans-European student community, your circle of friends will grow, your intellectual horizons will alter and your experiences will challenge your preconceptions daily!

Among some of the best European Studies courses are those which enable you to spend up to one year studying and gaining additional qualifications from partner universities and polytechnics in different parts of Europe. These courses normally last for four years. It is possible to graduate not only with a British but also with a European qualification.

If you want such a course, make sure that you look beyond language departments. The social sciences and law, and increasingly English and science departments, provide rich hunting grounds. If your main interest is language you would do well to choose a course that has a high European studies component and one which does not restrict you to the study of European literature. Many departments now offer the chance to study commercial language alongside literature, culture and politics.

In short, European Studies courses offer you numerous options and they often benefit from excellent schemes such as Erasmus and Lingua initiated by the Commission of the European Community. Erasmus is designed to promote student mobility. Many European Studies courses from a wide variety of disciplines are linked to European universities and polytechnics through Erasmus networks. This is a sort of twinning arrangement which makes it possible for students to do parts of their degrees in a number of European states. A new scheme called Tempus, modelled on Erasmus, is being introduced to expand mobility and exchanges to Eastern Europe.

If you choose to do a course in European Studies, you will be immersed in a dynamic and rapidly changing field. Your outlook is almost bound to change. You are likely to come into contact with students from all across Europe. You will have the chance of studying alongside them both at home and on the European continent. Your intellectual, social and employment horizons will expand considerably as a result.

In short, European Studies is predominantly about understanding the 1990s. How and why Europe is shaped as it is. What its role and place in the world is. Where it is going. What problems it confronts. How it resolves them whether they are economic, political, environmental, social, cultural, scientific, commercial or technical. Europe encroaches on all aspects of our lives and all aspects of education.

Studying Europe and the dynamic changes within the European Community which may lead to a federal United States of Europe is enlightening, exhilarating and invigorating. The 1990s are set to be a new European Age. How better to understand and shape it than to study it first?

Helpful reading: J Lodge (ed), *The European Community and the Challenge of the Future*, (Pinter, London, 1991); Brian Morris, Klaus Boehm, Maurice Geller, *The European Community* (3rd edition), (Macmillan Press, London, 1991).

Fine Arts
Dr Alex Potts, School of Fine Arts, East Anglia University

This area of study is often called art history, and with some justification. The visual arts – painting, sculpture and architecture – are usually studied from an historical point of view although critical analysis still plays a very important role. Even to be placed in an historical context, a work of art must be interpreted and this requires visual sensitivity – much as the reading of poetry requires a feeling for language. Of course no history can dispense with interpretation, no history is merely an objective recording of facts. Studying the history of art makes one all the more aware of this precisely because visual images can be so ambiguous, so difficult to interpret.

The history of art can be approached in a number of different ways and often one's approach varies with different periods and different art forms. Central to most discussions of the visual arts, however, are the notions of style and stylistic development (see Meyer Shapiro, 'Style' in A L Kroeber, ed, *Anthropology Today* – Chicago University Press, 1965; and in M Philipson, ed, *Aesthetics Today* – New York: World Publishing, 1961). We are all struck by the way visual forms change with time, one instance being changing fashions in clothes. The coherence of such changes is what enables the art historian to date a work of art on the basis of visual evidence, by classifying it with known objects in a similar style. Much more is involved, however, than placing works of art in chronological order. One wants to know, for example, why styles take on the particular aspect they do, how and why they change. This may be explored by focusing mainly on visual forms and defining their character and evolution, as in Heinrich Wölfflin's *Principles of Art History* (New York: Dover, 1950). Such preoccupation with style is a characteristic feature of art history.

No work of art, however, can be properly understood without reference to the ideas it expresses. These in turn must be illuminated by the social and cultural values of the society that produced the work of art. Some historians would go so far as to say that the visual arts should be conceived as the reflection of more general, social and cultural factors. But even though art history and social and cultural history are of necessity connected, links between the two that go beyond vague references to the spirit of the age can be hard to define. Jakob Burckhardt's celebrated *The Civilization of the Renaissance in Italy* (S G C Middlemore, trans, London: Phaidon, 1960), for example, though a basic text for anyone interested in Renaissance art and written by an authority on the subject, never actually specifies how the visual arts relate to the cultural values which he elicits from the writings and social and political history of the time. Recent attempts to link art and culture have often focused on subject matter, giving rise to a branch of art history variously called iconography and iconology (see Erwin Panofsky's *Studies in Iconology* – New York: Harper & Row, 1962). The religious beliefs embodied in an altar piece, for example, can be studied by looking at the subject depicted and the particular religious symbols used.

The interpretation of symbols and allegories, or iconographical analysis, is often as fruitful an approach to understanding a work of art as stylistic analysis. Content, however, can never be separated from style, for an idea is always modified by the way it is represented in a particular medium. Only by joint consideration of both styles and subject matter can one avoid a simplistic view of art as either pure form or mere illustration of cultural and social history (see Timothy J Clark's *Image of the People* – London: Thames & Hudson, 1973). Take a portrait, for example. Our understanding of it is undoubtedly aided if we know something about the particular person whom it represents. Some aspects, however, could be misunderstood if one interprets the portrait as a straightforward likeness. A certain rigidity, say, may owe more to the artistic conventions of the period than to the person's actual appearance.

Studying art and its history, you can see, will entail far more than learning how to identify and date works of art. This specialisation, connoisseurship as it is often known, can in any case perhaps best be learned by inspecting and classifying actual objects in museums or galleries. Studies in fine arts will involve you in trying to understand the varying character and significance of visual images from different historical periods. In most UKCPUs you will be obliged to focus on a few select periods of Western European art, such as the Renaissance and the nineteenth century. A small number of institutions, however, do offer facilities enabling you to choose courses anywhere within the period from Greek times to the present day. One or two places also offer courses in non-Western art. As your studies proceed, you will find your awareness of different styles and their meanings becoming more precise, but this process will never be cut and dried. No amount of historical fact, for example, will teach you to distinguish between good and bad art. The attraction of the subject lies on the contrary in trying to come to terms with images whose significance has never been satisfactorily explained and which always demand new interpretations.

As entrance requirements, most courses ask for at least one foreign language to O-level standard or equivalent, but few places specify particular A-level subjects. An A-level in history, English or a modern language can be as good a preparation for a fine arts course as one in art or art history.

HELPFUL READING: E H Gombrich, *Art and Illusion* (London: Phaidon, 1960).

Food Science and Nutrition
Professor R A Lawrie, Nottingham University

Prominent among the few unchanging aspects of the Earth is our need for food. It is essential for life. What is new is the relatively recent vast increase in the number of people who depend on sustenance for which the time and phase of consumption are substantially different. In our industrialized world there are few people nowadays who personally produce the food which they themselves require. Most depend on farmers and food factories. This circumstance, in turn, has created a much increased need to preserve the quality and safety of food from the time it is produced until the time it is eaten. It has thus become necessary to develop scientific understanding of food commodities so that control of their production and distribution can be effected with minimum wastage instead of being subject to the uncertainties which are unavoidable with traditional procedures based on empirical observation.

In the United Kingdom the systematized study of food has grown into a discipline in its own right since the end of the Second World War. A course in Food Science was established in the Royal Technical College, Glasgow, in 1949; and, as the University of Strathclyde, that body offered the first degree course in 1959. Since then about a dozen other degree courses in Food Science and Technology have been established, a fact which clearly reflects the increasing opportunities for men and women trained in the subject.

It should be mentioned that the term 'Food Science' is sometimes used to refer to the extension of knowledge in the field and the term 'Food Technology' to the application of that knowledge; but, in practice, both terms are largely interchangeable.

Because the eating quality and nutritive value of food commodities are determined by a long sequence of events from conception in the animal or germination in the seed, through the phases of growth and maturity, harvesting, preservation and preparation to consumption and human nutrition, the field covered by food science and nutrition is exceedingly wide. A great variety of careers is available. These are satisfying in that they cater for most aptitudes and interests and in that they are evidently most important for the well-being and survival of mankind.

Careers in food science and nutrition can be successfully pursued in many contexts. Apart from the more obvious openings in the food industry itself, there are many opportunities in related spheres, such as the manufacture of food ingredients, food packaging and food plant. The aptitudes and interests of some men and women may be more appropriately displayed in the control of food products by legislation, analysis and public health. Posts are available in research institutes supported by government or trade associations, in educational establishments (technical colleges, polytechnics and universities), and in industry. Others, especially after their experience and expertise have developed, find fulfilling and remunerative roles as consultants. For those with a flair for writing and communication there are openings in presenting the science of nutrition and food to the public in journalism, publishing and advertising. Many young people wish to travel in the early years after qualification. For these, there are numerous opportunities in industrial firms overseas, and in research and teaching in developing countries.

Within all these broad areas the type of work available is also varied eg product and process development, research, food control, management work study, scientific catering, teaching.

Not infrequently such posts require a knowledge of nutrition; but for those interested in dietetics as such (hospital almonry, nutritional catering, diet control), a diploma in dietetics is necessary; and courses for this are available.

Those who intend to follow a career in food science and nutrition may enter the profession by several routes. Those who wish to be recognized as food scientists and technologists would normally seek to obtain a degree, while those who seek to be technicians would qualify by following Ordinary or Higher National Diploma courses or those offered by the City and Guilds Institute. Those who are already qualified in some other discipline may obtain specific expertise in food science and technology by following relatively short conversion courses; or by working for a research degree.

A useful list of courses, at various levels up to degree, is published by the Institute of Food Science and Technology, 20 Queensberry Place, London SW7 2DR. The Institute is the incorporated professional body representing Food Science and Technology in the United Kingdom. Membership is available in various grades, according to qualifications, experience and expertise. It confers recognition of status within the profession without academic qualifications.

HELPFUL READING: G C Birch, M Spencer and A G Cameron, *Food Science*.

Geography
Professor M D I Chisholm, Cambridge University

There was a time when geography was regarded as an easy option, skimming the surface of many interesting topics but never getting to grips with anything. Much has changed in the last twenty years. Public debate about education often emphasises the disadvantages of specialisation, and in many universities interdisciplinary and multidisciplinary courses of study have been established in an attempt to meet this situation. The breadth of geographical study, bringing together topics concerning the physical environment (eg geology, soils, hydrology and climate) and socio-economic matters (eg patterns of economic development, urbanisation and industrial location), is now regarded as a strength rather than a weakness. This is particularly true given the growing importance of problems concerned with ecological management and the planning of cities and regions. Although maintaining a wide range of interests, geography also has developed some hard skills which have widespread application. Most departments teach basic statistics and introduce students to the use of computers; for these studies all that is required is a logical mind and an ability to think in numerical terms, something which many students with an arts background do readily enough. There is also growing emphasis on field observation and the use of basic laboratory techniques to analyse aspects of the natural environment (eg soil conditions and surface run-off).

Although there is a good deal of variation in detail, most university courses require the student to study across the whole field of the subject in his first year. Thereafter a choice of courses may be made, and attention can be increasingly focused on selected topics in either human geography or physical geography, or both. This offers a route to specialised studies in the third year for those who wish it. These specialised studies vary in character from one department to another, ranging from the study of particular regions/nations, through advanced statistical methods, micro-climatology, hydrology, the processes of change in urban areas, and regional planning/development in selected countries. By careful selection of topics, students can also maintain a broad spread of interests, something that may be specially important for those who are undecided as to what they wish to do on completing their studies.

Over a three-year programme, students have the opportunity to study developed and developing regions, and to examine the phenomena of the physical environment in several climatic regions. Such studies in both human and physical geography are undertaken with staff who are person-ally familiar with the areas in question. In addition to study of the actual world and of the nature of geographical variation, another essential for the student is learning to conceptualise the world in abstract terms. The importance of distance as a basic organising principle for all economic and social interaction (eg freight traffic, telephone calls) and for the choice of optimum locations (eg for hospitals and factories) quickly becomes appar-ent; these are all fields where geography is applied to the solution of real problems. Other live and intriguing areas of study are how people perceive the environment and respond to their perception, modelling hillslope development, the water budget of river basins, climatology (though meteorology – concerned with weather and weather forecasting – is sometimes taught as a separate subject outside geography) and the analysis of soils, which provides an important background both to topographical evolution and agricultural development.

The overwhelming majority of students have an A-level in geography. In some universities there are faculty requirements limiting the possible range, but otherwise almost any combination of supporting A-levels is acceptable. The common ones on the science side are geology, physics, chemistry, biology and mathematics; on the arts side history, economics, English and languages figure prominently. After graduating, a remarkably wide range of jobs is open to geographers. While many still enter the teaching profession, having taken a one-year Certificate in Education, many others become planners (for which further training is also necessary), join the civil service or such organisations as the Soil Survey and River Boards, enter industry or commerce in a wide range of capacities. The job prospects for geographers are good over a wide and increasing range of employments.

HELPFUL READING: R Abler, J S Adams and P Gould, *Spatial Organisation* (Englewood Cliffs, New Jersey: Prentice-Hall, 1971); R J Chorley, ed, *Water, Earth and Man* (London: Methuen, 1979); P Haggett, *Geography: a modern synthesis* (New York, Evanston, San Francisco and London: Harper & Row, 1979).

Geology
Professor T R Owen, Swansea, University of Wales

Geology is the study of the Earth. It has to do with rocks, minerals and fossils, and with the interior of the Earth as well as its surface layers. It unravels the fascinating history of our planet, which goes back over 4,500 million years, and one can study rocks in West Greenland and Canada that are almost that old. The story is one of changing climates, changing patterns of land and sea, evolving life.

Any subject that goes into depth about all the above must be fascinating, but today geology is a lot more than that. It is adjusting after a major revolution following the revelation in 1967 of the concept of plate tectonics. This revolution can be compared with the impact of Darwin's theory of evolution in biology and with Einstein's theory of relativity in physics. I consider myself lucky to have lived at this time. In the words of Prof S Toulmin: 'In the world of science . . . the second half of the twentieth century is proving to be a period of perpetual revolution and scientists are learning to live with the fact.'

I came to college in the 1930s intending to study geography but had to take geology as my main subject because at that time there was no honours school in geography in my college. I say this because I want to assure anyone that you can take a degree in geology starting from scratch. It's a marvellous subject because it pulls together lots of other subjects –

biology, geography, physics, chemistry, mathematics, etc. It helps a lot if you have studied some of these subjects at A-level, particularly if you want to become a professional geologist. But even without these background subjects you can really enjoy geology at college because geology is a cultural subject, a marvellous thinking exercise. It is both a 'doing' and a 'thinking' subject. A student of geology is a Sherlock Holmes. There are fascinating clues to be observed and problems to be solved.

Geology is also an outdoor subject. One studies rocks not only in the laboratory and the lecture room but also in the field. My student geological excursions are some of my most pleasant memories – the great thrill of finding my first fossils, of reaching the top of Snowdon, of making my first geological map in Spain or France: making marvellous friendships.

What about this geological revolution? It really all started at the beginning of the century when Alfred Wegener put forward his theory of continental drift. There followed a great debate but in general the theory was abandoned, mainly because there seemed to be no adequate mechanism for shifting continents. Then came a revival of interest with rapid exploration of ocean floors, the marvellous discovery of fossil magnetism in rocks and the theory of sea-floor spreading. The names of Blackett, Runcorn, Dietz, Hess, Matthews and Vine figure prominently in this exciting story. The revolution was proclaimed when the whole story was unfolded at the Goddard Symposium in 1967. We know now that the Earth's outer shell – the lithosphere – is broken into some seven major slabs or 'plates' (plus many more micro-plates) which are continually moving relative to one another. New oceanic crust is made when plates move away from one another. The Atlantic is widening whereas the Pacific is closing. When plates move towards one another, the denser plate – particularly when formed of oceanic crust – descends beneath the lighter plate, a process known as subduction. The descending plate melts and molten magma ascends to form lines of volcanoes. Deep-seated earthquakes are also a feature of subduction zones. The western zone of South America is a classic example. There are also areas of the world where plates are slipping sideways against one another. The San Andreas fault zone of California is an example as last year's tragic earthquake has shown.

We now have a coherent picture of geological processes. What were previously isolated geological items – volcanoes, earthquakes, mountain chains, sedimentary troughs, great fractures – can now be welded into a compact whole. Moreover, we can now truly follow the important geological principle, 'The present is the key to the past'. What is happening today helps us to unravel past geological history. The application of plate tectonics helps us to understand the British scene 500 million years ago. We now know that an ocean (long since closed completely) once separated Scotland from England and Wales. (Scottish devolution could have happened as early as 800 million years ago.)

The great advances in sea-floor studies around the British Isles are part of the new excitement in geology. Application of an exciting branch of geology called geophysics has given us a kind of X-ray picture of the deep structures beneath the North, Irish and Celtic Seas. New finds of oil and gas have resulted, finds of great importance to the UK economy. More-over, all this new geological information has now to be incorporated into our revised reconstructions of British (and European) geological history. It may well be that the Atlantic Ocean once tried its best to begin where is now the North Sea.

I have not said anything about geology courses. There are various kinds in colleges, polytechnics and universities, and all sorts of combinations of subjects are permitted. One can combine geology with oceanography, geography, biological sciences, physics, chemistry, civil engineering, energy studies, etc. Or one can take geology in combination with arts subjects, if one chooses. Look at the UKCPU prospectuses to find out what is possible. Field courses are a marvellous part of all geology courses. You'll enjoy them immensely.

Yes, geology has a new 1989 excitement – for everybody. Take geology as a first degree, either to be a geologist or, if you wish, just to get to know something about a truly fascinating Earth and the way it works. Mankind will one day derive tremendous benefits from these early days of the revolution. Why not join it now?

HELPFUL READING: Peter J Wyllie, *The Way the Earth Works* (New York: Wiley & Sons, 1976).

History
Dr Maurice Keen, Balliol College, Oxford University

St Thomas Aquinas defined man as 'a social and political animal' and history is the study of man's record as just that – and a little bit more too. A question that is often asked in history general papers is 'What is the difference between prehistory and history?' The answer is that pre-historians and archaeologists study tangible things that men of the remote past have left behind in the way of artefacts and the remains of buildings; in doing so they study man as a social animal, and very often, from their evidence, they also uncover something of the political structure of a past society. However, a new dimension of study – history – opens at the moment when the person studying the past can establish contact with statements that come direct from an articulate individual who lived in a past period and who can tell us of his internal reactions to his outside environment. History is not just about man's experience as a species, but also about the experience of individuals with inner feelings and opinions and ambitions which are still communicable, even across major barriers of time.

Your first duty as a historian, therefore, will be to learn to listen. Moreover, you must learn to listen critically since you will hear a great many people talking, and men in the past were just as divided as they are now by differences of status, situation and attitude. Like men today, they were often the victims of their own prejudices, and they were equally prone to handling the truth carelessly. This is, of course, as true of historians themselves as it is of the people who made history, which is why in the study of history there is no substitute for the original sources.

Naturally it is important to read what other historians have said about their special fields, but history books are not to be mistaken for infallible guides to the final truth. They are valuable rather as interpreters, to put you in touch with the past and so into a position where you can form your own judgment about it. The final test of a history book is whether what the author says rings true when his words are set alongside those of the people about whom he is writing.

Because of the need to listen carefully, languages will be important to you as a historian. This is obviously true in the superficial sense: anyone who wants to specialise in French or Spanish history, for example, must be able to catch the special nuances of people's words. But a historian must also learn to speak the 'language of the past'. The different environments of past ages and the differences in the range of possibilities in social, economic and technological terms caused people to value different priorities and to talk and think about their situation in ways that are different from those natural to us. The historian must be able to grasp these differences imaginatively in order to understand what the people that he studies are saying.

This, I believe, is what above all makes history an educational subject in the best sense of the term. Many problems in any age – perhaps most of them – arise from men's inability to appreciate and to make allowance for differences of opinion and attitude that stem from differences in upbringing, in physical and economic environment, in cultural background and in individual reactions. The study of history cannot, of course, solve the problems that arise thus but it can and should teach us to approach them in an intelligent way. For the same reason the study of ancient history can be as relevant and educational as the study of the recent past: seeking to understand the ways of those remote in time is a useful introduction to understanding modern people who are divided from us by barriers of distance and culture. The process is, of course, a two-way one: what anthropologists can tell us about primitive societies of our own time may illuminate, for example, the thought-world of the early Anglo-Saxons.

Listening and looking imaginatively with a critical ear and eye, therefore, are the keys to understanding **how** things happened in the past. Just how different that is from understanding **why** things happened remains an endlessly debatable topic. In the end you will have to form your own judgment about it. Does history have an inner logic of its own? To what extent do such impersonal factors as physical environment, technological development and economic relations allow individual endeavour and action to have a decisive impact? A school of Marxist historians believes that we can perceive a coherence in history, based in the dynamic working out of impersonal factors, and that in the understanding of this lies the key to the improvement of the human condition. Others, as I myself, do not believe that history shows as efficient a measure of coherence as this, and claim simply that its study is a humanising exercise which helps us to understand more about both others and ourselves. These are only two lines of approach, around which a lot of debate focuses at present: there is of course an infinity of alternative approaches. History is a very broad and important subject (nothing that is human is irrelevant to it) and it is bound to raise controversy. It is also an exciting subject because it brings continual contact with people of the past.

History is a subject that requires a lot of patient work, and there are a number of ancillary skills which are very helpful. In terms of A-levels, you will obviously be wise to offer history and, if at all possible, a modern language (or Latin). Many UKCPUs insist on at least one O-level pass in a language as a course requirement for history, and some prefer two. Mathematics or economics can be very useful: historians nowadays are much more statistically minded than they once used to be. Geography is another subject that can directly cross-fertilise with history. An A-level in classical studies or classical civilisation (offered by some GCE boards) can be helpful, especially if the degree course covers ancient history.

The syllabuses of history courses vary a great deal, and so do regulations about the subjects that may be studied in combination with history. Some (eg York University) encourage students to spend a part of their time working on a long essay or mini-thesis, which can count towards the degree; some (eg Oxford University) lay emphasis on the study of continuous British history as an essential part of the course; some (eg Durham University) offer a course in economic history as a degree course in its own right. The prospectuses of individual UKCPUs will give you the relevant information and it is worth looking at them carefully.

HELPFUL READING: I Berlin, *The Hedgehog and the Fox Ch.1* (London: Weidenfeld & Nicolson, 1953); E H Carr, *What is History?* (London: Macmillan, 1961); R G Collingwood, *The Idea of History* (Oxford University Press, 1946); J Le Goff and P Nora (eds.) *Constructing the Past* (Cambridge University Press, 1985).

Hotel and Catering Management
J O'Connor, Oxford Polytechnic

The provision of hospitality to the traveller has always been an important service and the origins of inn-keeping and tavern-keeping may be traced at least as far back as Ancient Rome. The profession of hotel and catering management as practised today is, however, vastly more diverse and complex than that pursued by the inn-keepers of Rome or the entrepreneurs who built the Savoy and the Ritz in London a century ago. Hospitality management, a term used to include hotel, catering and institutional management, is now truly international: our customers come from all over the world, many British companies have international interests and many young managers find it valuable to work abroad in the development of their careers. Whether pursued for profit or to provide a service, as in institutional management, hospitality is a business concerned with meeting the needs of consumers, with employing people with diverse skills and with investment, often heavy, in buildings, plant and other resources. The task of the modern hospitality manager is to make the best use of the investment of his employer and of his staff's skills in satisfying the needs of his consumers. This is more difficult today than it was at the turn of the last century and it will be more difficult still at the turn of this century when consumers will anticipate better value than ever before.

Education and training for hospitality management are constantly evolving and degree courses in this field are of fairly recent origin. In the last twenty years, twenty UKCPUs have developed degree courses, ten at honours level, in this subject. The structure and content of these courses varies significantly amongst the institutions. Most, but not all, are four-year sandwich courses; those which are not require students to gain industrial experience in their long vacations. A minority of courses specialise in preparation for one sector of the industry, eg institutional management or catering, but most are broadly based and aim at giving students the opportunity to become familiar with the industry in general before deciding upon a particular career pathway. The common core of all these courses is the study of the provision of food, drink and accommodation outside the home. These studies are technical and often scientific, involving laboratory work in training restaurants as well as the use of computers and scientific equipment. A second prime component will be business studies covering economics, accountancy and law. The third, and perhaps most important, cluster of studies will be those concerned with human behaviour, covering psychology, consumer studies and the management of people. Some institutions offer options in European languages. The range of subjects to be covered is therefore much wider than in the conventional honours degree and there is the additional demand upon students that they must integrate these studies into the vocational framework. To embark upon a course of this type and to complete it successfully requires motivation and flexibility in the student, but, since such attributes are essential for the hospitality manager, for those who possess them, the course and the subsequent career can be extremely rewarding. Most applicants to courses will prefer to test their suitability for the industry by seeking some work experience in the school holidays or at weekends. It is certainly not wise to enrol on a course of this nature unless you are quite clear that hospitality management is the career for you, with all that this implies in terms of unsocial and often long hours of work. It is a career which requires almost constant contact with people, whether customers or employees; you should, therefore, feel confident that you will enjoy working with and leading groups of people before embarking on this particular career pathway.

Entrance requirements for courses in this field do not usually demand specific A-level subjects, but applicants should enquire directly of the UKCPUs for details. Most courses are heavily over-subscribed so it is best to apply early, preferably by mid-December of the year preceding entry. Most admissions tutors like to interview candidates.

What will it be like after graduation? One thing is certain: your training will not be finished, thus you will probably decide to join a company with a graduate training scheme, usually of one or two years' duration, to widen your experience and develop managerial skills. Even if you are a born entrepreneur it is unwise to buy your own restaurant or hotel immediately.

You may decide to work for an international hotel company, join the forces as a catering officer, enter hospital catering or go into the catering division of a large industrial company where you might be involved in anything from head office restaurants to supplying an oil rig in the North Sea. Pubs, clubs and students' residences all require trained management, as do hamburger chains or luxury hotels. Whatever you decide upon, don't expect every weekend off – you are likely to be most busy when everyone else seems to be on holiday!

HELPFUL READING: D Taylor, *Fortune, Fame and Folly: British Hotels and Catering from 1878–1978* (London, IPC Business Press, 1977). *The Caterer and Hotelkeeper* publishes a career supplement each year, which is obtainable from booksellers or the publishers. The Hotel and Catering Training Board publishes *The College List* (HCTB, 1986). Videos, giving a general introduction to careers in the industry may be borrowed from your local Careers Office or from the HCTB. The Hotel, Catering and Institutional Management Association provides guidance on courses and publishes a reference book annually, obtainable from: HCIMA, 191 Trinity Road, London SW17.

Industrial Relations
Professor K F Sisson, Warwick University

Industrial relations is a relatively new subject at UKCPUs. Only one or two offer degrees or joint degrees in the subject at undergraduate level, although the number of postgraduate courses is greater. More commonly industrial relations is offered as an option in its own right or key elements will be included in courses bearing such labels as industrial sociology, labour economics, organisational behaviour, and personnel management. The rapid growth in the number of such options and courses reflects the fact that industrial relations has become a subject of major economic, political and social importance.

So what is industrial relations? Essentially, it has to do with work or employment relationships, the organisations and groups which take part in the management or control of these relationships, and the processes which are involved. The typical syllabus is likely to include the study of the management strategies and policies; the structure and control of work organisations; trade unions (their membership, structure and organisation – both inside and outside the workplace); the structure and processes of bargaining and consultation; and the role of government. The latter, in particular, has been assumed as growing in importance in recent years. The government is not only the employer (or, at least, paymaster) of some 6½ million people in the public services and nationalised industries, it also sets the legal framework and the economic context of industrial relations. For a more detailed list of the subjects covered, consult G S Bain, *Industrial Relations in Britain: Past Trends and Future Developments* (Oxford: Blackwell, 1983) or K Sisson, *Personnel Management in Britain* (Oxford: Blackwell, 1989) which are likely to be the standard texts for many courses.

The subject is anything but uncontroversial. Industrial relations touches on some of the most sensitive issues of the day – ways in which people are managed, the functions and power of trade unions, the role of the law, the contribution of collective bargaining in inflation, the prospects for industrial democracy, to name but a few. Clearly the outcome of such issues will have a significant effect on the balance of power between groups in society. Moreover, although many, but not all, who teach industrial relations might agree in broad terms with my definition of the subject, their method of approach to it is likely to be very different because they will inevitably hold different values about the issues involved.

Differences of approach are also likely according to the type of department which is offering the course or option in industrial relations. The increase in the number of universities and polytechnics offering the subject has, in many cases, been associated with the rapid growth in the number of first degree courses in business studies and management sciences. When industrial relations forms part of these courses there is a danger of teaching moving too quickly from description to prescription. That is to say, the institutions are described, industrial relations 'problems' identified – largely from a management perspective – and a range of possible solutions discussed. But the student is given insufficient time to study the processes at work and so develop an adequate framework within which to explain and interpret developments.

On the other hand, the teaching of industrial relations is also provided by more established academic departments like economics and sociology. Here there is likely to be greater emphasis on analysis and explanation but essentially from the point of view of the parent discipline. In this case the danger is that issues will be interpreted **only** in the light of the theories and explanatory frameworks of that discipline. For example, the economist might be tempted to treat trade unions as a special case of monopoly, while the sociologist might see them as essentially class organisations. Clearly both these approaches have something to offer, but exclusive preoccupation with one or the other is likely to give rise to limited understanding of the significance of trade unions. To concentrate on their economic aspects is to ignore the rights which trade unions have won to represent their members on a wide range of issues. Collective bargaining is not just concerned with pay or with hours of work; it often concerns such matters as discipline, dismissal, promotion, training and the organisation of work. Thus it is as much a political as an economic process. By the same token, if we see trade unions as essentially class organisations we are likely to overlook a large number of important organisations representing white collar and professional workers.

To sum up, industrial relations is not a discipline in the sense that many other subjects claim to be. Rather it is an area of study – and a very important area. It is by its very nature interdisciplinary and multidisciplinary, bringing insights from many of the social sciences together in an integrated fashion. It also requires a historical perspective. For these reasons it helps, but is not essential, to have done an A-level in one of the social studies. Those who teach industrial relations cannot and should not pretend that its study will provide easy answers. It does, however, provide an opportunity to gain much greater understanding of significant issues of today. For students who are prepared to think for themselves it can be immensely rewarding.

Information Technology

R S Burgess, Newcastle Polytechnic

Information Technology (IT) is a term introduced in the early 1980s to describe the coming together of other previously separate technologies and disciplines, namely computing, telecommunications and systems. Few people in the industrialised world have not had some contact with IT. IT is affecting us all, in the home, at work and in our social activities. Commerce, industry and government are becoming increasingly dependent on its application to function more effectively and efficiently. In the home we can access information via our television sets using teletext and programme some of our home appliances to be semi-automatic. Many of us are lucky enough to have a personal microcomputer to help us in our work or play. Our letter boxes regularly deliver us unwelcome bills produced by IT. Those privileged to have money in a bank can obtain cash at any time of the day through dispensers which are a part of the bank's IT system. IT helps us travel: road, air and rail traffic are controlled by computers as are airline reservation systems. Space travel would of course be impossible without computers and sophisticated telecommunications. IT provides us with some of our leisure activities through games machines. Many of our newspapers are produced using IT. Scientists were of course the first major users of computers back in the late 1940s and they would be unable to do much of their present day research without large computers. IT is having a major impact within the office in the form of word processing and electronic mail. Large businesses and government organisations have been using computers for nearly a quarter of a century for processing their financial and other data and this type of use is quickly spreading to the smaller businesses. Perhaps the biggest impact of IT in the short-term future will be on manufacturing industry where the use of computer-aided design, real-time systems, computer-controlled machine tools and robots is expected to mushroom.

It is the fastest growing industry worldwide and this growth has occurred over the last 40 years. Indeed the growth has been exponential and there are no signs of it slowing down. Perhaps the two most significant advances responsible for this growth were the invention of the microchip (which dramatically reduced the cost of computing power), and the developments in telecommunications – in particular laser technology, which enables people to communicate with computers, and computers to communicate with each other over long distances. It is these two developments in particular that have brought IT into the home and onto the high street and made IT all-pervasive. It is difficult to predict where IT is going and what will be the ultimate consequences for society. In the short term, two of the most significant and exciting developments will be in intelligent systems and voice recognition systems where machines and robots will be programmed to act and communicate more like humans.

However IT is not just about the technology of computers and telecommunications. To exploit this technology to the benefit of a particular application requires quantum leaps of human creative thought and effort so that the wood of an application can be seen for the trees of the technology. So not only is there a need for skilled manpower to create the technology but there is also a more significant requirement for skilled IT application specialists so IT may be successfully exploited. There is an acute shortage of well educated and skilled IT manpower in the UK and worldwide and all recent reputable reports suggest that the situation is getting worse rather than better. Therefore there will be good career prospects and rewards for IT graduates, both women and men, for the foreseeable future.

The majority of UKCPUs offer courses in IT at undergraduate level. Many of these courses will be offered by the computing departments but some may be offered by engineering or business studies departments. Such courses are offered under a variety of titles including computer engineering, computer science, computer studies, computing, data processing, information systems, information technology, software engineering and systems analysis. In some cases the title of the course will reflect the nature and emphasis of the course, but not always. All the courses will involve a study of the fundamental IT topics of telecommunications, computer systems hardware and software, programming and systems analysis and design. However some may have a greater emphasis on hardware and electronics (eg computer engineering and information technology courses), some on software and programming (eg software engineering, computer science and computing courses) and some on systems analysis and design and business applications (eg data processing, information systems and systems analysis). Courses may contain other supporting topics, such as mathematics, statistics, electronics, business applications, industrial applications or human behaviour and communications. There are also business studies courses with a major component of IT, aimed at producing graduates with the IT skills needed in modern business. Before applying for a course, look closely at the course description to ensure the nature and emphasis of the course matches your likes and aspirations.

IT is a vocational subject and hence very practically-based. Many courses, particularly those in polytechnics and colleges of higher education are 4 year sandwich courses, the third year being spent in industry practising and enhancing the skills already learnt. A large proportion of your time will be spent in practical assignments such as: programming a microprocessor in assembler language; programming a robot; building an electronic circuit; interfacing a device to a microcomputer; programming a computer using a third or fourth generation programming language; interviewing staff who are role-playing users in order to determine the requirements of a proposed computer-based application system; specifying and designing a new computer-based application system using software aids. The practical nature of the course will usually culminate with a major individual project in the final year of the course.

Students who have successfully studied computing are at an advantage both in terms of obtaining a place and in their first year studies although it is not normally a prerequisite for entry. Many courses do not specify named subjects in their A-level requirements for entry, although a few specify mathematics. At present both the IT industry and undergraduate courses are very male dominated. There are many reasons why this should be so but none of them are to do with IT being only suitable for men. None of the IT skills require male-only qualities. So come on you girls IT can be for you as well as us men!

HELPFUL READING: Jacquetta Megarry, *Inside Information* (BBC, 1985); *About Information Technology* (Hobsons, 1986); Chris Evans, *The Mighty Micro* (Coronet, 1979) – a bit out of date, but a classic! Chris Evans, *The Making of the Micro* (Gollancz, 1981).

Latin American Studies
Dr Simon Collier, Essex University

This study area is unlike most (though not quite all) the others discussed for your benefit in this guide. The big difference is that it isn't a **subject** in its own right so much as a number of subjects focused on a specific **region** of the world. Why study this particular region at all? You may well ask. Latin America (by which we usually mean the twenty republics of Central and South America) is not an area which is as well known as it might be in this country. If you follow the serious newspapers regularly, you see remarkably little reporting on events in Latin America. Only lurid and dramatic happenings get anywhere near the British headlines – the revolution in Nicaragua, the civil war in El Salvador, or the short, sharp war between Britain and Argentina over the Falkland Islands in 1982 (**that** did get into the headlines, of course, and the background reports on that occasion may have taught people quite a lot about modern Argentina). In some ways, this normal absence of news from the region is rather surprising. The relationship between the UK and Latin America used to be very much stronger than it is today. If anything, it seems at present to be getting weaker. British trade with the region continues to decline, although the last twenty years have seen a definite growth in Latin American Studies as an academic activity.

The chances are, therefore, that you have a fairly good reason for considering this study area at all. It may be that your family has had some sort of connection with one of the Latin American countries, or even that you yourself spent part of your childhood there and would like to return some day. It is possible that a particular Latin American theme has somehow taken your fancy – the ancient civilisations of the Aztecs and Incas, perhaps, or the work of the great Mexican mural-painters, or the glamorous and tragic story of Evita Peron, or the background to the

Falklands conflict. It may just be that you are in an adventurous mood and are tempted to try something 'different' in the way of a first degree. It is a good temptation, but be careful. Sad though it is to have to say this, the number of possible careers directly connected with Latin America is strictly limited. So perhaps the best piece of advice that can be offered is, simply, that you should think long and hard before considering Latin American studies as a first degree.

But let us suppose that you have thought about it a bit, and want to take matters further. What kinds of things are involved in the study of Latin America? Certain subjects are unavoidable, and the first which must always be mentioned is language. Eighteen of the twenty Latin American republics speak Spanish, while Brazil, the largest country of the region, speaks Portuguese. (The tiny republic of Haiti, in the Caribbean, is French-speaking.) Mastery of Spanish or Portuguese (and if possible both) is quite essential for this study area. You should not be unduly deterred. They are not, for English-speakers, the most difficult languages in the world by a long chalk.

For most people, language is not an end in itself. It simply provides an instrument for communication and for further learning. The basic aim of Latin American studies is (indeed, must be) to enable you to build up a well-rounded and comprehensive picture of the region. There are several key subjects which can be called into play. Geography, for instance, can explain a great deal about the physical environment in which Latin Americans live and the ways in which this has helped or hindered their economic growth. Sociology, too, can probe some of the pressing dilemmas of the present day: the population explosion, over-rapid urbanisation, acute social stratification, and the extreme poverty which is still such a depressing feature of most of the Latin American countries. Politics and government, likewise, can shed light on some of the recurrent modes of political behaviour in the area, not least the tenacious phenomenon of militarism – the tendency to military dictatorship, sometimes very harsh, which was such a prominent feature in the 1970s, though the tide turned back towards democracy in the 1980s. The study of Latin American culture must also be included in the broad picture. The international impact of certain writers from the region has been outstanding in recent decades. The great Chilean poet Pablo Neruda, and that strangely compelling Argentine genius, Jorge Luis Borges, have perhaps been the best-known figures of recent years, but a very impressive younger generation of novelists – Julio Cortazar (Argentina), Carlos Fuentes (Mexico), Mario Vargas Llosa (Peru), Isabel Allende (Chile), and Gabriel Garcia Marquez (Colombia), to name only five – has also staked a decisive claim to world attention.

Behind all these subjects there looms history, without which none of the others really falls into perspective. For those who study it, history is fascinating in itself, but from the angle of this study area it has the merit of helping to explain how things got to be the way they are. Latin America is often described, perhaps rather misleadingly, as part of the so-called Third World. If it is, it is easily the most developed part. But by the standards of

Western Europe or the USA, Latin America remains a region of enormous problems, a region where 'development' remains the supreme imperative of modern times. Mass poverty of a kind no longer visible in Europe is still an all too normal feature of Latin American life. What keys does the past provide for understanding Latin American underdevelopment? The nature of Spanish and Portuguese colonisation in the sixteenth century? The extremely lop-sided distribution of land in colonial times? The inability of the landowning elites, after independence, to 'modernise' the republics they now ruled? The influence of foreign economic interests – first British and later on American? All these question marks represent highly important historical debates, which are closely tied in, of course, with the kinds of issues examined by sociologists, economists and political scientists for the contemporary period.

Some of Latin America's dilemmas seem peculiarly her own; others look familiar enough from the viewpoint of Africa and Asia, too. The value of Latin American studies lies not in providing final or definite answers to the modern problems of the region, but in helping you to become very much better informed and more sensitive about the nature of the problems themselves. The opportunity to deepen your acquaintance with a richly colourful part of the world – exotic and puzzling, stimulating and depressing – is one which is well worth taking, providing that you really **want** to take it. Otherwise not. But if you are really keen, you probably will not regret it.

HELPFUL READING: Simon Collier, Harold Blakemore and Thomas E Skidmore, eds, *The Cambridge Encyclopedia of Latin America and the Caribbean* (Cambridge University Press, 1985); J Franco, *The Modern Culture of Latin America* (London: Pall Mall Press, 1967).

Law
Professor Geoffrey Wilson, Warwick University

One of the problems with law as a subject of University study is that for most people still at school it is one of the great unknowns. Though there are A-level courses in law they give little idea of what a University course ought to be like and, in any event, there are more important subjects to do at school than law.

One of the most common reasons students applying for places give for reading law is that students are thinking of becoming solicitors or barristers. For those who eventually decide to practise as lawyers a law degree does have the practical advantage of providing them with the opportunity of getting exemption from the First Part of the professional examinations as well as giving them a better idea of what might be involved in practice, and laying a foundation of legal knowledge that should stand them in good stead as lawyers in the years to come. One does not have to study law to be a lawyer but three or four years on a law degree does provide the chance of a more thoughtful and grounded introduction to the way the law works than can readily be acquired by practising it. One of the motives of the legal profession in supporting legal education at UCKPUs is that it means they are getting recruits educated for them at someone else's expense; the notion that law studied in an academic environment provides a broader training also no doubt plays a part.

The study of law at UKCPUs has never been recommended entirely on the basis that it provides a good training for future lawyers. Most law schools would agree that the study of law has advantages for students who do not intend to practise, or who thought they might want to and then change their minds, or for those who simply do not know. They would point to the intellectual training involved in the close reading of texts, statutes and the judgments in decided cases, in the isolation of the relevant from the irrelevant and the identification and disposal of the main issues in complex problems and situations, and in the practice of rational argument according to the ground rules of English legal reasoning. They would emphasise too the special characteristics of legal reasoning that it is not simply abstract and academic, not simply logical, but reasoning with a view to reaching a decision; that even though it is conducted in an academic environment and at one remove from the real world, it is dealing with real world problems, real legislation, real cases, real facts, real judgments. It is, in short, reasoning of a practical kind. In this respect law as a degree subject can provide a convenient halfway house between school and the real world, not as academic as A-levels, not as practical as real-world decisions, but somewhere in between. The only hesitation one might have in endorsing this justification for the study of law is that, in the hands of some law teachers, in some law schools, real life situations have given way to hypothetical factual situations used as a means of testing students' understanding of basic legal principles which are so bizarre that an ability to deal with them has a closer analogy to the ability to master the detailed rules of a complicated board game than anything resembling a real life situation. Even this and the jokey names that go with them like Oddball who sets out to sell shoddy goods to Clueless which are eaten by his shaggy dog Wagtail and so on, like crosswords have their avid fans and supporters, but of course the more the emphasis is placed on the bizarre and the cardboard cut-out figures who take part in these turnabouts, the less one can really argue that the study of law is closely related to the study of real life. In this respect, as in others, a glance at a law school's examination papers may sometimes give a clue to the prevailing ethos in it.

To the arguments that law is a suitable subject of study for future lawyers and when done well provides a good general training in rational analysis, discussion and decision, most law schools would probably add the importance of law and the legal profession in the community at large. Here it stands shoulder to shoulder with other subjects which study important aspects of society, such as economics or politics, looking at society from one important perspective, that of the part law plays in it. And along with law, go the legal profession and the machinery of justice, criminal and civil. It does not need much effort to see that individuals, companies and groups cannot avoid the impact of law and lawyers which extends into family life, labour relations, the organisation of companies, commercial and business relationships, taxation, social security, the environment, consumer questions, the business of buying, selling and renting houses, and all the millions of contacts between them and public authorities of one kind or another. In other words the study of law is as important as the law itself.

For the most part English law schools concentrate on English law and the English legal system. But over the years there has been a growing interest in what goes on outside the United Kingdom as well. Courses in international law have long been common. To these have been added an increasing number of courses on foreign legal systems, in particular the European, such as France and Germany, and the European Economic Community generally. One law school has even experimented with a course in Japanese law. The growing interest in foreign legal systems has been accompanied by the creation of formal links between UK law schools and law departments in foreign universities and the introduction of special degree courses which include a year abroad. These developments not only provide new opportunities for students, they may also break down some of the more parochial concerns that have been the hallmark of legal education since it was established in England in the nineteenth century.

Of course law schools vary in their strengths and weaknesses. Different schools emphasise different aspects of legal study and, as with other subjects, one needs to follow up a general interest in the prospect of studying law with a closer look at what each has to offer. Equally important to what is offered is the spirit of the place and here one is pretty well bound to be dependent on rumour and reputation, but even a day's visit may help and this goes for the question of studying law itself. Although there is a lot of law around for those still at school, it is largely invisible, but although it is invisible it is not inaccessible. All courts are open to the public. Many solicitors' firms welcome inquiries and some even offer opportunities for part time work. Visits of this kind can help to give some idea at least of the atmosphere in which the professional lawyer works.

As to the kind of person who is likely both to enjoy and do well at law that is more difficult. Law is a discipline: the reasoning is logical, rational and disciplined. It often has quite restricted views as to what is relevant in a particular situation which might not correspond to every man's scope, for imagination it is limited. It can appear pedantic, painstaking and inhibiting, but for those attracted by the prospect of pragmatic, concise and concrete argument about, not the whole world and its problems, but at least a part of it (or the whole of it but seen from a relatively limited perspective) it deserves very serious consideration, especially for those who look upon a degree course as the opportunity for a new start.

HELPFUL READING: *Report of the Ormrod Committee on Legal Education* (Cmnd 4995 London HMSO 1971); Sir Leslie Scarman, *New Dimensions of English Law* (London: Stevens, 1975); Glanville & Williams, *Learning the Law* (London: Stevens, 1978).

Library and Information Studies
Dr Margaret Evans, Loughborough University

What do courses in library and information studies offer students today? First, they provide a sound professional education that enables students to take up posts in the wide range of information careers now available. Information professionals are eagerly sought by all kinds of organisations, including libraries and information services, in both the public and private sectors, as well as all those organisations developing the management of their information resources, in such wide-ranging fields as marketing, charity and welfare, education or commerce. The market for information professionals is expanding rapidly, as the significance of information increases in our society, and the young information worker can anticipate a challenging and varied career. Inevitably therefore, as courses are vocationally oriented to a greater or lesser extent, you will learn a variety of skills as a preparation for an information-related career.

Some of these skills might surprise you. In the past, there was a great deal of emphasis on 'cataloguing and classification' in courses, as a means of organising knowledge for the library user. Professional librarians spent a great deal of their time in preparing material for use. Today there is rather less of this traditional 'cat and class' in degree programmes, as a result of the impact of computerisation on the organisation of information, which has freed librarians and information professionals for more creative professional work. You are as likely now to study the design of expert systems that help the information manager in accessing information as you are to learn about classifying books using a variety of classification schemes. The emphasis in most courses today is on the exciting developments in information management, made possible by the increasing sophistication of technology. This means that 'computer literacy' is essential for students: keyboard skills are developed in students from the very beginning of courses. However, most students coming into departments of library and information studies have either little or no previous computer experience and this is recognised in the teaching methods. Computer programming as such does not usually figure much, although for those who wish to specialise in this there is often the opportunity to do so.

Knowing how to organise information is one of the key skills expected by employers, but equally important is knowing how to manage that information in the context of a library or information service. The kinds of management skills developed in students are therefore very similar to those you would find on a business studies course. All libraries today are in the business of information provision, and even public libraries have to ensure they provide the kind of service expected by a demanding client group – the ratepayers. Many libraries or information services are also engaged in selling their services: university and polytechnic libraries, for example, are being encouraged to market their business information services to local industries. Information professionals therefore need to know what users want, be able to design services to meet those needs, and to monitor the quality of services and promote them to their potential users. Courses include a considerable element on the basic management skills needed to achieve this: resource management, managing people and marketing. Teaching methods often include the use of case study materials to emphasise the practical application of theories to the work situation in a variety of settings.

Inevitably, information professionals will spend a great deal of their time in communicating – to users, to other information services through the extensive national and international information networks, and also to information providers such as publishers or database producers. It is therefore essential to communicate effectively, whether verbally or in writing. There will usually be an element in courses that develops these skills and helps students to feel confident in their interactions with users and other information professionals. Report writing and abstracting, and presenting skills, feature considerably, often as an adjunct to other areas of study; as do foreign languages and, for those looking to 1992 and the single European market for their career development, it makes considerable sense to take advantage of this aspect of a degree programme.

So far I have concentrated on the development of the various necessary skills, which can of course be transferable across a range of information-related careers (one of the many advantages of a degree course in library and information studies). There are as well huge areas of knowledge that you will gain. The history of knowledge and of information transfer is intrinsically fascinating and you will be introduced to the honourable contribution made to our culture by authors, publishers, libraries and other learned institutions. In addition to the 'core' areas of study, such as organising information, and managing libraries and information services, there is also a range of optional elements for specialist study that caters for students' particular subject and career interests. This includes subjects as varied as health and welfare information management, publishing, archives administration and records management, children's and school librarianship.

Added to the areas of knowledge that make up the library and information studies curriculum most courses offer either another 'minor' subject or will comprise one half of a joint honours degree programme; so you can add subjects such as English, geography, a modern European language, social science or computing to your repertoire. However, even in a single honours course, the range of study areas is both so broad and deep that most students find themselves intellectually fully stretched by their course!

Contacts between the real world of information provision and departments of library and information studies add considerably to the content of courses: these contacts can take many forms. Students are encouraged to take up work placements during the long vacations; to take a sandwich year out either in the UK or in institutions overseas; and to undertake project work in libraries and information services as part of their course assessment. Visiting information professionals also give lectures and take seminars.

Courses in library and information studies are stimulating and rewarding, both intellectually and vocationally. Graduates in this subject can feel confident that their broadly based liberal education has prepared them for an interesting and varied career.

HELPFUL READING: R C Benge, *Libraries and Cultural Change,* (Bingley, 1979); A Toffler, *The Third Wave,* (Collins, 1980); D J Urquhart, *Principles of Librarianship,* (1981).

Linguistics
Dr Michael Garman, Reading University

First degree courses in linguistics started in this country only in 1964 but they are now already to be found, in a variety of forms, at many UKCPUs. They range from single subject courses, through combined subject courses (often with a modern language), to packages where linguistics sits with a number of components (as in communication-studies courses). This rapid growth (in what is still essentially a non-school subject) has led to a situation in which it will pay you well to select your course with some care (more of this later). But first we must look at the general area that any course would be expected to cover.

One obvious goal for students of language is acquiring fluent control of particular languages (often for practical reasons); another, perhaps less immediately obvious, is to understand language as such. Linguistics is more directly concerned with the second of these goals although it is impossible and undesirable to separate them entirely. As such, it is really a continuation of work that was begun by grammarians in the ancient world, as a branch of the study of man. But the methods and scope of the modern subject set it apart from the earlier traditions of language study. So when, and in what ways, did modern linguistics begin?

In one sense, towards the end of the eighteenth century: in 1786, Sir William Jones observed that Sanskrit, the ancient classical language of the Indian subcontinent, was 'possessed of a stronger affinity' with the European classical languages, Greek and Latin, 'both in the roots of the verbs and in the forms of grammar, than could possibly have been produced by accident'. For language scholars in Europe and elsewhere there was a unified research enterprise here, in uncovering the historical facts of this non-accident; the task, which filled the following century, was to place historical linguistic relationships on a scientific basis, so that languages could be placed within 'families', and, where necessary, long-extinct linguistic forms could be reconstructed in a convincing way. This formative period, of comparative philology, saw the development of techniques of linguistic analysis which transformed the study of language and laid the basis of modern linguistics.

But in another sense it is the work of Ferdinand de Saussure, a Swiss-French comparative philologist, which marks the beginning of the modern subject, around the turn of this century. He recognised the limitations of a purely **historical** approach, based largely on **written** forms of languages, and dealing mainly with development of **individual words or sounds**. In the 'structuralist' tradition that de Saussure inspired, the **whole language system** was the object of description, the system as it exists **at a particular point of time** (like the analysis of the pattern on the chess-board halfway through the game), and earlier emphasis on just the written forms of language was counteracted. This tradition saw the systematic description of thousands of previously unknown, or inadequately known, languages, most of them having no script, many imperilled by the advance of civilisation, scattered over North and South America, Africa below the Sahara, SE Asia and elsewhere. It was during this period, above all, that the main components of language structure and their associated fields of study became established in a recognisably modern form: **phonetics**, the study of speech, its acoustic properties and the neurophysiological basis of its production and perception; **phonology**, the study of the sound systems of particular languages; **morphology** and **syntax**, dealing with the grammatical elements (stems, affixes) of a language and the ways in which they combine to form words, phrases and sentences; and **semantics**, the study of meaning in language.

For most of us, though, there is another part to the answer. Our concern now, starting mainly with the work of Noam Chomsky in the late 1950s, is to go beyond the limits of a particular corpus of data, and to try to describe, not so much the data as the human reality which underlies it. We are as concerned with the next, unuttered, sentence, as with the one just recorded. And we have learned to build models of the language ability which we are trying to understand: while they are, as yet, only partially successful, these models have already taught us a good deal about what it means to **explain** (rather than **describe**) the nature of language. Furthermore, a particular feature of modern linguistics in this sense is the development of specialist research areas, many of which allow for the practical application of theoretical models. To mention some of the more important: **sociolinguistics** examines the nature of social and regional variation in language; **psycholinguistics** looks at the ways in which language abilities are developed and maintained in the individual, and the study of language development in young children has seen particularly vigorous activity in recent years; **second language learning** is another field in which psychological and linguistic factors have to be handled together, and where a great deal of research is currently going on; **language pathology**, the study of language disorders, is currently attracting the attention of an increasing number of linguists (and specialist degree courses have recently been established in this field at certain UKCPUs; and **computational linguistics** is now making significant advances in the modelling of natural language performance, and the development of expert systems for automatic and flexible production and perception of speech by machine.

So, if you do decide on linguistics, you will be entering a world where great advances have been made, many of them quite recently, where practical applications are opening up, and where rapid developments are still taking place. The intellectual excitements are many, and career prospects are generally good, but there are reasons for you to be careful in your course selection: first, check whether the subject will be presented as complete and entire in itself (in a sense, it **is**, but the danger is that you may end up doing entirely theoretical linguistics with not much chance of deepening your knowledge of some language); secondly, try to find out if the course you are considering is dominated by one particular school of thought (in which case things may be presented in a very coherent fashion, but you will not easily discover the advantages of other approaches in a subject where it is far too easy to recognise just one golden path); above all, beware of the course which makes linguistics easy by leaving out the hard bits and putting in their place an assorted collection of attractive, but unfounded, speculations. After two millennia of language study we are getting close to some fascinating and difficult issues concerning an incredibly complex human ability: this is not the time to have your head filled with trivia!

HELPFUL READING: D Crystal, *What is Linguistics?* 3rd edn (London: Arnold, 1974); F Palmer, *Grammar* (Harmondsworth: Penguin, 1983); P Trudgill, *Sociolinguistics* (Harmondsworth: Penguin, 1983); J D O'Connor, *Phonetics* (Harmondsworth: Penguin, 1974); J Lyons, *Language and Linguistics* (Cambridge: CUP, 1981).

Marine Technology
Professor J B Caldwell, Newcastle University

This study area is about the sea, and mainly about designing and building things that go to sea. Ships, of course, but other things too; from boats and barges to the large structures and systems which will be needed as mankind looks increasingly to the sea for a multitude of purposes. The oceans have been described as our last resource, and the exploring, and harvesting, and preserving of this resource will pose some fascinating challenges to the marine technologist of the future.

His work is a reflection of, and a response to, our need to use the sea. Throughout history the principal uses have been firstly to move people and goods and weapons around the globe, and secondly to harvest some of the many varieties of food which exist in the sea. The centre-piece of these activities is the ship in its multifarious forms, sizes and functions. Through many centuries the art of creating ships evolved by trial and error and experience, but with the Industrial Revolution came the need to design and build ships in new materials with new forms of propulsion, without the benefit of prior experience. And so there emerged the profession of naval architecture, signalled formally by the founding of the Institution of Naval Architects more than 125 years ago. Since then the main task of the naval architect has been the designing and building of all kinds of ships and craft for both civil and military uses, from ferries to frigates, tankers and trawlers, icebreakers and hydrofoils, containerships to cruisers.

Nor should we overlook the part played by naval architects in the growing business of leisure activities at sea, whether on luxury cruise ships, or just messing about in boats. The design of both types of vessel depends on the same basic principles of naval architecture. And indeed it is through pleasure sailing in their young days that many boys (and some girls, too) have their interest aroused in ships and the sea, and take their first steps towards a career in naval architecture.

The naval architect is a special kind of engineer. Sea-going craft and structures are mobile communities with a job to do. They must be safe, habitable, efficient, economical both to build and to operate. They must as far as possible combine this 'fitness for purpose' with attractive appearance – there is still scope, thank goodness, for the naval architect to exercise his art as well as his science. His particular art is synthesis, the blending together of the often conflicting requirements of shipowner, shipbuilder, safety and legislative authorities, and seafarer. Within his field of work a variety of specialist skills has grown up (eg in structures, hydrodynamics, propeller design, computer applications) and most naval architects develop one or more of these specialisms alongside their general overview of design. But because the use of the sea is influenced by so many things – political, economic, social, legal, as well as by continuous development in science and technology – the naval architect, as the creator of the vehicles and systems, must have a wide-ranging and forward-looking view of life. In an age of increasing specialisation he must remain a determined and highly professional generalist.

Alongside the naval architect there has grown a very closely related profession, that of marine engineering. The marine engineer – and this is where the definitions can get a little confusing – can have two fairly distinct roles. One is as an operator of the machinery and systems on board ship; the other, which is the real counterpart of the naval architect, is as the designer and builder of this equipment. Again, variety is a feature of his work; ships can be propelled by steam turbines, gas turbines, slow- or medium-speed diesel engines and electric motors, and many combinations of these are possible. The basic source of energy to push a ship along has changed through the centuries from wind, muscle-power, coal, oil and other special chemical fuels to nuclear fission. It is one of the fascinations typical of marine technology that the days of wind propulsion, or of coal used in new forms, may come again if technological developments and relative fuel costs make them feasible and economic. So just as the naval architect needs to take a broad informed view of the way in which progress in science and technology can contribute, so also must the marine engineer seek to harness his skills and knowledge of mechanical, electrical and control engineering, dynamics, noise, vibrations and the like, to the special needs of the marine environment. It is one thing to design and install a land-based power system, quite another to ensure that a 20,000 kW marine diesel engine, with its many associated auxiliaries, will continue to work reliably for perhaps twenty years despite violent motions of the ship, extremes of temperature, a highly corrosive environment and crews who increasingly are sensitive to noise or vibration.

Marine engineers and naval architects work closely together, and the professional education and training which they receive reflects their common interest in engineering for the sea. Mathematics and science – especially physics - provide the basis for degree-level education, not as ends in themselves, but for their usefulness when applied to solving the problems confronting the marine technologist. In most degree courses the general plan of study is similar. A foundation year of engineering science, mathematics, computing and some introductory work in marine technology is followed by an increasing emphasis through the second and third years on 'professional' studies. In the final year there may be a wide choice of specialised marine topics, and the student can begin to look forward to various career possibilities in choosing subjects for advanced study. Employment opportunities are many and varied, because all phases of the creative process – research, development, design, approval, production, commissioning, operation, trouble-shooting, education, training – require skilled professionals. And, as argued above, the scope of the work of the naval architect and marine engineer seems certain to increase.

Onto this widening tapestry of marine activity has recently appeared a third component – ocean engineering. As yet it is not as clearly defined as a profession as marine engineering and naval architecture, but ocean, or offshore, engineering is being used as a term to embrace a whole complex of engineering activities ranging from sea-bed technology (placing foundations for ocean structures, or pipes or cables) through underwater engineering (problems of submersible design, communication, visibility, life-support, safety etc), up to engineering on the surface (mothering craft, production platforms, artificial islands, protective structures, wave-energy devices etc). Of course many of the problems encountered in offshore engineering centre on the age-old difficulties of coping with the sea. So it is not surprising that naval architects and marine engineers – often working together with civil, mechanical, electrical, medical, electronic or other engineers – are finding new scope for their particular talents and interests.

What's in a name? If we use the term marine technology to embrace these three activities – naval architecture, marine engineering and ocean engineering – if nothing else perhaps it serves to underline the essential community of interests between these disciplines. Technology itself, like money, is neutral; it is the use we make of it which is good or bad, and which can sometimes excite the proper opposition of the environmentalist. But civilised use of the sea is essential to the future of mankind. It is to this end that the marine technologist must direct his professional skills and his social responsibilities.

HELPFUL READING: *A Career as a Naval Architect* (London: Royal Institution of Naval Architects, 1987); *Careers in the Marine Engineering Profession* (London: Institute of Marine Engineers, 1986); *Education and Careers in Marine Science and Technology* (London: Society for Underwater Technology, 1987); Tony Loftus, *The Last Resource: Man's Exploitation of the Oceans* (London: Penguin Harmondsworth, 1972); *Ships and Shipping of Tomorrow* (MacGregor Publications, 1983).

Maritime Studies
Alston Kennerley, South West Poly

With the waters of the World occupying some 70% of its surface area and the gradual decline in resources found on land, it was only to be expected that man's attention would increasingly be directed towards the exploitation of the sea's resources. The growth of marine related activity over recent decades provides evidence enough for this, and it seems certain that the scale of man's involvement with the seas will continue to grow.

Maritime Studies (or Marine Studies or Nautical Studies) is concerned with man's activity on and under the surface of the sea; and, of necessity, with the interface between the land and the sea, the coastline and ports. The nature of this activity may be expressed in general terms according to the uses man makes of the sea: for transportation, for exploitation of its living resources (sea food), or its non-living resources (energy and minerals), for recreation and for military purposes. None of these are new uses, but what is new is the extent to which they have been developed, and the global scale of activity and interest. Each of these uses has scientific, technological, commercial, legal and social aspects, and it will be appreciated that in fact most traditional areas of study have a maritime dimension. Courses in Maritime Studies are designed to provide a marine emphasis and to embrace and integrate traditional areas of study.

Most established undergraduate courses in Maritime Studies have been built around the transportation use, with the ship as a focus. This alone provides quite a diversity of subjects which are important to all uses and provide a basis for career opportunities in most areas of marine activity.

Recently developed courses embrace an even fuller range of marine subjects, and by adopting a modular structure, permit prospective students to devise their own programme of studies, and move the emphasis of study from the transportation use to one of the other uses suggested above.

The sea is a much more demanding environment than the land and Maritime Studies courses always provide opportunity for the study of the natural environment in which ships and marine structures must operate. Meteorology is of course concerned with the study of weather patterns, in this case in the marine context, with a view to predicting changes. Oceanography takes in every aspect of the oceans of the world but is particularly concerned with the nature of the waters, the currents and tides. Hydrography deals with the science of marine surveying, the process by which information about the sea bed is created. It includes marine cartography, the mapping of this information for use by mariners and others.

Hydrographic charts are an essential tool for marine navigation, the subject concerned with the safe movement of ships across the seas. This is much more than the proper use of hydrographic information. Positioning, using the wide range of radio aids to navigation, is important as are navigation management and communication, while also taking account of the natural environment, the ship and its cargo, and the density of shipping particularly in areas such as the Straits of Dover.

The traditional name given to the design of ships, naval architecture, demonstrates its links with the design of engineering structures, including for example those for offshore oil and gas extraction, with which it shares many principles. It is also concerned with the behaviour of marine vehicles in the sea, especially stability, and is closely related to shipbuilding. The study of the propulsion of ships, marine engineering, includes auxiliary machinery for ships' domestic services and deck machinery such as winches.

The handling and stowage of cargoes has both technological and scientific aspects, and is also a key element in the commercial success of shipping. Maritime business or sea transport is concerned with the commercial side of shipping including finance, management and operation and has related studies in marine insurance, marine law and port operations.

Some courses may include other aspects of man's use of the seas. Fisheries Studies will include: marine biology, especially the behaviour of fish; fishing technology concerned with the design and use of fishing gear; marine acoustics, in the context of modern fish hunting; fish farming, fish processing, and fisheries economics, including marketing, management and the legal regime. Forthcoming developments in maritime studies include programmes in marine resources, concerned with mineral and biological resources, pollution and resource management and marine recreation, increasingly important for careers.

From the foregoing it will be clear that courses in maritime or marine studies are very much applied studies and closely related to the modern uses that man makes of the seas. The subjects can be combined to suit those who have backgrounds in the sciences or in social studies.

HELPFUL READING: To explore the content of Maritime Studies a little further start with one of the few books providing something of an overview. Perhaps the best is *The Times Atlas of the Oceans*, edited by A D Couper, Times Books, 1983, which has short articles on most of the subject areas indicated and provides suggestions for further reading. Also useful is *The Oxford Companion to Ships and the Sea*, edited by Peter Kemp, OUP, 1976. *The Commanding Sea*, edited by Clare Francis and Warren Tute, BBC and Pelham Books, 1981, has a more relaxed style and is well illustrated.

Mathematical Studies
R Daniel Hirsch, City of London Polytechnic

We all notice and are curious about the world and we all have the intelligence to understand and satisfy an increasing part of that curiosity. Indeed we see patterns and study them. For example, we see that three boys and four boys together form a group of seven boys, and that *therefore* three girls and four girls together form a group of seven girls. This we do at an early age, and we develop this ability quite naturally. We seek out patterns. And then we go further and ask if there are new properties that we may use to our advantage.

Mathematical study simply formalises this natural progress. It can lead to very practical and useful results such as applications of the calculus – marginal revenue for the accountant, velocity for the physicist – or matrix techniques, frequently employed in advanced statistics. It can also lead to further theoretical results, that is to say statements that are not immediately obvious and perhaps not immediately applicable – the work of logicians and algebraists of the last hundred years, culminating in the building of the computer, is an excellent example.

The investment of our time, energy and intellect in this advanced study yields great pleasure and proof of human achievement. It is available to all and most communities seek out and reward us for such progress.

Undergraduate work in mathematics, whether for application or theory, can be divided roughly into two categories, the analytic and the algebraic. The analytic approach consists of being given a particular system, for example the real numbers, and then cutting up or analysing its properties. Thus we may be led to fine (unexpected) details about the number system we use, so commonly; to differential equations that describe the physical, economic or social changes in the world; to study of optimising techniques etc. The algebraic approach consists of being given a particular structure and then examining what common properties are shared by all systems with that same structure – for example, your right hand gives a faithful copy of your left hand and the number 5 is associated with any other faithful copy. This structural approach leads to algebra, logic, computer science etc.

It is usual and clearly sensible to start off with a programme of study that includes all these elements in the first year. Thereafter we go our various ways and (usually) devote more of our time to that area of work that is most fun and where we feel we are going to make most progress. This can vary from finding out why you cannot trisect an angle, examining the foundations of geometry, to 'building' wind tunnels, constructing a transportation matrix, developing techniques of numerical analysis and generally to almost any mathematics that has stood up to the test of experience. It is not always easy but equally it is not always difficult. It is always fascinating whether you are 'good at maths' or not, for much of this depends on your natural ability and perception. You can start with sorting out a football coupon, go on to counting the number of people shaking hands at a party, and finish with a model of some hydrocarbon molecules. All you need is what you already have – human curiosity and intellect to satisfy it.

Enjoy it!

Mechanical and Production Engineering
Emeritus Professor M W Thring,
Queen Mary and Westfield College, London

Mechanical and Production Engineering are the very foundation of our industrial civilisation, providing the machines and the power to drive them that enable one man's work to achieve more than ten men could do unaided. The industrial revolution, in which Britain led the way for the first hundred years, was entirely dependent on the work of inventive engineers. It could have taken place with a different economic, religious or political system, but the development of steam engines and machine tools were essential. It is also true that steam and hot air engines were developed by engineers decades before scientists formulated the first and second laws of thermodynamics.

So far the industrial revolution has enabled the people who were replaced by machines in one industry to be employed in a new one which is a part of the rising standard of living. However, like all exponential growth, this growth of standard of living, and the use of fossil fuels and mineral ores on which it is based, must level off. Other factors limiting the rise in wealth of the developed peoples are space limitations, consumer resistance to new gadgets, and the fact that the undeveloped countries desperately need some share of the limited resources of the earth. The use of energy per capita in the poor areas is less than one-tenth of that in the rich areas.

The world's economic system is creaking badly, with rising unemployment in both rich and poor countries, loans on which even the interest is unpaid, and millions of humans starving while vast sums of money are spent every year on weapons, nuclear power, giant dams that make electricity no one can afford to buy and upset the environment irreversibly, supersonic flight and the space race. Failures, disastrous to humans, occur every year because man has used engineering for short sighted purposes instead of looking to the future.

Thus mechanical and production engineers have a vital role to play in solving the problem of giving mankind a stable world in the 21st century. They can be in the forefront of developing the machines that will solve the following problems: to enable all adults in the world to have the opportunity of earning a fully adequate standard of living for themselves and their families using primarily local resources on a permanent basis; to use the limited mineral resources of the world in such a way that as they become exhausted the system can be maintained by recycling of metals and the use of renewable energy sources; to eliminate completely all potentially disastrous large systems and reduce to a very low level all small scale accidents; to reduce chemical pollution of air, land and water to undetectible levels, and not to burden the earth with any unnatural radioactive elements.

The mechanical engineer can play a central role in reducing the consumption of fossil fuels which cause the rise in CO_2 in the atmosphere which in turn is one of the main causes of the 'greenhouse effect'. This consumption can certainly be halved without any real sacrifices. Examples are given below. Similarly the mechanical engineer can develop refrigeration cycles which do not require the use of CFCs which are having such a disastrous effect on the ozone layer.

Of course the inventive engineer cannot solve these problems alone, but he or she must be at the spearhead of the solution because they are the only professionals who can foresee the machines that can be developed to solve them. Other professions constantly make wrong judgments because of their lack of engineering understanding. One example of this is that Britain has not developed the use of CHP (Combined Heat and Power, where boiling water from power stations is used for heating purposes instead of being thrown away) because those who drew up the terms of nationalisation of electricity did not understand the practical implications of the second law of thermodynamics. Another example is the export of tractors and high technology agriculture to the 'Third World'. Only the engineer can envisage the machines necessary to give really appropriate help to their agriculture: a possible machine is a 'mechanical bullock', a cultivator with legs that could be powered by steam from a boiler fired by agricultural refuse.

One of the most important problems of the developed countries is that our high standard of living is based on a steadily rising consumption of energy from fossil fuels (coal, oil and natural gas). The average use in the rich countries is about 6 tons of coal equivalent per head per year (TCE/ c.a). Thirty years ago we all believed that nuclear fission energy would enable us to continue this extravagant use of energy even when fossil fuels were exhausted. Now we know that, because of the high capital cost of power stations and the thermodynamic limitations of generating electricity from heat, we can never hope to have electricity cheap enough to replace fossil fuels for low grade heating or use it for any rail-less transport. Moreover we have a much greater experience of the hazards of radioactive materials that are a necessary consequence of nuclear fission power generation.

The mechanical engineer has therefore to develop machines to achieve the following:

(1) enable us to use far less fossil fuel without losing any of the really valuable results of the industrial revolution. I have calculated that this could be done using only 1 TCE/c.a. in the developed countries with cold winters, while in the undeveloped countries about ½ TCE/c.a. could bring them the most important benefits if the engineers really put their minds to it. The machines for these purposes have already been invented but need appropriate development. Examples are a diesel/electric parallel/hybrid car engine that could give over 100 mpg; aeroplanes using half as much fuel per passenger mile as present-day jets; a coal fired steam loco giving smokeless combustion and as good efficiency and performance as a diesel loco. There is very much more coal in the world than oil and gas.

(2) enable people to avoid all hazardous situations in their work. We can develop 'Telechirs' (hands at a distance) so that all work down mines, undersea, in radioactive or explosive situations or in fires can be done with full manual skill and visual and tactile feedback by people sitting in comfortable control cabins in a safe place. This would have the further advantage of increasing many-fold the amounts of coal and oil available to us.

(3) enable us to relieve intelligent humans of totally boring and repetitive jobs. First generation robots are already being used for paint spraying, spot welding, feeding all kinds of machines on repetitive operations such as stamping, die casting, plastic moulding and lathes, and for grinding and

inspection. Some simple assembly is being done, but we are a long way short of the human skill on this even when we use second generation robots with sensory adaptiveness. Second generation robots will certainly enable humans to avoid the more repetitive tasks, but the need to make long lasting consumer goods to save raw materials and fuel will reduce the number of identical objects being made and there must be a return to individual craftsmanship and personal responsibility to provide worthwhile jobs for all.

Every attempt to look into the future shows that we cannot have a peaceful, stable world in which one-third of the world's population uses over 80% of the energy and other limited resources while the remaining two-thirds has an ever falling standard of living as forests are cut down, deserts grow, soil blows away and even wood fuel for cooking vanishes. The mechanical engineer can provide the spearhead of the advance to solve these problems. Energy for electric lighting, water pumping, wood sawing and agriculture can be provided by windmills, solar concentrators, burning agricultural refuse and small hydropowered generators. In the case of solar or refuse heated boilers the steam can be condensed at 100°C and the boiling water used for cooking, thus saving the direct use of wood or charcoal. Leaf fractionation presses can act as 'mechanical cows' and produce 'grass milk' from any locally grown green leaves.

The use of high quality engineering design and invention to solve these problems, vital to the survival of humanity, can be just as exciting as the design of high technology gadgets or weapons and infinitely more satisfying to the conscience.

I hope that this survey of the problems that can be solved by mechanical and production engineers of the next generation shows that these subjects, far from being 'old hat', are the ones that would make the key contribution in the transition to a stable world in which man lives in peaceful equilibrium with his surroundings. 'Where there's a will there's a way.'

HELPFUL READING: M W Thring (1) *The Engineer's Conscience* (Northgate: MEP 1980); (2) *Robots and Telechirs* (Ellis Horwood 1983).

Medicine
Dr David Sturgeon
University College and Middlesex School of Medicine

The most important aspect of studying medicine is the enormous range of possible careers to which it can lead – from transplant surgeon to medical journalist, from general practitioner to research scientist.

You should realise that being a medical student is just the first step on a long road of learning, which continues after qualification, whether it be a three year general practice vocational training course, or the ladder of hospital specialist training. For a good overview of both the course structure, and career prospects, see the recommended reading.

The first two years, the pre-clinical course, are like an extension of

A-levels, and certainly no more intellectually demanding. This does not mean that the subject matter is not different – it is. You will follow courses in biochemistry, physiology, histology, cell biology as well as medical sociology and psychology. But the intellectual difficulty to passing exams in these subjects is no greater than at A-level.

You should not worry about exactly which subjects you have studied at A-level. The pre-clinical biological science subjects build only very indirectly on A-level knowledge. Very many students have not studied A-level biology, and indeed the minimum requirement at London University is that a student should have A-level chemistry, mathematics and physics at GCSE level. Arts A-levels are, and should be, no bar to medical school entry.

There is one other important aspect of pre-clinical studies. There is a definite tension between the declared aim of providing a basis of scientific knowledge on which the clinical teaching can stand, and the interests of the pre-clinical teachers, in teaching their subjects as 'pure science' entities in themselves. As well as medical students, they will be teaching those studying for a three year degree in the same subject, often in the same lectures. Thus biochemistry is often taught for the sake of biochemistry 'per se', rather than with a specific clinical medical relevance.

In some courses (eg London) the bias is towards 'pure science', in others (eg Nottingham) greater efforts are made to integrate the pre-clinical and clinical courses, making pre-clinical studies more practically relevant.

The pre-clinical course can be a daunting time for many students, with intensive lectures and examinations, while at the same time there is little or no contact with patients. Some students, nonetheless, glimpse the fascination of the biology of human existence through the morass of facts. However, in many medical schools, this period also brings the opportunity to spend an optional third year (automatic at Oxbridge), studying one subject in greater depth, be it biochemistry or the history of medicine.

The three year clinical course is an introduction to the hospital specialities and brings you into contact with patients. Suddenly students must wear shirts and ties. A white coat and a stethoscope give the appearance of already being a doctor, a distinction many patients are determined to accord you despite the large badge saying 'medical student'. There are still many facts to be learnt, but now in the context of patients' illnesses. Practical skills must also be acquired – the art of examining patients, the taking of blood and histories. As a teacher, my contact with students is in psychiatry. However, I see the psychological medicine which I try to teach as being integral to the whole of medical practice. Relating to patients is the most challenging, but also the most rewarding part of the clinical course. This challenge is most acute in talking to patients who are having to cope with death and disability, two subjects which are largely taboo in 'everyday' life. It is not at all easy for both doctors and medical students to remain within the confines of these taboos when confronted with 'difficult' situations.

As a medical student, you will be under many pressures – not least to assimilate huge amounts of information – but you will also have to face these 'difficult' situations in all areas of medicine, from surgery to psychiatry. It is important to be aware of patients' feelings in these situations as well as using scientific knowledge to diagnose treatable illnesses and to be aware of the interaction between these feelings and illness. In my own field, I have been involved in studying the effects the emotional atmosphere in the family has on the relapse of patients with schizophrenic illnesses.

My job: To give you some idea of what you might end up doing if you choose psychiatry as a speciality, this is what I do.

I have a number of patients in my care on a ward. I also see patients referred to me as out-patients and also patients on medical, surgical and other wards who have psychiatric or emotional dificulties. It is in these settings that I do most teaching of medical students. One afternoon a week I work in a health centre seeing GP referrals, and another afternoon I see patients with their families. I also find some time to do research and write books – and articles.

HELPFUL READING: Learning Medicine: Peter Richards, BMA, 1990. Living Medicine: Peter Richards, BMA, 1990.

Metallurgy and Materials Science
Vernon John, City University

Every single thing which is made, be it a humble paper clip or a highly complex construction composed of many thousands of components such as an aircraft, is produced from one or more materials. It is of the utmost importance that a good understanding of the science and technology of all materials exists in order that the selected materials are used wisely, effectively and economically. So the role played in industrial society by metallurgists, materials scientists and technologists is crucial and the possession of a degree in one of these study areas can lead to a wide range of career possibilities including research, development, manufacturing, management and marketing in spheres as diverse as microelectronics, aerospace, off-shore engineering and general manufacturing industry.

In the nineteenth century metals emerged as the major materials for engineering construction and metallurgy became an academic discipline (the first professorial chair in metallurgy in Britain was established a little under 100 years ago). Nowadays the spectrum of engineering materials comprises a wide range of metals and alloys, a continually increasing number of polymeric materials, ceramics (including new industrial ceramics) and glasses, stone, concrete, bituminous materials, timbers, and very many composite materials. This led to the creation of degree courses in materials science and technology. The pace of development in both materials and processing techniques is rapid and exciting. Some examples of developments of the last decade include materials for the electronics industry with impurity levels measured in parts per billion; single crystal turbine blades for aero gas turbines; ceramics which may be formed to shape by processes similar to those used for polymer materials; polymers for high temperature service; and high performance composites for aerospace applications.

The subject matter of degree courses in metallurgy and materials science develops from the basic A-level knowledge of physics, chemistry and mathematics but then, in my opinion, these two applied sciences are much more interesting than studies in the natural sciences. When I was an undergraduate I transferred from natural sciences to a degree course in metallurgy for this reason and have never regretted the change.

Now to the question, what is metallurgy and materials science? I will deal first with metallurgy – the study of all aspects of metals, from their extraction from ores through to the efficient utilisation of metals and alloys in engineering hardware. As you can imagine, this is an enormous spectrum of activity and it is convenient to divide it into a number of areas.

Extraction metallurgy is concerned with the production and refining of prime metals from their ores. The metallurgist in this sector is also involved with mineral dressing and the preparation of ore concentrates in a form suitable for successful extraction operations. This part of the subject is orientated towards chemistry, but there is also overlap with geology and mining.

Physical metallurgy, a major branch of the subject, deals with the structure, constitution and properties of metals and alloys. It is firmly based on theoretical physics and includes atomic structure and the crystalline nature of metals. The study expanded enormously after the 1940s and knowledge of the physical factors which affect the properties of materials has been increased beyond measure through the use of all the tools of modern research.

Mechanical metallurgy is a term which describes the study of metalforming, that is the ways in which a metal or alloy can be converted into a useful shape by means of processes such as casting, rolling, forging and machining. There are many aspects to be considered in this field, including the analysis of the forces involved in the processing machinery and equipment, the analysis of the plastic deformation of the materials being processed, the structural and property changes which occur in the metal being shaped, and the advantages and limitations of the various shaping techniques. There is overlap here with mathematics, computing and branches of engineering – notably mechanical and production engineering.

In addition to the areas mentioned above, courses in metallurgy also contain other important topics including failure mechanisms and failure prevention, corrosion, welding technology, test and evaluation methods and selection criteria.

Materials science and/or technology is a broader study area than metallurgy, dealing with the range of materials available to the engineer, metallic and non-metallic. Like the courses in metallurgy, these deal with the structures of materials and the development of properties, the production and fabrication of materials, and behaviour in various engineering service conditions.

To me the most interesting and useful section of the subject area is materials/engineering. In this area basic materials knowledge is integrated with engineering design and manufacturing engineering. As engineering designs and the materials available become more sophisticated, it becomes increasingly important to use materials both effectively and efficiently. The selection of a material to fit a particular engineering requirement and the choice of a manufacturing process are complex problems, and solving them offers a perpetual challenge to the materials engineer and designer.

There are wide differences between many of these courses, some being highly theoretical and mainly containing applied physics, while others are more orientated towards materials engineering. I am of the opinion that many teachers of metallurgy and materials have taken the wrong path in recent years by deleting basic engineering studies in order to make room for larger doses of the more esoteric aspects of metal physics. I can do no better here than to quote from a speech made in 1978 by the then president of the Institution of Metallurgists:

> . . . much of the sophisticated fundamental academic metallurgy included in courses today, though intellectually challenging, is of little use in the practical world of industry and has displaced subject matter which was taught in earlier years and which is practical and of value.

Before selecting a course you need to decide whether to practice as an engineer or to remain fairly firmly within the world of science. Under Engineering Council regulations, only those courses with a substantial engineering content and a balance between theory and applications will be fully accredited as leading to Chartered Engineer status; these accredited courses lead to BEng and MEng. Courses with a greater bias towards science are expected to continue at some colleges; they lead to BSc but will not have Engineering Council accreditation.

Any young person with an aptitude for science subjects could find this study area interesting and stimulating. After completing a course with a technological bias, the young graduate should be able to progress into a career in engineering with wide and varied possibilities and, in common with all other members of the engineering family, will be dealing with people as much as with things.

HELPFUL READING: J E Gordon, *The New Science of Strong Materials, or Why You Don't Fall Through the Floor* (Harmondsworth: Penguin, 1968).

Microbiology
Professor John Postgate, Sussex University

If you study microbiology, you will encounter a fascinating world of invisible, or barely visible, creatures who together encompass all the processes of which terrestrial life is capable.

What does that mean, you ask? Well, although fish and people, for example, live in very different environments, their life processes are really very similar: they breathe oxygen, they eat organic food, they reproduce sexually, they consist of enormous numbers of rather similar cells, they live out their lives and then die. Even plants are really much the same fundamentally, except that they mostly do not eat organic food; instead they use solar energy to make their organic matter from carbon dioxide. What makes microbes so different, then? Be patient – first I must tell you a little about what microbes are.

They are creatures, almost always single cells, which can only be seen satisfactorily through a microscope. A few, such as amoebae and certain sulphur bacteria, are just discernible with the naked eye; most microbes are visible only under a microscope; the viruses are so small that even the most powerful optical microscope is inadequate and scientists have to use the electron microscope to see them. Some microbes are very simple plants – yeast, moulds and certain algae are examples. Others, like the amoeba, are tiny primitive animals. But the majority, the bacteria, are neither plants nor animals; they constitute a different 'Kingdom' of living things, called the Prokaryotes. (Actually, they comprise two such Kingdoms, and no one is quite sure where viruses fit in, but these are details you would learn later.)

Microbes are everywhere: in the air, in soil, in water, on our skin and hair, in our mouths and intestines, on and in the food we eat. They change, often improve, our food; they make us vitamins inside ourselves; they can protect us from undesirable microbes. Yet most people are scarcely aware that they exist and, as 'germs', they have a bad press. Their unpopularity arises for a very simple reason: a few kinds of microbe can actually cause disease, a few can actually spoil food, can actually destroy valuable materials. And these are about the only times most people notice them at all.

In a microbiology course you will naturally learn about microbes in disease, about the bacteria which cause 'old fashioned' illnesses such as tuberculosis, scarlet fever, typhoid and so on, illnesses that have become rare today because of the effectiveness of modern drugs and antibiotics. You will learn how our natural immunity to disease works and how, when it breaks down, we become ill. You will be taught precisely how drugs and antibiotics work to help us recover. You will discover that, though a few awkward bacterial diseases persist, the viruses are today's major problem: infinitesimal fragments of barely living material which can cause illnesses ranging in severity from the common cold to AIDS. And you will learn how the war against such nasties is slowly being won. Smallpox has been eradicated using a combination of hygiene and inoculations; polio is in retreat; modern genetic engineering is providing new ways to attack other virus diseases. And sooner or later you will turn your mind from people and learn of microbes in animals and plant diseases. You will be told of, and see, the ways in which microbes can attack non-living material, corroding concrete and iron pipes, spoiling leather, wood, paper and even glass or plastics; you will learn of the troubles they can cause in oil technology, mining, machining and even film processing, not to mention the part they play in food spoilage and water pollution.

But you will also learn of the good, useful side of microbes. You might at first find mundane and boring their crucially important part in sewage treatment and waste disposal, but persevere; in a pullulating morass of sewage sludge flourishes a fantastic newly-recognised Kingdom of living things called the Archeabacteria – but I do not have space for further enlightenment here. You will be told how microbes, including archeabacteria, clean up our fouled lakes, rivers and beaches, even deal with exotic industrial effluents; how they decompose plant material, corpses and excreta to renew soil fertility. How they make the soil fertile: they add essential nitrogen to soil, help plants to get at phosphate, keep up the supply of sulphur compounds which plants and animals need. How, by recycling the detritus of plants and animals they constantly renew the supplies of oxygen, carbon dioxide, nitrates and even water on which all life on this planet depends. So vital are microbes to the lives of higher organisms that our own nutrition depends on them and some animals – sheep, cows and termites, for example – carry microcosms of specialised microbes around in their guts, to digest materials which the animals alone could not tackle. Plants, too, often have 'helper' microbes in their roots or leaves; you will learn that symbiosis with microbes is the 'name of the game' in biology – a simple fact which non-microbiologists too often forget. Then you will learn about biotechnology, how we exploit these beneficial aspects of microbes, sometimes in new and fascinating ways: scientists can splice alien genes, even genes from animals or plants, into the DNA of microbes, which can then be made to produce valuable materials such as human insulin; bacteria which attack plants can actually be recruited to add new and useful genes to plants, creating new varieties.

The impact of microbes on our well-being, on our society, on our economy and industry, are all exciting topics, and they ensure that microbiologists have a better chance than many of finding good jobs. But for me, a lifelong professional microbiologist, there has always been a deeper fascination in the way microbes do these things. This brings me back to my opening remarks. You and I need air to breathe, organic matter to eat, and we must keep ourselves wet and reasonably warm (inside at least) to survive. Then we live out our lives and die. Yet most bacteria are potentially immortal: they only die if some stress kills them (you can get into quite a philosophical tangle here if you have a taste for that sort of thing). More practically, many bacteria need no air; some breathe sulphates or nitrates, others split, not burn, organic food. Yet others transform iron compounds or sulphur. Some live in boiling water, others in sub-zero brines. Spores of certain bacteria survive drying for at least 300 years; other bacteria are so fragile they die seemingly as soon as you look at them.

The microbiologist soon learns how constrained is the biology of mankind and gains new insights into the potential of terrestrial life, hints of what life was like in the early days of this planet's history and, most exciting, intimations of how life might have developed elsewhere in the universe.

HELPFUL READING: John Postgate, *Microbes and Man* (Pelican Books, 1986).

Modern Languages

Professor Dennis Ager, Aston University

Despite the title, no degree courses are limited to the study of a foreign language. They involve the student in learning one or more languages, **and** in covering a programme of literary studies or studies of linguistics, history, politics, social and economic structure of the relevant country. The reason for this is not that learning a language is thought to be too easy – far from it! – or not intellectually demanding; rather that learning a language at an advanced level is a matter also of learning to see the world the way foreigners see it, from within their own cultural and historical traditions. There is no point in being a graduate in Arabic if you don't understand Islam; and a graduate in German who has never heard of Goethe or Hitler is literally not able to understand what Germans are talking about. Ideally, of course, a graduate in languages would be an expert in the history of the relevant country, in its present-day political, social and economic problems and in its relations with other countries, in its cultural, literary, intellectual and artistic achievements; and be able to assess and compare these with a similar awareness of his own country. In practice, within a three or four year degree course some selection has to be made and a lot of ground left to the initiative of the individual student; individual degree courses will therefore look very different from each other.

It is possible to start a language course from scratch at most UKCPUs, with the exception of French or German (although in some UKCPUs you can now start from GCSE or *ab initio* even in these languages). Success in language learning comes easily to some; they seem to have an ear for the sound patterns of foreign tongues and are able to reproduce particular sounds accurately and to perceive and use the quirks of a foreign grammar very quickly. For those of us who are less fortunate some effort is involved, but since the French and the Japanese are also human beings this effort is almost certain to be crowned, eventually, with success. There are very few people who are unable to achieve something approaching perfection in the linguistic skills in a foreign language; the recipe is a mixture of high motivation, persistence, intelligence and practice. Modern learning aids – language laboratories, video tape recorders, computer and calculator dictionaries – can speed up the process, as can carefully designed teaching sequences; but there is no substitute for understanding that a language is a means of communication between human beings, and that the spoken language is, in this function, vastly more important than the written. In a degree course, however, one is often dealing with more written material than spoken; and the necessity for precision and often finicky accuracy which is a characteristic of some languages in their written form imposes a discipline which is not necessarily characteristic of the spoken language. It is possible, for example, to make oneself understood in general outline in speaking German without too much attention to the difference between n and m at the end of adjectives; in the written form, however, confusion of this sort is rightly seen as an indication of ignorance.

At degree level mastery of the skills of speaking, writing, reading and listening to the foreign language itself is often accompanied by practice in such skills as translating and interpreting; in some UKCPUs also by summarising or abstracting, essay writing and paraphrasing and final examinations are often now constructed to test a range of skills. Departments vary in the degree of importance they accord to the language skills; some delegate all the language learning work to a language centre and even conduct all their own lecturing in English; others carry out all the work in the foreign language, using native speakers in addition to their own staff. Colloquial assistants – young native speakers appointed to strengthen the learning of the spoken language – used to be a normal feature of all language departments; sadly in the present round of economies some are not being replaced. Many courses now last for four years, with an integrated year abroad – an absolutely essential experience for the linguist – and perhaps also with vacation courses.

Until about 30 years ago the language was always studied in order to understand its literature; and many degree courses today still concentrate heavily on literary criticism. It is usual to provide general survey courses, showing the nature of the literary production of the relevant country over, say, the last 400 years, and in addition to ask students to examine an author, or sometimes even one noteworthy book, in considerable depth. Departments with literary interests (mostly in universities) may concentrate on one aspect or period, may offer courses in practical criticism, and may organise lectures by topic, period, genre or author. Few such departments would claim their courses are vocationally useful; some indeed pride themselves that literary courses are essentially and necessarily useless, and that their graduates received an education which will enable them to derive personal pleasure from reading, to understand and assess intellectually what they read, and to be aware of the artistic achievements, in literature, of the foreign society. Nonetheless, career opportunities for all linguists, from whatever type of course, are varied; usually better than most other arts subjects, and, of course, they open up the prospect of work abroad. Some departments now offer courses in the other arts – film and drama, occasionally fine arts and music – in addition to literature; and yet others provide background lectures in history or institutions to enable students to 'place' the texts they study.

Linguistics is often studied as another accompaniment to language; usually the linguistics of the relevant language often limited to a survey of the historical development of the present-day language, medieval forms of the language and phonetics. Other departments offer a detailed analysis of the contemporary language, while others may be covering dialects or sociolinguistics, analysing the different ways the language is used by different social groups.

Logically, as language is a means of communication between human beings, a linguist should be interested in the nature of the interactions between human beings in the **foreign society**. These interactions take place within the social framework and against the background of the political and economic structure of society, as well as depending on personal relationships, family traditions and the working environment. Some popular courses in modern languages, regrettably only a few, enable students to study these matters, not as background to literature, but as main subjects. Studies of political history can be carried out, as can studies of literature, in a void – divorced from language; for linguists it is important that there be a close integration of these studies with the language, so that, although the techniques of the political scientist or the sociologists are used to analyse and comprehend the facts of the situation in a different society, the aims and purposes of the analysis remain those of the linguist; that is, the study of interaction and the improvement of one's understanding of the foreign society and people. Some caution needs to be exercised in looking at UKCPU publicity material describing such 'non-literary' courses however: many really contain only the smallest component, usually called 'Institutions' or 'Intellectual history', not devoted to literature. Serious study of political history, social structure and policy, or economic trends, is as intellectually demanding as any other area of study, and needs adequate study time and adequate staff.

Particularly with 1992 and the new Europe in mind, courses in eg International business, International management are more widely offered. Some of these offer dual qualifications, some split the undergraduate year between two or more centres in more than one country. Most are intended to train the Euro-managers of tomorrow and are often offered by a network of collaborating language departments and business schools here and abroad.

In essence the study of modern languages is a study of people, whether as individuals or in the mass, in the very aspect of existence which marks out the human being as unique and special. So studies of the framework of society should include the historical dimension and should examine the political, social and economic structure against which contemporary problems arise. Again, students will follow courses of a general survey kind and will balance this with detailed study of a particular topic or problem. Degree programmes with this type of syllabus tend to be regarded by employers and others as more vocationally relevant, enabling graduates to use their linguistic knowledge effectively and providing a wider understanding of the foreign country than can be obtained from courses limited to literary topics alone.

Potential students should read prospectuses of individual departments with care. UKCPUs differ in orientation and course content; there are also differences of course structure to be aware of. You can study one language or two. It is often possible to study one language plus another subject, not a language – French plus civil engineering, German plus architecture – with no necessary link between the two subjects. A particularly popular combination is a language plus business studies or economics. Sometimes a link is made (eg in a Russian and sociology degree, the sociology is taught in Russian, and the Russian is the Russian of sociology). Many polytechnics have established such programmes, and the titles vary considerably, as do the proportions of language-related work. Finally, languages often find a place within degrees in other subjects, historians find a knowledge of one or more invaluable, but their requirement is for reading ability; engineers, too, need languages but their prime need is for just enough French or Russian to get the gist of specialist reports plus enough spoken foreign language to understand the main point of a conversation or technical presentation. European studies degrees usually fall within this type, requiring only sufficient knowledge of French or German as will enable students to cope with original texts – the main interest is usually in politics or sociology or history.

Music

Professor Brian Trowell, Oxford University

We all know what an Art is: a means of original creation and self-expression in some particular medium. In the case of a performing art such as music, we must add that it is a means of imaginative re-creation, of practical interpretation. The long training of the executant reminds us of an earlier meaning of 'Art' in the sense that has given us the word 'artisan': a body of specialised practical training in the 'mystery' of a craft which was taught and regulated by a medieval trade union, a guild such as the shoemakers or goldsmiths. From the same period comes the usage preserved by our universities, in which an Art was a body of higher learning and theoretical speculation, not in the modern sense of a liberal art or humane letters, but in the more general sense of a science, an organised complex of knowledge. Music, with its complexities of measurement and proportion, was then regarded (as in some respects it still may be) as an Art allied to mathematics: geometry was mathematics made visible, music was mathematics made audible, and astronomy was mathematics in movement; all four were known as the 'quadrivium'. Today – though music has kept its mathematical associations and even increased them in the study of acoustics, temperament, electronic and computer applications, and complex notation – we have come to view music as a liberal or humane Arts subject in the university curriculum. That is because music is an expressive art in the modern sense: its history and theory need to be studied as manifestations of what it was like to live, think and feel in cultures and periods different from our own, just as with any other art. We also need to re-interpret the old music that still forms the basis of our current repertory, from Purcell to Webern, to attempt the revival of forgotten or unexplored music and edit it for modern performance; and, besides restoring to the public its musical patrimony, we also have the duty of helping to elucidate and smooth away the difficulties that many modern composers face in getting their music performed and understood in a period of bewildering change. That involves us in the development of the theory of music and in musical analysis, though this branch of enquiry also enjoys a long history which must be studied in relation to the music of the past. As if that were not enough, we must also try to relate our studies of Western European music to our knowledge of non-Western music. Apart from the study of folk-music, which reminds us, amongst other things, that our horn or flute belongs to a family that is world-wide, we need to realise that there are other classical traditions of theory, aesthetics and notation in other lands, some of them older than our own.

Not all departments of music do all these things, but I have said enough to show some of the ramifications of the study of music in a university. Universities are primarily concerned with knowledge, with the interpretation of existing knowledge and the creation of new. One needs all kinds of knowledge to pursue the study of music in this way, from languages and 'straight' history to electronics and anatomy, and that is why the 'universitas' was invented, as a repository of universal learning. A professor or lecturer in music is pledged to advance musical learning, and a department of music will also contain a few – sometimes many – postgraduates, who are working to advance the boundaries of knowledge by research. In the close collegiate life of a university campus, and particularly in the intimacy of a music department with its collaborative music-making, this attitude of excitement over the acquisition of new knowledge inevitably spreads to the undergraduate members as well.

But music is a performing art as well as an Arts subject. Its study at once is a science, an art in the modern sense, and a craft. That is not generally the case with Arts subjects. Very few university English departments in this country teach 'creative writing': their approach is critical, historical, analytical. Historians do not go out of their universities and make history. (Perhaps they should, you may say: they seem to in France.) Yet music departments contain composers, and all music students have to be able to perform to a certain level, and some are good enough to specialise in performance, as in composition. That means that some parts of a university music curriculum overlap with the kind of studies taught at a high professional level by the music colleges, who in some cases, these days, number among their teachers historians and theoreticians of real distinction. The aspiring student, who may know very little about either type of musical education and may not be able to seek advice from recent graduates of both kinds of institution, can find it very hard to make the right decision.

The main emphases in the attitudes of music college and university department are clear enough. Common sense will tell the would-be professional performer (particularly the string-player) that he or she will form a more realistic view of future possibilities by constant comparison with fellow-students of high excellence. By the age of eighteen, though, an outstanding youngster may already have formed such a view, and indeed studied at a music college. Someone entering university with a very secure technique will not lose it (except through his or her own fault, playing in every concert in sight without practising). In a university in or near a large city with a college of music, a student may study with the same teachers that he or she would have met with by applying to the conservatory in the first place. For singers, it can be a positive advantage not to concentrate on vocal technique seriously at too early an age; many have profited by improving their musical skills first at a university and then going on to a college of music. Young conductors may gain invaluable experience by working with university groups. Performers in general get many more chances to perform in public on a university campus than they will at a music college – particularly pianists. At many universities there are choral, instrumental and organ scholarships which can help a little in these days of reduced grants. Those interested in the performance of early music, or of very new music (with expensive electronic facilities) may be much better served in a university; composers will find themselves working in a collegiate society which reflects the variety of interests and human types of the outside world much more widely than a monotechnical music college.

Against all this must be set the fact that a university course in England or Wales is normally of only three years, and that will contain a good deal of non-practical academic study which will not always allow adequate time for practice. In addition, there are wide variations from department to department in the provision for practical study (which you may have to pay for) and indeed for all aspects of the curriculum. Your guarantee in all this is the entrance interview, at which you should ask searching questions after careful prior study of any brochures or syllabus-descriptions that are sent to you. At this time of flux and reductions in university funding, you should also ask about the institution's plans for its music department over the next five years. You should also enquire about the nature of individual tutorial provision; do you have a personal tutor for everything, or can you count on expert tutorial advice for each separate subject?

If you wish to go first to a university and later to a music college, you should consider the matter of grants unusually carefully. If you wish to proceed to postgraduate study at a university, remember that to receive a British Academy studentship you will need a degree, not a diploma, though the two are regarded as equal in other professional respects. If you intend to enter the honourable, vitally important and potentially very rewarding career of school music-teaching, you would (if you took the university route) receive a mandatory year's grant for a Postgraduate Certificate of Education to cover the fourth year after a BMus. This route would normally allow you rather more study of the subject that you are going to teach, as opposed to ancillary matter connected with educational theory, than you would get at a college of education (good though some are); in school music, it is the ability to perform and direct that inspires enthusiasm and emulation . . .

Above all, if you are attracted by the university path, you should ask yourself whether, in addition to practical competence, you have a real intellectual interest in knowledge about music, and indeed about any of the many other subjects that you may take alongside music in a combined studies degree or as a subsidiary. These are not normally available in a music college. Try to learn another language on your way through the course, even if informally. Not only does so much great vocal music come with foreign words attached, but you will be able to read what foreign composers and scholars have written about music in their own authentic tone of voice.

Near Eastern and Islamic Studies
Professor H T Norris, SOAS

It is reported that T E Lawrence once remarked that a year spent in the Near East was worth at least ten years spent anywhere else. His adventures took place in Arabia which, viewed retrospectively, was a land of romance and nostalgia. Prior to the First World War, and even to the end of the 1960s in some parts of Southern Arabia, the Middle East and the Muslim World in Africa and in Southern and Eastern Asia were very much the habitat of Colonial Service adventurers, of desert explorers, both men and women, and pith-helmeted archaeologists and anthropologists. Many spectacled Orientalists studied and taught in closeted colleges, compiling lexicons and attempting poetic translations of Arabic, Persian and Turkish masterpieces. Arabic and Islamic Studies, in fact, have been respected academic disciplines in this country for many generations, the former since the seventeenth century.

Today our horizons are very different. Ours is the age of hostage taking, the Palestinian struggle, Salman Rushdie's 'Satanic Verses', the revival of fundamentalist Islam in Iran and in many parts of the Orient and Africa in protest against the West and its materialist values. Tourism has opened the whole Arab World to sightseers. The Alhambra is a visited building, Petra and Wadi Rumm in Jordan so commonplace a scenic backcloth, and the artistry of the Arab lute (*al-ud*) or the Algerian protest music group 'Rai' so familiar a sound on disc, that one is liable to forget how very recent was the re-discovery of the historical sites of the Arab world or their archaeological exploration.

All this is true, but whatever a student's reason for selecting Arabic, whether it be for a career in Banking or in Law or a fascination in the history and art of the Middle East, he, or she, will need to know something of the languages of Islam, especially Arabic. The latter is taught as a spoken language in many language schools and in courses on tapes. Nonetheless, in order to master the written language, whether Medieval Classical or Modern Literary Arabic, most students will need to devote three to four years of study to it at a university. The complexities of Arabic grammar, officially Classical Arabic, are considerable and it takes time to explore the riches of Islamic literature, the ancient poets, the Koran, the mystical flights of the *Sufis*, not to speak of recent literature; Egyptian novels, Palestinian plays from the occupied territories, short stories from Tunisia, the exiled poets in Latin America and contemporary Arabic journalism. Ideally, a student needs to spend up to a year abroad to become fluent in a dialect, often very different from literary Arabic, whether in Tunisia, in Egypt, in Jordan or in the Gulf.

A student is able to study all, or most, of the subjects mentioned above at one or other of the universities and polytechnics where Arabic and Islamic Studies are taught in this country. He, or she, is advised to peruse the handbooks and, if the need arises, to ask for a detailed syllabus of the course. Enquiries should be made as to how the course is taught and when it is examined; whether by a single subject degree, by tripos or by course units, and whether Arabic and Islamic Studies might be combined with other Oriental languages or with other disciplines. At London University (SOAS), for example, Arabic is a four year degree course with a choice of up to fourteen course units. It is common to combine it with politics, economics, law or another oriental or African language. After a first year intensive study of modern literary Arabic, which, incidentally, can also be examined after one year to qualify, in part, for a *Certificate in Arabic*, a student can to some extent choose his, or her, subjects. At most British universities, now, where Arabic is taught, the majority of students who combine the language with a discipline (combined languages sometimes precludes it) will want to spend their second year in Egypt (for example the University of Alexandria) where there are now well organised courses and the cost of study there is paid by the local education authority if the student qualifies for a grant. It is an essential part of the degree course.

During the third and fourth years of study the subjects which a student may select range from the Arabic novel and contemporary poetry, to Islamic Law, an Arabic dialect, Hispano-Arabic Literature, Popular Arabic Literature, Arab Musicology, and the history and culture of the Islamic Middle East.

Apart from social sciences or Arts subjects, Arabic can be combined at SOAS with Hebrew, Turkish, Berber and Hausa, and other combinations are possible. Most universities, where Arabic is taught, have excellent libraries of lexicons, encyclopedias and language tapes, and there are normally facilities for an intensive study of the spoken language, particularly Egyptian and Gulf dialects.

An Arabic degree is a useful qualification. However, a student should be warned that the language is difficult and in order to understand it and use it correctly it is essential to combine it with a study of Islam. It is a mistake to think that Islam can be grasped without some knowledge of Arabic. The Koran needs to be read in Arabic. A translation is only a reflection of its poetry and its message. An Arabic student will need to be strongly motivated, though Arabic literature and Islamic culture have rich rewards to offer in compensation for much hard study. Students find it an adventure and it appeals to a variety of temperaments. Therefore expect every type of student, British or non-British, to be your boon companion when the wine cup of the Islamic East is passed to you in order to taste its nectar!

HELPFUL READING: *Islamic Surveys* (Edinburgh University Paperbacks); *The Cambridge History of Islam* (CUP); *The Arab Background Series* (Longman and Librairie du Liban); A J Arberry, *British Orientalists* (London, 1943) and *The Koran Interpreted* (Oxford, 1964); M Brett and W Forman, *The Moors* (Orbis, 1980); Peter B Clarke, *West Africa and Islam* (E Arnold, 1982); Michael Cook, *Muhammad* (Oxford, 1983); Leila Ahmad, *Edward W Lane* (Longman, 1978); B Lewis, *The Arabs in History* (Hutchinson University Library, 1950); L H Melikian, *Jassim, a Study of the Psychosocial Development of a Young Man in Qatar* (Longman, 1979); Dorothee Metlitzki, *The Matter of Araby in Medieval England* (Yale, 1977); Sari J Nasir, *The Arabs and the English* (Longman, 1979); R Nicholson, *A Literary History of the Arabs* (Cambridge University Press, 1930); W Thesiger, *Arabian Sands* (Longman, 1959); J O Voll, *Islam, Continuity and Chance in the Modern World* (Westview and Longman, 1982); E L Ranelagh, *The Past We Share* (Quartet Books, 1979).

Nursing Studies
Professor Penny Prophit, Edinburgh University

At some time in life, every human being requires intelligent, kind, compassionate and competent care. It may come as a surprise to some that UKCPUs provide professional education in nursing, but on reflection it is obvious. This is especially true if you consider yourself a potential recipient of care, for nurses should gain their knowledge from a broad and liberal education, and from the level of competence in the discipline which such an education develops. Nurses are with patients in their most vulnerable moments, and the challenges of nursing are human challenges, demanding much of the nurse but also giving much. A degree course helps to prepare whole people to care for whole people, not just physically but also emotionally. In fact, nursing involves head, heart and hands. Nurses are best placed to be advocates for the patient, to interpret messages from other disciplines, and to assist the patient to cope with and find meanings in suffering and illness. Nursing is truly more than offering a pair of hands and feet: nursing is concerned with the human response to illness and with helping people to help themselves. As Florence Nightingale put it, 'nurse the patient, not the disease'!

Nursing is an exciting and demanding profession: it is not a career choice for the fainthearted. Nurses are to be found not only in hospitals, but also in the community and in situations which focus on the promotion of better health. As the health care system increases in complexity and scope, and as knowledge and technology advance, the responsibilities of the nurse who professes a service to others will continue to expand and diversify. Degree programmes in nursing vary in emphasis and provide a vast array of opportunities, from working with sick children suffering from an illness such as cancer, to the fast-moving pace of accidents and emergency settings. There is the joy of helping at the birth of a baby, as well as the experience of sorrow associated with pain, suffering and death. In a very real sense, nursing is a preparation for living and provides wonderful opportunities for learning about life and oneself.

In their work nurses make use of knowledge from many areas. In some spheres, biological insights play a major role and in others, social and psychological perspectives are very important and more appropriate. Nurses work in a multidisciplinary team. They need all the skills involved in listening, communicating and comforting those who are often deeply troubled. They also need a thorough understanding of the problems faced by the handicapped and chronically ill, and of the stress endured by families trying to cope with sufferers in the community. How the sick, the disabled and people at risk cope with adversity depends to a large extent on the society in which they live. Ethnic and social differences between patients, and between patients and nurses, must be acknowledged and understood. The social sciences foster such understanding and a knowledge of theology and philosophy helps with the ethical and moral challenges often encountered in health care situations.

Though the UK was rather later than the USA and many of the

developing countries in realising the need for degree level study, it is well ahead of its European partners. There are now numerous degree courses available in UKCPUs. They came into being gradually and each new course is partially patterned on having an emphasis on the biological and natural sciences or on the social sciences. It is important to explore the focus of the various programmes offered. In some, nursing is situated in faculties of medicine or of social sciences. In others, nursing may be the major component in a social science degree. Yet others have sandwich courses with BSc or BA joint honours degrees, for example nursing with economics or sociology. There is no general agreement on the school subjects for entry; for some courses science subjects are important while others favour a much broader educational background, believing that there are advantages in having students whose interests and enthusiasms differ widely and whose supporting studies span a wide range of disciplines. Any talent, gift or strength a nurse possesses will be of benefit to patients.

It is said that we have the sick with us always. There are many career opportunities in nursing. They are particularly open to graduates, as evidence shows that nurses qualifying from degree programmes are highly proficient and competent clinical practitioners who have much to offer and obtain greater satisfaction in nursing. Both men and women enjoy the varied career opportunities nursing has to offer, not only in direct practice, but also in management and research opportunities.

International opportunities abound in nursing, whether in highly advanced technological settings, or by mission work in developing countries. An increasing number of nursing graduates obtain research degrees and take new masters degree courses.

The time is right, the opportunities are there; the challenges are for the person who wants to grow, to give, to care. How about you?

Pharmacology
Dr Robin Hoult, King's College London

Pharmacology concerns the uses of drugs and the ways in which they and other biologically active chemicals affect the body. Particular emphasis is on the molecular mechanisms by which these chemicals alter biological processes at the cell and tissue level. Pharmacology is highly relevant to everyday life, not only because of the important therapeutic uses of drugs but also because of issues such as drug misuse and addiction. It is also exciting because research is proceeding at an ever-increasing pace, bringing with it the development of powerful new drugs as well as new insights into the molecular mechanism of the body's physiological functions.

Pharmacology is generally only offered as a degree subject in universities and polytechnics which have schools of medicine or pharmacy. Entry requirements are similar as for pharmacy (see below), although two good grades including chemistry may be sufficient for certain polytechnic courses.

For the study of pharmacology it is necessary to have a good understanding of the functions and integration of living systems, particularly in mammals (physiology), and of the molecular basis of these systems (biochemistry and cell biology) because only with this fundamental knowledge can we begin to understand how drugs work and their applications in therapeutics. Thus, in the first year of most pharmacology degree courses it is usual to study biochemistry and physiology as well as some or all of the following: cell biology, organic chemistry, physical chemistry, botany or zoology, statistics and design of experiments.

Chemistry is relevant to pharmacology for two main reasons. The first is that the principles of physical chemistry apply to the chemical systems of the body and to the molecular functions of cells, and the second is that the pharmacologist considers the actions of chemicals and drugs on body functions in terms of chemical interactions with specific receptor sites on tissues. Also, of course, it is the organic chemist who synthesises new substances (the potential new drug or medicine) which are later investigated by the pharmacologist.

Like all natural and medical sciences, pharmacology is above all an experimental subject – that is, most of our knowledge about drug action is based on careful measurement of effects of chemicals upon animals or man.

Much of this work, however, involves testing drugs on isolated tissues, organs or cell systems prepared from animals, rather than upon the whole animal itself. This means that a long time is spent in the laboratory learning experimental methods. A common problem is that even the simplest experiments often show variable results, usually due to the expected biological variation between animals, although sometimes it happens because of inexperience or error. As a result experiments may have to be performed a large number of times to be sure of the real result and a good knowledge of statistics and experimental design is important for their interpretation.

The second and third years are generally spent on courses in specialised aspects of pharmacology and advanced courses in related subjects or disciplines. Many are concerned with specific categories of drugs in terms of their site of action in the body (eg chemotherapy of infectious and parasitic diseases; cardiovascular, renal or endocrine or central nervous system pharmacology; drugs affecting the blood, nervous, muscular or reproductive systems). Others cover the ways in which drugs work (eg drug receptors and membrane structure – these topics illustrate the close links between pharmacology and biochemistry; drug addiction; administration and metabolism of drugs; experimental techniques for analysis of drug action; interaction of drugs with nerves, hormones, etc). Thus there are two different approaches to the study of pharmacology – the systematic one, which concerns the application of drugs to organ systems and disease treatment, and the analytical one, which is concerned with the way in which drugs work at the molecular level.

In some courses, students have the opportunity of an extra-mural year, working in an industrial or research laboratory, as part of a specialised research team. This option is offered between the second and third years, and is an exciting and useful preparation for the final year's study.

Many pharmacology graduates enter the pharmaceutical industry straight away as a BSc honours degree is a good starting point for several positions such as marketing, medical information and product registration (none of which involve laboratory work), as well as for pharmaceutical research. Other graduates continue their studies and obtain higher degrees, either by taking specialised MSc courses which offer specific career opportunities or by carrying out supervised research for a PhD degree (sometimes this can be done whilst employed in the pharmaceutical industry). PhD graduates usually continue to do research as a career, either in universities, hospitals, industry or in the scientific civil service (these options are also open to BSc graduates). Because of the multi-disciplinary nature of the subject, pharmacologists often carry out research in conjunction with scientists from other disciplines, such as biochemists, immunologists and molecular biologists.

HELPFUL READING: *Careers in Pharmacology* (London: British Pharmacological Society, 1989, available from the Society's secretary, Astra Neuroscience Research Unit, 1 Wakefield Street, London WC1N 1PJ).

Pharmacy
Dr Robin Hoult, King's College London

A definition of pharmacy which gives a good general idea of what undergraduate pharmacy courses are about is 'the application of physics, chemistry and biology to the study of medicinal products'. In other words pharmacy is concerned with every aspect of substances used to prevent or treat disease in humans and animals. Thus the pharmacist must be an expert in the production and quality-control of a wide range of both natural and synthetic substances and also in their application and dispensing for therapeutic purposes. This explains why a pharmacy degree involves the study of many subjects – and why stringent requirements have to be satisfied before anyone is allowed to practise as a pharmacist. In fact one year's practical training in a registered pharmacy is necessary before a pharmacist can register and practise on his own. This is taken either after graduation from a three-year course or is sandwiched into the degree course making a four-year course.

Pharmacy courses are offered by several universities and polytechnics, often ones with medical schools attached since some of the subjects which make up pharmacy are also common to medicine. Traditionally there is a quartet of sciences which form the basis of pharmacy and which are studied in the first two years of a pharmacy degree course. They are pharmaceutical chemistry, pharmacology, pharmaceutics and pharmacognosy. Pharmaceutical chemistry is concerned with the synthesis, properties and analysis of substances used in medicine, and its study may include compulsory foundation courses in chemistry and possibly physical sciences.

Pharmacology is the study of the effects and mode of action of chemicals which modify the functions of the living organism, particularly those which are used in the treatment of disease. A working knowledge of physiology, biochemistry and cell biology is necessary for its study and introductory courses in these subjects are generally offered in the first two years. The subject can also be studied independently (see above).

Pharmaceutics occupies a principal place in pharmacy courses and involves detailed study of the properties, formulation, preparation and presentation of medicinal drugs. Microbiology usually figures as a component of pharmaceutics, firstly because of the need to avoid inadvertent contamination of medicines with bacteria and fungi, and secondly because of the importance of disinfectants, vaccines, immunisations and antibiotics in medicinal practice.

Pharmacognosy, the final member of the quartet of sciences, is the study of natural products used in medicine or as sources of drugs. This is still a highly relevant subject even though most drugs are now synthesised rather than obtained from plant or animal sources. Other subjects on the pharmacy degree syllabus include medicinal chemistry, pharmaceutical engineering science, the law and practice of pharmacy, experimental pharmacology, biopharmacy (the principles affecting the absorption and fate of drugs in the body), computer science, forensic pharmacy, together with management and dispensing practice.

By the third year, courses usually become specialised and the student may undertake extended research or practical projects under supervision. Naturally, each institution has its own specialities and its own teaching style and atmosphere. One emerging speciality is clinical pharmacy, involving direct contact with hospital practice. However, lectures and practicals usually form the most important component of the formal instruction, generally supplemented by tutorials, directed reading and studies, and sometimes by self-instructional teaching materials.

For entry, three good A-levels are required from biology, chemistry, mathematics and physics. Students without biology at A-level must have a GCSE pass. Chemistry is very important both because of its relevance and because it is thought a good indicator of a student's likely performance; a good grade at A-level is usually obligatory.

Most of us think of a pharmacist as the person who is responsible for the dispensing of medicines in a chemist's shop (and who can give specialist advice about the choice of products for the treatment of minor illnesses), and indeed many students study pharmacy with this career specifically in mind. However, there are plenty of other career options either in hospital pharmacies or in industry (eg in the research and development of new drugs and in their production and marketing) or else in the academic field in either research or teaching.

HELPFUL READING: *Pharmacy as a Career* (London: Royal Pharmaceutical Society, 1988, available from the Royal Pharmaceutical Society of Great Britain, 1 Lambeth High Street, London SE1 5JN).

Philosophy

Professor Antony Flew, Reading University

Philosophy is not a mainstream A-level subject. So if you decide to do degree work in it you and all the rest of your class will be, as near as makes precious little matter, starting level. But, just because there isn't anyone either teaching or learning the subject in your school, you may well not know what philosophy would involve. Or else, much worse, you may think you do know and be wrong.

No doubt you will have seen series or articles or TV interviews in which people in the eyes of the media were invited to sound off about their philosophies of life. The word 'philosophy' there was being used in a perfectly respectable sense. But it was a sense only rather distantly and rather indirectly related to that in which the word is construed when we speak of philosophy as a discipline pursued in universities and polytechnics.

It is difficult to explain to people who have never done any what, in this present sense, philosophy is. (Would you care to try to explain what mathematics would involve to someone who had been to a school in which no one had learnt any at all?) This difficulty is one of several good reasons why anyone considering this as a degree subject is well advised to try for one of the institutions – Keele, for instance, or Reading – giving students opportunities of sampling one or two new things before they have finally to commit themselves on what subject or subjects they will read for honours.

The same difficulty led one most distinguished and well-loved Cambridge professor, G E Moore, always to begin his replies to the question, 'What is philosophy?' by pointing towards his bookshelves: 'It is what all those are about.' So let me too start by saying that philosophy is the main subject of most of the writings of Plato; of Aristotle's *Meta-physics* and *Nicomachean Ethics*; of large parts of the works of St Thomas Aquinas, Duns Scotus and William of Ockham; of the *Discourse* and *Meditations* of Descartes; of Berkeley's *Three Dialogues* and *Princi-ples of Human Knowledge*; of Hume's *Inquiry concerning Human Understanding*; of Kant's *Critique of Pure Reason*; and finally, in our own century, of Moore's own books, of Bertrand Russell's *Our Knowl-edge of the External World* and *Mysticism and Logic*, and of Wittgens-tein's *Tractatus Logico-Philosophicus*.

If you do decide to do philosophy you will certainly be introduced to many of these classics. However, unless and until you have been thus properly introduced, you had perhaps best stick to books written fairly recently, and books written as introductions. Try, for instance: G Vesey (ed) *Philosophy in the Open* (Milton Keynes: Open University Press, 1974); or Bertrand Russell *The Problems of Philosophy* (first published 1912 but since 1967 available as an Oxford University Press paperback); or A Flew *Philosophy: An Introduction* (London: Hodder and Stoughton Teach Yourself Series, 1980). And, whatever you do, don't set out for an interview without readying yourself to say something lively about some philosophy book which you have recently worked through. They probably want to sign you up. But you do need to give them some help!

You will not find many facts in any philosophy book, and those which you do find will be mainly facts about what particular philosophers have said. What you should find is arguments, and the more the better. So one good test for telling whether you are a person who could become fascinated by philosophy is to ask yourself whether you care about the validity or invalidity of arguments, and the sufficiency or insufficiency of evidence offered, as well as about the truth or falsity of conclusions reached, and the acceptability or otherwise of cases presented. If you do not, then certainly philosophy is not for you.

Consider, for example, the much disputed issues of 'freewill or pre-destination' and 'freewill or determinism'. The strictly philosophical questions here are not the questions of theological or scientific fact. They are not, that is, the questions: whether on the first day of creation God wrote what the last day of reckoning shall read; nor whether everything that happens, including everything which people do, could on the basis of a full knowledge of the laws of nature and the past condition of the whole universe, in principle be predicted. They are, rather, the questions: whether the idea of a creator God – not only all foreseeing, but also the sustaining cause of our every action and our very existence – is logically compatible with the ideas of human responsibility and human choice; and whether the sciences, and in particular the human sciences, logically presuppose or imply some form of determinism. If so, is this a sort of determinism or is it not logically compatible with our everyday talk and our everyday assumptions about human choice and action?

The philosophical questions about freewill and determinism and pre-destination, therefore, like other philosophical questions, though they may arise out of suggestions or discoveries about what is as a matter of fact the case, are themselves not questions of this factual sort, but questions about what does or does not follow from what, and what is or is not logically incompatible with what else. It is this fact which makes philosophy the outstandingly excellent pure mental training. Certainly it is not career-linked in the way in which law, say, and medicine both are. Certainly too it is not, unlike the usual school subjects, something which graduates can hope to earn their livings by teaching. But when you are competing for any of the other jobs done by arts graduates there is no call whatever to be shy about admitting that you read philosophy. Philosophy is, and is by many known to be, an incomparable exercise in intellectual gymnastics – just the right preparation for those intending to get to the top in one of the new information industries.

If you are still worried either about making yourself unemployable or about broaching a quite unfamiliar subject, then you could compromise. What about a joint honours degree in which you combine your new way-out, other-worldly interest in philosophy with the study of some safe, familiar, bread-and-butter subject?

Physics
Dr P E Hodgson, Oxford University

I've been interested in atoms ever since I was a very small boy. I was fascinated by the idea that all the things of everyday life, including our own bodies, are made up of billions of tiny particles. I resolved to find out all I could about them and now, many years later, I'm more interested than ever.

Naturally physics was my favourite subject at school, though mathematics was a close second. It was so immensely satisfying to have clear-cut problems that could be solved precisely and definitely by applying general principles and theorems of great power. However one worked out the problem, the answer was always the same – so different from other areas of study where vague discussions went round and round and any rules were notable mainly for their exceptions.

Physics is written in the language of mathematics, so an easy familiarity with algebraic equations, vectors, trigonometry and the calculus is a basic requirement. Once this language is mastered, we see that it is an elegant and powerful way of saying difficult things about the world in a very simple way. One equation can sum up the behaviour of a vast range of phenomena, and from it we can easily calculate what will happen in many different circumstances. Mathematical studies thus form an essential basis and companion to the physics course. If you study physics at university you will probably spend about half your first year studying mathematics, and later on you will be using it continually.

A university physics course is not a soft option for the flabby-minded. It is tough, rigorous and demanding, and can easily provide a worthwhile challenge to the most flexible and energetic minds. Parts of it, mainly at the beginning, involve some rather routine learning, but it becomes more and more interesting as time goes on.

Most of the second year is spent on classical physics, and you have the chance of exploring Newton's classical mechanics in some detail. You will see how to calculate the paths of the planets and the orbits of satellites and projectiles. The kinetic theory of gases shows how the same laws apply to the realm of the very small, and by considering the collisions of a swarm of atoms we can understand the ways gases behave. Then we see how electricity and magnetism are unified by Maxwell's equations, and how a study of the frequencies of spectral lines gives us a glimpse into the structure of the atom itself. Perhaps at this stage we begin some elementary quantum mechanics and begin to wrestle with the unfamiliar ideas of wave packets and transition probabilities.

The third year is more interesting still. Modern physics, based on the pioneering work of Einstein and Planck, is explored in depth. We see how the ideas hammered out in the 1920s by Sommerfeld and Bohr, Dirac and Pauli provide a sound basis of understanding of the structure of atoms. A course in solid-state physics shows how, at least in principle, we can calculate the properties of all materials from what we know about their constituent atoms and the way they are bound together. Delving deeper, we learn how Rutherford discovered the nucleus of the atom and began to probe its structure. In the 1930s the unstable mesons were discovered and since then a whole host of elementary particles. We enter the subnuclear world in all its fascinating complexity. In the last decade our understanding has grown apace, and now we see that the particles we called elementary are themselves built up of even more elusive particles called quarks. Many puzzles remain, and the search goes on.

All too soon the course is over, and then what? I was lucky and was able to stay on and start research into the particles of the cosmic radiation. I climbed mountains in Switzerland and studied the way the nuclei broke up when they were hit by cosmic ray particles. Later on I made theoretical studies of nuclear reactions and nuclear structure, and I am still doing this now. I also give lectures and tutorials to the physics students at Oxford and try to pass on to them some of the interest and excitement of physics. The more I learn the more I marvel at the complexity and yet underlying simplicity of the world.

Of course, not everyone is able to stay on after the degree. Most physicists leave the university and they enter a wide variety of occupations where they can use their knowledge of physics. Some teach physics in schools. Others go into industry and help to make manufacturing processes as efficient as possible, and also initiate new processes and even whole industries such as the atomic energy and computer industries. Others range further afield. One of my students is now a psychologist, another a lawyer, another a priest, and certainly the habits of exact thinking learnt in physics are of enduring value to them. There are also branches of physics that may not receive much mention in the university course that yet can provide satisfying careers both in the university and outside, such as geophysics (concerned with the structure of the earth), astrophysics (the structure of the stars and galaxies) and atmospheric physics (the composition of the atmosphere and the weather).

Increasingly after graduation, with experience of life, one sees how profoundly physics has moulded our whole society. What would our lives be like without electricity, or radio, or computers, to take a few examples? With this realisation comes a feeling of responsibility for seeing that as far as possible science is used for the good of man. We are aware of the damage that can be done by misapplied science, and this can only be prevented if people understand the potentialities of science. This in turn depends on scientists taking time off from their scientific work and explaining it in simple language.

At a deeper level we see that science raises, often in an acute form, all those problems about freedom and authority, power and responsibility, the individual and the state that we often so inconclusively discussed in our schooldays. As physicists we isolate one aspect of reality, mainly the quantitatively measurable, and find that it can be put in order. The much greater problems of life do not admit of such easy solutions. We also come to learn how science developed as an integral part of our Christian culture and realise that, from its first beginnings to the dominant position it occupies today, science is an organic part of the historical development of man.

So do not think that science, and particularly physics, is a dry, remote activity, fit only for desiccated robots who care nothing about other people. It is on the contrary a vital strand of our very humanity and if you have the essential ability and interest you can contribute more to your fellow man through the study of physics than in any other way.

HELPFUL READING: R P Feynmann, *Lectures on Physics* (Reading, Massachusetts, and London: Addison-Wesley, 1963); S L Jaki, *The Relevance of Physics* (University of Chicago Press, 1970).

Physiology
Dr D J Begley, King's College, London

> *General physiology is the basic biological science toward which all others converge. Its problem is to determine the elementary conditions of vital phenomena.*
> (Claude Bernard, *An Introduction to the Study of Experimental Medicine*, 1865)

Physiology is undoubtedly the most open-ended of the biological sciences and for this reason is also probably the most challenging. A physiologist is constantly attempting to explain how organisms work by a careful and critical analysis of well planned research and experiment. He can work at any number of levels within the organisation of a species. At the cellular level he can study how cells function or move, or how the nervous impulse is transmitted and how messages are received and interpreted by the cell. Alternatively he may focus on individual organs or tissues of the body (eg the brain or the liver) or on complete systems (eg the nervous or endocrine), studying how they control and regulate function. Or his interest can be in how several organs and systems interact (eg to maintain the constancy of the composition of the blood) or in the important area of developmental physiology (ie how the fertilised egg interprets and unfolds its genetic potential and develops into the mature adult). Or he may study the organism as a whole and its responses to external stimuli and environmental change.

In recent years, interest has certainly been concentrated on cellular physiology as powerful new research tools have increasingly miniaturised the scales at which living systems can be experimentally manipulated. Of course, there is still much to be discovered in other areas but studies into these must be built on firm foundations at cellular levels. Recent advances in cellular physiology have revolutionised the ways in which we examine and interpret higher function (eg in the working of the brain).

Because physiology forms the meeting point for a number of biological sciences, the physiologist utilises experimental methods and tools derived from related disciplines – for example the electron microscope from anatomy, radioactively labelled molecules from biochemistry, x-ray analysis from biophysics and from pharmacology new substances which mimic or modify the action of natural molecules in the body. It also means that the physiologist's armoury of experimental techniques is constantly expanding.

As a result of its interdisciplinary nature, physiology draws freely from and contributes widely to the other biological sciences. It is not uncommon, for instance, for the staff of a modern physiology department to be composed of academics whose initial training was perhaps in medicine, biology or physical science as well as in physiology.

A physiology undergraduate studies subsidiary subjects for at least the initial years of his course and the central nature of physiology allows him to take full advantage of courses offered in other biological sciences. Similarly physiology forms an essential but subsidiary part of subjects such as biology, zoology, botany and pharmacology, and a large number of physiology departments are actively involved in teaching medical as well as science students. This often enhances the already stimulating background for the undergraduate.

There are a large number of physiology departments in universities and polytechnics but it is not a subject offered by every institution and the emphasis placed on the subject can vary from department to department. Some may direct most of their research and teaching towards animal and comparative physiology, examining how similar functional problems are solved in different species; others may lay more emphasis on human physiology and the application of the science to medicine. The intending student would therefore be well advised to examine closely the various prospectuses available and to visit departments before making his final choices for application. The A-levels required by physiology departments may vary slightly but generally passes in biology and chemistry together with either physics or mathematics are acceptable.

HELPFUL READING: *Physiology – Education and Career* (London: Physiological Society, available from the Society whose address can be obtained from any university physiology department).

Politics and Government
Peter Dawson, LSE

Politics, political science, political theory and institutions, government – these are some of the names by which university departments teaching in this field are known and, although the specific subjects which they teach may differ, their broad concern is the same. The simplest way of describing this concern is to say that it is with the exercise of governmental power within and between nation states. Beyond that it is a concern with the processes by which power is acquired and used, and the restraints both material and ethical which may be placed upon it.

The oldest and most persistent strand of political studies is political philosophy with an ancestry which goes back at least as far as Aristotle and Plato. Political philosophy involves a concern – or 'engagement' – with the basic concepts of the discipline (eg politics, government, power, authority) and with the rights and obligations of both rulers and ruled, and much else. It cannot be assigned however to a separate and remote compartment. Philosophical considerations underlie all aspects of the study of politics and most enquiries tend to lead back to such concerns.

Some people distinguish political thought as a separate field from political philosophy. It entails an examination of the ideas of certain prominent thinkers and of their significance in their own and in subsequent times. Plato, Aquinas, Machiavelli, Rousseau and Marx would be just a few of the names which fall within this category.

Next there is a large area of empirical studies and theorising about them which may, for convenience, be divided into three parts. The first is the study of individuals and their motivation and behaviour in different political roles (eg voters or leaders). The second is the study of groups from the organised and articulate (eg political parties or pressure groups) to those with a possibly more diffuse voice who are less organised (eg racial or religious groups). Third is the study of governmental institutions – parliamentary assemblies, courts, cabinets, civil services – and constitutionally defined offices of leadership or direction (eg those of presidents, prime ministers and ministers). Public administration as an academic study is principally concerned with this third part.

These three types of study may be conducted in relation to the politics and government of our own or of any foreign country. Western European countries and North America have long been a subject of scrutiny, but with the growth since 1945 of Soviet, East European and Chinese studies and over the past twenty years of Third World studies there is now no country in the world whose political arrangements are not directly or indirectly the subject of research and publication.

Comparative politics – the methodical and simultaneous study of several political systems – has been one of the major developments of political science in recent years. The study has been aided by an accompanying elaboration of the concept of political systems. A primary concern in comparative politics is to show by examination of a number of countries how apparently similar institutions and structures may perform different functions or, conversely, how the same function may be performed by different structures. It becomes possible for example to analyse in some detail how political parties or the mass media perform widely varying roles in different countries, or how the functions attributed in the UK to Members of Parliament may elsewhere be performed by civil servants or influential, non-elected intermediaries.

Another aspect of comparative politics is the attempt to classify political societies and order them in generic groups. It tends to lead to an examination of such terms as totalitarianism, pluralism and participation. Closely related to this approach is the examination of political ideas or bodies of widely held beliefs like nationalism, socialism or conservatism. But by now the circle is almost closed since this sort of concern brings one into close proximity again with political philosophy.

A final area of concern is international politics or international relations, which in some universities is taught within a separate department but elsewhere is covered under politics or government. Essentially it is the study of politics between states and of such institutions as the United

Nations and the European Economic Community which constitute forms of international government. The various approaches outlined above are equally appropriate in this field.

It must now be clear that the study of politics cannot be undertaken in isolation from other disciplines. It enjoys common and overlapping boundaries with numerous other subjects, sharing many of their concerns and using some of their methods of study. History, above all, has a prominent place. At a basic level a large part of what we are able to study is historical in that it is accomplished fact, but also at a more elaborate level we can only provide intelligible accounts of political arrangements by trying to understand how and why they have evolved, by recognising the phenomenon of change and seeking to discover its causes. Sociology, economics and law are close relatives of politics, while geography, anthropology and psychology are more distantly placed; and mathematics, including statistics and computer applications, is being admitted ever more frequently to the family circle.

What are the principal methods of studying politics as an undergraduate? It remains above all a 'book' subject, pursued by reading the works of other scholars, but there also exist opportunities, which vary from topic to topic, to use primary sources such as official publications and newspapers both contemporary and historical. Novels, plays, poetry and other artistic works may have their relevance and there is an increasing use of survey data (eg public opinion samples), which in some instances is prepared by students themselves. In recent years there has been some use of simulation techniques either involving role playing and/or using computers as a method of both research and of teaching.

Few universities specify particular A-level subjects for students wishing to specialise in political studies. British constitution and other directly related subjects have tended in the past not to be regarded as a specially favoured qualification. On the other hand A-level studies in history, a modern language or mathematics would provide a useful grounding for a potential student in this field.

A more detailed and very readable account of the study of politics is Jean Blondel, *The Discipline of Politics* (Butterworth, 1981). Alternatively *Introducing Political Science* edited by Lynton Robins (published jointly by Longman and the Politics Association).

Psychology
Professor Keith Oatley, Glasgow University

'Know thyself' said the inscription on the temple at Delphi; and I suppose it is something like this idea that leads most of us into psychology. But how should we acquire that knowledge?

For most of this century the answer that has been widely accepted in psychology departments of universities is that we can best find out about ourselves using the methods of natural science. So psychology tends to be modelled on sciences like biology, and a common definition is 'Psychology is the study of behaviour and mental processes'. Just as biologists' and physiologists' interest is in how bodies of living things work, so psychologists concern themselves with how people behave and how their minds work.

A good deal of knowledge has indeed been produced in this way. Careful observation, results of experiments, and theories interpreting these kinds of evidence form the core of most psychology courses. A book specially written for people wondering whether to study psychology is A M Colman's *What is Psychology, The Inside Story* (Hutchinson). It emphasises this natural scientific viewpoint and gives a sample of what is to be expected in university and college psychology courses. Also with this viewpoint, but with more detail, is a book that is widely used at universities and colleges, *Introduction to Psychology* by R L Atkinson, R C Atkinson, E E Smith & E R Hilgard (Harcourt Brace Jovanovich). It, or an equivalent, is available in most public libraries.

Psychological research has made exciting advances in recent years. The observational and experimental study of childhood is an example which has important implications for education. Try M Donaldson's book *Children's Minds* (Fontana). Another approach which has become important at universities is cognitive psychology; the study of how knowledge is represented mentally, and used in such activities as seeing, conversing, understanding and thinking. A good book introducing cognitive psychology is *The Computer and the Mind: An Introduction to Cognitive Science* (Fontana) by P Johnson-Laird. Despite the title this book is not too hard to approach. It explains how the computer has become important in helping us understand mental processes like thinking, memory, perception, language and so on. A series of books that describes in straightforward terms some of the recent advances in psychology, including its applications to practical problems, is *Psychology Survey* (British Psychological Society). Volume 5 was edited by J Nicholson and H Beloff; and the most recent, volume 6, is edited by H Beloff and A Colman.

So, one might think, this is how one could get to know about child development, thinking and suchlike, but still something remains elusive: these approaches have not necessarily given us knowledge of our own selves.

In using the methods of natural science investigators can stand more or less outside the system they are studying. We might be made of molecules, but we can still study molecular reactions in a test tube without interfering too much. We might ourselves be products of evolution, but we can study some evolutionary processes by looking at fossils or doing genetic experiments on fruit-flies. But with ourselves and our own minds, it's not clear that we can always stand outside in this way – or at least not without missing something important.

So for some psychologists, the methods of studying the natural world are not appropriate to investigating the human world, which after all is a world of culture as much as of nature. In the distinctively human world psychologists are not so much finding out about mental mechanisms as about what we as people are up to, by ourselves, with each other and in society. Rather than asking 'What makes a person tick?' we can ask about what things mean to people, or about how people construct their personal and interpersonal realities. Most characteristically this is the area of social psychology, and its closely related disciplines of sociology and anthropology. Try reading one of E Goffman's books, for example *The Presentation of Self in Everyday Life* (Pelican). The idea of looking for human meaning is also the impulse behind much clinical psychology, where understandings are applied to healing emotional crises to which we are subject at various times in our lives. A good introduction to these issues is J Kovel's *Complete Guide to Therapy: From Psychoanalysis to Behaviour Modification* (Pelican), or K Oatley's *Selves in Relation: An Introduction to Psychotherapy and Groups* (Methuen). Certainly, nearly all the time, there is lively discussion about how we should proceed – for a good taste of this, concerning one of psychology's best known inventions try L Kamin's *The Science and Politics of IQ* (Penguin).

Psychology is applied to an enormous range of practical problems (and there is even an important branch called applied psychology). With a BA or BSc in psychology you will be able to work in industry, communications or research, and psychologists are employed in fields as diverse as the media and the civil service. To work as a clinical, educational or applied psychologist, you will need to follow your first degree with a further one to two year course (MA or MSc) which will give you specific training and qualifications.

Doing an undergraduate course with at least half your time spent on psychology would be a typical requirement for going on to such a vocational course. Most British degree courses in which students spend the larger part of their time doing psychology are officially recognised by the British Psychological Society. Graduating from such a course qualifies you for membership of this Society, a professional body that looks after the interests of psychology in Britain. If you think you might want a career in psychology it is a good idea to check that courses for which you apply are recognised in this way. You can find out more about careers and qualifications by sending £1.25 to the British Psychological Society, St Andrews House, 48 Princess Road East, Leicester LE1 7DR requesting their booklet *How About Psychology? A Guide to Courses and Careers*.

As to what you need to be accepted for a psychology course at university or college, the requirements are usually quite flexible; typically maths at GCSE or equivalent, and usually three A-levels, or in Scotland four Highers, in arts or science subjects.Biology, sociology or indeed psychology itself at A-level are useful. But do not worry if you are not taking these particular subjects. The real qualifications are knowing a bit about psychology before you apply, eg from friends already at college or university, or from books like the ones I have mentioned, an interest in people, an enthusiasm for ideas, and a preparedness to think for yourself.

Public Administration

Barry J O'Toole, Loughborough University

Public administration is about the very essence of politics: it is about power. Power is the ability to get people to do something that they would otherwise not have done. Its sources can be physical strength or simply the ability to persuade. In public administration power is derived from authority. In other words, public officials, whether elected politicians or permanent functionaries, can get things done because they have the legitimate right, derived from election or law, to get those things done.

The study of public administration is concerned with the who, the why, and the how of this legitimate exercise of power. In Britain the study is all the more exciting because the public official, be that person politician, civil servant or local government officer, generally exercises power in secret. The world of the public official is a dark and hidden world – a world which is formally 'public', but which in reality is 'private'. It is a world governed by conventions, traditions and precedents – but it is a world in which conventions, traditions and precedents can be broken if it suits those people who operate within it.

Who are these people and what exactly do they do? First of all what are the institutions of public administration in Britain? Starting at the very top, in central government, there is the cabinet. The cabinet, which derives its legitimacy from parliament, and ultimately from the electorate, is the supreme policy-making body. In the cabinet sit the senior ministers of the government. These people are usually supported by huge departments of state which carry out their policies. In the departments are the civil servants. Civil servants are appointed by publicly known and non-party-political criteria; they serve the government of the day. At the very top of the civil service hierarchy they are responsible for advising ministers about policy and for putting those policies into effect. Civil servants derive their legitimacy from their official positions and from their expertise, in particular their expertise in how government works. They are not the 'faceless, pliable, sexless creatures' of myth; they are rather 'cloistered politicians' or 'statesmen in disguise'. In other words, they exercise a real and constant influence on public affairs.

Central government, in essence the cabinet and the civil service, is responsible for creating the policy framework within which the other organs of the state operate. These other organs of the state include the local authorities, the nationalised industries and the quasi-autonomous bodies (QUANGOs) such as the Sports Council or the National Health Service (certainly the most important of the semi-independent authorities).

Local government has the primary responsibility for implementing the practical aspects of public policy. The various local authorities are providers of education, public housing and social services; they build roads and footpaths; they cater for the arts, libraries and leisure; they take away our refuse and clean our streets; they police our neighbourhoods. In essence the local authorities provide much of the physical and social framework without which civilised society could not exist.

The people who carry the burden of responsibility for the provision of these services are the local councillors, deriving their legitimacy as elected politicians; and the local government officers, deriving their legitimacy from their official position and from their specific expertise in aspects of local service provision. These people work in bureaucratic structures, often in large departments, with long hierarchical chains and governed by volume upon volume of rules, regulations and procedures. However, any organisation is only as good as the people who work within it; and clearly there are other factors which play a part in how local government operates. Students of public administration are not simply concerned with structures and functions of local authority departments and the local council; they will also seek to raise questions about what sort of people local councillors and officials are; what motivates them; and what are the economic, political and social boundaries within which they work. In other words, public administration, at all levels, is about people, politics and power.

Much has been written about the role of power/authority/legitimacy in the study of politics. Public administration is about the practical aspects and applications of those concepts. Students of public administration will therefore be expected during their studies to deal with the theoretical elements of the study of politics as well as with the empirical evidence of political activity in public organisations. They will also be asked to tackle such problems as communications in organisations, motivation, decision theory, policy making and leadership. Who are the leaders in public organisations: temporary politicians or permanent officials? Who are the decision makers and policy determinators? Who is responsible for motivating public officials? How are they motivated: by pay or by power? All these questions, and many others, will be raised while studying public administration. Why are they important? They are important because the answers to them affect every aspect of our lives. What public people do has a direct bearing on the business of private individuals. Furthermore, these questions are important in another sense. As citizens in a democracy surely it is our duty to find out as much as we can about how those who have charge over our political destiny go about discharging their responsibilities. The more we know the less they are likely to be irresponsible. Therein lies the challenge of studying public administration: on the whole there is so little that is known.

Public administration is usually taught in universities as part of a wider degree in politics or government. In certain polytechnics it is more likely to be taught as an entirely separate degree. Whatever the model used the methodology for the study of public administration will draw upon the related disciplines of economics, history, management, philosophy and sociology amongst others. It is a varied, stimulating and rewarding subject and will stretch the critical and intellectual faculties to their fullest.

HELPFUL READING: Richard A Chapman, *Ethics in the British Civil Service* (Routledge 1988); Richard a Chapman, *The Art of Darkness* (University of Durham, 1988); John Greenwood and David Wilson, *Public Administration in Britain Today* (George Allen & Unwin, 1989).

Religious Studies and Theology
Professor John R Hinnells, Manchester University

Religion is a potent driving force both in contemporary society and in past history. It has inspired some of the most noble, creative and generous actions. Equally it has been associated with the most savage cruelty, oppression and degradation. A balanced understanding of many major events commonly involves an appreciation of the religious factors at work. Whether it is in Northern Ireland, the Middle East, liberation movements in Latin America, independence movements in post-colonial Africa, the Church and 'Solidarity' in Poland or conflicts in the Punjab – religion and politics are commonly interwoven. Religion may inspire people, or it may be used by people, but it is commonly a significant dimension for the study of human life.

Many people describe contemporary British society as secular and say that religion is declining. I think that is wrong. Formal membership of the established churches may be dropping, but that is not an adequate measure of the state of religion in the country. Such an opinion ignores the growth of new religious movements, the ecstatic movements, what people (in biased tones) describe as the 'cults', and the central importance of religion in Asian and Afro-Caribbean communities here. Recent research has demonstrated that people who have migrated, or feel victims of prejudice, commonly reassert their identity in and through religious traditions. Much of contemporary British law, custom, values etc are (for better or worse) the product of a particular religious tradition. It is, in my opinion, impossible to understand our own society without an understanding of the plethora of religious influences which make it what it is.

Religion is crucial not only in the understanding of politics and society but also of the arts. Until recent times the church was the main patron of the arts – painting, music, architecture, drama. The influence of a patron is often crucial. The church not only commissioned works of art it also dictated the form, content and style of much of that art. The church often repressed the artist – not only through the mass destruction following the Reformation, but also in more recent times when its stance on, say, the depiction of the nude, the condemnation of some aspects of drama or literature, has been, frankly, narrow minded. Looking to other cultures, it is hardly possible to understand many of the art forms without the religion of which they are an essential part – whether it is the great civilizations of China and India, or of the small scale societies in Africa or the North American Indians. One of the fundamental failings of so many art histories, in my opinion, is that they study the arts as though they were produced for the 'antiseptic' atmosphere of most art galleries and museums, whereas in countless societies, including the pre-modern West, artefacts are produced to be used eg in rituals, to inspire devotion or to teach the illiterate.

Does a student have to be religious to study religion? Obviously many are, and in Britain that usually, but not always, means Christian. Some people study religion in order to find a faith for themselves; some study

Christianity because they believe it will confirm or develop their faith. A few study religion because they want to enter the religious ministry. What must be emphasised is that a university or polytechnic is a secular institution and not a priestly seminary. Within a department of religious studies there will be people of various faiths, and many of none. In theory a student's own religious position should make no difference to their studies. That is, of course, an ideal situation – and neither students nor staff are ever ideal! Most people like to think they have no prejudices. In my experience that is self delusion. We all have our prejudices. The danger time is when we are not aware of them. At least one major benefit of the study of religion is that it compels people to recognise their prejudices and to analyse them.

How should one study religion? There are as many answers to this question as there are departments which study it. In some departments religious studies means basically studying the Christian bible. One argument for this is that it, more than any other single document, has affected the course of western civilization. The scholarly methods used to study that text (or collection of texts) are intellectually demanding and diverse (eg languages, archaeology, literary studies, Roman history etc). But if you are interested in studying Asians in Britain then, frankly, it is not relevant. If you want both, make sure both are available.

For myself, I believe strongly that religion has to be studied from many points of view. The study must necessarily bring together a range of disciplines – anthropology, sociology, languages, history, art, archaeology, philosophy. It is only when there are students from these and other departments, people from different religions, as well as specialists in religion, that I find discussions come alive. Personally I accept the old dictum 'he who knows one knows none', ie that the study of any one religion is not the study of religion and such a focus precludes a balanced view of even that one phenomenon. It is only by a study of several that you see what is distinctive of each. But I am biased – comparative religion is my subject!

There are countless other branches to the study of religion not even hinted at yet. Religious studies more than any other subject wrestles with some of the ultimate issues: the concept of God; life after death; the nature of good and evil and ethical issues – what are the arguments for and against euthanasia, surrogate motherhood, nuclear power? If anyone thinks any of these are simple clear cut issues they have evidently not thought them through! Thinking things through is perhaps the most important part of studying religion.

What do people do after studying religion? The answer is 'almost anything'. Twelve months ago all my graduates, and post graduates, went into business management. That was an unusual percentage, but it illustrates the point that not all students enter the religious ministry. Careers followed by my students in the last few years include teaching, social work, civil service, the media, publishing, the Foreign Office, the armed forces, airport management, personnel management. Quite a number go overseas. Doubtless colleagues could add considerably to the list. Generally employers respect the subject because it is widely seen as a serious, stringent academic discipline, involving a range of types of study thereby demanding an intellectual flexibility.

My strongest advice (apart from 'narrow minded people need not apply'!) is – think through what your motivations are, then visit the departments you think offer contrasting stimulations and judge for yourself at first hand which one suits you. Do not be misled by a prospectus, or by a beautiful location amid shady trees (or big city night life), or where your teacher went (places change). Because of the importance of religion, and the wide range of subjects it involves, there is no more stimulating, challenging, exciting and relevant subject in the curriculum. Try it!

HELPFUL READING: J Dunn, *Unity and Diversity in the New Testament* (SCM, 1981); J R Hinnells, *Handbook of Living Religions* (Penguin, 1985); Leroy Long Jr, *Survey of Christian Ethics* (Oxford, 1982); D Pailin, *Groundwork of Philosophy and Religion* (Epworth, 1986); N Smart, *Religious Experience of Mankind* (Fontana, 1971).

Sociology
Dr Jason Ditton, Glasgow University

Sociology is the scientific study of society, OK? You could make it sound more pretentious, but it wouldn't help much. In fact its very subject matter makes it difficult to define more exactly. You can see this if you compare social sciences with, for example, natural sciences. The units of physics, atoms, do not read physics books and then get together to confound the physicists' theoretical predictions, do they? But that is exactly what the units of sociology, people, do to social theorists' predictions. Look what happened to Marxism in Western Europe after the 1848 revolution: many of the policies which the dominant classes initiated after the revolution seem to have been formulated precisely to confound Marx's predictions of victory for the working-classes.

Sociology is a science, but it is obviously qualitatively different from the conventional natural sciences. Sociology has its 'units' for analysis and to be very precise these are not so much people as the interactions that take place between people. It is from these basic units – which are studied with normal scientific rigour, although out in the world rather than in the laboratory – that sociologists are able to build up low-level conceptual pictures of ideas like social status, social role, and social class, and from them middle-range theories of more general societal features like organisation, change and conflict. In turn these concepts help to build grand models capable of explaining the operation of, and differences between, various societies.

Well, that's what sociologists **do**. But, and this is the case with all disciplines which are by their very nature responsive to changes in their subject matter, you can get more of an idea of what sociology **is** by first erasing some common misconceptions. Firstly, sociology isn't new. So those who think it might be an easy course because sociologists haven't had time to write many books about it are in for a weighty surprise. (Don't worry, most of us started with the same cosy delusion.) The idea probably took root because most UK sociology courses are fairly new, which means that it doesn't matter much which A-levels you do although arts or social science subjects might help you through the first few weeks of a degree course. However, sociology isn't new. Most basic social theory, particularly the work of sociology's big Three – Karl Marx, Max Weber and Emile Durkheim – has a pedigree dating from the nineteenth century. If you want a taste of timeless social theory, read Karl Marx's *Communist Manifesto* (Harmondsworth: Penguin, 1967).

Of course, sociology is about people, but it is not – to dispel a common view of the discipline as half social work, half public relations – about 'dealing' with them. You won't get much of a chance to research real live people actively and personally on a typical 3-year course, although you will get a chance to study systematically sociological analyses and descriptions of what life is like for other people. A brilliant example of what your and other people's life is like as seen through the eyes of a sociologist is Erving Goffman's *The Presentation of Self in Everyday Life* (Harmondsworth: Penguin, 1959).

Another common misconception is that sociology is obvious, that it is just common sense or, worse, merely trivial. Admittedly some sociological findings do seem obvious and pure common sense once sociologists have revealed them for everybody else, but that isn't the whole story. Everybody always knew, of course, that the newspapers and television coverage of news was biased against the working-class. But who could have backed his opinion with hard facts until the Glasgow University Sociology Media Group published their exhaustive and yet very readable study of the UK media? (For a short, lively and up-to-date account of the Group's work, see their *Really Bad News* – London: Writers and Readers, 1982.)

A final common but erroneous idea is that sociology analyses those bits of society which are left after economics, psychology and anthropology have carved off their bits. In fact the reverse is true. Sociology can be distinguished from all other disciplines through its ability not only to analyse society without the use of other disciplines (which is its chief function) but also to analyse competently the operations of all other disciplines. Natural science itself has become a target for some sociologists. They enquire: how do scientists make discoveries? Is it some sort of magical process? How is it that, occasionally, several scientists simultaneously but individually discover the same thing? Coincidence? If you want to know how it actually happens, take a look at Thomas Kuhn's *The Structure of Scientific Revolutions* (University of Chicago Press, 1970).

Finally, to judge sociology, don't just read those books with titles which begin with such phrases as 'An Introduction to . . .', or 'Teach Yourself . . .', or end with the words '. . . for Beginners' (except for *Marx for Beginners*, a good spoof by Rius, London: Beginners Books, 1976). No, read a bit of real sociology. For example why not take a look at those human warehouses which dominate current societal handling of certain groups – hospitals (the sick), prisons (the criminal), public schools and army camps (those in training), monasteries (those in retreat) and mental institutions (the insane)? One thing that they all have in common is that they have been studied, sociologically analysed and enchantingly described in Erving Goffman's *Asylums* (Harmondsworth: Penguin, 1968). Try reading it, and see this for yourself.

Speech Sciences

Dr Jane Maxim & Dr Sheila Wirz, The National Hospitals College of Speech Sciences

When people talk to each other, a complex series of messages are sent out, received, understood and then responded to. The processes involved in human communication require the interaction of several brain functions, neuromuscular mechanisms, sight and hearing. Listening for most people involves paying attention to what is being said, to facial expression and body posture. Such complex processes may break down or not develop along normal patterns. Speech sciences is the study of these processes of both normal and abnormal human communication.

Several UKCPUs have degrees in this area which usually appeal to students interested in speech therapy, audiology or the education of children with special needs. Not surprisingly, this science requires students to look at a range of widely differing subjects in order to acquire the integrated knowledge necessary to understand human communication. Speech sciences crosses the boundaries between science and the arts, including within the area anatomy, physiology, psychology, phonetics, linguistics, sociology, education, medical sciences and speech pathology and therapeutics.

In order to fulfil the demands of a course rooted in both the science and arts fields students need good analytical skills: in other words they need to enjoy problem solving. They also need an ability for creative and lateral thinking in order to put their scientific knowledge to realistic clinical use. However good an analysis of a communication problem is, there is still the need to present treatment in a form which is acceptable and enjoyable to the client. A child with delayed language development needs treatment through play to change their language pattern.

It may seem incredible that we still know so little about human communication but it is certainly the most complex of human functions and, perhaps, because of this complexity we are still only at the start of solving this particular jigsaw puzzle. As an example, let us consider how we understand just one word. We know that when it is heard, the acoustic and phonetic or speech sound properties have to be decoded. The brain then has to decide whether it has heard that particular word before. If it has then the word is processed to the semantic system where its meaning is retrieved. But even within this simple process, we still know very little about where words are stored in the brain and how they are stored in the semantic system.

For the student who is academically adventurous and sees research as a possible future goal this field still holds many possibilities. For that same reason this is not a field for those seeking ready made solutions. Clients with communication disorders may have the same diagnoses but the severity of the problem and the way in which it affects that particular client mean that an individual programme of therapy has to be worked out for each client. Many students wishing to enter the field feel that they want to help such individuals but such a desire to help must be coupled with a real curiosity about human behaviour and what can motivate the individual to change that behaviour. Clients with exactly the same diagnosis have very different degrees of severity and very specific individual needs. The child with cerebral palsy or the adult with multiple sclerosis both have problems with neuromuscular coordination but the treatment needed may vary from a programme to help mildly unintelligible speech to the provision of a complex computer system through which the client may communicate.

In common with other science degrees, speech sciences requires laboratory work. This component has two different strands: work in the laboratory concerned with speech and audiological sciences and clinical work which takes place in a variety of settings. The laboratory work therefore has a dual purpose: to enable the student to understand normal and abnormal speech processes and to help the student apply that knowledge in a clinical setting. Knowledge applied in a clinical environment also needs to be applied in a way which is appropriate for the client–therapist relationship; in other words the student learns how to apply personal and communication skills in a professional and effective way. The application of these skills also has to be done with a compassionate understanding for that particular individual. In some client groups the cause of the disorder may be a psychological disturbance, manifesting as, for example, a voice disorder. In such a case the student learns how to differentiate a voice disorder resulting from vocal abuse and poor vocal production from a voice disorder which requires counselling or referral to the psychiatric or psychology service.

Most courses in speech sciences begin with a year's study of foundation subjects which usually include human anatomy and physiology, psychology, phonetics, linguistics and research design and statistics. In any science degree the last subject is usually a basic component without which the student is unable to understand research methodology and critically evaluate research.

Students are introduced to clinical work first by structured observation of normal communication – observing the development of children as babies, in nursery schools and at primary schools; maybe also observing elderly people so as to gain perspective of development across the whole life span. Students then go on to acquire their clinical skills in a variety of settings, most commonly community clinics, main stream and special schools, hospitals and rehabilitation centres. Some may have clinical placements in homes for the elderly, centres for adults with severe learning difficulties and psychiatric units. The timing and length of these clinical placements tends to vary between courses. Most courses mix weekly clinical placements with longer periods in a particular setting while others use a sandwich course model. This will help the necessary development of above average communication skills and knowledge of the range of alternative communication options used with communicatively-impaired people.

For anyone who likes problem solving and has an ability to listen and communicate, this area offers the possibility of a satisfying and varied professional life with continuing scope for widening knowledge. Research possibilities and postgraduate courses are available.

Several UKCPUs now offer degree courses in speech sciences, varying in length between 3 and 4 years. Different titles usually reflect something of the flavour of the course. These include: linguistics and language pathology, speech and language pathology, clinical communication studies, remedial linguistics, speech and psychology, medical sciences (speech) and speech sciences. Graduates with satisfactory clinical profiles may also be recommended for clinical licenses to the College of Speech Therapists.

HELPFUL READING: These are not about speech sciences and speech therapy directly. Some are explorations of the issues of language development or of communication breakdown. But if you find them interesting and thought provoking then this may be the study area for you. Jean Acheson, *The Articulate Mammal*, 2nd edition (Hutchinson, 1983); David Crystal, *Listen To Your Child* (Penguin, 1986); Oliver Sachs, *The Man Who Mistook His Wife For A Hat* (Picador, 1986).

Strategic Studies
Dr Gerald Segal, Bristol University

War is the continuation of politics by other means and therefore the study of war is a continuation of the study of politics. The subject of strategic studies was once more generally known as war studies and was primarily the preserve of military historians dissecting ancient battles or arguing over the effectiveness of modern hardware. But especially in the past decade, the subject has had spectacular growth under its more modern headings of defence studies or security studies. Some have even gone as far as calling it peace studies. Whatever the name, most teachers, students and writers are concerned with the interaction between military power and politics.

As a result of this modernisation of the subject, people have been attracted to the subject for a number of reasons. Many are deeply concerned about the threat of war, especially nuclear war, and want to understand how to prevent or control it. Others have come to realise that it is impossible to understand politics or economics without understanding the impact that war has on both. The recent conflict in the Gulf between Iran and Iraq that threatens to shut oil supplies and affect Western economies is a case in point. The subject is also taught to military professionals to broaden their minds and produce 'thinking soldiers'. Many people are simply interested in a better understanding of issues that so dominate today's media, for example the wars in Central America or arms control talks between the superpowers.

Most people are attracted to the sweeping scope of the subject. In order to cover the issues, one needs a bit of history, economics, technology and politics. While each course will stress different dimensions, any good course will at least try to keep them all in perspective. While no specialised previous knowledge is required, what is most useful is a broad mind and a willingness to consider a range of problems and policies.

History is a usual starting point, if only because past wars have shaped the modern map and political realities. Without understanding the way in which the Second World War or colonial wars were fought, it is impossible to understand why the world is divided as it is. Why are there two Germanys or two Koreas and why do the Arabs and Israelis fight over tiny bits of land? To what extent should we learn lessons from past wars, for example in preventing the type of appeasement that led to the outbreak of the Second World War? Others would suggest the main lessons for the modern day come from the First World War and the risks of conflict resulting from bungling and entangling alliances.

Economics is a fundamental aspect of strategic studies because states need certain levels of economic strength before they can fight certain types of war. Poor peasant economies, as in China or Vietnam, will tend to use strategies of 'people's war' and can defeat even the most developed and technologically advanced adversary. There are also smaller guerilla movements in Africa which fight from the bush and avoid direct engagements. Rich states with their modern communications will also always be vulnerable to terrorism. But these rich states can also afford modern weapons and develop nuclear arsenals, and even though this provides little defence against terrorism, the faster they grow economically, the less burdensome is the cost of war.

An obsession with technology is often the reason why some are attracted to strategic studies before they realise that it is only part of the subject. But without appreciating the impact of technology, the course of war and politics is hard to grasp. The invention of gunpowder helped destroy the feudal age of chivalry and castles. The invention of aircraft helped spread the impact of war and made cities more vulnerable to attack. The invention of new technologies of communication meant spying could be carried out from a distance and armed forces could be directed from the safety of a headquarters on a different continent. The invention of nuclear weapons revolutionised the strategy of war, making certain types of war unthinkable, and producing the no-peace-no-war called a cold war. New weapons such as Cruise missiles or SS-20s may be minor modernisations of technology but their deployment can have a major impact on international politics as we have seen in the past decade.

The link between strategic studies and politics is perhaps the strongest. On the level of domestic politics, there is the question of how important the armed forces are in running the state. Do military dictatorships have distinctive types of policies and do they make war more often? As modern, developed states have more complex relations between industry, the armed forces and government, then how important is the military–industrial complex in making policies? Some states are so politically divided that they degenerate into civil war and strategic studies seeks to understand why these wars are fought and who makes policy. Is there a 'national security state' that undermines democratic control or rule by an ideologically motivated movement?

The politics of international affairs is obviously a central dimension of the subject. States are often paranoid about their security while others may be genuinely covetous of their neighbours' land, people or resources. Strategic studies explains why wars break out, how they are managed and how they are ended. In the age of superpower crises, the concern is with such events as the 1962 Cuban missile crisis, the Soviet invasion of Afghanistan in 1979 or the American attacks on Libya in the 1980s. As war between the great powers becomes less likely, there is much discussion of nuclear deterrence, arms races, and arms transfers. But attention is also focused on the more peaceful pursuits of arms control, disarmament and non-provocative defence. States pursue these policies as continuations of their strategies of security, but they sometimes learn to develop common security rather than merely national security. In the send, strategic studies is about two sides of the same coin: war and peace.

HELPFUL READING: J Baylis et al, *Contemporary Strategy* (London: Croom Helm, 1987); B Buzan, *An Introduction to Strategic Studies* (London: Macmillan, 1987); E M Earle, ed, *The Makers of Modern Strategy*, 2nd edn (Princeton: Princeton University Press, 1986); L Freedman, *The Evolution of Nuclear Strategy*, 2nd edn (London: Macmillan, 1986).

Town and Country Planning
Professor Margaret Roberts

The overall aim of the planner is to see that our cities, towns and countryside are best arranged to meet people's needs – that there are enough and appropriate houses, schools, hospitals, factories, offices, shops, open spaces, roads, railways and so on. It is not, of course, the planners themselves who provide all these, but they meet their aim in two complementary ways. First, they have to deal with requests for planning permission to build. Secondly, planners can encourage the provision of what they know to be lacking in an area by using their knowledge to influence possible providers, especially through the plans which are regularly produced.

Sometimes such changes happen in a 'grand design' – like the massive development now taking place in London's docklands, or in the post-war programme of 'new town' building. But, mostly, land use change occurs through a continuous series of individual proposals for buildings or plots of land – to alter what is there already, or build for the first time. The planner has to reach a conclusion about each such proposed change – is it acceptable in planning terms? How does the planner decide?

The planner will in each case consider the proposed scheme, along with what the law requires and allows; the overall planning aims of the local authority; the planner's knowledge about the broader area in which the proposed development is to be located; and the problems and needs of the local community. To be able to do all this, the planning authority has to hold a very substantial and up-to-date bank of information about its area and community, and keep good links with local groups and organisations so that it knows their views.

People often want to become planners because they feel a commitment to making places better for people to live in. This commitment may well come from their own personal experience – say of life in a run-down inner city area, where every day they have seen people living in poor housing, children attending schools without enough play space, streets choked with cars alongside out-of-date public transport. Or perhaps they have grown up in the country and watched the landscape alter as farming methods changed, rural communities losing population as fewer people were needed to work the land, and the habitats of wild plants and animals being destroyed. But, to be effective, an intending planner has to acquire knowledge and skills, as well as a sense of purpose. The common core of planning courses is laid down by the planners' professional body – the Royal Town Planning Institute.

This core includes study of sociology. Britain today is a complex urban society containing a great variety of cultures, levels of wealth, and types of living arrangement. The planner needs to understand how people's life patterns and opportunities are affected by social structures. In recent years there have been important efforts made to attract people from a greater diversity of backgrounds into planning, so that the profession becomes representative of the whole community for which it is planning, and thus has a more solidly-founded understanding of everyone's requirements.

Also essential to a planner is some understanding of economics – of the production and distribution of wealth, of what determines variations in income levels, both of people and of whole areas. Planners have become increasingly involved in economic planning, especially at the local level, and in trying to encourage job creation which requires them to have some knowledge of the operations and motivations of firms.

Another group of subjects includes law, government and politics. Planning is founded on legal powers which are constantly being updated by the central government; and it is essential that all planners understand how their functions and responsibilities fit into the broader legal and political framework of Britain.

At some stage the student planner will look at what is called the development process – in other words the operations of organisations involved in the financing, building, letting and managing of development. This will include study of their objectives, how they are influenced by financial, legal and other factors, and how planners interact with them so the best possible outcome from development is secured for the community, as well as the individual developer.

Through the course, more will be learned about the physical aspects of planning, about natural resources and conservation, buildings and architecture, landscape and townscape, and the value of how things look as well as how they function. A deeper study will be made too of particular land uses – housing, transport, commercial, industrial and recreational – and of different types of policy – especially social and economic.

As well as the 'core' material, each course will have its own particular flavour of specialism. Some courses are specialised as a whole, for example urban planning. Others will offer students a choice of option subjects relating, say, to different kinds of planning work such as countryside planning, transport, recreation, conservation or housing. In most cases the specialism of a course will relate to the area in which it is located, and the planning needs of that city or region.

To bring all this to life for students there will be project work looking, in the way that a planner does, at a number of contrasting places – to see how they have been shaped in the past, what are the pressures for change, and how these may best be met. Studying all aspects of the way a settlement functions includes getting information from a variety of different sources in order to build up a picture of the place and its people. Information sources used will include statistics and reports, interviews, looking at buildings and their use, observing traffic flows, checking how satisfied people are with different facilities such as shops, playgrounds and so on. With the information thus brought together, students will try to apply the ideas and theories that have been discussed in their studies.

Skills needed by a planner are varied. A study of planning will equip you with the necessary skill and confidence you will need in writing and speaking, in maths, statistics and computing, in graphics, drawing and design. Project work will take you through all the methods a planner uses to analyse the needs and problems of different areas and groups of people, and to prepare planning proposals, schemes and plans. You will also get practice in dealing with applications for planning permission. There will be role playing, for example a public inquiry (which may be held when agreement cannot be reached on a planning matter).

You will certainly find that a planning course is stimulating. There is interest to be found in the wide range of subjects covered, and the intellectual challenge offered. There is satisfaction to be gained from its clear relevance to contemporary life. There is personal confidence to be won from the valuable knowledge and skills which you will acquire, many of which are not only useful to planning but are very versatile and applicable widely in life.

HELPFUL READING: David Kirby and Richard Carrick, *Planning in Britain, An Introductory Framework* (University Tutorial Press, 1985), which is very clear and helpful and is organised largely in terms of different land uses; *Town and Country Planning*, a report to the Nuffield Foundation (Nuffield Foundation, 1986), which discusses what planning is trying to do, how well it is working and what the main issues are for the future.

Veterinary Studies
Professor E J L Soulsby, Cambridge University

Veterinary medicine is concerned with the health and welfare of all animal species with the exception of one – man! This is a very wide field of endeavour, requiring extensive and intensive study, but the opportunities at the end of the course are remarkably diverse and can fit almost any aspiration.

The majority of applications for veterinary studies are motivated by the desire to enter veterinary practice having had some contact with a veterinary surgeon in practice, or having been influenced by books, television programmes or movies about veterinarians. However, there is an increasing number of young people who see veterinary medicine as one of the professions that addresses the complex issues of the inter-relationships between man and animals at national and international levels; particularly how animals fit into the scheme of things, be it as part of intensive food production, as essential sources of draught power in Third World countries or as companion animals.

The course is long, five years (six at Cambridge) so tenacity of purpose is also important. All veterinary courses start with detailed study of basic sciences such as anatomy, biochemistry, physiology and the like. These are necessary preparation for the clinical parts of the course which follows further study of disease producing agents, how diseases occur and how animals resist infections. In many instances ill health in intensively managed livestock involves complex interactions between genetic factors, feeding and housing and is dealt with on the basis of maintaining health with maximum productivity and in which animal welfare is of increasing importance. In contrast ill health in companion animals is an individual rather than a herd problem and medical and surgical treatments are determined by factors other than economics.

Each veterinary school in the UK has a teaching hospital where students learn at first hand how to examine animals, diagnose their problems, advise owners and apply treatment under the supervision of clinical teachers. This must be the most exciting part of the course and the thrill of healing a sick animal is a unique and lasting experience.

Eventually the day of graduation as a veterinary surgeon comes when new members of the profession are admitted to the Royal College of Veterinary Surgeons, the body responsible for overseeing veterinary education in the UK. Each new graduate declares that he or she will be 'committed to the welfare of the animals under my care'. This is an important commitment as well as a solemn obligation and it has stood the test of time since the veterinary surgeon is regarded as an unbiased arbiter and is expected to act as such in his professional life.

The veterinary profession is numerically small; there are approximately 10,000 in the United Kingdom of which about 8,500 are actively working. The majority are in private veterinary practice and the rest are employed in government service, in university veterinary schools, in research institutes or by animal welfare societies. Those in research may become specialists in, for example, fish diseases, zoo animal medicine, farm animal, companion animal or wildlife studies or disciplines of the basic sciences. Quite a number of British veterinary graduates serve overseas, especially in developing countries where animals are especially important to agriculture, either as producers of meat and milk or the provision of motive power for transport or cultivation. Even in this world of mechanisation, on a global basis 85% of the energy required in agriculture is derived from animals; in developing countries 90% or more of energy is derived from animals.

Whatever the motivation and aspirations of the veterinarian-to-be, entry requirements are stringent and the number of applicants far exceeds the number of places available, about 335 nationally at this time. Generally two As and a B at A-level are required and several of the six veterinary schools in the UK conduct interviews, so some experience with a veterinary surgeon and strong motivation are important.

HELPFUL READING: *A Career as a Veterinary Surgeon* (The Royal College of Veterinary Surgeons, 32 Belgrave Square, London SW1X 8QP); *The British Veterinary Profession 1791–1948* by I Pattison (London: J A Allen, 1983); *Animals in Society: A Veterinary Viewpoint*, The Hume Memorial Lecture, November 1985 (University Federation for Animal Welfare, 1985); *Companion Animals in Society* (Oxford University Press, 1988). The novels by James Herriot provide an excellent humorous introduction to the life of a country veterinary surgeon in the late 1930s and 1940s.

Welfare Studies
Professor Olive Stevenson, Nottingham University

It is a pity that the word 'welfare', like 'charity', has been debased. It is a word of great importance and delicacy and expresses an aspiration that our citizens will 'fare well'. The much maligned phrase 'welfare state' carries an implication that through the organisation of service we will take responsibility for each other in times of need. It means that we do not want to leave it to chance or to informal acts of kindness, important though these things are. Industrialised societies generate social problems too large and too serious to be coped with by friends or voluntary activity alone. Every western country has 'welfare services' organised by the State, even those which resist the intervention of the State as far as possible. So the phrase 'welfare state' is one to be proud of, not to sneer at. It is not about scroungers or creating dependency on the State. These are minor matters in comparison with the central aim of creating a society in which the sick, the old, the disabled and others who are socially vulnerable, are cared for generously and sensitively.

Since 1980 we have seen a shift to the right, unparalleled since the war, in political ideology. With it has gone a resistance to any increase in State involvement in welfare and a challenge to some of the assumptions which governments of both colours had accepted since 1945. This change of political emphasis reflects a real shift in the prevailing political philosophy; it has been given force by an economic policy which stresses the need to reduce public expenditure in all areas, including welfare services. The most recent manifestation of these changes is to be seen in the White Paper on Community Care. In this, whilst local authorities are to play a lead role in planning services, they are encouraged (perhaps compelled, by financial controls) to make much greater use of the private and voluntary sectors for the provision of services. We may expect, therefore, to see an expansion in these sectors, for example in residential care for vulnerable groups and in the provision of community services such as 'meals on wheels' and domiciliary support. It is likely that social policy graduates and social workers will increasingly find employment within these sectors, in addition to their traditional 'home' in the statutory sectors.

All this is central to welfare studies. So whether you want to pursue courses in social policy (a better name for what is sometimes called social administration), or to qualify as a social worker, you will inevitably be drawn into a political debate to a greater extent than in the 1970s when the issues were less contentious.

Welfare studies draws upon a number of disciplines in the social sciences. You can expect a mixture, varying in balance, of politics, economics and sociology, which are used selectively to focus upon the central issues and problems of the subject. For example: how do you define and measure poverty and social need? What factors create unemployment and what effect does it have on society, families and individuals? How do citizens obtain redress for their grievances? If you are undertaking a social work course, to this will be added other subjects, mainly psychology and law, relevant to your chosen career. You will also undertake substantial periods of fieldwork, underpinned by teaching of social work theory and practice.

Realistically, students will be asking about job prospects. If you want to qualify as a social worker, your job prospects are at present very good. Most students think of social work as 'fieldwork in the community'. Much of this work focuses upon child protection. But there is another important area in which trained staff are urgently needed. This is in residential and day care where it is generally accepted that social workers have an important contribution to make to the care of the very vulnerable, dependent people – the very old, the young, the disabled, for example. Although efforts have been made to improve the status, training and pay of residential staff and day care staff, it has been an uphill struggle. Yet the quality of this provision is vitally important.

It is not so easy to assess job prospects for those who study social policy because the range of options is wider and more diffuse. Possible openings, as well as those mentioned above, are in hospital administration or the civil service, but a sound education in the social sciences, with a welfare slant, opens a good many doors. It is important to remember you do not have to nail your colours to the mast and opt for a career in social work when you read the general area of welfare studies. That can come later.

What is needed is a sense of perspective about the present situation, in which social science studies generally have been devalued. Social scientists with an applied element in their studies, continue to be needed across a wide range of public services. And public services will not – cannot – disappear, whatever the political rhetoric! They are integral to the fabric of the developed society. For example, if one thinks about the consequences – social, emotional and physical – of unemployment on the individuals concerned and on their families; or of the feelings and attitudes of young blacks in the inner cities who believe that our society has failed them; or of the growing numbers of frail elderly people in our society – these and many other social problems require intervention, both administrative and professional. Welfare studies is an excellent preparation for any career directly concerned with service to the community.

The position on A-level grades varies considerably across the wide range of educational institutions. It is broadly true, however, that students wishing to read 'welfare studies' do not need A-level grades as high as those entering the traditional professions such as law. It does not matter in what subjects you have your A-levels. But if they are in the sciences, it is advisable to have had some practice in essay writing before you turn up!

Zoology
Professor R McNeill Alexander, Leeds University

Zoology is about animals, including the whole range from flagellate protozoans, which are on the border between the animal and plant kingdoms, to humans. It is about corals, beetles, dinosaurs, lions and all the rest.

Zoology is about all aspects of the structure and lives of animals. It includes the biochemistry of animals – not so much the universal processes of the tricarboxylic acid cycle and suchlike, which are studied mainly in biochemistry courses, but more special processes such as the metabolic tricks that enable tapeworms to live in the anaerobic environment of our guts. It includes the structure of animals, of their cells, their organs and their whole bodies, the amazing diversity of form in the animal kingdom and the ways in which structure is adapted to different ways of life. It is about how animal bodies work, dealing with all aspects of physiology but taking special notice of differences between animal groups. If you study physiology at university you will learn how 'typical' muscles (in practice that means frog muscles) work, but if you study zoology you will learn also about many other kinds of muscle: the muscles of insect wings with their built-in resonance, the special muscles that lock clams shut, and so on. Zoology includes the behaviour of animals, how their nervous systems control their behaviour and why particular behaviour patterns have evolved.

It includes animal ecology, the study of the interactions of animal populations with each other, with plants and with the physical environment. Behavioural ecology asks what are the best ways to behave, that will be favoured by natural selection: should a redshank eat every worm it finds or just the big juicy ones, should a stag fight a rival and risk injury, and so on. Finally zoology includes evolutionary theory, both the basic theory of how evolution works, and the evolutionary history of animals.

Biology courses include all forms of life, plants and micro-organisms as well as animals. This generally means that they have to concentrate on general principles and either rush through the animal kingdom or deal in detail with only a few selected animal groups. By choosing zoology instead of biology you will get a fuller treatment of animals and you will probably be able, if you wish, to get some knowledge of plants and micro-organisms by taking appropriate subsidiary courses.

Zoology is not all like the natural history programmes on television. It *is* about gorillas and whales and strange animals in exotic places, but there is a lot more to it than that. It involves painstaking work in laboratories with advanced, complex equipment. It involves difficult concepts, some of them mathematical. It involves muddy fieldwork (it usually rains) and messy, sometimes smelly dissections.

You should be prepared for dissection (that means cutting up *dead* animals). Some schools now do little or no dissection, and zoologists at UKCPU do much less than in the past, but a limited amount of dissection is generally regarded as an essential (and very rewarding) part of a degree course in zoology. You cannot really appreciate how an animal is built until you yourself have taken it apart, and zoologists need dissecting skills for many kinds of research. Nearly all the zoologists I know have a profound respect for life and are careful not to cause pain to animals, but feel that it is justifiable to kill a few members of common species both for research and for teaching, and also of course to use animals that have died naturally. If you feel otherwise you probably ought to avoid zoology (and most other biological subjects).

Nearly all zoology lecturers believe that animals evolve and regard the theory of evolution by natural selection as the central theory that gives meaning to the whole subject. It is nevertheless possible (and not very uncommon) for students who do not believe in evolution to study the subject. They will not be penalized, provided that they remember that only scientific arguments have a place in science.

Zoology is not an easy option for students who have trouble with physics and mathematics. Zoologists use physics to explain how nerves, muscles and cilia work; to sort out the osmotic problems of life in fresh water; to understand the heat balance of desert animals; and for many other purposes. The mathematics we use is not just statistics (though that is important). We use mechanics to explain how people and other animals run, how fish swim and how birds fly; we use computer models to develop ecological theories; and we use calculus to work out optimum strategies for behaviour and reproduction. We also use chemistry as is well known. Though physics, chemistry and mathematics are all important, most zoology lecturers realize that some students find them difficult, and teach accordingly.

Many people study zoology simply because they are interested in animals (an excellent reason). Others have more practical motives. Zoology is the essential basis for conservation work, and for understanding the effects of pollution. It deals with agricultural pests, with parasites that cause disease in humans and farm animals and with vectors (such as mosquitoes) that transmit diseases. It is important for commercial fisheries and for aquaculture. Finally, much of our understanding of humans comes from research done by zoologists on other species.

HELPFUL READING: Knut Schmidt-Nielsen, *How Animals Work* (Cambridge University Press: a brilliant little book on comparative physiology); Richard Dawkins, *The Blind Watchmaker* (Longman: a thought-provoking account of evolutionary theory); Stephen Jay Gould, *Ever Since Darwin* (Pelican Books: essays on various topics).

Index

AA 109
Abbreviations 78
Aberdeen University 102
Aberystwyth 103
Academy of Live and Recorded Arts 106
Access courses 79
Access fund 41, 79
Accommodation 50
Accountancy 500, 577
Accountants 96
Acoustic engineering 500
Acoustics 96, 500
Acquired Immunity Deficiency Syndrome 52
Acting 500, 636
Actuarial studies 500
Actuaries 96
ADAR 27, 79
Administration (Public) 557, 717
Advertising design 500
Advocates 96
Aerodynamics 501
Aeronautical engineering 501, 579
Aesthetics 501
African studies 501, 582
Afro-Asian studies 501
Agricultural botany 501
Agricultural chemistry 501
Agricultural economics 501
Agricultural engineering 501
Agriculture 79, 502, 584
Agronomy 502
AIDS 52
Aircraft engineering 502
Air force 93, 96, 502
Air pilots 97
Air transport engineering 502
Air travel 70
Akkadian 502
A-level 25, 80
ALRA 106
Alternative prospectuses 15
American colleges, 80
American studies 502, 586
Amharic 503
Analogues 503
Anatolia 503
Anatomy 503, 588
Ancient history 503
Anglia 107
Anglo-Saxon 503
Animals 503

Animal science 503
Animation 503
Anthropology 503, 591
Applicant's calender 20
Application dates 20
Application forms 21
Applying 20
Applying for a grant 36
Arabic 504
Aramaic 504
Archaeology 504, 593
Architects 97
Architectural Association 109
Architecture 504, 595
Army 93, 504
Arrival 52
Art and design 504, 596
Art and design application 27
Art and Design Admissions Registry 27, 79
Art at university 81
Art colleges 80
Art history 504, 655
Artificial intelligence 505
AS-levels 25, 81
Asian studies 505, 602
Assyriology 505
Aston University 110
Astronautics 505
Astronomy 505
Astrophysics 505
Audio-visual communication 505
Automotive engineering 505
Avery Hill College (See Thames Poly)
Avionics 505
Awards 35, 36, 38

Bacteriology 505
Balliol (Oxford) 341
Bangor 112
Bangor Normal College 114
Banking 505
Banks 42, 44, 45
Bantu, 506
Barristers 97
Barts 406
Bath College 115
Bath University 116
BEd 100
Bedford College 118
Bedford College London (See Royal Holloway & Bedford)
Behavioural science 506

Belfast University 119
Benefits of a degree 10
Bengali 506
Biblical studies 506
BIJ 71
Biochemical engineering 506
Biochemistry 506, 604
Biological chemistry 507
Biology 507, 607
Biomedical electronics 507
Biophysics 507
Biosocial science 508
Biotechnology 508, 609
Birkbeck College 121
Birmingham Conservatoire 122
Birmingham Poly 123
Birmingham School of Music (See
    Birmingham Conservatoire)
Birmingham University 125
Bogus degrees 81
Bolton Institute 127
Books 13, 53
Botany 508, 612
Bournemouth Poly 128
Bradford & Ilkley 130
Bradford University 131
Brasenose College (Oxford) 342
Bretton Hall College 132
Brewing 509
Brighton Poly 134
Bristol Old Vic Theatre School 136
Bristol Poly 137
Bristol School of Osteopathy 140
Bristol University 138
Britannia Royal Naval College 210
British Institute in Paris 140
BRNC 210
Brunel University 144
Buckingham University 145
Buckinghamshire College 147
Buckland 148
Budgeting 33
Building 509
Building studies 509
Building surveying 509
Building technology 509
Bulgarian 509
Bullying 75
Bulmershe (See Reading University)
BUNAC 73
Burmese studies 509
Business 509
Business administration 509

Business economics 510
Business studies 510, 614
Byzantine studies 510

Camberwell College of Arts 149
Camborne School of Mines 151
Cambridge University 152
Cambridgeshire College of Arts and
    Technology (See Anglia)
Camp America 73
Canadian studies 511
Canterbury College of Art (See Kent
    Institute)
Carbon dating 511
Cardiff 185
Cardiff Institute 187
Caribbean studies 511
Caring 511
Carpet design 511
Catalan 511
Catering 511, 535, 664
CATS 82
CCAT (See Anglia)
Cell biology 511
Cellular pathology 511
Celtic studies 511
Central European studies 511
Central London Poly 375
Central St Martins 189
Central School of Art and Design (See
    Central St Martins)
Central School of Speech and Drama
    190
Ceramic science 512
Ceramics 512
Changing courses 53
Changing UKCPUs 53
Charing Cross & Westminster 191
Charities 43
Chelsea College of Art 193
Cheltenham & Gloucester College 194
Chemical engineering 512, 616
Chemical physics 512
Chemistry 513, 619
Chester College 196
Chinese 513
Chiropody 51
Choosing 16, 17
Christ Church College 197
Christ Church (Oxford) 343
Christ's (Cambridge) 155
Church history 513
Churchill (Cambridge) 156

Cirencester 198
City Poly 199
City University 201
Civil engineering 514, 621
Clare (Cambridge) 157
Classical studies 514
Classics 514, 623
Clearing scheme 27, 28, 29
Climate 514
Clothing 514
CNAA 82
Coaches 71
Coastal engineering 514
Colchester Institute 202
College 82
College of Librarianship, (See
  Aberystwyth)
College of Medicine, Wales 463
Colleges of education 28
Colleges of higher education 28, 83
Commerce 514
Communication engineering 514
Communication studies 515, 625
Community arts 515
Community charge 34
Community Service Volunteers 83
Community studies 515
Community work 568
Company educational trusts 43
Comparative literature 515
Computer engineering 515
Computer science 515
Computer technology 516
Computing 516, 627
Concessions 69, 71
Conditional offers 24
Conflict 517
Conservation 517
Construction 509
Continuing education 84
Contraception 64
Control engineering 517
Corpus Christi (Cambridge) 158
Corpus Christi College (Oxford) 345
Correspondence courses 84
Corrosion 517
Cosmetic technology 517
Cost benefit 10
Costs of a degree course 10
Council for National Academic
  Awards 82
Counselling 517
Country planning 566, 727

Courtauld Institute 204
Coventry Poly 205
Cranfield 206
Cranwell 207
Credit Accumulation and Transfer
  Scheme 82
Credit transfer 82, 84
Crewe & Alsager College 207
Criminology 517
Crop technology 517
CSV 83
Cultural studies 517
Cuneiform studies 517
Cybernetics 517
Czech/Slovak 517

Dance 518, 629
Danish 518
Dartington College of Arts 209
Dartmouth 210
Data processing 518
Decision theory 518
Deferred entry 11
Degrees 86
Degree equivalent courses 85
Demography 518
Dentistry 518, 632
Dentists 97
Department of Education of Science
  87
Derbyshire College 211
DES 87
Design 518
Deviance 519
Dietetics 519
Dietitians 97
Digital microelectronics 519
Dip HE 87
Diploma in Higher Education 87
Disabled students 54
Discounts 69
Discretionary grants 36
Divinity 519
Docks 519
Doctors 97
Dorset Institute (See Bournemouth
  Poly)
Downing (Cambridge) 159
Drama 87, 519, 634
Dropping out 55
Drugs 55
DSS 75
Duncan of Jordanstone 213

Dundee Institute 214
Dundee University 216
Durham University 217
Dutch 519

Ealing College 219
Earth sciences 519
East Anglia University 220
East London Poly 222
EBS 229
ECCTIS 88
EC 3, 89
EC students 47
Ecology 520
Econometrics 520
Economic history 520
Economics 520, 640
Edge Hill College 223
Edinburgh College of Art 225
Edinburgh University 226
Education 521, 642
Education college application 28
Education Counselling and Credit
    Transfer Information Service 88
Educational trusts 43
Egyptology 521
Electrical engineering 521, 644
Electromechanical engineering 522
Electronic engineering 522, 644
Electronics 523
Embroidery 523
Embryology 523
Emmanuel (Cambridge) 161
Energy engineering 523
Energy studies 524
Engineering 524
Engineering mathematics 524
Engineers 97
English 524, 646
Enrolment 65
Entomology 525
Entrance requirements 15
Environmental archaeology 525
Environmental engineering 525
Environmental health 525
Environmental science 525, 648
Environmental studies 525, 651
Equine studies 525
Erasmus 89
Ergonomics 526
Essex Institute (See Anglia)
Essex University 228
Estate management 526

Ethics 526
Europe 3, 89
European Business School 229
European business studies 526
European Community 3, 89
European Community students 47
European studies 526, 653
Exam results 23
Exeter (Oxford) 346
Exeter College of Art (See South West
    Poly)
Exeter University 231
Expenditure 33
Exploration 527
External degrees 91

Failure 26, 27, 75
Falmouth School of Art 232
Fashion 527, 600
Fees 34
Fermentation 527
Filling in forms 21
Film education 91
Film making techniques 527
Film music 527
Film studies 527
Finance 56, 527
Fine art 528, 597
Fine arts 528, 655
Finnish studies 528
Fisheries management 568
Fishery science 528
Fitzwilliam (Cambridge) 162
Flats 50
Flights 70
Flying 528
Food science 528, 657
Footwear 528
Forensic science 528
Forms 21
Forestry 529, 584
French 529
Freshwater biology 529
Fuel science 529
Furniture design 529
Furniture production 529

Gays 57
Genetics 529
Geochemistry 530
Geography 530, 659
Geology 530, 660
Geophysics 531

German 531
Girton (Cambridge) 163
Glasgow College 233
Glasgow College of Building 235
Glasgow School of Art 236
Glasgow University 237
Glass 531
GLOSCAT (See Cheltenham &
  Gloucester College)
Goldsmithing 531
Goldsmiths' College 238
Gonville & Caius (Cambridge) 164
Government 531, 712
Grants 35, 36, 38
Graphic design 532, 598
Greek, ancient/classical 532
Greek, modern 532
Guildhall School 240
Gujarati 532
Guy's Hospital (See United Medical
  Schools)

Halls of residence 50
Handicapped students 54
Harbours 532
Hardship funds 41, 57
Harper Adams 242
Harrow College (See PCL)
Hatfield Poly 242
Hausa 532
Health 69, 533
Hebrew 533
Hellenistic studies 533
Heriot-Watt University 244
Hertford (Oxford) 347
Hertfordshire College of Agriculture
  and Horticulture 79
Heythrop College 245
Highers 16, 99
Highway/traffic 533
Hindi 533
Hindustani 533
Hispanic studies 533
History 533, 662
History of art 534, 655
History of science 534
HIV 52
Holborn College 246
Holidays 72
Home economics 534
Home-based students 58
Homerton 248
Homosexuals 57

Horticulture 535, 584
Hotel management 535, 664
Housing 50
Housing administration 535
Huddersfield Poly 250
Hull University 251
Human biology 535
Human communication 535
Human movement 536
Human sciences 536
Humanities 536
Humberside Poly 253
Hungarian 536
Hydraulic engineering 536

IB 16
Iberian studies 537
Icelandic 537
Illustration 537
Immunology 537
Imperial College 254
Income and expenditure 33
Independence 58
Indian studies 537
Indonesian studies 537
Industrial design 537
Industrial engineering 537
Industrial relations 537, 666
Industrial studies 537
Informatics 538
Information design 538
Information science 538
Information studies 538, 675
Information technology 91, 538, 668
Institute of Archaology 257
Institute of Education 258
Institutes of higher education 28
Instrumentation 538
Insurance 58, 538
Interior design 538
International Baccalaureate 16
International relations 539
International students discount
  scheme 69
International student identity card,
  69, 71
Interpretation 539
Interrail cards 71, 74
Interviews 23
Investment 539
Iranian studies 539
Irish studies 539
Islamic studies 539, 700

IT 91, 538, 668
Italian 539

Japanese 539
Jesus (Cambridge) 166
Jesus (Oxford) 348
Jewellery 539
Jewish studies 540
Jews' College 260
Journalism 540
Jurisprudence 540

Keble (Oxford) 349
Keele University 261
Kent Institute 262
Kent University 263
Kibbuts 73
King Alfred's College 266
King's (Cambridge) 167
King's College London 267
King's College School of Medicine 268
Kingston Poly 270

La Sainte Union 272
Laban Centre 273
Labour 540
Lady Margaret Hall (Oxford) 350
Lampeter 274
Lancashire Poly 276
Lancaster University 277
Land administration 540
Land economy 540
Land surveying 540
Landscape architecture 540
Landscape studies 540
Languages 541, 694
Laser 541
Latin 541
Latin American studies 541, 670
Law 541, 672
LBS 291
LEA 92
LEA grants 35, 36
Learning 59
Leeds Poly 279
Leeds University 280
Leicester Poly 282
Leicester University 284
Leisure studies 542
Lesbians 57
Levant 542
Libraries 59
Library studies 542, 675

Life science 542
LIFS 299
Lincoln (Oxford) 351
Linguistics 542, 677
Literature 542
Liverpool Institute 286
Liverpool Poly 287
Liverpool University 289
Loans 39
Local education authorities 92
Local travel 7
Logic 542
London 60
London Bible College 290
London Business School 291
London College of Dance 293
London College of Furniture (See City
    Poly)
London College of Music 294
London College of Printing 296
London Contemporary Dance School
    297
London Hospital 298
London Institute 81
London International Film School 299
London School of Economics 305
London University 300
Loughborough College of Art 302
Loughborough University 303
LSE 305
Lucy Cavendish (Cambridge) 168
Luton College 306

Magdalen (Oxford) 352
Magdalen (Cambridge) 169
Maidstone College of Art (See Kent
    Institute)
Malay 542
Manadon 308
Management 542
Manchester Business School 309
Manchester College (Oxford) 353
Manchester Poly 311
Manchester University 313
Mandatory grants 35
Mansfield (Oxford) 354
Manufacturing engineering 543
Marathi 543
Marine architecture 543
Marine biology 543
Marine engineering 543
Marine technology 679
Maritime studies 544, 682

Marketing 544
Materials science 544, 689
Materials technology 544
Mathematics 97, 544, 683
Mature students 26, 41, 60, 93
MBS 309
Mechanical engineering 545, 684
Media and production 545
Media studies 546
Medical laboratory science 546
Medicinal chemistry 546
Medicine 546, 687
Medieval studies 547
Mediterranean studies 547
Merchant Navy 97
Mergers 93
Merton (Oxford) 355
Mesopotamia 547
Metallurgy 547, 689
Metaphysics 547
Meteorology 547
Microbiology 547, 691
Microelectronics 548
Middle East studies 548
Middlesex Hospital (See University
    College London)
Middlesex Poly 314
Military education 93
Mineral processing technology 548
Mineralogy 548
Mining 548
Minimum entrance requirements 15
Modern languages 548, 694
Money 31
Moral philosophy 548
Movement studies 548
Music 548, 697
Mycology 549
Mythology 549

Napier Poly 316
National Bureau for Students with
    Disabilities 55
National Council for Drama Training
    87
National Extension College 317
National Film School 318
National Hospitals College of Speech
    Sciences 319
National Union of Students 94
Nautical studies 549
Naval architecture 549
Naval engineering 549

Navy 93, 549
Near East studies 549, 700
NEC 317
NELP (See East London Poly)
Nene College 320
Neurobiology 549
Neuroscience 549
New College (Oxford) 356
New Hall (Cambridge) 171
Newcastle Poly 322
Newcastle University 323
NEWI 327
Newnham (Cambridge) 172
Norfolk Institute 325
Norse 549
North Cheshire College 326
North East London Poly (See East
    London Poly)
North East Wales Institute 327
North London Poly 328
North Staffs Poly (See Staffs
    Poly)
Northern Ireland 94
Northern School of Contemporary
    Dance 330
Norwegian 549
Norwich School of Art (See Norfolk
    Institute)
Nottingham Poly 330
Nottingham University 332
Nuclear science 550
Nuclear technology 550
Nurses 98
Nursing 550, 702
NUS 94
Nutrition 550, 657

Oak Hill College 333
Occupational psychology 550
Occupational Therapy 55
Oceanography 550
Offers 24, 25
Office organisation 550
Offshore engineering 550
Open days 15
Open University 94, 335
Operational research 551
Ophthalmic optics 551
Organisational behaviour 551
Organisational studies 551
Oriel (Oxford) 357
Oriental studies 551
Ornithology 551

Orthoptics 551
Osteopathy 551
OU 94, 335
Overseas students 47, 61
Overseas travel 70, 72
Oxford Poly 336
Oxford University 337

Packaging technology 551
Painting 551
Paisley College 374
Parasitology 552
Parental contributions 37
Parents 62
Part-time work 41
Pathology 552
PCAS 28, 95
PCL 375
Peace studies 552
PEL 222
Pembroke (Cambridge) 173
Pembroke (Oxford) 358
Performance arts 95, 552
Persian 553
Personnel administration 553
Peterhouse (Cambridge) 174
Petroleum engineering 553
Petrology 548
Pharmacology 553, 703
Pharmacy 553, 705
Philosophy 553, 707
Philosophy of science 554
Phonetics 554
Photography 554, 599
Physical education 554
Physical science 554
Physics 554, 709
Physiology 555, 711
Physiotherapists 98
Physiotherapy 555
Planetary physics 555
Plant science 555
Plastics 555
Plymouth Poly (See South West Poly)
PNL 328
Polish 555
Political economy 555
Politics 555, 712
Poll tax 34
Pollution 556
Polymers 556
Polys 28, 95 – for specific Polys, see
   name eg Birmingham Poly

Polytechnic applications 28
Polytechnic Central Admissions
   System 28, 95
Portsmouth Poly 377
Portuguese 556
Poverty 62
Pregnancy 64
Preston Poly (See Lancashire Poly)
Printing 556
Printmaking 556
Probation 556
Production engineering 557, 684
Professional qualifications 96
Programming 557
Prospectuses 14
Psychology 557, 714
Public administration 557, 717
Public health 557
Public relations 557
Publishing 558

Quality control 558
Quantity surveying 558
Queen Margaret College 379
Queen Mary & Westfield 380
Queen's College Glasgow 382
Queen's (Oxford) 359
Queens' (Cambridge) 165

Racism 64, 72
RADA 383
Radar 558
Radio 558
Radiographers 98
Radiography 558
Railcard 72
Rail travel 71
Rapid Results College 384
Ravensbourne College 384
RCA 395
RCM 396
Reading difficulties 65
Reading University 386
Recreation 558
Reference books 13
References 23
Regent's Park (Oxford) 360
Registration 65
Religious studies 558, 719
Renaissance studies 558
Ripon & York St John 387
Risk 559
RMA 417

RNEC 308
Robert Gordon's Institute 389
Robinson (Cambridge) 176
Roehampton Institute 391
Rolle (See South West Poly)
Romanian 559
Rose Bruford College 392
Royal Academy of Dramatic Art 383
Royal Academy of Music 393
Royal Academy Schools 394
Royal Agricultural College 198
Royal Air Force College 206
Royal College of Art 395
Royal College of Music 396
Royal Free 398
Royal Holloway and Bedford 399
Royal Military Academy 417
Royal Military College of Science 425
Royal Naval Engineering College 308
Royal Navy 93
Royal Northern College of Music 401
Royal Scottish Academy of Music &
    Drama 402
Royal Veterinary College 404
Rumanian 559
Rural environment studies 559
Russian 559
Russian studies 559

Safety 65, 559
St Andrews University 405
St Anne's (Oxford) 361
St Bartholomew's Hospital 406
St Catharine's (Cambridge) 177
St Catherine's (Oxford) 362
St Edmund Hall (Oxford) 363
St Edmund's (Cambridge) 179
St George's Hospital 408
St Hilda's (Oxford) 364
St Hugh's (Oxford) 365
St John's (Cambridge) 179
St John's (Oxford) 366
St Mark & St John 409
S Martin's College 410
St Martin's School of Art (See Central
    St Martins)
St Mary's College 412
St Mary's Hospital 413
St Paul & St Mary (See Cheltenham &
    Gloucester College)
St Peter's College (Oxford) 367
St Thomas's Hospital (See United
    Medical Schools)

Salford University 415
Sandhurst 417
Sandwich courses 99
Sanskrit 559
Scandinavian studies 559
Scholarships 46
School of Oriental and African Studies
    428
School of Pharmacy 418
School of Slavonic & East European
    Studies 437
Scientific graphics 559
SCOT 379
Scotland 99
Scottish Agricultural College 79, 80
Scottish Centre for PE 419
Scottish College of Textiles 420
Scottish Education Department 99
Scottish highers 16, 99
Scottish studies 560
Sculpture 560
Seale-Hayne Agricultural College (See
    South West Poly)
Secretarial studies 560
Seismology 560
Selection 23
Self-catering 65
Selwyn (Cambridge) 180
Semiconductors 560
Semitic languages 560
Serbo-Croat 560
Sex 67, 68
Sexual harassment 67
Sexually transmitted diseases 67
Sheffield Poly 422
Sheffield University 423
Shipbuilding 560
Shortlists 16, 17
Shrivenham 425
Sidney Sussex (Cambridge) 181
Silsoe College 426
Silversmithing 560
Sinhalese 560
Skill: National Bureau for Students
    with Disabilities 55
Slade School of Fine Art 427
Slavonic studies 560
Slovak (See Czech/Slovak)
SOAS 428
Social administration 561
Social anthropology 561
Social biology 561
Social history 561

Social psychology 561
Social science 561
Social security benefits 46
Social statistics 562
Social studies 562
Social work 562
Social workers 98
Sociology 562, 721
Soil science 562
Solicitors 98
Solid state electronics 563
Solid state physics 563
Somerville (Oxford) 368
South America 563
South Bank Poly 430
South East Asian studies 563
South Glamorgan Institute (See Cardiff Institute)
South West Poly 432
Southampton University 435
Soviet studies 563
Space 563
Spanish 563
Spanish studies 563
Speech sciences 563, 723
Speech therapists 98
Speech therapy 563
Sponsorship 43
Sports studies 564
Spurgeon's College 436
SSEES 437
Staff-student sex 68
Staffs Poly 439
Stage management 564
Standby fares 69
Statistics 564
STCTT 71
STDs 67
Stirling University 440
Strategic studies 725
Strategy 18
Strathclyde University 441
Student concessions 69, 71
Student fares 70
Student health 69
Student health service 69
Student loans 39
Students' unions 70
Student travel office 71
Study areas 573
Studying 70
SU 70
Subject mixes 573

Sunderland Poly 443
Surrey University 444
Surveyors 98
Surveying 564
Sussex University 446
Swahili 564
Swansea 447
Swedish 564
Systems analysis 564

Talmud 565
Tamil 565
Teachers 98
Teaching 100, 565
Technical graphics 559
Teesside Poly 449
Telecommunication engineering 565
Television 565
Textile technology 565
Textiles 565, 600
Thai studies 565
Thames Poly 451
Thames Valley College 45
Theatre arts 634
Theatre design 565, 639
Theology 566, 719
Third world 566
Three dimensional design 566, 600
Topographical science 566
Tourism 566
Town planning 566, 727
Town planners 99
Toxicology 566
Trains 70
Transatlantic flights 70
Transfers 53, 84
Translation 539
Transport 70, 99
Transport studies 566
Travel 70
Trent Poly (See Nottingham Poly)
Trinity & All Saints 453
Trinity (Cambridge) 182
Trinity (Oxford) 370
Trinity College Carmarthen 454
Trinity College of Music 455
Trinity Hall (Cambridge) 183
Tuition fees 34
Turkish 567
Typing 72
Typography 556

UCCA 29, 100
UCL 461
UEA 220
UKCPUs 6
Ulster University 456
UMDS 459
UMIST 458
Unconditional offers 24
Unions 70
United Medical Schools 459
United States 567
Universities 29, 100
Universities – for specific universities,
    see name eg Aberdeen University.
    For Universities of London and
    Wales, see also individual colleges
    eg Birkbeck College and
    Cardiff.
University applications 29
University Central Council on
    Admissions 29, 100
University College London 461
University College (Oxford) 370
University of Manchester Institute of
    Science & Technology 458
University of Wales Institute of
    Science & Technology (See
    Cardiff)
Urban estate management 567
Urban studies 567
Urdu 567
UWCM 463
UWIST (See Cardiff)

Vacation work 72
Vacs 72
Valuation 567
Value of a degree 10
Veterinary studies 567, 729
Veterinary surgeons 99
Victimisation 75
Victorian studies 567
Vietnamese studies 567
Virology 567
Visual communication 568
Voluntary service 83

Wadham (Oxford) 371
Wales 100
Wales College of Medicine 463
Wales Poly 465
Wales University 466
War studies 568
Warwick University 466
Water resources 568
Watford College 468
Welfare 75
Welfare studies 568, 731
Welsh Agricultural College 80
Welsh College of Medicine 463
Welsh College of Music and Drama
    469
Welsh studies 568
West Glamorgan Institute 470
West London Institute 472
West Surrey College of Art & Design
    473
West Sussex Institute 474
Westfield (See Queen Mary &
    Westfield)
Westminster College 475
Westminster Medical School (See
    Charing Cross & Westminster)
Wildlife management 568
Wimbledon School of Art 476
Winchester School of Art 478
Wolfson (Cambridge) 184
Wolverhampton Poly 479
Wood technology 568
Worcester College 480
Worcester (Oxford) 373
Work 41, 72
Writtle 482
Wye College 482

Year off 11
York University 484
Youth Hostel Association 74
Youth work 568
Yugoslav studies 568

Zoology 568, 733
Zulu 568